| Gastrow |
| **Injection Molds** |
| 102 Proven Designs |

Gastrow

Injection Molds

102 Proven Designs

Edited by
K. Stoeckhert

with contributions by
K. H. Blauert, H. Bormuth, J. Gaiser, H. Gemmer, H. Geyer,
R. Großmann, W. Hartmann, G. Henkel, A. Hörburger, M. Müller,
E. Oebius, W. Sander, D. Schulz, L. Sors, M. M. Trapp t, P. Unger,
H. M. Wolff

Hanser Publishers, Munich Vienna New York

Distributed in the United States of America by
Macmillan Publishing Co., Inc., New York
and in Canada by
Collier Macmillan Canada, Ltd., Toronto

Distributed in USA by
Scientific and Technical Books
Macmillan Publishing Co., Inc.
866 Third Avenue, New York, N. Y. 10022

Distributed in Canada by
Collier Macmillan Canada Distribution Center,
539 Collier Macmillan Drive, Cambridge, Ontario

Distributed in all other countries by
Carl Hanser Verlag
Kolbergerstr. 22
D-8000 München 80

Translated by K. A. Alex (Chapters 1 — 3) and E. J. Tremmel
(Chapters 4 — 7)

CIP-Kurztitelaufnahme der Deutschen Bibliothek

Gastrow, Hans:
Injection molds: 102 proven designs / Gastrow.
Ed. by K. Stoeckhert. With contributions by
K. H. Blauert . . . [Chapters 1–3 were transl.
by K. A. Alex and chapters 4–7 by E. J. Tremmel]. – Munich; Vienna; New York: Hanser;
New York: Macmillan; Toronto: Collier
Macmillan, 1983.
   Einheitssacht.: Beispielsammlung für den
   Spritzgieß-Werkzeugbau (engl.)
   Orig.-Ausg. auch u. d. T.: Gastrow, Hans:
   Der Spritzgieß-Werkzeugbau in 100 Beispielen

   ISBN 3-446-13663-0 (Hanser)
   ISBN 0-02-949440-0 (Macmillan)

ISBN 0-02-949440-0 Macmillan Publishing Co., Inc., New York
Library of Congress Catalog Card Number 83-06 2286

Copyright © Carl Hanser Verlag, Munich 1983
Printed in Germany by Courier Druckhaus, Ingolstadt

Preface

Dipl.-Ing. *Hans Gastrow* has been publishing examples of mold construction for injection molding since the mid-fifties. These were collected and published in 1966 in the first German edition of this book, which was widely acclaimed because there had been, until then, no other collection of its kind. The injection molding industry stood at the beginning of its great upturn and ideas for constructing good and economically feasible molds were received with great interest. Shortly after the publication of the first edition, Gastrow died. The second edition, published in 1975, kept the objectives set by the first. It does not aim to be a textbook but illustrates selected problems of injection mold construction with interesting and commercially tested solutions. Some of the examples from the original *Gastrow* were retained; others, from younger specialists, were added. The present English translation of the third German edition remains true to this principle. Along with a large number of new examples, principles of construction are also treated. At the time of the second edition's publication, some of them did not possess their present topicality, as for example, hot-runner molds. The solutions to the problems illustrated include molds from the simplest technology to the most complex multi-stage molds.

The publishers and editor extend their thanks to the authors for their collaboration and their willingness to be deeply involved in diagrams, descriptions of mold functions, and to present detailed ideas on design, and the translators Dr. Kurt Alex and Elmar Tremmel who prepared this English edition.

The editor is especially indebted to Dr.-Ing. W. Hoffmanns, without whose extensive work in preparing the texts which accompany the examples, this book could never have been written.

Summer 1983   Publishers and editor

Table of contents

Abbreviations of contributing authors

Bl	= Blauert	Mü	= Müller
Bo	= Bormuth	Oe	= Oebius
Gr	= Gaiser	Sa	= Sander
Ga	= Gastrow	Sch	= Schulz
G–G	= Gemmer und Geyer	So	= Sors
Gn	= Großmann	Tr	= Trapp
Ha	= Hartmann	Un	= Unger
He	= Henkel	Wo	= Wolff
Hö	= Hörburger		

List of design examples

1 General

1.1 Classification of Injection Molds

A critical evaluation of a large number of injection molds for parts fulfilling a variety of applications results in the identification of certain classes and groups that differ from each other in their construction in some basic manner. Of course, for the sake of clarity such a classification cannot contain all combinations that are possible among the individual classes and groups. It is also quite conceivable that new knowledge and experience will make an expansion necessary.

Such a classification does, however, serve its purpose if it transmits the collected experience in mold design in detail and in the clearest manner possible. When faced with a new problem, the mold designer can then see how in similar cases such a mold is designed or has to be designed. Moreover, there should also be an attempt to evaluate the collected experience and create something even better instead of simply following previous designs.

A basic requirement of any mold that is intended for use on an automatic injection molding machine is that the molded parts be automatically ejected from the mold without the necessity for secondary operations (degating, machining to specified dimensions, etc.).

From a practical standpoint, a classification of injection molds should be based on the main design features and manner of operation. These include:

– The type of gating and means of degating
– The type of ejection used for the molded parts
– The presence or absence of external or internal undercuts on the part to be molded
– The manner in which the part is released from the mold

The following discussions and examples are organized on the basis of the above listing. Cross references to other sections are provided whenever necessary.

1.2 Methodical Mold Design

Figure 1.2/1 presents a flow chart outlining a procedure to be followed for methodical mold design.

In general, the requirements and design possibilities are considered in relation to each other in a preliminary mold design. This initial design is intended to be corrected without a great deal of time and effort and provides a useful basis for discussion and further work in planning the production (e.g., specification of the number of cavities and selection of the injection molding machine). It is not necessary that this initial design be complete to the last detail. In many cases, dimensioned hand sketches will already be satisfactory for practical purposes.

It is only after the part design has been completed and all requirements that affect the design of the mold have been clarified that the final mold design can be prepared. This design then serves as working instructions for the mold maker.

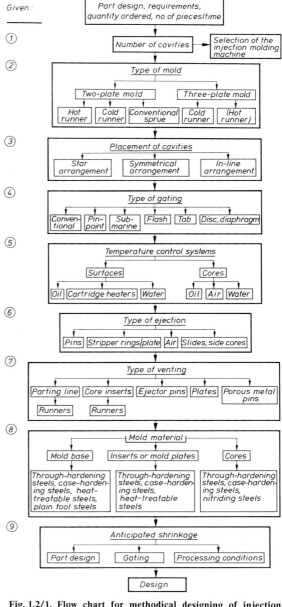

Fig. 1.2/1. Flow chart for methodical designing of injection molds.

1.3   Wall Thickness Calculation For Large Container Injection Molds

Wall thicknesses of small injection molds are generally established on the basis of experience. Since small injection molds usually involve hardened inserts in mold plates, deflection or cracking of mold walls subject to the injection pressure seldom occurs. However, the situation is quite different with large molds. On the one hand, the high-grade steel should be used as sparingly as possible, since every excess dimension makes the mold more expensive. On the other hand, it is not easy to gain a feeling for the forces to which the walls of injection molds for deep containers are subjected. Accordingly, the mathematical principles that may be used to calculate the necessary wall dimensions are discussed in the following.

The example uses a box-shaped container with a base of 50×12 cm and a height of 40 cm such as that used for battery cases.

Pressure in the cavity

It can be assumed in general that on completion of filling, an average pressure of about 400 bar exists in the cavity. The injection pressure is usually considerably higher, but because of flow resistances in the cavity, the pressure at the end of the flow path is considerably less than at the gate. Since, however, with a warm mold and high melt temperature the pressure gradient in the cavity may be considerably less than under normal production conditions, and the walls of the mold are not permitted to deform even under this load, an internal cavity pressure of 400 bar must be assumed to be safe.

Mold clamping force

With most injection molded parts, the height of the part in the opening direction of the machine is little in relation to the base area of the part. With such parts, the sizing of mold side walls is not of prime importance. The internal cavity pressure acts primarily in the direction of the mold clamping force. This force must be greater than the base area of the molded parts multiplied by the internal cavity pressure, in the present case 400 bar. The container to be manufactured has a base area of $50 \times 12 = 600$ cm². If flash is to be avoided on the part, the mold clamping mechanism must provide a clamping force of at least $600 \times 400 \times 10 = 2\,400\,000\,\text{N} = 2.4\,\text{MN}$.

Sizing the mold wall for the bottom surface

The thickness of the mold wall for the bottom surface is not critical, because the opening in the stationary platen of the machine is relatively small and forces acting on this area can be absorbed by the stationary platen, which is usually quite thick. However, the mold clamping plate should not be too thin, since it usually contains cooling water channels and is thus weakened.

In the present case, it is assumed that the cavity for the container to be manufactured has been machined into a solid steel block, although, taking into consideration the difficulty of machining at a depth of 40 cm, it would naturally be more practical to have a separate bottom plate.

Calculation of the large side wall

With a filled mold, each of the large side walls with dimensions of 50×40 cm is subjected to a force of $50 \times 40 \times 4000 = 8$ MN. This number already provides an indication that these side walls must be very thick if they are not to deflect an impermissible amount when subjected to the injection pressure. Provided that the cavity for the container is machined into a steel block, the maximum load for the enclosing walls occurs at the open end of the steel block. Figures 1.3/1 and 1.3/2 show vertical and horizontal sections through the mold: (a) is the core, (b) the stripper plate and (c) the so-called cavity, i.e., the steel block in which the cavity for the container has been machined. Guide pins to locate the core with respect to the cavity are not shown. With the mold as shown in Figures 1.3/3 and 1.3/4, it is preferable to locate the mold halves without guide pins.

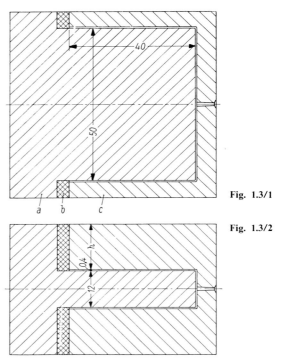

Fig. 1.3/1

Fig. 1.3/2

Figs. 1.3/1 and 1.3/2. Section through the mold for a box-type container with a base of 50×12 cm and a height of 40 cm.

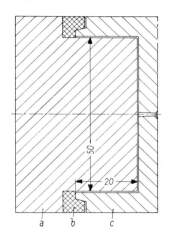

Fig. 1.3/3

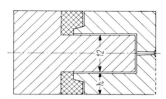

Fig. 1.3/4

Figs. 1.3/3 and 1.3/4. Mold for a box-type container with a height of only 20 cm.

Figs. 1.3/1 to 1.3/4. *a*, core; *b*, stripper plate; *c*, cavity.

To calculate the wall thickness, imagine a strip 1 cm wide cut out of the open end of the cavity. Along a length of 50 cm, a force of $50 \times 1 \times 4000$ N $= 0.2$ MN then acts on the 1 cm wide strip.

Even considering the alloy steel used for the cavity, a bending load σ_b of 200 N/mm^2 should not be exceeded so that an adequate safety factor remains in the event of overloading.

The following equations may be used for the calculation, where the letters have the following meanings:

$$W = \text{moment of resistance} = \frac{b\,h^2}{6} \text{ [cm}^3]$$

$$I = \text{moment of inertia} = \frac{b\,h^3}{12} \text{ [cm}^4]$$

b = width in cm
h = height in cm (wall thickness)

The wall is subjected to a bending load. For the load calculation, assume fixed ends. The following equations then apply:

$$W = \frac{P\,l}{12\,\sigma_b} \text{ [cm}^3]$$

$$f = \frac{10\,P\,l^3}{384\,E\,I} \text{ [mm]}$$

where
f = maximum deflection [mm]
P = total load [N]
l = length of the area subjected to load [cm]
E = modulus of elasticity = 210 000 N/mm^2

The necessary moment of resistance W is calculated from the load $P = 200,000$ N as

$$W = \frac{200,000 \times 50}{12 \times 20,000} = 41.5 \text{ cm}^3$$

From this the required wall thickness h is calculated as $\sqrt{41.5 \times 6} = 15.8$ cm. Thus the wall must be 16 cm thick. The maximum deflection under load at the critical location must still be checked.

For a wall thickness of 16 cm and a width of 1 cm, the moment of inertia I is

$$I = \frac{16^3}{12} = 341 \text{ cm}^4$$

This results in a deflection of

$$f = \frac{10 \times 200,000 \times 50^3}{384 \times 210,000 \times 341} = 0.09 \text{ mm}$$

Hence the wall thickness of the molded part will be almost 0.1 mm thicker in the center than at the edge.

Calculation for the narrow side walls of the cavity

As the container is narrow in relation to its lateral areas, a calculation of deflection is not necessary. The tensile load for a strip 1 cm wide is:

$$\sigma_z = \frac{200,000}{2\,h \times 1}$$

Assuming a permissible tensile load of 200 N/mm^2, the wall thickness is $h = 5$ cm.

Calculation for a low container

If the depth of the container to be manufactured is considerably smaller in relation to the lateral area (compare Figures 1.3/3 and 1.3/4), it is possible to achieve better load conditions and thus thinner side walls by having the circumference of the open end of the cavity c engage the stripper plate b with a taper. For the large side walls, this represents the load on a beam fixed at one end and supported at the other. The following calculation results for the 20 cm long × 1 cm side strip cut out of the 50 cm wide side wall of the cavity:

$$W = \frac{P \times l}{8 \times \sigma_b} = \frac{20 \times 400 \times 20}{8 \times 2000} = 10 \, cm^3$$

$$h = \sqrt{10 \times 6} = 7.7 \, cm$$

The cross-sectional load for the narrow sides is in this case the same as for the large sides. Accordingly, the required wall thickness is 7.7 cm.

It will now be calculated for the 40 cm high container whether significant reductions in wall thickness, and thereby material savings, can be obtained by having the stripper plate absorb the forces experienced by the open side walls of the cavity. For the calculation,

the same loading situation as for the low container may be assumed, i.e., a beam fixed at one end and supported at the other. The length of the beam must then be taken to be 40 cm.

$$W = \frac{P \times l}{8 \times \sigma_b} = \frac{20 \times 400 \times 40}{8 \times 2000} = 40 \, cm^3$$

$$h = \sqrt{40 \times 6} = 15.5 \, cm$$

Compared to the previously calculated wall thickness of 15.8 cm for the large side walls, absorbing the injection pressure in the stripper plate in the present case, i.e., a deep cavity, provides no advantage. Nevertheless, for large box-type containers, locating by means of guide strips will be preferred to locating by means of guide pins, since the greater bearing surface provides a better guarantee against shifting of the core.

1.4   Effect of Draft on the Design of an Injection Mold

Example 1. Four-cavity mold for a coil case

For functional reasons, the draft that must sometimes be employed in an injection mold appears contrary to that required for easy part removal.

The requirement in this example is to produce a slip-together protective coil case consisting of two identical halves of which four are produced simultaneously in one mold.

The conventional means of construction in which the outer surfaces of the part are formed in the stationary mold half and the part is stripped from the core on the moving mold half cannot be used, because the requirement that two identical halves be assembled into one case makes it necessary that one half of the case exhibit external draft in one direction while the other half exhibit draft in the opposite direction or no draft at all.

Between the two walls with opposite draft there is a gap of about 1 mm in the center of the case wall. The inner walls of the case, which enclose the two coil cores, must also have opposite draft in order to engage one another. The stated requirement eliminates formation of the outer walls of the case in the stationary mold half, because the exterior draft would be in the wrong direction along at least half the circumference.

If the case half were formed on the movable mold half up to the radius leading to the top surface, the side walls, which are only 0.5 mm thick, would normally

have to be simultaneously released from the core and cavity surfaces.

Since it is known that such thin walls tend to stick in the cavities in spite of careful polishing of the steel surfaces, the ejector pins that act on the bottom of the case would simply push through the case wall without ejecting the side walls.

This problem can only be solved by releasing the exterior and inner walls sequentially and not simultaneously. It does not matter whether the exterior surface and then the interior surface is released or vice versa.

In the present example, the side walls of the case are formed by a movable mold plate that can travel forward with the ejector motion for a certain distance as the part is being stripped from the cores. Once the part has been separated from the core, the exterior part surfaces release from the movable mold plate due to shrinkage and the part can be easily ejected.

By no means does the release motion have to occur over the entire opening stroke. For the usual case of draft in one direction, a release motion of only a few millimeters usually suffices to facilitate ejection, in the course of which the exterior and inner surfaces may be released in sequence.

Should the mold now be made with individual hardened cavities (inserts) or should the cavities and openings be machined in hardened steel plates? In the latter

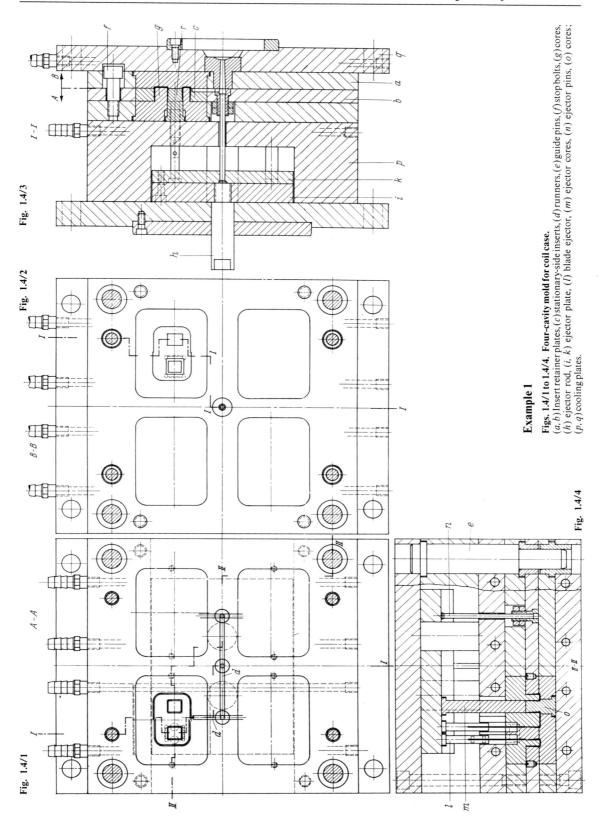

Fig. 1.4/3

Fig. 1.4/2

Fig. 1.4/1

I–I

B–B

A–A

Fig. 1.4/4

Example 1

Figs. 1.4/1 to 1.4/4. Four-cavity mold for coil case.
(a, b) Insert retainer plates, (c) stationary-side inserts, (d) runners, (e) guide pins, (f) stop bolts, (g) cores,
(h) ejector rod, (i, k) ejector plate, (l) blade ejector, (m) ejector cores, (n) ejector pins, (o) cores;
(p, q) cooling plates.

case, considerable distortion on hardening, which may have a detrimental effect especially on the bores for the guide pins, is to be expected.

Of course, the decision also depends to a significant degree on the facilities available at the mold-making shop. If a coordinate grinding machine is available, distortion hardening is less important, since the bores for the guide pins can be ground again after the plates have been hardened.

For mold plates as large as those necessary in the present example, however, the simplest way to avoid distortion hardening is to place cavities in insert retainer plates of tempered steel. Temper-hardening to a value of 1000 to 1100 N/mm² is practical, because with insert-type construction the runners also are located in these plates to some extent and normal structural steel is too soft for this purpose. The mold described in the following is designed in this manner.

The insert retainer plates (a) and (b) enclosing the runners are of quenched and tempered steel that has been brought to a value of 1000 to 1100 N/mm² before final machining. Insert retainer plate (b) contains the stationary-side inserts (c) in which the exterior shape of the case as well as the submarine gate and runners are machined. The motion of this insert retainer plate

on the guide pins (e) is limited to about 10 mm by four stop bolts.

The mold first opens between plates (a) and (b). The molded parts and runner remain on the movable half and the cores (o) are withdrawn from the molded part.

As soon as the ejector rod (h) is actuated, the ejector plates (i) and (k) and the blade ejectors (l) are moved forward, thereby actuating ejector cores (m) and the runner ejector pins (n). Insert retainer plate (b) also moves during the first 10 mm of ejector stroke until it is stopped by bolt (f).

So that the blade ejectors (l) must only eject the outer surface of the inner wall at first, core (r) moves for a distance of about 6 mm. Thereafter the molded part has been released enough by the draft of the walls such that the blade ejectors can eject the part from both cavities without undue force.

As the mold closes, the ejectors are returned to their original position by the ejector cores (m) with the aid of cores (o).

The mold is cooled adequately by four channels each in the plates (p) and (q). Since nylon (polyamide) is to be processed, it is useful to first run hot water through the channels until the mold has reached the operating temperature.

1.5 Temperature Control of Injection Molds

The designing of the cooling system of an injection mold is often considered to be only of secondary importance. Neither the sizing nor the design are given adequate attention. An improperly designed cooling system can result in hidden stresses in small parts, distortion in larger parts with relatively thin walls and even crack formation. Furthermore, insufficient cooling reduces the economics of molding by increasing the cycle time. In the following, the complicated process of cooling injection molds is investigated in somewhat simplified form, useful equations are derived and the procedure to be used for sizing a cooling system on the basis of the equations is discussed.

Sizing of cooling systems is without a doubt no simple task and something with which mold designers are in general not familiar. The task is very complex so that even in the technical literature it is hard to find a satisfactory answer to certain questions. The heat transfer equations are known in part and today computers and programmable pocket calculators are available to solve them. Nevertheless, solving the problem is often made difficult by the conditions encountered. For instance, the wall of the cavity is warmed periodically by the injected plastics melt. As a result, the temperature difference between the mold and the cooling water is increased and the cooling action becomes greater. After the mold has been opened and the molded part ejected, the cavity is cooled additionally by the ambient air. Accordingly, the temperature of the surface of the cavity changes cyclicly (see Fig. 1.5/1). The problem becomes even harder to solve because the injected plastics melt comes in contact with only a portion of the mold – the cavity – while the mold is cooled over its entire height and width by cooling channels. In addition, the cooling water is warmed during its passage through the mold so that the temperature difference between mold and cooling water changes.

Calculating the cooling system of injection molds

Total amount of heat to be removed

The total amount of heat to be removed Q is given by the following equation:

$$Q = n \times \Delta i G \quad \text{kJ/h} \tag{1}$$

where n = number of shots per hour, Δi = difference in enthalpy of the plastic on entering the mold ($t_{1\,max}$) and at the end of cooling ($t_{1\,min}$) in kJ/kg and G = shot weight including runner in kg.

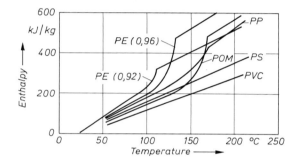

Fig. 1.5/2. Enthalpy of various plastics resins as a function of temperature.

The value of Δi can be obtained from Fig. 1.5/2 for some plastics. In addition, the following approximation holds:

$$\Delta i = c_p(t_{1\,max} - t_{1\,min}) \tag{2}$$

where the specific heat c_p may be obtained from handbooks or information provided by the material manufacturer.

The amount of heat removed by natural cooling

Heat is removed from the mold naturally by convection. In contrast, the heat removed by radiation is an order of magnitude smaller and may be neglected. The amount of heat removed by convection Q_1 is given by the following equation:

$$Q_1 = \alpha_1 F(t_{2\,m} - t_0) \tag{3}$$

where α_1 = heat transfer coefficient in kJ/(m² h °C), F = mold area in m², $t_{2\,m}$ = mean mold temperature

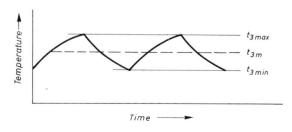

Fig. 1.5/1. Temperature of the cavity surface as a function of time.

in °C and t_0 = temperature of the ambient air in °C. The following equation is given by Mihajev for α_1:

$$\alpha_1 = A_3 \Delta t^{1/3} \tag{4}$$

The value of A_3 is given in tabular form[1] on the basis of experimental results. With the aid of a regression calculation, the following equation is obtained for $0\,°C < t_{2\,m} < 300\,°C$:

$$A_3 = \left(0.25 + \frac{360}{t_{2m} + 300}\right) \times 4.1868 \tag{5}$$

Accordingly,

$$Q_1 = 4.1868 \left(0.25 + \frac{360}{t_{2m} + 300}\right) F(t_{2m} - t_0)^{4/3} \tag{3a}$$

The amount of heat so calculated is valid for vertical, flat walls, since it is for this situation that the value of α_1 applies. For horizontal, upward-facing surfaces, a deviation of $+30\,\%$ arises, while for horizontal, downward-facing surfaces, one of $-30\,\%$ results. Thus this leads to no errors for injection molds.

If the amount of time needed to open the mold and eject the finished parts represents too high a fraction of the overall cycle time ($> 30\,\%$), the area along the mold parting line must be taken into consideration accordingly.

Mean wall temperature of the wall cavity

The plastics melt entering the cavity is cooled by the cooler mold wall, which in turn is warmed. In order to remove from the mold the amount of heat remaining (Q_2) after that removed by natural convection (Q_1) has been subtracted ($Q_1 = Q - Q_1$), a temperature difference is needed and is obtained from

$$Q_2 = \alpha_2 f(t_{1\,m} - t_{3\,m})\tau \quad \text{kJ/h} \tag{6}$$

as

$$(t_{1\,m} - t_{3\,m}) = Q_2 / \alpha_2 f \tau \tag{7}$$

where f is the area of the molded part in m^2, τ is the ratio of injection and holding time to the overall cycle time and α_2 is the heat transfer coefficient between the plastic and mold = 1549 kJ/(m^{2}h °C)[1].

It is known from the science of heat transfer that for heat exchange between two media where the temperature of one medium increases and that of the other decreases, a logarithmic temperature average must be used instead of the mean temperature t_m:

$$(t_{1\,m} - t_{3\,m}) = \frac{0.4343\,[(t_{1\,max} - t_{3\,min}) - (t_{1\,min} - t_{3\,max})]}{\lg\left(\dfrac{t_{1\,max} - t_{3\,min}}{t_{1\,min} - t_{3\,max}}\right)} \tag{8}$$

[1] M. A. Mihajev, *Wärmeübertragungen aufgrund praktischer Berechnungen* (Hung.) Budapest, 1953.

In eq. (8) $t_{1\,max}$ is given by the process. Likewise, an optimum mean temperature for the cavity $t_{3\,m}$ and what would appear to be a practical temperature fluctuation $t_{3\,a}$ of the cavity wall of, for instance, $\pm 10\,°C$ may be assumed. From these values, $t_{3\,min}$ and $t_{3\,max}$ must be calculated:

$$t_{3\,min} = t_{3\,m} - t_{3\,a} \tag{9}$$
$$t_{3\,max} = t_{3\,m} + t_{3\,a} \tag{10}$$

Next, the difference $t_{1\,max} - t_{3\,min}$ and the difference $t_{1\,m} - t_{3\,m} = Q_2 / \alpha_2 f \tau$ must be calculated. Using these two values, the difference $t_{1\,min} - t_{3\,max}$ is obtained from Fig. 1.5/3 as the point of intersection. If too high a value of the temperature of the molded part $t_{1\,min}$ (above the possible ejection temperature) results, the calculation must be repeated with another value of $t_{3\,a}$.

Thermal resistance of the mold

The quantity of heat to be removed from the injection molded part must be transmitted via conduction from the wall of the cavity through the body of the mold to the cooling water flowing through the cooling channels.

The heat flow between parallel surfaces can be calculated with the Fourier equation as follows:

$$Q = \frac{1}{\delta} \Phi \times \Delta t \quad \text{kJ/h} \tag{11}$$

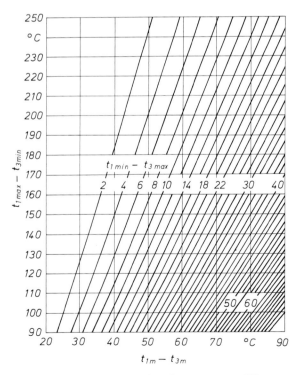

Fig. 1.5/3. Chart for determining the temperature difference $t_{1\,min} - t_{3\,max}$

It is useful to write this relation in the following form:

$$Q\frac{\delta}{l\Phi} = \Delta t = t_{3m} - t_{4m} \tag{11a}$$

where δ = distance between cavity and cooling channel in m, l = length of the cooling channel in m, Φ = cross-sectional area of the surface through which heat is flowing between the cavity and cooling channel in m^2 and t_{4m} = temperature of the wall of the cooling channel in °C. The value $\delta/l\Phi$ is called the thermal resistance; it is usually designated in the literature as R_v.

Equation (11) holds only for the case of parallel surfaces, where the cross-sectional areas of the incoming and outgoing heat flows are identical. This is not the case with injection molds. Here the cavity represents the "warm" surface and the cooling channel the "cold" surface, so that it becomes necessary to determine the value of Φ more accurately.

Assume that the cross-sectional area through which heat is transferred is defined by planes and that its dimensions increase in proportion to the distance from the origin. Of course, such an assumption is only approximately valid, since heat is also conducted outside the delineated region. In accordance with the principle of least resistance, however, it may be assumed that the majority of the heat flows along the straightline path mentioned above, so that it appears permissible to neglect the heat conducted outside this cross-sectional area.

If Φ is a function of the distance x, the following equation holds:

$$d R_v = \frac{1}{\lambda}\frac{d x}{\Phi(x)} \tag{12}$$

or

$$R_v = \frac{1}{\lambda}\int_0^L \frac{d x}{\Phi(x)} \tag{12a}$$

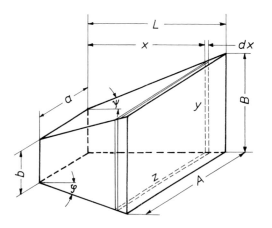

Fig. 1.5/4. **Method for calculating the thermal resistance of the mold.**

where λ = thermal conductivity [steel: λ = 176 kJ/(m h °C)], L = (mean) distance of the cooling channel from the cavity in m (see Fig. 1.5/4).

Let it further be assumed that the smallest cross section has dimensions a and b (see Fig. 1.5/4) and that the largest cross section has dimensions A and B. For location x, the following equation can than be written:

$$\Phi(x) = zy \tag{13}$$

If $\tan\varphi = M$ and $\tan\psi = m$, it follows

$$z = a + Mx \tag{14}$$

and

$$y = b + mx \tag{15}$$

and thus

$$\Phi(x) = (a + Mx)(b + mx) \tag{16}$$

hence

$$R_v = \frac{1}{\lambda}\int_0^L \frac{d x}{(a + Mx)(b + mx)} \tag{12b}$$

On integration, the following is obtained:

$$R_v = \frac{1}{\lambda}\left(\frac{1}{Mb - ma}\right)\ln\left(\frac{\dfrac{ML + a}{mL + b}}{\dfrac{a}{b}}\right) \tag{17}$$

or

$$R_v = \frac{1}{\lambda}\left(\frac{2.3\,L}{(A - a)\,b - (B - b)\,a}\right)\lg\left(\frac{A}{a}\right)\left(\frac{b}{B}\right) \tag{17a}$$

For $A/B = a/b$ the value $0/0$ results. For this case,

$$R_v = \frac{1}{\lambda}\frac{2.3\,L}{a\,B} \tag{17b}$$

For cores and similar internally cooled thick-walled components, the following is obtained

$$R_v = \frac{2.3}{2\,\pi\,\lambda\,l_{Kern}}\lg\left(\frac{d_2}{d_1}\right) \tag{17c}$$

where l_{core} = core length in m, d_1 = core inside diameter in m and d_2 = core outside diameter in m.

Since in injection molds several cavities and numerous cooling channels are often present, the thermal resistance between each cavity and each cooling channel must be calculated separately and used to obtain an overall thermal resistance as

$$\frac{1}{R_v} = \sum \frac{1}{R_{vi}} \tag{18}$$

Using R the condition that the desired amount of heat reaches the cooling channel may be formulated as follows:

$$Q_2 R_v = t_{3m} - t_{4m} \tag{19}$$

or

$$t_{4m} = t_{3m} - Q_2 R_v \tag{19a}$$

Heat transfer between cooling channel and cooling water

In the cooling channel, the cooling medium must absorb the heat by convection. To this end, turbulent flow must be assured and the requirement that

$$Re = wd/v \geqq 2320 \qquad (20)$$

must be fulfilled (Re = Reynolds number, w = flow velocity of the cooling medium in m/s, d = diameter of the cooling channel in m, v = kinematic viscosity in m²/s). Values of v are given in Fig. 1.5/5.

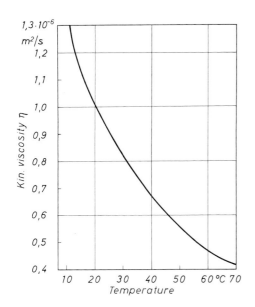

Fig. 1.5/5. Kinematic viscosity of water.

Between Re values of 2320 and 6000 there is a transition state where turbulent flow is not assured. It is to be recommended that Re numbers of 3000 to 6000 be provided, from which the following equation results:

$$wd = (3000 \text{ to } 6000)\, v \qquad (21)$$

The amount of heat to be removed hourly is

$$Q_2 = Q - Q_1$$

For Q_2 it follows that:

$$Q_2 = \gamma \frac{d^2\pi}{4} 3600\, w(t_{5\,\text{out}} - t_{5\,\text{in}})\, c \text{ kJ/h} \qquad (22)$$

where t_5 = cooling water temperature and c = specific heat in kJ/kg °C. For water, $\gamma = 1000 \text{ kg/m}^2$ and $c = 4.19 \text{ kJ/kg °C}$.

Inserting the expression for w from eq. (21), $w = (3000 \text{ to } 6000)\, V/d$, in eq. (22), it follows that:

$$d = \frac{Q_2}{(9 \text{ to } 17)\, v\, (t_{5\,\text{out}} - t_{5\,\text{in}})\, 10^9} \text{ m} \qquad (23)$$

In practice, values of d between 0.008 and 0.025 m are common, while values of w vary between 0.5 and 5 m/s.

The amount of water flowing through the cross-sectional area of the cooling channel is given by:

$$s = d^2 \pi w/4 \quad \text{m}^3/\text{s} \qquad (24)$$

or

$$S = 2830\, d^2 w \quad \text{m}^3/\text{h} \qquad (25)$$

Usually the flow velocity is obtained from the pressure drop in the cooling system:

$$w = \sqrt{\Delta p\, d/l} \qquad (26)$$

where Δp = pressure difference between cooling water inlet and outlet and l = total length of all cooling channels (including fittings, elbows, etc.).

The inlet temperature of the cooling water encountered under actual conditions should be employed. When open-circuit water cooling is used exclusively $t_{2\,\text{in}}$ is not over 20 °C, while with closed-circuit cooling the temperature of the water is often not below 25 to 28 °C.

For convective heat transfer – as in the present case of heat transfer to a flowing medium – the following holds:

$$Q_2 = \alpha_3\, \varphi(t_{4\,m} - t_{5\,m}) \qquad (27)$$

where α_3 = heat transfer coefficient between mold and cooling water in kJ/(m²h °C), φ = surface area of the cooling channel in m² and $t_{5\,m}$ = mean cooling water temperature in °C. The heat transfer coefficient α_3 is a function of the flow velocity w and the diameter d of the cooling channel[2,3]:

$$\alpha_3 \approx 7348\,(1 + 0.015\, t_{5\,m})(w^{0.87}/d^{0.13}) \qquad (28)$$

Actually, the logarithmic mean of t_5 ought to be used in eq. (28), which is not done here, however, because of the factor 0.015. Values of $d^{0.13}$ and $w^{0.87}$ can be obtained from Figs. 1.5/6 and 1.5/7. For the commonly

2 S. Kenig and M. R. Kamal, *SPE-J*, vol. 26, no. 7, 1970, p. 50.
3 H. Gröber, S. Erk and U. Grigull, *Wärmeübertragung*. Berlin, 1955.

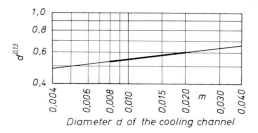

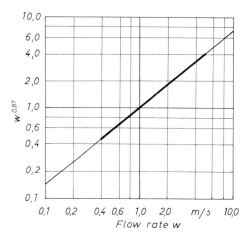

Fig. 1.5/6. Chart for determining the value $d^{0.13}$.

Fig. 1.5/7. Chart for determining the value $w^{0.87}$.

encountered values of d and w, it may be assumed that $d^{0.13}$ is approximately 0.55 and that $w^{0.87}$ is approximately w, so that eq. (28) is simplified to:

$$\alpha_3 \approx 7348\,(1+0.015\,t_{5\,m})\frac{w}{0.55} \qquad (28a)$$

The surface area φ of the cooling channels is given by

$$\Sigma\varphi = d\,\pi\,l \qquad (29)$$

where l = total length of cooling channels in m. It then follows that

$$Q_2 = 7348\,(1+0.015\,t_{5\,m})\frac{w}{0.55}\,d\,\pi\,l\,(t_{4\,m}-t_{5\,m}) \qquad (27a)$$

and with eq. (25) the required total length of the cooling channels is obtained as:

$$l = \frac{Q_2\,d}{14.78\;S\,(1+0.015\,t_{5\,m})\,(t_{4\,m}-t_{5\,m})} \qquad (30)$$

Experience with sizing of cooling systems

Practical experience has shown that it is useful to design the cooling system of an injection mold in accordance with its operation and the space available, and to check and, if necessary, to change the diameter,

length and placement of the cooling channels. In simpler cases, it is sufficient to determine the required amount of cooling water, the cross-sectional area of the cooling channel and the flow rate required to guarantee turbulent flow and the pressure drop necessary for this flow rate, assuming a value for the temperature difference $t_{5\,\mathrm{out}} - t_{5\,\mathrm{in}}$ of the cooling water. The pressure drop and temperature difference must be checked when testing the mold to ensure proper operation of the cooling system.

With more complicated molds, a calculation should be made using the procedure discussed above. While a certain amount of reserve can be provided, it should be recalled that an oversized cooling system serves no useful purpose from either a technical or an economical standpoint. The factor α_3 determined in eq. (28) applies only in the case of heat transfer between water and a cooling channel with a metallic surface. In the presence of scale or oxide films, the heat transfer is reduced by orders of magnitude. Accordingly, it is recommended that the water used be as soft as possible. To avoid corrosion phenomena, it is recommended that the cooling channels be phosphatized.

The transfer coefficient α_3 applies only with turbulent flow. With laminar flow, the heat transfer is considerably less, which is why turbulent flow must be en-

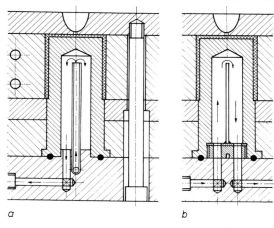

a b

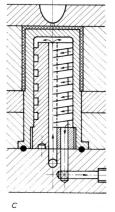

Fig. 1.5/8. Cooling of a mold core.
(a) Poor cooling effectiveness because of an increase in cross section, (b) improved cooling effectiveness through the use of a baffle, (c) most effective design for affecting the flow velocity.

c

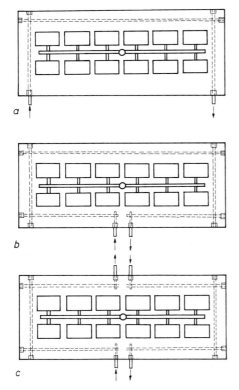

Fig. 1.5/9. Placement of cooling circuits.
(*a*) nonuniform cooling, (*b*) better arrangement, (*c*) most effective placement of two circuits.

sured by all means. Special attention must be given to those locations where the flow cross section increases. Here, the required velocity must be achieved through the use of baffles or other means.

As an example, Fig. 1.5/8a shows an incorrect design. As a result of the increase in cross section, the velocity of the cooling water drops considerably and the effectiveness of the cooling is reduced. In Fig. 1.5/8b, an increase in cross section is avoided through the use of a baffle. In Fig. 1.5/8c, the flow velocity is affected in the desired manner through the use of a helical channel in the core. When placing cooling channels, it must be born in mind that the cooling water becomes warmer in the mold and that as a result the heat transfer is reduced. In large molds, several circuits are to be provided in such a way that the inlet of one circuit is located in the vicinity of the outlet of another circuit (see Fig. 1.5/9). In the stationary mold half, the inlet of the cooling water must be placed near the warmest location of the mold, i.e., in the vicinity of the sprue bushing, which is often cooled by a separate system.

It is also unsuitable to place the cooling channels too close to the surfaces to be cooled, even though this results in greater cooling effectiveness, because the cooling is nonuniform. A distance of 3 to 6 *d* from the surface to be cooled is recommended.

Sample calculation

The cooling system of the mold shown in Fig. 1.5/10 is to be checked.
    Larger sides: $2 \times 42.5 \times 20 = 1700$ cm^2
    Small sides: $2 \times 27.5 \times 20 = 1100$ cm^2
    Bottom: $40 \times 25 = 1000$ cm^2
All sides have openings occupying 30 % of the surface area. The surface area of the molded part is thus
    $0.7 (1700 + 1100) + 1000 = 2960$ cm^2
The wall thickness is 1.5 mm. The volume of the molded part is thus 450 cm^3. The material used, PVC, has density of 1.38 g/cm^3, so that the weight is 620 g.

Referring to Fig. 1.5/2, the enthalpy is 251 kJ/kg at 180 °C and 41.8 kJ/kg at 60 °C. Hence 209.35 kJ/kg have to be removed by cooling. The cycle time is 20 s, corresponding to 180 cycles/h. It consists of 7 s for injection, 5 s for holding pressure and 8 s for opening and closing the mold.

The amount of material processed per hour is thus $180 \times 0.62 = 113$ kg. The amount of heat to be removed per hour is $113 \times 209.35 = 23{,}657$ kJ.

In accordance with eq. (3), the amount of heat Q_1 is removed by natural cooling. The surface area of the mold F is required to calculate this quantity. Without going into greater detail, it consists of the outer surface areas $= 1.08$ m^2 and the inner surface areas, which have to be considered for 40 % of the cycle and have a value of 0.40 m^2. This results in a value of $F = 1.48$ m^2.

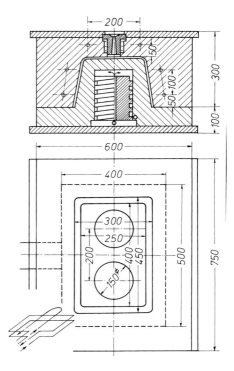

Fig. 1.5/10. Injection mold for producing a basket.

The mean mold temperature $t_{2\,m}$ is 60 °C; the ambient temperature is 20 °C. It then follows from eq. (3a) that:

$$Q_1 = 4.1868\left(0.25 + \frac{360}{60 + 300}\right)1.48 \times 40^{4/3} =$$
$$1047\,\text{kJ/h}$$

and

$$Q_2 = Q - Q_1 = 22\,610\,\text{kJ/h}.$$

Since the cavity can be cooled better than the core the amount of heat to be removed Q_2 is divided into two parts:

$$Q_{2G} = 14\,235\,\text{kJ/h},$$
$$Q_{2K} = 8\,375\,\text{kJ/h},$$

and the cooling system is designed accordingly. Equation (7) should be used:

$$t_{1\,m} - t_{3\,m} = Q_{2G}/\alpha_2 f \tau.$$

The area f is calculated to be 0.38 m², so that

$$t_{1\,m} - t_{3\,m} = \frac{14\,235}{1549 \times 0.38 \times \left(\frac{7+5}{20}\right)} = 40\,°\text{C}.$$

For $t_{1\,\text{max}} = 180\,°\text{C}$, $t_{3\,\text{max}} = 70\,°\text{C}$ and $t_{3\,\text{min}} = 50\,°\text{C}$, and with $t_{3\,\text{max}} - t_{3\,\text{min}} = 130\,°\text{C}$ and $t_{1\,m} - t_{3\,m} = 40$ °C, a value of $t_{1\,\text{min}} - t_{3\,\text{max}}$ of 6 °C is obtained from Fig. 1.5/3, so that $t_{1\,\text{min}} = 76\,°\text{C}$.

The thermal resistance of the mold body is calculated using eq. (17) for each cooling channel individually. Without going into detail, it follows from eq. (18) that:

$$\frac{1}{R_v} = 4\left(\frac{\lambda}{1.2} + \frac{\lambda}{1.57}\right) + 2\frac{\lambda}{1.02} = 7.88\,\lambda$$

With a thermal conductivity for steel of $\lambda = 176\,\text{kJ/}$ (m h °C), $1/R_v = 1390\,\text{kJ/m h °C}$ or

$$R_v = 0.00072\,\text{h °C/kJ}.$$

Using eq. (19) it follows that

$$Q_{2G}\,R_v = 14\,235 \times 0.00072 = 10.2\,°\text{C}$$

so that from eq. (19a) the mean wall temperature of the cooling channel is calculated to be

$$t_{4\,m} = 60 - 10.2 = 49.8\,°\text{C}$$

If values of $t_{5\,\text{in}} = 20\,°\text{C}$ and $t_{5\,\text{out}} = 50\,°\text{C}$ are assumed for the cooling water temperatures, i.e., $t_{5\,m} = 35\,°\text{C}$, it follows that $t_{4\,m} - t_{5\,m} = 14.8\,°\text{C}$. In addition, $t_{5\,\text{out}} - t_{5\,\text{in}} = 30\,°\text{C}$. The required cooling water flow rate is thus calculated to be

$$S = \frac{14\,235\,\text{kJ/h}}{125\,600\,\text{kJ/m}^3} = 0.113\,\text{m}^3/\text{h}.$$

Using eq. (30):

$$l = \frac{14\,235 \times 0.01}{14.78 \times 0.113\,(1 + 0.015 \times 35) \times 14.8} = 3.80\,\text{m}$$

The actual length of the cooling channels totals 6.20 m.

The flow velocity of the cooling water is calculated from eq. (24) as

$$w = \frac{4 \times 0.113}{3600 \times 0.01 \times \pi} = 0.4\,\text{m/s}$$

The Reynolds number is calculated to be $v = 0.72 \times 10^{-6}$ or 5550; turbulence is thus ensured.

The amount of heat to be removed from the core is 8375 kJ/h. With $\lambda = 176\,\text{kJ/(m h °C)}$ and taking into consideration that the core is cooled by two channels, the thermal resistance is calculated from eq. (17c) to be

$$R_v = 0.00115\,\text{h °C/kJ}$$

The mean wall temperature of the cooling channel is thus calculated to be

$$t_{4\,m} = 60 - 8375 \times 0.00115 = 50.4\,°\text{C}$$

With conditions identical to those above, the required cooling water flow rate is

$$S = \frac{8375}{125,600} = 0.066\,\text{m}^3/\text{h}$$

From eq. (30)

$$l = 2.94\,\text{m}$$

The actual length of the cooling channels totals 4.70 m, of which 75 % = 3.50 m may be assumed effective.

The flow velocity of the cooling water is calculated to be $w = 0.36\,\text{m/s}$, resulting in a Reynolds number of 4000. Turbulence is therefore ensured.

Design guidelines for cooling systems of injection molds

The temperature control system of a mold must fulfill two functions:
1. Provide the most uniform possible temperature distribution in the mold
2. Remove heat from the filled cavity

In reality, most practical cases generally involve compromises between the two requirements of:
1. Technical quality of the injection molded parts as a function of the uniformity of the temperature distribution in the mold and the level of the mold temperature
2. Economical cycle times through rapid removal of heat from the filled cavity.

Which of the requirements is of greater importance when designing the mold temperature control system depends on the material and the properties required in the finished part.

The thermodynamic system of an installed mold

The thermodynamic processes occurring in an installed mold are:
1. Heat conduction (heat transfer within a material),
2. Convection (heat transfer from a liquid or gaseous medium to a solid material or vice versa),
3. Radiation (heat transfer by means of electromagnetic radiation)

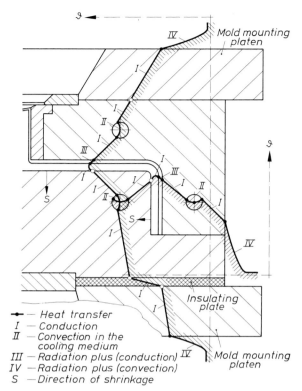

- ← Heat transfer
- I — Conduction
- II — Convection in the cooling medium
- III — Radiation plus (conduction)
- IV — Radiation plus (convection)
- S — Direction of shrinkage

Fig. 1.5/11. The thermodynamic system of an installed mold.

As heat is transmitted from the injection molded part to the temperature control medium, ambient air or mold mounting platens the above-mentioned processes occur individually or in parallel (e.g., convection + radiation at the mold surface). In Fig. 1.5/11 the individual processes and the temperature distribution in a mold are illustrated qualitatively. The mold is in contact with the ambient air and the mold mounting platens or insulating platens.

The total amount of heat to be removed from an injection molded part can be obtained from the enthalpy curve as follows:

$$Q_{ab} = G_s \times (i_E - i_{mA}) \, kJ \qquad (31)$$

G_s = weight of injection molded part in g
i_E = enthalpy on entry into the mold in kJ/g
i_{mA} = enthalpy at mean ejection temperature in kJ/g

Placement of temperature control systems in molds

Even today the placement of cooling channels by the mold designer is often the last work before the mold is made. The result is that cooling channels are placed wherever there is just enough space available. Cases are also known where the mold maker made the cooling channels without drawings while machining the mold.

Such an approach to temperature control in a mold can lead to difficulties and for molds intended for the production of precision parts must be relegated to the past. Precision injection molding requires that the mold designer already consider temperature control within the framework of the basic conception of a new mold. It goes without saying that side cores, slides, or loose mold components may be necessary to form a part and that an ejector system is needed to eject the part. Given this situation, the designer must at least attempt to reach a compromise solution that provides optimum temperature control in the mold.

Temperature control for flat parts

The following basic considerations refer to a mold used to manufacture flat, rectangular parts, but the knowledge gained may be applied to other injection molds.

The physically ideal situation would be to have one cooling channel each of width b_T identical to that of the article b_A in each mold half in the immediate vicinity of the cavity. However, except for parts of little width, the cavity shape would change under the effect of the injection pressure.

Adequate dimensional stability of the cavity subjected to the injection pressure is obtained by interrupting the physically ideal cooling channel with walls. This technically optimum form is used primarily for helical, spiral or curved cooling channels and less often for straight cooling channels. It requires as a prerequisite a firmly established partition of the mold by the cooling channels and usually time-consuming milling or turning, and it often creates sealing problems. Cooling channels with a round cross section may be made quite readily and for this reason are used very often. However, round cooling channels with a diameter d_T identical to the width b_T of the rectangular cooling channel have reduced cooling effectiveness.

Nevertheless, one advantage of molds with drilled cooling channels must be pointed out. It is only through the use of rigid molds that the tolerances required for precision injection molding are attained. Molds with single-piece mold plates or cores and drilled cooling channels exhibit greater rigidity than molds with multiple-piece mold plates or assembled cores having identical dimensions. From a purely theoretical standpoint, the areal moment of inertia J (cm^4) as a design index of the stiffness is greater by a factor of 4 for a single-piece plate than that of a plate divided in the center, assuming identical thickness.

The bending stresses and sheer stresses arising between the cavity and cooling channel under the action of the injection pressure lead to local deformation of the mold cavity. Lindner has investigated the placement of cooling channels for various widths and diameters and a permissible deformation of max. 2.6 µm. An effective cavity pressure of 1000 bar (14,500 psi) and a mold made of steel grade St60 (modulus of elasticity = 2.1×10^9 N/mm^2) were assumed.

The values obtained are listed in the table under point 4 in Fig. 1.5/12.

In general, the diameter of the cooling channels varies over a range of 8 to 15 mm. Only in exceptional cases are cooling channels with smaller dimensions used because of space restrictions. The cooling effectiveness of such channels is slight and the danger of obstruction great. Cooling channels with larger dimensions are provided in the mold if the design requires a large distance between the cavity and cooling channel or heat transfer occurs between one mold plate and another.

With regard to mold stiffness, the cooling channels can be placed at a distance s (Fig. 1.5/12, point 4) from each other. Molds, however, require for their operation sprue bushings, ejector systems, slides, cores and cavities. These design elements require space and affect or determine the spacing of cooling channels in a mold. The result is a greater spacing of cooling channels than that required from considerations of mold stiffness.

There are basic differences between the cooling in a mold for mass-produced articles and that in a mold for precision parts. For mass-produced articles, "hard" cooling is preferred to achieve short cycle times, and greater dimensional fluctuations, a coarse, inhomogeneous structure and greater stresses in the molded part are expected. Hard cooling means close spacing of the cooling channels to the cavity and low mold temperatures.

① Physically ideal shape

Width of article b_A =
width of cooling channel b_T

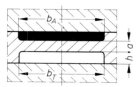

② Technically optimum shape

Condition: Temperature control while retaining sufficient rigidity of the mold cavity when subjected to injection pressure → interruption of the physically ideal shape by partitions

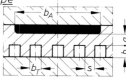

③ Easily provided shape

Condition: As under ②, however, smaller thermally effective surface area with circular shape if $d_T = b_T$

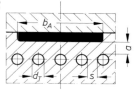

④ Dimension of cooling channels

b_T, d_T, h (mm)	6	8	10	12	14	16	18	20
a (mm)	4	6	8	12	15	20	25	30
s (mm)	4	6	7	8	10	11	12	14

Fig. 1.5/12. Design and dimensions of cooling/heating channels.

With the production of precision parts, close dimensional tolerances and good mechanical properties are required. This necessitates "soft" cooling. With regard to mold filling and the mechanical properties, a mold temperature in the vicinity of the crystallite melting point at the moment of injection and slow cooling to the ejection temperature would be ideal. However, this is unrealistic because of the inertia of molds with respect to a short cyclic temperature change and the requirement of a reasonable cycle time and can thus be used only to provide a general guideline.

A high mold temperature is a prerequisite for injection molding of precision parts. The location and diameter of channels necessary to achieve soft cooling are determined by various, often opposing, requirements. These requirements are discussed in the following as a function of the design feature.

Spacing between cooling channel and mold cavity

The larger the spacing, the more uniform is the temperature in the mold cavity and the greater is the temperature rise at the surface of the cavity during injection. This has positive consequences with respect to distortion, the mechanical properties of the parts and mold filling. The smaller the spacing, the more rapidly is heat removed and the shorter is the cycle.

Spacing between cooling channels

The smaller the spacing between the cooling channels, the more uniform is the mold temperature. If, however, the design requires a larger spacing between cooling channels, the spacing from the cavity and the channel diameter must also increase.

With increasing wall thickness, more heat must be removed. Hence it follows that the channel diameter must increase.

Diameter of cooling channels

On the basis of the indicated requirements and the knowledge gained, an attempt must be made to approach the dimensions given in Fig. 1.5/13 for the placement and channel diameter necessary to achieve soft cooling. The relations between the size of the cooling channels and uniform heat removal are illustrated by the isotherms shown.

If the spacing between cooling channels is determined by the design, the channel diameter should be selected to be at least one third of the spacing between the cooling channels. The relations given here are to be considered guidelines and goals. There will without a doubt be molds where these relations cannot be attained and with which precision parts are manufactured. However, this does not undermine the validity of the relations given.

Parallel flow cooling requires that the cooling channels' supply be located in the vicinity of the gate and, in general, it is utilized only with helical, spiral and curved cooling channels. With drilled cooling channels, parallel flow cooling is associated with a great

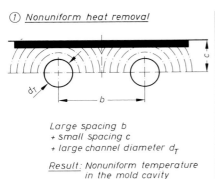

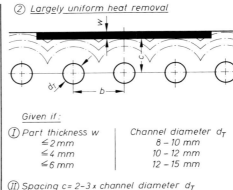

① Nonuniform heat removal

Large spacing b
+ small spacing c
+ large channel diameter d_T

Result: Nonuniform temperature
in the mold cavity

② Largely uniform heat removal

Given if:

① Part thickness w | Channel diameter d_T
≤ 2 mm | 8 – 10 mm
≤ 4 mm | 10 – 12 mm
≤ 6 mm | 12 – 15 mm

② Spacing $c = 2$–$3 \times$ channel diameter d_T

③ Spacing $b = $ max $3 \times$ channel diameter d_T

Fig. 1.5/13. Diameter and placement of cooling/ heating channels in precision molds. The channels are surrounded by concentric isotherms (idealized).

deal of effort and for this reason is found only seldom. A substitute for such cooling is provided by local turbulence (increase in cooling effectiveness) in the region of the gate.

In this regard, series and parallel connection of cooling channels must be discussed. The stationary and movable mold halves should always be cooled separately. This requires that two chillers be used. Whenever several cooling channels are connected in series, the temperature of the cooling medium rises with increasing length. This leads to temperature variations in the mold cavity. Series connection of cooling channels is advantageous if it results in parallel flow cooling. If the cooling channels for several cavities in a multiple-cavity mold are connected in series, there is the danger of significant dimensional differences among the parts. In general, parallel connection of cooling channels is more advantageous than series connection. Parallel connection results in a largely uniform mold temperature, but when using a central supply requires that the flow resistance of the cooling channels be identical. If this is not so, the cooling effectiveness of the channels will differ.

Molds with cooling channels usually require seals to prevent leakage of the cooling medium. The location of the seals has an effect on any problems encountered during assembly. Seals located between two mold plates or, for round mold components, at the point of a change in cross section are largely problem-free. An attempt should be made to utilize such designs. Gaskets placed in the direction of assembly, e.g., between the mold plate and an inserted core, run the danger of being damaged or displaced during assembly. With inserted cores having drilling cooling channels, such sealing problems are avoided through the use of threaded pipes.

Cooling systems for cores with small dimensions

Cooling of long cores small in diameter or width and used to form blind holes, through holes, grooves and slots is sometimes very problematical and re-

quires appropriate design measures in the mold. In almost all cases, the resin shrinks onto the core after injection and thus provides for direct heat transfer. Between the cavity and molded part, however, a gap forms in which the heat is conducted only poorly. Accordingly, the greatest amount of heat is transmitted to the core.

Core dia. Core width d (mm)	Description	Design
≥ 3	Heat removal by air while mold is open	Air
≥ 5	Copper pin or thermal pin (heat pipe) as heat conductor to temperature control medium	Cu
≥ 8	Bubbler cooling (bubbler cooling with spiral)	
≥ 40	Spiral cooling	
Hollow core $s \geq 4$	Cooling of hollow core by means of double spiral	

Fig. 1.5/14. Core cooling systems.

If not enough heat can be transmitted to the body of the mold and if the core is not cooled adequately by an appropriately designed channel, the temperature in the core increases as production continues. A thermal overload results. The consequences are: an increase in cycle time until production is stopped and, for cores with a square or rectangular cross section, the danger of side wall collapse or distortion. Figure 1.5/14 illustrates possible designs for cooling long cores with small diameters or widths.

Core diameter or width d ≧ 3 mm

Air may be used to cool cores with diameters or widths of 3 mm and above. The air cools the core either from the outside during the ejection time, e.g., through appropriately placed openings in a stripper ring, or flows through a channel in the core. The advantage of the former method is to be found in its applicability to cores with diameters or widths under 3 mm and to cores used to form blind holes and slots. The disadvantage is the poor cooling effectiveness.

Cores containing a central channel are better because of the good cooling they provide. The air may flow during the entire time the mold is open (time for opening and closing the machine and for ejecting the part). If, however, this time is not adequate to remove the heat, air cooling may be used during the entire cycle time with an appropriate mold design (discharge of the air through holes in the stationary mold half).

This cooling system requires through holes or slots in the part to be molded and, depending on the air pressure, tends to produce whistling.

It goes without saying that with the aforementioned cooling systems very significant temperature fluctuations occur at the core in the course of a cycle. The ideal situation for precision injection molding with largely constant mold temperatures specified by means of measurements cannot be realized here. It should, however, be pointed out very clearly that these cooling systems do provide opportunities for removing the heat from thin cores in a reliable manner and thereby eliminate the consequences (thermal overloading, increase in cycle time) of not doing so.

Core diameter or width d ≧ 5 mm

With this design principle, the good thermal conductivity of copper or its alloys is utilized. A copper pin is press-fitted into a blind hole centrally positioned in the core. This copper pin protrudes into a cooling channel and can thus conduct the heat from the core to the cooling medium. An increase in diameter of the copper pin once outside the core improves the heat conduction and heat transfer to the cooling medium as a result of the greater surface area. This cooling system and those described in the following may be employed with all core designs (cores for forming of blind holes, through holes, slots and grooves). A more recent development is the use of so-called thermal pins (heat pipes) instead of copper pins. Heat

transport in these copper pins is based on the phase change (liquid/vapor and vice versa) of an encapsulated medium[4].

Core diameter or width d ≧ 8 mm

In cores with a diameter or width of 8 mm and above, a bubbler cooling system may be used to advantage. The core is channeled down the center (blind hole) and a tube with an outside diameter smaller than that of the channel is introduced. The temperature control medium (oil or water) is fed to the tip of the core through the tube and controls the core temperature during the return flow. In cores used to form tubular parts with central gating, this cooling system fulfills the requirement for "parallel flow cooling".

Besides being used in thin cores, bubbler systems are also used in valve ejectors and opposite sprues to ensure rapid removal of the heat that is concentrated locally at the point of melt entry and deflection.

Bubbler systems are possible with tubes down to 1.5 mm in outside diameter. These capillarylike tubes are used primarily as syringe needles. Since it is difficult to obtain such tubes, many mold makers use the needles from disposable syringes in their molds. When using capillarylike tubes, clean oil or water as the temperature control medium is a basic prerequisite, as otherwise deposits and corrosion would lead to obstruction and thus inhibit operation in a very brief period of time. Even when using oil as the temperature control medium, a bevel at the end of the tube to increase the discharge opening is necessary. Such a bevel is not necessary for tube outside diameters greater than 4 mm.

Cores greater than 20 mm in diameter permit the use of a tube with a spiral. The spiral creates turbulence in the flowing temperature control medium and thus improves the effectiveness. For economic reasons, baffle strips are occasionally used in core cooling channels. The temperature control medium flows to the tip of the core in one half of the channel and returns through the other half. The result is a nonuniform temperature distribution in the core. Such cooling systems may be justified for the injection molding of mass-produced particles, but not for the production of precision molded parts. The disadvantages of this type of cooling system can be largely eliminated through the use of twisted baffles.

Core diameter or width d ≧ 40 mm

With cores greater than 40 mm in diameter or width, bubbler systems no longer satisfy the requirements. To achieve the desired effect, an additional core is placed inside the core used in molding the part. This inner core has a channel down the center and a spiral at the end that leads to a helical channel on the outer surface. This type of core cooling also satisfies the requirement for parallel flow cooling.

───────────────

[4] G. Wübken: *Kunststoffe*, vol. 71, 1981, pp. 850–854.

Cooling by means of two channels that meet at the tip of the core or are interconnected by means of a cross channel leads to varying temperatures in the core. While this design principle may be justified in cores used to form grooves and slots, the bubbler system is to be preferred for cores used to form round or rectangular openings.

The intensive cooling system used in molds for producing yogurt cups may also be used in molds for precision injection molding. The cooling fluid flows to the tip of the core through a channel down the center and cools the core during the return flow through numerous channels uniformly spaced around the circumference. The advantage of this design is that it does not weaken the core to any great extent.

Hollow cores

Hollow cores are known primarily from their use in the production of areosol caps from HDPE. When these parts were initially produced, cooling of the hollow core did not receive any special attention. The re-sults were long cycle times for a relatively thin-walled part. It was only when the hollow cores were cooled by means of a double helical system that a cycle time appropriate to the wall thickness could be achieved. The cooling liquid flows through one spiral to the tip of the core and returns through the other spiral.

Hollow cores are also found in molds used to produce caplike parts that are ejected by means of valve ejectors. In order to provide cooling of a hollow core, a wall thickness of at least 4 mm is necessary. The hollow core is divided into an inner core and an outer core having identical wall thickness. Two spirals with identical pitch and an interconnection at the tip of the core are machined into the outer core and inner core. In the assembled state, the spirals and interconnection overlap. The inner core is adhesively bonded, soldered or welded to the outer core at the end.

With hollow cores having a wall thickness greater than 5 mm, the two spirals can be machined on the inner core and thus save some of the work involved in the mold construction.

Example 2. Chassis mold with four slides

The mold illustrated in Figs. 1.5/15 to 1.5/19 is used to manufacture the chassis for an electrical machine. Components with very close tolerances as to the relative spacing must then be mounted on the chassis. The chassis are molded of glass-fiber-reinforced polyacetal. The cavity is filled via a hot runner and two conventional gates (conical). The chassis is required to exhibit optimum mechanical properties, minimal distortion and close tolerances. These requirements are decisive for placement of the cooling system in the mold. The cooling system is divided into seven circuits.

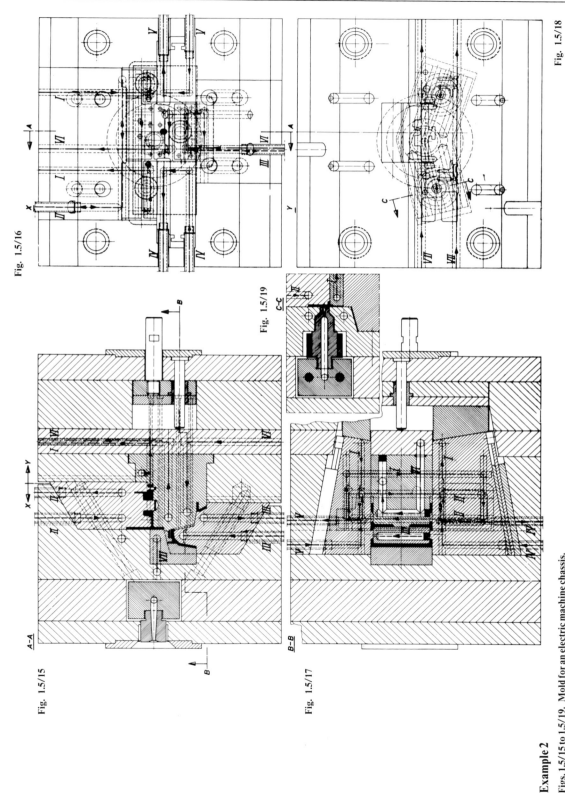

Fig. 1.5/16

Fig. 1.5/18

Fig. 1.5/15

Fig. 1.5/17

Fig. 1.5/19

Example 2

Figs. 1.5/15 to 1.5/19. Mold for an electric machine chassis.
Identification of the cooling systems: (*I*) outer stationary cores, (*II*, *III*) slides, (*IV*, *V*) core slides, (*VI*) main stationary core, (*VII*) runner plate.

Example 3. Injection mold for cover components of ABS

When designing a mold, not only the properties of the material to be processed but also constructional aspects should be taken into consideration in order to keep the mold costs low. In the present case, the objective is to build an injection mold for the production of cover components of ABS. The mold is to be designed using standard mold components. The molded part should exhibit as few changes in wall thickness as possible in order to facilitate filling of the mold. The resulting design uses a sprue and runner with pinpoint gating (see Figs. 1.5/20 to 1.5/22). An additional requirement was to provide especially good cooling. Ac-

cordingly, the inserts (a) and (b) in the stationary mold half were each provided with a peripheral cooling circuit (k_1). In addition, insert (a) was provided with spiral cooling (k_2) and insert (b_1) with bubbler-type cooling (k_3). The cores (c) and (d) in the movable mold half are provided with peripheral and bubbler cooling. To prevent deflection of the support plate (e), support pillars (g) are placed between the clamping plate (f) and the support plate (e). The return spring (h) retracts the ejector (i) from the mold parting line, thereby ensuring that the parts can fall freely.

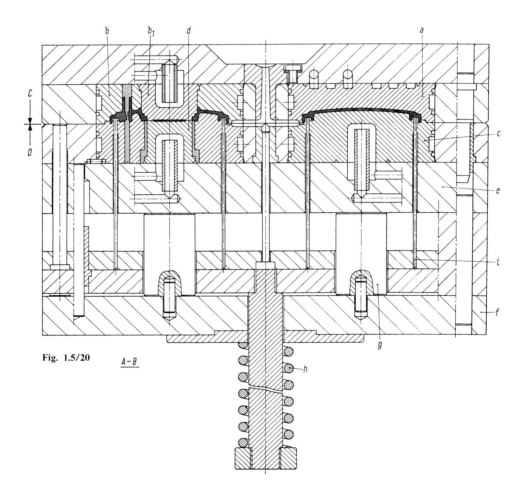

Fig. 1.5/20 $A - B$

Example 3

Figs. 1.5/20 to 1.5/22. Two-cavity injection mold for cover components of ABS, designed using standard mold components.
(a, b, b_1) inserts in stationary mold half, (c, d) cores in movable mold half, (e) support plate, (f) clamping plate, (g) support pillars, (h) return spring, (j) ejector, (k_1 to k_2) cooling channels.

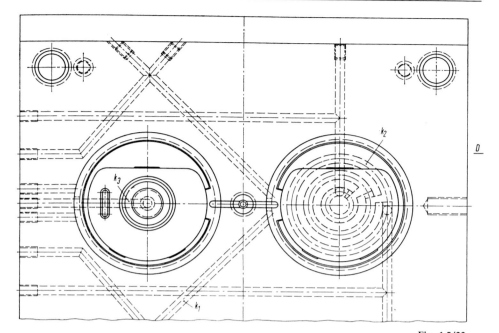

Fig. 1.5/22

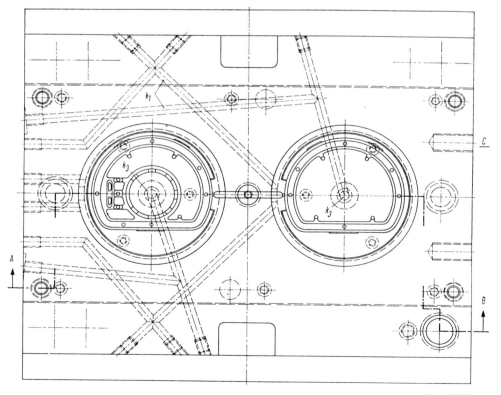

Fig. 1.5/21

Example 4. Four-cavity injection mold for production of ABS cases

The objective in this case is to mold rectangular cases with dimensions of 38×30 mm and 55 mm in height. The wall thickness was to be about 2 mm. Because of its low shrinkage, ABS was specified as the resin. Since a rapid cycle with this material could result in orientation in the case wall, and thus considerable internal stress, particular attention must be given to providing a good possibility for cooling/heating when designing the mold. Furthermore, the mold is to be designed using standard mold components. The result is a four-cavity mold (see Figs. 1.5/23 and 1.5/24). The molded parts (a) are filled via a sprue (b) and run-

ner (c) with tunnel (submarine) gate. As the mold opens, the sliding plate (d) with the slide is moved toward the center of the mold by the cam pin (e), thereby releasing an undercut in the interior of the molded parts so that they are ejected. The cavity retainer plate (f) on the stationary half of the mold is provided with four cooling channels (g) 9 mm in diameter through which the cooling water flows. The cooling channels (i) in the cores (h) on the movable mold half are provided with baffles (k) to direct the flow of the cooling medium.

Symbols used for the temperatures

t_1 = temperature of the plastic resin
t_2 = temperature of the mold body
t_3 = temperature of the wall of the cavity
t_4 = temperature of the wall of the cooling channel
t_5 = temperature of the cooling water

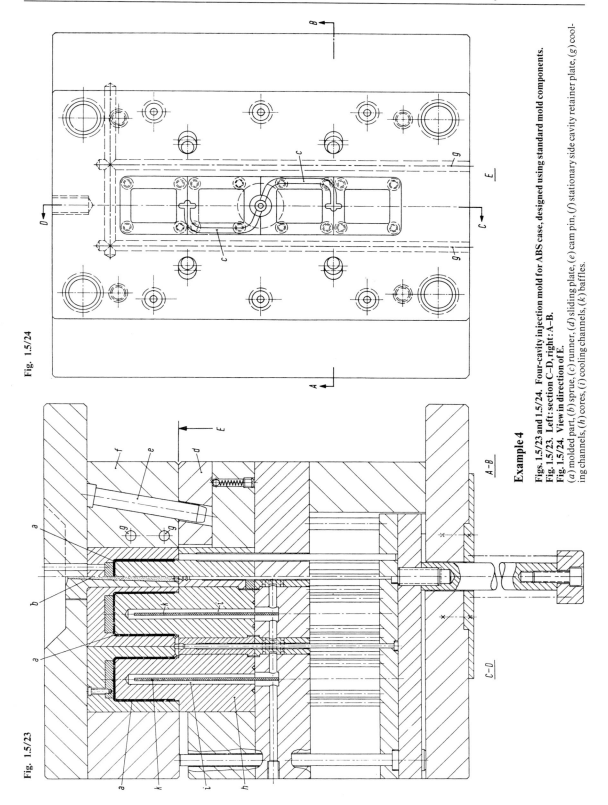

Fig. 1.5/24

Fig. 1.5/23

Example 4

Figs. 1.5/23 and 1.5/24. Four-cavity injection mold for ABS case, designed using standard mold components.
Fig. 1.5/23. Left: section C–D, right: A–B.
Fig. 1.5/24. View in direction of E.
(*a*) molded part, (*b*) sprue, (*c*) runner, (*d*) sliding plate, (*e*) cam pin, (*f*) stationary side cavity retainer plate, (*g*) cooling channels, (*h*) cores, (*i*) cooling channels, (*k*) baffles.

A–B

C–D

1.6   Fastening of Inserts

Round inserts

Multiple-cavity injection molds are usually so designed that round or rectangular inserts of high-grade tool steel, which is hardened, are placed in mold plates of unhardened, but possibly tempered, steel that can still be machined. An attempt should always be made to construct a mold in this manner, as the use of insert retainer plates can significantly reduce the tendency for distortion on hardening, which often occurs with larger mold plates. Since such insert retainer plates are usually bolted to other mold components, the simplest way to fasten round inserts is by means of a retaining shoulder. To prevent unwanted rotation with circular or in-line arrangements, the inserts are placed so close to each other that flats on the retaining shoulder of the inserts touch (Fig. 1.6/1).

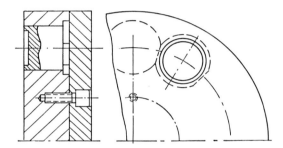

Fig. 1.6/1.   Insert with retaining shoulder.
The shoulders of the inserts are provided with flats to prevent rotation.

If the inserts cannot be placed close enough together, rotation is prevented through the use of locating pins (Fig. 1.6/2). In order to still be able to drill the locating holes for the pins after hardening and grinding the inserts, about 2 mm on the edge of the retaining shoulder is removed after carburizing so that the shoulder remains soft during hardening. To permit radial alignment of the inserts, they must be provided

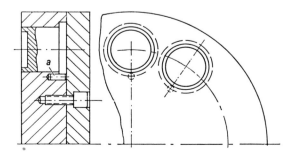

Fig. 1.6/2.   The insert is secured axially and radially by a small pin.

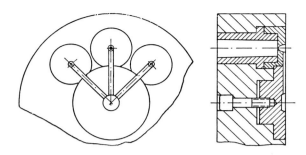

Fig. 1.6/3.   Securing the insert axially from both sides.

with a fit that permits rotation once they are installed (slide fit).

It occasionally happens with automatic degating molds that it is necessary to fasten inserts without retainer plates. The design shown in Fig. 1.6/3 provides such a possibility. It has the advantage that the inserts are held in position both axially and radially. At the same time, the runners are located completely in hardened steel.

Rectangular inserts

Because of their shape, many injection molded parts require rectangular inserts. These in turn require retainer plates, which are held in place by the guide pins and guide bushings. The holes for guide pins and guide bushings are drilled through both the retainer plates and support plates behind them at the same time. The guide pins and bushings are then fitted into the plates and the pockets for the inserts are machined into the joined plates. The cooling is most effective, of course, if the cooling channels are located directly in the inserts. If, however, the inserts have many cores

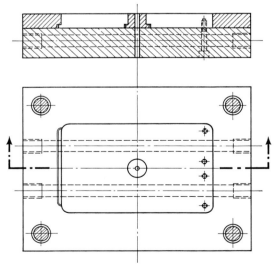

Fig. 1.6/4.   Rectangular inserts.

between which there is no place for cooling water channels, these channels must be located in the support plate or stationary clamping plate.

Whenever possible, the inserts should be fastened in the retainer plates without the use of a retaining shoulder (Fig. 1.6/4, right). This means, of course, that they must be bolted to the support plate to prevent them from falling out. Inserts without shoulders can be ground all around, which simplifies manufacturing the pockets in the retainer plates. Often, however, no place for cooling water channels remains when fastening the inserts. In this case, the inserts must be fastened in the retainer plate by means of a shoulder (Fig. 1.6/4, left). Shoulders placed on two opposite sides are usually adequate, so that the two other sides may be ground smooth.

1.7   Determining the Most Economical Number of Cavities for Injection Molding[5]

There are considerable differences in price and energy consumption between injection molding machines with identical ratings, but produced by different manufacturers. The investigations that have appeared to date with the objective of determining the most economical number of cavities have not taken these differences into account. The machine hour costs were incorporated into the calculations only as a function of the machine rating. In the following, the most economical machine and number of cavities for the production of a specific part will be determined on the basis of respective machine hour costs.

The determination of the most economical number of cavities for injection molding has already been the object of extensive discussions[6, 7]. In the course of these discussions, each of the individual authors has approached the solution to this problem from a different side, where, nevertheless, the hourly costs of the machine used play an important role. In one case[6] the machine hour rate is considered exclusively as a function of the clamping force of the machine. From Table 1 of this work, the machine hour rate can be determined from the machine costs and the machine operating time (Table 1.7/1).

In the other case[7] the maximum shot weight of the machine provides the basis for the machine hour rate (Table 1.7/2).

The costs of a machine hour include:

– The amortization costs of the machine (which are a function of the purchase price)
– The energy costs
– The maintenance and service costs
– Overhead (heating, lighting, material handling, administration, etc.) and
– Wages

It is known that machines with identical ratings but produced by different manufacturers exhibit considerable differences in purchase price, which influences the machine hour rate considerably through the amortizations costs. The purchase price of a new, modern machine is much higher than that of a machine bought, for instance, 10 years ago but having an identical rating (identical shot volume). There will also be differences in maintenance and service, energy costs and wages. Experience has shown that when taking these aspects into account differences that may be up to 100 % can result for certain machine hour rates for identical machine ratings. Accordingly, a value for the economical number of cavities determined on the basis of flat machine hour rates will not be completely satisfactory. Therefore a more refined calculation that takes into account the above-mentioned situation must be applied.

While such a computational method is sure to provide reliable results, in a large plant it will require considerable effort when a choice is to be made between machines from various manufacturers and having different ratings. The following procedure leads to a rapid and exact determination of the most economical machine and number of cavities for production of a given part.

Table 1.7/1.   Machine hour rate[5] (incl. wages)

Machine size kN	250	500	1000	1500	2250	3000
Machine hour rate DM/h	12.50	15.—	17.30	19.50	23.50	28.50

Table 1.7/2.   Machine hour rate[6] (without wages)

Shot weight g	10	20	50	80	160	300	550	1000	1200
Machine hour rate DM/h	4.—	4.50	5.—	8.—	10.—	12.—	20.—	24.—	28.—

[5] Reprinted in part with the permission of VDI-Verlag from the book *Qualitätsformteile aus thermoplastischen Kunststoffen,* by Geyer, Gemmer, Strehlow, 2nd ed., 1974.

[6] J. Pröls, lecture, 12th Plastics Colloquium, SKZ, Würzburg/W. Germany, 1971. Abridged in *Kunststoffe,* vol. 62, 1972, pp. 33–34.

[7] F. Dralle and H. Gemmer, *Kunststoffe,* vol. 62, 1972, pp. 158–165.

Let Q represent some characteristic parameter of the processing machine (e.g., for injection molding machines, the shot weight or the shot volume, or possibly the clamping force; for compression presses, the compression force) and q represent the corresponding characteristic parameter of the molded part (e.g., the weight or volume, or the compression pressure needed to mold the part). It then follows that

$$x = Q/q \tag{1}$$

cavities are possible. If n is the quantity to be produced, the number of cycles necessary for this quantity is given by

$$n/x = nq/Q \tag{2}$$

With a cycle time of t [s], the required manufacturing time is given by

$$T = nqt/Q \text{ s} \tag{3a}$$

or

$$T = nqt/3600\,Q \text{ h} \tag{3b}$$

If the operating costs of the machine, including wages, are given as U [DM/h], the manufacturing costs (not including material costs) are given by

$$K_M = nqtU/3600\,Q \text{ DM} \tag{4}$$

With the costs K_G for producing that part of the mold that is unaffected by the number of cavities and the costs K_W for producing the mold inserts ($K_W = xK_{W1}$, with $K_{W1} = $ costs for producing one cavity), the manufacturing costs K for a certain part (not including material costs) are given by:

$$K = K_M + K_W + K_G \tag{5}$$

or

$$K = nqtU/3600\,Q + K_{W1}Q/q + K_G \tag{5a}$$

These costs are a minimum when

$$dK/dQ = 0$$

i.e., when

$$-\frac{nqtU}{3600\,Q^2} + \frac{K_{W1}}{q} = 0 \tag{6}$$

Rearrangement of the above gives

$$U/Q^2 = 3600\,K_{W1}/nq^2\,t \tag{6a}$$

Next, the value of U/Q^2 for each machine available must be established and recorded. When selecting the most economical machine for a given part, the value of the right side of eq. (6a) must be determined with the

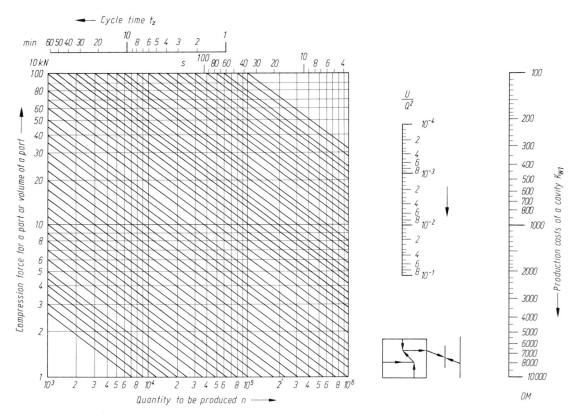

Fig. 1.7/1. Nomograph for selecting the most economical machine and number of cavities.

Table 1.7/3. Sample calculation. Total quantity required $n = 3\,000\,000$ pcs; part-dependent clamping force per cavity $q = 180\,kN/pc$

<table>
<tr><td rowspan="8">Data from [1], Table 1</td><td>1</td><td>Machine variable Q</td><td>kN</td><td>250</td><td>500</td><td>1000</td><td>1500</td><td>2250</td><td>3000</td></tr>
<tr><td>2</td><td>Machine-limited number of cavities</td><td>pc</td><td>1</td><td>2</td><td>4</td><td>6</td><td>10</td><td>14</td></tr>
<tr><td>3</td><td>Machine time required for the total quantity needed</td><td>h</td><td>22 600</td><td>11 700</td><td>6050</td><td>4170</td><td>2500</td><td>1780</td></tr>
<tr><td>4</td><td>Machine costs for the total quantity needed</td><td>DM</td><td>283 000</td><td>176 000</td><td>105 000</td><td>81 000</td><td>58 800</td><td>50 800</td></tr>
<tr><td>5</td><td>Mold costs, base</td><td>DM</td><td>22 500</td><td>16 500</td><td>11 800</td><td>6300</td><td>7500</td><td>10 000</td></tr>
<tr><td>6</td><td>Mold costs, inserts</td><td>DM</td><td>11 500</td><td>13 800</td><td>18 400</td><td>13 800</td><td>23 000</td><td>32 100</td></tr>
<tr><td>7</td><td>Number of molds needed</td><td>pcs</td><td>5</td><td>3</td><td>2</td><td>1</td><td>1</td><td>1</td></tr>
<tr><td>8</td><td>Total production costs per piece</td><td>DM/pc</td><td>0.107</td><td>0.069</td><td>0.045</td><td>0.034</td><td>0.030</td><td>0.031</td></tr>
<tr><td rowspan="6">Calculated from the above values</td><td>9</td><td>Machine hour costs $U(4:3)$</td><td>DM/h</td><td>12.50</td><td>15.—</td><td>17.70</td><td>19.50</td><td>23.50</td><td>28.50</td></tr>
<tr><td>10</td><td>Square of the machine variable Q^2</td><td>$10^2\,kN^2$</td><td>625</td><td>2500</td><td>10 000</td><td>22 500</td><td>50 700</td><td>90 000</td></tr>
<tr><td>11</td><td>Characteristic index $U/Q^2\,(\cdot\,10^{-4})$</td><td>DM/h kN²</td><td>2</td><td>0.6</td><td>0.173</td><td>0.0865</td><td>0.0464</td><td>0.0317</td></tr>
<tr><td>12</td><td>Mold base costs per 1 mold K_G (5:7)</td><td>DM/pc</td><td>5100</td><td>5500</td><td>5900</td><td>6300</td><td>7500</td><td>10 000</td></tr>
<tr><td>13</td><td>Cost K_{W1} for 1 insert $(6:(2\cdot 7))$</td><td>DM/pc</td><td>2300</td><td>2300</td><td>2300</td><td>2300</td><td>2300</td><td>2300</td></tr>
<tr><td>14</td><td>Cycle time $t\,\dfrac{2\cdot 3\cdot 3600}{3\,000\,000}$</td><td>s</td><td>27.2</td><td>28</td><td>29</td><td>30</td><td>30</td><td>30
30</td></tr>
</table>

known values of K_{W1}, n, q and t. Then that machine whose value of U/Q^2 comes closest to this value must be found. This machine is the most economical one for the job involved. If the selected machine is not suitable for some technical reason, e.g., the platens are too small, the next-best machine must be selected. The number of cavities is given by eq. (1).

The calculation is facilitated through use of the nomogram given in Fig. 1.7/1. The inventory number of each machine available can be recorded to the left of the U/Q^2 axis.

It should also be mentioned that depending on the different meanings of the quantity Q, different nomograms can be prepared. Accordingly, the most economical injection molding machine or compression press can be selected with respect to clamping force, shot weight or compression force. Experience has shown that it suffices to consider the shot volume or compression force for injection molding machines and compression presses respectively, and then examine the so-selected machine with respect to the remaining specifications (clamping force, mold mounting dimensions, etc.).

While the values of the quantities K_{W1} or t are still uncertain in the initial phase of mold planning, sufficiently accurate values should be established in order to give the mold planner reference points. At a more advanced stage of the project, the calculation can be checked, if necessary, with the more accurate data now available. It should also be pointed out that a somewhat larger number of cavities increases the cost of producing the mold relatively less than a smaller number of cavities does, particularly as a larger number of cavities permits the use of modern manufactur-

ing methods (e.g., hobbing, the use of Cu-Be mold sets or precision casting), which significantly reduces the costs of mold making[6].

As an example for the procedure described, the calculation for one case[5] will be presented. From Table 1.7/3, the cycle time t is obtained as 30 s and the costs K_{W1} for a mold insert as DM 2300.00. An additional 10 to 15 % for the costs of increasing the mold base size due to an increase in the number of cavities must also be added.

The result is:

$$\frac{3600\,K_{W1}}{n\,q^2\,t} = \frac{3600 \times 2530}{3\,000\,000 \times 324 \times 30} = 3.14 \times 10^{-4}$$

According to Table 1.7/3, this value of U/Q^2 corresponds best to the 3000 kN machine, which should be used as long as the remaining technical data are satisfactory. According to the other procedure[5], the 2250 kN machine is the most economical. The difference of 0.001 DM/piece (see line 8 in Table 1.7/1) is negligibly small. It results from the costs for the mold base for this size machine probably having been assumed too high in the case mentioned[5].

With such slight differences, use of the larger number of cavities is generally more practical, since this machine will require less time to produce the quantity needed.

Today there is a definite trend to produce highly technical small parts in multiple-cavity molds. In view of this fact, it should be clarified before completing the design of the mold whether a multiple-cavity mold can be considered for production of the parts in question.

The number of cavities is ultimately determined by

- The technical capabilities and facilities available
- The quality requirements
- The delivery deadlines
- Economical considerations

In order to make a decision, the most economical number of cavities must first be determined. Next, the most economical number of cavities so determined must be evaluated in conjunction with the above-mentioned requirements.

To establish the most economical number of cavities, a procedure has been developed

- Where the individual plant capabilities and part-related factors are taken into consideration
- That is independent of time-related aspects
- That does not require a great deal of calculation
- That uses information and numerical values taken as the basis of a calculation performed in accordance with economical principles
- That eliminates the fear on the part of the mold designer or planner of having designed or conceived an uneconomical mold

A prerequisite for determining the most economical number of cavities, however, is exact knowledge of the market possibilites for the planned molded part, i.e., the total quantity needed must be specified exactly if uneconomical production is to be avoided. The total quantity needed is the number of pieces on which the entire calculation is based for a given period of time. This period of time selected should not be too long, as otherwise difficult to determine market-oriented and financial aspects that cannot be incorporated in a long-term calculation may play a role.

By definition, the most economical production is achieved when the costs of the particular molded part are as low as possible.

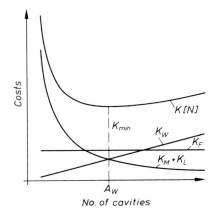

Fig. 1.7/2. Theoretical dependence of the machine costs (K_M), wages (K_L) mold costs (K_W), material costs (K_F) and manufacturing costs (K) on the number of cavities.

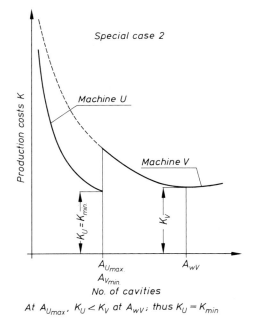

Case 1: For several injection molding machines, the economical number of cavities falls within the limiting number of cavities $(A_{(N)min}, A_{(N)max})$.

Case 2: The manufacturing costs on the next-smaller injection molding machine with the maximum number of cavities are below the manufacturing costs on the injection molding machine with the economical number of cavities.

Fig. 1.7/3. Special cases encountered when determining the economical number of cavities.

From both theory and practice it is known that

- The machine costs and wages decrease with an increasing number of cavities
- The mold costs increase with an increasing number of cavities
- The material costs of production – barring exceptions – are not affected by the number of cavities in a production mold

The sum of these costs yields the manufacturing costs, which, when plotted as a function of the number of cavities, passes through a minimum at the most economical number of cavities A_W (Fig. 1.7/2).

Since the machine hour rates for the machine sizes under consideration cannot be plotted as a mathematical function of the number of cavities, there is the danger that the economical number of cavities determined will not lead to the most economical production. To eliminate the possibility of uneconomical production, two special cases must be investigated (Fig. 1.7/3).

These special cases are encountered only seldom in actual practice, but in the initial stages of a project it cannot be established whether the present investigation is such a special case. Accordingly, the limits of the above procedure should always be ascertained.

Table 1.7/4. Definitions and symbols for determining the most economical number of cavities

Symbol	Definition	Unit
$A_W(N)$	Economical number of cavities for a specific injection molding machine	Pieces
A_{Ws}	Most economical number of cavities	Pieces
F	Costs that result from manufacturing and inserting a cavity in the mold base	DM/piece
G	Weight of the molded part	kg/piece
g	Runner weight per molded part	kg/piece
$K(N)$	Nominal manufacturing costs incurred when producing the molded parts on a specific injection molding machine	DM
K_t	Actual manufacturing costs	DM
L	Wage rate (prorated)	DM/h
$M(N)$	Machine hour rate for a specific injection molding machine	DM/h
(N)	Designation of the injection molding machine	
Q	Total quantity ordered	pieces
R	Raw material price	DM/kg
t_z	Molding cycle	s
WG	Costs for the mold base and design costs	DM
$A_{(N)max}$	Maximum possible number of cavities for a specific injection molding machine	Pieces
$A_{(N)min}$	Minimum possible number of cavities for a specific injection molding machine	Pieces

The most economical number of cavities can also be determined from the flow diagram given in Fig. 1.7/4. The above-mentioned special cases are incorporated in this flow diagram.

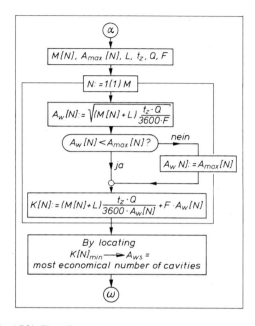

Fig. 1.7/4. Flow diagram for determining the most economical number of cavities (see Table 1.7/4 for definitions).

It must, however, also be pointed out that in the equation used to determine the manufacturing costs $K(N)$ all the cost factors independent of the number of cavities had not been taken into account. The nominal manufacturing costs will differ in any case from the actual manufacturing costs and, in this form, can only serve as the basis of a calculation if the material costs of production, costs of the mold base and design costs are taken into account.

The actual manufacturing costs K_t are calculated from the following equation (with the most economical number of cavities):

$$K_t = (M+L)\frac{t_z \times Q}{3600 \times A_{ws}} + F \times A_{ws} + WG + (G+g) \times Q \times R \qquad (7)$$

To simplify determination of the economical number of cavities A_W, the nomograph shown in Fig. 1.7/5 was developed. Use of this nomograph is illustrated for three examples. When determining the economical number of cavities, however, the limits should still be ascertained.

The manufacturing costs $K(N)$ are plotted as a function of the number of cavities for these three examples in Fig. 1.7/6.

It can be seen that the graph of the costs as a function of the number of cavities is consistent with that shown in Fig. 1.7/2.

As mentioned in the beginning, the number of cavities cannot be established only on the basis of economical considerations. The following questions must be asked after the most economical number of cavities has been calculated:

– Can the quality requirements – primarily those concerning shape and dimensional tolerances – be met with parts molded in the multiple-cavity mold? The part properties will, without a doubt, be impaired with an increasing number of cavities.
– Is it technically feasible to make a functional mold with the calculated most economical number of cavities? The requirement here is that the cavities be

produced with considerably greater dimensional accuracy than the molded parts.
– Is an injection molding machine suitable for the mold with the most economical number of cavities available for production?
– Is a symmetrical distribution of cavities over the working area of the mold possible for the most economical number of cavities?
– Does the delivery deadline permit construction of a mold with a large number of cavities?
– Will the output from a mold with the most economical number of cavities permit the order to be filled on time?

Construction of a mold with the most economical number of cavities is justified only if these six questions can be answered in the affirmative. If only one question can be answered in the affirmative, the factor relating to this question should be used as the basis for determining the number of cavities.

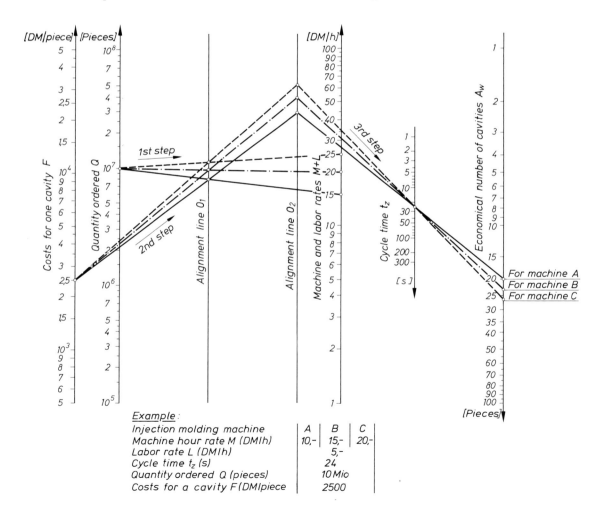

Example:

	A	B	C
Injection molding machine			
Machine hour rate M (DM/h)	10,-	15,-	20,-
Labor rate L (DM/h)		5,-	
Cycle time t_z (s)		24	
Quantity ordered Q (pieces)		10 Mio	
Costs for a cavity F (DM/piece)		2500	

Fig. 1.7/5. Nomograph for determining the economical number of cavities (with example).

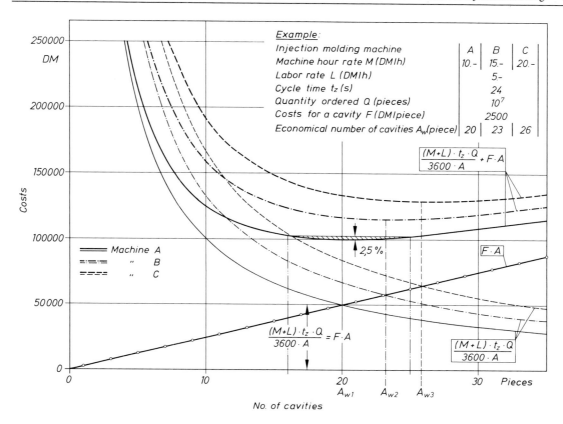

Fig. 1.7/6. Dependence of machine costs, wages, mold costs and manufacturing costs on the number of cavities (example).

1.8   How Can the Costs for Making Injection Molds Be Reduced?

The precision demanded of injection molds increases continually. Fierce competition requires greater and greater productivity from and service life for injection molds. The situation is aggravated by a pronounced shortage of experienced skilled labor, so that very often difficult work on complicated molds must be performed by individuals who are not sufficiently familiar with the necessary techniques.

In many mold making shops, much time is lost through requests for more detailed information and subsequent deliberations, because satisfactory drawings that would permit construction of the mold are lacking. Even today there are many shops that make injection molds worth thousands from a hand sketch. Once such a mold has reached that stage of completion (generally after a great deal of material has been wasted) where thoughts are given to the cooling, it is often found that there is no space for cooling water channels. In desperation, a few coils of copper tubing, the cooling capacity of which is usually quite small, are then soldered around the outside of the mold.

If for injection molds built in this manner the hours spent with deliberations, requests for additional information, repeated work and the like are conscientiously recorded, it is found that 30 to 40 hours, and often even more, could have been saved if the work had been better organized.

This loss of productive work, however, does not mean only lost earnings. Since the machine tools are generally idle during such further deliberations and consultations, the cost of the mold is actually considerably higher because of the wages paid and operating costs incurred during such wasted time.

The situation described above is then often further aggravated by a factor that results in an even greater cost. Once the mold has been finally completed and tested, most often significantly later than the agreed-on date, this and that shortcoming, requiring extensive rework and change, is found. Additional time is lost and costs are incurred, and the customer becomes only more dissatisfied.

The obvious question is how such undesirable cost increases can be avoided. An essential prerequisite is careful job planning. This involves not only those questions related to production of the mold but also those intended to clarify technical details. Often the ordering party is not quite certain how many cavities are needed in the mold. Accordingly, the machine in which the mold is supposed to run and the productivity of this machine must be established on the basis of an estimated need and the machines available before specifying the number of cavities. This requires in particular knowledge of the clamping force of the machine as well as the plasticating capacity. Once these questions have been clarified, an exact drawing of the

part to be molded must be prepared if it is not already available, and tolerances should be specified from the very beginning if dimensional accuracy is required of the molded parts. The question of tolerances has a significant effect on the costs of the mold and they should therefore be established unambiguously in conjunction with the customer. The tolerances listed in standards are not satisfactory in many cases. On the other hand, tolerances closer than those listed in the standards often lead to a considerable increase in the amount of work needed to make injection molds. With excessively close tolerances, the productivity may also drop noticeably, as the range of operating conditions is restricted, and with excessively stringent requirements for dimensional accuracy the molded parts may even have to be sorted, which results in a considerably higher reject rate.

An essential aspect of this preliminary work is clarifying how the part should be molded with as few gates as possible, taking into account the flow conditions and physical properties required. Often an individual familiar with mold making will be able to provide valuable suggestions concerning slight changes to the part that will greatly simplify making the mold. Any such changes, however, must not impair the part performance expected by the customer, and it is therefore best that they be discussed personally with the designer.

Once all these questions have been clarified with the customer, the actual preparation for the mold making begins. The first step is preparation of an assembly drawing of the mold by an experienced designer. The costs incurred here are well spent in any case, since it is only at the drawing board, and not from hasty sketches, that all factors that affect proper operation of a production injection mold can be reviewed. Since erasing and changing a design drawing are considerably less expensive and simpler than changing the finished mold, it is only in this manner that the most economical construction and reliable operation of the mold can be achieved. An experienced designer can look at a design drawing and tell whether, for instance, the part will release properly, adequate cooling has been provided, etc. To the extent that there is close cooperation among the operators of individual machine tools in small mold making shops, a carefully prepared assembly drawing, which must include the parts list and all dimensions of individual components, generally suffices. This is true especially when a single individual performs all of the planning, turning, grinding, drilling operations, etc., in the course of making the mold. From the assembly drawing he will be able to establish which fits are required for the individual components, even when this is not indicated in the assembly drawing.

The situation is different, however, in a larger shop where the individual machining departments are separated from each other. In this case, drawings of the individual mold components are worthwhile. However, since the fit requirements cannot be reviewed in relation to other parts, these drawings must contain exact tolerances (ISO fits) if unnecessary inquiries for more detailed information and expensive rework of the individual components are to be avoided. Instructions are also necessary on the drawings if, for instance, several inserts are to be drilled simultaneously for the purpose of exact alignment of holes, or if a second plate is to be drilled only after a previously hardened plate in order to avoid any displacement as the result of distortion on hardening. It goes without saying that machining instructions such as finish machining, grinding, polishing, etc., are also to be indicated on these drawings.

In a properly organized machine shop, the individual mold components arriving for final assembly from the various machining departments should fit together in such a way that the mold maker has to make only minor adjustments to fits. His actual job is assembly of the mold and final finish and polishing. If the necessary machine tools (grinding machines, lathes, milling machines, drill presses, etc.) are available to him, considerable time and effort and especially time-consuming explanations can be saved.

The number of working hours that can be saved in such a strictly organized mold making shop is astonishing. The higher overhead incurred in a larger shop due to the greater number of machines and the expenses for organization can be more than offset by the considerable time savings. Finally, this results not only in a reduction of the production costs but above all in a shortening of the delivery times, which in very many cases is critical for obtaining the job. While in a small shop a single individual performs almost all necessary machining operations on a mold, in a large shop the planning, turning, grinding and drilling operations needed to produce the individual components can take place simultaneously, so that the time required to complete the mold can be reduced significantly.

Example 5.   Six-cavity mold for measuring spoons

The considerations that led to the design of a six-cavity mold for measuring spoons will be discussed in example 5.

The requirement was to achieve a guaranteed output of 1600 measuring spoons per hour from an automatic injection molding machine with a maximum plasticating capacity of 8 kg/h. For economic reasons, the number of cavities in the mold was to be kept as small as possible. For reasons associated with melt flow, the part had to be gated at the center of the bottom of the spoon, since after test molding with the gate on the handle the bowls of the spoons split too easily along the resulting weld line.

Although a four-cavity mold would have been adequate to produce the required quantity with a readily achievable seven shots per minute, a six-cavity mold was designed. This was done on the one hand with a view to providing a certain reserve capacity with respect to the required quantity, but above all because of the complicated part removal situation in the self-degating mold that was needed in this case. With a six-cavity mold, the guaranteed production rate could be achieved with 4½ shots per minute, so that 13.5 s were available for a molding cycle. With favorable cooling possibilities for the thin-walled measuring spoon, this provided sufficient time to ensure that the runner system and six measuring spoons could drop safely out of the mold. The 1600 pieces per hour, including the runner, require a plasticating capacity of 6.4 kg/h, so that even in this regard the machine plasticating capacity of 8 kg/h provides a certain reserve.

Figures 1.8/1 to 1.8/7 show the mold design. The measuring spoons are arranged in two rows of three spoons each, with a pinpoint gate at the center of the bottom of each spoon.

In order to ensure good cooling of the cores used to form the bowls of the spoons, an inside ejector, which would have been adequate, was not used. Rather, the cavity plate on the movable half was designed to function as a stripper plate. Since, however, the parts cannot fall from this plate automatically because of the cavities engraved for the handles, a spring-loaded ejector 2 mm in diameter was provided at each handle to knock the individual spoons out of the flat handle cavities in the stripper plate after this plate had stripped the bowls of the spoons off the cores. To ensure trouble-free production of the mold, individual drawings of the mold components were prepared.

Example 5 (right side)

Figs. 1.8/1 to 1.8/7. Six-cavity mold for a measuring spoon.
(*1*) Nut, (*2*) ejector plate, (*3*) ejector rod, (*4*) movable side clamp plate, (*5*) core plate, (*6*) rear ejector plates, (*7*) bar, (*8*) front ejector plate, (*9*) return pin, (*10*) ejector housing, (*11,12*) cavity plates, (*13*) socket head hex bolts, (*14*) stripper plate, (*15*) stationary side clamp plate, (*16*) socket head hex bolts, (*17*) locating ring, (*18*) sprue bushing, (*19*) spring bumper pads, (*20*) compression spring, (*21*) socket head hex bolts, (*22/23*) O-ring, (*24*) gasket, (*25*) guide strips, (*26*) cooling water connection, (*27*) round head bolts, (*28*) locating pin, (*29*) leaf spring, (*30*) rivet, (*31*) latch, (*32*) release bar, (*33*) socket head hex bolts, (*34*) cooling water tube (bubbler), (*35*) O-ring, (*36*) compression spring, (*37*) spring-loaded pin, (*38*) ejector pin, (*39*) core, (*40*) core pin, (*41*) runner insert, (*42*) guide pin, (*43*) set screw, (*44*) guide bushing.

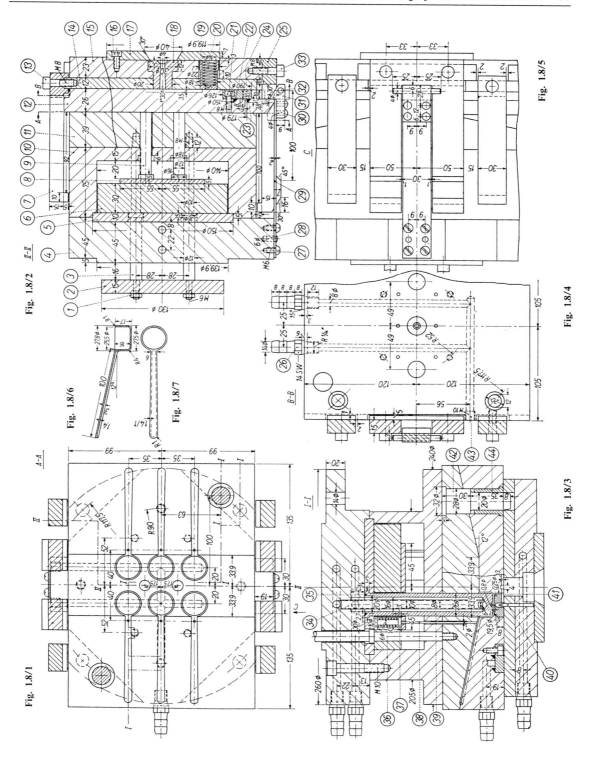

Fig. 1.8/1
Fig. 1.8/2
Fig. 1.8/3
Fig. 1.8/4
Fig. 1.8/5
Fig. 1.8/6
Fig. 1.8/7

Example 6   Injection mold for a square six-liter container (ice cream container)

The core halves of these and similar molds should if possible be machined from a single piece of steel. Only in the ideal case is filling so uniform that the melt issuing from the gate fills the cavity symmetrically. In practice, however, it is continually observed that, in accordance with the law of least resistance, the melt flows faster on one side of the core or the other, thereby exerting a considerable lateral pressure against the core and forcing it to the opposite side. As a result, the wall thickness of the molded part is not uniform, and it becomes difficult to release the molded part because the core tends to spring back into its original position as the cavity pressure drops, thereby wedging the molded part in the cavity.

Often, important factors preclude an optimum design: it may be difficult, expensive and time-consuming to procure an appropriately sized, specially forged piece of steel, or shaping the core may require a great deal of machining and this expensive work must be performed on very large milling machines, and lathes (e.g., for a pail mold).

The present example does not show the optimum mold design, but rather a practical alternative, namely a mold with an assembled core. Such a mold does not require a special forging. It can be made quicker and less expensively, and if produced with a high level of precision provides all prerequisites necessary to ensure an exceptionally long service life even for long production runs.

The mold was designed by E. Fristedt of Rantil Plast AB, Karlskrona, Sweden, for a rectangular container to be molded of high-density polyethylene.

A continuous raised edge was specified for the bottom. The upper edge is designed for use with a snap-on cover of low-density polyethylene. The mold used for this cover ist quite conventional and thus requires no description. Because the upper edge of the container was required to be flash-free and rounded, a stripper plate had to be provided instead of ejector pins, which would have been simpler. Because of the injection molding machine to be used, the core retainer plate (a) could only be 115.0 mm thick in the present case, as a result of which the core retaining recess could only be 55.0 mm deep, which is dangerously close to the minimum necessary for such a tall core. The effectiveness of the stripper plate as an additional core support should not be overestimated; it is virtually nonexistent. If injection molding machines providing a larger mold mounting height are available for a mold designed in this manner, the additional mold height must be used to strengthen the core retainer plate.

While ideally the cavity half should also be machined from a single piece, the present example shows an inserted bottom plate (b), which was chosen because of the required raised edge, the recess for which could not have been machined conventionally at the bottom of the cavity. Furthermore, the separate bottom plate offered the advantage of being able to place two large cooling channels around the sprue. The core is provided with nine baffled cooling channels, i.e., with quite adequate cooling capacity. In addition, the core has four conventional air valves.

What the ideal mold, with its respective core and cavity halves each machined from a single piece, offers inherently, namely stability, must be achieved in the design described here through accuracy of fit. It is practical to proceed as follows:

The core (c) ground to provide a precision fit in the core retainer plate (a) is inserted and bolted tight. The core is hardened, the retainer plate (a) tempered. The stripper plate (d), either with an inserted, hardened stripper ring (not shown) ground to provide a precision fit to the core or machined from a single piece of nitrided steel, is put in place. Strips of aluminum or brass sheet metal having exactly the thickness corresponding to the distance between core and cavity in the closed mold (i.e., the wall thickness of the molded part plus the necessary additional amount for shrinkage) are placed on all four sides of the core. Next, the tempered cavity plate (e) is put in place. The resulting assembly is now clamped together firmly, if possible by means of at least four through bolts with nuts or by means of external clamps. In an appropriately sized drill press, the four guide bores as well as the bores for the horizontal locating pins (f) provided on each side to ensure permanent alignment of the cavity plate (e) and stripper plate (d) are now drilled.

After disassembly of the mold, the guide pins (g) and guide bushings (h) and (i) are pressed into the guide bores.

While it may be theoretically true that the components of such a mold are guided and fit together best if the guide bores are drilled in each piece separately on a jig boring machine and then finished on a coordinate grinding machine, the procedure described above guarantees very accurate guidance and a uniform wall thickness for the molded part even though the mold may be built in a less extensively equipped workshop.

The stripper plate (d) requires some comment. In the present design there is a completely straight fit between core and stripper plate. Doesn't this mean that the core and stripper plate might seize at this spot? The answer is: Experience has shown that if the guiding elements are provided as described and ground to a precision fit, seizing is not to be expected.

The straight fit between core and stripper plate offers the advantages of being simpler to make, and later in production, of ensuring that there will be neither flash nor any displacement. With each closing, the clamping force repeats the assembly and clamping of

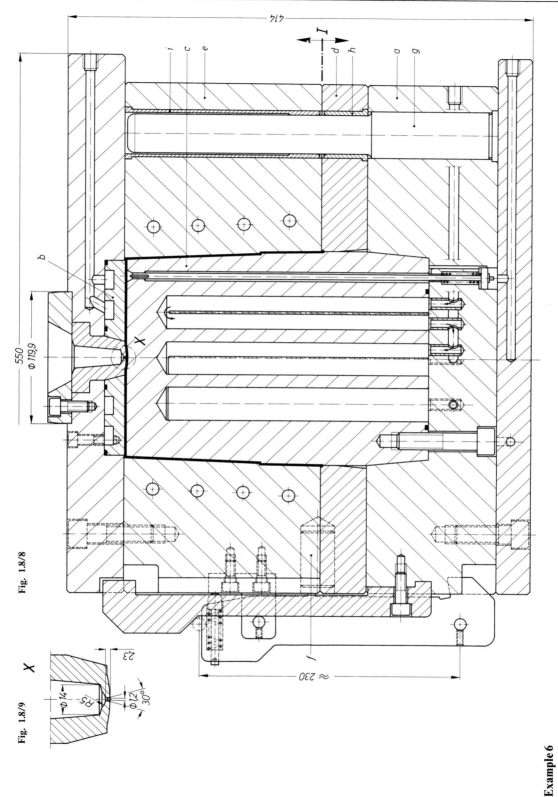

Fig. 1.8/8

Fig. 1.8/9

Example 6

Figs. 1.8/8 and 1.8/9. Injection mold for square six-liter container.
(*a*) Core retainer plate, (*b*) bottom plate, (*c*) core, (*d*) stripper plate, (*e*) cavity plate, (*f*) locating pin, (*g*) guide pin, (*h*, *i*) guide bushings.

the individual components into a solid block. While a tapered fit between core and stripper plate eliminates any possibility of seizing because the parts do not touch until the end of the closing stroke, such a fit is more expensive and does not eliminate the possibility

of flash formation or displacement. The latter could occur, for instance, if the core expanded somewhat more than did the stripper plate as the result of warming and would already be in contact with the taper before completion of the stroke of the plate.

Examples 7, 8 and 9. Alternative mold designs for a pump impeller

There are often several alternative mold designs for injection molding of thermoplastics. An automatically operating mold with high output ist not always the most favorable. Rather, the type of mold for which the sum of mold making costs and manufacturing costs for injection molding (including secondary operations) are lowest, or whether, because of a possible bottleneck in the mold making shop, another version that may have higher production costs may be more advantageous must be examined on an individual basis.

Of the costs to manufacture injection molded parts, a considerable portion is associated with mold amortization, so that lower mold costs considerably improve the economics of injection molding. The following equation applies when determining the production costs K_M (in DM) of a part (without material costs)

$$K_M = \frac{n \times q \times t \times U}{3600 \ Q} = \frac{n \times t \times U}{3600 \ x} \tag{1}$$

where n = quantity to be produced, q = volume of a part in cm³, t = cycle time in s, U = machine operating costs in DM/h, Q = shot volume in cm³ and $x = Q/q$ = number of cavities in the mold.

The production costs K_W (in DM) of the mold (as a function of the number of cavities) are

$$K_W \approx x \times K_{W1} \tag{2}$$

where K_{W1} = production costs of a cavity in DM. According to the analysis of Sors[8], that machine is most economical for which

$$\frac{U}{Q^2} = \frac{3600 \times K_{W1}}{n \times q^2 \times t} \tag{3}$$

Rearranging eq. (3) gives

$$\frac{Q^2}{q^2} = x^2 = \frac{n \times t \times U}{3600 \times K_{W1}} \tag{4}$$

Inserting the expression for x obtained from eq. (4) in eq. (1) it follows that

$$K_M = \sqrt{\frac{n \times t \times U \times K_{W1}}{3600}} \tag{5}$$

If this value of x is inserted in eq. (2), it is interesting to note that the same result is obtained for K_W. This means that optimum conditions occur when the fraction of mold making costs proportional to the number

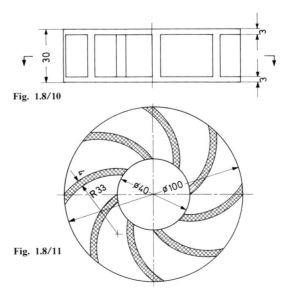

Fig. 1.8/10

Fig. 1.8/11

Figs. 1.8/10 and 1.8/11. Pump impeller.

[8] L. Sors, *Kunststoffe,* vol. 65, 1975, pp. 120-122.

of cavities equals the part production costs (without material costs).

The part production costs are composed primarily of the labor costs and operating costs of the injection molding machine, and together yield a certain hourly rate. Starting with the fact that when making the molds both machine work and manual work (albeit with higher labor costs than for injection molding, but with no machine costs) are performed, it may be assumed that the hourly rate for injection molding does not differ considerably from that for mold making. The con-

clusion is that optimum conditions occur when the time to make a mold is approximately equal to the production time for injection molding. Expressed in another way, this means that the number employed in the mold making shop should be about equal to the number employed in the injection molding operation, assuming the same number of shifts.

This fact determines within certain limits the degree of automation for molds. The productivity of automatic molds is high, and the production time resulting from injection molding is reduced through their use.

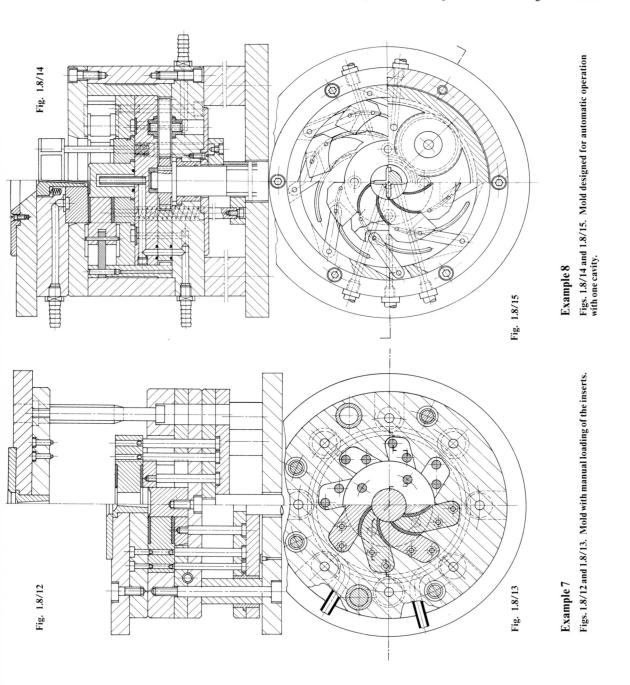

Fig. 1.8/14

Fig. 1.8/15

Example 8

Figs. 1.8/14 and 1.8/15. Mold designed for automatic operation with one cavity.

Fig. 1.8/12

Fig. 1.8/13

Example 7

Figs. 1.8/12 and 1.8/13. Mold with manual loading of the inserts.

Nevertheless, the time needed to make such molds is considerably greater than that for molds that do not operate automatically.

Since the same part can be produced in molds with differing degrees of automation, the various possibilities must be considered and evaluated in order to achieve optimum economics. Such an evaluation starts preferably with a simple, nonautomatic mold the mold making costs of which are estimated along with the production costs of the parts to be molded (without material costs). Next, the costs incurred through use of a mold with a higher degree of automation, and perhaps a fully automatic mold, are determined in the same manner.

The mold thus determined to be optimum is not always the best in every case. The particular conditions in the plant, e.g., the available capacity of the mold making shop or injection molding department, can result in other solutions. The following example will serve to elucidate the above discussion.

A quantity of 60,000 pump impellers as shown in Figs. 1.8/10 and 1.8/11 is to be manufactured out of PVC. Figures 1.8/12 and 1.8/13 show a simple mold with a single cavity in which the spaces between the impeller blades are filled by inserts. These inserts are

Table 1.8/1. Production costs (in cu = cost units) with mold shown in Figs. 1.8/12 and 1.8/13

	Cost rate [cu/h]	Required time [h]	Cost [cu]
Quantity: 60 000 Machine time 30 s Load 8 inserts at 3 s per insert 24 s Cycle time 54 s Time required for production $\left(\dfrac{60\,000 \times 54}{3600}\right)$		900	
Hourly rate for operating the injection molding machine (energy, depreciation and other incidental costs)	80		
Hourly wage of the operator at the injection molding machine 16 cu (social security contributions = 25 %) 4 cu	20		
Cost rate of production	100		
Production costs for injection molding without material costs (900 × 100)			90 000
Time required to make the mold		450	
Average hourly wage in the mold making shop (machine and manual work) 20 cu (social security contributions = 25 %) 5 cu Miscellaneous costs (= 400%) 80 cu	105		
Costs to make the mold without material costs (450 × 105)			47 250
Total production costs			137 250

Table 1.8/2. Production costs with the mold shown in Figs. 1.8/14 and 1.8/15

	Cost rate [cu/h]	Required time [h]	Cost [cu]
Quantity: 60 000 Machine time: 30 s Time required for production $\left(\dfrac{60\,000 \times 30}{3600}\right)$		500	
Hourly rate for operating the injection molding machine (energy, depreciation and other incidental costs)	80		
Production costs for injection molding without material costs (500 × 80)			40 000
Time required to make the mold		700	
Average hourly wage in the mold making shop	105		
Costs to make the mold without material costs (700 × 105)			73 500
Total production costs			113 500

Table 1.8/3. Production costs with mold shown in Figs. 1.8/16 and 1.8/17

	Cost rate [cu/h]	Required time [h]	Cost [cu]
Quantity: 60 000 Machine time 30 s/3 part Time required for production $\left(\dfrac{60\,000 \times 30}{3 \times 3600}\right)$		166.7	
Hourly rate for operating the injection molding machine (energy, depreciation and other incidental costs)	100		
Production costs for injection molding without material costs (166.7 × 100)			16 700
Time required to make the mold		880	
Average hourly wage in the mold making shop	105		
Costs to make the mold without material costs (880 × 105)			92 400
Time required for assembling and welding the molded pieces (30 s/piece = 60 000 × 30/3600)		500	
Hourly wage for secondary operations 12 cu Social securing contributions (= 25%) 3 cu Miscellaneous costs (300%) 36 cu	51		
Costs of secondary operation (500 × 51)			25 500
Time to make the assembly and welding fixture		50	
Production costs for the fixture (50 × 105)			5250
Total production costs			139 820

removed from the mold manually along with the molded part. After manually placing new inserts in the mold, the next cycle begins. The inserts are removed from the molded part with the aid of an extraction device. This relatively simple mold requires the continuous presence of an operator at the machine.

With the design shown in Figs. 1.8/14 and 1.8/15, the inserts are withdrawn by means of levers that move in internally splined cylinders. The mold operates automatically; the operator may be eliminated. The costs

to make this mold, however, are more than for the first mold.

Figures 1.8/16 and 1.8/17 show a two-level stack mold with three cavities per level. The impeller is then assembled from two different parts (Figs. 1.8/18 to 1.8/21). The part with the blades has two 3 mm pins per blade, while the mating piece contains notches to accept the blades and holes for the pins. The two parts are assembled and the pins protruding through the holes are riveted. While this mold does produce three

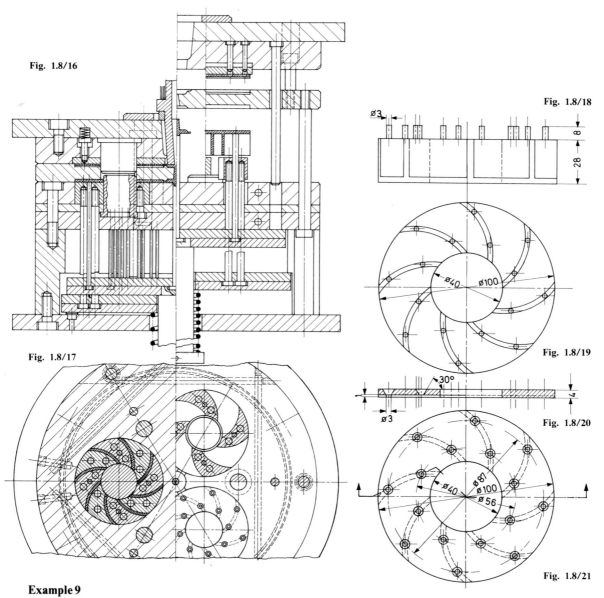

Fig. 1.8/16

Fig. 1.8/17

Fig. 1.8/18

Fig. 1.8/19

Fig. 1.8/20

Fig. 1.8/21

Example 9

Figs. 1.8/16 and 1.8/17. Two-level stack mold with 2 × 3 cavities.

Figs. 1.8/18 to 1.8/21. Assembly of the parts produced in the mold shown in Figs. 1.8/16 and 1.8/17.

parts per cycle, they must be assembled and riveted together, which results in additional costs.

Which of these three alternatives is the most economical is indicated by an evaluation of the respective production costs and shown in Tables 1.8/1 to 1.8/3. According to this evaluation, the second alternative with overall production costs of about 113,000 cost units is the most economical.

It goes without saying, of course, that under certain circumstances, e. g., limited mold making facilities or capacities for secondary operations, another version may be more advantageous for a particular operation in spite of the higher production costs. Other results are also obtained if the molds are provided by the customer. The present evaluations are based on conditions in Hungary. With other initial conditions in other countries, they could quite easily lead to different results. In any case they show that there ist no universally valid economic optimum, but rather that various alternatives should always be investigated and that while economy is an important aspect, it is not always decisive.

Process-based design of injection molded parts

Example 10. Mold for V-belt pulley

Internal and external undercuts on injection molded parts cause the costs for both mold making and mold maintenance to increase considerably, since slides and their actuating mechanisms become necessary. Moreover, with increasing use of the mold, the reliability drops due to the wear of precisely these additional components.

The nylon V-belt pulley shown in Fig. 1.8/22 is an example of a practical design showing how slides in the mold can be avoided. If the V-belt pulley were of a one-piece design, two or three slides per cavity would be required to form the V-belt groove in the pulley. Any flash formed in the groove with this mold design could be removed only with a great deal of effort. If the flash were not carefully removed, there would be a danger of damaging the V-belt. By dividing the pulley across the axis of rotation, the mold design shown in Fig. 1.8/23 becomes possible. Furthermore, the snap connection required for assembly may also be achieved without the use of slides. The two halves of the pulley were designed to be identical, so that the mold inserts are identical and any two pulley halves may be assembled together.

The three-plate mold (Fig. 1.8/23) operates fully automatically. Opening begins at parting line I, since plates (3) and (4) are held together by pin (25) and latch (24) until the bar (23) releases the latch (24) via the adjustment screw (27). Further opening movement of (3) and (4) is prevented by the stop bolts, so that parting line II also opens, and the molded parts may be ejected by the ejector pins (17). After removing the diaphragm gates, the molded parts may be snapped together to form the V-belt pulleys.

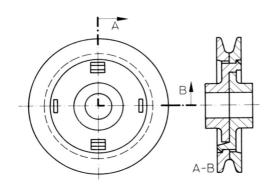

Fig. 1.8/22. Nylon V-belt pulley, assembled from two identical parts by means of a snap connection.

Example 10 (right side)

Figs. 1.8/23 to 1.8/26. Four-cavity injection mold for nylon V-belt pulley halves.
(1, 2) Stationary side clamp plates, (3) upper cooling plates, (4) upper cavity retainer plate, (5) lower cavity retainer plate, (6) support plate, (7, 8) ejector plates, (9, 10) movable side clamp plates, (11) support pillar, (12) lower cavity insert, (13) upper cavity insert, (14) core pin, (15) insert, (16) flat bar, (17) ejector pin, (18) sprue bushing, (19) locating ring, (20) O-ring, (21) sprue ejector, (22) guide pin, (23) release bar, (24) latch, (25) latch pin, (26) pivot pin, (27) adjustment screw, (28) spring, (29) screw, (30) cooling water connection, (31) stop bolt, (32) ejector rod, (33) spring, (34) pin.

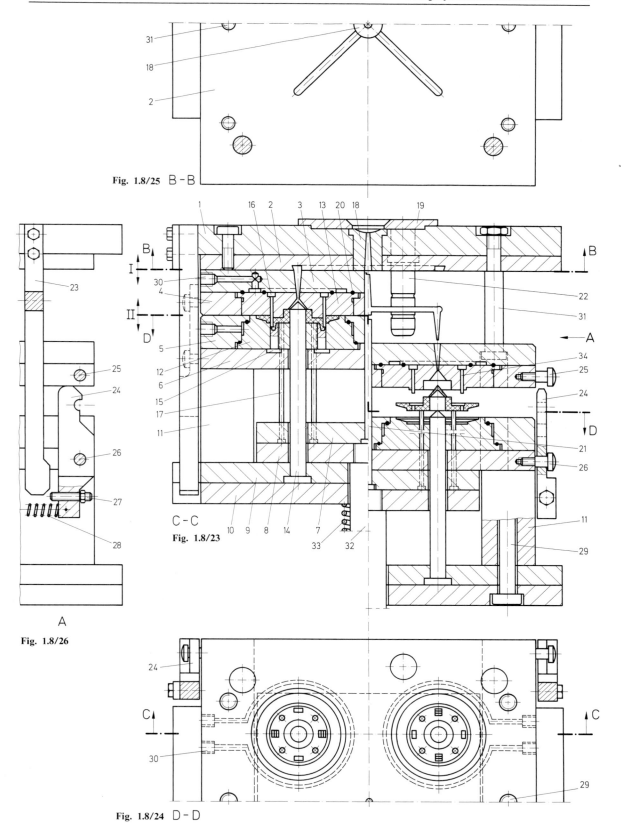

Fig. 1.8/25 B-B

Fig. 1.8/23 C-C

Fig. 1.8/26 A

Fig. 1.8/24 D-D

1.9   Mold Opening Force and Ejector Force for Cylindrical and Conical Injection Molded Parts

G. P. Gilmore and R. S. Spencer investigated the effect of pressure, temperature and time on the molding process some time ago[9]. They established that the stress level in the cavity, which is encountered during opening and is the determining factor for the mold opening force, depends on the duration of the holding pressure (second-stage injection pressure). When holding pressure is applied for only a short period of time and the mold is not yet "sealed," the stress level in the cavity can drop to zero as the result of return flow of melt, thereby permitting easy opening of the mold. The measurements were made on a box-shaped molded part with a wall thickness of 4.3 mm. Results from more recent investigations are now also available from G. Menges and H. Bangert[10].

In the view of H. Gastrow the situation is completely different with thin-walled parts. Here the time until the mold is sealed is so short that back flow of melt from the cavity cannot take place. For the opening force of a thin-walled cup mold, it is not the pressure drop resulting from back flow of melt that is the determining factor, but rather the stress level in the cavity and core of the mold resulting from the high injection pressure.

Shrinkage

The difference between two length measurements (dimensions) is designated the (linear) shrinkage. One is taken directly from the mold while the other is obtained as the corresponding dimension on the molded part, in both cases at room temperature. Shrinkage thus has dimensions of mm. It is usually related to the specified dimension of the molded part and expressed in percent as the relative shrinkage.

From experience it is known that the shrinkage of otherwise identical parts varies: the amount of shrinkage depends on the scatter.

The shrinkage depends on a number of variables that are not constant or cannot be easily held constant during the molding process. Accordingly, no fixed numerical values can be specified for shrinkage and scatter. For polystyrenes and commonly encountered injection molding conditions, a relative shrinkage of 0.4 to 0.6 % may be expected.

According to measurements made by Gilmore and Spencer, the ratio of the volume of polystyrene at pressure P and temperature t to the volume at 0 pressure and a temperature of 24 °C is a function of the temperature and pressure. Accordingly, the melt is com-

pressed at the high injection pressure and occupies a smaller volume than at normal pressure. This compressibility, however, is of secondary importance for the following discussion if it is assumed that with thin-walled parts a back flow of melt, and thus a reduction in the stress level in the mold, cannot occur. The determining factor for the opening force of a thin-walled cup mold is solely the elastic deformation of the steel due to the high injection pressure.

To simplify the calculation, a mean linear shrinkage of 0.4 % will be used in the following. This figure is based on the cavity dimension in the unstressed state and on the dimension of the molded part at room temperature. It may be assumed that at an injection pressure of about 1000 bar (external injection pressure according to Gilmore and Spencer), which results on average in an internal injection pressure of about 500 bar in the narrow cavity, the cavity and all microscopic depressions are completely filled by the flowing plastics melt. On conventional injection molding machines, the internal injection pressure is also maintained during the cooling time in order to prevent shrinkage by supplying additional melt at least until solidification takes place as the result of cooling at the cold cavity walls. This is intended above all to prevent the formation of voids and sink marks on the surface. This holding pressure ceases to have any effect at the moment solidification of the melt (sealing) occurs at the narrowest spot in the flow path (gate).

If for polystyrene, for example, it is assumed that the temperature of the melt in the cavity at which continued flow through the gate stops is 120 °C and the injection temperature is 200 °C, the shrinkage occurring during cooling in the mold from 200 to 120 °C would be eliminated through continued supply of melt, i.e., it is not included in the assumed shrinkage of 0.4 %. The relative shrinkage would thus increase with a smaller gate cross section, since it may be assumed that with a smaller gate the continued flow of melt would stop sooner and the melt in the cavity would have an even higher temperature. This is also probably the reason why previous investigations of shrinkage led to such considerably differing results[11]. The greater shrinkage of thick-walled parts can be explained quite simply from this standpoint, since in general the ratio of gate thickness to wall thickness becomes smaller with increasing wall thickness. The result is that for a thick-walled part there is a considerably higher temperature in the cavity at the moment the gate solidifies, thereby giving rise to greater shrinkage on cooling to room temperature.

The stresses in a cup mold can be compared with those in a piece of rubber hose slipped over a cylinder. A two-dimensional stress state exists in the hose. Axially stress relaxation is prevented by friction between the hose and cylinder surface, and circumferentially by the cylinder itself. Across the wall thickness of the

[9] G. D. Gilmore and R. S. Spencer, *Mod. Plast.*, vol. 27, 1950, pp. 143–150.
[10] G. Menges and H. Bangert, *Kunststoffe*, vol. 71, 1981, pp. 552–557
[11] J. Hemmersbach, *Kunststoffe*, vol. 32, 1942, p. 339.

hose (radially), stress relaxation can take place because the outside diameter is free to change. The result is that the two-dimensional stress leads to a two-fold reduction in wall thickness as long as the hose does not move on the cylinder and a stress exists in both the axial and circumferential directions. If the hose is removed from the cylinder, the axial and circumferential stresses are relieved, and the wall thickness increases.

Analogously, the three-dimensional shrinkage of the cup in the closed mold initially results in a reduction in wall thickness equal to three times the linear shrinkage. This is reduced to simple linear shrinkage only after ejection, whereupon the stresses in the other directions may relax. The amount of relative shrinkage at ejection depends on the mean temperature of the cup at the moment of mold opening. If the mold is opened at the usual solidification temperature of the plastics melt, i.e., at about 70 °C, less shrinkage may be expected at the moment of mold opening than if cooling is continued to a temperature of 20 °C. If for the sake of simplicity it is assumed that the shrinkage is proportional to the temperature drop and that continued flow of melt during holding pressure ceases at a mean temperature of 120 °C in the cavity, and if the mean temperature is permitted to reach at least 40 °C before the mold is opened, the linear shrinkage at the ejection temperature is

$$0.4 \times \frac{(120-40)}{(120-20)} = 0.32\%$$

Based on the above, the three-dimensional shrinkage is $3 \times 0.32 = 0.96\%$. The wall thickness of the cup is less than the spacing between cavity and core by an amount corresponding to the three-dimensional shrinkage. If the cavity walls were absolutely rigid, it ought to be possible to easily remove the cup from the cavity (even assuming a theoretically smooth surface) since the cup has become smaller as the result of shrinkage. At the same time, the cup has shrunk onto the core and thus moves with it. Unfortunately, the situation is different in reality.

Stress state in the mold after injection

The opening force of a mold is a function of numerous factors. These include in particular the deformation of the mold by the internal injection pressure, the shrinkage of the molded part, the surface quality of the mold and the coefficient of friction between the molded part surface and cavity or core surfaces.

Cavity filling takes place at a pressure of approximately 500 bar. At this pressure, both the cavity wall and core experience elastic deformation. The inside diameter of the cavity increases and the core diameter decreases.

If D_{Ma} = the outside diameter of the cavity in mm
$\quad D_{Mi}$ = the inside diameter of the cavity in mm
$\quad D_{Ka}$ = the outside diameter of the core in mm

D_{Ki} = the inside diameter of the core in mm (the core is hollow because of the cooling channel)
E = the modulus of elasticity of steel 2.1×10^5 N/mm^2
m = Poisson's ratio = 3.33 = extension/lateral contraction
Q_m = the ratio of $D_{Mi}/D_{Ma;}$
Q_k = the ratio of $D_{Ki}/D_{Ka;}$ (from Dr. Ing. Paul Leineweber: Passung und Gestaltung)
p = pressure on the injected melt (internal injection pressure) = 500 bar

the inside diameter of the cavity increases due to the injection pressure p by

$$\Delta_{Mi} = p \, K_m \, D_{Mi} \, [\text{mm}]$$
where
$$K_m = \frac{(m+1)+(m-1)Q_m{}^2}{m \, E(1-Q_m{}^2)}$$

In like manner, the outside diameter of the core is reduced due to the injection pressure by

$$\Delta K_a = p \, K_k \, D_{Ka} \, [\text{mm}]$$
where
$$\Delta K_k = \frac{(m-1)+(m+1)Q_k{}^2}{m \, E(1-Q_k{}^2)}$$

Accordingly, the cavity increases in size by

$$\frac{\Delta_{Mi}+\Delta_{Ka}}{2}$$

due to the assumed pressure of 500 bar acting on the inside and outside surfaces of the cup during injection. Without any shrinkage, a cup having an outside surface area of 200 cm^2, i.e., about 50 mm in diameter and 100 mm high, an opening force of 157 cm$^2 \times 500$ bar $\times 0.1 = 79,000$ N would be required if the coefficient of friction were 0.1. The above assumes theoretically smooth wall surfaces and that the opening force is proportional to the pressure.

In the event of microscopic irregularities and depressions, the opening force would be considerably greater, since the material filling the depressions would have to be sheared off or an additional surface pressure would result due to the elastic deformation of the cavity wall. Thus shrinkage plays a decisive role in reducing the opening force. Since the linear shrinkage is approximately proportional to the wall thickness, it is understandable why it becomes increasingly difficult to open a mold the thinner the mold wall becomes.

If the linear shrinkage is greater than $\frac{\Delta_{Mi}+\Delta_{Ka}}{2}$, the opening force becomes zero to the extent that theoretically smooth surfaces are assumed and no vacuum forms.

Effect of shrinkage on the mold opening force

Using a practical example, the effect of shrinkage on the mold opening force will now be investigated, assuming initially theoretically smooth and cylindrical surfaces. The effect of draft on the work required to open a mold will be shown later.

A cup 50 mm in diameter, 100 mm high and having a wall thickness of 1.5 mm is to be molded. Accordingly, the cavity of the associated cup mold has an inside diameter D_{Mi} of 50 mm and, with a wall thickness of 20 mm, an outside diameter D_{Ma} of 90 mm. With a cup wall thickness of 1.5 mm, the core outside diameter $D_{Ka} = 47$ mm. The cooling channel in the core $D_{Ki} = 25$ mm. The cup height $l = 100$ mm.

For the cavity

$$Q_m^2 = \frac{D_{Mi}^2}{D_{Ma}^2} = \frac{50^2}{90^2} = 0.31$$

and for the core

$$Q_k^2 = \frac{D_{Ki}^2}{D_{Ka}^2} = \frac{25^2}{47^2} = 0.283$$

Thus, K_m equals

$$\frac{4.33 + (2.33 \times 0.31)}{3.33 \times 22 \times 10^3 \times 0.69} = 0.1 \times 10^{-3}$$

$$\Delta_{Mi} = 5 \times 0.1 \times 10^{-3} \times 50 = 0.025 \text{ mm} = 25 \text{ μm}$$

(increase in cavity inside diameter due to injection pressure)

The value of K_k equals

$$\frac{2.33 + (4.33 \times 0.283)}{3.33 \times 22 \times 10^3 \times 0.717} = 0.068 \times 10^{-3}$$

$$\Delta_{Ka} = 5 \times 0.068 \times 10^{-3} \times 47 = 0.016 \text{ mm} = 16 \text{ μm}$$

(reduction in core diameter due to injection pressure)

The total increase in spacing cavity and core is therefore:

$$\frac{\Delta_{Mi} + \Delta_{Ka}}{2} = \frac{25 + 16}{2} = 20.5 \text{ μm}$$

Assuming within the temperature limits of 120 to 40 °C (cessation of holding pressure to the moment of mold opening) a linear shrinkage of 0.32 %, i.e., a spatial shrinkage of 0.96 %, the reduction in wall thickness is $1.5 \cdot 0.0096 = 0.0144$ mm $= 14.4$ μm providing that the spatial shrinkage of 0.96 % in the closed mold results only in a reduction in wall thickness. The increase in wall thickness as a result of the elasticity of the cavity and core when subjected to the injection pressure has not been considered here, since it is an order of magnitude smaller than the wall thickness.

The increase in wall thickness by 20.5 μm is therefore offset by a reduction of 14.4 μm due to shrinkage.

The pressure of 500 bar during injection has thus been reduced to

$$\frac{20.5 - 14.4}{20.5} \times 500 = 14.9 \text{ N/mm}^2 \text{ as the result of}$$

shrinkage.

The opening force, however, still amounts to 14.9 N/mm² × 157 cm² × 0.1 = 23,200 N, if the coefficient of shrinkage is once again 0.1.

With a solid core, i.e., without a cooling channel, the constant K_k would equal

$$\frac{2.33}{73.3 \times 10^3} = 0.0318 \times 10^{-3} \text{ and}$$
$$\Delta K_a = 5 \times 0.0318 \times 10^{-3} \times 47 = 0.0075 \text{ mm}$$
$$= 7.5 \text{ μm.}$$

The total increase in spacing between cavity and core would therefore equal $\frac{25 + 7.5}{2} = 16.25$ μm.

The pressure of 500 bar would thus drop to $\frac{16.25 - 14.4}{16.25} \times 500$ bar $= 5.7$ N/mm² and the opening force to $157 \times 57 \times 0.1 = 8950$ N.

The use of a small cooling channel in the core therefore can lead to considerably increased ease of mold opening.

An increase in cavity wall thickness has the same effect. A strength calculation alone leads to a much too thin wall; consequently the cavity and the ejection forces required are increased significantly by too weak a wall.

With an infinitely large cavity outside diameter,

$$K_m = \frac{4.33}{73.3 \times 10^3} = 0.0591 \times 10^{-3} \text{ and}$$
$$\Delta_{Mi} = 14.8 \text{ μm}$$

With a solid core, the total increase in spacing between cavity and core would then be $\frac{14.8 + 7.5}{2} = \frac{22.3}{2}$ $= 11.2$ μm and there would be no residual stress.

Effect of surface quality on the mold opening force

An exact calculation of the effect of the surface and its quality is not possible as this would require knowledge of the shape, height and number of depressions in order to calculate the shear forces and forces associated with elastic deformation. Furthermore, such a calculation is pointless since it is impossible to establish the shape, number and size of surface irregularities produced by a machining method.

A comparison of the surface quality that may be achieved by machining with the differences between deformation of the steel and shrinkage of the melt will, however, serve to illustrate what an exceptionally great effect the surface quality has on the opening force. The calculation shows that a difference of

6.1 μm, resulting from deformation of the cavity and core on the one hand and shrinkage of the melt on the other, already requires an initial opening force of 29,800 N. If numerous other microscopic irregularities of the same order of magnitude must also be considered – for instance, the height of the grinding marks on a finish-ground cavity is only 6 μm – a doubling of the opening force may be expected.

The height of grinding marks is 2.5 to 6 μm for finish grinding. A finish-ground surface is thus not acceptable for those locations at which initial part release is to take place, especially when the grinding marks run transverse to the opening direction. The situation would be more favorable if the grinding marks would lie in the direction of mold opening, but this is not possible with grinding.

The importance of smoothing ground surfaces in the direction of mold opening is clear from the above considerations. The deciding factor in such smoothing is that all protrusions be removed while changing the shape of the surface as little as possible. Such smoothing of the surface, however, is not possible with a soft-backed abrasive (buffing), but rather should be done manually with polishing stones shaped to match the surface curvature, starting first with the coarser grit and then using progressively finer grit.

It is not so much a question of the brightness of the surface as of the elimination of all microscopic projections and depressions that hinder movement of the sliding surfaces (dry friction). In this regard, subsequent chrome plating should also be warned against since the almost unavoidable irregularity of the chrome layer is more likely to cause damage than help.

The quality of the steel used, especially its uniform structure and freedom from porosity, can be quite important. Accordingly, only electric steel should be employed. It goes without saying that the surface hardness also plays a decisive role since a hard surface can be polished much better than a soft one. In any case, the smoothing must be continued until no marks transverse to the opening direction of the mold can be seen with the most powerful magnifying glass.

It is only if all these measures are taken that a cup mold can be reliably expected to open first at the desired surface. If these requirements are not met, it is possible that the core will be withdrawn from the cup first, an undesirable situation with regard to part ejection.

Retention on the core of the mold

At the beginning of opening, the retention force tending to keep the part on the core is almost identical to that experienced by the outer surface of the cup, assuming that the surface finish of the cavity and the core is the same. While it is true that the surface pressure has been increased somewhat by the shrinkage, this is only of secondary importance when compared to the state of stress in the steel cavity and core caused by the injection pressure in light of the slight wall thickness of the

cup and low modulus of elasticity of the plastic. In addition, the surface area of the core is less than that of the cavity due to the wall thickness of the cup, as a result of which the increase in retention force attributable to shrinkage is more or less offset. It is to be recommended, however, that circular grinding marks on the core be left or at least that the smoothing by hand polishing not be performed to as great an extent as with the cavity. The requirement of achieving greater retention on the core is met most practically by smoothing the core circularly, i.e., perpendicular to the direction of opening.

As the following calculation shows, the surface quality of the core is of secondary importance for ejection from the core. On opening of the mold, complete stress relaxation of the cavity wall takes place. The core, however, can relax only to that stress state associated with the shrunk cup. Assuming that even now the shrinkage can act only in the direction of the cup wall thickness because relaxation is prevented axially by friction on the core and circumferentially by the core itself, the shrinkage in the direction of the cup wall thickness must be taken as three times the linear shrinkage, i.e., 0.96 %, as long as the cup is retained on the core. The stress state can be determined by means of a simplified calculation for the wall of the cup, which is thin in relation to the diameter. The tensile stress σ_z on the circumference resulting from shrinkage is $0.0096 \times E$, where the modulus of elasticity of the usual molding compounds is $E = 30 \times 10^4$ N/cm^2. Thus $\sigma_z = 0.0096 \times 30 \times 10^3 = 2880$ N/mm^2.

This tensile stress results in a surface pressure p given by

$$p = \sigma_z \times \frac{2 \times s}{D_{Ka}} = \frac{2880 \times 2 \times 0.15}{4.7} = 1.84 \text{ N/mm}^2$$

The surface area of the core is $4.7 \pi \times 10 - 148$ cm^2

With a coefficient of friction of 0.1, the initial force required for ejection from the core is

$$148 \text{ cm}^2 \times 1.84 \text{ N/mm}^2 \times 0.1 = 2720 \text{ N}$$

Surface irregularities have not been taken into account in this calculation. With 0.96 % shrinkage, the stress state in the cup wall corresponds to a decrease in diameter of $0.0096 \times D_{Ka} = 0.0096 \times 47 = 0.45$ mm $= 450$ μm. Assuming that the greatest depressions on the core surface are 6 μm (finish-ground), the increase in ejection force due to these irregularities is about $\frac{85 \times 6}{225} = 22.6$ N, i.e., of secondary importance. Although the stress resulting from shrinkage of the bottom of the cup has not been taken into account, it is of a magnitude that may also be neglected.

It can be seen from the above considerations that, for ejection of a thin-walled part from a core, the surface quality of the core is only of secondary importance. It is thus quite possible to eject thin-walled parts from almost cylindrical cores without scoring so long as the cores have been polished well axially. It is, however, absolutely impossible – as is confirmed by practice – to withdraw a thin-walled part without any external draft from a closed cavity without damaging the surface.

Where cylindrical inner and outer surfaces are absolutely necessary on a thin-walled part, there is no other possibility than to place the cavity surfaces along a mold parting line and to eject the part from the core after opening these surfaces.

Effect of draft on work of opening and ejection

A slight amount of external draft has hardly any effect on the initial opening force. Yet the slightest amount of draft has a significant effect on the tendency to score. Scoring, i.e., destruction of the surface, occurs whenever the product of frictional force × distance, i.e., the work of friction, is so great that the relatively sensitive molding compound is heated past the softening point. With rough surfaces, adhesion in depressions of the cavity wall may, under certain circumstances, lead to destruction of the surface on only the slightest motion. In the case of the cup mold, an increase in diameter of 12.2 µm already suffices to reduce the opening force from 23.200 N to zero. With a draft of 1:50 this corresponds to a mold opening stroke of $50 \times 12.2\,\mu m = 0.61$ mm.

The work of friction is then

$$\frac{23,200}{2} \times 0.61 \times 10^{-3} = 7.0\,\text{J}$$

Even if surface irregularities of the same order of magnitude are taken into consideration (finish-ground surfaces), the friction, and thus the work of opening the mold, will hardly exceed 15 J, i.e., 0.1 J per cm^2 of surface area. Such an amount of work can be withstood quite readily as a shock by the moving masses of the machine and mold. Care must be taken, however, that the initial opening force of 23,200 N is transmitted to the masses represented by mold and machine by sufficiently strong bolts or other means of fastening, since the core mass and speed are relatively low and hence can provide only a slight amount of impact work.

Without draft the work of friction would be $\frac{23,200 \times 0.1}{2160} = 1160$ J, which would result in destruction of the surface. With a surface roughness of 0.6 µm, the work of friction would almost double. The great importance of a conical design for thin-walled cup-shaped parts can thus be seen from this example. Because of the greater expansion of the thin cup wall, the situation is different for the core. The reduction in diameter due to shrinkage was 450 µm at an initial ejection force of 2720 N. With identical draft of 1:50, the work of ejection is $\frac{50 \times 272 \times 0.45 \times 10^{-3}}{2} = 30.6$ J, i.e., of the same order of magnitude but distributed over a greater distance of $50 \times 0.45 = 22.5$ mm.

Determining the shrinkage with a cup mold

The shrinkage of injection molding compounds can be determined in a very simple manner without precision methods of measurement with the aid of a cup mold having minimal draft. After having cooled to room temperature, the cup can be pushed onto the core only a certain amount without using force. This is a measure of the linear shrinkage. If l_1 is the distance (measured with a sliding caliper) of the rim of the cup after it has been slipped onto the core from the mold parting line and k the draft (e.g., 1:50), the linear shrinkage of the diameter $= D \times l_1 \times k$, i.e., the relative shrinkage is $k \times l_1 \times 100$ %. In the manner, for instance, the effect of the duration of holding pressure (second stage injection pressure) on the shrinkage could be determined, especially if a sufficiently large gate were located directly on the bottom of the cup. All effects associated with irregular wall thickness, and which lead to varying results for shrinkage measurements on other parts, as well as the effect of different sized gates would thus be eliminated, and the exceptional amount of scatter found with all previous shrinkage measurements ought to disappear, assuming uniform injection temperature and uniform duration of holding pressure. For such experiments, opening of the mold must be delayed after cessation of holding pressure until the cup wall has cooled to at least 40 °C.

Practical consequences

The above investigations make no claim to universal validity. They were conducted only for a cup mold and, furthermore, a fixed shrinkage was assumed. Nevertheless, certain conclusions that are of practical importance may be drawn. These are summarized below.

To reduce the opening force, the cavity surfaces must be smoothed in the direction of mold opening. This work should be done manually with initially coarser and then progressively finer grits. Subsequent chrome plating is generally detrimental since the surface becomes more irregular as a result. Electric steel should be used if possible for the cavity. In contrast, round grinding marks on the core should be left in order that the core not be withdrawn from the part first during mold opening. Although a slight amount of external draft has almost no effect on the initial opening force, the draft does result in considerably reduced work of friction during molding opening, to about $\frac{1}{100}$ in the example shown. The tendency to scoring is also reduced accordingly.

In practice, use is made of the fact that a mold subjected to holding pressure for only a short period of time opens more easily. The shrinkage is greater in this case because of the higher temperature of the melt in the cavity, as a result of which the opening force is reduced.

1.10 Protection of Injection Molds

For problem-free production of high-quality and dimensionally correct injection molded parts, injection molds require special care both during handling and storage as well as during operation. Molded parts that remain in the mold can lead to damage as the mold closes to begin the next cycle and such damage may jeopardize further use of the mold. Accordingly, measures are often taken that do not permit closing of the mold until it is assured that all molded parts have been ejected and ejectors returned. With single-cavity molds, a photoelectric eye that senses the falling injection molded part suffices. With multiple-cavity molds, this method can no longer be used. In this case, the following possibilities exists:

– Platen preposition
– Multiple-pulse ejection (pulsating ejector)
– Electromechanical mold protection
– Air blow-off device
– Ejector plate return safety

The majority of the above measures concern additions to the machine and will not be discussed here since they have no effect on the design of the mold. The ejector plate return safety, however, does require modifications to the mold. These are discussed in the following.

Example 11. Ejector plate return safety

If ejectors are located behind movable side cores or slides, the ejector plate return safety checks whether the ejectors have been returned to the molding position. If this is not the case, the molding cycle is interrupted.

This safety requires a receptacle on the movable clamping plate along with a switch on the mold that is actuated when the ejector plate is in the retracted position. The ejector plate return safety thus functions only if the molding cycle utilizes platen preposition, i.e., after the molded parts have been ejected, the clamping unit closes to the point at which the ejector plate is returned to the molding position by spring force. Only then does the control system issue the "close mold" command. In molds requiring a long ejector stroke, spring return of the ejector plate is often not sure enough. For such cases, there is an ejector return mechanism that fulfills this function. Attachment of the ejector plate return safety is shown in Figs. 1.10/1 to 1.10/6.

This single-cavity mold is used to produce an angle fitting (1). Two long side cores (2) meet at an angle of 90°. The somewhat shorter side core is pulled by a cam pin (3), while the longer core is pulled by a slide (4). The difficulty is that blade ejectors (5) are located under the two cores and must be returned to the molding position after having ejected the finished part before the two cores are set as the mold closes and possibly damage the blade ejectors. Possible consequences include not only broken blade ejectors but also a damaged cavity. Either of these could result in a lengthy interruption of production. For this reason, a helical spring (6) that permits operation with platen preposition is placed on the ejector rod. This spring then returns the ejector plate. To ensure proper operation, a microswitch (7) is mounted to the clamping plate (8), while a pin (10) that actuates the switch is mounted in the ejector plate (9). After connecting the cable with the switch housing of the movable clamping plate, the ejector plate return safety is complete.

Example 11 (page 50)

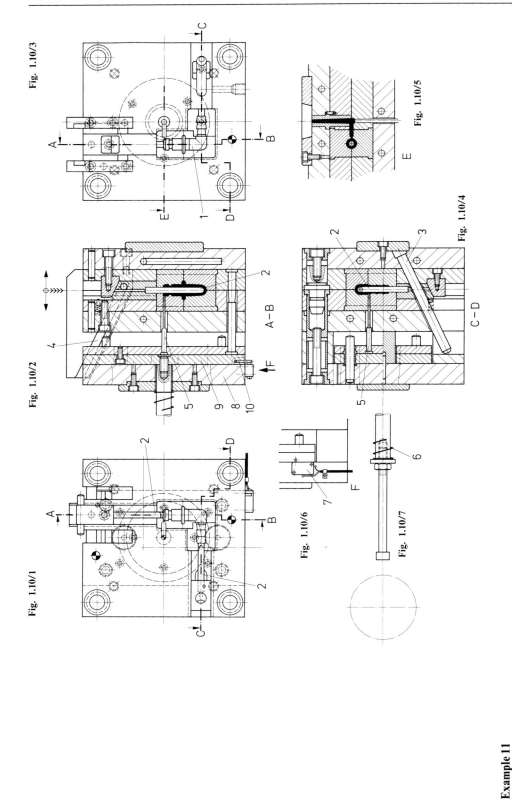

Fig. 1.10/3

Fig. 1.10/5

Fig. 1.10/2

Fig. 1.10/4

Fig. 1.10/1

Fig. 1.10/6

Fig. 1.10/7

Example 11

Figs. 1.10/1 to 1.10/6. Injection mold for angle fitting.
(1) angle fitting, (2) side cores, (3) cam pin, (4) slide, (5) blade ejector, (6) helical spring, (7) microswitch, (8) clamping plate, (9) ejector plate, (10) pin.

2   Runner Systems and Gating

2.1   Sizing of Sprues and Runners

Sprues, runners and gates fulfill the function of conveying the plastics melt from the nozzle of the injection unit to the individual cavities. While it is true that they may be reused in the form of regrind, their presence nevertheless means a reduction in the performance of the injection molding machine inasmuch as they must be plasticated in the barrel. With smaller parts, they may account for 50 % or more of the actual shot weight.

Sprue

The sprue may be considered the continuation in the mold of the channel in the nozzle. Single-cavity molds where the sprue leads directly to the molded part are said to have *direct sprue gating*.

Very often, the performance of a single-cavity injection mold is determined by the cooling time of this sprue. In addition to providing adequate cooling of the sprue bushing, the diameter of the smallest opening in the sprue bushing should be kept as small as possible and permitted by proper filling of the cavity. No universally applicable rules can be given here, since filling of the cavity depends on very many factors.

The sprue should have 1.5° of draft. Greater draft may simplify removal from the sprue bushing, but

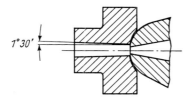

Fig. 2.1/1. Practical cross section of a runner.

with a longer sprue results in a greater diameter and thus longer cooling time. The nozzle orifice should be about 0.5 mm smaller in diameter than the smallest opening in the sprue bushing (Fig. 2.1/1) so that there is no undercut at the end of the sprue to hinder removal.

Runners

In multiple-cavity molds, the plastics melt must flow to the individual cavities through runners in the mold parting line. The same basic rules that apply to the sprue apply also to the cross section of these runners. An additional factor that must be considered is

that the cross section is also a function of the length of the runner, since it may be assumed that the pressure lost in a runner increases at least proportionally with the length. In all likelihood it will probably increase more than proportionally, since the cross section is reduced by solidification of the melt along the walls, and the more so the greater the distance from the sprue. Because the sprue and runner system represent lost material and lost plasticating capacity, the runners should be designed to be as short as possible and with the smallest possible cross section. The length of the runners is determined by the number of cavities in the mold and the geometrical arrangement of the individual cavities.

Shape of runner cross section

The smallest surface area, and therefore the least amount of cooling in relation to the cross-sectional area, is provided by a full round runner. It should be thus employed whenever possible. The melt solidifies last in the center of a round runner. Accordingly, the plastics melt will continue to flow the longest under holding pressure down the center of a full round runner. Hence gates (the locations where the runners enter the cavities) should be so designed that melt flows through them into the cavity via a circular or rectangular cross section fed from the center of the runner. Friction of the plastic melt at the smallest cross section of the runner provides for local heating of the steel around the gate so that melt can be forced in under holding pressure a longer period of time to compensate for shrinkage before the gate freezes.

Full round runners cannot be used when flat slide surfaces must move relative to the runners. In such cases, a recessed half-round runner may be employed (Fig. 2.1/2). The advantage of this shape is that it has to be machined on only one side of the mold plate. However, a recessed half-round runner with the same radius of curvature as a full round runner of identical diameter contains 12.5 % more material.

Fig. 2.1/2. Design of the sprue and size of orifices.

Shape of the gate

The gate, i.e., the opening between the runner system and cavity, should give rise to as small a pressure drop as possible. It is thus useful to have a tapered reduction in cross section from the runner to the gate opening in the cavity. If the molded parts are small and no particular value is placed on invisibility of the gate location, the gate shown in Fig. 2.1/3 is recommended, i.e., the gate is tapered like a wedge from the runner to the molded part. The part can then be broken off the runner relatively cleanly. If thicker parts are to be cut off the runner by using a pliers or cutter, it is better to use the gate shown in Fig. 2.1/4. In this case, however, the narrowest section should be kept as short as permitted by the cutter to avoid significant pressure drop.

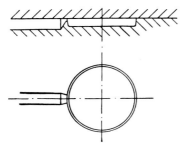

Fig. 2.1/3. Gate tapered toward molded parts.

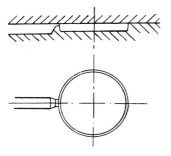

Fig. 2.1/4. Gate for thicker part.

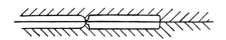

Fig. 2.1/5. Gate for full round runners.

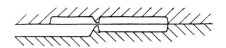

Fig. 2.1/6. Gate for rectangular runner cut into one side of the mold.

With full round runners, the gate shown in Fig. 2.1/5 is practical, as melt flows from the center of the round cross section into the cavity. The same effect can be achieved with runners machined into one side of a mold plate by using the gate shown in Fig. 2.1/6.

The *tunnel (submarine) gate* represents an especially advantageous design, since it permits automatic degating of the part from the runner system during opening of the mold. The melt flows into the cavity through a short tunnel at the end of the runner. With proper tunnel design, it is possible to ensure that the gate will be hardly visible so that no secondary degating operations will be necessary on the molded part. It has been found that this type of gate is suitable not only for polyethylene (for which it was originally developed), but rather that parts of polystyrene, nylon (polyamide) and other resins can also be molded successfully in this manner.

Certain aspects as discussed in the following, however, must be observed. The part surface where the gate is located should either have a greater amount of draft or be stepped immediately after the gate opening, as otherwise scratches can easily occur behind the gate. Figures 2.1/7 to 2.1/9 show a few practical designs for this type of gate.

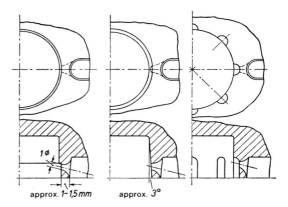

Figs. 2.1/7 to 2.1/9. Types of tunnel gates.

Example 12. Eight-cavity injection mold for sleeves

The problems encountered when molding sleeves are usually: the core should not deflect during injection, as this would result in a varying part wall thickness; and the greatest amount of heat should be removed from the core by means of direct cooling to reduce the cycle time.

The parts shown in example 12 (Figs. 2.1/10 and 2.1/11) are sleeves of linear polyethylene for electric Christmas tree lights (electrified candles). The cavities are placed in a circle so that the flow length to each cavity is identical. The parts are gated at one end via two tunnel gates. The advantage of two gates is that the core (1) is subjected to injection pressure from two sides and is thus held in the center. In addition, this type of gating ensures that the melt flows into the cavity uniformly, thereby ensuring proper venting. Air might possibly be trapped if the melt were to enter from only a single gate. Since the sleeve is continuous, it is easy to center the core by providing a slight taper (about 5°) that enters a centering piece (2) as the mold closes. By providing a small flat surface on the circumference of this centering piece it is possible to vent the

air from the cavity. Stationary side inserts (3) provide for optimum cooling, since the cooling water can be brought close to the cavity through the use of two interconnected channels. Sealing is provided by O-rings. The core has about a 6 mm diameter channel into which a 4 mm tube (4) with angle fitting is screwed. The cooling water flows in through this tube and returns in the space between the tube and channel wall. The runner system is machined into only the stationary side of the mold. It is retained on the movable half of the mold by undercut pins (5). Once the mold is open, the sleeves are stripped off the cores by the stripper plate (6). Simultaneously, the runner system is stripped off the pins. Since the tunnel gates are sheared off the parts as the mold opens, the molded parts and runner system drop out of the mold separately.

Because the molded parts have already been separated from the runner at the time of ejection, the runner system cannot be utilized for ejection. Accordingly, the ecjection mechanism for the individual molded parts must be so designed to ensure that each individual part is removed.

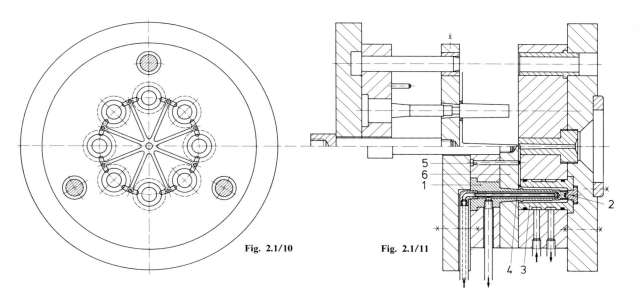

Fig. 2.1/10   Fig. 2.1/11

Example 12

Figs. 2.1/10 and 2.1/11. Eight-cavity injection mold for sleeves.
(1) Core, (2) centering piece, (3) insert, (4) tube, (5) pin, (6) stripper plate.

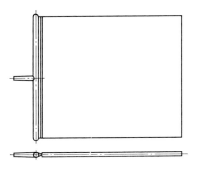

Fig. 2.1/12. Flash gate.

Flash gate

If large flat parts are molded by means of direct sprue of pinpoint gating, severe warpage due to different rates of shrinkage in the flow direction and transverse to the flow direction results, especially with resins exhibiting high shrinkage (polyethylene). This warpage can be largely suppressed if such rectangular parts are gated along their entire width from a parallel runner (Fig. 2.1/12). While there are still different rates of shrinkage along and transverse to the flow direction, these can no longer result in warpage of the rectangular plates, but only affect the different shrinkage allowances taken into consideration in specifying the dimensions of the cavity.

2.2   Self-Degating Molds (Three- And Four-Plate Molds)

To eliminate the secondary operation of degating, injection molds in which the parts are automatically degated from the runner system by the opening motion of the mold were already developed by Gastrow in 1938. Granting of the patent filed to cover this technique was imminent, but was not pursued after the end of World War II so that the technique of self-degating is not protected by any patent.

Principle of self-degating

Self-degating requires two parting lines in the mold. In the first parting line, melt is distributed from a central sprue through runners and flows through risers in an intermediate plate at the end of which the gate to the cavity is located. The parts to be molded are located in the second parting line of the mold. During the opening motion of the mold, the parting line containing the runner system opens first and the runner system is held on the stationary side in order that the gate in the intermediate plate be severed from the molded part. Suitable measures must be taken to ensure that the runner system and sprue are ejected once this parting line has opened a suitable amount. The second parting line containing the molded parts now opens. After this second parting line has opened the necessary amount, the parts are ejected in the usual manner.

The sequential opening of two parting lines requires a sufficiently large opening stroke for the mold, a situation that unfortunately has not been taken into consideration in the design of many injection molding machines. A relatively large mounting height for the mold is also necessary, especially for deep parts, in order to provide enough space for the actuating mechanisms for the two-step opening.

Pinpoint gate

Surprisingly, it has been found that with the so-called pinpoint gate (and this is always the type in a three- or four-plate mold) very small gate openings suffice if certain prerequisites are fulfilled. It has also been found that thin walls can be filled better with pinpoint gating than with a gate located in the parting line. It is also easier to prevent sink marks in thick-walled parts with pinpoint gating than with a larger gate placed in the parting line.

The explanation is probably that with proper design of the pinpoint gate, even though there is a severe pressure drop at the restriction, the sudden heating of the melt as a result of this pressure drop results in better flow into the cavity.

Local heating of the steel around the gate is a further consequence, as the result of which melt can continue to flow into the filled cavity through the pinpoint gate under holding pressure to compensate for shrinkage because the local increase in temperature of the steel surfaces prevents premature freezing of the gate. However, an essential prerequisite for easy filling of the cavity and maintenance of holding pressure is that the runners be large enough to prevent premature solidification of the melt on the one hand and too great a pressure drop during flow through the runners on the other. The pinpoint gate always requires high injection pressure from the very start of injection.

This prerequisite can always be fulfilled in hydraulically actuated machines. If, on the other hand, the injection rate is limited by the type of drive, as is the case with spindle and toggle drives in plunger machines, the pressure may be too low to force the melt through the pinpoint gate at the plunger speed attainable because of the high flow resistance at the restricted cross section. In this case, the pinpoint gate must be opened up to reduce the flow resistance.

Example 13. Self-degating injection molds for flat parts

With self-degating, it is possible to locate the gate at the center of gravity of a part, i.e., in the center of round discs, for instance. Very often, this is more useful than edge gating for reasons associated with flow. On the one hand, the flow paths are reduced by a half; on the other, weld lines, which always have reduced strength, are avoided. It is also often possible to place the pinpoint gate at a location where it is invisible if the molded part is subsequently glued to another part. In the following example (Figs. 2.2/1 to 2.2/4), small covers that are subsequently glued to another part are to be produced. Since the gate may protrude by 0.1 to 0.2 mm after degating, it is placed on the back of the cover in a slight depression so that it will not interfere with the bonding of the cover.

To achieve a cleanly severed gate, degating must take place with firmly closed mold inserts. With flat parts, this can only be achieved by positively retaining the runner on the stationary side of the mold and having the mold open first along the runner parting line. To provide this sequence of mold opening, the stationary-side retainer plate (a) must be actuated by powerful spring washers (b) that provide a force greater than that needed to sever the pinpoint gates. During this motion, each riser is positively held on the stationary side by undercut pins (c). The sprue and runner system are thus retained on the stripper plate (d), while the parting line between plates (a) and (d) opens. Since the spring washers (b) act only over a short distance, the second parting line in which the covers are located must be kept closed by other means in order that sufficient room to eject the runner system be first provided

in the runner parting line. To this end, the retainer plates (a) and (e) are held together by a latch (f) that is released by a bar (g) bolted to the movable side clamping plate only after the runner parting line has opened the necessary amount. During this initial opening motion, the retainer plate (a) is guided on three stripper bolts (h) and shortly before the end of its opening motion comes in contact with the nut (i). These nuts are fastened to guide bushings (k), which have a shoulder behind the stripper plate (d). At the end of the opening motion of the runner parting line, the stripper plate (d) is pulled forward by about 10 mm until the nut (l) comes up against the washer (m). This limits the opening motion of the retainer plate (a), and the runner is pulled off the undercut pins (c). The sprue has also been withdrawn 10 mm but is not completely free of the sprue bushing. Since it is only sitting loosely in the sprue bushing, release of the springs (n) causes it to be forcefully ejected so that the runner system can now drop. A prerequisite for proper dropping of the runner system, however, is that the nozzle does not exhibit stringing, as is the case with polystyrene if no suitable nozzle shutoff is provided, because otherwise the runner will remain hanging.

During the continued opening motion of the mold, the parting line between the two retainer plates (a) and (e) now opens until the ejector rod (o) is actuated and pushes the ejector plates (p) and (q) forward. The sleeve ejectors (r) that strip the individual covers off the cores are held by shoulders between these two plates.

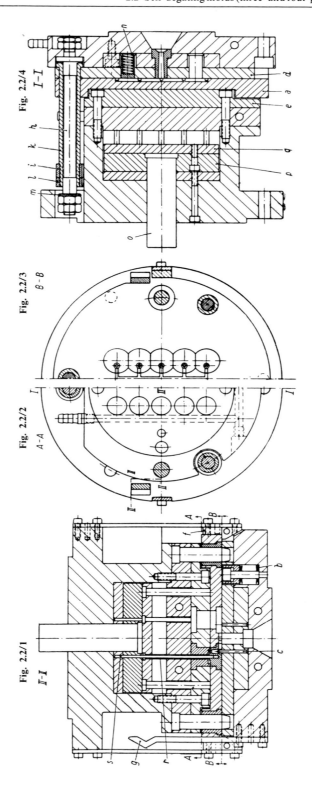

Fig. 2.2/1
II-I

Fig. 2.2/2
A-A

Fig. 2.2/3
B-B

Fig. 2.2/4
I-I

Example 13

Figs. 2.2/1 to 2.2/4. Ten-cavity self-degating mold for covers.

(a, e) Insert retainer plates, (b) spring washers, (c) undercut pins, (d) stripper plate, (f) latch, (g) release bar, (h) stripper bolts, (i) nut, (k) guide bushing, (l) nut, (m) washer, (n) spring, (o) ejector rod, (p, q) ejector plates, (r) sleeve ejector.

Example 14. Self-degating injection molds for externally gated deep parts

Deep parts, e.g., drinking cups, can be molded in multiple cavities only when center-gated because with edge gating the cups would exhibit a tendency to break as a result of the unavoidable weld lines. Example 14 shows a four-cavity mold for drinking cups with pin-point gating at the bottom of the cup.

The operating and construction are basically quite similar to those of the previous example for flat parts. With deep parts, however, the spring-washer action for the injection-side insert retainer plate and latching of the two mold halves can be eliminated, since the adhesion between the cup and the core and cavity surfaces is great enough to ensure that the two mold halves are held together to sever the pinpoint gate and carry the injection-side insert retainer plate to the stop position as it moves along the three stripper bolts.

In order to avoid variations in the wall thickness of the cups, the two mold halves must be aligned very accurately with respect to each other. Guide pins alone are not enough in this case. The two mold halves are thus not only guided by two guide pins (*a*) but are further aligned with respect to each other by means of dual tapered seats in the stripper plates (*b*). The large contact area of the seats guarantees that there will be no variations in the wall thickness even in the event of guide pin wear in the course of extended production. The cores (*c*) must be press-fitted into the retainer plate (*d*) with adequate length to ensure that they will not be displaced in the event of melt flowing on one side.

The cores (*c*) and cavity inserts (*e*) are cooled by annular channels that are sealed by O-rings. The bottom of the cup is formed by a separate insert (*f*) in order to make lengthwise polishing of the cavity side walls easier. On opening of the mold, the cups are retained on the cores (*c*) from which they are then ejected by stripper plate (*b*) as it is actuated by the ejector rods (*g*). These are fastened to the ejector bar (*h*).

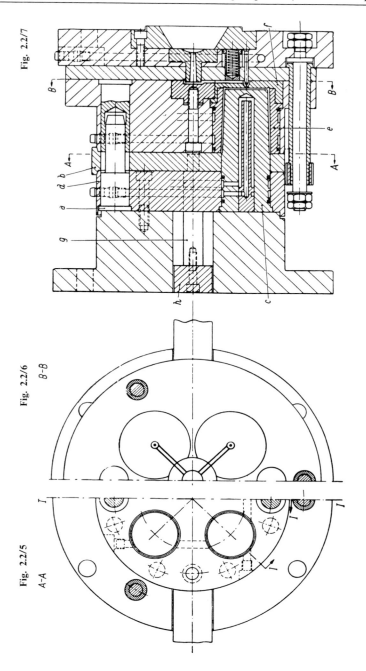

Fig. 2.2/7

Fig. 2.2/6

B-B

Fig. 2.2/5

A-A

Example 14

Figs. 2.2/5 to 2.2/7. Four-cavity mold for drinking cups with pinpoint gate on cup bottom.
(*a*) Guide pin, (*b*) stripper plate, (*c*) core, (*d*) insert retainer plate, (*e, f*) inserts, (*g*) ejector rod, (*h*) ejector bar.

Self-degating of tubular parts without internal threads and of parts with metal inserts

Example 15. Internally gated deep parts

There are parts where it is desirable to gate on the inside so that no gate mark whatsoever is visible on the outside. Such parts include, for instance, covers for cans and lipstick holders, half spheres that are to be glued together to form a full sphere and others. The following example shows a mold for internally gated lipstick holder covers (Figs. 2.2/8 to 2.2/11). Internal gating is generally limited to relatively short parts as otherwise the risers become too long.

Once again the mold has two parting lines. The runner system leading from the sprue to the risers is located in the first parting line between plate (a) and the stripper plate (b), while the molded parts drop out in the parting line between stripper plate (c) and cavity insert (d) after they have been degated.

The relatively long risers resulting from the depth of the molded parts, together with the sprue, require a long opening stroke for the runner parting line if adequate space for ejection of the rather bulky runner system is to be provided. This results in a relatively large mounting height for the mold, which must also hold the correspondingly long stripper bolts (e).

The mold operates as follows:

During the initial opening motion, plate (a) is separated from stripper plate (b) by about 3 mm through the action of the spring washers (f). The sprue and runner system are retained on the injection side by undercut pins (g) at the risers. The internal gates in the molded covers are severed by the initial opening motion and the runner parting line opens for a distance of about 100 mm until the nut (h) runs up against plate (a). Adhesion of the molded parts in the cavities (d)

and on the cores (l), together with the friction between the guide pins (i) and the guide bushings (k), keeps the cavity inserts (d) and plate (a) together. The cores (l) are held in plate (a) by means of retaining shoulders that fit into corresponding recesses. Once nut (h) comes up against plate (a), the stripper plate (b) is moved 10 mm in the direction of opening until nut (m) is stopped at washer (n). This motion strips the risers off the undercut pins (g) and pulls the sprue out of the sprue bushing (o) by 10 mm. The springs (p) can now relax and forcibly eject the sprue and runner system. Stripper plates (c) are located between the cavity inserts (d) and cores (l) and are bolted to the ejector plate (q). During the continued opening motion of the mold, the covers are retained on the cores (l) while the outer surface is released from the cavity inserts (d). This parting line continues to open until the shoulders of the three stripper bolts (r) come up against he backing plate (s). With further opening motion, the ejector plate (q) and the individual stripper plates (c) attached to it are actuated and strip the covers off the cores.

The example just described represents a limiting case for internal gating. Whenever the length of a part is greater than the diameter, internal gating should be used only in special cases since the long risers are undesirable and removal of heat from the long cores creates difficulties. The cores, namely, receive heat not only from the molded parts but also from the melt in the risers. Removal of this heat becomes more difficult as the diameter of the core decreases because it is not possible to place effective cooling in the cores.

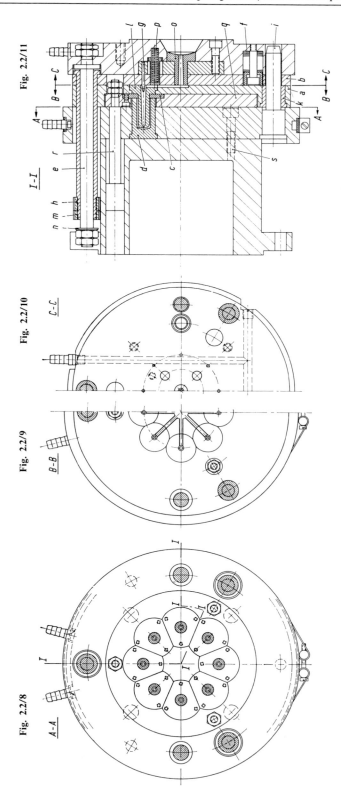

Fig. 2.2/11

Fig. 2.2/10

Fig. 2.2/9

Fig. 2.2/8

Example 15

Figs. 2.2/8 to 2.2/11. Eight-cavity mold for lipstick holder covers.
(*a*) Plate, (*b*, *c*) stripper plate, (*d*) cavity insert, (*e*) stripper bolts, (*f*) spring washers, (*g*) pin, (*h*) nut, (*i*) guide pin, (*k*) bushings, (*l*) cores, (*m*) nut, (*n*) washers, (*o*) bushings, (*p*) springs, (*q*) ejector plate, (*r*) stripper bolts, (*s*) backing plate.

Example 16. Parts with molded-in metal inserts

Automatic self-degating is also practical for parts where metal inserts are to be molded-in during injection. Example 16 describes a mold (Figs. 2.2/12 to 2.2/15) used to produce four battery holders for pocket flashlights and in which two lead wires must be sealed liquid-tight in polyethylene. The difficult aspect is that the 1.5 mm thick wires should not be displaced as the melt enters the cavities. Displacement can be prevented only by guiding the wires in sleeves (a) along their entire length. As the melt enters the cavities, it pushes back the sleeves and the wires are uniformly encapsulated. The parts are ejected jointly by the forward motion of the guide sleeves (a), which stop in the full forward position, and by a stripper plate (b), which acts on the entire circumference of the holder.

Automatic ejection of the sprue and runner system by springs is not possible with the relatively soft polyethylene. Instead, they must be removed by hand once they have been stripped off the undercut pin (c) by the stripper plate (d). Since the mold must be run semiautomatically anyway because of the need to insert the lead wires, manual removal of the sprue and runner system does not play a decisive role. As for the rest, operation is analogous to that described above for automatic self-degating molds.

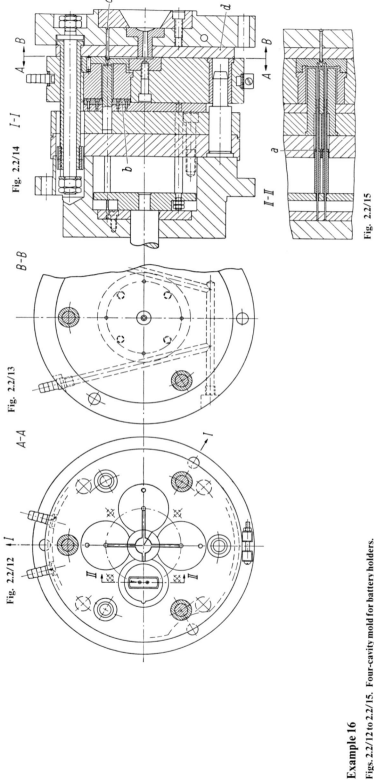

Fig. 2.2/14   I–I

Fig. 2.2/15   I–II   a

B–B   Fig. 2.2/13   A–A

Fig. 2.2/12

Example 16

Figs. 2.2/12 to 2.2/15. Four-cavity mold for battery holders.
(a) Guide sleeve, (b) stripper plate, (c) cores, (d) stripper plate.

Example 17. Injection mold for ballpoint pen barrels with metal sleeves

In high-quality ballpoint pens, it is sometimes required that a metal sleeve be molded into the barrel to guide the refill. Since it is hardly possible to load this metal guide sleeve automatically, the mold can be operated only in a semiautomatic mode. The sleeves are then placed in the cores while the mold is open.

Usually, the other end of such ballpoint pen barrels has an external thread that is automatically released by means of slides. If, however, very strict requirements as to the concentricity of this thread with respect to the pen barrel and the absence of a seam (witness line) are to be met, those components of the cavity that form the threads must be unscrewed.

Automatic unscrewing of this external thread would require a more complex and expensive mold, and for this reason would not be worthwhile, especially since the mold cannot run automatically because of the metal sleeves that must be inserted. Accordingly, it is more practical to place threaded rings in the mold and then unscrew them from the molded pen barrels by hand or with the aid of a motorized unscrewing tool. Because of the two inserts per cavity that must be loaded, it is not practical to design the mold with more than four cavities. Furthermore, one operator per machine would not be able to unscrew the threaded rings from the pen barrels within the molding cycle with more than four cavities per mold.

The pen barrels should be molded via two pinpoint gates at the threaded end. Since the gates are then located on the inside of the barrel, the gate locations will be invisible. The relatively close arrangement of the four cavities with respect to each other permits the design of this automatic self-degating mold to be simplified, because it is possible to actuate the runner plate containing the gates from the ejector side by means of bars. The construction of such a mold is described in the following (Figs. 2.2/16 to 2.2/18).

The cavity inserts for the pen barrels are extremely difficult to make of hardened steel, especially in light of the stringent requirements for a mirror finish in the long, narrow cavities. It is much simpler and less expensive to produce these inserts by electroforming. This requires only an exact metal or acrylic model onto which a nickel-cobalt layer is deposited. This layer is then reinforced by a backing layer of electrolytically deposited hard copper. The electroformed insert is then machined to size externally and pressed into a hardened steel sleeve (a). Polishing of the electroformed cavity is not necessary as long as the model was polished satisfactorily. The steel sleeves are cooled by water flowing from insert to insert as shown in section A-A. To ensure concentricity of the thread with respect to the pen barrel, the threaded insert rings (b) are aligned by the taper on the sleeves (a). Two sets of rings are needed in order that one set can be placed in the mold while the other set is being removed from the molded parts during the next molding cycle. The guide pins (c) provide for preliminary alignment of the mold halves but alone cannot guarantee concentricity of the thread with respect to the pen barrel, especially when wear of the guide pins can be expected after prolonged use of the mold. To eliminate any possibility of distortion due to hardening, the insert retainer plates (d, e, f, g) remain unhardened and utilize identical diameters for the retaining pockets so that they can be bored together.

The mold is designed as a conventional three-plate mold with automatic degating, i.e., plates (d) and (f) are held together by latches (h) during opening at the first parting line A-A. Undercuts at the ends of the runners initially hold the runner system in the runner plate (i) so that the two gates at the threaded end of the pen barrel are severed. After an opening stroke of about 60 mm, which provides just enough space for the sprue and runner system to drop out, plates (d) and (f) are unlatched. Simultaneously, ejector plate (k) is actuated, stopping plate (f) and causing the parting line between plates (d) and (f) to open as the mold continues to open. The threaded insert ring (b) containing the threaded end of the pen barrel is withdrawn from its conical seat in the sleeve (l) and must be unscrewed by hand after the parts drop out of the machine. After a further opening stroke of 85 mm, ejector plate (k) is actuated for a second time by ejector bar (m), causing the molded parts to be ejected from the cavities by pins (n).

Before the mold closes for the next cycle, the metal sleeves must be placed on the cores (o) and the threaded rings (b) loaded. Since these threaded rings contain the gates, they must be loaded in a certain orientation in order that the runners in plate (i) connect to the two gates. To ensure proper orientation, alignment pins (p) that engage in grooves in the threaded insert rings (b) are provided.

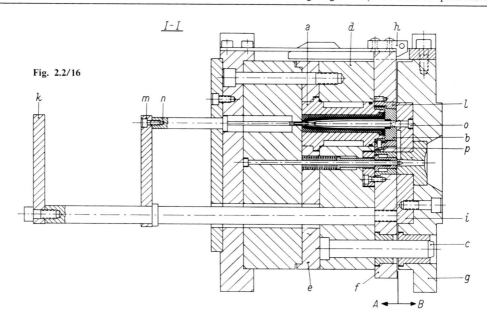

Fig. 2.2/16

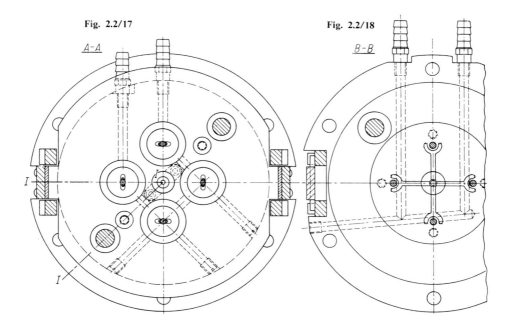

Fig. 2.2/17

Fig. 2.2/18

Example 17

Figs. 2.2/16 to 2.2/18. Semiautomatic four-cavity mold for ballpoint pen barrels.
(*a*) Steel sleeves for electroformed cavities (backed with electrolytically deposited hard copper), (*b*) insert rings, (*c*) guide pins, (*d, e, f, g*) insert retainer plates, (*h*) latch, (*i*) runner plate, (*k*) ejector plate, (*l*) bushing, (*m*) ejector plate, (*n*) ejector rod, (*o*) core, (*p*) alignment pin.

Example 18. Injection mold for small gears

Because of their good running properties, nylon gears are used for small drive mechanisms, clocks and similar purposes. Accordingly, in designing injection molds for such gears it is preferred that the various gears be produced as a set in one mold if possible. With counters where some gears are needed three to five times while others are used only once, this means that the mold must have a relatively high number of cavities.

Number of cavities in the mold

Since the gears are usually very small, the highest possible number of cavities in the molds is desired in order to better utilize machine capacity. Nevertheless, it is unavoidable that the ratio of runner weight to actual part weight be exceptionally high. This cannot be avoided since the hot-runner principle cannot be employed with nylon (polyamide). Compared to machining, however, production of these gears by means of injection molding yields such significant economic advantages in addition to the improved smoothness of running and service life that the relatively high proportion of wasted melt is acceptable since this material can be recycled for less critical uses.

Gating of the gears

Gating of the gears at the edge is not acceptable since this would disrupt proper engagement of the gear teeth. There is thus no other possibility than to use a pinpoint gate on the face of the gear. In view of the good flow characteristics of nylon, a gate diameter of 0.5 to 0.6 mm is quite adequate and is hardly visible on the surface; it also does not interfere with operation of the gears.

Ejection of the gears

Ejection is difficult especially with very small gears having eight to ten teeth since there is then no surface available on which ejector pins can be used. Often the space between the root diameter of the gearing and central hole is only a few tenths of a millimeter in size. In such cases, the gears can be ejected only by means of a sleeve ejector, the smallest diameter of which equals that of the core pin used to form the central hole and the outside diameter of which is somewhat smaller than the root diameter of the gearing (see Figs. 2.2/21 and 2.2/24 to 2.2/27). For gears with a molded central shaft (Fig. 2.2/22), it is most practical to eject directly at the shaft itself. Ejection by means of ejector pins is shown in Figs. 2.2/21, 2.2/23 and 2.2/27. Figure 2.2/20 shows a view of the runner system on the injection side of the mold.

Producing the gear inserts

Since it is hardly possible to produce the cavity inserts by means of profile milling with the accuracy that is so necessary especially for the tooth profile on such small gears, only two possibilities remain. The first involves producing a hob with the necessary shrinkage allowance and then hobbing and hardening the insert. This somewhat older method yields satisfactory results in all cases even though it cannot always be employed, e.g., if a double gear with different numbers of teeth is to be molded in one piece. It is impossible to produce such a hob. It might be thought that such an insert could be assembled from two parts. Since, however, the gears are only 0.8 to 1 mm thick, the wall thickness would be too weak for the height of the tooth. The more practical method for producing such inserts is without a doubt *electroforming*. This requires making an exact master of the desired gear in metal or acrylic with the necessary shrinkage allowance. This presents no difficulties since the teeth of the master can be rolled, milled or shaped in the case of internal gearing. Gears having different pitch diameters can be combined. They need only be screwed, soldered or cemented on a plate in the parting line of the mold and have the size of the final insert diameter. Double-toothed gears can be produced only in one piece for reasons of ejection if the outside diameter of the smaller gear is smaller than the inside diameter of the larger gear.

A 2 to 3 mm tick layer of a nickel-cobalt alloy is electrolytically deposited on this master and is then reinforced by a backing layer of electrolytically deposited hard copper. After electroforming is complete, the outside diameter is machined to permit press-fitting into a case-hardened insert. Today it is possible to produce such electroformed inserts with a surface hardness of 55 to 60 Rockwell C. The accuracy of reproduction is extraordinarily high as even microscopic details of the master are transferred to the electroformed cavity. Since it is also possible to suspend a large number of the small gears in an electroforming bath, the time required to produce the cavities is acceptable even when two to three weeks are expected for the deposit to be completed. In turn, no other secondary operations whatsoever are necessary with the exception of external machining. Even the production of cavity inserts for helical gears by means of electroforming is quite simple.

Mold design

As mentioned above, only molds with pinpoint gates come into consideration for small gears. The large number of inserts that must usually be incorpo-

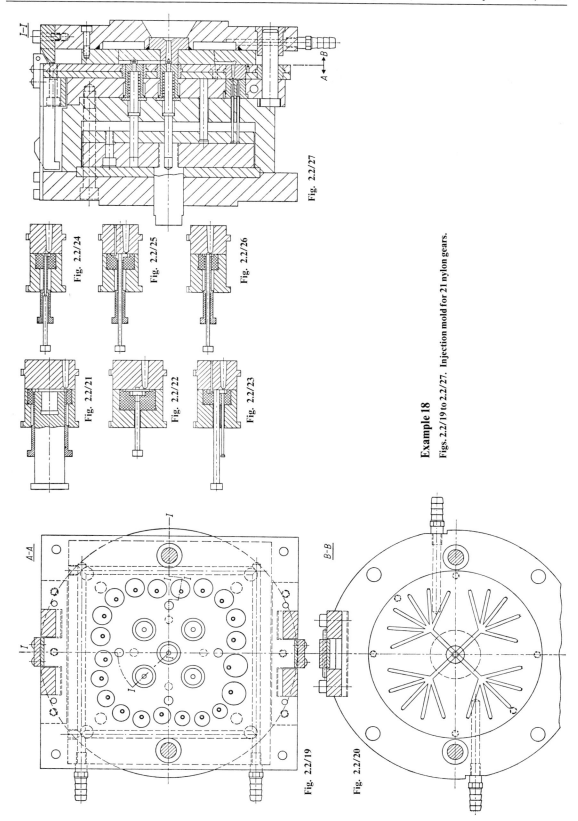

Fig. 2.2/27

Fig. 2.2/24

Fig. 2.2/25

Fig. 2.2/26

Fig. 2.2/21

Fig. 2.2/22

Fig. 2.2/23

Example 18

Figs. 2.2/19 to 2.2/27.   Injection mold for 21 nylon gears.

Fig. 2.2/19

Fig. 2.2/20

rated in a single mold places special requirements on the construction of the mold. Example 18 therefore describes a 21-cavity mold for such small gears, with special emphasis on the mold making aspects (Figs. 2.2/19 to 2.2/27).

The number of cavities resulted from the need for one gear as shown in Fig. 2.2/21, one gear as shown in Fig. 2.2/22, five gears as shown in Fig. 2.2/23, three gears as shown in Fig. 2.2/24, five gears as shown in Fig. 2.2/25, one gear as shown in Fig. 2.2/26, and five gears as shown in Fig. 2.2/27, i.e., a total of 21 gears for a particular drive mechanism. These had to be placed in a mold in such a way as to guarantee trouble-free automatic operation and permit good cooling/heating with hot water.

An arrangement of the inserts as shown in Figs. 2.2/19 and 2.2/20 proved practical. Four sets of secondary runners emanate from four points that function as retention points for the runner system and are fed from the sprue by means of four primary runners. The secondary runners are almost identically long and lead to the individual pinpoint gates. Slight differences in the length of the secondary runners result from the different distances of the gates from the center of the gears due to the varying number of teeth on the gears.

The advantages of the arrangement chosen are that the cooling channels can be brought quite close to all inserts and that the runner system is as short as possible. The length of the secondary runners is enough to withstand the bending on release from the undercuts.

Guidelines for the construction of the mold

The very close tolerances demanded of such gears not only with regard to their diameters but also with regard to the concentricity of the central hole or shaft with respect to the gear teeth require extremely accurate alignment of the pockets in the insert retainer plates. Accordingly, these cannot be hardened, since otherwise distortion might occur. In machining these plates, aligned pockets in the various retainer plates should be bored together, if possible on a jig boring machine or another suitable machine tool with a rotary table und adjustment by coordinates.

After external machining of the plates, including surface grinding, the holes for the guide pins and guide bushings are first bored and the pockets for the inserts are then machined simultaneously with the guide pins and bushings installed. The recesses for the retaining shoulders of the pockets can be made later since the shoulder diameter has about 0.2 mm clearance and the axial alignment of the recesses with respect to the pockets is not as critical. All fits for inserts in the assembled retainer plates are based on ISA tolerances H7 for the pockets and j6 for the outside diameter of the inserts. This combination results in the minimum tolerance for easy assembly.

The electroformed inserts and their sleeves utilize a fit of H7-n6 and must be press-fitted together. It is recommended that the retaining shoulder for the cavity inserts and other inserts be left soft if they are to be secured to prevent rotation. This is achieved most simply by providing an additional 2 mm all around on the insert and then removing it after carburizing and before hardening. This area will then remain soft on hardening so that the holes for the locating pins can be drilled in the hardened and ground inserts.

The moving parts (ejector sleeves and ejectors) should be given a fit based on the combination H7-f6. Depending on the diameter, a length of 5 to 10 mm suffices for such fits. Beyond this length, the bore can be opened up by 0.2 to 0.3 mm.

To prevent the formation of flash on the molded part, the inserts should protrude 0.05 mm past the retainer plates. This adjustment is best made after initial assembly of the mold and grinding of the inserts to a common height. The required grinding allowance must thus be added to the thickness of the gears in advance. The 0.05 mm projection of the inserts is then achieved by subsequent grinding of the retainer plates without the inserts.

Example 19. Mold for bushings with concealed gating

A flanged bushing is to be injection molded in such a way that any remnants of the gate are concealed or as little noticeable as possible. The bushing would normally require a two-plate mold with a single parting line. The molded part would then be released and ejected along its axis, which coincides with the opening direction of the mold. The gate would be located on the outer surface of the flange since it is in contact with the mold parting line.

In order to satisfy the requirement for an "invisible" gate, the cavities (two rows of four) are placed between slides carrying the cores (Fig. 2.2/28) even though there are no undercuts. From a central sprue the melt flows through conical runners in the cores to pinpoint gates located on the inner surface of the bushings. As the slides move during opening of the mold the gates are cleanly sheared off flush with the adjacent part surface. The flexibility of the plastic selected is sufficient to permit release of the end of the runner from the angled runner channel. The parts are now free and can drop out of the mold.

Example 19

Fig. 2.2/28. Mold for bushings with concealed gating.
Illustration: Erikssons Verktygsindustri, Gislaved/Sweden.
(*1*) Stationary-side clamping plate, (*2*) stationary-side backing plate, (*3*) wedge, (*4*) slide, (*5*) movable-side backing plate, (*6*) injection-side cavity half, (*7*) ejector-side cavity half, (*8*) core, (*9*) sprue bushing, (*10*) locating ring, (*11*) part ejector, (*12*) sprue ejector.

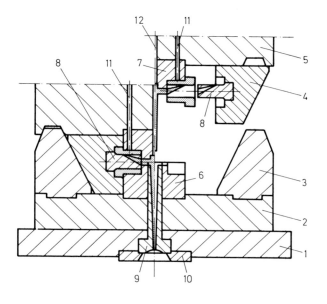

2.3   Molds with Internal Punch-Action Degating

Example 20. Multiple-cavity injection mold with central punch-action degating

If, for instance, dials with a central hole are to be produced, edge gating is not satisfactory for high-quality requirements. A weld line would result behind the core used to form the central hole, and the surface quality and strength of the dial would be reduced. In this case, there is no other possibility than to mold a solid dial and then make the hole subsequently. Edge gating is also unacceptable if a thicker edge is required on the dial as in the present case. With edge gating of such a part, the melt would flow preferentially around the edge. The result is that during final filling the melt flows toward the center of the dial and the air cannot escape from this area. Accordingly, a dial having a thicker edge must be gated in the center. If, however, a hole is required exactly at this location in the dial, this hole must be produced subsequently. A solution is provided in the mold designed in the following, where central gating is used for the part and the required hole is automatically produced by punch-action degating during opening of the mold.

Externally, the mold shown in Figs. 2.3/1 and 2.3/2 resembles the molds with two parting lines that have been repeatedly described previously. The runners are located in parting line (A). The mold first opens at this parting line as long as the latches (a) hold plates (b) and (c) together. The two mold halves are unlatched as the release pins (d) travel along the release bars (e). After this opening of the runner parting line, plate (c)

is held by stops on the release bars (e), and the mold opens at the second parting line between plates (b) and (c).

The difference with respect to a pinpoint-gated mold is that the dial is gated over the entire cross section of the future hole, whereby a concentration of stress such as that which results around a pinpoint gate is largely avoided. The punch-action degating and simultaneous creation of the hole occurs during the initial opening at the runner parting line (A) by having the spring (g) extend the punch (f) toward the nozzle while plates (b) and (c) are still latched. During this motion of the punch, the portion of the runner around the retaining pin (h) is simultaneously released from its tapered channel. The runner system is initially released from the retaining pin by the action of the strong sprig washers (i) on the stripper plate (k). After the spring washers have relaxed, the springs (l) provide for further motion of the stripper plates (k).

The runner system is initially held on the sprue puller (m), which is positively pulled out of the sprue on opening of the mold at the parting line between plates (b) and (c) as plate (b) is held by the stop on the release bar (e). The runner system is then ejected at parting line (A) by the sudden relaxation of spring (n). The dials are ejected by the sleeve ejectors (o) as ejector rod (p) is actuated.

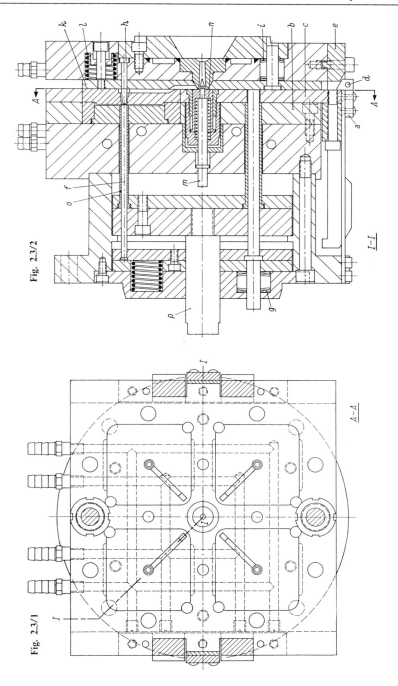

Fig. 2.3/2

Fig. 2.3/1

Example 20

Fig. 2.3/1 and 2.3/2. Four-cavity mold for dials.
(*a*) Latches, (*b, c*) mold plates, (*d*) release pin, (*e*) release bar, (*f*) punch, (*g, l, n*) springs, (*h*) retainer pin, (*i*) spring washers, (*k*) stripper plate, (*m*) sprue puller, (*o*) sleeve ejectors, (*p*) ejector rod.

Example 21. Injection mold for producing covers

In this example, the objective was to design a three-cavity injection mold for the production of polystyrene covers. The mold was constructed using standard mold components as shown in Figs. 2.3/3 to 2.3/6 and has four parting lines, *I* to *IV*. To avoid variations in wall thickness as much as possible and to permit offset printing of the molded parts, a flash gate as depicted in Fig. 2.3/4 was selected in lieu of central gating.

On opening of the mold, the spacer pin (*a*) is withdrawn from parting line I, thereby opening parting line II as shown in Fig. 2.3/3. The force exerted by spring pack (*b*) prevents shifting of the molded part (*c*) between the movable cores (*d*) and (*e*).

Spring pack (*f*) then causes opening of parting line *III* and closing of parting line *I*. Simultaneous displacement of the cutter insert (*g*) in the direction of the arrow automatically degates the molded part. The molded parts and runner system are then ejected on actuation of the ejector pins (*h*) as shown in Fig. 2.3/6. The spacer pins (*i*) and (*k*) prevent damage to the cores (*d*) and (*e*) during mold closing.

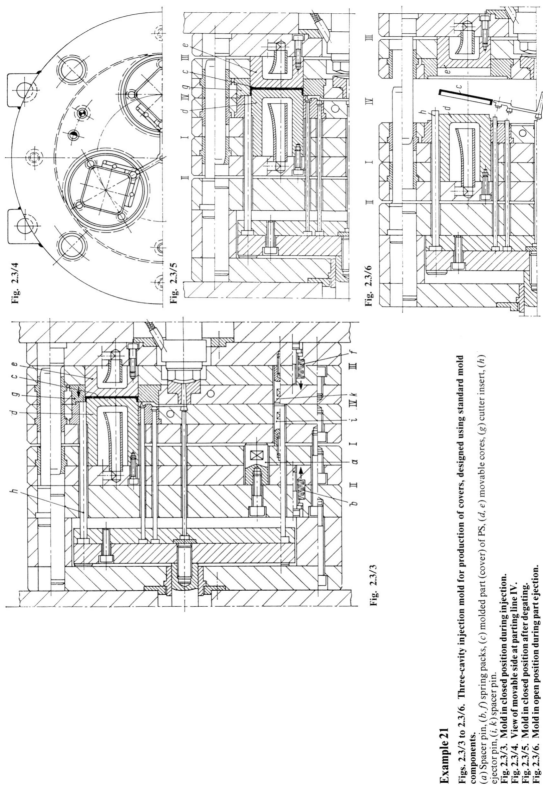

Fig. 2.3/4

Fig. 2.3/5

Fig. 2.3/6

Fig. 2.3/3

Example 21

Figs. 2.3/3 to 2.3/6. Three-cavity injection mold for production of covers, designed using standard mold components.

(a) Spacer pin, (b, f) spring packs, (c) molded part (cover) of PS, (d, e) movable cores, (g) cutter insert, (h) ejector pin, (i, k) spacer pin.
Fig. 2.3/3. Mold in closed position during injection.
Fig. 2.3/4. View of movable side at parting line IV.
Fig. 2.3/5. Mold in closed position after degating.
Fig. 2.3/6. Mold in open position during part ejection.

2.4   Molds with Internal Mechanical Shear-Action Degating

By shifting or rotating an insert in a mold with respect to the cavity, the molded parts may be degated from the runners. Such molds are not complicated at all and, if properly made, operate in an extremely reliable and clean manner. Such shear-action degating, however, is limited to parts having sharp, straight edges along which the slide may travel during the degating action or where the possibility exists to gate from below, i.e., from the flat side of the molded part. In either case, degating is possible only at the outer

edge. This method nevertheless offers the advantage that parts with a bevel or radius that must normally be gated at this bevel or radius may be gated on the flat side and the gate will be cleanly sheared off during opening of the mold without the need for secondary operation. It does not matter whether the parts are ejected by pins or a stripper plate since it is also possible to place the moving slide containing the gates in the stripper plate.

Example 22.   Eight-cavity mold for sight glasses

Example 22, shown in figs. 2.4/1 to 2.4/4, describes an eight-cavity mold for sight glasses such as those used in oil level gauges. In placing the eight parts in the mold, care must be taken that the flow paths to the molded parts are as equal as possible. Experience has shown that the reversal of flow direction that is necessary for the four inner parts with this arrangement has no effect whatsoever on the flow resistance. The rheological properties of most plastics melt differ significantly from those of an ideal fluid. The viscous melt slowly flows through the runners and into the cavities so that even with the apparently unfavorable arrangement resulting from the sharp reversal the eight cavities are filled uniformly. The runners are machined into a slide (a) having a travel of about 3 mm on the ejector side of the mold. The gate extends under the surface of the molded part for about 1.5 to 2. mm. With the mold closed, the gate is directed radially toward the center of the molded part. The slide is held in the indicated position by the offset cam (b) and is shifted to the left on opening of the mold. As the mold opens, the sprue must first be withdrawn from the sprue bushing (c) before the slide is shifted. The offset cam thus provides for a stroke somewhat longer than the length of the sprue before actuating the slide. It is

only after the mold has opened this amount that the offset cam causes the slide to shift by about 3 mm. Measures must also be taken to ensure that shifting of this slide can occur without destroying the undercut used to hold the runner system on the ejector side of the mold. This is achieved by elongating the ejector guide bushings (d) in the direction of slide motion to ensure good shutoff of the elongated undercut used to retain the runner system. The ejector pins (e) must be flush with the ejector guide bushings (d) and slightly crowned at the end. The purpose of this is to prevent formation of a small plastic chip at this location during the shearing action of the slide. The crowned end of the ejector pin acts like a wedge as the slide shifts so that the undercut for the runner system is lifted slightly during the shearing action and a chip does not form.

In molds having such shear-action degating, care must be taken that the molded parts on the ejector side of the mold provide adequate resistance to the shear forces. With a completely smooth surface, such shear-action degating on the surface is not possible unless the part has several holes and can be held on core pins during shearing of the gate as in the present example, where there are two mounting holes for the sight glass.

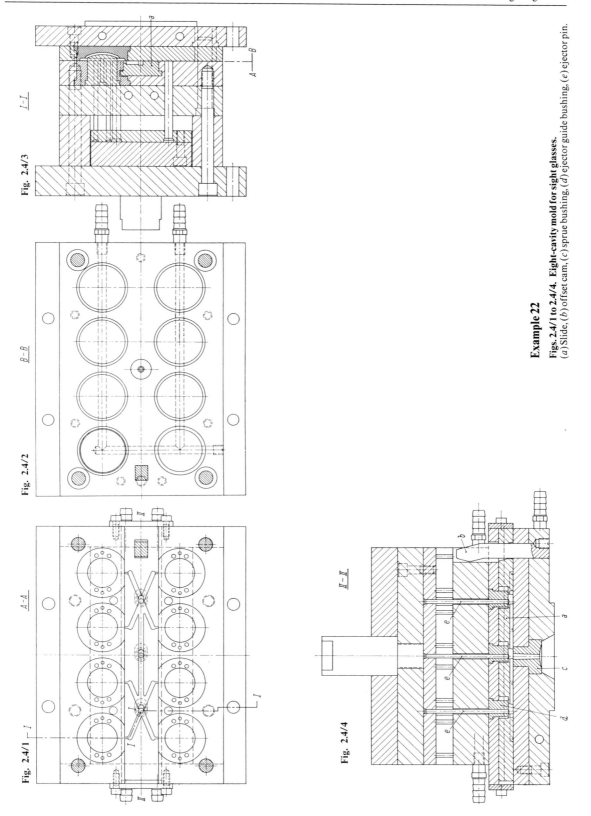

Fig. 2.4/3

I–I

Fig. 2.4/2

B–B

Fig. 2.4/1

A–A

Fig. 2.4/4

II–II

Example 22

Figs. 2.4/1 to 2.4/4. Eight-cavity mold for sight glasses.
(*a*) Slide, (*b*) offset cam, (*c*) sprue bushing, (*d*) ejector guide bushing, (*e*) ejector pin.

Example 23.   Universal injection mold for watch crystals.

Watch crystals with various diameters and curvatures are needed in great quantities. They are produced almost exclusively from acrylic by injection molding. The great variety of shapes forces the use of injection molds with interchangeable inserts in order to keep the mold costs within reasonable limits. In addition, it is required that these molds produce watch crystals on which the gate is as invisible as possible and where the degating occurs automatically.

By arranging the inserts in two rows, the parts can be degated on opening of the mold by shifting a slide containing the runner system and gates.

In the mold for example 23 (Figs. 2.4/5 to 2.4/11), the inserts are placed in a circle and the parts are degated by rotating an insert containing the runner system as the mold opens. The inserts (a) for the back and (b) for the face of the watch crystals are fitted into slides (c) and (d) respectively and are held against the runner plate (f) and sprue bushing (g) by bolts (e). Since the runner plate (f) and sprue bushing (g) partially overlap the inserts (a) and (b), the inserts are prevented from falling out.

Sprue bushing (g) is tightly bolted to the stationary-side clamping plate (h), while runner plate (f), which contains the runner system, is mounted in bronze

bushing (i) and may be rotated in plate (k). During the initial opening motion of the mold, this runner plate is actuated by means of two gear segments (l) and (m) that are operated by an offset cam (o). The cam is so designed that the runner plate (f) rotates by about 15° over an opening stroke of about 60 mm.

The runners are machined into the runner plate (f) and the watch crystals are gated from the back through an opening of about 1 mm. Figure 2.4/10 shows the cross section of the gate. The dovetail-shaped gate provides a sharp cutting edge and thus clean degating of the molded part over an area of about 1×0.8 mm.

To prevent the watch crystals from rotating as the gate is being sheared, either a small flat on the core or a few points that simultaneously identify the cavity may be provided if necessary.

In order that no ejector marks be visible on the watch crystals, they are stripped off the cores by the rotary motion. After the runner plate (f) rotates 15°, a cam located on the edge of the runner plate (see secs. *III-III*, Fig. 2.4/9) slips under the watch crystal and lifts it off the core (a) so that it may drop.

The runner system is ejected in the usual manner at the end of the opening stroke by actuating the ejector rod (p).

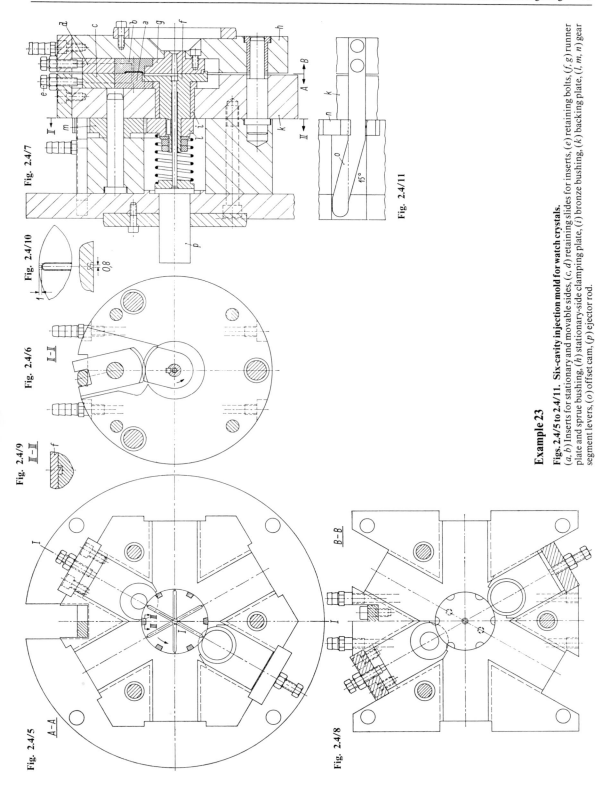

Fig. 2.4/7

Fig. 2.4/11

Fig. 2.4/10

Fig. 2.4/6   I – II

Fig. 2.4/9   I – II

Fig. 2.4/5   A – A

Fig. 2.4/8   B – B

Example 23

Figs. 2.4/5 to 2.4/11.   Six-cavity injection mold for watch crystals.
(*a, b*) Inserts for stationary and movable sides, (*c, d*) retaining slides for inserts, (*e*) retaining bolts, (*f, g*) runner plate and sprue bushing, (*h*) stationary-side clamping plate, (*i*) bronze bushing, (*k*) backing plate, (*l, m, n*) gear segment levers, (*o*) offset cam, (*p*) ejector rod.

2.5   Insulated Sprue Bushing

For relatively large parts that are produced in single-cavity molds, the so-called insulated sprue bushing has been used quite successfully. With the insulated sprue bushing, the nozzle of the injection molding machine opens into a conical chamber from which the plastics melt flows into the cavity through a gate of about 1 to 1.5 mm in diameter. The heavy sprue formed by the chamber is retained on the nozzle by an undercut as the nozzle retracts from the mold and must be removed by hand or by means of a suitable tool. It can then be returned to the machine and reprocessed. This mode of operation requires good accessibility to the nozzle, which is not the case for all injection molding machines. Especially well suited for this techniques are machines where the injection unit is retracted from the mold after each injection cycle so that the nozzle is readily accessible. An even more useful technique is to leave the partially solidified sprue on the nozzle and inject through the still-fluid core. If, however, the molded part requires the application of holding pressure for a very long period of time because of a heavy wall thickness, this method can no longer be used because the sprue solidifies completely.

The difficulty lies in sizing the chamber of the insulated sprue bushing such that the center remains fluid but the steel walls of the sprue bushing do not become too hot, as otherwise a smooth surface on the injection molded part cannot be achieved around the gate.

With this mode of operation, it is of course also possible to retract the nozzle by about 10 mm. This is necessary in order not to remove too much heat from the sprue. It is also useful to partially insulate the sprue bushing from the rest of the cold mold by an air gap of about 1 mm. However, in the area where the sprue bushing forms a part of the molding surface care must be taken to ensure proper cooling of the bushing by fitting it precisely into the cavity wall.

Another measure that may be taken to ensure that the center remains fluid is to insert a protruding copper tip into the nozzle. This copper tip ensures on the one hand that the sprue is firmly attached to the nozzle and on the other that heat will be conducted from the heated nozzle into the sprue through the thermally conductive copper. The copper tip should be designed such that there is a gap of about 1 to 1.5 mm between the tip and the wall of the sprue bushing. In addition, an approximately 3 mm hole should be provided crosswise to permit insertion of a silver steel rod for screwing the tip into the nozzle. An insulating layer of plastic then solidifies around the copper tip and contributes significantly to keeping the melt inside the copper tip fluid for as long as possible. This technique is not suitable for nylon (polyamide), since the solidification point is too high.

Intense cooling of the cavity plate around the sprue bushing is decisive for proper operation of the insulated sprue bushing.

Example 24. Hot sprue bushing with three gates

For the production of an almost cylindrical container with a funnel-shaped end and a height of about 230 mm, a small diameter of about 60 mm and large diameter of about 127 mm, the cavity half of the mold was machined from a solid piece. The core was also turned from a solid piece with a generously dimensioned base and then fitted into an accurately ground conical seat (Fig. 2.5/1).

In view of the relatively small quantity of parts that was to be produced, bubbler coolers placed symmetrically around the vertical axis of the cavity and core were deemed satisfactory. The gate would normally have been centered on the bottom of the molded part. However, the function of the part dictated the presence of a cylindrical recess about only 12 mm in diameter at this location. A gate at the bottom of the recess would have surely subjected this section of the mold to so much heat that the measures that would have been necessary to provide adequate cooling would have made the part prohibitively expensive. Accordingly, a novel design was utilized: a heated

sprue bushing with three pinpoint gates around the upper edge of the recess. In this manner, overheating of the gate area was to be avoided.

The heated sprue bushing is unique in that it consists of three precisely machined components that fit into one another and prevent any leaks whatsoever both axially and radially, thanks to the design of the center piece, which is heated internally by a cartridge heater. A design providing good flow and heat transfer characteristics was selected for the end of the center piece (which could also be called a torpedo or probe as in hot-runner systems) and the corresponding section of the sprue bushing. The copper electrode used for the electrical discharge machining of the sprue bushing is shown in Fig. 2.5/2 along with a wax casting of the end of the bushing. This concept was successfully used in production. The three melt streams already combine at the bottom surface and the fear that long weld lines would be visible along the cylindrical side walls of the container proved to be unfounded.

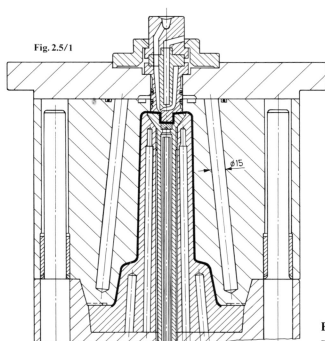

Fig. 2.5/1

Fig. 2.5/2. Copper electrode (right) used to produce the inside of the sprue bushing with three pinpoint gates and wax casting of the sprue bushing.

Example 24

Fig. 2.5/1. Illustration of the sprue bushing for an injection mold used to produce a container by means of three pinpoint gates.
Mold maker: Sydsvenska Verktygs AB, Helsingborg/Sweden.

2.6   Insulated-Runner Systems

Example 25. Six-cavity insulated-runner mold for PE covers

It is only natural to extend the insulated sprue bushing concept to create an insulated-runner system for multiple-cavity molds. It was observed even in long unheated runner systems that the plastics melt remains fluid enough at least in the center of the runner to permit repeated injection as with an insulated sprue bushing even if the mold plates in which the runner system is located are cooled. The solidified melt on the surface of the runner channel provides exceptional thermal insulation for the inner fluid core.

The entire cross section of the runner will, of course, solidify in time and provisions must be made to ensure easy removal of the solidified runner system at the end of a shift or after a long interruption. This is accomplished most simply by placing the runner system in a parting line of the injection mold that normally remains closed but may be easily opened to permit removal of the solidified runner system.

The insulated-runner system has proved especially suitable for polyethylene. Nevertheless, polystyrene and all thermoplastic resins that have a wide softening range may be processed utilizing this technique.

Compared to hot-runner molds with heated runner systems, such molds are considerably simpler in design and less expensive to make than self-degating three- and four-plate molds with cold-runner systems. They also do not require as large a mold mounting height or opening stroke as do such molds, since the opening stroke for a second parting line is eliminated.

They are thus suitable for use wherever large quantities of molded parts are to be produced fully automatically with maximum economy and without any waste whatsoever. In example 25, a six-cavity insulated runner injection mold for airtight covers of polyethylene is described (Figs. 2.6/1 to 2.6/3). The inner edge of the cover exhibits a bead that engages in a groove in the container to be sealed and holds the cover on the container. To ensure proper sealing of the cover, an inner collar with two sealing lips is provided. These difficult-to-release undercuts require special measures to ensure proper ejection. The undercuts are machined into an annular core (a) which has a certain amount of travel (about 8 mm) during the initial portion of ejection and is then stopped. This is necessary to first release the cover with its inner collar from core (b) so that the sealing lips can pass over the annular core (a) as ejection continues. If this travel of the annular core did not take place, the sealing lips would be sheared off during ejection. Ejection is accomplished by means of a sleeve ejector (c) and stripper plate (d), which contains the inserts (e) used to strip the beaded edge off the annular core.

Cavity inserts (f) are used to form the outer surface of the cover and are cooled individually by annular channels. These inserts contain the risers in which the plastics melt remains fluid long enough to permit repeated injection through a small gate of 0.6 to 0.8 mm in diameter. To ensure that this small gate does not freeze, it should be designed with about 10° taper toward the cover and the length of the gate should not be greater than its diameter. This requires the use of a tough steel for the insert, since if a case-hardened steel were used there would be the danger that the very thin wall around the gate would break.

If a circular witness line can be tolerated on the molded part, it is practical to place the riser in a separate insert, since it can be expected that the gate will wash out in the course of time because of the high flow velocity during filling. It is naturally much simpler to replace the riser insert than the entire insert for the molded part.

Use of a separate riser insert is to be recommended especially for rectangular inserts that may further contain engraving. This provides the additional advantage of being able to insulate the riser bushing from the cavity insert by an air gap so that the riser may be kept warmer than the insert.

The riser opens into the runner system, which is machined in both the insert retainer plate (g) and the clamping plate (h). The diameter of the runner depends on the cycle time that can be achieved, but if possible should not be smaller than 16 to 18 mm in order to avoid premature solidification of the plastics melt in the core of the runner.

After a lengthy interruption, the runner will have naturally cooled and solidified so far that repeated injection is no longer possible. The mold must than be opened at the runner parting line and the solidified runner system removed. Under certain circumstances, this may be necessary after the first shot at the start of a shift, since for trouble-free operation the mold plates must have first reached a certain temperature.

To permit easy removal of the runner system, four latches (k) are placed on stud bolts (i) screwed into the retainer plate (g). Normally these latches are fastened to the clamping plate (h) so that the runner parting line remains closed during mold opening. If the runner system is to be removed, these latches are loosened while the mold is closed and fastened to plate (d). If the mold is now opened, the runner parting line separates and the solidified runner system can be removed.

Example 25

Figs. 2.6/1 to 2.6/3. Six-cavity insulated runner mold for snap-on PE overcaps

(*a*) Annular core, (*b*) core, (*c*) sleeve ejectors, (*d*) stripper plate, (*e, f*) inserts, (*g*) insert retainer plate, (*h*) clamping plate, (*i*) stud bolt, (*k*) latch.

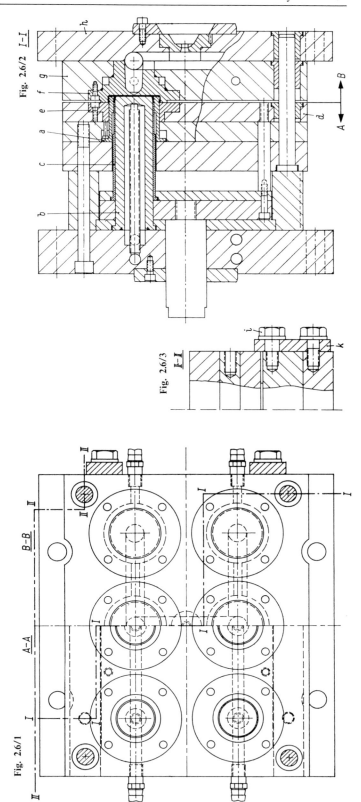

Fig. 2.6/2 *I–I*

Fig. 2.6/3 *I–I*

Fig. 2.6/1

2.7 Hot-Runner Molds

Hot-runner molds offer significant processing advantages. Of primary importance is the material savings that results from elimination of the runner system. A hot-runner system represents in essence an extension of the machine nozzle through which the plastics melt flows directly into the cavities. For parts having identical weights, the amount of material to be plasticated is less than that required in a cold-runner mold by the amount needed to fill the runner system. The required recovery time, and thus the overall cycle time, is shortened by a corresponding amount, leading to increased machine productivity. The use of hot-runner systems is suited especially for multiple-cavity molds, molds for small parts and molds for quality parts subjected to high loads where no regrind may be processed. The processing and economic advantages of hot-runner molds are often achieved by converting cold-runner molds even if the entire runner system cannot be eliminated because of the mold design. As a rule, however, considerable savings of time and material are achieved.

Although these advantages speak for the use of hot-runner molds, their general use does confront certain difficulties and problems. There is furthermore the need for additional temperature controllers and heating systems. Some general rules for proper design are discussed in the following.

Heat balance considerations [1]

The most commonly encountered problems with hot-runner molds – regardless of the hot-runner system used – occur because of inadequate heat balance. This shortcoming may be the result of very different causes.

For instance, problems with externally heated hot-runner nozzles with wound heating elements may be the result of too little heat transfer surface, which leads to complete failure of the hot-runner system. Identical problems may occur when using cartridge heaters if a proper seat is not provided. In this case, the insulating action of the resulting air gap between the cartridge heater and bore may lead to a heat buildup in the cartridge on the one hand and at least locally inadequate heating on the other even though the heating capacity has been properly determined. The heat buildup in the cartridge is often the cause of premature failure, i.e., shortened service life. Tubular heating elements that have been embedded in thermally conducting cement in coarsely machined channels have proved quite successful. Since these tubular heating elements can be individually adapted to local requirements in accordance with the layout of the hot-runner manifold, they can contribute to an improved heat balance in many cases. When proper procedures are followed, i.e.,

– Entrapped air in the thermally conducting cement is avoided
– All surfaces of the tubular heating element and channel are coated with the thermally conducting cement
– The instructions of the manufacturer with regard to curing of the thermally conducting cement are observed

tubular heating elements exhibit a long service life and little susceptibility to failure. Because of the brittleness and tendency of the thermally conducting cement to crumble, the channels must be covered. For thermal reasons (see below), this is accomplished preferably with bright cold-rolled or polished aluminum plates fastened to the hot-runner manifold.

The requirement for a uniform heat balance in the hot-runner manifold includes especially the requirement for as few local temperature differences as possible, as this is a necessary prerequisite for identical temperatures at the tips of the probes (torpedos) when these are heated indirectly by the hot-runner system. To achieve as few temperature fluctuations in the hot-runner manifold as possible

– The mass of the block should be as high as possible
– The heat losses should be as low as possible
– The temperature should be controllable.

In determining the heating capacity, specific values of 150 to 300 W/kg of hot-runner manifold have proved successful. It should be noted that in particular too high a specific heating capacity (> 300 W/kg of the hot-runner manifold) can lead to large, undesirable fluctuations of the hot-runner manifold temperature. The use of quasi-continuous controllers with reduced power output during start-up is to be recommended for controlling the temperature of the hot-runner manifold. It must, however, be borne in mind that even with the most elaborate temperature control system problems of heat balance cannot be corrected if at the same time measures to minimize the heat losses are not taken.

For instance, temperature differences of up to 60 °C (!) were measured as the consequence of *convective heat losses* resulting from a chimney effect (Fig. 2.7/1) in a four-nozzle hot-runner mold. Continuous production of parts to specifications was not possible in spite of an otherwise properly laid out hot-runner system. The chimney effect was easily eliminated by covering the open sections of the mold. This measure led to a significant reduction in temperature differences.

The goal of a uniform temperature can be achieved relatively easily through very simple, physically meaningful measures based on the laws of heat transfer. The temperature difference between the hot-runner manifold and the mold plates may be up to 300 °C. More or less heat may be lost by *radiation* depending

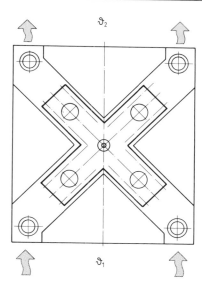

Fig. 2.7/1. Illustration of the cause of convective heat losses due to the chimney effect resulting from open sections of the mold $(\vartheta_1 < \vartheta_2)$

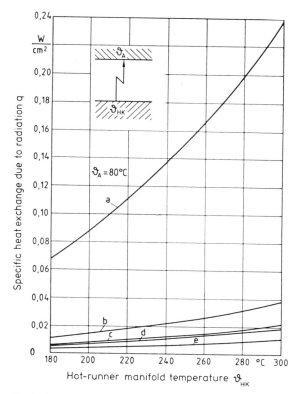

Fig. 2.7/2. Heat losses due to radiation from various surfaces in the hot-runner mold.
(a) Slightly rusted steel–slightly rusted steel, (b) bright steel–bright steel, (c) aluminum–slightly rusted steel, (d) aluminum–bright steel, (e) aluminum–aluminum.

on the type of surface. This is true especially for surfaces with temper colors or even more for slightly rusted steel surfaces.

To minimize these losses at little cost, it is recommended that bright drawn or polished aluminum plates be fastened to the surfaces of the hot-runner manifold (Fig. 2.7/2, curve c). The use of coverings for the mold plates enclosing the hot-runner manifold provides an additional but relatively slight improvement (Fig. 2.7/2, curve e). As can be seen for the conditions illustrated in Fig. 2.7/2, the radiant heat transfer between two slightly rusted steel surfaces can be up to an order of magnitude greater than that between surfaces of aluminum and rusted steel.

Further heat losses occur as the result of *conduction* in the support pads and locating bushings (example 26, Figs. 2.7/7 to 2.7/12, items *17, 18*). Since these losses are proportional to the areas of contact, these should be kept as small as possible while observing a maximum permissible force per unit area of about 300 N/mm² for the supporting components. These relatively high surface forces necessitate the use of hardened steel support components, as such high mechanical loads would otherwise lead to plastic deformation of the heated probes (torpedos). Designs in which locating bushes have not been used for reasons of simplicity have no proved successful.

The fits for the probe shank, locating bushing and locating bushing seat in the hot-runner manifold should always be a combination of H7/m6. Electrical discharge machining has not proved useful because of the relatively rough surfaces that result and the danger of melt penetrating into the seat.

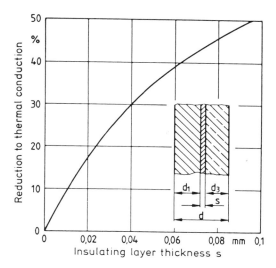

Fig. 2.7/3. Reduction of thermal conduction by a plastics-filled gap (s) between the probe shank (d_3, copper) and locating bushing (d_1, steel).
The example shown is based on the following data:
$d = 10$ mm, $d_1 = 5$ mm, s, $d_3 =$ variable, thermal conductivities of steel, $\lambda_{St} = 17$ W/(m × K), plastic resin $\lambda_K = 0.31$ W/(m × K), copper $\lambda_{Cu} = 395$ W/(m × K).

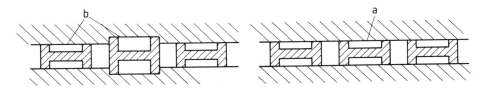

Fig. 2.7/4. Illustration of a favorable (right) and unfavorable (left) design of support component with one and two reference planes respectively (the so-called double fit).
(*a*) One plane, (*b*) two planes.

An insulating layer of 10 μm, for instance, already leads to a reduction in heat transfer by about 10 %.

Control of the hot-runner manifold temperature can be accomplished quite simply. In many cases, a thermocouple and temperature controller suffice. By consistantly following laws of heat transfer, temperature fluctuations of only a few degrees may be achieved at the probe tips, thereby fulfilling an essential prerequisite for production of precision molded parts. Closed-loop control should always be preferred over open-loop control, keeping in mind, however, that an attempt should be made to achieve maximum reliability with as little expense as possible.

Experience permits the general conclusion to be drawn that the most commonly encountered cause of greater or fewer problems and mistakes with hot-runner molds can be traced to poor attention to heat losses. Heat losses always lead to impermissibly large temperature differences in the hot-runner manifold. The results are fluctuating part quality with respect to tolerances and properties and/or solidification of the melt during the molding cycle, that is, failure of the system. The expense to minimize heat losses is generally low and is always justified as well as necessary for the reasons mentioned, since even a process-controlled injection molding machine cannot correct for the effects of temperature differences or impermissibly high temperature fluctuations in the mold.

Multiple fits (double fits) [1]

The hot-runner manifold is generally located in the mold and connected to the mold plate by means of support pads and locating bushings. In order to prevent impermissibly large amounts of deformation and at the same time reliably prevent leakage, certain tolerances as to the shape and location of the sealing surfaces with respect to one another are required. This is achieved without the need for a great deal of machining by having the pressure pads (example 26, Figs. 2.7/7 to 2.7/12, item *17*), for instance, in contact with only one common plane (Fig. 2.7/4, right). This is accomplished by grinding the support pads to a common

height with the aid of a surface grinder. Occasionally, two or more planes are provided (Figs. 2.7/4, left, and 2.7/5, left) for reasons of locating and positioning the hot-runner manifold, but these have not proved useful in practice because of the differing percentages of contact area resulting from the double or multiple fits, not to mention the increased amount of machining necessary. Differing percentages of contact area (= different surface pressures) are often the cause of leakage in multiple-cavity molds, especially in the region of sealing surfaces, e.g., between the probe locating bushing and the gate insert. Melt can be forced into the air gap between the hot-runner manifold and mold plates and completely fill it. As a result of the higher thermal conductivity of the plastics resin compared with that of air, this leads to a drastic distortion of the heat balance, since heat losses increase considerably. Compensating for these heat losses by raising the hot-runner manifold temperature generally causes thermal degradation of the plastics melt, because the permissible processing temperature range is exceeded. In addition to the thermal degradation and unpleasant odors, lower toxic limits may also be exceeded, which is impermissible for obvious reasons.

The pressure pads and locating bushings should be fitted with an overal interference of 0.05 mm. The resulting surface pressure should not exceed about 300 N/mm^2. By also taking the thermal expansion into account, reliable sealing is ensured so long as multiple fits are avoided.

End plugs [1]

Inadequate attention to the design and fitting of an apparently incidental component such as the end plug in the hot runner (example 26, Figs. 2.7/7 to 2.7/12, item *13*) is often the cause of leakage or problems when changing colors. The end plugs in hot runners must meet the following requirements. They must:

– Be absolutely leakproof
– Have no "dead corners"
– Be secured against rotation
– Be removable

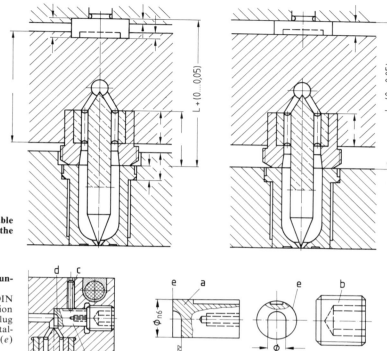

Fig. 2.7/5. Favorable (right) and unfavorable (left) design (multiple fits) for supporting the hot-runner manifold.

Fig. 2.7/6. Two-piece design of the hot-runner end plug.
(*a*) Hot-runner end plug, (*b*) set screw (DIN 913, 10 k), (*c*) set screw to prevent rotation (DIN 915), (*d*) radiused recess in the end plug matched to surrounding surfaces after installation to provide a smooth transition, (*e*) sharp-edged face of the end plug.

A proven design is shown in Fig. 2.7/6. This two-piece end plug seals primarily at its face. The necessary surface pressure is achieved by means of the set screw. Adequate sealing in the region of the cylindrical seat must also be provided, which experience has shown requires a press fit.

The radiused recess should be matched to adjoining surfaces after installation with the aid of a spherical cutter, for instance, to provide good flow and a smooth transition. Care must be taken to ensure that the edges of the sealing face are not chamfered, as this would form a groove. The resulting "dead corner" could then be the cause of difficulty when changing colors. It should be borne in mind that machining of the mounting hole with the aid of a reamer may be the cause of inadequate sealing and/or "dead corner," because of the tapered cut. Accordingly, use of a spot facing cutter, bent finishing tool or other similar tool with the aid of which an accurate fit for the end plug may be achieved is recommended when machining the mounting hole.

Processing of abrasive and/or corrosive molding compounds [1]

Abrasive and/or corrosive thermoplastic molding compounds, e.g., glass-fiber-filled nylon (PA), generally cannot be processed in hot-runner molds with plated probes of electrolytic copper or wrought cop-

per alloys without rapidly increasing wear. The wear resistance of these metallic materials can, however, be improved considerably through electroless hard nickel plating [2, 3]. Plating thicknesses of 20 to 30 μm are sufficient.

Even for the processing of unfilled polypropylene, probes of copper and its alloys should generally be electroless hard nickel plated, as this will prevent oxidation of the probe surfaces in contact with the plastics melt. Unplated probes, for instance, exhibited after a relatively short period of use groovelike wear that could be the cause of striations and discolorations in the molded part and possibly even premature failure of the hot-runner system.

For the processing of thermoplastic fluoropolymers, the probe as well es all mold surfaces coming in contact with the melt should be plated to prevent corrosion, since the formation of slight amounts of aggressive fluorine-containing compounds cannot be prevented. Here, too, electroless hard nickel plating has proved to provide adequate surface protection that is less expensive than using high-alloy, corrosion-resistant steels.

Avoidance of stringing [1]

When processing polyacetal copolymers, stringing (which generally occurs only with relatively large gates) may be eliminated by lowering the hot-runner manifold temperature ϑ_{HK} by a few degrees, and thereby lowering the temperature ϑ_l at the probe tip when the probe is indirectly heated by the hot-runner manifold.

When processing unfilled polypropylene, for instance, stringing cannot always be avoided through this measure. In this case, a slight shortening of the probe length l_T by $\Delta l_T = 0.2$ to about 1 mm has proved effective. Through this measure the gate area (considered as a heat sink) is supplied with a reduced amount of heat, as a result of which stringing can generally be eliminated. When processing polypropylene with extremely short cycle times, a special modification of the material that affects the rate of crystallization has also proved useful.

Example 26. Four-cavity hot-runner mold for polyacetal copolymer tumblers

In designing a four-cavity hot-runner mold for polyacetal copolymer tumblers weighing 21 g each (Figs. 2.7/7 to 2.7/12), a hot-runner system utilizing indirectly heated probes[1] was chosen in preference to one with direct heating of the nozzle probe, e.g., by means of a cartridge heater [4].

The heated and temperature-controlled manifold block serves as the heat source. Heat flows to the probe and gate area, ensuring that the melt remains fluid. The indirect heating requires very little in the way of temperature control hardware. Local overheating and the resulting thermal degradation of the melt can be prevented by maintaining the specified processing conditions. The forces are transmitted from the manifold block (11) to the mold plates (1, 3) via the support pads (17) and locating bushings (18). Surface pressure adequate to ensure absence of leakage throughout the system is provided by a slight interference fit. The shank of the probe (19) is shaped like the spider die commonly used in extrusion (with spokes between the openings with air foil cross sections; Figs. 2.7/11 and 2.7/12). Compared with the performance of straight-sided probe support spokes, this results in better homogeneity of the melt stream.

This hot-runner system is comparatively simple to manufacture. In addition to its reliability, the low manufacturing costs, minimal requirement for auxiliary equipment and gentle processing capabilities constitute the major advantages in its favor. Furthermore, a large number of various thermoplastic resins may be processed with it.

The reader is referred to the literature [1, 5] for information concerning selection of material for the probe (torpedo) and its design.

---

[1] Development of Hoechst AG.

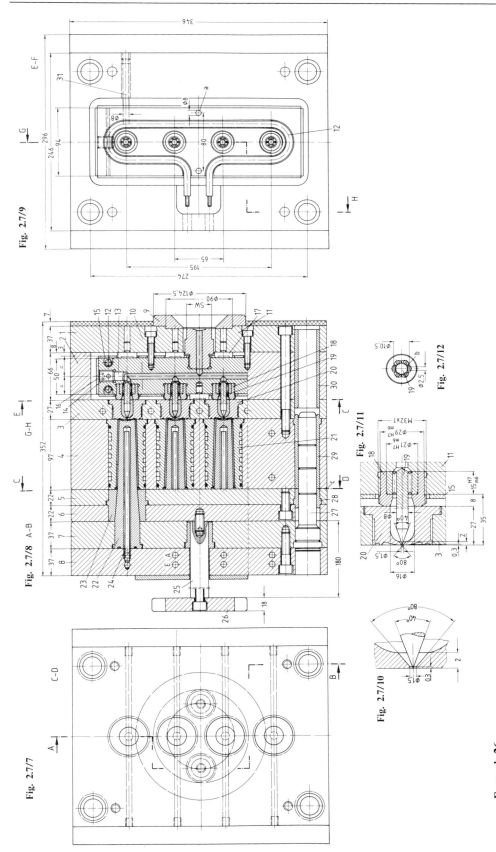

Fig. 2.7/9

Fig. 2.7/8 A–B

Fig. 2.7/7

Fig. 2.7/11

Fig. 2.7/12

Fig. 2.7/10

Example 26

Figs. 2.7/7 to 2.7/12. Four-cavity hot-runner mold for polyacetal copolymer (Hostaform®) tumblers.
(*1*) Stationary-side clamping plate; (*2*) spacer for hot-runner manifold; (*3*) nozzle plate; (*4*) cavity retainer plate; (*5, 6*) ejector plates; (*7*) core retainer plate; (*8*) movable-side clamping plate; (*9*) locating ring; (*10*) runner channel; (*11*) hot-runner manifold; (*12*) tubular heating element, 8.5 mm dia; 220 V/1200 W; total length 600 mm; heated length 500 mm; (*13*) runner end plug; (*14*) set screw; (*15, 16*) aluminum cover plate; (*17*) support pad; (*18*) locating bushing; (*19*) probe (torpedo); (*20*) gate insert; (*21*) cavity; (*22*) core; (*23*) stripper ring; (*24*) bubbler tube; (*25*) ejector rod; (*26*) ejector bar; (*27*) guide pin; (*28, 29*) guide bushing; (*30*) locating bushing; (*31*) thermocouple.
(*a*) Hot-runner manifold pinned to mold plate, (*b*) rounded openings, (*c*) parting line, (*A*) cooling water outlet, (*E*) cooling water inlet.

Example 27. Hot-runner injection mold for aerosol can caps

The mold shown in Fig. 2.7/13 was designed for economical production of 1.5 million aerosol can caps in nylon with no wasted material or secondary finishing operations. This was accomplished through utilization of a hot-runner manifold (13) with spring-loaded needle shutoff nozzles. The nozzles are closed by the force of the spring. With increasing melt pressure as injection starts, the shutoff needle (17) is forced back by the melt, thereby opening the path into the cavity. As the pressure drops, the needle closes the nozzle orifice and prevents stringing during part ejection. To prevent heat losses, the hot-runner manifold is covered with insulating plates. The BeCu nozzle inserts are screwed into the hot runner manifold and heated by it.

The design of the cap incorporates an internal collar and therefore requires two-stage ejection. As the mold opens, the parting line between plates (4) and (5) separates, simultaneously releasing the part from the cavity (22). After the ejector sleeve cap (45) is stopped during the continued opening motion, the core (24) connected to the movable clamping plate (14) is withdrawn from the molded part by the stopping of plates (5) to (7) and (9) to (12). Plate (8), which is also connected to plate (14), stops against plate (9) and forces it, plate (10) and the ejector rod (38) in the direction of the opening motion, thereby releasing the latch (41), which had previously hindered the relative motion of ejector plate (6), (7), (9) and (10) with respect to (5), (11) and (12), so that the annular core (23) is withdrawn from the part, permitting it to fall freely out of the mold. Engagement of the latch (41) in the second groove in ejector rod (38) ensures return of the ejector plates in the proper order as the mold closes.

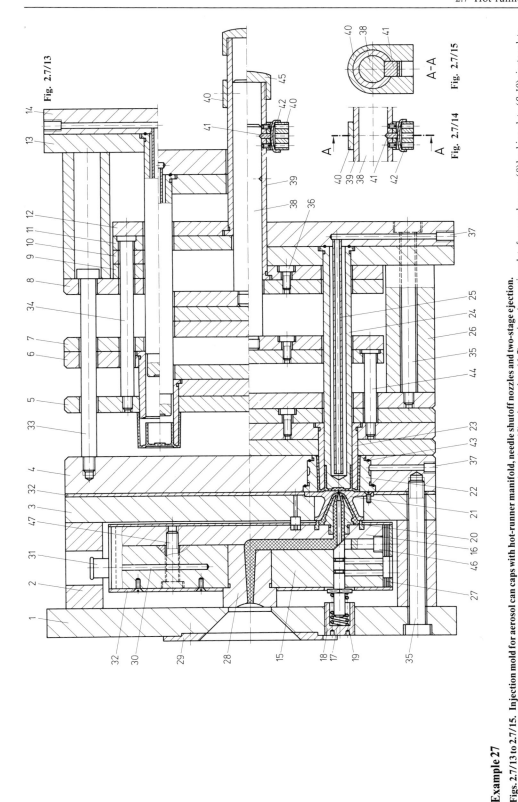

Fig. 2.7/13

Fig. 2.7/14

Fig. 2.7/15

A–A

Fig. 2.7/15

Example 27

Figs. 2.7/13 to 2.7/15. Injection mold for aerosol can caps with hot-runner manifold, needle shutoff nozzles and two-stage ejection.
(1) Stationary-side clamping plate, (2) spacer ring, (3) nozzle plate, (4) cavity retainer plate, (5) stripper plate, (6, 7) retainer/mounting plate for annular core, (8) backing plate, (9, 10) ejector plate for the annular core motion, (11, 12) ejector plate for the stripping motion, (13, 14) movable-side clamping plates, (15, 16) heated plates of the hot-runner manifold, (17) shutoff needle, (18) adjusting screw, (19) spring for shutoff needle, (20) BeCu nozzle insert, (21) insulated gate insert, (22) cooled cavity insert, (23) annular core, (24) cooled core, (25) bubbler tube, (26) spacer ring, (27) heating element, (28) sprue bushing, (29) locating ring, (30) thermocouple well, (31) connection for electrical heating, (32) insulating plate, (33, 34) spacer bolt, (35, 36) assembly bolts, (37) cooling water connection, (38) ejector rod, (39) ejector sleeve, (40) latch housing, (41) latch, (42) leaf spring, (43) O-ring, (44) spacer bolt, (45) ejector sleeve cap, (46) runner end plug, (47) assembly bolt.

Note: The guide pins and associated bushings for ejector plates (9, 10, 11, 12) are not shown.

Example 28. Hot-runner mold for a sight glass

For a combined dryer and conveyor for thermoplastic resin, a sight glass was needed, for which the mold shown in Figs. 2.7/16 to 2.7/20 was designed. The sight glass was supposed to exhibit good transparency and withstand temperatures of up to 110 °C, for which reasons polycarbonate was selected as the material. A special feature of the sight glass is a vertical lip running around the circumference inside the edge. Usually sight glasses are edge-gated. Studies of how the cavity fills and correction to the gate ensure that the flow front forms a line to prevent the entrapment of air that would lead to the formation of weld lines. This is assisted by an overflow opposite the gate through which the displaced air can escape.

However, with edge-gating the circumferential lip near the edge would cause the melt to first fill the edge region and then to flow together in the center. Accordingly, the present sight glass had to be center-gated.

Of the four types of gates possible in this case, the hot-runner system was selected, since a sprue gate would leave too large a gate mark and require secondary finishing operations. Furthermore, the sprue (or riser in an insulated runner mold or three-plate mold with pinpoint gating) would be too long as the molded part must be ejected from the stationary half of the mold, since the outer surface of the sight glass is required to be completely smooth. In addition, formation of waste in the form of a sprue that could not be reground and used again for transparent parts is avoided.

An open nozzle (1) with female thread is screwed into the barrel of the injection molding machine. This nozzle has a BeCu tip (2) that fits into the decompression chamber (3) of the hot sprue bushing. A decompression chamber is necessary to prevent drool out of the hot sprue bushing when the nozzle (1) is retracted.

The hot sprue bushing holds for cartridge heaters (4) with a total heating capacity of 1000 W. The heating capacity should not be too low in order to have reserve capacity available if needed. The temperature of the hot sprue bushing is sensed by a resistance thermometer with a bayonet connection (5) that is especially suited for such molds because of the great depth of penetration. This sensor is connected to a solid-state control unit that also provides the electrical power to the receptacle box (6). The controller rating is 1600 W. The contact surfaces of the hot sprue bushing must be kept as small as possible to keep heat transmission to the mold at a minimum. An insulating plate (7) prevents material from penetrating into the area of the cartridge heaters. A BeCu nozzle (8) with a tip that reaches to the cavity and forms an annular gate is screwed into the hot sprue bushing. The advantage of such nozzles is clean degating directly at the part. In conventional nozzles with a central orifice a small stub often remains on the molded part, and there is the further danger that stringing may occur because the fluid core is larger than with the present nozzle. With regard to nozzle designs for hot-runner manifolds in general, it should be pointed out that the nozzle threads should be larger in diameter than the nozzle body if possible. This will ensure better heat transfer from the hot-runner manifold to the nozzle tip.

Whenever high-quality parts are desired, the temperature of the mold should be kept as uniform as possible and sufficiently high, up to 130 °C for polycarbonate. It is known from experience, however, that this is not always possible. Inserts, for instance, often prevent an optimum solution or make it more difficult. In the present case, however, there are no such difficulties. It was possible to provide spiral channels on both sides through use of inserts (9) and (10).

After the melt has been injected through the hot sprue bushing and has solidified, the mold opens at the parting line. After an opening stroke of 45 mm, the latches (11) pull the ejector plate (12) forward so that the ejector sleeve (13) ejects the sight glass. As soon as the part has been ejected, the latches are disengaged by the release bar (14). As the machine closes, the ejector plate (12) is returned to the molding position by four push-back pins (15).

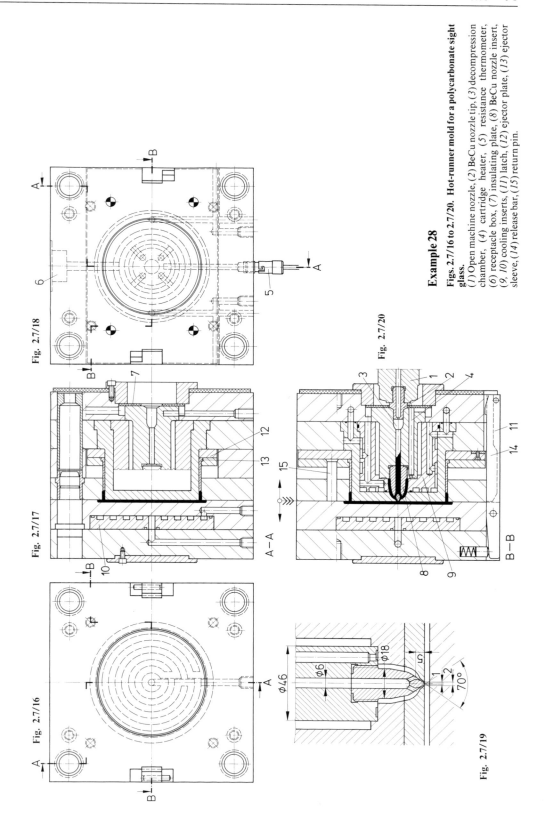

Fig. 2.7/18

Fig. 2.7/17

Fig. 2.7/16

Fig. 2.7/19

Fig. 2.7/20

A – A

B – B

Example 28

Figs. 2.7/16 to 2.7/20. Hot-runner mold for a polycarbonate sight glass.

(*1*) Open machine nozzle, (*2*) BeCu nozzle tip, (*3*) decompression chamber, (*4*) cartridge heater, (*5*) resistance thermometer, (*6*) receptacle box, (*7*) insulating plate, (*8*) BeCu nozzle insert, (*9*, *10*) cooling inserts, (*11*) latch, (*12*) ejector plate, (*13*) ejector sleeve, (*14*) release bar, (*15*) return pin.

Example 29. Thirty-two-cavity hot-runner mold for production of precision parts for atomizer pumps

A two-plate mold with a cold runner system (Figs. 2.7/21 and 2.7/22) was used as the production mold for packings for atomizer pumps (the piston pump principle). In this mold, ejection of the molded parts and runner system took place separately via synchronized ejector mechanisms (*12*), (*13*) and (*14*), (*15*), the latter being actuated subsequent to extension of ejector mechanisms (*12*) and (*13*) which severs the molded parts from the tunnel gates. To provide the most economical production possible, the mold was designed with 32 cavities. Each part is molded via a single tunnel gate with a diameter of 0.8 mm. After extensive mold trials, LDPE was selected as the suitable material for the packings (Fig. 2.7/25), which had to be produced with high precision. With a total weight of 11.2 g (= 32 × 0.35 g) for the molded parts, the weight of the runner system in this mold design was 10.03 g (Fig. 2.7/26). The ratio of part to runner volume was 1.1:1.

As part of a campaign to improve production efficiency, the mold was supposed to be redesigned at the lowest possible cost and in the least amount of time to reduce the volume of the runner system and shorten the cycle time, if possible, through use of a suitable hot-runner system. After detailed study of various hot-runner systems, the system utilizing indirectly heated probes (torpedos) [4] was selected for reasons of

– Simple and problem-free conversion
– Lowest temperature control requirements
– Low space requirement
– Little susceptibility to trouble
– Low maintenance requirements
– Low cost

The design is shown in Figs. 2.7/23 and 2.7/24. For space reasons, the hot-runner manifold (H pattern) (*21*) was designed with eight copper probes (*22*) (E-Cu F 37; DIN 40500). The probes were electroless hard nickel plated by the Kanisil technique [6]. To ensure adequate integrity of the probe locating bushing in the limited space available, the probe shank was made as long as possible (18 mm).

With a weight of 12 kg for the hot-runner manifold block, a heating circuit consisting of two tubular heating elements (*23*) with a total heating capacity of 3.5 kW was provided. This corresponds to a specific heating capacity of about 300 W/kg of hot-runner manifold. To provide good heat transmission the tubular heating elements are embedded in thermally conductive cement. To reduce heat losses due to radiation, the surfaces of the hot-runner manifold are covered with bright-rolled aluminum plates (*24*). The hot-runner manifold is controlled with the aid of only one temperature controller.

As a result of the conversion of the mold, the weight of the runner system was reduced to 4.15 g (Fig. 2.7/27). This corresponds to a volume reduction of 59%. The ratio of part to runner volume changed to 2.7:1. Through the reduction of recovery time and shot volume, it was possible to reduce the cycle time by 25%.

Use of the hot-runner system in conjunction with a shortening of the flow paths led to noticeably lower pressure drop along the runner compared with that of the original mold design. This resulted in greater part density and better dimensional accuracy. The volume of the runner system could be reduced even further if the entire mold were redesigned.

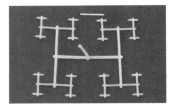

Fig. 2.7/26. Runner system before mold conversion.

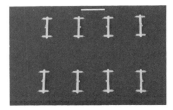

Fig. 2.7/27. Runners between hot-runner manifold nozzles and molded parts after mold conversion.

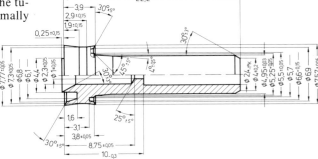

Fig. 2.7/25. LDPE plunger packing for atomizer pump
Company drawing, Calmar Albert GmbH.

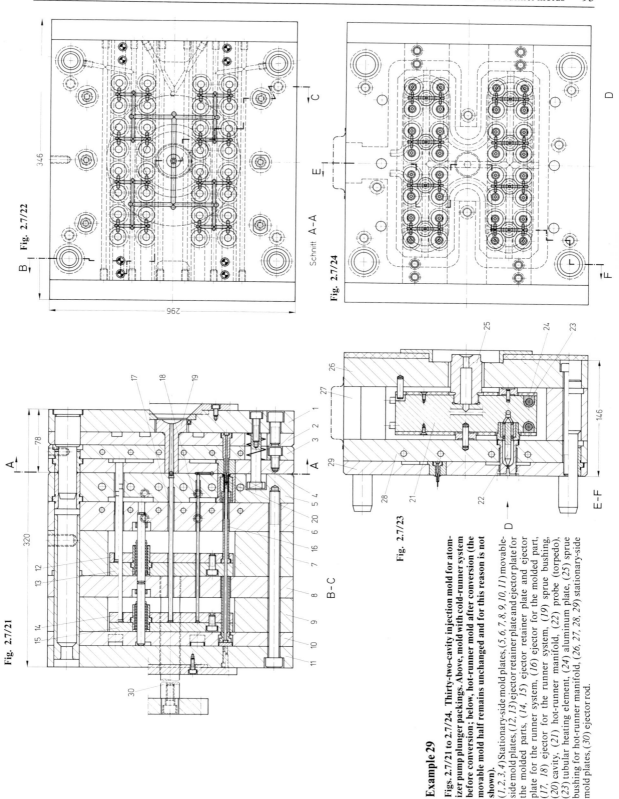

Fig. 2.7/21

Fig. 2.7/22

Schnitt A–A

Fig. 2.7/24

Fig. 2.7/23

Example 29

Figs. 2.7/21 to 2.7/24. Thirty-two-cavity injection mold for atomizer pump plunger packings. Above, mold with cold-runner system before conversion; below, hot-runner mold after conversion (the movable mold half remains unchanged and for this reason is not shown).

(1, 2, 3, 4) Stationary-side mold plates, (5, 6, 7, 8, 9, 10, 11) movable-side mold plates, (12, 13) ejector retainer plate and ejector plate for the molded parts, (14, 15) ejector retainer plate and ejector plate for the molded part, (16) ejector for the runner system, (17, 18) ejector for the runner system, (19) sprue bushing, (20) cavity, (21) hot-runner manifold, (22) probe (torpedo), (23) tubular heating element, (24) aluminum plate, (25) sprue bushing for hot-runner manifold, (26, 27, 28, 29) stationary-side mold plates, (30) ejector rod.

Example 30. Four-cavity hot-runner mold with unscrewing for threaded closures

A four-cavity mold is required to injection mold threaded closures with no waste. If one excludes regranulation and recycling of the regrind, this condition can be met only through the use of a hot-runner mold. The mold shown in Figs. 2.7/28 to 2.7/34 differs in no way from a conventional three-plate mold with a cold-runner system in regard to the core design with a cooling and unscrewing mechanism, which is installed on the stationary mold half. The melt, however, is supplied through a hot-runner manifold (2) into which the machine nozzle (1) injects. This manifold distributes the melt to four nozzles (3).

The hot-runner manifold (2) should be designed sufficiently large in size to provide the advantage of a more uniform heat balance. To achieve a certain amount of insulation between the manifold and mold, a large air gap (4) is provided around the manifold. For the same reason, the two manifold locating rings (5) are designed with as little contact area as possible. The hot-runner manifold (2) is then forced against the annular surface of the gate inserts (7) by the bolts (6). It is held in the proper position by the pin (8), which prevents rotation about the manifold locating ring (5). The runners (9) in the manifold form an H pattern to provide equal flow-path lengths.

To prevent melt drool from the hot-runner manifold (2) when the machine nozzle (1) is retracted, a decompression chamber (10) is provided to permit expansion of the melt in the hot-runner manifold (2). As the BeCu nozzle tip (11) is once again inserted into the decompression chamber (10), the melt is forced back into the hot-runner manifold as if by a piston. The accumulation of drooled material, which can lead to improper operation after a short period of time, is thus avoided. The design of the nozzles (3) is of prime importance for clean degating of the threaded closures from the nozzles in the hot-runner manifold. All four nozzles must be identical in dimensions and condition. This is absolutely necessary for uniform filling of the cavities. The nozzle (3) is screwed into the hot-runner manifold (2) and projects into the nozzle well of the gate insert (7), where it is surrounded by an air gap that later becomes filled with melt. The nozzle well (a)

(Fig. 2.7/35) should be as close as possible to the outer surface of the threaded closure (b) to keep the gate land (c) as short as possible. In designing the closure, a depression (d) was provided so that the gate vestige would not protrude above the surface of the molded closure. With this type of nozzle design, however, it is difficult to obtain a short gate vestige. After the melt has been injected into the cavity (f) through the nozzle channel (e) the cooling time begins for the molded part. As the mold then opens, the gate is severed at its weakest point (c). This entails the danger of stringing from the fluid core of the nozzle channel (e). Since it is not possible to mold a clean threaded closure in this manner, the nozzle design shown in Fig. 2.7/36 should be employed.

In this nozzle, the channel (h) is not drilled quite so deeply and then divides into two or three smaller channels (i). By incorporating these smaller channels (i), the nozzle tip (k) is retained in its entirety and is continually surrounded by hot material. The great advantage of this nozzle design is that on opening of the mold the gate is severed at its weakest point (l) without stringing because the fluid core has only a very small cross section. By adjusting the length of the nozzle tip, the length of the gate can be established exactly. The gate can even be so designed that the BeCu nozzle tip extends to the surface of the molded part and in this manner almost completely avoids the formation of a gate vestige.

Satisfactory temperature control is achieved through the use of high-capacity cartridge heaters (12) that are placed in the manifold in such a way as to provide the most uniform possible heat transfer to the runner channel. The electrical connecting cables for the cartridge heaters are placed in channels (13) outside the mold and brought to a junction box. A thermocouple well (15) is placed in the hot-runner manifold, and a means for attaching the thermocouple is provided in the mold frame (14). The well should extend as far as possible toward the center of the manifold to ensure a stable temperature reading for control of the manifold temperature.

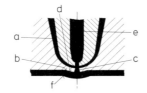

Fig. 2.7/35. Nozzle with straight-through melt flow from the nozzle channel.
(a) Nozzle well, (b) outer surface of the threaded closure, (c) gate, (d) depression, (e) nozzle channel, (f) cavity.

Fig. 2.7/36. Nozzle with lateral discharge openings from the nozzle channel.
(g) BeCu nozzle insert, (h) nozzle channel, (i) lateral discharge channels, (k) nozzle tip, (l) gate.

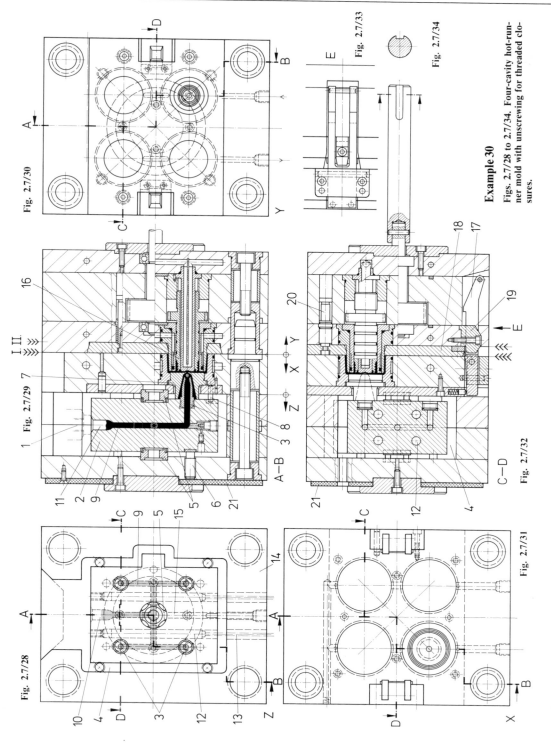

Fig. 2.7/30

Fig. 2.7/29

Fig. 2.7/28

Fig. 2.7/31

Fig. 2.7/32

Fig. 2.7/33

Fig. 2.7/34

Example 30

Figs. 2.7/28 to 2.7/34. Four-cavity hot-runner mold with unscrewing for threaded closures.

(*1*) Machine nozzle with female thread, (*2*) hot-runner manifold, (*3*) BeCu nozzle insert, (*4*) air gap, (*5*) locating ring for hot-runner manifold, (*6*) bolts, (*7*) gate insert, (*8*) pin, (*9*) channels in hot-runner manifold, (*10*) decompression chamber, (*11*) BeCu nozzle tip, (*12*) high-capacity cartridge heater, (*13*) channels for electrical connecting cables, (*14*) mold frame, (*15*) thermocouple well, (*16*) threaded core, (*17*) latch, (*18*) stripper plate, (*19*) release bar, (*20*) stop bolt, (*21*) insulating plate.

Before the unscrewing action begins, the mold opens at the first parting line to cleanly degate the threaded closure from the nozzle (*3*) and to relax a certain amount of stress between the molded part and cavity, thereby greatly facilitating the unscrewing. This opening stroke may be very short; it is limited by a switch mounted on the mold. After the first mold parting line opens for this short stroke, the threaded cores (*16*) are unscrewed. The movable mold half then opens further until the latch (*17*) engages the stripper plate (*18*) and pulls it forward. This motion strips the threaded closures off their cores. The release bar (*19*) then disengages the latch (*17*) and further motion of the stripper plate is prevented by stop bolt (*20*). The mold now continues opening to the full-open position and the threaded cores are screwed back into the molding position. The mold can now close for the next cycle.

Example 31. Compact 24-cavity mold for HDPE shotgun shells with edge gating

Economical production of small injection molded parts often requires the use of multiple-cavity molds. The higher the number of cavities, the more branched and complex is the runner system and the more difficult is the operation of such molds. Uniform filling of all cavities – a prerequisite for the desired uniform quality of all molded parts – requires uniform conditions for the melt flowing in the runners, i.e, although the melt must be cooled in the mold in order to eject the solidified parts and the runner system in the shortest possible amount of time, the cooling of the runner system must not be so intense that the melt already solidifies on the way to the cavity.

The runner system required to produce a large number of small parts in one cycle often weighs as much as the molded parts. For many applications, the runner system can be returned to the process in the form of regrind. For precision molded parts and parts subjected to high loads, this is not the case, so that this material represents waste. Additional costs are incurred in either case, either as a result of the reduced value of the waste material or as a result of the investment and energy costs required for regrinding the material and conveying it back to the machine.

The desire to save these material costs and at the same time have problem-free melt conveying systems led to the development of a system with a design exhibiting particular advantages in regard to distribution of the melt to the individual cavities. This system[2] is exhibited in the present example of a compact 24-cavity mold (Figs. 2.7/37 to 2.7/41) used to produce HDPE shotgun shells (Fig. 2.7/42).

Uniform temperature control of the melt between the nozzle of the injection molding machine and the gates is essential for operation of the melt conveying system used to achieve runnerless injection molding. This is provided through the use of BeCu as the material for the manifold (*23*) and heater casts (*21*) for the nozzles. The heater casts are produced by means of a pressure casting technique that guarantees absolute contact between the high-capacity tubular heating element and alloy, thereby ensuring ideal heat transfer from the heater element to the nozzle material. The high thermal conductivity of the BeCu makes heating of the melt conveying manifold (*23*) unnecessary. It is heated adequately by the attached heater casts.

The compact design of the heater casts promotes good heat transfer to melt up to the gate orifice. A large cross section can be used up to this area for the flowing melt, which is thus subjected to little shear. The melt that accumulates around the tip of the heater cast pro-

2 System Hot-Edge®, Mold-Masters.

Fig. 2.7/42.   HDPE 12-caliber shotgun shell, edge-gated.

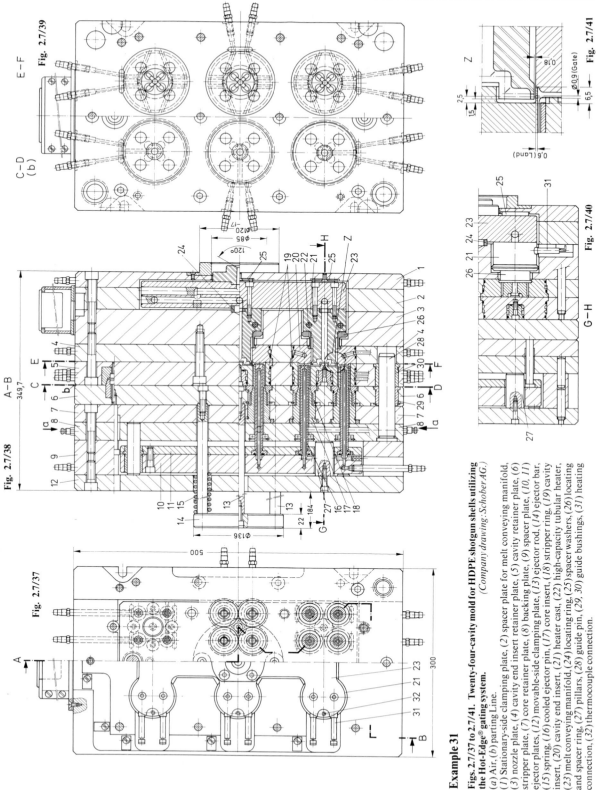

Fig. 2.7/39 E – F

Fig. 2.7/41

Fig. 2.7/40 G – H

(b) C – D

A – B

Fig. 2.7/38

Fig. 2.7/37

Example 31

Figs. 2.7/37 to 2.7/41. Twenty-four-cavity mold for HDPE shotgun shells utilizing the Hot-Edge® gating system. *(Company drawing: Schober AG.)*

(a) Air, (b) parting Line.

(1) Stationary-side clamping plate, (2) spacer plate for melt conveying manifold, (3) nozzle plate, (4) cavity end insert retainer plate, (5) cavity retainer plate, (6) stripper plate, (7) core retainer plate, (8) backing plate, (9) spacer plate, (10, 11) ejector plates, (12) movable-side clamping plate, (13) ejector rod, (14) ejector bar, (15) spring, (16) cooled ejector pin, (17) core insert, (18) stripper ring, (19) cavity insert, (20) cavity end insert, (21) heater cast, (22) high-capacity tubular heater, (23) melt conveying manifold, (24) locating ring, (25) spacer washers, (26) locating and spacer ring, (27) pillars, (28) guide pin, (29, 30) guide bushings, (31) heating connection, (32) thermocouple connection.

vides good thermal insulation, as does the air gap around the manifold and the spacer ring (26) of high-strength steel with minimum contact areas. This results in melt temperatures that may be a few degrees lower than normally used. Heat marks at the gates are likewise avoided. Compared with tunnel (submarine) gates, the edge gating system shown (Fig. 2.7/41) permits the cooling time to be shortened from 15 to 20 %. The melt solidifies in the gate orifice, so that stringing is avoided on ejection. During mold opening, the molded parts are retained on the movable side sufficiently to sever the solidified gates from the parts. In Fig. 2.7/42 the gate is located on the outer edge at the bottom of the shell between the two inner ribs and is barely visible. The solidified gate slug is forced against the core in the cavity during the next shot and because

of its small size is completely remelted by the following melt stream, so that there is no reduction in part quality.

The good thermal conductivity of the materials used and the compact design with gating of four cavities at each nozzle provides such uniformity of temperature throughout the entire system that only one thermocouple is required at the interface between one of the heater casts and the melt conveying manifold to control all heating zones. The continuous digital controller used provides an automatic "soft start" that provides the heaters with 50 % of the rated power up to a temperature of 100 °C and then with full power. An integrated alarm reacts on deviations of ± 9 °C from set point to automatically shut down the entire heating circuit and prevent overheating of the melt.

Example 32. Four-cavity hot-runner mold for polyacetal copolymer high-strength ski bindings

In the past five years ski bindings have undergone a rapid development leading to an as yet incomplete conversion of entire ski bindings from metal (aluminum die casting, sheet metal) to high-quality engineering plastics. On the basis of the previous standard, the plastic parts have to meet correspondingly high quality requirements.

Originally, plastics found application in the area of downhill ski bindings as functional components, e.g., as cams for opening or closing the binding. The present state encompasses housing components, including the inside functional components that must absorb all forces. A typical example is the ski binding shown in Fig. 2.7/43.

On the basis of preliminary trials, four-cavity, three-plate split-cavity molds were selected to produce the components of this heel binding. This satisfies the requirement to produce four parts economically and with the same high quality. The high quality with regard to dimensional accuracy (precision injection molded parts) as well as strength (rigidity and toughness) can be achieved during long-term production only with optimum processing parameters.

The production rates provided by a conventional mold led to the investigation of the possibility of utiliz-

ing a hot-runner system (Figs. 2.7/44 to 2.7/48). In this way it was possible to eliminate the runner system, which weighed about 50 g. With a molded part weight of about 258 g, this translates into a material savings of about 20 %. Recycling of the regrind was not possible

Fig. 2.7/43. Ski binding. In front, a housing component of the binding (Company photo: Salomon).

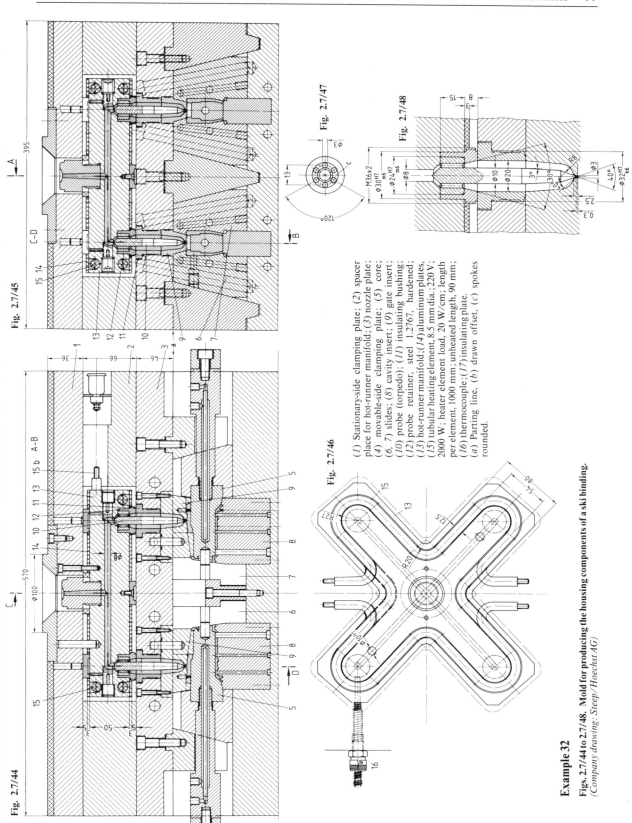

Fig. 2.7/44

Fig. 2.7/45

Fig. 2.7/47

Fig. 2.7/48

Fig. 2.7/46

(1) Stationary-side clamping plate; (2) spacer place for hot-runner manifold; (3) nozzle plate; (4) movable-side clamping plate; (5) core; (6, 7) slides; (8) cavity insert; (9) gate insert; (10) probe (torpedo); (11) insulating bushing; (12) probe retainer, steel 1.2767, hardened; (13) hot-runner manifold; (14) aluminum plates; (15) tubular heating element, 8.5 mm dia.; 220 V; 2000 W; heater element load, 20 W/cm; length per element, 1000 mm; unheated length, 90 mm; (16) thermocouple; (17) insulating plate.
(a) Parting line, (b) drawn offset, (c) spokes rounded.

Example 32

Figs. 2.7/44 to 2.7/48. Mold for producing the housing components of a ski binding.
(Company drawing: Steep/Hoechst AG)

in production of these parts, since ski bindings represent safety components as the link between an individual and ski.

On the basis of the stringent requirements to be met by the molded parts, special attention must be given not only to maintenance of the optimum machine parameters but also to the heat balance of the mold. This means that

– Temperature differences between the hot-runner manifold and probe tips should be as small as possible
– All cavities should have optimum and uniform temperature control

The system selected utilized indirectly heated probes [4, 7] (see also examples 26 and 29). On the basis of its basic design, this system provides for maintenance of a very uniform hot-runner manifold temperature. In order to eliminate the normally negligibly small effect of the unheated end portions of the tubular heating element on the region around the probes, the design shown in Figs. 2.7/47 and 2.7/48 is recommended to provide identical amounts of heat to each gate. The probe temperatures are almost identical. Uniform filling of the cavities in multiple-cavity molds is thus ensured. This feature of the system is one of the essential prerequisites for the production of high-quality injection molded parts. This applies equally to the maintenance of close dimensional and weight tolerances, but especially to the mechanical properties of the molded part.

The heating system for the hot-runner manifold (13) is controlled from only one point (thermocouple 16). The specific heating capacity is about 220 W/kg of hot-runner manifold. The tubular heating elements (15) are embedded in the hot-runner manifold (13) with thermally conducting cement. To reduce heat losses due to radiation, the manifold is covered with bright aluminum plates (14). The four probes (10) are made of copper (E-Cu F 37; DIN 40500) and were modified slightly for the existing mold. On opening of the mold the slides (6, 7) open first and the cores (5) are then pulled hydraulically. Individual temperature control is provided for the slides, cores and mold plates.

With the conversion of a conventional mold to a design utilizing a hot-runner system, a direct comparison of the two approaches is possible. It was found that the high quality level was maintained. Further advantages resulted from a shortening of the cycle time, since the recovery time was reduced, as well as from an improvement of the thermal homogeneity of the melt due to the better degree of utilization of the machine capacity, which should only be between 40 and 70 % when high quality standards must be met.

Additional hot-runner molds
Examples 2, 46, 48, 49, 69, 72, 100, 101 and 102.

Bibliography for section 2.7
[1] P. Unger and A. Hörburger, *Kunststoffe*, vol. 71, 1981, pp. 855–859.
[2] Publication of Fa. H. Schnarr OHG, Aschaffenburg, on chemicals Nickel ®Kanigen.
[3] W. Metzger, *Plastverarbeiter*, vol. 30, 1979, pp. 142–145.
[4] A. Hörburger, *Plastverarbeiter*, vol. 20, 1969, pp. 797–800.
[5] P. Unger, *Kunststoffe*, vol. 70, 1980, pp. 730–737.
[6] Publication of Fa. H. Schnarr OHG, Aschaffenburg, ®Kanisil 2000.
[7] K. H. Blauert and P. Unger, *Kunststoffe*, vol. 71, 1981, pp. 209–211.

3. Ejection Systems

3.1 General

Injection molding compounds exhibit a certain amount of shrinkage, i.e., in a cooled condition the volume is somewhat smaller than in a heated condition. If parts with accurate dimensions are needed, allowances must be made for this shrinkage when establishing the dimensions for the cavities. Shrinkage also causes the molded parts to sit tight on the cores, since usually parts are ejected after they have cooled down. As a result, special measures are required to be able to eject finished parts.

These measures include first of all careful polishing of all mold surfaces that come in contact with the plastics melt as well as a certain draft in the direction of draw. Since self-acting slight lubrication of the mold surfaces that come in contact with the molded parts is possible only in rare cases, there is a danger that scratches and cracks will develop when the mold is opened or the parts ejected, particularly if the molding compound is very hard. A mirror finish, which is easily obtained by buffing a hard steel surface, is in no way adequate; it is far more important to grind and polish the areas in the direction of ejection with an oilstone in order to eliminate any scratches and indentations. Wherever possible the surface should be lapped, since even microscopic scratches and indentations are filled with plastics melt under the high injection pressure, thus preventing smooth ejection. Proper surface finishing takes up a considerable portion of the total mold production time (see Sec. 1.9).

Ejection of flat parts

Only completely flat parts, which in addition must have a pronounced draft toward the direction of ejection, can be ejected without special ejector pins on the parts themselves. However, this requires the runner system, that is, the channels between the sprue and the molded part as well as the gate, that is, the small opening leading from the runner to the cavity, to be of sufficient strength in order to be able to eject the actual molded parts from the center by means of the ejector pin. The sprue ejector pin is alway required, since the sprue adheres relatively firmly in the sprue bushing, even though the bore has a draft of approximately 1.5 to 2°. To make sure that the sprue is pulled out of the sprue bushing on the stationary half of the mold, a well with a depth of about 4 to 5 mm should be provided on the movable half of the mold in line with the sprue. This well, with the help of grooves or reverse draft, retains the sprue on the movable half of the mold when the mold opens. A sprue ejector pin is located in the extension of the well to eject the runner system with the molded parts connected to it as the ejector rod actuates the ejection mechanism in the machine. To make sure

that the runners are ejected from the machine, it is advisable to place a spring on the shoulder of the ejector pin (as shown in Figs. 3.1/1 and 3.1/2), which, by extending the ejector pin, ensures proper ejection after the sprue undercut has been ejected. If flat parts have only a slight draft on the outer surface or have holes, ejector pins must be placed on the parts themselves (Fig. 3.1/2). Their diameter and number depends on the depth of the parts in the direction of ejection. As a rule, the parting line between the movable and stationary halves of the mold should run in such a way that the molded part is retained more strongly by the half from which it is to be ejected than by the other half. Generally this will be the movable half of the mold.

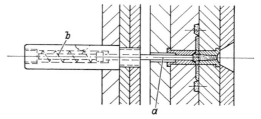

Fig. 3.1/1. Ejection of a flat part without the use of ejector pins. (*a*) Sprue ejector pin, (*b*) spring.

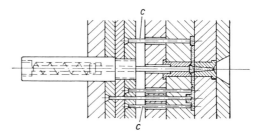

Fig. 3.1/2. Ejection of a flat part by means of ejector pins. (*c*) Ejector pin.

However, in special cases, it may be advisable to choose a parting line that will cause the molded parts to be retained more strongly by the stationary half than by the movable half. In such cases special measures must be taken to eject the molded part from the stationary half during opening.

Generally a molded part will sit more tightly on the half on which it can shrink onto the cores. However, this is only the case if this core is of sufficient length relative to the outer surface. In the case of a container, the core for the interior will generally be located on the movable half, because the molded container shrinks tightly on this core, whereas the exterior will be located on the stationaryhalf. In special cases the part can be made to adhere more strongly on the movable half through appropriate variation in draft and polishing.

In cases of doubt in which it is difficult to decide whether the molded part is more likely to be retained by the stationary half or the movable half, it is possible to apply a spring force to suitable ejectors to assist in loosening the part from the stationary half to make sure that the part is carried by the movable half and is not retained by the stationary half when the mold opens. The springs need only travel within a narrow range of approximately 2 to 3 mm since the part, once it is detached, is certain to be carried by the movable half.

Ejection of deep, hollow parts

In the case of very deep, hollow parts, which shrink very firmly onto the cores, individual ejector pins are no longer adequate, since the individual ejector pins are likely to pierce the bottom of a deep container. Such cases require ejection by means of a stripper plate (Fig. 3.1/3). The stripper plate covers the entire rim of the container and pushes the molded part off the core as the ejector rod actuates the ejection mechanism. It is also possible to locate this stripper plate on the stationary half of the mold, either to assist in loosening certain parts for which the core has to be located on the stationary half, in which case strong springs act on the stripper plate, or in ejecting, say, large lids gated on the inside from the stationary half of the mold.

Ejector sleeves

Ejector sleeves are used in cases where containers and tubular parts cannot be ejected by means of a stripper plate. Figure 3.1/4 illustrates such an example. To prevent the ejector sleeves from making scratches on the polished mold surfaces, which would interfere with smooth ejection, the external and internal diameter are made 0.1 to 0.2 mm smaller or larger than the respective mold surfaces. During the ejection process they slide by without making contact with the interior and exterior. Since for the most part the ejector sleeves consist of thin-walled tubes, which are difficult to harden without deforming them, it is advis-

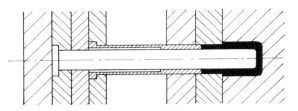

Fig. 3.1/4. Ejection by means of an ejector sleeve.

able to make them of high-strength steel and to harden and temper them to 900 to 1000 N/mm² before finishing.

Ejection becomes a particular problem if, in addition to long internal surfaces, longer external surfaces must be released at the same time. Such a case applies to a part as shown in Fig. 3.1/5. One solution is to release the internal and external surfaces sucessively. For this purpose the core can be displaced axially, requiring travel of only a few millimeters. As the ejector sleeve advances the molded part, it is initially retained on the core until the core and its shoulder reach the fixed stop. During the ejection process the external surface is released first. The core ceases to move as soon as it reaches the stop and the molded part is ejected from the core.

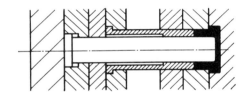

Fig. 3.1/5. Core designed for axial displacement.

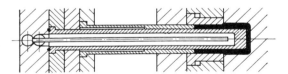

Fig. 3.1/6. Cavity insert designed for axial displacement, stationary core.

Figs. 3.1/5 and 3.1/6. Ejection of parts with long inner and outer surfaces.

Figure 3.1/6 illustrates a different approach to the same problem. However, in contrast to the approach in Figure 3.1/5, this time the core is stationary and the cavity insert for the external surface is movable, so that the molded part is first released from the core and then ejected from the cavity. This design is advantageous if long cores are cooled internally, since it is easier to provide for the supply and return of cooling water in a stationary core than in a movable core.

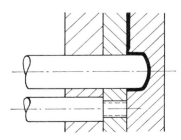

Fig. 3.1/3. Ejection of deep hollow parts by means of a stripper plate.

Ejection booster

There are a number of molded parts whose ejection from the mold requires great forces. This applies in particular to parts where two surfaces have to be released simultaneously, such as parts with very deep ribs or many thin partitions, such as slide trays, grids and similar parts. Almost always a thin blade ejector is located at each rib or partition, but one finds out during test runs that the ejection force of the machine is insufficient to release the part from the mold. In such cases, even very careful polishing of the cavity surfaces and greater draft on the partitions are not of much help, since the adherence is attributable less to the surface than to the deformation of the steel brought about by the injection pressure. The slight shrinkage of the thin partitions is not sufficient to offset the deformation of the mold. The partitions of the molded part may well be under a residual pressure of several hundred bars. It is obvious that a very high force is needed to release the molded part in such cases. But where should such a great force come from if the ejection force of the machine is inadequate?

The simplest solution is offered by a mechanical lever mechanism that will increase the ejection force within the mold two- or threefold at the expense of the ejector travel.

Figure 3.1/7 and 3.1/8 show such a lever mechanism, which about doubles the ejection force of the machine. It goes without saying that such a lever mechanism can only be built into a machine with sufficient space behind the movable platen, at least in a vertical direction. In machines with central mold height adjustment or in many foreign machines that do not have any space behind the movable platen in the first place, the attachment of such a lever mechanism to the mold is problematic.

The lever mechanism must be of sufficiently rugged design to be able to transmit the great forces exerted on

it. In particular, the bolts with which it is attached to the movable half of the mold must be of sufficient strength to withstand these stresses.

Essentially, the lever mechanism consists of a somewhat modified ejector rod (a), which is attached into the movable plate in the customary manner, and the backup plate (b) which is bolted onto the mold. Lever (d) is supported by the strong shaft (c) in this backup plate. The lever is designed in such a way that it is able to rotate through whatever angle is necessary to eject the parts.

Since most of the time the actuating point of the lever is below the machine center line due to the central position of the ejector rod (a) an actuating surface below the machine center line must be provided. In the case in question, this is achieved by bolting a plate (e) to the ejector mechanism of the machine.

Ejector return mechanism

Positive (early) ejector return

Ejector plates of molds are usually retracted with the aid of push-back pins or springs with the mold closed. In the case of molds with slides or core pulls, the ejector pins can sometimes not be located anywhere but directly behind the slides. In such a case the ejector pins must be retracted before the slides are closed, otherwise the pins – or, even worse, the slides – cannot be prevented from being damaged when the mold closes.

In such cases the ejector plate with which the pins are advanced is generally retracted by a strong spring as soon as the mold begins to close, as shown in Figure 3.1/9. However, the force of the return spring may not be sufficient to retract the ejector pins due to the considerable restraining forces developed at the ejector pins. As a result, the cores advance toward the protruding ejector pins as the cam pins are inserted into the slides, thus damaging the mold.

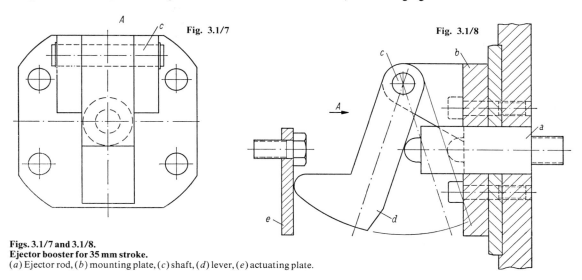

Fig. 3.1/7   Fig. 3.1/8

Figs. 3.1/7 and 3.1/8.
Ejector booster for 35 mm stroke.
(a) Ejector rod, (b) mounting plate, (c) shaft, (d) lever, (e) actuating plate.

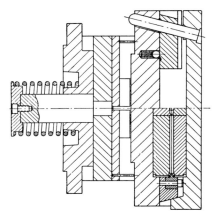

Fig. 3.1/9. Mold in which the ejector plate is returned by a spring as the mold closes. If the force of the spring is inadequate, the mold will be damaged.

Many molds have been destroyed in this manner. A way had to be found of achieving a positive (early) return, i.e., without the spring force, as soon as the mold begins to close. The retraction device for the ejector plate described below solves this problem in a relatively simple manner.

Figure 3.1/10 shows the retraction device with the mold closed; instead of the normal ejector rod a latch rod(b) is screwed into the rear ejector plate (a). Eight slots in the latch rod ensure good spring action of the eight latches, especially when hardened and tempered collet steel is used. A latch sleeve (d) is screwed into the movable-side clamping plate (c) of the mold and secured by a slotted nut (e). The normal ejector rod of the injection molding machine is replaced with a specially designed actuating rod (f), which actuates the rear ejector plate as it seats in the bottom of the latch rod. As the ejection mechanism advances, the eight latching teeth of the latch bolt catch behind the shoulder on the actuating rod (f). During the ejector travel, they are held within the bore of the latch sleeve (d), so that during the ejector return stroke a positive connection between the actuating rod (f) and the latch rod (b) is provided. Figure 3.1/11 shows the ejector plate in the forward position, that is, with an open mold.

When the ejector plate (a) is retracted as the mold closes, the latches release by spring action. By adjusting the latch sleeve (d) in the movable-side clamping plate (c), the return stroke can be set exactly.

Fig. 3.1/10. Mold closed.

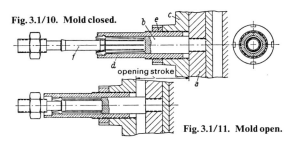

Fig. 3.1/11. Mold open.

Figs. 3.1/10 and 3.1/11. Mold with positive (early) ejector return: retracting without the use of spring.
(a) Ejector plate, (b) latch rod, (c) movable-side clamping plate, (d) latching sleeve, (e) slotted nut, (f) actuating rod.

3.2   Flat Parts with and without Ejectors

Example 33. Eight-cavity injection mold for brush handles

Flat parts such as the shoe polish brush handle produced in the mold shown in Figure 3.2/1 require only a relatively simple mold design. It is practical to design the movable-side clamping plate and ejector housing (*c*) in such a way that it can also be used for other similar molds. The same applies to the ejector rod (*d*) and the ejector plate (*e*). The ejector retainer plate (*f*) will have to be made new each time, since the spacing between the ejector and push-back pins (*g*) and (*h*) respectively will differ depending on the size of the parts to be produced. In the present case, use of a sprue bushing and return pin bushing was dispensed with in order to further simplify the mold. In general, however, use of at least a sprue bushing is recommended, since the nozzle seat in the stationary-side cavity plate may be easily damaged if the machine is improperly

set up and subsequent installation of a sprue bushing in this hardened plate will be difficult. With large mold plates, it is practical to have a separate locating ring (*i*) for the stationary-side cavity plate (*b*). The advantage here is that both cavity plates can be ground flat and with parallel surfaces, which is important in view of the possibility of distortion on hardening. Because of their replaceability, guide bushings (*k*) should always be used, since especially in older machines that no longer provide exact guidance of the mold halves the guide pin bearing surfaces are subjected to considerable loads that may make replacement of guide bushings and guide pins necessary after a short period of time. A new bushing with a somewhat smaller inside diameter can be rapidly produced. The old guide pin can then usually be reground to be made

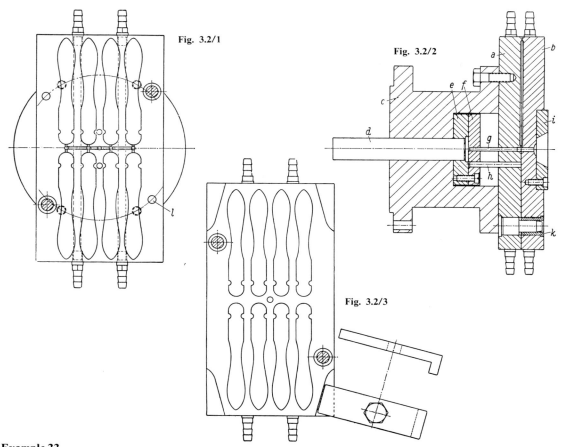

Fig. 3.2/1

Fig. 3.2/2

Fig. 3.2/3

Example 33

Figs. 3.2/1 to 3.2/3 Eight-cavity mold for brush handles.
(*a, b*) Cavity plates, (*c*) movable-side clamping plate and ejector housing, (*d*) ejector rod, (*e*) ejector plate, (*f*) ejector retainer plate, (*g*) ejector pin, (*h*) push-back pin, (*i*) locating ring, (*k*) guide pin, (*l*) two locating pins.

serviceable once again. Keeping this wear in mind, the diameter of guide pins should not be smaller than 16 mm if possible. For reasons associated with grinding, a smaller diameter is also undesirable.

A locating ring for the movable-side cavity plate (a) on the clamping plate and the ejector housing (c) is impractical, because in the event of distortion on hardening flat grinding of the recess is more difficult than flat grinding on a surface grinding machine. It suffices if the cavity plate (a) is held in the proper position on the clamping plate and ejector housing (c) by two locating pins (l). Because of their length, it is best to drill the cooling channels from both sides and provide hose connections at each end. This provides the opportunity to connect all cooling channels in series through the use of appropriate hose connections or to run them in parallel.

The well at the end of the sprue ejector pin should be provided with a slight undercut (5°) to ensure that the individual parts attached to the runner system are retained on the movable mold half and not in the stationary cavity plate (b).

3.3   Deep Parts Utilizing Ejectors

Example 34. Injection mold for a housing

The housing is relatively complicated in design and must furthermore be molded with high dimensional accuracy. Four mounting holes are positioned around the outer edge and together with the sealing lip around the edge are ribbed to improve rigidity. Two rounded partitions are located inside the housing, the larger of which is slotted on the sides. In addition, the side of the housing has a rectangular opening with a lip for welding. The material to be used is polypropylene.

The two-cavity mold is shown in Figs. 3.3/1 to 3.3/7 and has two slides (a) that form the rectangular openings in the side of the housings by means of the side cores (b) and an interconnecting opening between the curved partitions by a cylindrical core pin (c). The inside surface faces the injection side and is formed primarily by the core insert (d), which is held against the core plate (f) by the core retainer plate (e). Inserts (g) and (h) are used to form the curved partitions and are held against the clamping plate (j) by the insert retainer plate (i). The outside of the housing faces the ejector side and is formed by the cavity insert (k). The parts are molded via a sprue (l) and a cold-runner system in the main parting line I-I and are edge-gated.

It should be noted above all that, because of the sealing lip around the edge, the slide (a) must pass through the cavity insert (k) on the movable side. The resulting bridge (m) is designed as a separate component and is screwed to the insert (k).

The mold uses three cooling circuits.

Cooling circuit A:

This circuit consists of the channels in the movable-side cavity inserts (k) and is reached via extension tubes.

Cooling circuit B:

This circuit is located in the stationary-side core inserts and consists of several channels.

Cooling circuit C:

The inserts (g) and (h) used to form the curved partitions are cooled by channels with baffles (n). The cooling medium for the series-connected core cooling circuit is supplied through channels in the clamping plate (j).

The mold first opens at parting line II-II, since the latch (o) holds plates (e) and (f) together. In this manner, the curved partitions are released first while the mold is closed (main parting line). This measure is necessary because the wall thickness of the partitions and their shape do not permit the use of sleeve ejectors. After the curved partitions have been released, the latch (o) is disengaged and permits the mold to open at the main parting line I-I. To facilitate the opening motion of the slides, four spring-loaded rods (p) providing a force of 1000 N each act on the core retainer plate (e). The slides (a) are actuated by the cam pins (q) and release the molded parts after a stroke of 50 mm. The upper slide is held by a spring catch (r), which is actuated by a rod (s).

The molded parts are ejected by a number of ejector pins (t) and ejector sleeves (u). The ejector sleeves (u) act at the mounting holes. Mold plates (e) and (f) move along the guide pin (w) and are held by the stop bolt (v) after being unlatched. Stop bolt (v) must be of adequate size, since it must withstand the entire opening force of the slide (a).

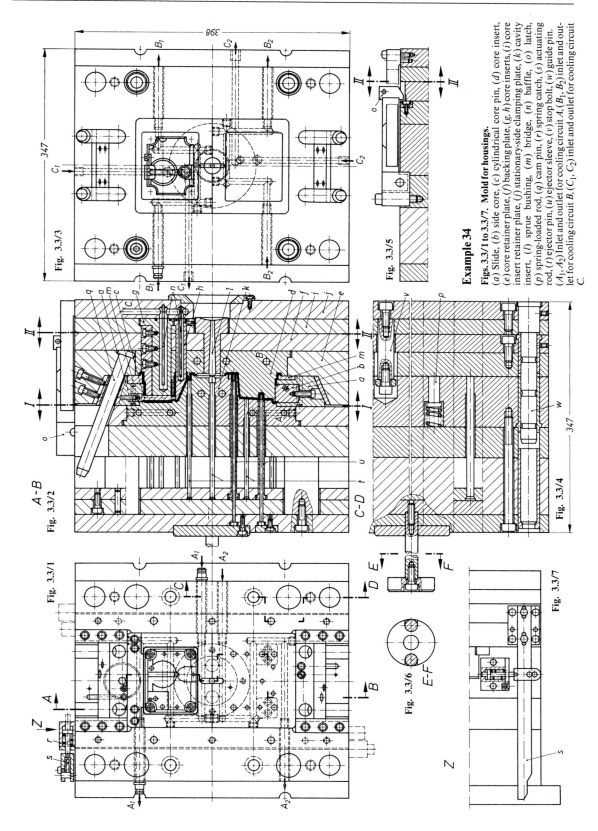

Example 34

Figs. 3.3/1 to 3.3/7. Mold for housings.
(a) Slide, (b) side core, (c) cylindrical core pin, (d) core insert, (e) core retainer plate, (f) backing plate, (g, h) core inserts, (i) core insert retainer plate, (j) stationary-side clamping plate, (k) cavity insert, (l) sprue bushing, (m) bridge, (n) baffle, (o) latch, (p) spring-loaded rod, (q) cam pin, (r) spring catch, (s) actuating rod, (t) ejector pin, (u) ejector sleeve, (v) stop bolt, (w) guide pin. (A_1, A_2) Inlet and outlet for cooling circuit A, (B_1, B_2) inlet and outlet for cooling circuit B, (C_1, C_2) inlet and outlet for cooling circuit C.

Fig. 3.3/3

Fig. 3.3/5

$A-B$
Fig. 3.3/2

$C-D$
Fig. 3.3/4

Fig. 3.3/1

$E-F$
Fig. 3.3/6

Fig. 3.3/7

Example 35. Injection mold for thin-walled sleeves

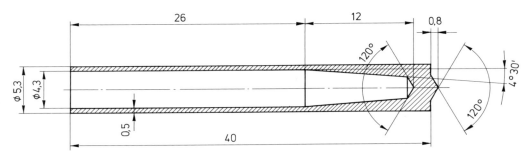

Fig. 3.3/8. Polyester sleeve.

A four-cavity mold with parting line injection was needed for a thin-walled sleeve having a length of only 0.5 mm for a length of 26 mm (Fig. 3.3/8). Parting line injection was necessary, because an extremely long hydraulic ejector was needed for the mold. The material to be molded was a polyester (polyethylene terephthalate) with good flow properties that is especially suited for thin-walled parts with a high flow length/wall thickness ratio.

To permit fully automatic operation, the sleeves were to be ejected separately from the sprue and runner system. Furthermore, the outer surface of the sleeves was not permitted to have any witness line. The closed end with conical tip had to be smooth and clean. The best solution thus appeared to be to gate the sleeve at its thick-walled end by means of two tunnel gates on opposite sides (Fig. 3.3/9).

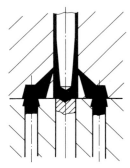

Fig. 3.3/9. Gating of the sleeve by means of two opposite tunnel gates.

Ejection without damaging the thin walls of the molded part takes place by first withdrawing the core (5) from the sleeve (1) while it is still completely contained in the cavity. The mold (Figs. 3.3/10 to 3.3/19) first opens at parting line (1). Parting lines (2) and (3) are held closed by latch (4). During the opening stroke, the cores (5) are cooled by means of compressed air introduced through openings (6). As the release bar (7) disengages the latch (4), parting line (2) is opened by means of bolt (8). Parting line (3) is held closed by means of latch (9). Undercuts (10) retain the runner system and in this manner shear off the tunnel gates (3). Opening at parting line (2) continues until the runner system can drop out properly. Release bar (11) then disengages latch (9) as plate (12) is held by stop (13), so that parting line (3) now opens. As the mold reaches the full-open position, the hydraulic ejector (14) is actuated, thereby ejecting the sleeve from the cooled cavity insert (16). Simultaneously, plate (17) actuates plate (18). The ejector pin (19) mounted in plate (18) is located behind the retaining undercut (10) for the runner system, which is now ejected. It does not drop out of the mold, however, until ejector pin (15) is retracted by the hydraulic ejector.

The position of ejector plate (17) is sensed by two roller switches, which are actuated by switch rods (20) and (21), and determine the machine sequencing. Ejector plate (18) is returned to the molding position by push-back pin (22) as the mold closes.

The closed end of the sleeve exhibits the same 120° tip as does the inner core to ensure that this inner core cannot be deflected toward one side as the sleeve is filled through the two gates (Fig. 3.3/9). In addition, the ejector pin (15) is spring-loaded (23). When the mold is closed, the end of ejector pin (15) seats against the inner core (5) and centers it in the corresponding recess.

As the melt enters the cavity, the core is held centered until the cavity pressure overcomes the force of the spring located behind ejector pin (15) and forces it to its retracted position. By this time, the core (5) is surrounded by melt to such an extent that it can no longer be deflected. This precautionary measure in the mold design was found to be absolutely necessary on test molding with the completed mold.

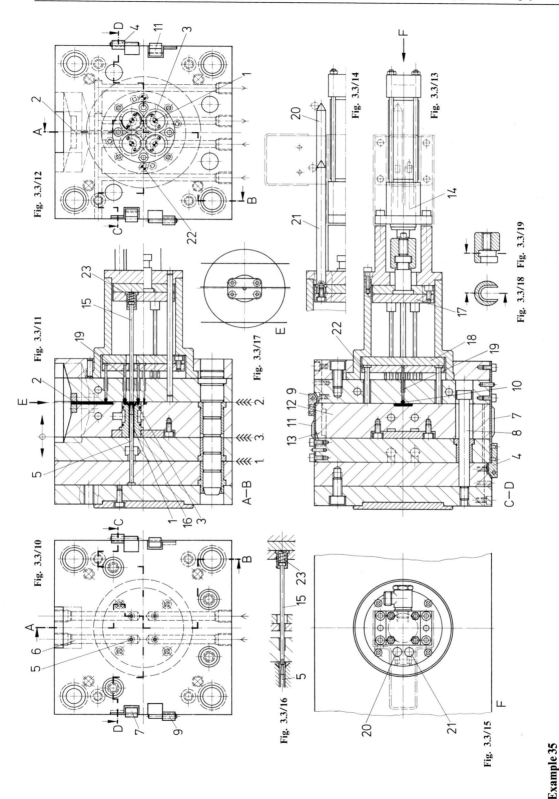

Fig. 3.3/12

Fig. 3.3/11

Fig. 3.3/10

Fig. 3.3/17

Fig. 3.3/16

Fig. 3.3/15

Fig. 3.3/14

Fig. 3.3/13

Fig. 3.3/18   Fig. 3.3/19

Example 35

Figs. 3.3/10 to 3.3/19.   Four-cavity injection mold for automatic molding of thin-walled polyester sleeves.
(*1*) Sleeves, (*2*) sprue bushing, (*3*) tunnel gates, (*4*) latch, (*5*) core, (*6*) opening for cooling air, (*7*) release bar, (*8*) bolt, (*9*) latch, (*10*) undercut, (*11*) release bar, (*12*) cavity retainer plate, (*13*) stop, (*14*) hydraulic ejector, (*15*) ejector pin, (*16*) cavity insert, (*17*) ejector actuating plate, (*18*) ejector plate, (*19*) ejector pin, (*20, 21*) switch rods, (*22*) push-back pin, (*23*) spring.

Example 36. Mold for long, thin, tubular parts

A time-tested rule of thumb used by injection mold-ers and mold designers alike says that neither the plas-ticating capacity nor the clamping force of a machine should be used at the full rated values. A utilization factor of 70 to 80% should be considered an accept-able level. In addition, the geometry of a mold and the forces occurring in a mold should have a balanced re-lation. This is not always easy to achieve, however, as is shown in the present example.

A large quantity of test-tube-like specimen tubes was to be molded in polystyrene. The tube was to have a flange at its larger end and a conical tip with axial opening at the smaller end. A four-cavity mold ap-peared both technically and economically reasonable. The length of the tubes, however, posed a problem. For the length of 170 mm, an opening stroke of 510 mm would have been required with a convention-al mold design. Since only 40 cm³ of melt would have been needed to simultaneously mold the four tubes, a small injection molding machine would have been adequate. As a rule, however, small machines do not have such a long opening stroke. The clamping force required was slight, since the projected area amounted to only a few square centimeters, so that only a small machine would have been required from this stand-point as well. Because the outside surface of the tubes was not permitted to show any witness lines, it was not possible to place the cavities in the plane of the parting line.

Accordingly, a mold (Figs. 3.3/20 and 3.3/21) was designed that projected through an opening in the movable platen where the ejector mechanism normal-ly would be mounted. A further slight modification of the machine was also required: the stripper plate (20) located in the stationary mold half leaves the nor-mal guide pins (21) during the last portion of its stroke and thus needs an auxiliary means of guid-ance. Accordingly, two holes were drilled in the movable platen, through which two extended aux-iliary guide pins (14) project. The stripper plate (20) runs in ball bearings (16) on these pins. To provide optimum filling, each cavity was provided with two tunnel gates.

Bolts (18) and (19) are located between the cavi-ty and auxiliary guide pin (14). Bolt (19) is mount-ed in the stationary-side clamping plate. Bolt (18) serves as the stripper bolt to actuate the stripper plate (20) located in the stationary mold half. This plate must not be actuated before the movable mold half has released the entire length of the molded parts. Accordingly, it is held in position by pins (22) that project into the runner system and become embedded in the solidifying melt. As soon as the movable mold half has released the molded parts, stripper bolt (18) actuates stripper sleeve (13), and the molded parts are stripped off the cores (6, 10) until the shoulder in sleeve (17) seats against the bolt (19) and stops further motion of stripper plate (20). The stripper plate is now sup-ported on the auxiliary guide pins (14) and is re-turned to the molding position as the mold closes. This design proved successful both technically and economically.

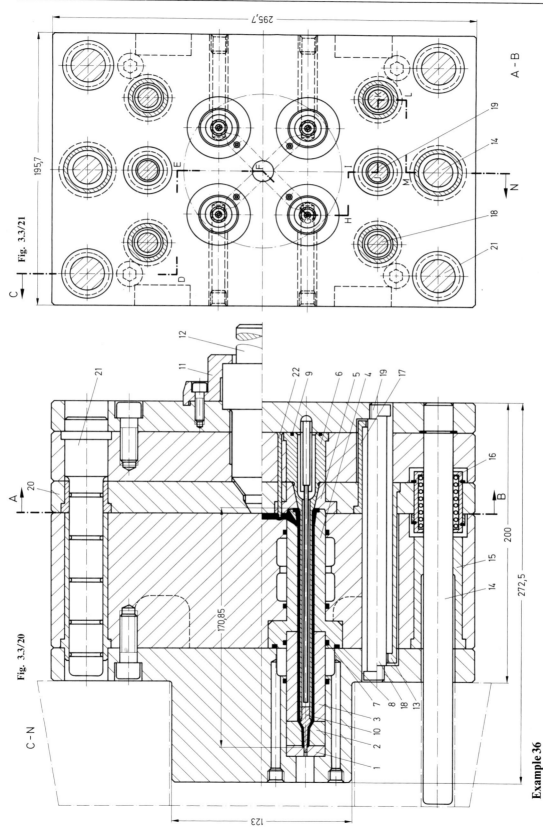

Fig. 3.3/21

Fig. 3.3/20

Example 36

Figs. 3.3/20 and 3.3/21. Four-cavity injection mold for test-tube-like polystyrene specimen tubes.
(1) Core tip support, (2) cavity insert for tip, (3) tip insert, (4) cavity insert for flange, (5) stripper ring, (6) core insert, (7, 8, 9) O-ring, (10) core insert tip, (11) locating ring, (12) hot sprue bushing, (13) stripper sleeve, (14) auxiliary guide pins, (15) guide bushings, (16) ball bearing, (17) stop sleeve, (18) stripper bolt, (19) stop bolt, (20) stripper plate, (21) guide pin, (22) sucker pin.
Mold design: Einar Fristedt, Karlskrona, Sweden.

3.4   Ejection by Means of Stripper Plate

Example 37. Four-cavity mold for a box and lid

Stripper plate combined with ejector pins

Example 37 involves a small, round box with an off-set lip so that the lid fits flush with the side. Ejection by means of individual ejector pins is difficult for such parts especially when the parts are deep and the walls thin. The offset lip is held in the mold so tightly that, unless a stripper plate is used, puncturing of the molded parts by the ejector pins is to be feared. The offset lip is thus best placed in a stripper plate. While the box is now cleanly stripped off the core by the stripper plate, it is retained in the stripper plate by the offset lip and must be removed by hand.

The question therefore arises as to how the parts that have been stripped off the core but are still retained in the stripper plate can be reliably ejected fully automatically.

This is possible if the stripper plate stops after a certain distance and ejector pins located inside the box are then extended to eject it from the stripper plate. This two-stage ejection must be performed by the central ejector rod, however, if the mold is not to become too complicated.

In the following a solution to this problem is described that has proved successful and offers the further advantage of not using any latches involving springs, which operate unreliably and easily give rise to trouble when high ejector forces are needed.

Figures 3.4/1 to 3.4/4 show an injection mold in which two boxes and matching lids are molded. To eliminate any need for secondary operations, the box and lid are tunnel-gated so that on opening, the approximately 1 mm diameter gate is cleanly sheared. The molded parts and runner system thus drop out of the mold separately.

On opening of the mold, both parts are retained on the cores (a) and (b) from which they are stripped by the stripper plate (c) at the end of the opening stroke. While the lid on core (b) can drop after the stripper plate has been actuated, the box itself is retained in the stripper plate (c) by the approximately 3 mm high offset lip. The motion of the stripper plate is stopped after a certain distance by ejector plate (d), which is connected to the stripper plate (c) by four sleeves (e). The ejector pins (f), which until now had accompanied the motion of the stripper plate (c), do not stop, but rather continue their forward motion and thereby eject the

boxes from the stripper plate. How does the sequential actuation of stripper plate and ejector pins occur?

First, there are two sets of ejector plates. The front plates (g) and (d) are connected to the stripper plate. Plates (h) and (i) actuate the ejector pins (f). For actuation of the stripper plate, ejector plates (g) and (d) have a central actuating sleeve (k) slotted like a collet.

The relaxed condition of this actuating sleeve is shown in Fig. 3.4/4, whereas Fig. 3.4/3 illustrates the spread condition. The sleeve is spread as the mold closes by the action of the push-back sleeves (e), which displace the actuating sleeves (k) with respect to the spreader (l) so that the slotted actuating sleeve (k) is spread by the shoulder on the spreader (l).

The two rear ejector plates (h) and (i), which actuate the ejector pins (f), are connected to the central ejector sleeves (m). With the mold closed (Fig. 3.4/3), the slotted actuating sleeve (k) rests against a shoulder inside ejector sleeve (m). As the ejector sleeve (m) is actuated via the spring pack (n), ejector sleeve (m) and the rear ejector plates (h) and (i) with attached ejector pins (f) are extended together with the front ejector plates (g) and (d) with the attached stripper plate (c). Since a considerable amount of force is necessary to strip the parts from the cores, the spring pack (o) becomes compressed during this motion. As soon as the parts are stripped off the cores, the spring pack (o) can relax, which causes a sudden forward motion of the stripper plate. This sudden motion is sure to knock the lids off the stripper plate. The front ejector plate (d) is now up against the backing plate so that the stripper plate can no longer move.

As a result of the motion of the stripper plate, the actuating sleeve (k) has moved in relation to the shoulder on the spreader (l), permitting the previously spread sleeve (k) to relax as shown in Fig. 3.4/4. In this relaxed position, however, the positive connection between actuating sleeve (k) and ejector sleeve (m) is interrupted, so that with further forward motion of the ejector sleeve (m) only the ejector pins (f) are extended, while the stripper plate is held stationary.

As the mold closes, the rear ejector plate (h) is first returned by the push-back pins (p) while the front ejector plate (g) is subsequently returned by the push-back sleeve (e). The actuating sleeve (k) is thereby once again spread in the ejector sleeve (m) as shown in Fig. 3.4/3.

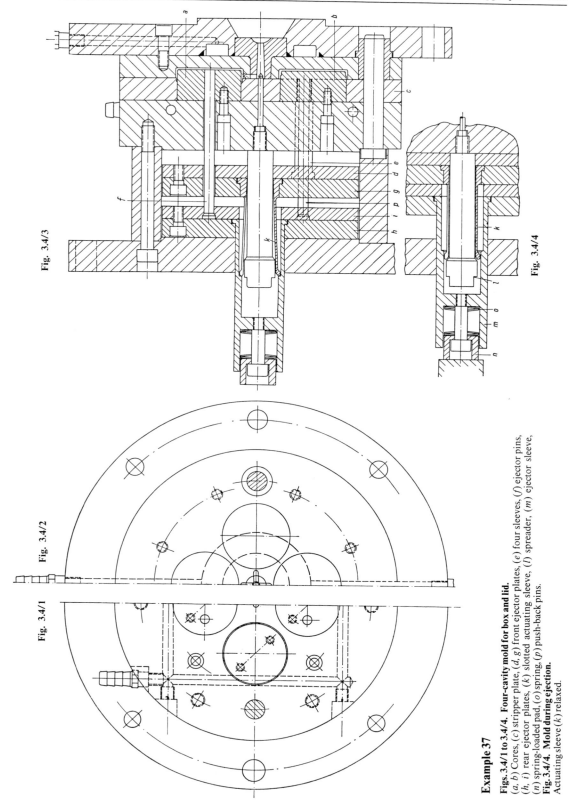

Fig. 3.4/3

Fig. 3.4/4

Fig. 3.4/2

Fig. 3.4/1

Example 37

Figs. 3.4/1 to 3.4/4. Four-cavity mold for box and lid.
(*a, b*) Cores, (*c*) stripper plate, (*d, g*) front ejector plates, (*e*) four sleeves, (*f*) ejector pins,
(*h, i*) rear ejector plates, (*k*) slotted actuating sleeve, (*l*) spreader, (*m*) ejector sleeve,
(*n*) spring-loaded pad, (*o*) spring, (*p*) push-back pins.
Fig. 3.4/4. Mold during ejection.
Actuating sleeve (*k*) relaxed.

Example 38. Mold for tablet tubes

It has been found that especially with tubes, which are relatively long in relation to their diameter, it is extremely difficult to prevent displacement of the core and avoid the resulting variation of wall thickness with all the detrimental consequences. As the result of uneven melt flow, the core is displaced toward one side even when a centrally positioned pinpoint gate is used on the bottom.

In the following, an injection mold is described in which displacement of the core is reliably prevented. It has been determined that gating from two opposite points on the open end of the tube already leads to considerably less displacement of the core than occurs when gating on the bottom. It is useful to design these two points as tunnel gates so that they are automatically sheared on opening of the mold and eliminate the need for any secondary operations.

With long tubes, however, even this type of gating is not enough to ensure completely uniform wall thickness. The core must be held in position until the melt reaches the bottom. This is accomplished in the mold shown in Figs. 3.4/5 to 3.4/8 as follows: To avoid an unnecessarily long sprue, the water-cooled cores (a) are fastened on the stationary mold half. The face of the core has a conical recess about 0.5 mm deep into which a conical protrusion on the movable core (b) is pressed by means of spring washers (c) when the cavity is not filled. As soon as the plastics melt fills the cavity to the bottom and flows into the annular space around the protrusion, the injection pressure overcomes the force exerted by the spring washers and displaces the movable core (b) by an amount corresponding to the thickness of the bottom. The entire bottom now fills with melt. A vent pin (d) with running fit in the movable core (b) to permit the compressed air to escape is provided to ensure that the melt will flow together properly at the center of the bottom.

As the mold opens, the spring washers assist in ejecting the tablet tubes from the cavities as well as in shearing off the two tunnel gates. The tubes are supposed to be retained on the cores, from which they are stripped by the stripper plate (e) during the final portion of the opening stroke. The runner system is initially retained by undercuts on the sucker pins (f). However, as soon as the stripper plate (e) is actuated, the runner system is pulled off the sucker pins (f) and drops out of the mold separated from the molded parts.

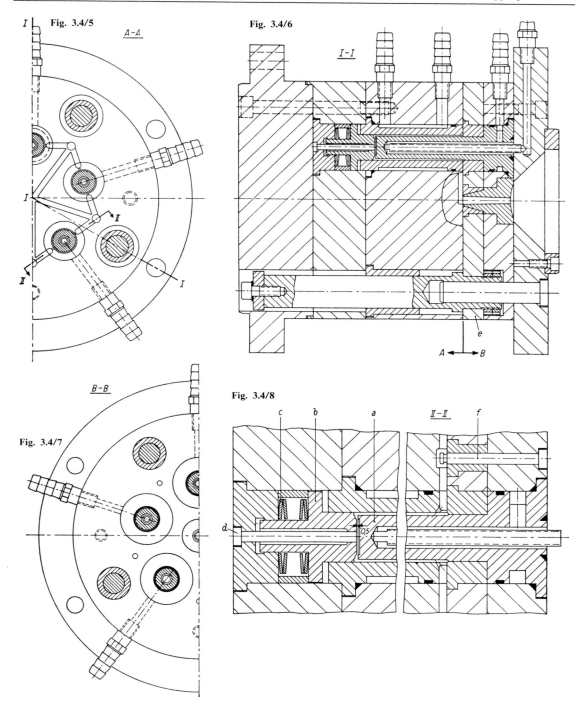

Fig. 3.4/5

A-A

I-I

Fig. 3.4/6

Fig. 3.4/7

B-B

Fig. 3.4/8

II-II

Example 38

Figs. 3.4/5 to 3.4/8. Five-cavity injection mold for long tablet tubes.
(*a*) Water-cooled core, (*b*) movable core, (*c*) spring washers, (*d*) vent pin, (*e*) stripper plate, (*f*) sucker pin.

3.5   Air Ejection

The various methods of mechanically ejecting molded parts from the open mold have been described with numerous examples. In the following, a method that is finding increasing use for large parts of polyethylene will be described. Polyethylene exhibits an undesirable tendency to stick on long cores, a disadvantage for mechanical ejection. Since it is also relatively soft, use of a stripper plate on thin-walled deep parts causes the wall to fold over, so that the part is rejected. A large central valve ejector on the bottom does not provide a remedy either, since the bottom can easily be punctured without releasing the long cylindrical side walls from the core.

It seemed only natural to introduce compressed air through a central valve ejector, and this method of ejection has been used successfully for a long period of time for large parts such as buckets, tubs and the like. It was also found that a small valve ejector in the core was quite adequate for introduction of the compressed air. Observation showed that the polyethylene wall was released from the core starting at the point at which air was introduced. An air cushion forms between the wall of the molded part and the core and in a very short period of time expands to such an extent that the part is lifted off the core by the compressed air.

An additional major advantage of this type of ejection is the reduced mounting height required for the mold, since the ejector mechanism, which is usually equal to the height of the core with mechanical ejectors, is no longer needed. Since the mold mounting height available in most machines is the limiting factor for deep parts ejection by means of compressed air means a considerable increase in the maximum possible depth of parts that may be molded in a given machine.

Use of compressed air for ejection also provides an additional advantage. The small compressed-air valve does not have to be in the center of the core. By placing it on the side of the core, space is gained in the center to permit installation of a high-capacity cooling system. This is especially important since it is very difficult to remove the heat from long cores by other means when it is not possible to install an effective cooling system.

The use of compressed air is not by any means limited to polyethylene. If the bottom surface of a part is approximately flat and large enough to flex somewhat under the action of compressed air, parts molded of polystyrene or other rigid plastics may be successfully ejected by means of compressed air. Often, the compressed air can be used to replace the long ejector stroke after a short mechanical ejection has released the parts form the cores. This can mean a considerably reduced mold mounting height. Use of air ejection is, however, limited to objects closed at one end. The parts cannot have holes.

It is not difficult to initiate ejection automatically through the use of electromagnetically or mechanically actuated compressed-air valves as the mold opens, so that the machine can be operated fully automatically. With electromagnetically actuated (solenoid) valves, it is practical to stop the flow of compressed air automatically after ejection by means of an adjustable timer or other mechanism. This should be done in any case to save on the relatively expensive compressed air. Air ejection provides an additional significant advantage in that ejection occurs gently, so that the scratches that can easily occur with mechanical ejection are prevented by the air cushion between the core and wall of the molded part.

Example 39. Test mold with both mechanical and air ejection.

In example 39 a mold providing both mechanical and air ejection is described (Figs. 3.5/1 and 3.5/2). The requirement was to design a test mold in which large cases could be molded of both hard molding compounds (polystyrene, nylon, etc.) and soft resins (polyethylene, PVC, etc.). In addition, use of a conventional sprue bushing or insulated sprue bushing was to be possible. The problem was solved by providing six half-round ejectors (a) around the edge of the

case and a central valve ejector (b) that simultaneously functions as central mechanical ejector. With soft resins, air ejection alone can be utilized without having to actuate the ejector rod (c). In this case, compressed air is merely introduced at connection (d) after the mold opens. Compressed air flows through three channels around the circumference of the slightly extended valve ejector and releases the case from the core. With hard resins, the ejector rod (c) is actuat-

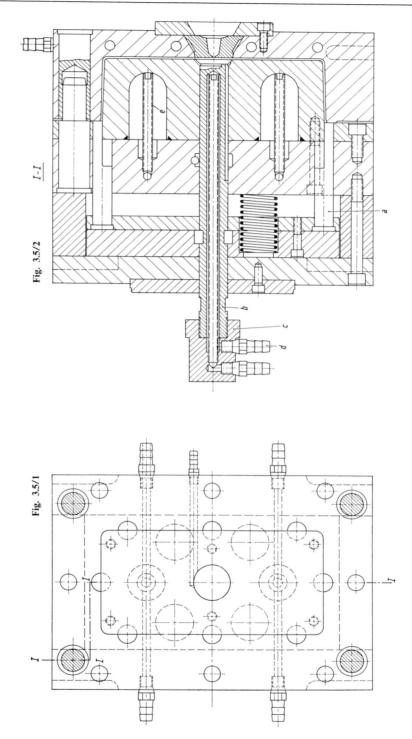

Fig. 3.5/2

I-I

Fig. 3.5/1

Example 39

Figs. 3.5/1 and 3.5/2. Test mold with both mechanical and air ejection.
(*a*) Mechanical ejector pin, (*b*) valve ejector, (*c*) ejector rod, (*d*) connection for compressed air, (*e*) bubbler tube for cooling.

ed, and the six ejector pins (*a*) as well as the center valve ejector (*b*) strip the case from the core. Compressed air can also be utilized in this case to perform the ejection after the part has been mechanically released from the core. Since the valve ejector is exposed to the entire heat flow through the gate, internal cooling extending to the head of the valve ejector is provided. The core itself is effectively cooled by means of two large cooling chambers into which the cooling water is introduced through tubes (*e*).

The requirement to permit optional use of either a conventional sprue or an insulated sprue was met by providing interchangeable sprue bushings. The insulated sprue bushing is relieved to ensure thermal insulation and thereby avoid excessive cooling when parts are molded by injecting through the still-molten core without removing the sprue, as is readily done with polyethylene.

Example 40. Injection mold with air ejection for polypropylene cups

In developing injection molding of thin-walled polypropylene packaging items, the greatest importance by far must be attributed to mold design. Thin-walled polypropylene cups cannot be produced economically and reliably in the types of molds used for polystyrene. Because of the greater enthalpy and lower thermal conductivity compared to those of polystyrene, the cooling must be more effective when processing polypropylene. Because of its reduced rigidity during ejection and greater tendency to shrink onto the core, ejection of thin-walled polypropylene cups by means of ejector rings creates problems. While air-assisted valve ejector systems can facilitate ejection, the less effective cooling possible with such a system does not permit extremely short cycle times. Roughening or draw polishing of the surface of the core is not a suitable solution for transparent cups because of the detrimental effects on the transparency. Air ejection by means of static or dynamic air valves is only of limited use in fast-cycling single-cavity molds, since at production rates of over 20 shots per minute rapid and exact closing of the valve is hindered by the air remaining in the valve stem.

The first mold for polypropylene cups with side air ejection was built in 1978. Preliminary tests with this novel ejection system for cups were so promising that the mold makers specializing in the production of cup molds adopted this system and improved it even further.

With side air ejection, stripper rings, which represent the most significant wearing part when producing cups by injection molding, can be eliminated. Figure 3.5/3 shows the design of such a core with side air ejection. With the mold illustrated in Fig. 3.5/4, acceptable cups were produced in a cycle time of 1.5 s using side air ejection exclusively.

This ejection system can also be employed with multiple-cavity and stack molds. However, exact control of the air, which is absolutely necessary for ejection, still presents certain difficulties.

With polypropylene, air must also be introduced at the bottom from the cavity side. This serves not only to prevent the formation of a vacuum but also to sever the tough gate.

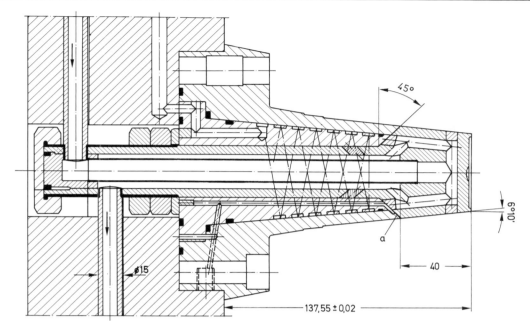

Fig. 3.5/3. Core of a cup mold with side air ejection, dimensions in mm.
(*a*) Annular gap with a width of 0.01 mm.
Mold drawing: Hoechst AG.

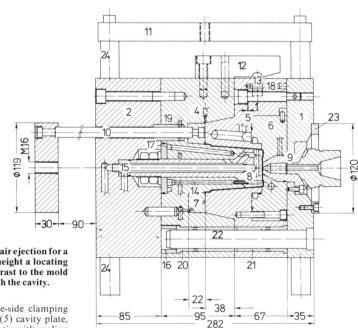

Example 40

Fig. 3.5/4. Single-cavity injection mold with side air ejection for a polypropylene dessert cup. To reduce the mold height a locating taper was provided parallel to the cavity, in contrast to the mold shown in Fig. 3.5/3, where the taper is in series with the cavity.
Company drawing: Fostag, Stein am Rhein.

(*1*) Stationary-side clamping plate, (*2*) movable-side clamping plate, (*3*) ejector plate, (*4*) core retainer plate, (*5*) cavity plate, (*6*) cavity bottom insert, (*7*) stripper ring, (*8*) core tip with cooling channels, (*9*) hot sprue bushing, (*10*) ejector rod, (*11*) strap for transporting the mold, (*12*) latch, (*13*) latch bolt, (*14*) static air valve, (*15*) central cooling water tube, (*16*) spacer sleeve, (*17*) sealing plate, (*18*) pinlift, (*19*) guide bushing, (*20*) guide bushing, (*21*) guide bushing, (*22*) guide pin, (*23*) locating ring, (*24*) strap mounting bolts.

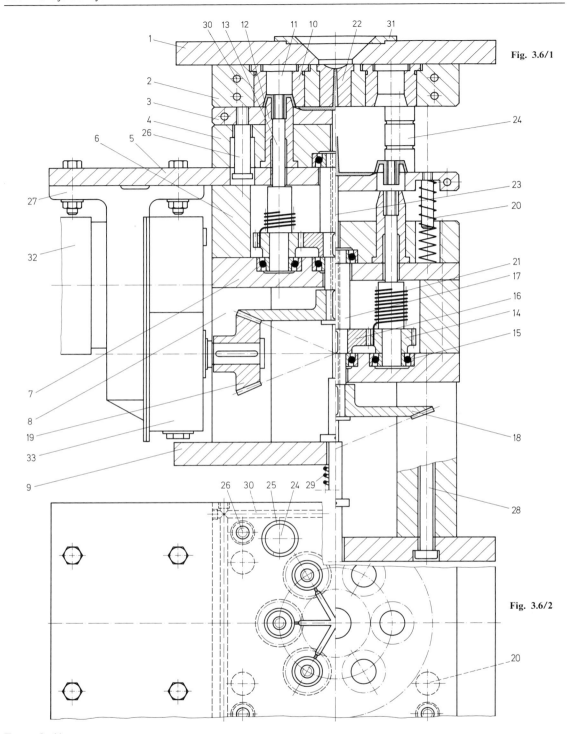

Fig. 3.6/1

Fig. 3.6/2

Example 41

Figs. 3.6/1 and 3.6/2. Injection mold with integral unscrewing mechanism with spring coupling.
(*1*) Stationary-side clamping plate, (*2*) stationary-side cavity retainer plate, (*3*) stripper plate, (*4*) movable-side core retainer plate, (*5*) backing plate, (*6*) support pillar, (*7*) ball bearing retainer plate, (*8*) support pillar, (*9*) movable-side clamping plate, (*10*) stationary-side cavity insert, (*11*) cavity bottom insert, (*12*) movable-side cavity insert, (*13*) thread-forming insert, (*14*) pinion gear, (*15*) ball bearing (series 61), (*16*) central spur gear, (*17*) ball bearing shaft, (*18, 19*) bevel gears, (*20*) springs, (*21*) spring couplings with 4, 6, 8, 10, 12 and 14 coils, (*22*) sprue bushing, (*23*) ejector pin, (*24*) guide pin, (*25*) guide bushing, (*26*) stop bolt, (*27*) motor mount, (*28*) bolts, (*29*) spring, (*30*) cooling water connection, (*31*) locating ring, (*32*) electric motor, (*33*) spur gear drive.

3.6   Unscrewing Molds

Example 41. Injection mold with unscrewing mechanism

It is often necessary to produce plastic parts with internal and external threads. In multiple-cavity molds a high torque may be needed to unscrew the thread-forming insert, especially if the mold has been used extensively and is exhibiting wear. Hard chrome plating of the threads usually does not help and may even be detrimental if because of the well-known "edge effect" more metal is deposited on the outer edge of the thread than in the root. This can result in variations in thread profile. In such cases involving manual removal, unscrewing of the molded part is time-consuming and possible only with a great deal of force. For automatic operation this means that an excessively powerful drive motor must be provided to overcome the adhesion between the molded piece and thread-forming insert. There have been extensive efforts to find a better design. Figures 3.6/1 and 3.6/2 show a proven solution to this problem. The thread-forming inserts (*13*) are connected via spur gearing to an electric motor (*32*). The motor drives a pinion (*14*) at each cavity by means of a central spur gear (*16*) and a pair of bevel gears (*18*) and (*19*). These gears are not keyed to the threaded insert (*13*), but rather are connected by means of a spring coupling (*21*). The number of coils in each spring, however, differs, e.g., each spring has one coil more than the adjacent spring. As the drive motor starts, the springs do not all tighten simultaneously but rather one after another, depending on the respective number of coils. As a result the torque developed by the motor acts only on one threaded insert at a time, so that a motor with a relatively low drive rating may be used. In addition, this system is hardly liable to give trouble.

Example 42. Injection mold for valve stems with internal threads

The valve stem illustrated in Figs. 3.6/3 and 3.6/4 is used to accurately adjust the flow rate of water. A rubber O-ring is placed in the groove on the larger portion of the shank for sealing. The part is gated at the tip of the valve cone. With such a design, a three-plate mold is needed. Since the valve cone is not permitted to have a witness line, a pair of slides is needed to form the sealing ring groove, so that the mold can be designed only with two cavities. The location of the slides prevents turning of the threaded core. Unscrewing is thus possible only via the integral molded handle, which has suitable driving surfaces. The stem is hollow at the handle end. This recess cannot extend further than the sealing ring groove, as otherwise the valve stem would be weakened too much. This results in a gating problem, namely, the formation of a free jet of molding material as the cavity is filled. This free jet (Fig. 3.6/5) can have a very detrimental effect on the valve cone. The free jet of material injected into the cavity cool slightly before it impinges on the core with the 60° tip. The

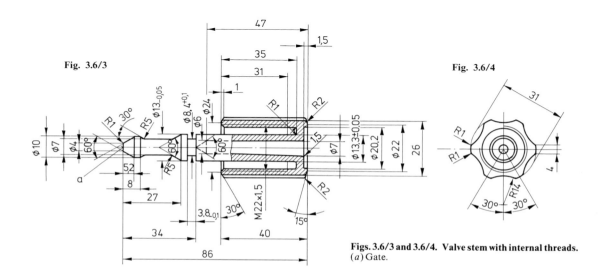

Fig. 3.6/3

Fig. 3.6/4

Figs. 3.6/3 and 3.6/4. Valve stem with internal threads.
(*a*) Gate.

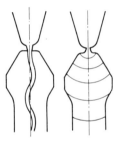

Figs. 3.6/5. Poor gate design results in formation of a free jet.

Fig. 3.6/6. Good gate design avoids formation of a free jet.

somewhat cooled stream of material is deflected to the side and may be forced to the outer wall, where it then remains and can form a very uneven and rough surface. This phenomenon can be avoided by using the gate illustrated in Fig. 3.6/6. As shown, the gate must widen toward the part. It is also important that the gate not have a sharp corner where it meets the part, but rather be rounded. It is only with such a design that the solid tip of the valve stem can be filled cleanly and with a smooth surface by means of fountain flow.

The only disadvantage of this design is that the gate vestige remains on the molded part, which is unimportant as far as proper functioning is concerned.

Section C–D (Fig. 3.6/10) provides a good view of the layout of the two-cavity mold (Figs. 3.6/7 to 3.6/11). It can be seen that the machine nozzle (*1*) has an internal thread into which a nozzle tip (*2*) is screwed that extends to the runner system (*3*), so that the undesirable sprue is eliminated. The cavities for the handles of the two valve stems (*4*) are machined into the rotating, geared insert (*5*). These engage with the drive gear (*6*), which is connected to the unscrewing unit (*8*) via the shaft (*7*). The slides (*9*) that form the groove for the sealing ring can be seen in section A–B (Fig. 3.6/8). The mold first opens at parting line (*I*), because the latches (*10*) still hold parting line (*III*) closed. The latch heads are riveted to spring steel bands. During this opening motion, the slide locking wedges (*11*) simultaneously separate from the outer locking wedges (*12*). The cam pins (*13*) force the slides (*9*) outward, releasing the groove for the sealing ring. The slides (*9*) are held in the open position by the ball catches (*14*). As this parting line opens, the gates (*15*) are immediately severed from the parts (*4*). The run-

ner system (*3*) is held on the stationary mold half by the undercut pins (*16*).

As parting line (*I*) opens, the motion to open the second parting line to eject the runner system (*3*) is initiated. Delayed opening of parting line (*II*) is controlled by packs of spring washers. At first, the push pin (*17*), behind which the stronger spring pack is located, holds the runner stripper plate (*18*) in its retracted position. As the force exerted by this spring pack decreases, the plate (*18*) is forced forward by the spring pack (*19*) until the motion is stopped by bolt (*20*). In the course of this motion, the runner system (*3*) is stripped off the undercut pins (*16*). The spring-loaded runner ejector pins (*21*) prevent the runner system (*3*) from sticking to plate (*18*), so that the runner system can drop freely out of the mold.

Once the mold has opened so far that the latches (*10*) are disengaged by the release bar (*23*) and the plate is resting against the stops (*24*), the opening motion of the machine is stopped. The unscrewing unit (*8*) is now actuated. The rotating motion is transmitted by shaft (*7*) to the drive gear (*6*) and from here to the inserts (*5*). Since, however, the threaded cores (*25*) are stationary, this entire portion of the mold, which runs in ball bearings (*26*) on the guide pins (*27*), is unscrewed and the threaded cores (*25*) are released from the molded parts. At the same time, the valve stems are withdrawn from the cavity insert.

Once the unscrewing unit (*8*) has stopped rotating, the mold opens at parting line (*III*), the main parting line. As soon as the ejector rods (*28*) are actuated, the ejector plate (*29*) moves forward. The molded parts are now ejected from the cavities (*5*) by the ejector pins (*30*), which are held in rotating inserts (*31*). The push-back pins (*32*) return the ejector pins (*30*) to their retracted position as the mold closes. This segment of the machine cycle and actuation of the unscrewing are controlled by the core pull sequencing of the molding machine. The unscrewing unit needs an additional pair of switch cams for its sequencing, because the rotating motion is required in only one direction.

The weakest point in the mold design is that the threaded cores (*25*) and internal core pins (*33*) cannot be reached with any liquid cooling. Accordingly, the mold was provided with air cooling. The main jet of air is split and directed against the stationary threaded cores (*25*) and internal core pins (*33*) through adjustable tubes. The air flow is started as unscrewing begins and stops only as the mold starts to close. With the aid of this air cooling, at least some of the heat absorbed by the cores can be removed.

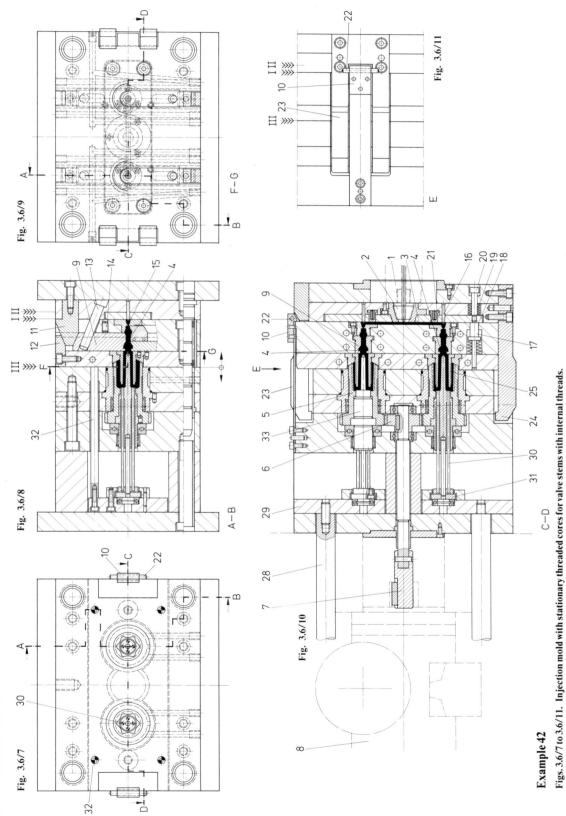

Fig. 3.6/9

F–G

Fig. 3.6/8

A–B

Fig. 3.6/7

Fig. 3.6/11

Fig. 3.6/10

C–D

Example 42

Figs. 3.6/7 to 3.6/11. Injection mold with stationary threaded cores for valve stems with internal threads.
(*1*) Machine nozzle; (*2*) nozzle tip; (*3*) runner system; (*4*) molded part (valve stem); (*5*) rotating, geared inserts; (*6*) drive gear; (*7*) shaft; (*8*) unscrewing unit; (*9*) slide; (*10*) latch; (*11*) cam locking wedge; (*12*) outer locking wedge; (*13*) cam pin; (*14*) ball catch; (*15*) gate; (*16*) undercut pin; (*17*) push pin; (*18*) runner stripper plate; (*19*) spring washers; (*20*) stop bolt; (*21*) runner ejector pins; (*22*) latch release pin; (*23*) release bar; (*24*) stop; (*25*) threaded core; (*26*) ball bearing; (*27*) guide pin; (*28*) ejector rod; (*29*) ejector plate; (*30*) ejector pin; (*31*) rotating inserts; (*32*) push-back pins; (*33*) internal core pin.

4 Types of Undercuts

4.1 Moldings with External Undercuts or Screw Threads

Example 43. Four-impression injection molding tool for producing a pressure nut[1]

A pressure nut with a 1 in BSP pipe thread (Fig. 4.1/1) had to be produced out of Polyacetal (POM). Mechanical rigidity and dimensional accuracy were required, but above all a low unit price was of importance. Contrary to the usual in-line arrangement due to the price and also for the sake of transferring the melt in good condition, four mold cavities were arranged in a square for these externally threaded moldings. In this way the volume of melt in the runner system could be reduced considerably below half of that required for the in-line system.

In the case where mold cavities are arranged in line, the moldings are released by the two split halves moving apart symmetrically to the center line. Cavities arranged in the square, however, require an additional movement to release the screw threads. An unconventional solution has been found in a delay device with angled bias guide (29) which retains the moldings in their position during the first stage of the opening sequence while the cores (31) are being pulled. During the next phase the external splits (27) are released and the four nuts are uncovered with the screw-threaded halves pointing to the outside.

In the third phase the external splits pull a sliding split (25) to one side, demolding the pressure nuts from the shared center bar (26).

Fig. 4.1/1. Sprue and gates of the four-impression tool (left) for producing the 1 in BSP pressure nut.
Works photo: Arcu, Altermo/Sweden.

---

[1] From *Plastforum* 12(1981)3, pp. 50–53.

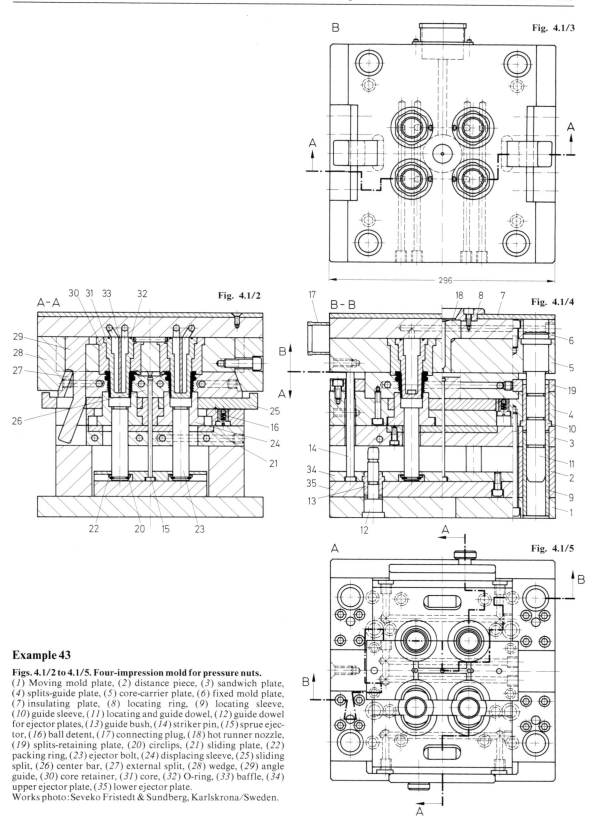

Fig. 4.1/3

Fig. 4.1/2

Fig. 4.1/4

Fig. 4.1/5

Example 43

Figs. 4.1/2 to 4.1/5. Four-impression mold for pressure nuts.
(*1*) Moving mold plate, (*2*) distance piece, (*3*) sandwich plate,
(*4*) splits-guide plate, (*5*) core-carrier plate, (*6*) fixed mold plate,
(*7*) insulating plate, (*8*) locating ring, (*9*) locating sleeve,
(*10*) guide sleeve, (*11*) locating and guide dowel, (*12*) guide dowel
for ejector plates, (*13*) guide bush, (*14*) striker pin, (*15*) sprue ejector, (*16*) ball detent, (*17*) connecting plug, (*18*) hot runner nozzle,
(*19*) splits-retaining plate, (*20*) circlips, (*21*) sliding plate, (*22*)
packing ring, (*23*) ejector bolt, (*24*) displacing sleeve, (*25*) sliding
split, (*26*) center bar, (*27*) external split, (*28*) wedge, (*29*) angle
guide, (*30*) core retainer, (*31*) core, (*32*) O-ring, (*33*) baffle, (*34*)
upper ejector plate, (*35*) lower ejector plate.
Works photo: Seveko Fristedt & Sundberg, Karlskrona/Sweden.

Example 44. Injection molding tool for the valve housing of a water-mixing tap[2]

A valve housing (Figs. 4.1/6 and 4.1/7) had to be designed and produced for a water-mixing tap. The problem when designing the tool (Figs. 4.1/8 to 4.1/12) resulted from the undercuts in four directions. Originally occurring considerable differences in wall thicknesses have been eliminated during optimization. Demands for high precision of the cylindrical valve seating mainly were being negatively influenced

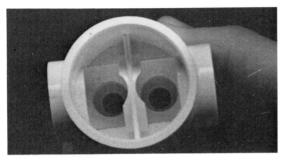

Fig. 4.1/6. View of the interior of the valve housing, showing the places of core penetration.
Works photo: ARCU, Altermo/Sweden.

Fig. 4.1/7. View of the exterior of the valve housing.
Works photo: ARCU, Altermo/Sweden.

by various recesses in the wall and adjoining partitions, which favored sink marks and ovality.

Polyacetal (POM) had been chosen as molding material. The complete molding had to have homogeneous walls, free from flow lines if at all possible, as the molding would be subjected to ever changing contact with hot and cold water during an estimated long life span. Inadequately fused weld lines would be capable of developing into weak spots and were therefore to be avoided at all cost.

Provision has been made for an electrically heated sprue bush (30) (Fig. 4.1/11) in order to avoid a long conical sprue gate, provide better movement energies for the melt and maintain its temperature until it enters the cavity. The resultant very short sprue channel leads to the gate on the edge of the pipelike housing, to be hidden by a part that is subsequently fitted to cover it. The gating, the predetermined mold temperature, the wall thickness at the critical positions and the resultant shrinkage have been employed as the basis for dimensioning the shape-giving parts.

Two cores each cross in the pipe-shaped housing, i.e., one core (16) each penetrates another core (19). This obviously presents a danger spot should the minutest deviation occur from the time- and movement-bound fixed coordination as well as from the accuracy in the mold.

The hollow cores (19) are kept still by mechanical delay during the first phase of the mold-opening process, whereas the crossing cores (16) are being withdrawn by an angle dowel each (31). Mechanical actuation has been preferred over a hydraulic or pneumatic one in this case in order to exclude the danger of a switching error (the so-called human factor) during setting and in operation.

The cores (16, 33) consist of a beryllium-copper alloy. They are cooled by heat conducting pins (27, 28).

[2] From *Plastforum* 12(1981)3, pp. 54–57.

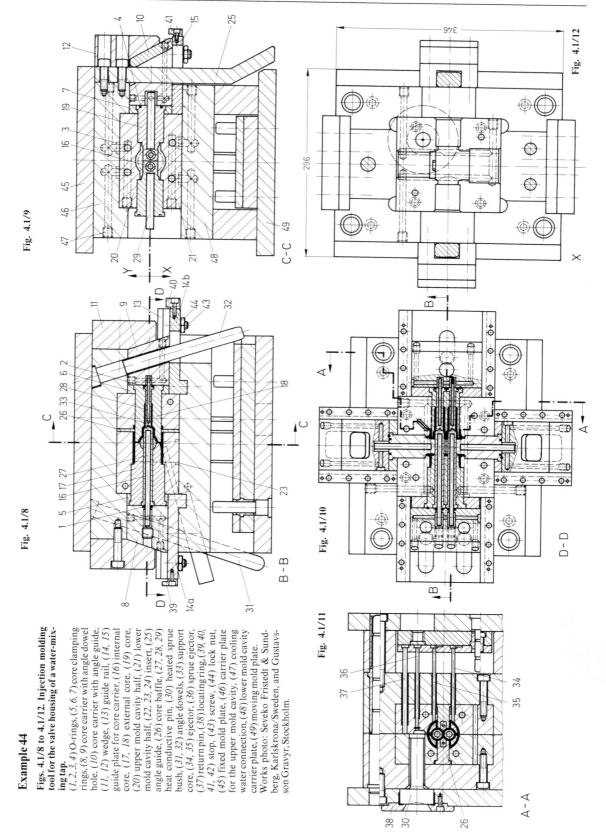

Fig. 4.1/9

Fig. 4.1/12

Fig. 4.1/8

Fig. 4.1/10

Fig. 4.1/11

Example 44

Figs. 4.1/8 to 4.1/12. Injection molding tool for the valve housing of a water-mixing tap.

(1, 2, 3, 4) O-rings, (5, 6, 7) core clamping rings, (8, 9) core carrier with angle dowel hole, (10) core carrier with angle guide, (11, 12) wedge, (13) guide rail, (14, 15) guide plate for core carrier, (16) internal core, (17, 18) external core, (19) core, (20) upper mold cavity half, (21) lower mold cavity half, (22, 23, 24) insert, (25) angle guide, (26) core baffle, (27, 28, 29) heat conductive pin, (30) heated sprue bush, (31, 32) angle dowels, (33) support core, (34, 35) ejector, (36) sprue ejector, (37) return pin, (38) locating ring, (39, 40, 41, 42) stop, (43) screw, (44) lock nut, (45) fixed mold plate, (46) carrier plate for the upper mold cavity, (47) cooling water connection, (48) lower mold cavity carrier plate, (49) moving mold plate.
Works photo: Seveko Fristedt & Sundberg, Karlskrona/Sweden, and Gustavsson Gravyr, Stockholm.

Example 45. A three-cavity injection mold for a cosmetic cream container with a threaded lid

A fine-threaded lid is usually used for the closure of cosmetic cream containers. When these are containers molded in plastic, the injection molding tool must usually, for aesthetic reasons, be such that no markings on the surface of the molding caused by the different mold parts are visible. Such marks are left behind on the molding when a simple two-part mold cavity is used. Tools with a screwing-off facility prevent this disadvantage, but they are complicated and expensive.

The three-cavity mold shown in Figs. 4.1/13 and 4.1/14 shows an alternative economical solution to this problem: the container wall is molded in a nonseparating cavity and a cavity separation takes place only in the area of the outer thread at the edge of the molding. The thread is molded by means of a three-part ring (15), which is held together in the closed mold by wedge-shaped pieces (16) (as shown in region

I of the main sectional drawing, or in the plan view, left, Figs. 4.1/13 and 4.1/14). The three-plate tool is so constructed that on opening, the first separation between plates (2) and (3) causes the sprue and runner to be ejected by means of the spring (33) and the pin (32) (illustrated in region II on the main sectional drawing). The striking of plate (4) against the head of stroke limiting screw (22) causes the separation of plates (4) and (5) to commence. This in turn causes the thread forming ring segments (15) to be drawn away from the wedges (16) and to be separated from each other by the springs (25), thus releasing the molded thread. Finally, the ejector (19) causes ejection of the molding (as illustrated in region III of the main sectional drawing and the plan view, right, Figs. 4.1/13 and 4.1/14). The internal cooling of the core (13) and external cooling of plate (5) result in short cycle times.

Example 45 (right side)

Fig. 4.1/13 and 4.1/14. A three-cavity injection mold for a cosmetic cream container with a threaded lid.
(1, 2) Fixed tool plates, (3, 4) upper mold cavity retaining plate, (5) mold cavity plate, (6, 7) base plates, (8) distance ring, (9, 10) ejector plates, (11, 12) movable tool plates, (13) cooled core, (14) insert for bottom molding, (15) three-parted thread forming ring, (16) wedge, (17) guide pin, (18) cooling water connection, (19) ejector sleeve, (20) ejector rod, (21) cooling water connection for core cooling, (22) stroke limit screw, (23) injection molding bush, (24) centering disc, (25) spring, (26) guide pin, (27) guide bush, (28) packing ring, (29) dowel pin, (30) connection screw, (31) spring, (32) ejector pin for feed channel, (33) spring.

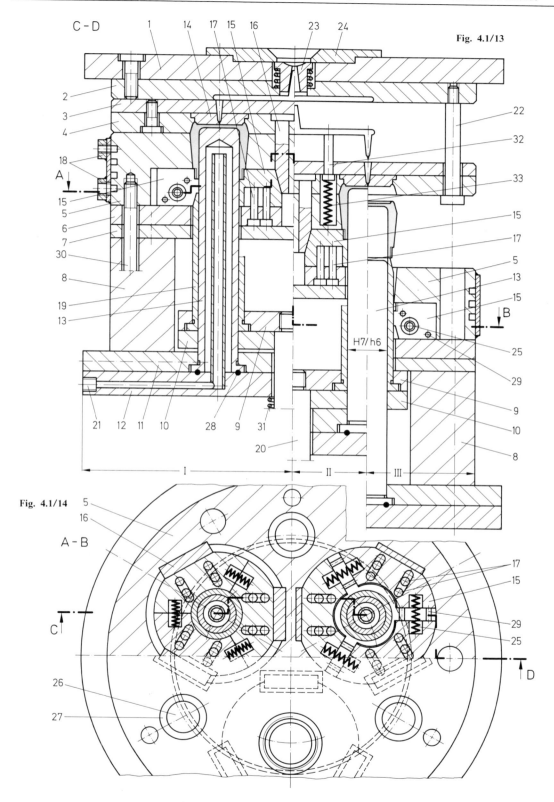

C – D

Fig. 4.1/13

H7/ h6

I   II   III

Fig. 4.1/14

A – B

Example 46. Eight-impression hot-runner injection molding tool for original closures

With complicated moldings, constructed of concentric circles and incorporating undercuts around their circumference, a multistage ejection sequence is necessary to prevent the undercuts from being torn off. The mold shown in Figs. 4.1/15 to 4.1/19 has been designed for such a part. At the start of mold opening, air pressure is applied to the cylinders in plate (2), resulting in split line (a) opening first. The part is demolded from the shape-giving sprue bush. With continuing opening movement spring (21) opens, and with it the parting plane (b) once the pistons (23) have contacted their end positions. With this the core sleeve (15) is withdrawn from the article. When the restricting bolts (16) have made contact, the main parting plane (c) starts opening. The undercut in the molding produced by mold cavity insert (26) is released by demolding it inwardly. Once the parting at (c) is sufficiently large, the pistons (24) are pressurized with compressed air to displace cores and ejectors (17) to (20), without there being any relative movement to each other, however. This pushes the molding out of cavity insert (27). That sequence runs off synchronously with the opening of split line (d). Final demolding can now take place by pushing the ejectors (19) and (20) forward, degating the moldings from the tunnel gates as well. The undercut formed by the core sleeve (17) is being stretched during demolding. When the mold closes, cores and ejectors (17) to (20) are pushed back to their base positions by the push-back pins (28).

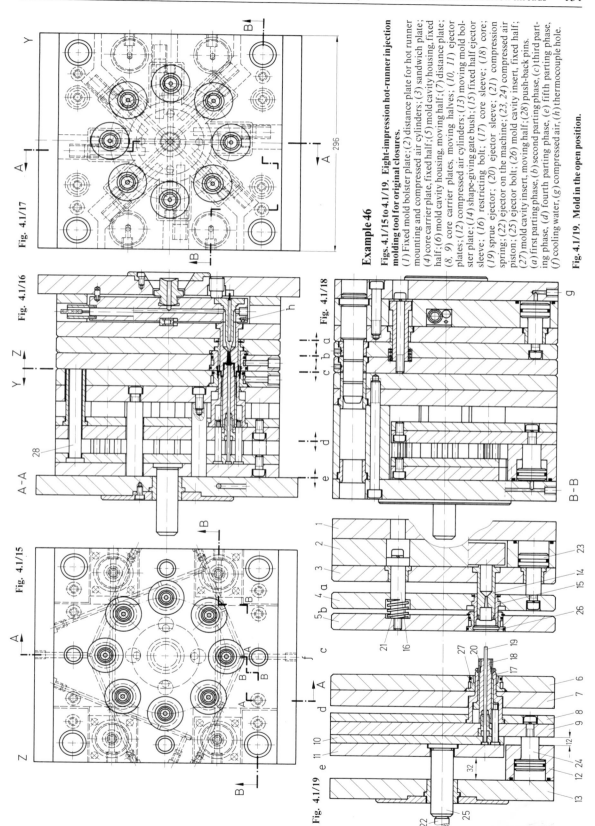

Fig. 4.1/17

Fig. 4.1/16

Fig. 4.1/15

Fig. 4.1/18

Fig. 4.1/19

Example 46

Figs. 4.1/15 to 4.1/19. Eight-impression hot-runner injection molding tool for original closures.

(*1*) Fixed mold bolster plate; (*2*) distance plate for hot runner mounting and compressed air cylinders; (*3*) sandwich plate; (*4*) core carrier plate, fixed half; (*5*) mold cavity housing, fixed half; (*6*) mold cavity housing, moving half; (*7*) distance plate; (*8, 9*) core carrier plates, moving halves; (*10, 11*) ejector plates; (*12*) compressed air cylinders; (*13*) moving mold bolster plate; (*14*) shape-giving gate bush; (*15*) fixed half ejector sleeve; (*16*) restricting bolt; (*17*) core sleeve; (*18*) core; (*19*) sprue ejector; (*20*) ejector sleeve; (*21*) compression spring; (*22*) ejector on the machine; (*23, 24*) compressed air piston; (*25*) ejector bolt; (*26*) mold cavity insert, fixed half; (*27*) mold cavity insert, moving half; (*28*) push-back pins.
(*a*) first parting phase, (*b*) second parting phase, (*c*) third parting phase, (*d*) fourth parting phase, (*e*) fifth parting phase, (*f*) cooling water, (*g*) compressed air, (*h*) thermocouple hole.

Fig. 4.1/19. Mold in the open position.

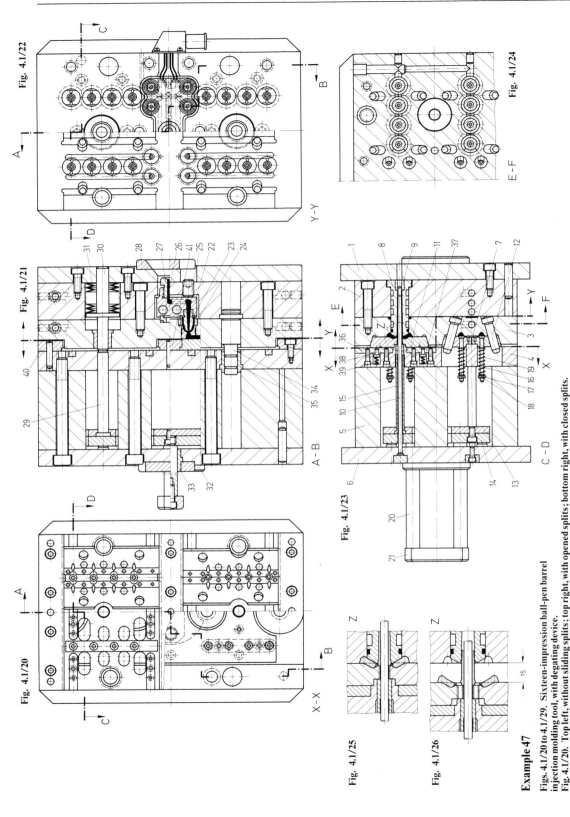

Fig. 4.1/22

Fig. 4.1/24

E – F

Fig. 4.1/21

A – B

Fig. 4.1/20

X – X

Fig. 4.1/23

C – D

Y – Y

Fig. 4.1/25

Fig. 4.1/26

Example 47

Figs. 4.1/20 to 4.1/29. Sixteen-impression ball-pen barrel injection molding tool, with degating device.
Fig. 4.1/20. Top left, without sliding splits; top right, with opened splits; bottom right, with closed splits.
Fig. 4.1/26. Detail illustration (individual detail Z) after 15 mm opening stroke.

(1) Fixed mold bolster plate, *(2)* sandwich plate with hot runner, *(3)* manifold plate, *(4)* base plate for splits, *(5)* distance plate, *(6)* moving bolster plate, *(7)* cover strip, *(8)* cavity, *(9)* core location, *(10)* core, *(11)* splits, *(12)* angle dowel, *(13, 14)* ejector plates, *(15)* ejector sleeve, *(16)* ejector pin, *(17)* end disc, *(18)* shaft circlip, *(19)* compression spring, *(20)* ejector bar, *(21)* outer ejector plate, *(22)* hot-runner block, *(23)* hot-runner nozzle, *(24)* antechamber bush, *(25)* pressure screw, *(26)* sprue bush, *(27)* hot-runner block location, *(28)* locating ring, *(29)* restraining bolt, *(30)* bolt with collar, *(31)* disc springs, *(32)* locating rings, *(33)* guide bush, *(34)* locating bolt, *(35)* locating sleeve, *(36, 37)* detent holder, *(38)* detent, *(39)* compression spring, *(40, 41)* splits guide.

Example 47. Sixteen-impression ball-pen barrel injection molding tool, with degating device

Side injection of small diameter moldings, such as ball-pen barrels, for instance, can nowadays only be accomplished in a multi-impression hot runner tool with standardized hot-runner nozzles, developed especially for side injection and marketed by such firms as MoldMasters, Thermoplay and Jetform. If one does not choose this system of gating, then there only remains the combination of hot- and cold-runner systems for fully automatic production without any sizeable losses of sprue. This type of solution is shown with the mold in Figs. 4.1/20 to 4.1/29. A centrally placed hot runner block (22) with eight hot-runner nozzles (23, 24) supplies four mold cavities each by way of two cold sprue channels. These lead the melt into the cavities from two sides via tunnel gates. This bilateral gating ensures additional core centralizing during injection. The gates are located on the locating ring of the ball-pen barrel and will later be covered by a decorative ring. The external screw threads of the ball-pen barrels are formed by two splits (11). These also house the gate runners.

It is important when demolding that axial displacement of the ball-pen barrels on the cores (10) is avoided until the splits (11) guided by the angle dowels (12) have opened. This detaches them from the tunnel gates, and the sleeves are simultaneously demolded from the cavity (8). This sequence is safeguarded by a spring disc packet (31), which retains the

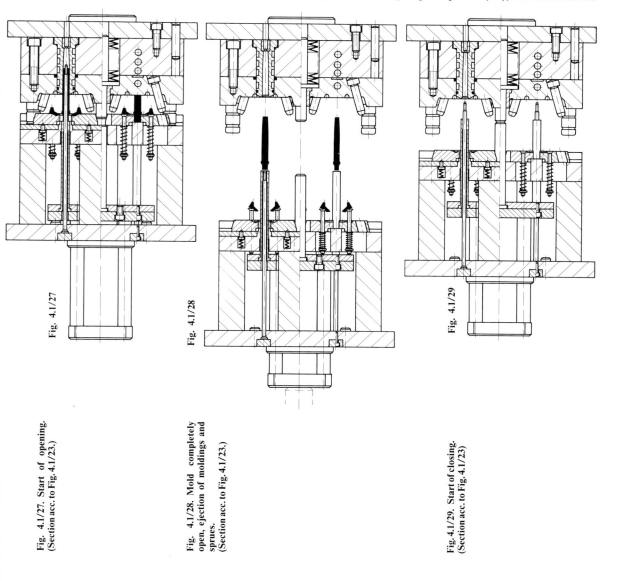

Fig. 4.1/27

Fig. 4.1/28

Fig. 4.1/29

Fig. 4.1/27. Start of opening.
(Section acc. to Fig. 4.1/23.)

Fig. 4.1/28. Mold completely open, ejection of moldings and sprues.
(Section acc. to Fig. 4.1/23.)

Fig. 4.1/29. Start of closing.
(Section acc. to Fig. 4.1/23)

ejector plates (*13, 14*) by pushing bolt (*30*) against bolt (*29*) until the collar on the former, housed in plate (*3*), bottoms. Because of the length of the ball-pen barrels, the mold requires a long opening stroke and the angle dowels (*12*) move out of the splits plates (*11*). They are retained in their open position by detents (*37*) to ensure the safe entry of the angle dowels (*12*) into the guide holes when the mold is being closed. The ejector on the machine is adjusted so that it meets with the outer ejector plate (*21*) when the molding has been withdrawn completely from the cavity. Then the ejector sleeve (*15*) pushes the molding off the core (*10*). During the progress of this movement the ejector plate (*13*) contacts the ejector pins (*16*), so that the sprues are ejected by them. The illustrations in Figs. 4.1/27 to 4.1/29 show the sequence of this demolding process.

Example 48. Eight-impression hot-runner mold for closure plugs

The shape of the closure plugs incorporates undercuts requiring a relatively complicated mold design with sliding splits to ensure problem-free demolding.

On the mold illustrated (Figs. 4.1/30 to 4.1/32) the elasticity of the thin walled PE molding is made use of for demolding, eliminating the need for sliding splits. It is necessary, however, that the core (*13*) is being pushed out of the mold cavity insert (*7*) to allow the molding to slide over the undercut in the side of the core.

As the ejectors (*17*) must only enter into the operation when the core (*13*) has been displaced, the ejector movement is controlled by ball catches. When the mold has opened, the cores (*13*) as well as the ejectors (*17*) are pushed forward between plates (*2*) and (*3*) by means of the ejector bar (*18*) and the ejector plates (*15, 16*). The in bush (*22*) engaged balls (*21*), which are being carried along by sliding splits bush (*19*), ensure that core (*13*) and ejector (*17*) move in parallel. The movement of core (*13*) is concluded and it is arrested when the core carrier plate (*14*) engages in catch (*23*). Simultaneously the balls (*21*) reach the screwed-in position of bolt (*20*). The flush alignment with the mold between sliding splits bush (*19*) and bush (*22*) is cancelled, so that only the ejectors (*17*) carry on moving with the ejector bar (*18*). This results in the ejectors overriding the face areas of the now fully extended arrested cores (*13*) and ejects the moldings. The plan view in Fig. 4.1/33 shows the final position of the opening movement. With mold closing, the ejectors (*17*) are pushed back by the bar (*24*) until the balls (*21*) are aligned with the ball raceway of bush (*22*). At that point plate (*2*) also reaches the push-back pin (*25*), which now also pushes back the core (*13*) parallel to the ejectors (*17*), which becomes feasible through the balls (*21*) being able to run into the larger diameter of bolt (*20*).

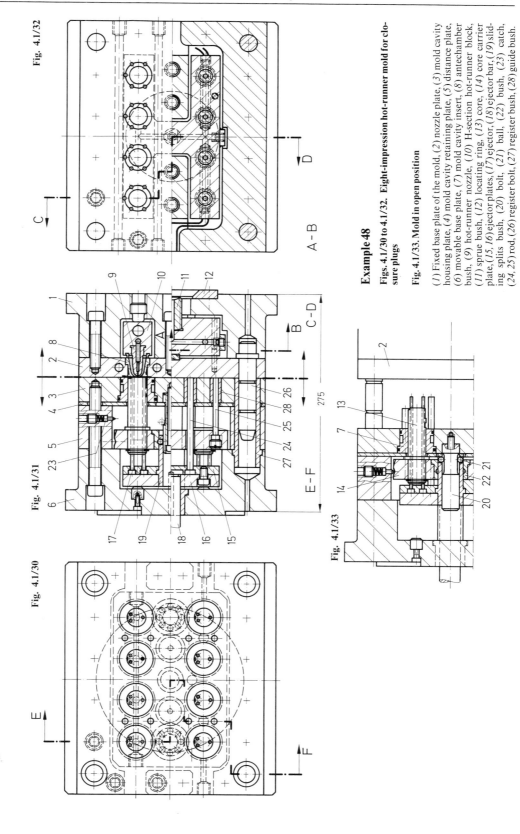

Fig. 4.1/32

Fig. 4.1/31

Fig. 4.1/30

Fig. 4.1/33

Example 48

Figs. 4.1/30 to 4.1/32. Eight-impression hot-runner mold for closure plugs

Fig. 4.1/33. Mold in open position

(1) Fixed base plate of the mold, *(2)* nozzle plate, *(3)* mold cavity housing plate, *(4)* mold cavity retaining plate, *(5)* distance plate, *(6)* movable base plate, *(7)* mold cavity insert, *(8)* antechamber bush, *(9)* hot-runner nozzle, *(10)* H-section hot-runner block, *(11)* sprue bush, *(12)* locating ring, *(13)* core, *(14)* core carrier plate, *(15, 16)* ejector plates, *(17)* ejector, *(18)* ejector bar, *(19)* sliding splits bush, *(20)* bolt, *(21)* ball, *(22)* bush, *(23)* catch, *(24, 25)* rod, *(26)* register bolt, *(27)* register bush, *(28)* guide bush.

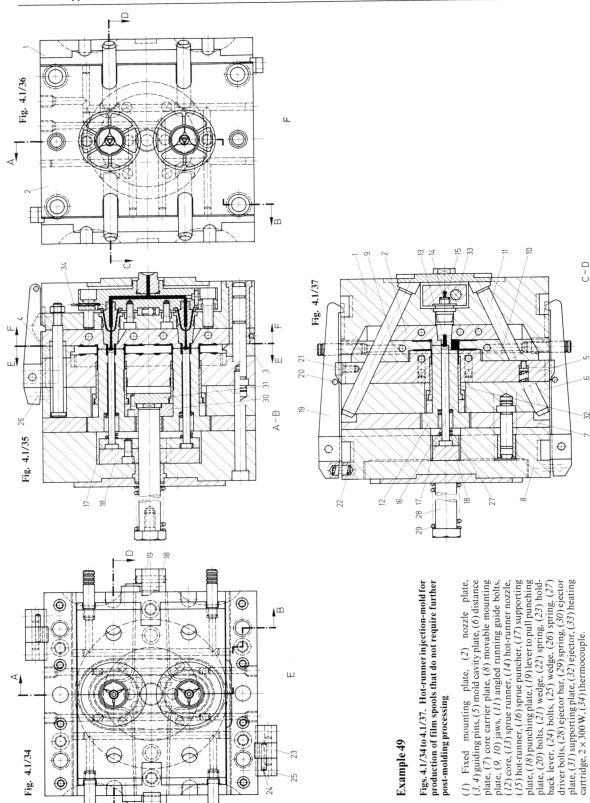

Fig. 4.1/36

Fig. 4.1/35

Fig. 4.1/34

Fig. 4.1/37

Example 49

Figs. 4.1/34 to 4.1/37. Hot-runner injection-mold for production of film spools that do not require further post-molding processing

(1) Fixed mounting plate, (2) nozzle plate, (3, 4) guiding pins, (5) mold cavity plate, (6) distance plate, (7) core carrier plate, (8) movable mounting plate, (9, 10) jaws, (11) angled running guide bolts, (12) core, (13) sprue runner, (14) hot-runner nozzle, (15) hot-runner, (16) sprue puncher, (17) supporting plate, (18) punching plate, (19) lever to pull punching plate, (20) bolts, (21) wedge, (22) spring, (23) hold-back lever, (24) bolts, (25) wedge, (26) spring, (27) driver bolts, (28) ejector bar, (29) spring, (30) ejector plate, (31) supporting plate, (32) ejector, (33) heating cartridge, 2 × 300 W, (34) thermocouple.

Example 49. Hot-runner injection mold for two film spools in impact resistant polystyrene

Because of their geometrical shape, film spools need injection molds (Figs. 4.1/34 to 4.1/37) with movable jaws (9, 10) which, in their closed state in the mold cavity, form the inner contour of the spool that later will allow the film to be wound on. Into the double-walled spool boss, suitable cores project inward from both sides (2, 12) to form the storage and make up rosettes. The central bores of the spools are formed in the ejector side of the tool by movable cores, which at a later state function as sprue breaks (16). A hot-runner sprue (15) with indirectly heated nozzles (14) in Be-Cu is used for feeding melt in the conical breakoff sprues (13) with three pinhole gates.

Demolding the spools takes place in such a way that first the conical sprues are separated from the nozzles (Fig. 4.1/38). Next the sprue is punched out the boss boring (Fig. 4.1/39) before the spool itself is finally ejected (Fig. 4.1/40). This ensures that any further work on the spools is eliminated.

Because of the need to stamp out the sprue in the tool and thereby reduce finishing costs it is only possible with this double-cavity tool to use a hot-runner system. A conventional three-plate mold with multicavities and a cold sprue would increase costs to an acceptable level. At the same time the hot-runner system reduces material losses arising from a cold sprue.

On opening, the mold parts that are screwed togeth-er and fixed to the movable bolster move with plates (4) to (8) and plate (2) which is held away from lever (23), away from the mold half, which is attached to the bolsters on the fixed half on the machine. In this way the sprue runner (13) is drawn out of plate (2). In the same way the conical sprue is separated from the heat conducting nozzles. During this opening movement, the jaws (9, 10), which are carried on the plate (5) by strips (3) and (4) are forced apart by the angled guiding bolsters (11), so that the film spools are released around its circumference. At the same time, the nose of lever (19) reaches and moves in the groove cut in plate (1), which is then drawn over rail (18) and against the force of springs (27), together with the sprue puncher (16).

This pushes the conical sprue with the sprue spider out of the spool hub boring until the end of lever (19) is lifted out of the groove by raising peg (20) on the wedge (21). Further opening movement of the mold causes the wedge (25) to reach the bolt (24), which then lifts lever (23), thus freeing plate (2) which functions as a lower support. The driver bolt (27) finally opens the tool completely by drawing plate (2) from the mold cavity. To finish off by moving the ejector (28) against the power of spring (29) over the ejector plates (30) and the ejector sleeves (32), the spools are pushed off the cores (12).

Fig. 4.1/38   Fig. 4.1/39   Fig. 4.1/40

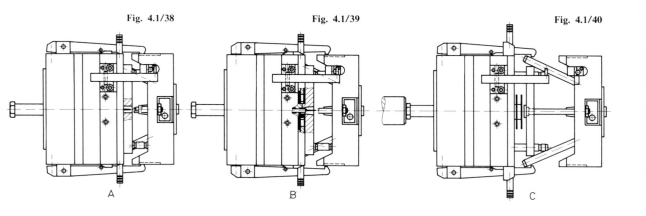

A   B   C

Figs. 4.1/38 to 4.1/40. Function of the mold during demolding.
Fig. 4.1/38. Sprue tears away.
Fig. 4.1/39. Sprue is punched from spool.
Fig. 4.1/40. Spool is ejected.

Example 50. Mold for a lid with three screw threads

The lid is a rotation-symmetrical molding with three screw threads. Threads *I* and *II* are of the same pitch and can be formed by a single screw thread core. The material employed is polyacetal. The size of the order (total number of units to be produced) is small.

The mold (Figs. 4.1/41 to 4.1/45) is of simple design. The external shape of the molding is formed by an insert (*c*), which is housed in mold plate (*b*) and secured against rotating. This insert is heated via a ring channel (heating/cooling system *A*). Screw thread *III* is formed by two splits (*d*). The part is injected through a diaphragm gate (*e*). The internal shape of the lid is obtained from a main core (*f*), which is housed in the mold plate (*p*) and is secured against rotating. This core is heated via an internal tube (heating/cooling system *B*). Its effectiveness is increased by the soldered-on spiral (*g*). The screw threads *I* and *II* are formed by a single screw core (*h*). Because of the low number of moldings required, the mold has been designed for the screw core (*h*) to be unscrewed outside the tool. The screw core is inserted into an ejector ring (*i*) and is retained by three sprung pressure catches (*k*). It is located by the cone (*l*) of the fixed core (*f*). The mold opens in parting plane *I-I* positively assisted by two latches (*m*). The thread-forming splits (*d*) are moved outward by this action. After a distance of 18 mm the latches are released through the control strips (*n*) and the mold opens in the main parting plane *II-II*. By actuation of the machine ejector the thread core (*h*) is pushed in the direction of the fixed half by three ejector pins (*o*) and the ejector ring (*i*) for a distance of 90 mm (height of the molding plus 10 mm). During the movement the screw thread core strips the molding off the fixed core (*f*). Then the molding, with the screw core (*h*), is pulled manually out of the stripping ring (*i*) without any danger of damaging the fixed main core (*f*). Unscrewing takes place outside the mold with the aid of an unscrewing device. To shorten the cycle time, several screw cores are employed. While one part is being unscrewed, the next molding is being produced.

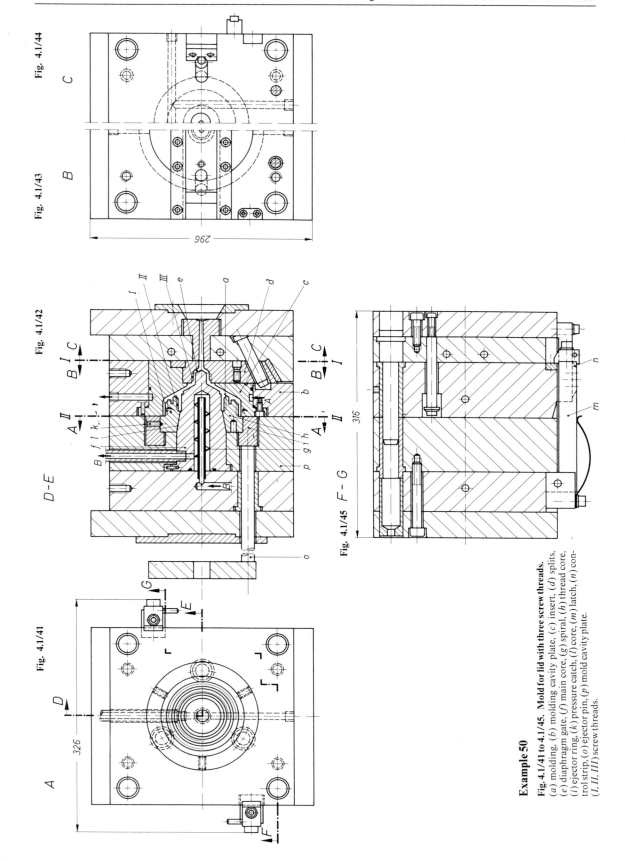

Fig. 4.1/44

Fig. 4.1/43

Fig. 4.1/42

Fig. 4.1/41

Fig. 4.1/45

Example 50

Fig. 4.1/41 to 4.1/45. Mold for lid with three screw threads.
(*a*) molding, (*b*) molding cavity plate, (*c*) insert, (*d*) splits,
(*e*) diaphragm gate, (*f*) main core, (*g*) spiral, (*h*) thread core,
(*i*) ejector ring, (*k*) pressure catch, (*l*) core, (*m*) latch, (*n*) control strip, (*o*) ejector pin, (*p*) mold cavity plate.
(*I, II, III*) screw threads.

Example 51. Four-impression mold for fountain pen barrel

The tool (Figs. 4.1/46 to 4.1/50) has been designed to mold the transparent front end of a fountain pen barrel onto the barrel proper, which has been produced in opaque material by a previous process. The gluing of two parts, often subject to shortcomings, is eliminated by this operation. The opaque barrels are pushed onto the pins (b) when the mold is open, the splits are out and the stripper plate (a) has been withdrawn. When the mold closes, the splits (c) shut. They are guided on T-section rails (d), which are bolted together with the cone body (e) in the direction of the cone areas. While advancing along these guides the splits open. Circular inserts (f, g) are bolted together with the splits, into which the external shape of the fountain pen barrel has been cut. It does not pay to have these shapes cut into the splits themselves, as precise location of the fountain pen bores to their outside diameter would be jeopardized due to hardening distortion. The inserts can be produced with sufficient concentric accuracy. There is also no difficulty in drilling the inserts in the splits and the nozzle flange together with the utmost precision because the bore is the same. However, this accuracy will only be preserved if the splits are not hardened. Fitting the splits with inserts is also useful because the latter can easily be replaced when worn. If, however, the splits themselves are tooled, the complete unit will have to be reproduced.

To avoid sink marks on the inside of the transparent tube, which could cause leaks around the piston, a ring gate is used. The articles are broken off the sprue after molding and faced-off on a lathe. In order that the barrels for molding on can be pushed onto the pins (b), the ejector plate (a) has to be withdrawn first. However, the ejector plate has been pushed forward by the ejector bar (h), which has contacted the machine stop when the mold is fully open. So that barrels can be inserted even when the mold is fully open, the following ejector arrangement has been made.

The ejector plate (a) has been connected to the two plates (k, l) and three dowels (i). A slotted sliding lock (m) (Fig. 4.1/50) through which the ejector bolt (h) is guided slides in a space between the two plates (k, l). The locking mechanism (m) is pushed into a reset in the ejector bar by a spring, thereby solidly interlocking the bar (h) with the ejector plates (k, l, a). When the ejector bar (h) contacts the machine stop, the ejector plate is pushed forward. At the completion of the ejection stroke, the interlock of ejector bar and sliding lock is released by the actuating rod (n). The ejector plates (k, l, a) are pushed back into their resting position by the strong spring (o). Despite the pushed-forward ejector bar (h), the ejector plate (a) is in the rear position. When the mold closes, the ejector is pushed back into its resting position by spring (p) and the interlock (m) snaps back into the recess in the ejector bar.

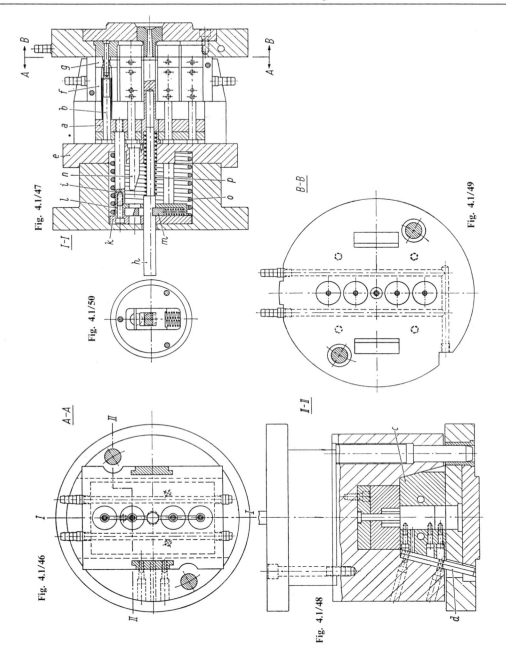

Fig. 4.1/47

I-I

B-B

Fig. 4.1/49

Fig. 4.1/50

A-A

Fig. 4.1/46

I-I

Fig. 4.1/48

Example 51

Figs. 4.1/46 to 4.1/50. Four-impression mold for molding on the transparent part of fountain pen barrels.
(*a*) Stripper plate, (*b*) pin, (*c*) splits, (*d*) T-shaped rail, (*e*) core body, (*f*, *g*) insert, (*f*, *g*) T-shaped bar, (*h*) ejector bar, (*i*) rod, (*k*, *l*) ejector plates, (*m*) interlock slide, (*n*) actuating rod, (*o*, *p*) spring.

Example 52. Injection molding tool for moldings of several parting lines vertical to the direction of opening

If parts with shallow undercuts are to be produced in a multi-impression tool, the mold will have to be furnished with multiple splits. The mold in Figs. 4.1/51 to 4.1/54 contains four little boxes, open at two sides, which have depressions in all four sides. The outer side walls of these boxes are bordered by four splits (a), which have been set into the base plates (b) with a conical collar. Into each one of these splits two guide dowels (c) are firmly pressed, which are at a slightly less acute angle than the cone splits. The cone angle of the splits must in any event remain outside the self-blocking limit of 10° (approx.), otherwise the splits will release only with difficulty when pushed forward, as they will be pressed against the conical contact area with great force by the injection pressure. It is also recommended to keep the angle of the dowels small enough that the splits can lodge behind the moldings sufficiently far during that part of their travel during which the moldings are still retained on the pins (d) to be able to demold them during their further advance. Push-back pins are not required for the ejector plate (e), as the angle dowels of the splits return the ejector plate when the mold closes.

Efficient pin cooling is achieved by equipping the cores with larger bores, into which the cooling water is fed via brass tubes (f). The cores are sealed with a plastic round cord ring (g). A triangular groove having the same area as the diameter of the core accommodates the O-ring, which is pressed into the groove to form a watertight seal when the retaining bolts for the core are tightened. The cooling water is supplied to the brass tube through a bore in the base plate (h). A second channel, connected to the cooling bore of the core, serves as return. The nozzle flange (i) is either cooled by a surrouding channel or a ring groove, as is the case here. The pressed-in ring (k) is sealed by the rubber ring (l).

The feed channels for the mold cavities are led to the four corners of the boxes. They have been milled into the core-retaining plate (m) and reach tight up to the box. The runner serving the cavity, the sprue itself, is situated on the ejector side and is cut into the splits approximately 1 mm deep.

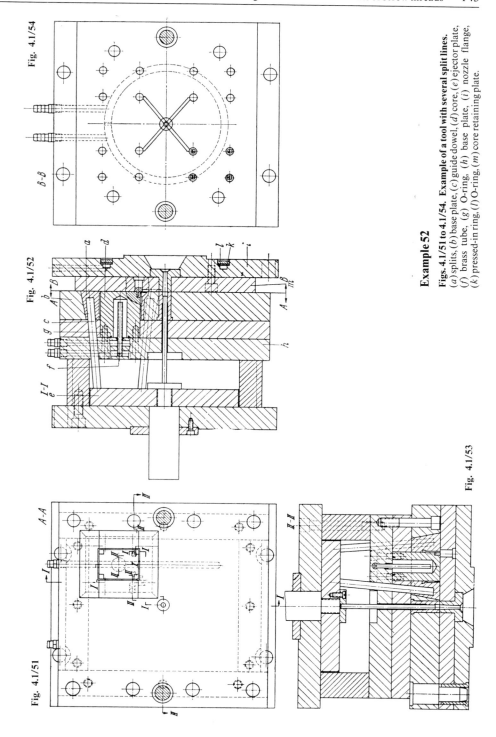

Fig. 4.1/54

Fig. 4.1/52

Fig. 4.1/51

Fig. 4.1/53

Example 52

Figs. 4.1/51 to 4.1/54. Example of a tool with several split lines.
(*a*) splits, (*b*) base plate, (*c*) guide dowel, (*d*) core, (*e*) ejector plate, (*f*) brass tube, (*g*) O-ring, (*h*) base plate, (*i*) nozzle flange, (*k*) pressed-in ring, (*l*) O-ring, (*m*) core retaining plate.

Example 53. Mold for pump housing and pump piston

The pump housing (a) and the pump piston (b) are rotationally symmetrical parts of different external undercuts and lateral perforations. The molding material is polyacetal. Due to the similarity of both moldings a mold has been constructed (Figs. 4.1/55 to 4.1/63) in which the piston (b) and the pump housing (a) can be produced simultaneously. The external shapes of the moldings are produced exclusively by two splits, which are divided into the splits carriers (c) and splits inserts (d). When damaged, only the inserts will have to be replaced. Various lateral perforations are molded by the cores (e) housed in the splits inserts.

Due to the height of the splits (146 mm, danger of tilting) and to achieve a large supporting cross section for the shut-off face (f), the angle dowels (g) have been mounted outside the splits' shut-off area. The splits are guided by the stripper plate (h). A cylinder secured on one side (i) in the splits-separating area additionally serves to locae the splits. The spure (k) and the center gating (l) for the moldings are also located in the splits-separating area. The internal shape-giving cores (n, o) are housed in the sandwich plate (m). They are secured against rotating by peeling. The core tips (p) are screwed in because of their liability to damage; they are replaceable.

The bushes (q) are wearing parts; they are fitted in the stripper plate (h). To ensure the reliability of the stripping operation, the bushes (q) and the fixed cores (n, o) are cone shaped.

The mold is temperated by five independent systems:

System A + B: Tempering of the fixed core (n, o) by cascade tempering.

System C + D: Tempering of the splits inserts (d) takes place via several channels linked together into area temperating systems.

System E: Tempering of the bolster plate (r) is by two parallel channels connected to each other by a cross channel.

The mold opens along the split line I-I. The splits are moved out simultaneously by the angle dowels (g), thereby releasing the external undercuts and lateral perforations. A relative movement of the splits-guiding stripper plate (h) to the sandwich plate (m) is prevented by the coupling of the mold ejector bar (v) with the hydraulic ejector on the machine (not shown). Demolding takes place through the operation of the hydraulic ejector on the machine and the stripping of the moldings by the two stripping bushes (q) in the stripper plate (h). Discharge of the moldings is initially ensured by an additional air spray (s).

The tempering cascades are of varying diameter due to the different core diameters. The supply line for the tempering medium should be equal to or larger in diameter than the remaining residual diameter for the returning tempering medium. This is a function of the heat convection constant α, which obtains its highest values at high flow speeds (turbulence). The cascade temperation in the core (n) illustrates that the exit of small-bore supply lines should be bias cut to enlarge the cross-sectional area.

With the pump piston the stripping bush contacts the piston skirt (t), whose external diameter is considerably larger than the piston diameter itself. This could have led to severe deformation when demolding the piston. To create a more favorable flow of forces, nonfunctional ribs were placed at (u).

Example 53 (right)

Figs. 4.1/55 to 4.1/63. Mold for pump housing and pump piston.
(a) Pump housing, (b) pump piston, (c) splits carrier, (d) splits inserts, (e) cores, (f) supporting cross section for the shut-off face, (g) angle dowels, (h) stripper plate, (i) cylinder, (k) sprue, (l) gate, (m) sandwich plate, (n, o) antiturning secured cores, (p) core tip, (q) bush, (r) bolster plate, (s) connection for air spray, (t) piston skirt, (u) rib, (v) ejector bar on mold, (x) illustrated without splits, (y) shown offset by 45°.

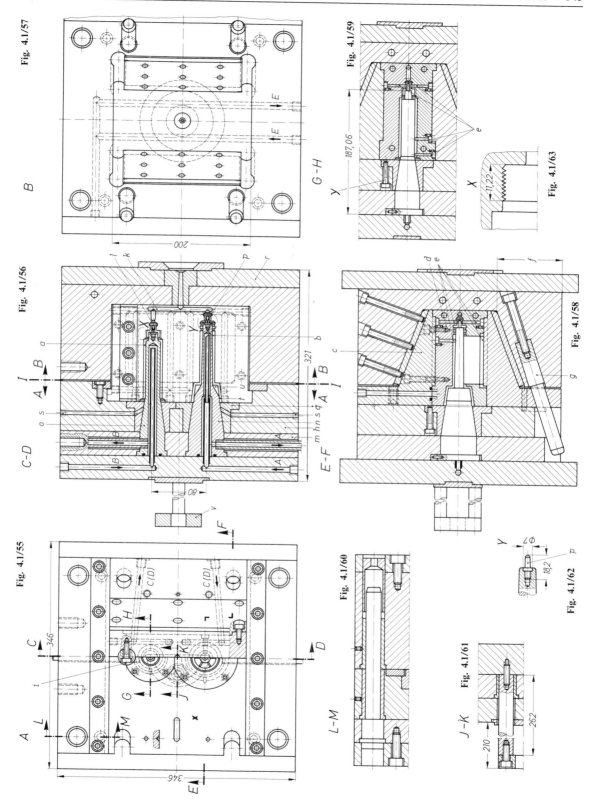

Fig. 4.1/57

Fig. 4.1/56

Fig. 4.1/55

Fig. 4.1/59

Fig. 4.1/63

Fig. 4.1/58

Fig. 4.1/60

Fig. 4.1/61

Fig. 4.1/62

Example 54. Facility for adjusting the lead-nut thread to compensate for wear

The thread cores of unscrewing tools often run in so-called lead nuts. These are subject to wear, which in turn leads to the situation where the cores no longer reach their predetermined position precisely. This results in flash on the moldings. Usually new threaded parts are required, costing money and time-consuming fitting work.

The detailed illustration in Figs. 4.1/64 to 4.1/66 shows a way around these costs and for reducing the down time of the tool considerably. In the case presented this probability was put into practice on a mul-

ti-impression mold for tapped dowels. The lead thread has been housed in the lead nuts (3), which are clamped between the mold plates (1, 2) in the split line. During the opening of the mold they are retained by the yoke (6). The axial position is determined by the machined-on flange and the central one by the toothed segment (4). The serrations on the circumference of the lead nut (3) (70 × 75, DIN 5481) contain 48 teeth. At a lead thread pitch of 12 mm an axial displacement of the bolt of 0.25 mm can be obtained if the lead nut is advanced by one tooth.

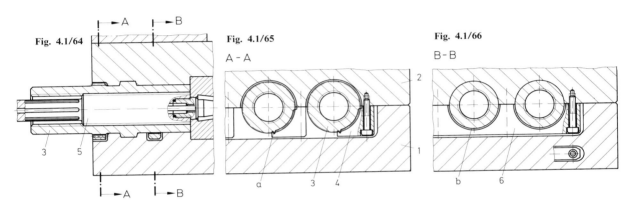

Example 54

Figs. 4.1/64 to 4.1/66. Facility for adjusting the lead nut thread to compensate for wear.
(1, 2) Mold plate; (3) lead nut; (4) tooth segment; (5) core spindle; (6) yoke;
(a) serration, 70 × 75, DIN 5481, 48 teeth; (b) 0.03 to 0.05 mm play.

4.2   Molding with Undivided External Threads

Example 55. Injection molding tool for battery closures with undivided external thread and sealing cone

The external thread and the sealing cone of battery closures are usually molded in splits tools, leaving a fine parting line seam.

If it has been specified that no parting line seam at all be visible, thread and sealing cone will have to be demolded by unscrewing. Figures 4.2/1 to 4.2/5 show such a tool designed as an eight-impression mold. Its construction and operation are described below:

To avoid an externally visible gate, an easily severed pin gate is situated inside the closure. The construction and operation of such molds have been described repeatedly. The external thread and the sealing cone of the closures are produced in the threaded sleeves (a). These are carried in bronze guide cartridges (b), which have the same screw pitch as the bat-

tery closures. The threaded sleeves are provided with gear teeth on the other side, where they are in mesh with the central pinion (c). This pinion is driven by a central spindle (d), with a screw thread of low pitch, by the opening and closing movement of the mold. When opening, the mold drives the sleeves (a) anticlockwise, and clockwise when closing. The closures grip the cores (e) sufficiently tightly through shrinkage during the unscrewing process, so that they remain stationary. The shape of the molding also ensures that it does not turn.

As soon as the threads have been released, the ejector pins (f) push against the clamping cover (g) and the closures are ejected by the ejector pins (h).

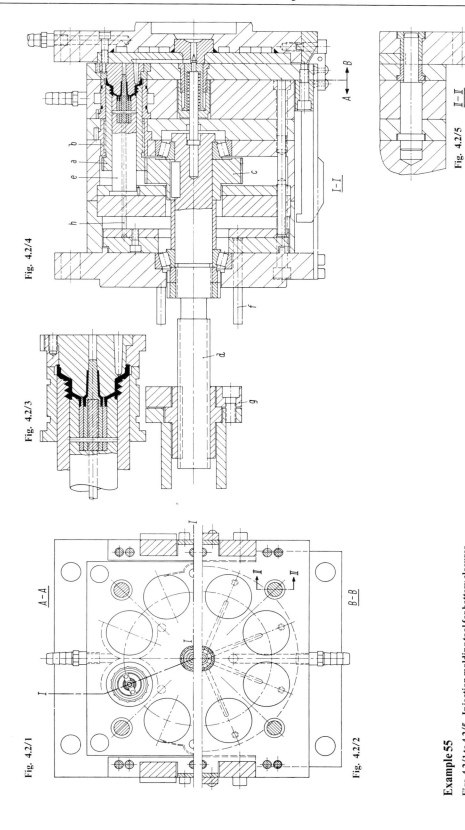

Fig. 4.2/4

Fig. 4.2/3

Fig. 4.2/5

I–I

I–II

A–A

B–B

Fig. 4.2/1

Fig. 4.2/2

Example 55

Figs. 4.2/1 to 4.2/5. Injection molding tool for battery closures.
(*a*) Thread sleeves, (*b*) guide cartridges, (*c*) pinion, (*d*) screw spindle, (*e*) cores, (*f*, *h*) ejector pins, (*g*) clamping cover.

Example 56. Injection molding tool for a Polypropylene container with a screw thread neck

This is the description of a three-plate injection molding tool for a polypropylene container that does not show any splits markings. Sprue and ejectors are designed for automatic operation.

Specifications

When the development of a household utensil had been concluded, the task of constructing a tool for the container of the utensil arose. A molding part drawing served as basis on which the geometrical shape, dimensions, permissible tolerances and polypropylene as material had been firmly established. The container concerned is an extensively rotation-symmetrical quality molding with relatively high demands on the surface, on dimensional accuracy (conditioned by assembly and operation) and on the mechanical loading of the polypropylene.

The injection molding tool has been constructed according to the principles of special-machinery design; in other words, according to a methodically assembled structural diagram of the constructive activities, (see ref. Chapter 1.2).

Number of cavities and selection of the injection molding machine

The technical feasibilities and the injection molding machines available for the production led to the stipulation for a single-impression tool. That was the reason why no research took place into finding the most economical number of cavities.

Mold lay-out

The design shown in Figs. 4.2/6 to 4.2/9 is a three-plate tool (split line *I* and *II*) with stripper plate (*p*). When the injection molding machine opens, the mold is forced to open in plane *I* by the latches (*b*). Through this movement the two thread-forming splits (*c*) are pulled out of the thread by the angle dowels (*d*), thereby demolding the screw-thread-conditioned undercuts. The latches are guided by the cam strips (*e*) and they release after 28 mm of travel. Mold plate (*f*) stops. The mold opens in the main parting plane (*II*). The bolster plate is guided by four additional guide bolts (*g*). This bolster plate is secured by end-stops (*h*).

Sprue system

The molding material is fed into the cavity via sprue, cold channel runners and gates (*i*). Despite the relatively high wall thickness of the molding (3.5 mm) attempts were successfully made to inject via four shear-gates (*i*) of 1.8 mm diameter each. The gates are sheared off during mold opening in parting plane (*I*). The gates are in the upper mold cavity. The choice of this gating system and its position offer the following advantages:

– Central gating. This ensures even mold filling.
– Position of the gate is outside the functional and visual areas of the molding.
– Feasibility of automatic production without post-molding operation of sprue trimming.

Tempering system

Uniform mold tempering to 50°C is necessary to satisfy the quality requirements. Effective tempering had also been asked for in order to achieve short cycle times. The mold was therefore equipped with five tempering systems *TS*, independent of one another:

System 1:   Temperation of the main core (*k*)
System 2:   Temperation of the jacket (matrix) (*l*)
System 3 + 4: Temperation of the thread-forming splits (*c*)
System 5:   Temperation of the contour-forming sprue bush (*m*) and the auxiliary core (*n*). The tempering effectiveness on the auxiliary core is increased by a copper bolt (*o*).

Ejector systems

The molding is stripped off the core by the stripper plate (*p*). This movement is effected by a hydraulically operated ejector on the machine. The stroke of the ejector plate (*p*) is limited by two bolts (*q*) with registers (*r*). The molding bead (*s*) in the ejector plate could cause it to stick on demolding. For that reason the air spray (*t*) has been provided, which is charged with compressed air at the end of the ejection process. This ensures certain discharge of the moldings. The sprue is pushed out of the retaining claw and ejected by a separate ejector system (*u*). The movement of this ejector is actuated by contact of the bolt head (*v*). This bolt serves to couple the machine's ejector with the ejector plate (*w*).

Materials used in the mold

The following materials were chosen for the individual parts of the mold:

– Shape-giving inserts: case-hardening steel, case hardened
– Mold plate and stripper plate: nitrited annealed steel
– Mold structures: tool steel, unalloyed

Shrinkage prediction

Shrinkage was assumed for this polypropylene molding to be 1.6%. Checks have confirmed that this shrinkage assumption was correct.

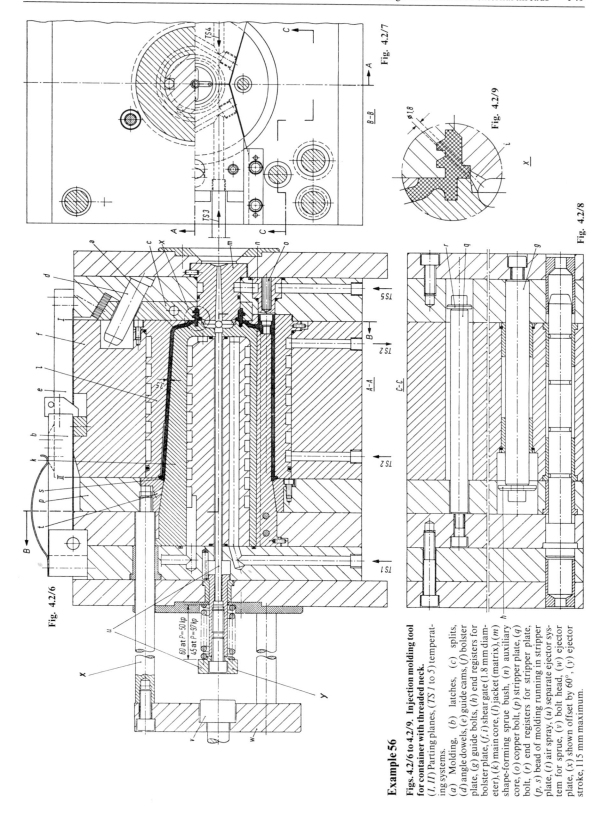

Fig. 4.2/7

Fig. 4.2/9

Fig. 4.2/8

Fig. 4.2/6

Example 56

Figs. 4.2/6 to 4.2/9. Injection molding tool for container with threaded neck.

(*I, II*) Parting planes, (*TS 1* to *5*) temperating systems.

(*a*) Molding, (*b*) latches, (*c*) splits, (*d*) angle dowels, (*e*) guide cams, (*f*) bolster plate, (*g*) guide bolts, (*h*) end registers for bolster plate, (*f, i*) shear gate (1.8 mm diameter), (*k*) main core, (*l*) jacket (matrix), (*m*) shape-forming sprue bush, (*n*) auxiliary core, (*o*) copper bolt, (*p*) stripper plate, (*q*) bolt, (*r*) end registers for stripper plate, (*p, s*) bead of molding running in stripper plate, (*t*) air spray, (*u*) separate ejector system for sprue, (*v*) bolt head, (*w*) ejector plate, (*x*) shown offset by 60°, (*y*) ejector stroke, 115 mm maximum.

Summary

PP containers completely fulfilling the quality requirements are being produced with the aid of the mold shown in Figs. 4.2/6 to 4.2/9. Before starting with the designing, the alternative of forming the complete outer shape of the container by splits was considered. However, this principle of construction has decided disadvantages over the one chosen. In general the construction principle applied has the following advantages:

– No separating markings caused by the splits occur within the visual area of the container, because the splits have been limited to the height of the screw thread. Also, the jacket (*l*) can be tempered by a circulating medium.

– Four shear gates are adequate for producing this molding. By choosing this gating system costs for the subsequent degating are eliminated.

– The ejector system has been designed to allow for automatic production.

Example 57. Injection molding tool for lid with two threaded studs

In Figs. 4.2/10 to 4.2/17 a mold for the production of lids (*a*) is illustrated. The lid consists of an almost rectangular plate with three pipelike studs (*b*) on its underside and two threaded studs (*c*) on the topside. The distances between the studs (*c*) differ lengthwise as well as across the lid (refer to view in direction *Y*). Talcum-filled polypropylene is the molding material.

Due to the shape of the molding it was necessary to execute the tool as a single-impression mold. The two threaded studs (*c*) are molded by two splits (*d*), which are mounted on a moving carrier plate (*e*) on the fixed half. The tapered sprue (*f*) is led through the carrier plate (*e*) into the splits separation plane and gated via a rectangle (*g*) into the molding. The external shape of the lid is formed by a fixed mold insert (*h*) and the bores are formed through three cores (*k*) retained in the mold clamping plate (*i*) of the moving half.

Mold temperation is by three tempering systems, which are independent of one another.

System A:
Temperating of the mold insert (*h*) in the moving half. For reasons of effectiveness the temperating medium is recirculated in this insert several times. Supply and return lines for the medium connect to the sandwich plate (*l*) (section *G–H*). O-rings (*m*) serve as seals.

System B + C:
Temperating of the two splits (*d*). The temperating

medium is redirected several times in this case also. Supply and return is via extension ferrules (*n*).

The lid is demolded by the following sequence of operations:

– To ease the movement of the splits, the mold is opened for about 0.2 mm in the main parting plane (*I–I*) via two spring-loaded bolts (*o*) (section *J–K*) to start with.

– Then the mold opens in parting plane (*II–II*) by four latches (*p*). The two splits (*d*) are guided to the outside via four angle dowels (*q*) simultaneously, releasing the screw threads (*c*) and the rectangular gate (*g*) in the splits separation.

– The latches (*p*) are released by the cam rails (*r*) after 28 mm travel. The mold then opens in the main parting plane (*I–I*). The stroke of the splits carrier plate (*e*) is restricted by two bolts with registers (*s*) (section *L–M*).

– Once the mold is fully open the ejector arrangement (*t*) is pushed forward by the hydraulic ejector on the machine (not shown) and the molding is ejected by a group of ejector pins (*u*) and ejector sleeves (*v*).

– The ejector in the mold and the ejector on the machine are firmly coupled together. The group of ejectors (*t*) is returned to the starting position by the hydraulic machine ejector when ejection has taken place. This operation is controlled by limit switches on the machine's ejector.

Example 57 (right side)

Figs. 4.2/10 to 4.2/17. Mold for lid with two screw-threaded studs.
(*a*) Lid (injection molding), (*b*) pipelike stud on the molding, (*c*) screw-thread stud on the injection molding, (*d*) splits, (*e*) carrier plate, (*f*) tapered sprue, (*g*) gate, (*h*) mold insert, (*i*) mold clamping plate, (*k*) core, (*l*) sandwich plate, (*m*) O-rings, (*n*) extension ferrules, (*o*) spring-loaded bolt, (*p*) latches, (*q*) angle dowels, (*r*) cam rails, (*s*) register bolts, (*t*) group of ejectors, (*u*) ejector pins, (*r*) ejector sleeve, (*w*) construction position top.

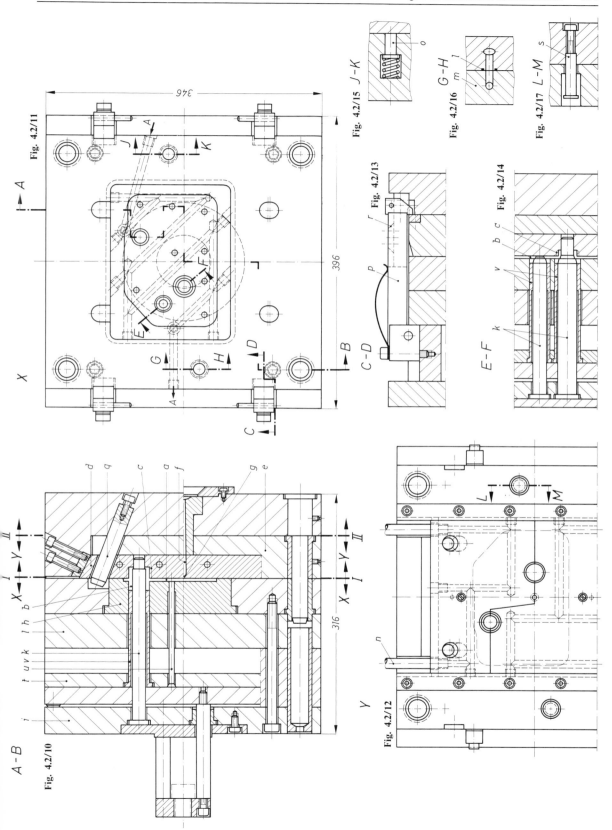

Fig. 4.2/11

Fig. 4.2/10

Fig. 4.2/12

Fig. 4.2/13

Fig. 4.2/14

Fig. 4.2/15   J-K

Fig. 4.2/16   G-H

Fig. 4.2/17   L-M

4.3   Moldings with Internal Undercuts

Example 58. Injection molding tool for curved pourer

Complicated demolding processes result from curved, hollow moldings, such as a pourer, for example. This particular one can be fitted with a retaining nut to be screwed onto the threaded pouring part of a bottle for drinks. The production of this molding calls for a curved core, requiring a stripper plate describing an arc that is matched to the contour of the molding.

The molding illustrated in Figs. 4.3/1 to 4.3/4 serves to describe the production of this type of pourer. For demolding the tool opens in the parting-line plane. To start with, the molding remains in the moving mold cavity of the mold plate (3), with the core carrier (9) being moved along the guide dowel (24) by springs (26) until stopped by the discs (27) following the opening movement. On further opening, demolding takes place from this mold cavity half as well and the freed molding rests on core (13) between the mold halves. When the hinged latch (32) housed in the retainer (31) reaches the pressure bolt (20), the latter through its downward movement rotates the ejector plate (10) against the force of spring (23) down around the fulcrum pin (11). The molding is pulled off the core. Due to the conical shape of the core an ejector stroke of approximately 5 mm suffices to drop the molding off the core.

With the mold closing movement the latch (32) moves into the traverse (31) via pressure bolt (20) without shifting the pressure bolt. When the injection unit moves back, it pulls the sprue out of the mold. The sprue must be removed from the machine nozzle after each shot in the version described here.

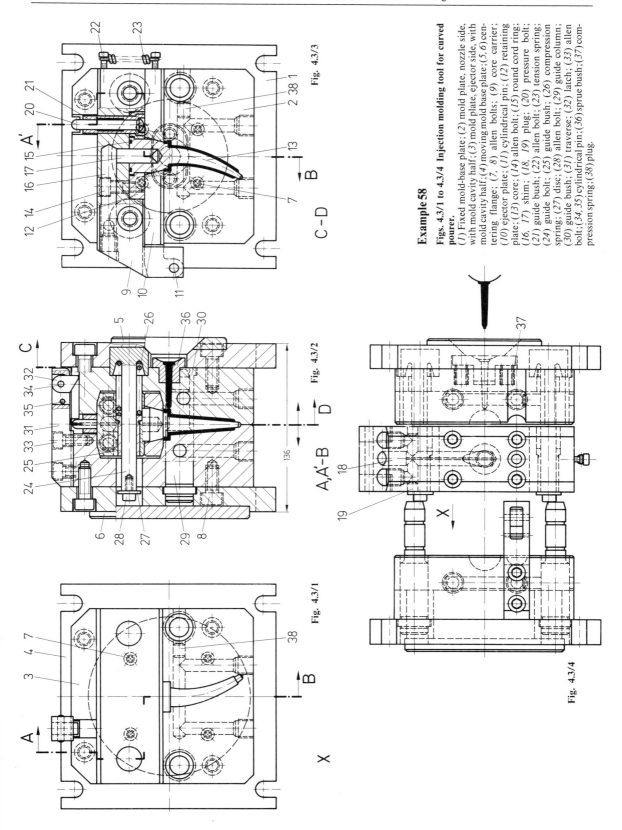

Example 58

Figs. 4.3/1 to 4.3/4 Injection molding tool for curved pourer.

(1) Fixed mold-base plate; (2) mold plate, nozzle side, with mold cavity half; (3) mold plate, ejector side, with mold cavity half; (4) moving mold base plate; (5, 6) centering flange; (7, 8) allen bolts; (9) core carrier; (10) ejector plate; (11) cylindrical pin; (12) retaining plate; (13) core; (14) allen bolt; (15) round cord ring; (16, 17) shim; (18, 19) plug; (20) pressure bolt; (21) guide bush; (22) allen bolt; (23) tension spring; (24) guide bolt; (25) guide bush; (26) compression spring; (27) disc; (28) allen bolt; (29) guide column; (30) guide bush; (31) traverse; (32) latch; (33) allen bolt; (34, 35) cylindrical pin; (36) sprue bush; (37) compression spring; (38) plug.

Fig. 4.3/1
Fig. 4.3/2
Fig. 4.3/3
Fig. 4.3/4

Example 59. Mold for parts with inner peripheral grooves

Examples of injection moldings with inner peripheral grooves are frames for spectacles and magnifying glasses. Grooves may also be required for instrument housings that have to be glazed. In standard practice, two solutions exist for designing articles of this nature.

- The part of the mold in which the groove is formed (actually a plate) is divided into four compartments that are withdrawn in pairs with the aid of toggles.
- While it is still capable of plastic deformation, the injection molding is forced out of the compartment of the mold in which the groove is formed.

The first case demands a mold of complicated design and therefore incurs high costs. Owing to the toggles and pivots required, it is susceptible to breakdown. In the second case, the rough treatment of the molding may cause slight deformation of the groove. This entails high reject quotas, or, if correction is possible, considerable expense. The design shown in Figs. 4.3/5 to 4.3/7 overcomes both disadvantages. It represents a two-cavity mold for the production of magnifying glass frames. At four points on the outside of the molding, there are small lenticular parts: three on the frame itself and one on the handle. They allow a grip for the ejector pins (*11*) and are subsequently removed.

There is a spiral slot on the plate (*19*) in which the peripheral groove is formed. The slotted plate is secured in the center by two bolts with hemispherical heads. A helical spring is thus formed. When the molding is ejected, this spring is withdrawn from the perforated groove without causing any deformation.

A mold of this comparatively simple design has given good results in practice.

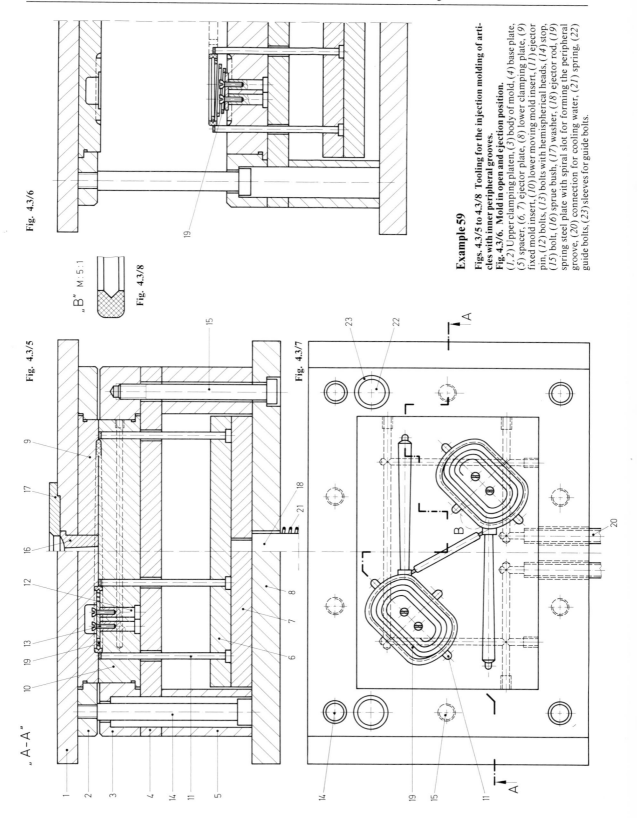

Fig. 4.3/6

"B" M: 5:1

Fig. 4.3/8

Fig. 4.3/5

Fig. 4.3/7

"A–A"

Example 59

Figs. 4.3/5 to 4.3/8 Tooling for the injection molding of articles with inner peripheral grooves.

Fig. 4.3/6. Mold in open and ejection position.

(1, 2) Upper clamping platen, (3) body of mold, (4) base plate, (5) spacer, (6, 7) ejector plate, (8) lower clamping plate, (9) fixed mold insert, (10) lower moving mold insert, (11) ejector pin, (12) bolts, (13) bolts with hemispherical heads, (14) stop, (15) bolt, (16) sprue bush, (17) washer, (18) ejector rod, (19) spring steel plate with spiral slot for forming the peripheral groove, (20) connection for cooling water, (21) spring, (22) guide bolts, (23) sleeves for guide bolts.

Example 60. Four-impression cold runner injection molding tool for screw caps

For the screw cap (Figs. 4.3/9 and 4.3/10) a fully automatic operating mold had to be constructed. It had been requested that the point of injection should lie centrally in a depression in the surface of the cap. The flutings on the circumference of the cap (Fig. 4.3/10) aid gripping; at the same time they can serve as an antirotation lock when unscrewing the threaded core. Two parting planes are required to achieve automatic degating of the molding.

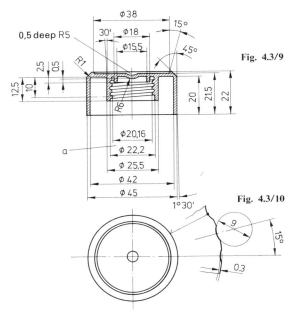

Fig. 4.3/9

Fig. 4.3/10

Figs. 4.3/9 and 4.3/10. Design and dimensions of the screw cap. (*a*) Transition radii, 0.5 RD22, DIN 168.

The main function of the mold construction (Figs. 4.3/11 to 4.3/17) is the injection of the molding material into parting plane *I*, the result of the arrangement of the unscrewing unit (*1*) on the fixed machine platten. Therefore an injection molding machine with the injection unit perpendicular to the clamping unit axis has to be employed. The four screw cap cores (*3*) are symmetrically placed around the driving pinion (*4*). Injection takes place at point (*2*) into parting plane *I*. From there the sprue channel disappears into the center of the mold where it divides into an H-like sprue runner (*5*), so that the flow length to all mold cavities is the same. With such long sprue channels as experienced here it is customary to extend them beyond the

gates. The pockets thus formed collect the advancing cold slugs of material during injection, thereby keeping them away from the cavities.

When the cooling time has elapsed, the central pinion (*4*) is driven by the drive shaft (*7*), which is housed in the hollow shaft of the unscrewing unit (*1*). The pinion (*4*) in turn drives the threaded cores (*8*). These alter the lead thread of the screw thread cartridges (*9*), which has the same pitch as the thread in the screw caps and is thus withdrawn. The number of core rotations and the unscrewing speed are adjustable. Once the screw thread has been demolded in this manner, the opening process in split-line *I* starts, as parting plane *II* is still being held shut by the latch. The molding is degated as the sprue is being retained on the moving half by undercuts. The cam rail (*14*) is mounted on the same side. This releases the latch (*13*) at that point in time when the register pin (*15*) makes contact and restricts the opening of parting plane *I*. Parting plane *II* is now allowed to open. During this process the claw (*17*) knocks against the stripper plate (*18*), taking this along with it and simultaneously ejecting the screw caps until the claw (*17*) is being lifted by the cam rail (*19*), thereby releasing plate (*18*). At the same time the registers of the guide pins (*20*) make contact and restrict the travel of plate (*18*). With continued mold opening the ejector bar (*21*) contacts the stop on the machine, so that the sprue is ejected by the ejector plates and the ejector pins (*22*). The distance pieces (*23*) ensure the rigidity of the mold within the area of this ejection mechanism.

Special care must be taken with mold cooling. Particular heat concentrations occur on the inner cores, onto which the melt is injected, and between the screw thread and the outside wall of the screw caps. Therefore, within the unscrewing core (*8*) a fixed core (*10*) is made use of which incorporates cooling channels divided by a baffle. The four cores are switched in series. Further cooling is accommodated in the ring core (*3, 11*). The cooling, effective on both sides of the unscrewing core (*8*), ensures the latter's trouble-free operation and avoids seizure of the metallic sliding surfaces. Further cooling is provided in the mold cavity (*12*) and in the moving mold plate (*16*). These cooling channels (*24*) ensure fast cooling of the sprue. Design care must furthermore be taken with the geared part of the mold. The recesses for the pinions must not be made any bigger than is absolutely necessary to keep weakening of the mold within bounds.

After the conclusion of the opening movement, the screw cores (*8*) are screwed forward again. Ejector plates and ejector pins (*22*) are returned to their starting positions again by a spring on the ejector bar (*21*).

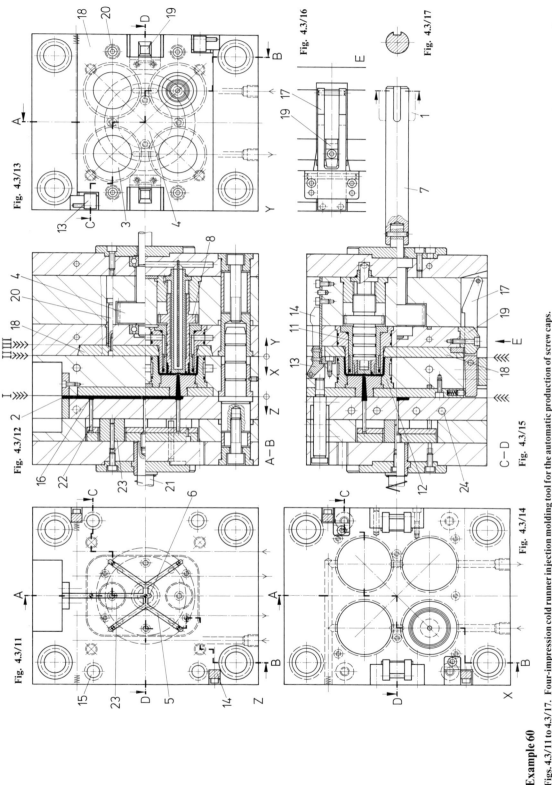

Example 60

Figs. 4.3/11 to 4.3/17. Four-impression cold runner injection molding tool for the automatic production of screw caps.
(*1*) Unscrewing unit, (*2*) injection point into the mold, (*3*) screw cap core, (*4*) drive pinion, (*5*) H-shaped sprue, (*6*) extended runners, (*7*) drive shaft, (*8*) screw core, (*9*) screw thread cartridge, (*10*) fixed core with through-flow cooling, (*11*) external core with cooling, (*12*) mold cavity insert, (*13*) latch, (*14*) cam rail, (*15*) register pin, (*16*) undercuts for the sprue system, (*17*) claw, (*18*) stripper plate, (*19*) guide cam, (*20*) guide bolt with register, (*21*) ejector bar, (*22*) ejector pin, (*23*) distance piece, (*24*) cooling channels, (*I, II, III*) parting planes.

Example 61. Injection mold for an ABS spectacle frame

The shape of a frame for protective goggles (Fig. 4.3/18) poses demolding problems for the mold designer. Undercuts on injection moldings are usually formed in the mold by means of jaws or slides. The production of the undercuts needed for subsequently fitting the lenses involves considerable design problems, especially since these slides would not lie at right angles to the direction of demolding. The present design of an injection mold for making a spectacle frame (Figs. 4.3/19 and 4.3/20) shows how, by using collapsible cores, the problem can be simplified. These cores can be obtained as standard mold units.

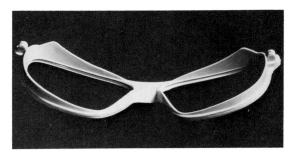

Fig. 4.3/18. Spectacle frame for protective goggles made of ABS (® Teluran, made by BASF AG, Ludwigshafen).

The cavity for the frame is formed by plates 5 and 6 (Fig. 4.3/19). The lens surrounds (undercuts) are formed by the core segment sleeves (*11*) of the collapsible cores (*9*) (Fig. 4.3/21). When the mold opens (Fig. 4.3/20) the moving mold half (*2*) is separated from the fixed mold half (*1*) by the platen (*4*), the frame being demolded from the cavity plate (*5*). During this operation, the pneumatic ram (*15*) of the cylinder (*14*) is subjected to compressed air via a control valve and the air inlet (*L*) of the cylinder, so that the parting surface between the guide plate (*13*) and support plate (*8*) remains closed.

After a certain opening stroke the air control valve is switched over and the compressed air is passed via an air inlet (*R*) to the second piston surface of the double-acting pneumatic cylinder. This causes the platen (*7*) and the collapsible core elements (*9*) in it to move in the opposite direction together with the support plate (*8*). Hence the center cores (*10*) of the collapsible cores (*9*), which move outward, are held fast by the sliding blocks (*16*) of the guide plate (*13*) and so they slide out of the core segment sleeves (*11*).

Before the opening stroke is limited by the pneumatic piston, the stop bolts (*18*) in the guide plate (*13*) carry along the outer sleeve (*12*) of the collapsible core elements via the fastening flanges (*17*) after a certain distance has been covered. This causes the cores of the segment sleeves (*11*) to drop toward the inside. The undercuts (lens surrounds) of the spectacle frame are thus exposed (Fig. 4.3/22).

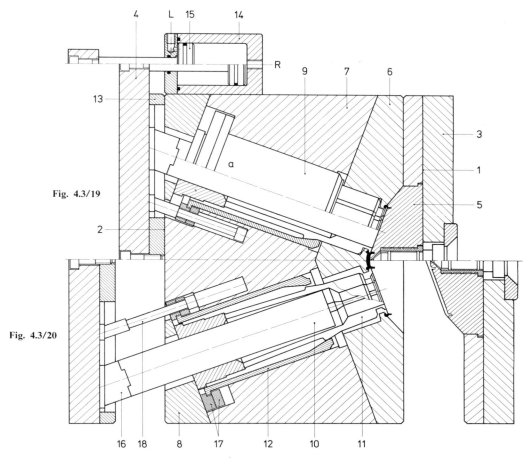

Fig. 4.3/19

Fig. 4.3/20

Example 61

Figs. 4.3/19 and 4.3/20. Injection mold for the spectacle frame.
(*1*) fixed mold half, (*2*) moving mold half, (*3*) fixed platen, (*4*) moving platen, (*5*) cavity plate, (*6*) cavity plate, (*7*) platen, (*8*) support plate (*9*) collapsible core element, (*10*) center core, (*11*) segment sleeve, (*12*) outer sleeve, (*13*) guide plate, (*14*) pneumatic cylinder, (*15*) double-acting pneumatic piston, (*16*) sliding block, (*17*) fastening flange, (*18*) stop bolt.
View top: Closed mold.
View bottom: Mold opened with collapsed core, demolding is possible.
a: Collapsible core; *L, R:* air inlet holes.

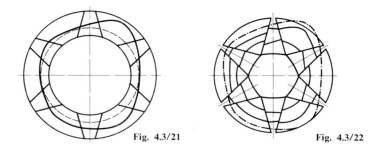

Fig. 4.3/21   Fig. 4.3/22

Figs. 4.3/21 and 4.3/22. Contour of spectacles near the lens surrounds on the core disc.
Fig. 4.3/21. Contour on the core during molding.
Fig. 4.3/22. Contour on the core during demolding.

Example 62. Injection mold for a slotted articulated piston from glass fibre reinforced thermoplastic polyester

For the injection molding of a slotted articulated piston (Fig. 4.3/23) from glass fiber reinforced thermoplastic polyester, which has a ball end and ball socket, a mold has been developed (Figs. 4.3/24 to 4.2/27) whose special feature is the core movements. These core movements are mechanically controlled by the opening movement of the mold. Specific opening positions must occur in the movement sequence before core pulling takes place.

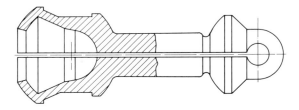

Fig. 4.3/23. Slotted articulated piston.

The molding is completely divided above the hole running through the ball end for assembly and demolding reasons. This division is achieved with two core sheets (7, 8), which are connected by pins to the mold halves (5, 6), which are let into the mold plates (3, 4). The ball end bore is produced with the core (11), which centers under the core sheet (7) via a spring-loaded core (16), which acts as counter bearing. The ball socket is formed by the core head (13), which sits on a rod. When the mold opens, the rod (14) moves

with the core head (13) at half the speed of the mold half fixed to the moving machine plate in the direction of the opening movement. The axis of the core head (13) is therefore always in the middle of the free space between the two mold halves because of the symmetry of the load-bearing lever system (15). As long as the bolt (23) has not reached the top end of the long hole in the rod head (14), the core head is not pulled out of the molded part. To enable the molding to follow the mold opening movement of the core head (13), the core (11) with the ejector sleeve (12) is moved synchronously to core head (13) through the rods (18) at the side of the mold, which are linked to the core holding plate (17) with the strap (19). Here, the centering cone of the core (11) is supported by the countercore (16), which is under spring load. When the mold has opened sufficiently, the bolt (14) pulls out the core head (13) from the molding via the rods (15). During this operation, the ball socket halves of the counter piston are pushed apart. The molding is held fast by the cores (11, 16) during this process. Afterward, the ejector sleeve (12) and sprue ejector rod (22) are pushed forward via the ejector rod (20) and the ejector plate (21), thereby separating the sprue from the molding.

The gating system was designed so that the molding is gated from two sides through a sprue gate and a cold runner immediately behind it, thereby achieving symmetrical mold filling. Central gating of the molding under the ball bore would be connected with high internal stresses in this part of the cross section. The consequence could be that this cross section breaks during demolding or subsequent assembly of the molding (bending open).

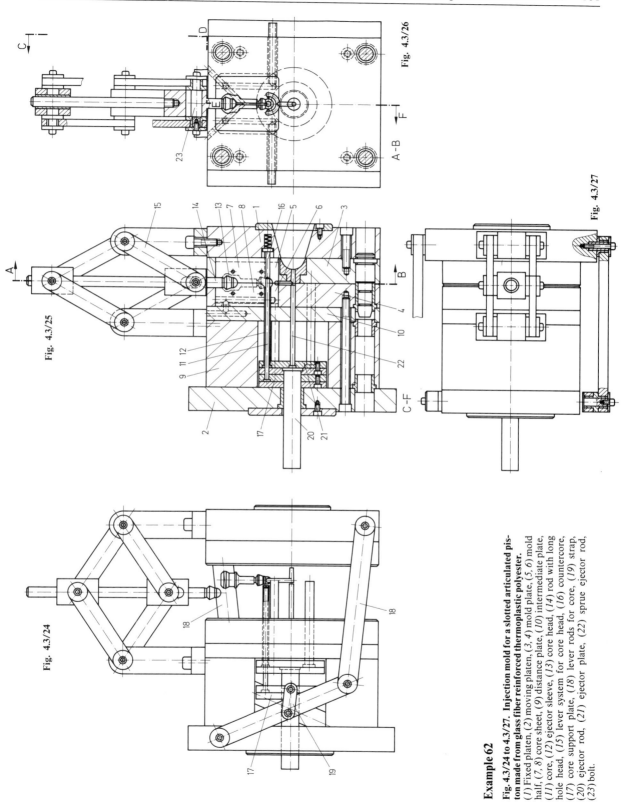

Fig. 4.3/24   Fig. 4.3/25   Fig. 4.3/26   Fig. 4.3/27

Example 62

Fig. 4.3/24 to 4.3/27. Injection mold for a slotted articulated piston made from glass fiber reinforced thermoplastic polyester.
(*1*) Fixed platen, (*2*) moving platen, (*3, 4*) mold plate, (*5, 6*) mold half, (*7, 8*) core sheet, (*9*) distance plate, (*10*) intermediate plate, (*11*) core, (*12*) ejector sleeve, (*13*) core head, (*14*) rod with long hole head, (*15*) lever system for core head, (*16*) countercore, (*17*) core support plate, (*18*) lever rods for core, (*19*) strap, (*20*) ejector rod, (*21*) ejector plate, (*22*) sprue ejector rod, (*23*) bolt.

4.4   Moldings with Internal Screw Threads

Example 63. Gating inside screw caps

The injection point on moldings, i.e., the spot where the melt from the sprue runner enters the mold cavity, should be as unobtrusive as possible, so that the looks of the molding are not spoiled. By injecting the material through a small hole on the circumference of the article a clean, automatic degating can be obtained on mold opening. However, this pinpoint gate is visible on the finished molding and can be a nuisance. One therefore endeavors to hide the gate as much as possible. One possibility is offered by pin gating inside a screw cap. This method of injecting also has the great advantage that the melt enters the cavity centrally without leaving any weld lines on the molding, which is of importance particularly with larger screw caps and lids. The 16-impression mold illustrated in Figs. 4.4/1 to 4.4/3 distinguishes itself by the particularly suitable design of the degating feature, which no longer requires a sandwich plate for stripping the sprue from the nozzle side on the mold. A much more reliable method for ejecting the sprue star can be employed with this design.

To achieve as short a gate for degating as possible, the parting plane for the star-shaped sprue is slightly conical. This results in a saving of sprue weight and a considerable shortening of the main sprue (sprue bush). Space is also gained for a reliably operating sprue-ejector system.

The screw-thread inserts (a) are fixed in this mold. The runners to the gates of the individual moldings are arranged centrally to the inserts. The 16 inserts are retained between the cover plate (b) and the insert plate (c), which are bolted together. A cooling water channel that runs around the inserts ensures intensive cooling of the screw-thread cores.

The bolted together plates (b, c) slide on the guide strips (d) for a distance of 90 mm during opening. These guide strips are connected with mold flange (e) on the nozzle half of the tool. During this travel of 90 mm the moving half mold fixing plate (f) is rigidly locked with plates (b) and (c) through the leaf springs (g) and the latches (h), so that the tool opens first in the parting plane of the sprue. Plates (b) and (c) are retained by the registers on the guide strips (d) after 90 mm of travel. Simultaneously, the latches (h) are released through the unlatching pins (i) running up onto protuberances on guide strips (d), thereby allowing the tool to open now in the main parting plane between plates (k) and (b).

The gates are severed from the moldings during the initial opening of the mold in the sprue plane as follows: After injection the gates are retained by severe undercuts in the retaining pins (l) in the fixed mold half, so that they are pulled out of the screw thread inserts (a), severing from the molding at their weakest point. Spring (o) pressing against the ejector sleeve (m) causes the ejector sleeve (m) and the retaining pin (n) to follow the initial opening stroke after a certain distance, limited by register, which approximately corresponds to the length of the gate runners.

Thus the gates to the individual moldings are pulled out of the channels. On further opening of the sprue plane the individual runners, centrally retained by the retaining pin (n) are pulled from the undercuts in the retaining pins (l). At the same time the main sprue is

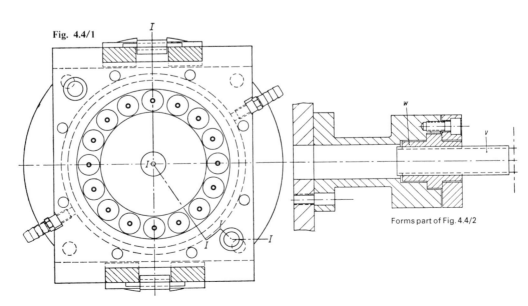

Fig. 4.4/1

Forms part of Fig. 4.4/2

released from sprue bush (p). After an opening stroke of 90 mm of the sprue plane, plates (b) and (c) are stopped by registers on the guide strips (d). The moving half of the tool, starting with plate (k) to the mold fixing plate (f), however, continues opening, carrying retaining pin (n) along by its collar. Now the retaining pin (n) is forced to release from the undercut in the center sprue. Caused by the resistance of the pull, the ejector sleeve (m) is moved back slightly against the force of spring (o). At that moment, when the pin releases from the undercut of the sprue, the ejector sleeve (m) shoots forward, ejecting the star-shaped sprue. A ring groove in the mold fixing plate (e) on the nozzle side provides cooling for the main sprue and the runners.

The external shapes of the screw caps have been cut into the spindles (q), whose external thread corresponds to the pitch of the screw caps. These spindles run in bronze leadnuts (r), which are housed in plate (s). They are secured by flats against rotating. These spindles are in mesh with the central drive gear (u) via pinions (t), which are keyed onto them. When the mold opens, gear wheel (u) is turned by the central drive shaft (v), which slides in a fixed nut (w).

On the initial mold opening in the sprue plane by 90 mm, the screw caps are unscrewed from the fixed screw thread cores (a). The distance of 90 mm corresponds precisely to the number of turns in the screw cap. As plates (b) and (c) are latched to the ejector plate of the moving half, the screw caps are not released from their cavities. After a little more than the 90 mm opening stroke the ejector pins (x), pushed back by springs (y), contact the sprung registers (z). During the continuing opening movement of the tool exceeding the 90 mm, the registers (z) are pushed back until the spring force overcomes the adhesion of the moldings in the cavities. Should the adhesion be greater than the spring force, the registers (z) will eventually bottom toward the end of the mold opening movement. During the remaining movement the ejector pins (x) advance relative to the spindles (q), releasing the moldings from their cavities in any case. The springs (j) can then relax and the screw caps are forcefully ejected from their cavities.

Example 63

Figs. 4.4/1 to 4.4/3. Sixteen-impression mold for tube closures, internally center gated. The point of injection is not visible externally.
(a) Screw core inserts, (b) cover plate, (c) insert plate, (d) guide strips, (e) mold flange, (f) mold clamping plate, (g) leaf springs, (h) latches, (i) delatching pins, (j) springs, (k) plate, (l) retaining pins, (m) ejector sleeve, (n) retaining pin, (o) spring, (p) bush, (q) spindles, (r) lead nut, (s) plate, (t) pinion, (u) gear wheel, (v) drive shaft, (w) nut, (x) ejector pins, (y) springs, (z) registers (for reasons of clarity the drive shaft (v) has been separated at the dotted line).

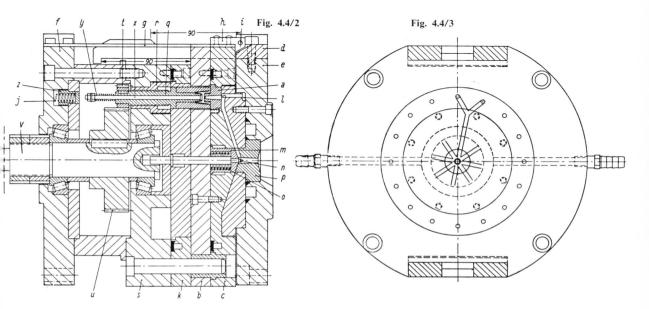

Fig. 4.4/2   Fig. 4.4/3

Example 64. Single-impression injection molding tool for larger moldings with internal screw thread

Comparison of rack drive vs. shaft drive

The toothed rack has the advantage over the shaft drive described (e.g., example 63) in that it is easier to produce, as the toothcutting operation can be more easily carried out than the milling of a screw threaded spindle of shallow pitch. However, it must be noted that worm gears, which are required for such tools in any case, can only transfer forces by meshing point contact, so that they are incapable of transmitting large forces. Therefore a shaft drive is better for the large forces required in multi-impression tools with screw thread cores, as with this type of transmission torque is transmitted through area contact of the wedge profile of the shaft or by line contact in the case of the gear wheels.

For single impression tools, and the same also applies to multi-impression molds with screw thread cores of small diameters, however, the *toothed rack drive* of the cores offers considerable advantages. Without reserve, even up to six in-line cores can be driven by one toothed rack. It is even possible to demold two rows of cores if two worm-geared shafts are provided. In principle therefore it is necessary that the moldings are arranged in line for toothed-rack drives in multi-impression tools whereas a shaft drive requires the moldings to be arranged in a circle, so that the screw cores can be operated by a pinion positioned centrally in the mold.

Single-rack mold

In the following the construction method of a single-impression mold is described, in which thermos flask cups are produced with approximately three internal turns of thread. To avoid waste, the mold has been designed as an antechamber tool, injecting externally in the center of the cup (Figs. 4.4/4 and 4.4/6). Intensive cooling of the external jacket and the core, enabling fast cooling, is necessary so that it is possible to keep on injecting through the small hole in the antechamber without the material freezing at that point. As the cup is produced in high density PE, which like all types of PE is most suitable for injecting through the antechamber, and as the wall thickness of the cup is relatively thin, injection can take place so fast that freezing at the point of injection is prevented. The antechamber is kept warm internally by a heat-conducting cone in copper or beryllium bronze, as described repeatedly already. The antechamber pin gate is sufficiently supported to degate the point of injection when sprue break occurs.

Insert (a) on the fixed half, giving shape to the cup exterior, is centered in the stripper plate (b) by a cone, eliminating the need for guide dowels. The stripper plate is pushed forward by four push rods (d) when the ejector plate (c) contacts the register. The threaded part must have been demolded first, though. The screw threaded part consists of the screw thread sleeve (e), which is carried on core (f). This core is water cooled internally by well-known methods. The thread sleeve has a worm gear thread that is meshed with the worm gear shaft (g). It also possesses a lead thread in its tail end, whose pitch is identical to that of the molding. The screw thread sleeve is carried on its outside in the lead nut (h) for once and in the bearing bush (i) at the other end. The transmission of the worm gear should advisedly be chosen as 1:1, as the degree of effectiveness is at its most favorable at that ratio for worm gear transmission.

The worm gear shaft (g) is carried in tapered roller bearings (k), and the worm gear drive is filled with grease to eliminate lubrication during operation. The worm gear shaft (g) is connected with the toothed rack (l) via a transmission gear. This transmission must be so matched that the screw threaded parts are demolded and the molding itself can be stripped off the core (f) by the stripper plate (b) during the sequence "mold opening" to "contacting the machine stop."

When mold closing, the screw thread sleeve must move forward till it contacts the screw core to ensure that no gap remains at that position, which could fill with material. Care must therefore be taken that no damage can occur within the gearing, should the machine have been wrongly set. This is achieved by not fitting a key between the gear (m) and the worm shaft (g), and simply tightening bolt (n) to obtain frictional contact. This friction/coupling would slip in case of wrong setting.

A further protection for the gapless contact of the screw thread sleeve (e) against the collar of core (f) is the set of disc springs (o) between the mold clamping plate of the fixed half and the rack (l). As this spring relaxes when the sleeve (e) butts up against the collar of core (f) in the closed mold position, it can safely be assumed that there will be no gap in that place and therefore injection molding material is prevented from intruding.

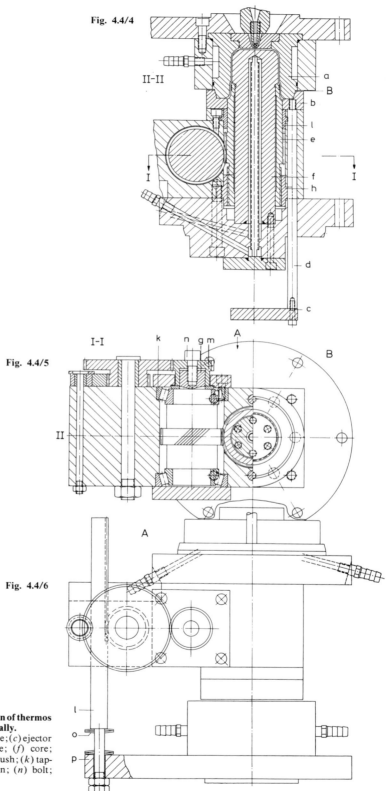

Fig. 4.4/4

Fig. 4.4/5

Fig. 4.4/6

Example 64

Figs. 4.4/4 to 4.4/6. Mold for the production of thermos flask cups with three turns of thread internally.
(*a*) Insert, fixed mold half; (*b*) stripper plate; (*c*) ejector plate; (*d*) push rods; (*e*) thread sleeve; (*f*) core; (*g*) worm shaft; (*h*) lead nut; (*i*) bearing bush; (*k*) tapered roller bearing; (*l*) rack; (*m*) pinion; (*n*) bolt; (*o*) disc spring; (*p*) clamping plate.

Example 65. Injection molding tool with motorized thread unwinding

Internal threads can be demolded through a coarse threaded spindle that slides in a fixed nut in the machine during the opening sequence. The rotary movement of this spindle, centrally situated in the tool, is transmitted to the pinions of the screw cores, which are arranged in a circle.

The number of screw core rotations is limited, however, with this transmission in the same way as the rack drive or segmental rack drive is restricted, so that only a limited number of turns can be unscrewed. With more than six or seven turns of thread the direct mechanical transmission to the screw cores fails, as the reduction ratio of maximally two to three rotations of the screw spindle to the screw cores becomes excessive. The same applies to the toothed rack drive. The rack would have to become so extended in that case that the space requirements in the machine would be inadequate. If more than six to seven rotations of the screw cores are required for unwinding, then the cores have to be driven by an electric motor.

It is one of the requirements for unwinding internally threaded moldings that the injection molded parts are secured sufficiently against turning in the moving half when the cores are being unscrewed. Should this condition not be fulfilled by the external design (hexagonal profile, ribs, grooving, etc.) it could be obtained by arranging retaining ribs directly around the threaded part itself within the thickness of the walls and to a depth of 0.5 to 1 mm in the molding. This prerequisite must, in other words, be fulfilled by the design of the molding itself.

A further "must" for the mold designer's attention concerns the extreme limits of the screw cores in the closing and opening movement of the mold. These precisely registered end positions of the screw cores determine the injection process as well as the start of mold closing. This in turn means that these end positions of the screw cores must actuate electrical contacts that initiate the injection process or the closing of the mold. It is only possible to time the unscrewing of the screw cores independently of the mold opening through that type of electrical control. This becomes necessary, for instance, when the time for the mold opening sequence is too short for unwinding the cores from multiple turns of thread.

If a great number of turns are to be unwound, it must be taken into consideration that the peripheral speed inside the formed screw thread cannot be randomly high if tearing of the thread surface is to be avoided. The permissible peripheral speed, however, is influenced by a series of factors, which have not all been clearly defined. Conicity of the screw cores, surface roughness of the thread and the polish as well as the influence of the various injection molding materials or their internal lubrications are among the determining factors.

Tests have shown that, surprisingly enough, a previously flawless and mirror polished core, which had then been microscopically roughened by acid, released considerably more easily from the molding than a highly polished core. It seems that the adhesion to the roughened surface is reduced compared with that to the polished surface. Peripheral speeds of 120 to 150 mm/s are obtainable if the above-mentioned conditions are fulfilled.

Determining the drive-motor capacity is still very uncertain. At present data concerning the torque required for unwinding the screw cores are still lacking. However, even these are determined by a series of very influential factors. Apart from the already mentioned ones concerning the speed of core rotation, the mold temperature, the injection pressure and the follow-up pressure time have to be added. For a start, one is forced to guess the motor capacity. However, one must have it clearly in mind that particularly with multi-impression tools and the larger core diameters as well as a greater number of thread turns the required capacity must not be underestimated. Experience shows that capacities of 0.7 to 1.5 kW are required for larger molds if the motor is not to be stalled under unfavorable conditions, such as too long a cooling time, too low a mold temperature, etc. The latest research has for the first time established static friction coefficients as functions of the influential parameters mentioned, on which realistic calculations for the torque required can be based.

An eight-impression injection molding tool for ⅜ in sockets approximately 25 mm long is subsequently described. A ⅜ in thread has a pitch of 19 threads per inch. This means that for unscrewing the 25 mm socket to enable it to be demolded, 19 turns of the screw thread cores are required. At a thread diameter of 17 mm the circumference is $17 \times \pi = 53.3$ mm. If one calculates for 150 mm peripheral speed, then 150/53.3 = 2.86 turns per second = 172 rotations per minute can be envisaged. Therefore 19 turns require 19/2.86 = 7.5 s. Should the injection process take 2 s and the follow-up pressure time take 3 s, then the injection molding process takes $2 + 3 + 15 = 20$ s, provided that the unscrewing of the thread cores starts at the time of mold opening and that the same time is taken for winding the screw cores in as it takes to unwind them. This means that three injection cycles per minute can be run.

As one polystyrene socket weighs approximately 6 g the machine would have to be of a plasticizing capacity of $6 \times 3 \times 8 \times 60 = 8.7$ kg/h. With the space requirements for the injection molding tool–mold height approximately 300 mm–the plasticizing capacity is available anyway.

The pitch circle diameter for eight inserts results from the insert diameter of 110 mm. The screw core

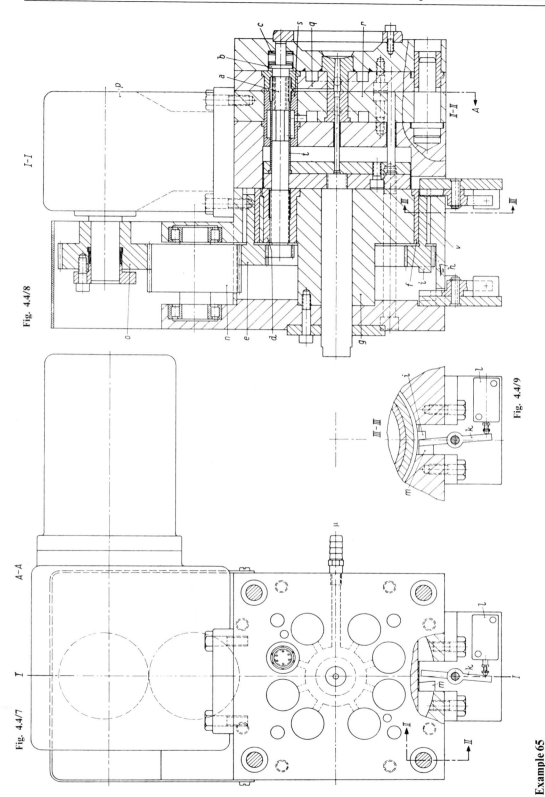

Fig. 4.4/8

Fig. 4.4/9

A–A

Fig. 4.4/7

Example 65

Figs. 4.4/7 to 4.4/9. Eight-impression socket mold with motorized thread unwinding.
(a) Screw cores, (b) cores on the fixed half, (c) set of disc springs, (d) lead nut, (e) planet gear, (f) bronze bearing bush, (g) center core, (h) housing, (i) register, (k) lever, (l) limit switch, (m) fixed register, (n) idler gear, (o) pinion, (p) gear box, (q) plate, (r) insert plate, (s) insert, (t) ejector sleeve, (u) supply air, (v) 6 mm pitch.

pinions are equipped with 20 teeth, modulus 1.25. The common transmission gear therefore is of a 135 mm pitch circle diameter or 108 teeth of modulus 1.25. The transmission ratio is 108/20 = 5.4. As 19 screw core turns are required before the molding can be ejected, 19/5.4 = 3.5 rotations of the gear ring are required. Four complete rotations are executed from register to register of the gear ring, which is equipped with 94 outside teeth, modulus 2 or 188 mm pitch circle diameter. This gear ring is driven by the driving of 44 teeth, modulus 2, via an idler gear. The transmission ratio driveshaft/gear-ring therefore equals 44 to 94 = 1 to 2.14. Hence the drive shaft has to turn at 172/5.4 × 2.14 = 68 rpm if the screw cores are to turn at 172 rpm.

For weight-saving reasons a geared three-phase motor of 2800 rpm is chosen. The geared motor is designed as a brake motor, as it has to operate from register to register, so that there is as little overrun as possible after switching off. It is also recommended to install a two-speed motor. It would then be possible to unscrew the cores at 172 rpm and screw them in at 344 rpm, which would shorten the cycle time by 3.7 s.

The eight-impression socket tool is shown in Figs. 4.4/7 to 4.4/9. The socket is externally ribbed to secure it against rotating and has been designed with a central bead connected to a tunnel gate as injection point. The screw cores (a) push against the fixed half cores (b) in the injection position. The cores at (b) are supported by substantial sets of disc springs (c). This arrangement ensures against flash across the face of the screw cores.

The screw cores (a) possess a lead thread on their driven side, which is of the same pitch as the socket, with which they are carried in a bronze lead nut (d); the screw core is equipped with 20 teeth at the same end (modulus 1.25) and the pinions, arranged in a circle, are in mesh with the gear ring of the planet gear, which has 94 teeth of modulus 2 on the outside.

This planet gear is carried by a bronze bearing bush

(f) on a core (g), centrally arranged in the mold. On its outer circumference the planet gear is meshed with the housing (h) via a screw thread of 6 mm pitch, so that the planet gear travels 6 mm to the right or the left with one complete turn depending on the direction of rotation. This axial displacement of the planet gear suits the following purpose:

As already explained, the planet gear should complete four turns before it contacts the register in either the one or the other direction. To achieve this, the registers (i) have been provided on both faces of the planet gear. They are a little lower than the pitch of the thread, so that they are overrun on the release turn after one rotation of the spur gear. The registers (i) move against levers (k), which actuate limit switches (l) with their opposite ends, resting solidly against supporting stops (m), which are fixed parts of the mold structure. In this manner the requirement has been taken care of that the bilateral end positions of the screw cores must be limited by registers and also that a limit switch must be actuated. It is possible, through these limit switches, to influence the movement program of the machine independent of the final screw core positions in the desired sequence by stoppage or switching. If required, the geared motor can even be switched to the high rotational speed by limit switch actuation. The external teeth of the planet gear mesh with the pinion (o) of the gear box (p) via the idler gear (n).

Plate (q) for the inserts on the fixed half is cooled by a ring channel for cooling water. The cores can only be cooled by compressed air. For this purpose an annular groove has been provided in the insert plate (r), which is supplied with compressed air. Two supply channels lead from this annulus to the hollow spaces in the inserts (s). The air is guided to the axial cooling channels in the cores from these hollow spaces through bores in the ejector sleeves (t). The high speed of the air inside the narrow bores of the cores results in an adequate cooling effect.

Example 66. 16-impression injection molding tool for screw caps

Screw caps for bottles and similar containers are required in vast numbers. If they are produced in HDPE, two advantages are gained. First, the caps will seal without any additional sealing discs, particularly if molded with an internal sealing cone, which enters the bottle mouth. Second, it is possible to demold the thread without having to turn the cores if it has been designed as a rounded thread, as is usually the case with such screw caps. The caps can then simply be stripped off the core, as the moldings are so flexible that the threads can be demolded without shearing off.

Such a 16-impression mold with external pin gating of the screw caps is subsequently discussed (Figs. 4.4/10 to 4.4/14). The central pin gating has the advantage of ensuring concentricity of the screw caps, which is not always the case with eccentric injection on the rim and the resultant uneven shrinkage. The screw caps are of greater strength as well, due to the absence of weld lines. If the injection point is of 0.6 mm diameter, terminating in lettering, for instance, the gating will hardly be visible if correctly designed. One way of making the gate as unobtrusive as possible is by providing some concentric ring pattern around it in the absence of any lettering.

The mold must be constructed as a so-called three-plate tool, i.e., the star-shaped sprue must be safely ejected in one plane and the screw caps in the second one. To eject the sprue reliably is not quite so easy.

The sprue-runner plane lies between plates (*a*) and (*b*). The channels for the runners are machined into plate (*a*). These channels possess an undercut at their terminations, which retains the runners on the fixed half during the first opening of the sprue plane. In that way the molding is degated as the gate is pulled out of the conical bore of insert (*c*). So that the molding is degated flush, the gate runner should terminate in the gate itself at a taper angle of 60°. Thus the gate is severed directly on the molding. To keep pressure

losses as small as possible, the length of the taper bore should not be greater than its diameter; 0.6 mm in the present case.

So that the mold opens in the gate-runner plane first, the insert plate (*b*) is interlocked with the moving half of the mold via latches (*d*) and leaf springs (*e*), which are bolted together with the mold fixing plate (*f*). In this instance the insert plate (*b*) slides on guide strips (*g*), which are bolted together with the mold fixing plate (*h*) of the fixed half.

After an opening distance of 100 mm the insert plate contacts the registers of the guide strips (*g*). In this position the release pins (*i*) have run up onto the 45° incline on the guide strips (*g*), thereby releasing the latches. The mold now opens between plates (*b*) and (*k*). The screw caps, which sit tightly on the cores (*l*), are pulled out of the cavity inserts (*c*). After an opening distance of approximately 50 mm the ejector bolt (*m*) touches the machine stop, pushing the stripper plate (*k*) forward via the ejector star (*n*) and the push rod (*o*), ejecting the screw caps from the core. Inserts (*c*) and cores (*l*) must be well cooled if high outputs are to be obtained. The cores contain a bore of 8 mm, which has to be extended as far as possible toward the injection point. A brass tube of 6.5 mm diameter intrudes into this bore to receive cooling water supplied from channels in plate (*p*). A second channel in plate (*p*) serves as return. O-rings pressing into a triangular groove seal the core inserts (*l*) from plate (*p*).

The cavity inserts (*c*) contain a machined annular groove through which the cooling water is fed. The sealing of insert plate (*b*) is effected by O-rings pressing into a triangular or rectangular groove.

Sharp edges in the transition from cooling water channel to groove have to be well rounded, as otherwise the seals will be destroyed when the inserts are pressed into the insert plate and they will lose their sealing faculty.

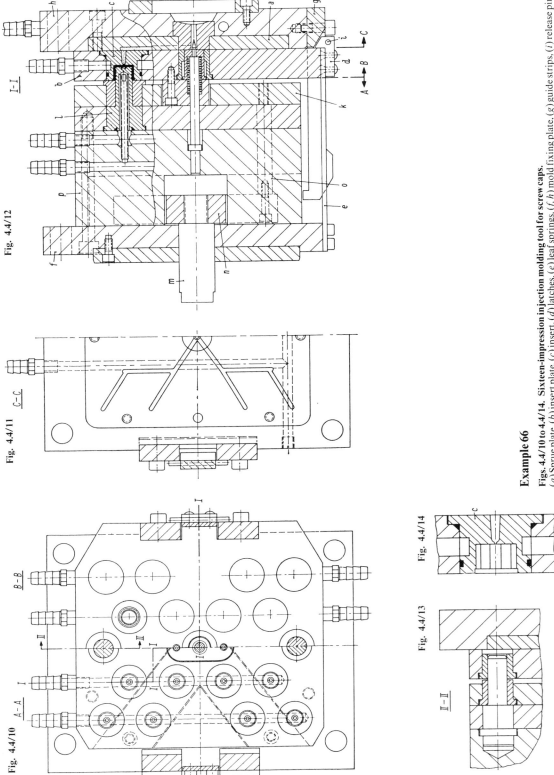

Fig. 4.4/12

Fig. 4.4/11   C-C

Fig. 4.4/10   A-A

Fig. 4.4/14

Fig. 4.4/13

I-I

B-B

II-II

Example 66

Figs. 4.4/10 to 4.4/14.   Sixteen-impression injection molding tool for screw caps.
(a) Sprue plate, (b) insert plate, (c) insert, (d) latches, (e) leaf springs, (f, h) mold fixing plate, (g) guide strips, (i) release pin, (k) stripper plate, (l) core, (m) ejector bolt, (n) ejector star, (o) push rod, (p) ejector plate.

Example 67. Eight-impression injection molding tool for the upper halves of cable clamps

The fully automatic production of the well-known upper parts of cable clamps requires a rather complicated injection molding tool (Fig. 4.4/15). A screw core of approximately seven turns of thread has to be unscrewed and a side split containing the retaining notches has to be pulled out. Furthermore, the mold must sever the gate cleanly from the sprue when opening, so that the eight upper cable clamp moldings discharge separately from the sprue.

Fig. 4.4/15. Upper parts for cable clamps.

To start with, we will examine the considerations leading to the construction of the mold. An injection molding machine of 225 mm mold height and a maximum opening stroke of 170 mm is available. To produce a reliable discharge of the moldings, separated from the sprue, a tubular ejector has been provided over the screw cores with an ejector stroke of 25 mm. The screw cores must therefore be screwed out for a distance of $170 - 25 = 145$ mm. At an 80 mm pitch of the center spindle imparting the rotational movement to the cores, this results in 145 to 80 = 1.8 spindle rotations, which have to be transmitted to the threads, so that approximately seven core rotations take place to the start of ejection. The transmission ratio between the central pinion, which is being turned by the spindle during the opening process, and the core pinion must therefore be 4:1, so that with a stroke of 145 mm $4 \times 1.8 = 7.2$ turns result. Once the diameter for the inserts producing the external shape has been established at 40 mm, a distance of 75 mm for the inserts from the center of the mold results, having taken the space for the four arms of the ejector star between the inserts into consideration.

Arrangement of the ejector

With modulus 1, which is quite adequate for the teeth of the pinions, the ratio of numbers of teeth at a 1 : 4 transmission results in 120 to 30 teeth.

As the ejector tubes have to be arranged in a circle of 150 mm diameter but an unrestricted passage of only 90 mm is available behind the mold fixing plate on the moving half, the ejector mechanism has to be housed within the diameter of 90 mm. This calls for a second ejector plate within the given mold height, and the

connecting bars between the ejector plates must fit outside the large gear wheel. The two tandem ejector plates enlarge the mold height by approximately 50 mm. For this reason those machines are at an advantage that possess as large a free access space behind the mold fixing plate of the moving half as possible to enable ejector bars to be fitted outside the large gear wheel diameter directly up to the ejector stop on the machine. On machines with a central setting nut for adjusting the mold height, which has its own advantages, this would hardly be possible, however, as the setting nut would have to be too large in diameter. These machines ought to have as large a mold height accommodation as possible in order to house the second ejector plate necessary and to account for the large ejection stroke within the mold.

Core splits

Demolding of the internal notches of the clamp is only possible if core splits containing these detends are pulled before ejection takes place. During this splits-pulling operation the cores can simultaneously be unscrewed. As the inserts for the exterior shape of the clamp are arranged in a circle because of the central spur gear drive of the screw cores, these splits have to be withdrawn radially toward eight sides. By contact between the end face of the splits against a sturdy conical ring care must be taken that no injection molding material can enter between the splits contact area and the insert surfaces, so that at that point no flash occurs.

The mold is illustrated in Figs. 4.4/16 to 4.4/18. The mold fixing plate (a) of the fixed half is bolted together with the conical ring (b) for the contact of core splits (c). A cooling water circulation channel has been arranged between the two, as direct cooling of the inserts (d) is hardly possible. A second cooling water circulation channel is housed within the inserts (d) in the insert plate (e).

Insert plate (e) is furnished with radial T-slots, in which the splits (c) with the detend-machining for the upper parts of the clamps slide. These splits are moved through the guide strips (f), which slide in the T-slots of the splits and which have been bolted together with the conical surface of ring (b). In the open position, when not in contact with the moldings, the splits (c) are detained in their position by ball detends (g).

The screw cores (h) are meshed through their gears with the central spur gear (i), their free ends being carried in lead cartridges (k), which are of the same pitch as the cable clamps.

The central spur gear is keyed onto the spindle (l), whose opposite end glides in a nut (m) with a six-turns left-hand thread of 80 mm pitch. This nut is bolted together with a nut carrier (n), which on its opposite side is fastened to the ejector plate (p) of the machine with the divided clamping cover (o). The clamping cover

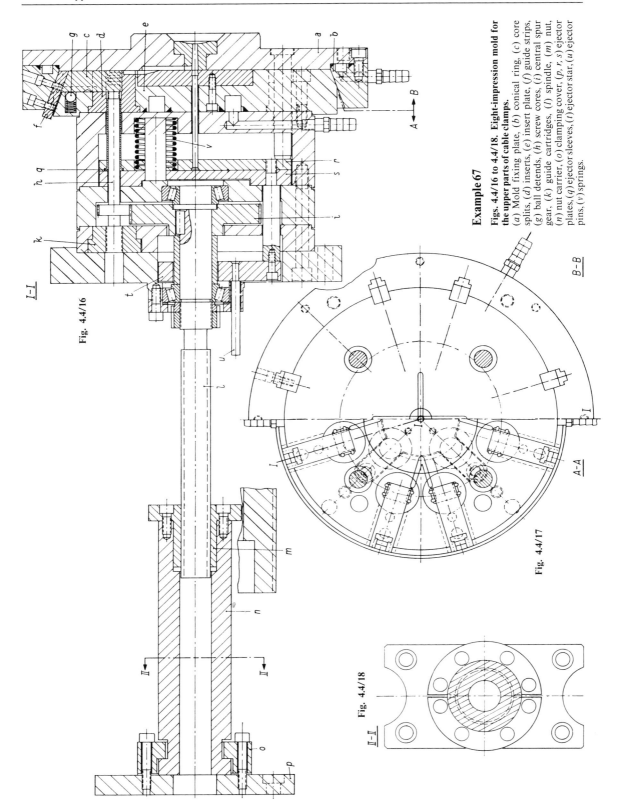

I-I

Fig. 4.4/16

A—B

B—B

Fig. 4.4/17

A—A

II—II

Fig. 4.4/18

Example 67

Figs. 4.4/16 to 4.4/18. Eight-impression mold for the upper parts of cable clamps.

(*a*) Mold fixing plate, (*b*) conical ring, (*c*) core splits, (*d*) inserts, (*e*) insert plate, (*f*) guide strips, (*g*) ball detends, (*h*) screw cores, (*i*) central spur gear, (*k*) guide cartridges, (*l*) spindle, (*m*) nut, (*n*) nut carrier, (*o*) clamping cover, (*p, r, s*) ejector plates, (*q*) ejector sleeves, (*t*) ejector star, (*u*) ejector pins, (*v*) springs.

enables the nut carrier (n) to be turned by hand after the mold has been fitted into the machine, so that the cores (h) contact the splits (c) when the mold is closed to prevent flash from forming at the contact areas.

The eight cores can be matched by remeshing, by one or even several teeth, until all of them are flush with the contacting plane of the splits (c) in their terminal position.

The ejector sleeves (q) slide over the screw cores (h) to a running fit. The collared ends of the sleeves are clamped between the ejector plates (r) and (s). The ejector plates are connected to the ejector star (t) by four push rods. The ejector pins (u), which are riveted in the ejector star (t), push against the nut (m) after an opening stroke of 145 mm, during which the screw

cores have been unwound from the moldings, so that the latter are ejected from the inserts (d) during the remaining opening stroke of 25 mm. To prevent the splits (c) from damaging the ejector sleeves (q) during mold closing, the ejector plates are pushed back by four strong springs (v) at the start of the closing movement. Should there be reservations that for any reason the springs might fail in pushing the ejector sleeves back in time, a microswitch can be fitted into the mold, which only closes when the ejector plates (s) and (r) are fully back. The control wiring for the directional solenoid valve "mold closing" is then fed through this microswitch. Then the mold can close only when the ejectors are in the fully retracted position. Severing of the injection point is achieved by tunnel gating.

Example 68. Injection molding tool for parts with internal threads in the parting plane

There are moldings with internal threads in the split line. These can practically be produced only by cores. Where it is a question of short runs, manually inserted screw cores will probably be employed, for the sake of economy, which will then be demolded by hand. As the cores stick tightly inside the moldings due to shrinkage, they are best unscrewed by a motorized device.

In the subsequently described injection molding tool (Figs. 4.4/19 to 4.4/23) air pistol grips are to be produced in large numbers. The mold therefore has to operate fully automatically. What makes the operation more difficult is the requirement for core pulling coaxial to the bilateral internal threads. These cores are for relatively long bores, apart from which there is also a rectangular perforation for the valve-actuating lever in the parting plane that also has to be demolded via a sliding split within that plane. The simplest way for driving screw cores in the split line is the toothed rack drive, which is employed in this case as well.

The polyamide pistol grip weighs approximately 45 g. The longest core pull coaxially to the thread is 65 mm. Only two grips can be housed in one tool, as the runners would become too long for these rather thick-walled moldings (up to 10 mm in wall thickness).

Screw-on guides for the core splits are required, as the guide length would otherwise need unnecessarily large tiebar spacings on the injection molding machine. The length of the internal thread is limited by the direct rack drive through the total length of the rack, which cannot exceed the mold height. The active length of the rack is reduced by the thickness of the fixed half mounting plate up to the parting plane and by the ejector stroke, if the toothed rack is to remain permanently in mesh with the core pinion.

With the smallest number of teeth on the core pinion being 13 and modulus 1, one core rotation requires a rack length of $13\,\pi = 40.8$ mm. At a distance of the parting plane from the mold mounting plate on the fixed half of 65 mm and a maximum mold height of 360 mm, an active rack length of 280 mm results after deduction of the ejector stroke ($360 - 65 - 15$ mm $= 280$ mm). During this opening stroke the screw core has to be unwound from the molding before it can be ejected. According to this calculation $280/40.8 = 6.9$ turns can be completed.

A $\frac{3}{8}$ in BSP thread has a pitch of 1.34 mm. The length of thread must therefore not be more than $1.34 \times 6.9 = 9.3$ mm. The thread on the right-hand side is of $\frac{3}{4}$ in BSP $= 1.81$ mm pitch. To be able to eject the part, however, altogether 21 mm will have to be unscrewed, as there is a cylindrical step present from the internal diameter of the thread that can only be demolded by unscrewing the core.

Therefore $21/1.81 = 11.6$ rotations are required. The toothed rack length is inadequate for a direct drive; hence the pinion driven by the rack must transmit a greater number of rotations.

At that point a toothed rack, which drives the threaded pinions of $\frac{3}{4}$ in BSP through an idler gear with a small and a large number of teeth, suffices as driving force for both screw cores.

If the small pinion of the idler gear is designed with 13 teeth, modulus 1.5, then for one rotation $13 \times 1.5 \times \pi = 61$ mm are required. The large drive gear therefore has to do $280/61 = 4.6$ turns if the rack is to stay in mesh. The transmission ratio from the large gear wheel to the threaded pinion must then amount to $11.6/4.6 = 2.5$ to 1. A ratio of 60/22 teeth has been chosen, equaling 2.8 : 1.

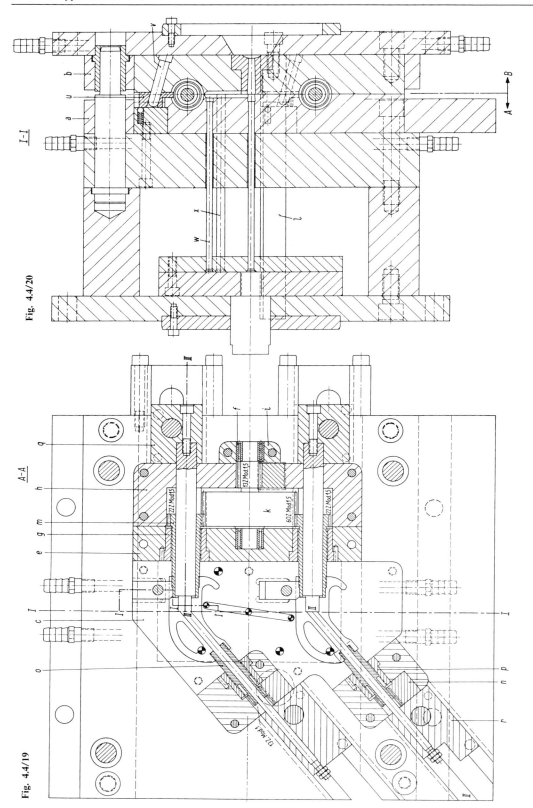

I-I

Fig. 4.4/20

A-A

Fig. 4.4/19

Example 68

Figs. 4.4/19 and 4.4/20. Injection molding tool for two polyamide pistol grips. For explanation of the reference letters refer to Figs. 4.4/21 to 4.4/23.

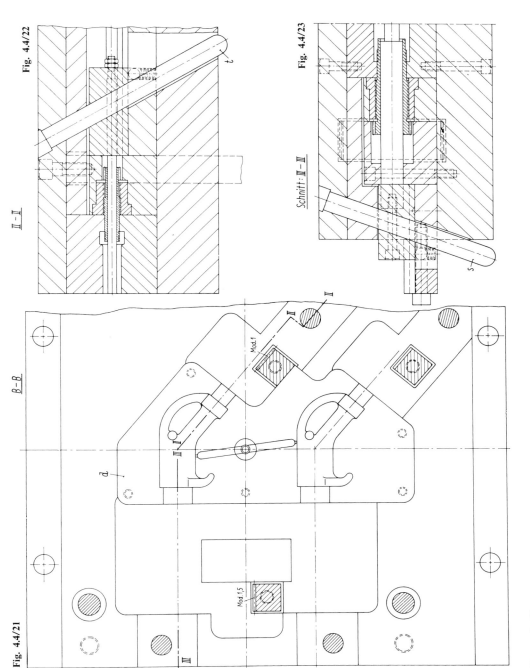

Fig. 4.4/21

Fig. 4.4/22

Fig. 4.4/23

II – II

B – B

Schnitt : III – III

Mod.1

Mod.1,5

Example 68

Figs. 4.4/21 to 4.4/23. Injection molding tool for two polyamide pistol grips, weight of each grip approximately 45 g.
(a) Bolster plate, moving half; (b) bolster plate, fixed half; (c, d) insert plates for cavity contours; (e) insert strip; (f) needle bearing for 60 teeth gear; (g) thread lead cartridges; (h) spur-gear housing; (i) insert for needle bearing; (k) spur gear and pinion; (l) rack modulus 1.5; (m) core sleeve; (n) rack modulus 1.0; (o) threaded pinion; ⅜ in BSP; (p) bronze thread guide cartridges; (q, r, u) splits; (s, t, v) angle dowels; (w) ejector pins; (x) push-back pins.

The mold is shown in Figs. 4.4/19 to 4.4/23. The inserts (c) and (d) for the mold cavities are fitted into the bolster frames (a) of the moving half and (b) of the fixed half. The insert strip (e) also contains a needle bearing (f) for the large gear wheel and screw thread cartridges (g). The bolster plate (a) furthermore accommodates the gear wheel housing (h) and a bearing insert (i) for the second needle bearing (f).

The toothed rack (l) is meshed with the small pinion of the double gear wheel (k), so that on mold opening the core sleeve (m) for the ¾ in BSP thread is rotated anticlockwise, thereby unscrewing the molding.

The two racks (n) drive the ¾ in threaded pinions (o), which are carried in bronze lead-screw cartridges (p) in the same way. Coaxial drilling cores, which are fixed in the splits (q) and (r) to be pulled by the angle dowels (s) and (t) in the usual manner when the mold opens, are led through both screw sleeves (m) and (p).

The upper perforations 17 × 5 mm in the pistol grips are created by the splits (u), which are actuated by the angle dowels (v). All three splits are secured in their terminal position by ball detends. At the end of core pulling the molding is ejected by ejector pins (w), which partially act directly on the molding and partially on the sprue runner. The ejectors are returned by two push-back pins when the mold closes.

Example 69. Eight-impression injection molding tool for screw closure. Mold construction incorporates rack-and-pinion drive by using standardized parts.

In the subsequently described design (Figs. 4.4/24 to 4.4/26) the screw cores are driven by racks that are being operated vertically by hydraulic pistons. The rack propulsion of the screw cores presupposes that hydraulic control equipment for operating the drive cylinders is available on the machine. It will also have to be ascertained that the racks do not butt against the machine bed in their bottom position with the vertical rack propulsion. This becomes critical in particular when many turns of thread are asked for, which necessitates a particularly long stroke of the toothed rack.

There naturally is also a possibility of employing compressed air pistons instead of hydraulic drive pistons with the racks. However, their considerably larger diameter compared with that of hydraulic cylinders–working pressure 12 bar against 175 bar–very often precludes their employment, as not enough space is available.

Rack-stroke-dependent electrical interlock contacts often have to be installed with toothed rack propulsion of screw cores. For instance, mold opening has to be prevented electrically until the screw cores have been unwound from the molding in such cases where core unscrewing takes longer than mold opening. This is essential, so that the ejector pins do not move forward while the screw cores are still in contact with the moldings.

With these tools the employment of standard items is very advantageous, as almost all mold construction parts can be bought-in ready-made, and so only the specific assembly parts have to be manufactured. At the least, a considerable amount of time is saved. The shape forming of the screw closures is effected by divided splits. So that these splits can be restricted in their length (danger of hardening distortion if they are too long) two rows of four screw closures each are provided. The splits (a) are guided by the cover strips (b), which are bolted together with the sandwich plate (c) (standard part). They are being kept shut in the closed position by hardened wedge strips (d) and (e). The housings for the inserts (g) and the grooves for the racks (h) are machined into the mold plates (f) (standard parts). A bronze guide strip absorbs the tooth pressure. The mold plate (f) should expediently be hard chromium plated on the upper surface on which the splits (a) slide. One saves hardening these machined plates, which could easily lead to distortion of internal bores.

The sandwich plate (i) (standard part) contains the housing bores for the lead cartridge inserts (k). The mold clamping plate (l) of the moving half, the rear ejector plate (m) as well as the front ejector plate (n), the distance strips (o) and the locating sleeves (p) are all standard parts.

A particular ejector device (type Ackermann) (q) ensures that the ejector pins (r) jump back immediately when they have pushed the moldings forward in the open mold, thus improving demolding.

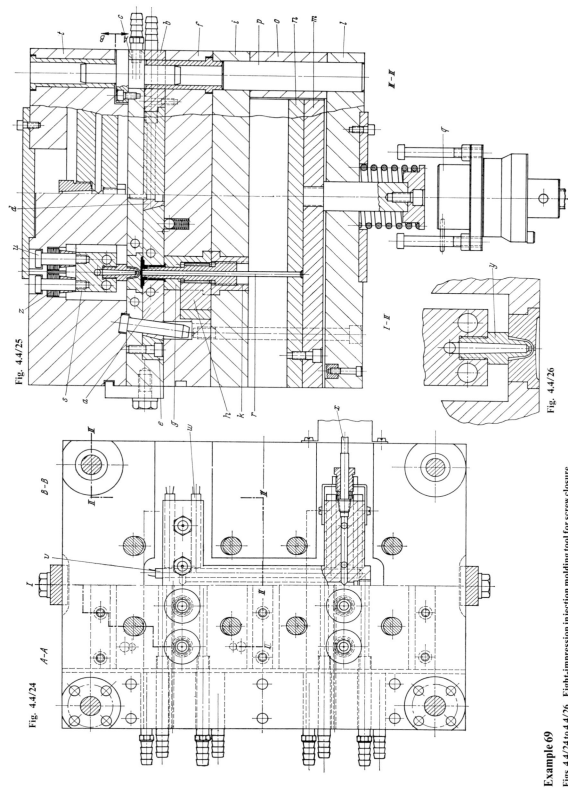

Fig. 4.4/25

Fig. 4.4/26

Fig. 4.4/24

Example 69

Figs. 4.4/24 to 4.4/26. **Eight-impression injection molding tool for screw closure.**
(*a*) Divided splits, (*b*) cover strips, (*c*) sandwich plate, (*d, e*) wedge strips, (*f*) mold plate, (*g*) inserts, (*h*) racks, (*i*) sandwich plate, (*k*) lead cartridge inserts, (*l, t*) mold clamping plates, (*m, n*) ejector plates, (*o*) distance strips, (*p*) locating sleeves, (*q*) ejector device, (*r*) ejector pins, (*s*) hot-runner body, (*u*) bolts, (*v, w*) cartridge heaters, (*x*) thermocouple, (*y*) heated nozzles, (*z*) disc springs.

Example 70. Two-impression injection molding tool for coupling sleeves

The coupling sleeve in Figs. 4.4/27 to 4.4/31 had to be produced in a PA 66 with 30% by weight glass fibre reinforcement. The injection molded part has a center hole, entered by tapped M10 holes that, starting from the peripheral surface, are opposite each other. As spigoted grub screws are screwed into each tapped hole to push against the centrally fitted shaft, it is not necessary to have a continuous screw thread in both bores, which would have called for a bridging screw core that would have had to cross the center core. Apart from problems with sealing, the unscrewing device also would have been in difficulty, as it would have had to perform a larger stroke. The employment of the molding allows for two separate screw cores to be operated independently of each other, however, so that they can be propelled by one rack each. To avoid further core pullings for the remaining shape of the molding, it is put perpendicularly into the parting plane of the mold by its symmetrical axis.

Concerning the direct propulsion of the screw cores by racks, a check must be made to ascertain that an adequate transmission can be achieved or if intermediate stages are required to avoid an excessively long rack stroke.

The pitch of the metric thread M10 is $h = 1.5$ mm. With allowing for a certain safety, an unscrewing distance of 11 mm must be taken up, which results in $11/1.5 = 7.33$ rotations of the screw core. At a pitch circle diameter of $d_o = 12$ mm and a modulus of $m = 0.8$ mm, the pinion of the screw core works out at $t = 12/0.8 = 15$ teeth and a pitch circle circumference of $12 \times \pi = 37.68$ mm. At 7.33 turns this results in a required rack stroke of $7.33 \times 37.68 = 276.19$ mm.

Standard hydraulic cylinders of 280 mm stroke are available. Divided by the division $d = \pi \times m = 2.5$ mm of the gear tooth system, this corresponds to 112 teeth on the rack, which with 15 teeth on the pinion turns the latter 7.46 times during one stroke. From this results an unscrewing distance of 11.19 mm, which is sufficient. It must be checked whether the space available on the injection molding machine allows the installation of the suspension and the hydraulic cylinder under the mold.

The mold design (Figs. 4.4/32 to 4.4/38) is such that two sleeves (1) can be produced at the same time. The unscrewing equipment has been installed in the fixed mold half (3) so that the hydraulic cylinder (14) does not have to participate in the opening and closing movement but can remain in its position.

The center bore of the coupling, which tapers toward the moving mold half, is molded by two cores (4) and (5) which are self-centering.

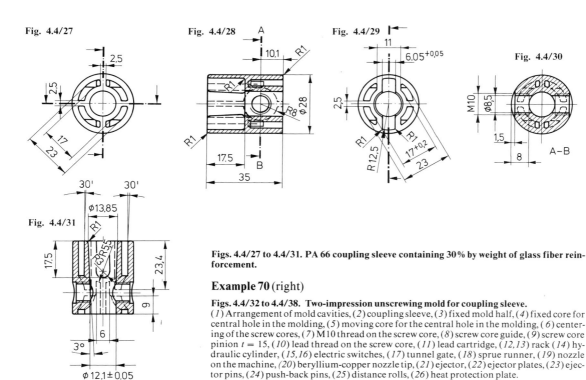

Fig. 4.4/27   Fig. 4.4/28   Fig. 4.4/29   Fig. 4.4/30   Fig. 4.4/31

Figs. 4.4/27 to 4.4/31. PA 66 coupling sleeve containing 30% by weight of glass fiber reinforcement.

Example 70 (right)

Figs. 4.4/32 to 4.4/38. Two-impression unscrewing mold for coupling sleeve.
(1) Arrangement of mold cavities, (2) coupling sleeve, (3) fixed mold half, (4) fixed core for central hole in the molding, (5) moving core for the central hole in the molding, (6) centering of the screw cores, (7) M10 thread on the screw core, (8) screw core guide, (9) screw core pinion $t = 15$, (10) lead thread on the screw core, (11) lead cartridge, (12, 13) rack (14) hydraulic cylinder, (15, 16) electric switches, (17) tunnel gate, (18) sprue runner, (19) nozzle on the machine, (20) beryllium-copper nozzle tip, (21) ejector, (22) ejector plates, (23) ejector pins, (24) push-back pins, (25) distance rolls, (26) heat protection plate.

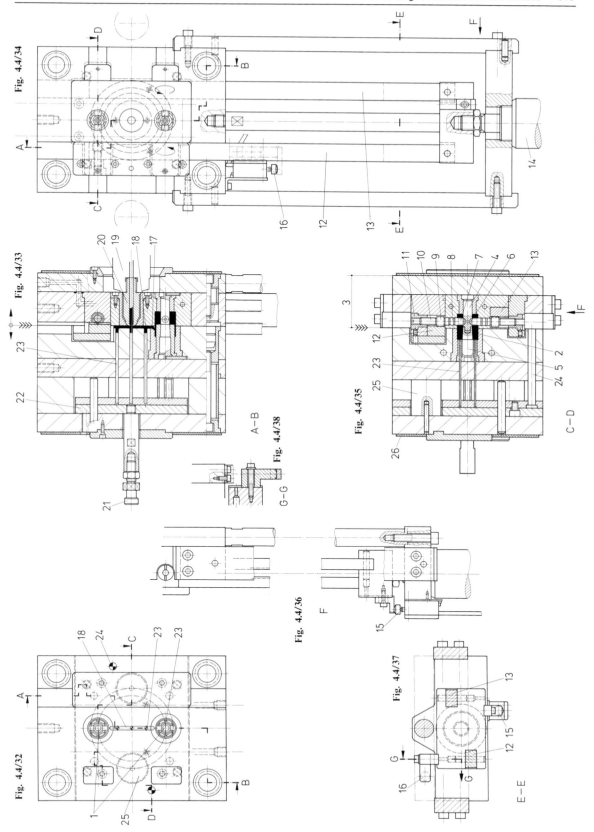

Fig. 4.4/34

Fig. 4.4/33

A–B
Fig. 4.4/38
G–G

Fig. 4.4/35

C–D

Fig. 4.4/36

Fig. 4.4/32

Fig. 4.4/37

E–E

The locating spigots (6) of the screw cores enter the core (4), rigidly fixed in the mold clamping plate, from both sides. The screw cores are made up of the locating spigot (6), the M10 screw thread (7), a guide (8), the 15 gear teeth (9), and the lead thread (10) at the other end, which runs in the fixed lead cartridge (11).

The two racks (12) and (13) have been arranged offset to each other so that opposite directions of rotation can be transmitted to the opposing screw cores. The hydraulic cylinder pushes the racks (12) and (13) up to unscrew the threaded bolts. The upper racks protrude from the mold and need to be guarded by a screen. For interlocking with the machine's control circuit of the cycle sequence, the racks contact switch (15) in the lower and switch (16) in the upper position.

By employing lateral tunnel gating (17), the coupling sleeves are automatically degated from the sprue runner (18). This is being directly injected through a beryllium-copper nozzle tip (20), which is screwed into the female thread of the nozzle on the machine (19) to avoid the conventional tapered sprue rod penetrating the fixed mold half (3).

The operating sequence of the unscrewing tool takes place as follows:

The racks are moved in by the hydraulic cylinders, unscrewing the screw cores from the moldings. Then the opening movement of the mold starts. When finished, the hydraulic ejector of the machine, to which is coupled the ejector bar (21), pushes the ejector plates (22) and through them the ejector pins (23) for the coupling sleeves and for the sprue runner forward. For safety, the push-back pins (24) also move out simultaneously. They have to return the ejector plate to the starting position in any case when the mold closes. Once the mold is closed, the racks are pulled up again and the new cycle can start with the injection process.

Example 71. Four-impression unwinding splits tool for screw caps

The screw caps are to be produced by injection molding. They have an internal thread, requiring unscrewing of the cores. The external shape is imparted by splits, as the surface structure of the molding does not allow any axial demolding movement. It is therefore expedient to arrange the mold cavities in line. The four-impression mold (Figs. 4.4/39 to 4.4/42) has an unscrewing device that makes use of the opening movement of the injection molding machine. A coarse threaded spindle (16) slides in a nut that has been installed outside the mold as a machine fixture. The turning movement thus obtained for the spindle (16) is directly transmitted to the internal in-line arranged cores (13) through the spur gear (17). The cores transmit the movement to the outer screw cores (13) through idler gears (18). The cores are guided by lead nuts (15). The two adjacent nuts are secured against rotation by flats.

As the opening movement releases the splits (7) and (8) simultaneously via the angle dowels (9) to demold the outside of the caps, they must be fixed against rotation. This is achieved by side gating each pair of adjoining moldings. These gates are of a sufficiently sturdy design to prevent the moldings from turning during core unscrewing. This is prevented by the shared gate runner. As the injection moldings remain in the moving half of the tool during the opening process, the sprue taper is pulled out of the sprue bush (11).

The return movement of the screw cores is insufficient for demolding the caps, although the thread has been released. Therefore air is blown on the moldings from the guide bushes (14) to assist them in dropping off the cores.

The incoming cooling water is directed against the reverse side of the screw core face by a cascade tube (23). The O-rings (24) arranged in the screw core bore as seals have been coated with Molycote. In the guide-nut area (15) they run on guide inserts (22). The running surfaces are hard chromium plated. These inserts at the same time serve to supply and return cooling water to and from the hollow screw cores for temperating.

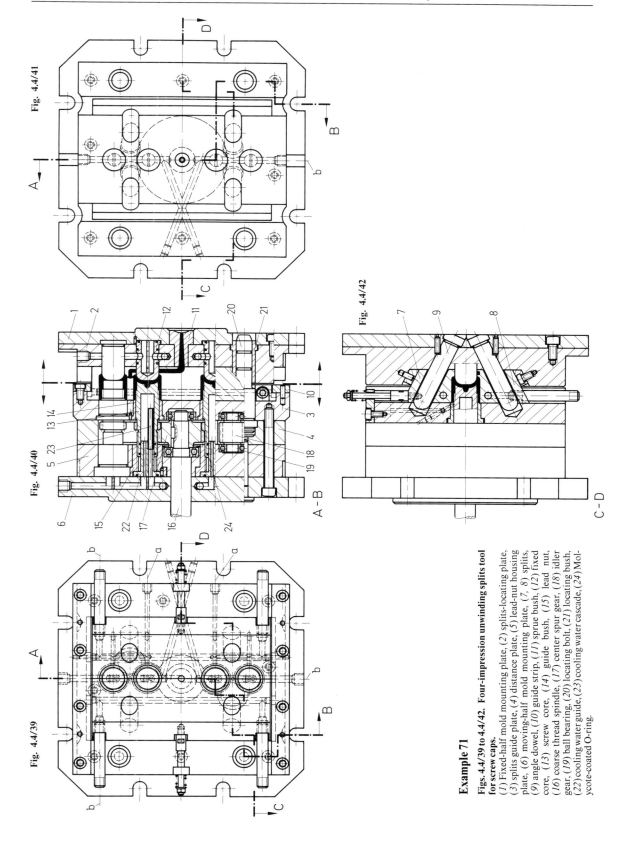

Fig. 4.4/41

Fig. 4.4/42

Fig. 4.4/40

Fig. 4.4/39

A – B

C – D

Example 71

Figs. 4.4/39 to 4.4/42. Four-impression unwinding splits tool for screw caps.

(1) Fixed-half mold mounting plate, (2) splits-locating plate, (3) splits guide plate, (4) distance plate, (5) lead-nut housing plate, (6) moving-half mold mounting plate, (7, 8) splits, (9) angle dowel, (10) guide strip, (11) sprue bush, (12) fixed core, (13) screw core, (14) guide bush, (15) lead nut, (16) coarse thread spindle, (17) center spur gear, (18) idler gear, (19) ball bearing, (20) locating bolt, (21) locating bush, (22) cooling water guide, (23) cooling water cascade, (24) Molycote-coated O-ring.

Example 72. Four-impression hot-runner mold for three-liter-bottle screw cap closures

A space-saving solution for the unscrewing gear trains of a screw-cap tool has been evolved in the design illustrated in Figs. 4.4/43 to 4.4/45. Once again, as with the tool in example 71, the opening movement of the injection molding machine is utilized for screw core propulsion. It has not been possible, however, to guide the coarse threaded spindle (24) in a nut fixed in the moving half of the machine, as an additional axial ejector movement is required. The spindle is firmly installed as a machine fixture on the mold mounting plate of the fixed half (2), whereas the coarse threaded nut (25) is mounted in the moving half of the mold and allowed to rotate. The turning movement is transmitted by chain-drive (sprockets 22 and 23) to the center shaft (21), which carries the center pinion (12). The gear teeth of the four thread cores (13), circularly displayed around the pinion (12), are in mesh with the latter. The cores are guided in running bushes (14) and lead nuts (15). The cooling water supply and return in the lead-nut zone are taken care of by the core housing (16). Two O-rings (72) in the screw core seal the cores and the core housings.

As the unscrewing process takes place parallel to the opening movement of the mold, the screw closure caps must be secured against rotating, as they are fully withdrawn from the the cavity already on mold opening, whereas the unscrewing phase is still progressing. A pin (59), protruding into each cavity in the lower rim area of the cap, serves as antirotating device. This feature subsequently requires an additional ejection movement, which is transmitted to the molding by the ejector sleeve (11), displacing the article from the pin (59). The ejector sleeve (11) is carried in the ejector plates (9) and (10). These are moved by the ejector rod (19), which is centrally housed in shaft (21). The pushback pin (36) ensures that the ejectors are returned when the mold closes.

The injection molding material is introduced into

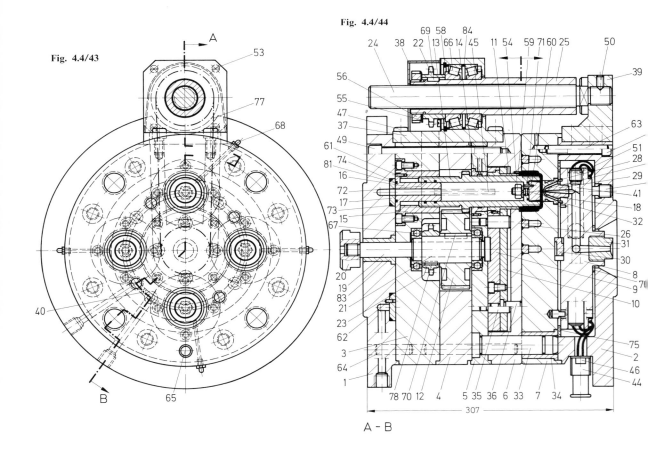

Fig. 4.4/43

Fig. 4.4/44

A - B

the mold cavities through a cross-shaped hot runner manifold (8) and a copper heat-conductive nozzle (29), which extends into the antechamber bush (28). Injection takes place through centrally positioned pin gates.

The construction of the mold, which requires an opening stroke of 205 mm, is such that it does not require machine-operated core actuation, allowing the tool to be mounted in any machine of suitable size.

Fig. 4.4/45

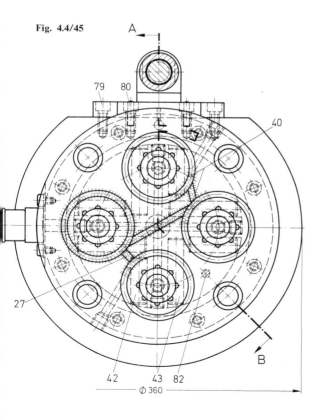

Example 72

Figs. 4.4/43 to 4.4/45. Four-impression hot-runner three-liter-bottle screw cap closure mold.

(1) Moving-half mold mounting plate, (2) fixed-half mold mounting plate, (3) retaining plate, (4) sandwich plate, (5) guide plate, (6) housing plate, (7) cavity plate, (8) manifold plate (hot-runner block), (9, 10) ejector plate, (11) ejector sleeve, (12) central gear wheel, (13) screw core, (14) running bush, (15) coarse threaded nut, (16) core housing, (17) washer, (18) core, (19) ejector bolt, (20) register, (21) central shaft, (22, 23) chain sprocket, (24) coarse threaded spindle, (25) coarse threaded nut, (26) ring, (27) leg, (28) injection point, (29) heat conductive nozzle, (30) distance piece, (31) sprue bush, (32) sealing ring, (33) guide column, (34) guide bush, (35) support bolt, (36) backing pin, (37) bearing block, (38) cover, (39) spindle housing, (40) separating web, (41) plug, (42, 43) cartridge heater, (44) electrical socket connection, (45) tube, (46 to 49) Allen bolts, (50 to 52) threaded studs, (53) cylinder bolt, (54) hexagonal nut, (55) tab washer, (56) grooved ring nut, (57) spring washer, (58) circlip, (59 to 65) cylindrical pin, (66) taper roller bearing, (67) grooved ball bearing, (68) grease nipple, (69, 70) shaft key, (71 to 74) O-ring, (75, 76) gasket, (77) roller chain, (78) shaft key, (79) Allen bolt, (80) cylinder pin, (81) O-ring, (82) cylinder pin, (83) bush, (84) distance ring.

Example 73. Unscrewing device for a junction-box injection molding tool

A polyamide junction-box injection molding tool had to be designed for fully automatic operation. Tapped holes in the corners of the box for fastening the cover had to be taken into account. These had to be produced within the same operating process. The particularity of this design (Figs. 4.4/46 and 4.4/47) is the elimination of a lead thread for unscrewing the screw cores. This simplifies mold construction with regard to the mechanical parts content. What had to be taken into consideration, however, is the mechanical arresting of the unwinding core by the lead thread, preventing its axial displacement in the cavity during the injection process. In the case presented here, a hydraulic counterpressure is built up at the end of the core before the plastics melt is injected into the cavity. This pressure must be at least as high as the maximum available injection pressure in the mold cavity. That is the reason why this part of the core has been constructed as a hydraulic piston. The radial movement of the screw core, which occurs during the demolding of the thread, allows for core cooling with far less wear of the sealing rings than with cores, which are being moved axially as well as radially.

Two each of the four tappings in the corners of the cover are unscrewed by hydraulic motors. Their high torque, compared with that of hydraulic cylinders, electric motors and lead-screw spindles, is transmitted through the stub shaft (*10*), chain sprocket (*9*) and roller chain (*11*) to the chain sprockets (*12*). These are connected to the screw core by a gear tooth profile, which transmits the torque to the core. The male gear shaft profile of the screw core (*13*) is axially displaceable in the female tooth profile of the chain sprocket (*12*).

The mold operates in the following manner:

Once the mold is closed the screw cores (*13*) are preloaded in the mold cavity by at least 120 bar. During the injection period, the follow-up pressure period and the cooling period this pressure is maintained to ensure the position of the screw core (*13*). Then the pressure is dropped to zero and the screw cores are unwound from the molding by the hydraulic motor (*8*) through the chain drive (*9, 11, 12*). During this operation the screw core moves back as it unwinds from the screw thread in the molding. The junction-box cover is retained in the cavity of the mold plate (*2*) during the subsequent opening of the mold. The box is released and demolded by pushing the cavity splits forward hydraulically.

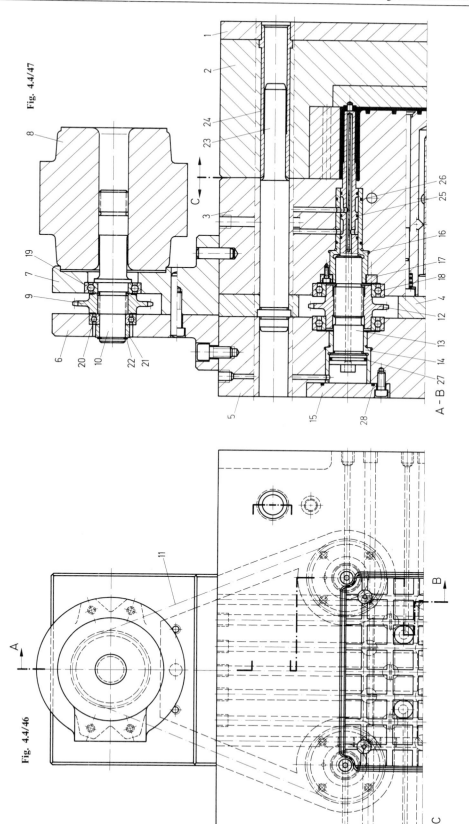

Fig. 4.4/47

Fig. 4.4/46

Example 73

Figs. 4.4/46 and 4.4/47. Unscrewing-device for a junction-box injection molding tool.
(1) Fixed-half mold mounting plate, (2) cavity plate, (3) core plate, (4) sandwich plate, (5) moving-half mold mounting plate, (6) bearing plate, (7) motor bearing, (8) hydraulic motor, (9) chain sprocket (number of teeth $z = 25$, chain pitch $t = \frac{1}{2}$ in, outside diameter of a gear wheel = 106.5 mm), (10) stub shaft, (11) single roller chain, (12) chain sprocket (number of teeth $z = 25$, chain pitch $t = \frac{1}{2}$ in, outside diameter of a gear wheel = 106.5 mm), (13) screw core, (14) hydraulic cylinder bush, (15) cylinder cover, (16) guide and cooling bush, (17) ring, (18 to 20) grooved ball bearing, (21) sandwich ring, (22) circlip, (23) guide dowel pin, (24) guide bush, (25 to 28) sealing rings.

5 Demolding Methods

5.1 Mechanical Core Pulling

Example 74. Injection molding tool incorporating curved core pulling

With certain applications the cores forming the bore in pipe bends and similar moldings have to be pulled in an arc. For as long as the angle of arc does not substantially exceed 90°, the cores can be pulled fully automatically.

In the following an injection molding tool is described in which two 90° pipe bends of different diameters are produced simultaneously (Figs 5.1/1 to 5.1/4).

The external shapes of the pipe bends have been machined into the inserts (a) and (b). The relatively shallow insert (a) on the fixed mold half is being cooled by cooling water channels in the bolt-on plate (c). Insert (b), on the moving half of the mold, has been provided with an annular cooling water groove. Further inserts (d) to (g) for the male thread are fitted into inserts (a) and (b).

The curved cores (h) and (i) are bolted and dowelled together with a curved lever on the shafts (k), describing an arc when the shafts (k) rotate. At the other end of the shafts (k) the drive gears (m) are clamped by annular springs (l). These annular springs have the advantage over keying the gears to the shafts that the gears can be firmly attached to the shaft in any given position. The drive gears (m) are meshed with a pinion, situated centrally in the mold, which is an integral part with the coarse threaded spindle (n) whose operation has been described repeatedly. The coarse thread spindle rotates on mold opening and the curved cores (h) and (i) are retracted from the pipe bend. They are positively guided into the molding position again when the mold closes.

5.2 Hydraulic Core Pulling

Example 75. Injection molding tool with hydraulic core pulling

It is expedient to operate long-stroke core pulling as required for pipe fittings, for instance, hydraulically. As core pulling strokes of up to 400 mm are required and cores have to be pulled sequentially, mechanical actuation through control profiles, as often advertised, has to be dismissed. Hydraulic operation has the added advantage that the movement sequences mold opening, core pulling, ejector operation, etc., can readily be interlocked through limit switches. The respective hydraulic cylinders are actuated by directional solenoid valves, which can be interlocked electrically through these limit switches until a certain sequence is concluded.

The advantages of hydraulic core pulling actuation are demonstrated with the example of a 100 mm diameter branch fitting. Hydraulic pumps are part of most injection molding machines, so that the oil supply for core pulling can be diverted from the machine's oil circuit. With mechanically driven machines an additional hydraulic pump will have to be obtained; if compressed air is available, core pulling can be operated by air-oil transmission. It is not recommended to operate the core pulling cylinders by direct air drive, as the movement is usually haphazard due to frictional resistance.

As there is a great variety of soil pipe fittings (different diameters, various branch angles and differing desings such as bends, single branches, double branches and pipe sockets), a *mother tool* (Figs 5.2/1 and 5.2/2) with swiveling hydraulic cylinders has been provided, so that in principle fittings of random choice and diameter can be produced in just one basic tool by an exchange of inserts and cores.

It is naturally recommended to have individual bol-

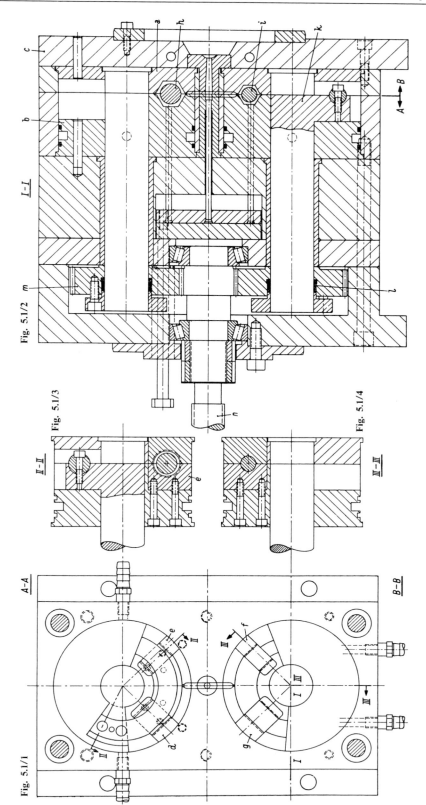

Example 74

Figs. 5.1/1 to 5.1/4. Injection molding tool with two curved cores (h) and (i).

(a) Insert in the fixed mold half, (b) insert in the moving mold half, (c) bolt-on plate, (d, e, f, g) inserts for male threads, (k) shafts, (l) annular springs, (m) driving spur gears, (n) coarse-threaded spindle with six turns of left-hand thread.

sters for each diameter and machine size, as it would prove uneconomical to mold fittings of 40 to 50 g on a machine of 500 g injection capacity. Even from the injection molding technology's point of view it would be inexpedient to produce minor parts on large machines. The hourly throughput rate of the plastics material in the plasticizing barrel and screw would then become too small. With rigid PVC in particular, employed for soil pipe fittings, decomposition manifestations would occur in the melt that would result in moldings of reduced strength characteristics, at the least.

A mother tool for fittings basically consists of a mold carrier (a) on the moving mold half, the T-slot machinings for the fixing bolts of cavity inserts (b) and the annular grooves for the bolts of the peripherally rotatable carrier (c) for the hydraulic cylinders. If the finished moldings are not to be removed manually but are to be demolded automatically, sufficiently large ejector plates (d) and (e) are to be provided additionally. Care must be taken with the latter, however, as the ejector actuation must lie in the center line of the machine, but the center of the mother mold is usually offset laterally to enable the fitting to be gated on its point of gravity. An exchangeable locating plate (f) is required to equalize this eccentricity between the machine center and the center of the mother tool. A micro switch (g) is built into the locating plate. The switch is only closed when the ejector return spring (h) has withdrawn the ejector (i) completely. Only then is the control solenoid for "core in" energized. This prevents the core from being pushed onto protruding ejectors, protecting both from damage.

The second major item of the tool bolster is the mold carrier plate (k) on the fixed half, with corresponding annular grooves for fastening the cavity inserts (l) on that side. There is also an eccentric locating plate (m) for the centering position of sprue bush (n). Further components of the mother tool are the swivel carrier (c) for the hydraulic cylinders (o) and (p) and the core-guide block (q), which slides in the carrier. The various cores can easily be mounted in this guide support and coupled firmly with the piston rod of the cylinder at the same time. Limit switches are mounted at top and bottom of carrier (c). The core movements are switched off or the next control sequence is interlocked through them, as the case may be. Actuation of

the upper limit switch should, if possible, be adjustable so that the strokes of the same cylinder can be set for longer or shorter distances.

Insert modules for the mother tool

Only the following modules are then still required for the mother mold to produce the single branch Y-piece illustrated: the two cores (r) and (s) with cover (t) and cooling insert, the cavity plates (b) and (l) with guide dowels, cooling insert, sprue bush (n) and mechanical core interlock (u) and (v), the ejectors (i) with ejector plates (d) and (e) as well as the locating plates (f) and (m). The cylinder carriers (c) are only slackened off and tightened up again with the new setting corresponding to the core angles. Where applicable, the upper limit switches have to be reset according to the stroke requirements of the cores. The bottom limit switches will not have to be altered, as the lower core position is always against register.

The movement sequences must progress to a predetermined control program. Starting with the injection process, the following movement sequence applies for the single branch fittings, controlled by the appropriate limit switches:

(1) Injection
(2) Follow-up pressure of plasticized material during cooling
(3) Screw return
(4) Cooling time without follow-up pressure
(5) Mold opening until the sprue has been released and the core interlock (u) or (v) has been cancelled;
(6) Withdraw the long (r) and the short (s) core completely from the fitting
(7) Open mold till it contacts the machine stop and the fitting is demolded by ejector (i)
(8) Close mold until the ejector (i) has been retracted completely, when the limit switch (g) will be actuated to initiate core pulling
(9) The long core (r) must be brought into the molding position under sequence 8
(10) When the main core is in position, move the short core (s) into place for molding
(11) Close mold completely when the mechanical interlocks (u) and (v) monitor the cores
(12) = l, Injection

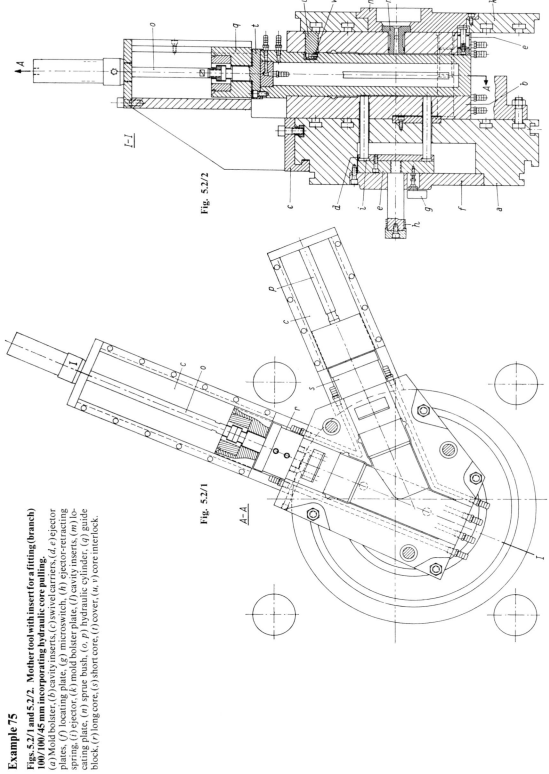

Fig. 5.2/2

I–I

Fig. 5.2/1

A–A

Example 75

Figs. 5.2/1 and 5.2/2. Mother tool with insert for a fitting (branch) 100/100/45 mm incorporating hydraulic core pulling.

(*a*) Mold bolster, (*b*) cavity inserts, (*c*) swivel carriers, (*d*, *e*) ejector plates, (*f*) locating plate, (*g*) microswitch, (*h*) ejector-retracting spring, (*i*) ejector, (*k*) mold bolster plate, (*l*) cavity inserts, (*m*) locating plate, (*n*) sprue bush, (*o*, *p*) hydraulic cylinder, (*q*) guide block, (*r*) long core, (*s*) short core, (*t*) cover, (*u*, *v*) core interlock.

Example 76. Injection molding tool with built-on hydraulic core pulling for automatic measuring tube production

A measuring tube for a liquid-distributing manifold was to be produced fully automatically. The molding had to be comparatively thick walled, as operating pressures of up to 10 bar and operating temperatures of up to almost 100 °C occur. It has proved expedient to inject from one face end to prevent unilateral stresses that would distort the tube to an unwelcome degree. In this case an injection molding machine capable of split-line injection is available. The smallest possible machine suitable can be employed without having to arrange the molding eccentrically in the tool (Fig. 5.2/3), which would only result in long flow paths and unfavorable one-sided machine loading. Hydraulic core pulling is employed, as mechanical cores are unsuitable for such lengths of stroke. Insert cores would be unacceptable, because the requirement is for automatic production of the molding.

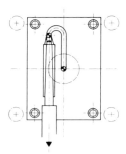

Fig. 5.2/3. Required positioning of the molding in the parting plane of the mold with the greatest possible utilization of the machine size and central injection.

The mold design (Figs. 5.2/4 to 5.2/9) starts with the central position of the measuring tube in the parting plane. To obtain the clean scale graduation surface necessary for reading off the flow rate, these divisions have been machined into the fixed mold half. The core of the measuring tube is now located precisely in the center of the mold cavity inserts. It is being centralized at the end of the tube as well as at the entrance.

The gate runner approaches the measuring tube via the end of the core in three adequately dimensioned sections. The core is circumcirculated uniformly by the melt through this type of gating and is furthermore centered accurately. Below the mold on the moving half core (3) is housed in a yoke (5), which is fixed in its direction precisely by guide rods (6). A cross plate (7), into which the hydraulic cylinder (8) has been screwed, is fitted to the end of the guide rods. The cylinder (8) has been additionally supported (9), to avoid any excessive vibrations from this long substructure

during the travel movements of the mold. The piston rod (10) of the cylinder is coupled to the yoke (5). Heating/cooling channels (11) have been provided on the fixed as well as on the moving mold halves. Of great importance also is the possibility of core tempering. The core has been drilled for this purpose and divided into two chambers with a cascade by a separating baffle (12).

Hydraulic cylinders as well as connecting hoses to the hydraulic circuit of the machine are not part and parcel of the core pulling equipment, as is often assumed. The size of the cylinders has to be matched to the pressures occurring in the mold. This then also becomes the decisive factor in establishing whether the core to be pulled can be held just by the cylinder pressure or if it has to be mechanically interlocked as well. In the example presented interlocking is not necessary. It has been proved advantageous for the cylinders to be equipped with cushioned registers in both movement directions. A considerably gentler operation can be obtained in this way.

It is essential for the operational sequence of the controls to monitor the position of core (3) in its most forward and rearmost position electrically through limit switches (13, 14) and pass this information on to the machine control.

To describe the operational sequence, it is assumed that the tool is fully open and void of moldings, i.e., in the starting position:

Core (3) is moved into the mold by hydraulic cylinder (8). The mold closes and the injection process starts. As soon as the injection, follow-up pressure and cooling times have elapsed the mold is opened for a few millimeters only. Due to the core (3) being mounted on the moving mold half, the measuring tube (1) with its scale (2) is demolded securely from the fixed mold half. Now core (3) is retracted completely from the measuring tube (1). The mold moves to the opening position and the hydraulic ejector of the machine moves forward. This is coupled up with the ejector bar (15), which pushes the ejector plates with their built-in ejector pins (16) for the measuring tube and the sprue forward, ejecting the completed molding from the tool. The core is moved in again and another cycle starts.

To make the mold more solid the hollow space required for the ejector plates is bridged by distance pillars (17). An essential particularity of this tool is the quartz-crystal pressure transducer (18) in the vicinity of the gate for assessing the mold cavity pressure, which is then controlled in accordance with the data received to prevent sink marks and to reduce internal stresses in the molding.

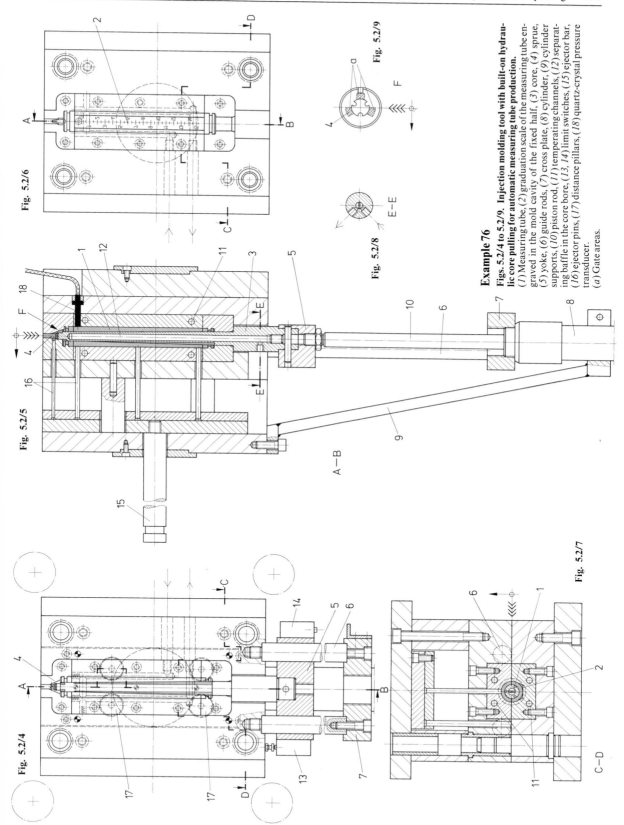

Fig. 5.2/6

Fig. 5.2/9

Fig. 5.2/8

Fig. 5.2/5

Fig. 5.2/4

Fig. 5.2/7

A–B

C–D

E–E

Example 76

Figs. 5.2/4 to 5.2/9. Injection molding tool with built-on hydraulic core pulling for automatic measuring tube production.
(*1*) Measuring tube, (*2*) graduation scale of the measuring tube engraved in the mold cavity of the fixed half, (*3*) core, (*4*) sprue, (*5*) yoke, (*6*) guide rods, (*7*) cross plate, (*8*) cylinder, (*9*) cylinder supports, (*10*) piston rod, (*11*) temperating channels, (*12*) separating baffle in the core bore, (*13*, *14*) limit switches, (*15*) ejector bar, (*16*) ejector pins, (*17*) distance pillars, (*18*) quartz-crystal pressure transducer.
(*a*) Gate areas.

Examples 77 and 78. Cable socket injection molding tool with hydraulic core pulling

Hydraulic core pulling equipment is usually required when long cores have to be pulled for which mechanical core pulling devices provide insufficient length of stroke. There are applications, however, which could be adequately served by mechanical core pulling, but where the employment of a hydraulically pulled core results in simplification of the mold design and therefore in economical advantages. This presupposes that the injection molding machine can be equipped with ancillary hydraulic equipment.

Fig. 5.2/10. Cable sockets of varying sizes.

The two principles of design will be compared in the example of tools for cable sockets (Fig. 5.2/10). Figure 5.2/11 (example 77) shows the mold construction incorporating mechanically operated splits, which has been chosen to give a better comparison with example 78 in this chapter. The parting plane of the mold runs vertically to the plane of the drawing along line (1) to the split (3). As this molding is exposed to view and meant to carry the manufacturer's name on the back of elbow (10), the molding is injected through a tunnel gate (2) on the peripheral rim in the split line (1). However, to be able to demold the part, half of the lower part of the molding had to be machined into split (3), although a cylindrical plug would have been quite adequate for the opening itself (4).

When the mold opens, the angled surface (6) releases, so that the pressure on the split (3) is cancelled via the wedge area (5). The split moves down, guided by angle dowel (7) and sliding on the surface of wedge (5). This leaves the molding resting freely on the core (9), to be pushed off by the ejector pins (8).

Figures 5.2/12 to 5.2/17 (example 78) show the employment of hydraulic core pulling. The molding lies in the split line, in the same way as in example 77. The parting plane also runs vertically to the plane of the drawing from top to bottom. Gating is also via tunnel gate (2), and injection takes place in the split line. Instead of the complicated split arrangement, a cylindrical plug forms the opening in the molding. The plug is moved by a small hydraulic cylinder (4) that is mounted below the mold on an adaptor (5). The two electrical switches (8) and (9) are fitted to plate (6). They are actuated by an S-shaped switching rod (7), signaling the upper and lower position of cylinder (4) to the ma-

chine controls. As a guide for a sliding split is not required on the moving half of the mold, the possibility of surrounding core (10) by a stripper plate (11) is given. This is linked with the ejector plates (13) by tie rods (12). Plate (11) acts simultaneously as push-back plate for the ejectors when the mold closes. The hollow space in the ejection system is well supported by the distance pillars (14). Core (3) does not have to be mechanically interlocked, as the effective area for the injection pressure is not very large. This force can be absorbed solely by the hydraulic pressure of the cylinder (4), which is cushioned in both terminal positions.

The operational sequence starts with mold closing. Then the core (3) is moved in by the hydraulic cylinder (4). This is followed by the injection and cooling time. When this is elapsed, core (3) is withdrawn from the molding. The mold moves into the open position, and the hydraulic ejector – coupled with the tool through the ejector bar (15) – actuates the ejector plates (13) and pushes the molding off the core (10) with the stripper plate (11) and the ejector pins (16). The mold is cooled in the mold cavity plate (17) as well as in the core (10).

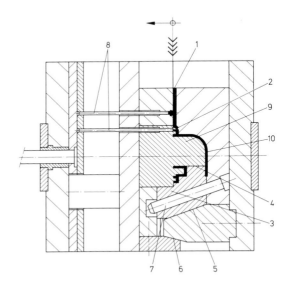

Example 77

Fig. 5.2/11. Cable socket injection molding tool with mechanical core pulling (sliding split).
(1) Parting plane and point of injection, (2) tunnel gate, (3) split, (4) opening, (5) wedge surface on the sliding split, (6) counter wedge surface, (7) angle dowel, (8) ejector pins, (9) core, (10) surface with manufacturer's lettering.

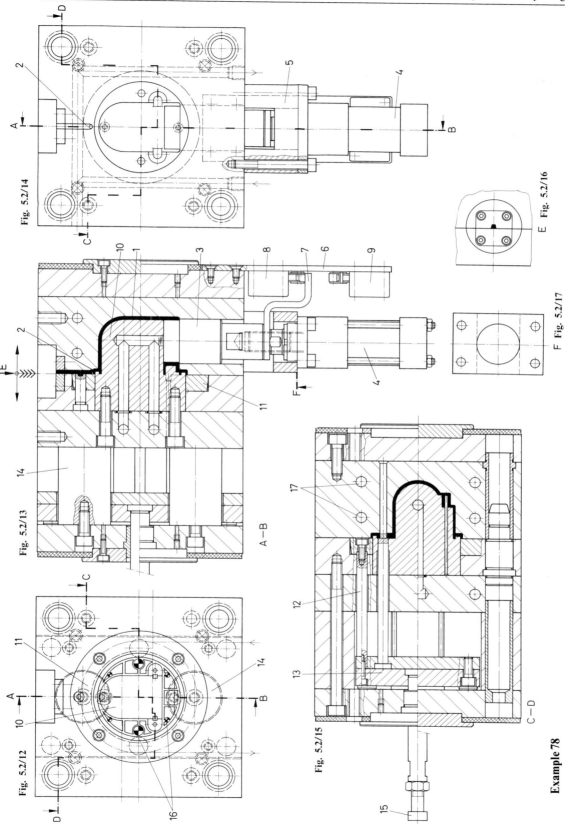

Fig. 5.2/14

Fig. 5.2/13

A – B

Fig. 5.2/12

Fig. 5.2/15

C – D

E Fig. 5.2/16

F Fig. 5.2/17

Example 78

Figs. 5.2/12 to 5.2/17. Cable socket injection molding tool with hydraulic core pulling.
(*1*) Molding, (*2*) tunnel gate, (*3*) cylindrical plug for forming the opening in the molding, (*4*) hydraulic cylinder, (*5*) adaptor, (*6*) plate, (*7*) switching rod, (*8, 9*) electrical switches, (*10*) core, (*11*) stripper plate, (*12*) tie rods, (*13*) ejector plates, (*14*) distance pillars, (*15*) ejector bar, (*16*) ejector pins, (*17*) mold cavity plate.

5.3   Sliding Splits on Stripper Plate

Example 79. Injection molding splits tool with core retraction for molding wire bobbins

Splits tools have already been described in which the splits are opened by the advancing ejectors. However, this principle is not applicable to all moldings of divided external shapes. Many moldings have to be retained in position on the cores during the opening movement of the splits, and ejection from the cores must only take place at the conclusion of the splits' opening movement. This stipulates that on mold opening the splits open fully and only then are the cores pulled out of the molding.

In principle this sequence of movements is covered by so-called sliding-splits molds, in which the splits for the external contours are opened by guide dowels during the initial opening movement. If, however, the moldings in the splits plane are relatively large surfaced, secure mold clamping can create difficulties with sliding splits tools. In this instance the mold design according to Figs. 5.3/1 and 5.3/2 has proved effective. The mold contains two wire bobbins to DIN 46 399, which are pin gated on a flange. The outer shapes are molded in exchangeable inserts (a) which are bolted together with splits (b). Split guides (c) are screwed on top and bottom to guide the splits on the stripper plate (d). These splits guides themselves are guided in the direction of the taper angle in guide plates (e), which are bolted together with the mounting plate (g) of the fixed mold half through the wedges (f). The stripper plate (d) is connected with the ejector plate (i) through the push rods (h). When the ejector plate (i) moves against the machine stop, the stripper plate, complete with splits, is pushed forward. The correct sequence of the movement process during mold opening is dependent on the stipulation that core (k) and splits (a) are firmly connected to each other via the material filled mold cavity. During mold opening the splits (a) are opened so far by the time the ejector plate (i) has contacted the machine stop that the distance between them is a little larger than the diameter of the bobbins to allow the latter to drop off the core. The splits (a) remain in the open position during further mold opening, while cores (l) and (k) are withdrawn from the bobbin. Splits (b) are still engaged in the guide plate (e) with their split guides (c) in this position, so that the push rods (h) are relieved of the weight of the splits when the mold is open.

This design ensures trouble-free mold seating of the splits areas even with moldings of large surfaces requiring 1000 kN clamping force in the splits plane and more. If the wedge strip (m) has been made adjustable by slight tapering, then positive mold seating can easily be regained by resetting when the wedge surface becomes worn.

Very high demands regarding absence of seams are made of wire bobbins in particular. These can only be accomplished by this type of design, ensuring extremely solid and positive mold seating.

This design also offers particular advantages regarding cooling of the splits. As the splits are unencumbered top and bottom, in contrast to the closed tapered splits mold, one or several cooling channels can be included.

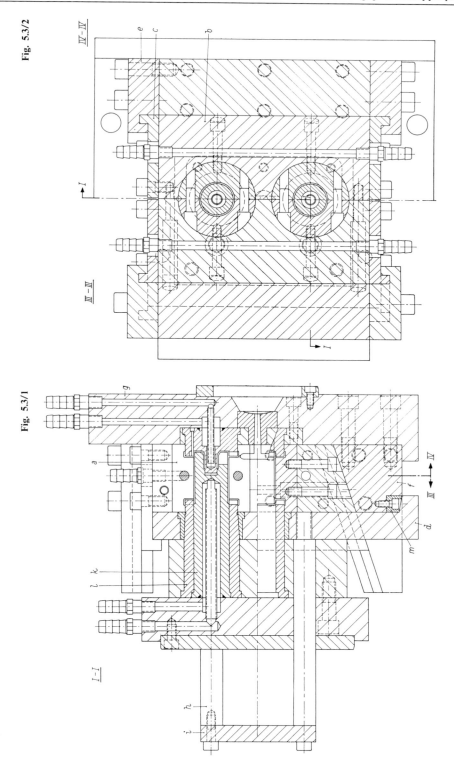

Fig. 5.3/2

Fig. 5.3/1

Example 79

Figs. 5.3/1 and 5.3/2. Double splits tool for 50 mm wire bobbin.
(*a*) Insert, (*b*) splits, (*c*) splits guides, (*d*) stripper plates, (*e*) guide plates, (*f*) wedge, (*g*) bolt-on plate, (*h*) push rod, (*i*) ejector plate, (*k, l*) cores, (*m*) wedge strip.

Example 80. Injection molding splits-tool with twice the ejection distance

A proven mold design for moldings with external undercuts and continuous bore, as represented by hose connectors, for instance, is subsequently described. The mold construction of this splits tool offers considerable advantages, with greater splits length in particular, as the tapered splits do not require an all-enclosing jacket as did splis tool described earlier.

The advantage lies especially in the fact that the clamping wedges for the splits can have ground contact surfaces and that the splits themselves can be equipped with intensive cooling. They are accessible top and bottom in the direction of the clamping areas, so that cooling channels can be continuous along the full length of the splits.

A further feature arising from this design is the possibility of designing adjustable clamping force seating in the direction of the splits closing surface for this mold. A considerable advantage is gained in being able to open the splits so wide that sufficient space is created to allow the moldings to drop out between the splits. For that reason considerably longer moldings can be accommodated in such a tool than is possible in splits molds of closed clamping jackets.

Figure 5.3/3 shows the two-impression mold in section along the line *I-I* of Fig. 5.3/4. In Fig. 5.3/4 a section is shown in direction (*A*), Fig. 5.3/5 shows one in direction (*B*) and Fig. 5.3/6 illustrates a cross section in direction *II-II*. Figure 5.3/7 reproduces the ejector assembly in the pushed-forward position.

The external configurations of the hose connectors have been machined into splits (*a*). Inserts (*b*) in these splits contain the threaded part of the hose connectors for the sake of easier working. The splits (*a*) are retained for flush mold seating by the wedges (*c*), which are bolted together with the ejector side of the mold. Wedge strips (*d*) have been provided to press these adjustable wedges against the splits. These wedge strips have been produced with a 1° taper to transfer the clamping pressure to the contact area of plates (*e*). On the opposite end wedges (*c*) are in contact with the hardened and ground wedge strips (*f*), also adjustable, and supported by the shoulder of the mold fixing plate (*g*) on the fixed half. Splits (*a*) are guided on the open facing sides by plates (*h*), which are bolted together with the wedges (*c*). These plates (*h*) grip the splits (*a*) through a spring or inserted wedge and guide these splits when advancing in the direction of the clamping taper.

Therefore the mold opens first in parting plane *A-B* while the splits are closed and the sprue is withdrawn from the sprue bush (*i*). After a certain opening distance in this plane the splits (*a*) have to be propelled forward sufficiently far to free the existing undercuts of the external configurations. The splits then have to be arrested and the moldings ejected off the cores. This means that two successive ejection strokes are required by contacting the machine register. This *double ejection process* is achieved by the following device:

The ejector mandrel (*k*) of the mold has been designed as a trip sleeve. Figure 5.3/3 shows the trip sleeve (*k*) in position, rigidly connected to sleeve (*l*) and at that through plate (*m*) and push rod (*n*) to stripping plate (*o*). By moving the stripper plate (*o*) forward the splits (*a*), guided by plates (*h*), are advanced and opened first. After an approximately 50 mm stroke the splits are opened sufficiently far to release the undercuts. This movement also trips the lock between trip sleeve (*k*) and sleeve (*l*) positively by the step on locking mandrel (*p*), which is screwed into the moving mold half tool plate (*q*). The eight sprung ends of the trip sleeve (*k*) collapse inward and the trip sleeve (*k*) can be pushed further forward, whereas plate (*m*) remains stationary. In this position the hose connectors remain only loosely on the slightly tapered cores (*r*), from which they have already been stripped by about 50 mm. They can then be stripped off the cores completely by an ejector (*s*) acting on the central sprue, as they are still firmly connected to each other by a relatively thick runner and gate. The central ejector (*s*) is bolted to the trip sleeve (*k*), so that by advancing the trip sleeve the hose connectors will be thrown off the cores. Figure 5.3/7 shows the final position of the trip sleeve.

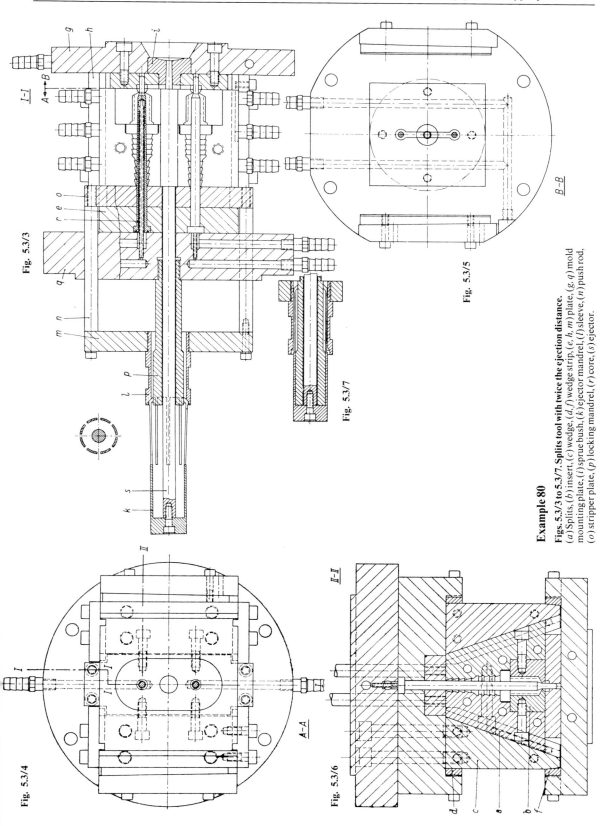

Fig. 5.3/3

Fig. 5.3/4

Fig. 5.3/5

Fig. 5.3/6

Fig. 5.3/7

Example 80

Figs. 5.3/3 to 5.3/7. Splits tool with twice the ejection distance.
(*a*) Splits, (*b*) insert, (*c*) wedge, (*d*, *f*) wedge strip, (*e*, *h*, *m*) plate, (*g*, *q*) mold mounting plate, (*i*) sprue bush, (*k*) ejector mandrel, (*l*) sleeve, (*n*) push rod, (*o*) stripper plate, (*p*) locking mandrel, (*r*) core, (*s*) ejector.

5.4 Splits on the Fixed Mold Half

Example 81. Eight-impression injection molding tool for fountain pen caps

Caps for fountain pens usually possess an internal thread on one side and an external one on the other for fastening the clip. To prevent harmful weld lines they ought to be gated for injecting at the closed end of the external thread. This requirement can only be fulfilled in the multi-impression version by a tear-off tool. The difficulty lies in the tear-off gate having to be in the splits containing the external threads for the cap.

If the screw cores for the internal thread are to be driven by a central spur gear, then it is not possible to arrange the caps in line, which would be expedient for the demolding of the divided external threads. In an eight-impression mold eight pairs of splits are required, which house the external thread and the screw thread for the molding. The male thread on the caps has been cut into the wedge splits pairs (a), which have been fitted at a taper of approximately 10° into moving plate (c), which moves in guide strips (b). Guide dowels (d) are set into plate (c) on the facing sides of the wedge splits, with the larger part of their circumference pointing in the direction of the wedge taper. They are secured by studs (e) with plate (c). Springs (f) push the splits against the collar of the guide dowels in the direction of opening when the mold opens, releasing the thread in that open position.

The inserts (g) for the external contours of the caps have been matched with the insert plate (h) and cover plate (i). Both plates are guided on guiding strips (b). These guide strips are provided with two registers. After an opening stroke of 72 mm between plates (c) and (i) the wedge-split plate (c) is retained by the first register and the interlock between this plate and the mold flange (l) on the moving half is cancelled simultaneously. This is managed by the release pins (m) running up on the cams of the guide strips (b). With the initial opening in the sprue-runner plane the narrowest part of the gate is torn off the caps. The gate is withdrawn from its bore by this action, aided by an undercut at the end of the runners, while the tapered splits are still closed. At the same time the central sprue, resting unaidedly on the sprue retainer (n), is withdrawn from the sprue bush (o). Sprue retainer (n) and ejector sleeve (p) run through an idling stroke initially, which is approximately commensurate with the sprue length for the molding, under pressure of spring (q) until the movement is terminated by a collar. During the continuing opening movement the retaining pin of the sprue retainer (n) is forcibly withdrawn from the center sprue. During this operation the bush (p) is initially pulled back against the tension of spring (q) in the opening direction. As soon as the retaining pin has been withdrawn from the sprue, spring (q) can relax, thereby forcibly ejecting the sprue-runner star. At the

end of a total opening stroke of 84 mm the cover plate (i) of the insert plate (h) contacts the second register on guide strips (b) and is retained by them. During further mold opening the caps, which are being retained firmly by cores (r), are withdrawn form the inserts (g). The mold now opens in the second parting plane between stripper plate (s) and insert plate (h) until the stripper plate (s) is being pushed forward, stripping the moldings off the cores (r).

Before the moldings can be stripped off, however, the internal threads have to be demolded. This is managed by rotating the threaded sleeves (t) anticlockwise through the central spur gear (u), so that the moldings have been released by the start of the ejector stroke. The central spur gear is driven by a flat thread spindle, running in a fixed nut mounted in the machine.

In the closed mold position the screw sleeves must contact a collar on cores (r) without leaving a gap. As the drive to all screw sleeves is positive, it is hardly possible to match all cores so accurately in length that this requirement can be satisfied. To balance this inaccuracy in length, powerful sets of disc springs (v) therefore support the cores (r). Slight differences in the longitudinal set of the cores (r) are bridged by these springs, so that gap-free contact of the screw sleeves with the collar on the cores is ensured.

Prerequisite for the high capacity of an injection molding tool is efficient abduction of the heat transmitted to the mold by the material melt. The most efficient cooling always results if the inserts are circumcirculated by cooling water directly. To fulfill these requirements, the inserts (g) are sealed by rubber or plastic O-rings and provided with a cooling water groove. The cooling water is fed through channels in insert plate (h) from insert to insert, ensuring extremely efficient cooling.

Cooling of the cores is difficult. Just that, however, is particularly important for the efficiency of the mold, as the heat from the long cores can be conducted away only with difficulty. Although the cores are fixed, water cooling can hardly be accommodated.

In such cases air cooling has proved extremely effective. Compressed air of 5 to 6 bar is available in most factories. The stripping inserts (w) are provided with a machined groove, which is supplied with air instead of water in a similar manner to insert plate (h). Three channels of approximately 1 mm diameter lead to the internal diameter of these inserts, which are closed off by the screw sleeves (t) when the mold is shut. As soon as the stripper plate (s) is being pushed forward, compressed air is blown at high speed through these channels onto the cores (r), giving intensive cooling.

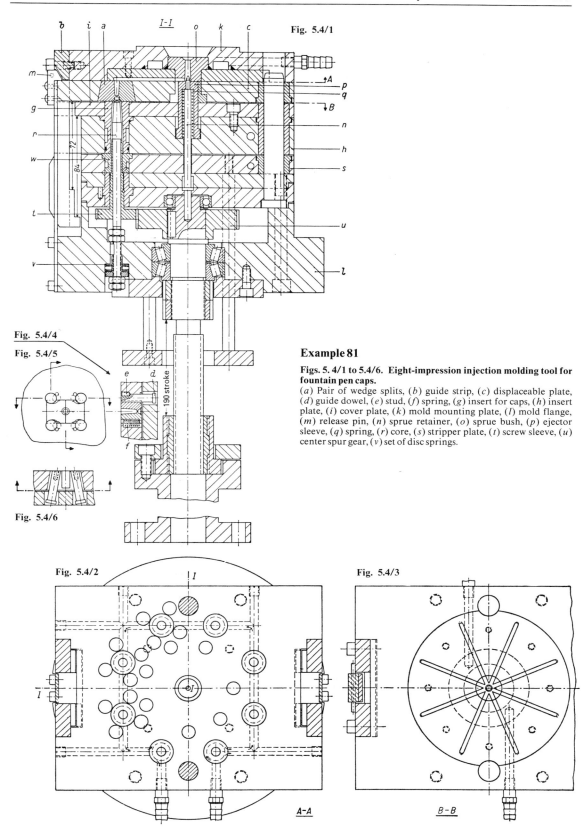

Fig. 5.4/1

Fig. 5.4/4

Fig. 5.4/5

Fig. 5.4/6

Fig. 5.4/2

Fig. 5.4/3

I-I

A-A

B-B

Example 81

Figs. 5. 4/1 to 5.4/6. Eight-impression injection molding tool for fountain pen caps.

(*a*) Pair of wedge splits, (*b*) guide strip, (*c*) displaceable plate, (*d*) guide dowel, (*e*) stud, (*f*) spring, (*g*) insert for caps, (*h*) insert plate, (*i*) cover plate, (*k*) mold mounting plate, (*l*) mold flange, (*m*) release pin, (*n*) sprue retainer, (*o*) sprue bush, (*p*) ejector sleeve, (*q*) spring, (*r*) core, (*s*) stripper plate, (*t*) screw sleeve, (*u*) center spur gear, (*v*) set of disc springs.

Example 82. Injection molding tool with sliding splits and long cores on the fixed half

Unilaterally closed tapered tubes approximately 150 mm in length and 35 mm in diameter had to be produced with a flange on the open side and a channel in the closed side as well as in the circumference. An injection molding machine of 300 mm maximum mold height and an opening stroke also of 300 mm was available.

Normally such pipes are accommodated in the mold in such a way that the core is located on the moving half, with the moldings being stripped off the core by a stripper plate or pipe ejector. With this type of construction, however, neither mold height nor opening stroke of the machine would have sufficed. A design therefore had to be found that resulted in the shortest possible mold height and a short ejector stroke. The solution was found by siting the cores on the fixed half and machining the external shape into the splits, in which the tubes are demolded off the core initially in the closed position. They then open sufficiently far to allow the tubes to drop out between the open splits with their flange. As the latter is 50 mm in diameter, the splits have to open at least 26 mm to each side so that the tubes can drop out. The mold is shown in Figs. 5.4/7 and 5.4/8.

The mold mounting plate (a) of the fixed half of the tool contains the cooling water supply and return channels for two cores each. A right-hand and a left-hand wedge plate (b) are bolted to the mounting plate. These wedge plates are supported on their open side by wedge strips (c), which are tapered longitudinally by 1°, thereby facilitating adjustment of the tapered splits seating, avoiding flash on the moldings in the parting plane. The splits (d) themselves, containing the external shape of the moldings, are guided by bolted on guide plates (e) on a plate, which is accommodated in the moving half mold mounting plate (h) and can be displaced on rods (g).

Two further guide plates (i) are bolted to the wedge plates (b). They contain guide grooves for the guide mandrels (k), which are firmly fitted in the guide plate (e). These guide grooves are fashioned in such a way that they initially keep the splits closed over a distance of 20 mm when the mold opens. Over that distance the moldings are disengaged from the cores. During further opening the splits are pulled apart sufficiently far to allow the molding to drop down between them when pulled off the core.

So that the molding does not get stuck on one side during opening of the splits, the round closed side of the tubes has been machined into an insert (l), which also contains the core pins for the holes. At the end of the opening movement the molding is ejected from these inserts by ejectors (m).

The ejectors are moved via ejector strips (n), which are actuated at the conclusion of the opening movement by pushing plate (f) forward with the push rods (g). The plate (o) is retracted by powerful spring discs (p) when the mold closes. This seemingly somewhat complicated actuation of the ejectors becomes necessary, as there is not sufficient space available for standard ejector plates within the mold height at disposal. It is self-evident that the mold must never be opened to such an extent that the splits (d) leave the guide plates.

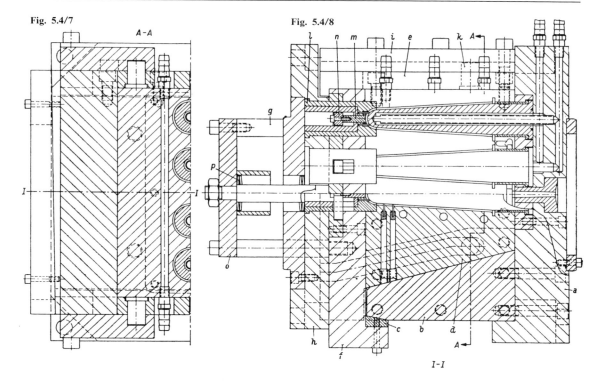

Fig. 5.4/7

A-A

Fig. 5.4/8

I-I

Example 82

Figs. 5.4/7 and 5.4/8. Injection molding tool for the production of 150 mm-long tubes; cores on the fixed half.
(a) Fixed half mold mounting plate, (b) wedge plate, (c) wedge strips, (d) splits, (e) guide plate, (f) plate, (g) rod, (h) moving half mounting plate, (i) guide plate, (k) guide mandrel, (l) insert, (m) ejector, (n) ejector strip, (o) plate, (p) disc springs.

6   Molds for Thermosets and Elastomers

Molds ought to be of optimum finish in order to make full use of the advantages of thermoset processing. This can be achieved to a great extent by observing the points listed below.

Rigidity

Although tools represent statically predetermined systems as a rule, an attempt should be made to ascertain the approximate magnitude of mold deflection under injection pressure by a rough calculation. That the deflection of thermoset tools can be considerably higher than that for thermoplastics tools has been shown by the mold cavity pressures ascertained by practical trials. As is well known, these reach between 250 to 500 bar for thermoplastics, whereas for thermosets this figure increases to 600 to 900 bar. The mold bolster for thermoset tools should therefore be thicker by approximately 50 %. It is advisable to fit additional support pillars in the area of the ejector plates to achieve satisfactory rigidity here as well. As preplasticized thermosets are of very low viscosity, even a slight flexing of the mold plates will result in flash on the moldings, thereby increasing the finishing operations. If a tool is equipped with side splits, the light mold cavity pressure must also be taken into account when designing the locking mechanism.

Wear

Thermoset materials are available in a multitude of resin and filler variations, which create enormous friction when coursing through the tool. This friction puts the wear resistance of the mold cavity steel to the test. For this reason alone those parts coming in contact with the material should be produced as inserts on principle. As many individual sections as possible are of great advantage for complicated mold cavities and core parts. In this way a replacement of the corresponding worn or broken parts is facilitated at low cost. Mold venting is also solved by this remedy, as air can be vented along the seating surfaces. A further advantage can be found in that only those inserts must be hardened (or produced in special steels), whereas for the mold bolster a heat treatable steel of up to 1000 N/mm² strength suffices. Through-hardening steels of late have come to replace the customary insert steels for shape-giving parts of the mold; this way indentation of the surface layer by hardened material remains into the soft substratum is avoided. Good experiences have been gained in this instance with a heat treatment steel of an approximate hardness of HRc 58 (very little distortion, easy to weld, polish and machinability excellent).

Additional hard-chromium plating of the shape-giving areas not only counteracts wear but also prevents the moldings from adhering to the tool. Polyes-

ter processing for instance thus called for chromium plated molds only (adhesion). The chromium layer furthermore presents an excellent protection against corrosion. If wear appears on it in the course of time, the wearing parts are stripped of chromium, then polished and newly chromium plated. Mechanical finishing is thereby avoided. The tolerances of dimensions that have to be strictly adhered to can be corrected at the same time. Re-chromium plating in good time prevents the steel surface from being attacked. With correct handling this can be achieved about three times without damaging the steel. The life span of the chromium plating is a function of the thermoset material to be processed and the shape of the moldings, i.e., the flow resistance in the tool. Statements from processors differ widely. They fluctuate between 60,000 and 100,000 shots.

The greatest wear does not take place in the mold cavities, however, but at the gates. In multi-impression tools in particular moldings are injected through a strip or film gate of approximately 0.6 to 0.8 mm width.

Due to the venturi effect on the molten material an extremely high degree of friction takes place at this point, resulting in very fast erosion of the steel. Because the runner channels are also subjected to this type of wear it is advisable to construct the complete sprue layout as an insert. The life span is further increased by producing the gate as a hardened steel insert (Fig. 6/1).

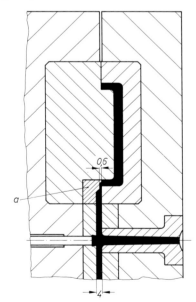

Fig. 6/1. Hardened steel insert for the gate.
(*a*) Hardened steel.

Gating

The shape and type of the gate employed depends on the design and layout of the tool and the moldings. Single-impression molds usually feature the tapered sprue rod, which ought to be kept as short as possible. A sprue bush is employed in the same way as with tools for thermoplastics materials. The hole diameter on the nozzle radius should be at least 3.5 mm. This applies to moldings of 5 mm maximum wall thickness. The bore should measure approximately 4 to 6 mm for larger wall thicknesses. The taper is $1\frac{1}{2}°$ and must be well polished to ensure trouble-free demolding.

Multi-impression tools require runners of equal length to each mold cavity. Pressure progress and simultaneous mold cavity filling are constant in that case (Fig. 6/2). The following formula for calculating the dimension of the gate cross section is useful: Gate cross section in mm^2 = volume of molding in cm^2 $\pm$ 50 %. Deduct for "soft" material (short-fibered filler: good prewarming) and add for "hard" material (long-

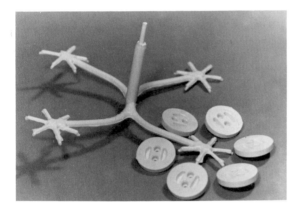

Fig. 6/2. Radial runner system for $4 \times 6 = 24$ impressions. Runners of equal length ensure uniform mold filling.

fibered filler: little prewarming, low injection pressure available). If it can be assumed, however, that a minimum gate thickness of 0.4 mm can be applied and that a film gate will be employed at the same time, the above formula becomes meaningless.

The influence of the dimensions of the molding on the gate cross section generally is as follows: thick walled, compact part–small gate cross section, i.e., high percentage of frictional heat; thin walled long part–large gate cross section, i.e., frictional heat fairly low, as otherwise the material would cure prematurely, due to the long flow path. The final dimensioning of the gate has to be done during balancing trials; the gate should pass sufficient material that the mold filling time does not exceed five seconds.

As with thermoplastics materials, the radial runner system should be retained on the moving half of the molding by undercuts (tapered bore with submerged ejector pin). It suffices to machine the channels for the runners into one half of the mold (preeminently on the ejector side). As already mentioned at the beginning of this chapter, chromium plating is essential in this case as well. Tunnel or pin gates are only employed for very soft formulations (good flow properties) and then mainly for solid moldings, which do not tend to distort. Even then the bore is quickly enlarged by wear and problem-free degating is no longer the case. To prevent the distortion of long, flat moldings it is preferable to site the gate at the narrow side (face); in this way the particles are aligned uniformly.

Venting

Venting is of particular importance since thermosets tend to create gas during processing, but this is determined by the type of resin and/or the resin content. There are various methods of venting, which find application according to the design of the mold cavities:
(a) Provide a venting slot approximately 5 to 8 mm wide and 0.03 mm deep at the end of the flow path. So that the slight flash created here does not stick to the mold plate, close the vent; this must be well polished or chromium plated.
(b) If there is an air inclusion inside the molding, this can be conducted away either by grinding a slight flat on the ejector pins or by a ground, separate pin. The ground area should only display a gap of 0.05 mm maximum.

Heating

The heating capacity to be installed amounts to approximately 30 to 40 W per kg of tool weight, calculating from experience. A high heating capacity decreases the heating-up time but results in wide-regulating band spread, which means a lack of constancy in mold temperature. The following pointers apply to the constructive design of the mold heating:
(a) Cartridge heaters in combination with heater bands create a homogeneous temperature impression (Fig. 6/3). If one does not use heater bands, then the insulation corners fitted to the tool can displace the isotherms.
(b) Usually the sprue rod shows a high temperature difference axially, i.e., the rod is not being cured uniformly right through, resulting in difficulties in demolding. Curing of the sprue rod determines the cycle time. Should this difficulty arise in practice, remedial action can be taken by installing separate sprue heating. It is understood that each mold half is heated and regulated separately. A separate temperature control must be provided for prominently protruding cores.

The tools are provided with particularly suited 10 to 12 mm thick insulating plates to keep the heat-transfer to the machine platens as low as possible.

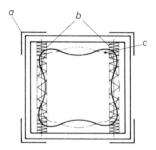

Fig. 6/3. Displacement of the isotherms in the tool through a combination of heater bands, cartridge heaters and insulation of the mold corners.
(*a*) Insulating corners, (*b*) cartridge heaters arranged to displace the isotherm, (*c*) isotherm.

The degree of demolding draught required must be obtained from the material manufacturers' data. This is generally about 1°, but not less than 2°, for polyester.

Thermoset moldings do not appear to suffer from shrinkage during the demolding phase, as is the case in thermoplastics processing. The moldings adhere to that part of the mold which shows the highest demolding resistance or where adhesion is caused by vacuum, created by the opening stroke. The molding should adhere to the moving mold half after opening in order to avoid demolding problems. This can be achieved by machining undercuts into the mold. A further possibility is the positive demolding of the parts from the fixed half through drag-link operated or spring-loaded ejector pins. The repeat-stroking ejector facility increases demolding reliability considerably.

Example 83. Injection-stamping (injection-compression) mold for a plate

Plates, cups, saucers and other tableware are often produced in thermoset materials, though predominantly in melamine resin molding materials. Apart from the compression molding process, which requires long cure times and wage-intensive manual operation, these moldings can also be produced on injection molding machines by the injection molding process.

As shown in Fig. 6/4, the plate is injected through a pin gate. This avoids subsequent removal of the sprue rod. With this type of gating the material is subjected to fierce orientation, which partially leads to high stresses. These effect distortion of the molding and lead so far that fissures occur around the gate. Therefore the plate could not possibly be produced by the standard injection molding process. For this reason the injection stamping process is employed here: the

Example 83

Fig. 6/4. Injection-stamping tool for a plate.
(*a*) Mold plate, (*b*) sandwich plate, (*c*) stamping plate, (*h*) nozzle undercut, (*k*) cartridge heater, (*m*) heater band, (*n*) insulating plate, (*t*) disc springs, (*v*) mushroom valve ejector, (*z*) stamping space.

mold closes to leave a gap of 6 to 8 mm, and then the material is injected. The machine closes as soon as the injection process is concluded, thereby pressing the material into the mold cavities. Stresses in the molding are minimized this way and a distortion-free article can be guaranteed.

The tool has to be designed as a dipping mold to make injection stamping at all feasible. However, since the plate does not allow the tool to be designed as a dipping mold, due to the radius on the outer edge of the plate, the mold has to be designed differently. In this particular instance it has been constructed as a three-plate mold, in which the central diameter acts as the stamping punch. The stamping procedure is as follows:

The mold closes until mold plate (a) touches the sandwich plate (b). A stamping gap (z) of approximately 6 to 8 mm is thus created. Now follows the accurately metered injection process, and at its conclusion the mold is closed. The material confined in the stamping gap is now compressed into the mold cavity by the plate.

The mold opens first between (c) and (b) due to the disc springs (t). Because the antechamber nozzle is still in contact at that moment, a vacuum is created in the space at (z), which retains the plate on the sandwich plate (b). Once the mold is fully opened, the nozzle retracts from the mold. Due to the undercut (h) the cured material is withdrawn from the antechamber. The vacuum can relax and the plate, which now only adheres to the mold plate (b), is lifted off by a pneumatically operated mushroom valve ejector (v). The material remaining on the nozzle is knocked off by a pneumatic cylinder-operated wedge.

Mold heating is by cartridge heaters (k). Twenty to 30 W heating capacity is recommended per kg tool steel. The antechamber should also be additionally provided with a heater band (m). The mold is equipped with insulating plates (n) to reduce heat transfer to the machine platens.

Example 84. Five-impression spindle-retracting tool for thermoset knobs

Machines and other lever-operated equipment require thermoset knobs in large quantities and of different sizes with and without internal screw thread. The most popular diameters are 25, 32 and 40 mm.

Injection molding with its shorter cycle times presents an alternative to the compression molding process, by which spheres of maximum wall thickness (approximately 15 mm) are produced in three minutes. At the beginning molds were produced in which the split line ran across the periphery of the knobs. The gate was about 8 mm wide and 0.8 mm thick on the sphere's circumference. This, however, had the disadvantage that the knobs became chipped when the sprue was broken off and these blemishes could not be removed by any finishing operation.

This problem is removed with a mold (Figs. 6/5 to 6/7) that features a 0.5 mm thick ring gate on the contact area for injecting the knobs. This requires two parting planes in the mold. To be able to produce at least three different sizes (with and without screw thread) in the same mold, all inserts must be interchangeable and the tool must incorporate spindle retraction.

The material is injected into the mold cavities via the ring gates when the cores are in and the tool is closed. When the cure time has elapsed, the hydraulic motor – which is accurately controlled by the core-pulling equipment on the machine – turns the chain-connected sun gear (1). This in turn rotates the toothed screw spindles (2) which unscrew the coupled screw core (4) from the knob via guide bush (3). To stop the knobs from rotating, the whole procedure takes place inside the closed mold. The mold then opens along split line (a) with the aid of the spring dowels (10). The center plate (5) is pulled along till it contacts the register (6). The sprue runner, retained on the moving half of the mold by an undercut in the ring-gate, separates from the molding and is ejected once the mold is open.

The ejector bolt (7) is coupled to the hydraulic ejector and can therefore be actuated repeatedly. The cores move in before the mold closes again. Should one of the spherical knobs not have dropped out by its own weight, the core will eject it during the slow-closing phase of the tool.

By exchanging the guide spindle (2), the guide bush (3) and the screw cores (4) various thread sizes can be accommodated. It is also possible to produce different sphere diameters by exchanging the inserts (8) and (9). If knobs without internal threads are to be produced, a smooth core is inserted instead of a threaded one.

The amount of flash on the circumference of the knob is negligible and hardly requires any finishing operation.

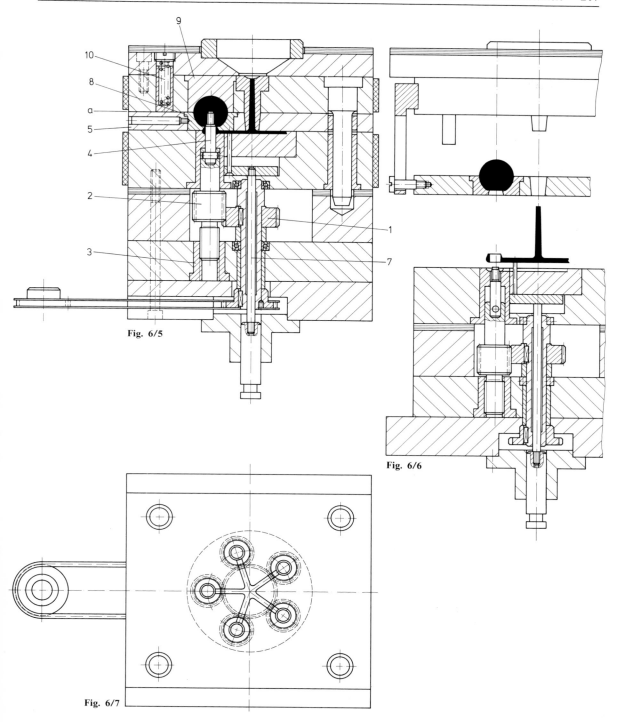

Fig. 6/5

Fig. 6/6

Fig. 6/7

Example 84

Figs. 6/5 to 6/7. Five-impression spindle-retracting tool for thermoset knobs.
(*1*) Sun gear, (*2*) screw spindle, (*3*) guide bush, (*4*) screw core, (*5*) center plate, (*6*) register, (*7*) ejector bolt, (*8, 9*) mold cavity inserts, (*10*) spring dowel, (*a*) parting plane.

Example 85. Thermoset-injection molding tool for thin-walled housing part

The housing part shown in Figs. 6/8 to 6/10 had to be injection molded in thermoset molding material. The thin-walled edges (0.3 mm) on the open side of the molding are of particular interest. The molding possesses rather thin walls all around and proves quite an ejection problem, as thermoset moldings do not necessarily adhere to the core but tend to remain in the cavity, unlike thermoplastic moldings. Undercuts are not the solution either as thermosets lack the necessary elasticity. Undercuts tend to break or shear off, leaving blemishes.

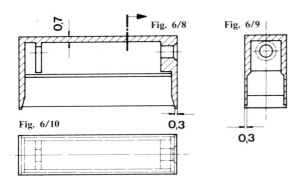

Figs. 6/8 to 6/10. Thin-walled housing part in thermoset material.

The only remaining answer is to eject the molding against the bottom side. As the molding is clamped against the core as well as the four outer walls, there is the danger of the ejector pins perforating the bottom of the housing. That is the reason why the internal core is withdrawn from the molding first of all and only then is the article released from exterior adhesion by the ejectors and demolded from the mold cavity.

This solution has been put into practice in the four-impression injection molding tool presented here by the introduction of two parting planes. The mold opens in the first parting plane through the spring-assisted jacks (3) after the housing parts have been injected and cured. During opening the tapered sprue (4) is pulled out of the sprue bush, which should have been polished longitudinally to allow the sprue to sep-

arate easily from the bush. The split (5) for producing the lateral holes in the housing is withdrawn via the angle dowel (6) at the same time and retained in its position by the spring-loaded catch (7). The first parting plane then opens, until the plate (8) contacts the latch (9), at which the second mold parting plane opens. By this procedure the core (10) is withdrawn from the housing. The injection molding is supported on its narrow sides (11) and by the two ejectors (12). The ejector plate (13) is connected to plate (8) by register bolts (14) so that the ejectors (12) do not alter their position on the housing during the opening of this parting plane. Once the mold has opened sufficiently far that the pin (16) on the register latch (9) has run up the release cam (17), the interlock latch (9) and plate (8) is cancelled and the moving half can continue on its opening stroke. It will travel on until the ejector rod (18) contacts the fixed machine stop (19), pushing the ejector plate (13) forward, thereby ejecting housings and sprue. A compression spring (20) has been mounted on the ejector rod (18) to pull the ejector plate (13) back when the mold closes. Once the housing part has been pushed out of the mold cavity in plate (8) by the ejector pins (12), the moldings could get stuck on the ejector pins. This would put the fully automatic operation of the machine in jeopardy. An ejector-retraction facility as part of the machine controls or repeat-stroking of the ejector system are very useful if not essential on thermoset-processing machines. With the ejector-retraction facility switched on, the moving mold half closes again for a settable distance, once the opening stroke is completed. In this way the ejectors can be retracted (employed for injection moldings with inserts or as an aid to ejection). With the "repeat-stroking of the ejector" facility on the machine, this sequence can be repeated several times, so that even those moldings will be ejected that otherwise would hang on tenaciously.

When the tool closes, the ejector plate (13) is returned completely by the push-back pins (21). Particular care must be taken with cavity venting on thermoset tools. In the case presented here it has been of great help that the core is well suited for venting.

After a short guide section in plate (8) it is relieved (22). This relief also serves as an unrestricted exit for any material possibly finding its way between core (10) and plate (8), so that seizure of the core is prevented.

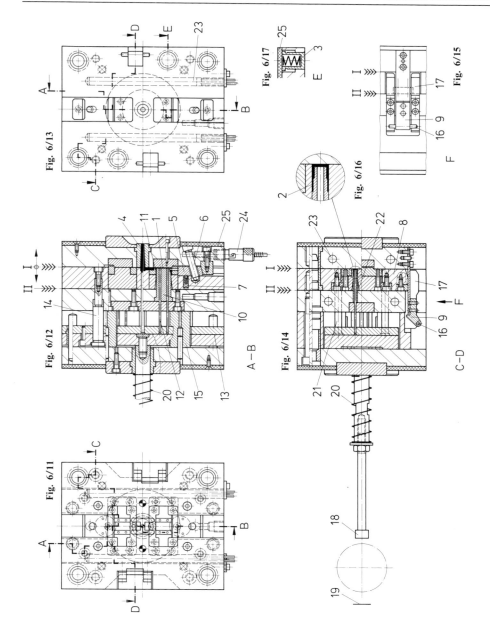

Fig. 6/13

Fig. 6/17

Fig. 6/16

Fig. 6/15

Fig. 6/12

Fig. 6/14

Fig. 6/11

Example 85

Figs. 6/11 to 6/17. Four-impression injection molding tool for thin-walled housing part in thermoset material.

(*1*) Housing part, (*2*) annular 0.3 mm thick rim of the housing part, (*3*) spring loaded jack, (*4*) tapered sprue, (*5*) split, (*6*) angle dowel, (*7*) spring loaded catch, (*8*) plate, (*9*) latch, (*10*) core, (*11*) narrow sides of housing, (*12*) ejector, (*13*) ejector plates, (*14*) register bolts, (*15*) reinforcing spacers for mold stiffening in the ejector plate spaces, (*16*) pin, (*17*) release cam, (*18*) ejector rod, (*19*) machine stop, (*20*) compression spring, (*21*) push-back pin, (*22*) relief around the core.

Example 86. Multi-impression injection molding tool for rings in elastomeric materials

Elastomer processing on injection molding machines has the advantage of shorter cure times compared with those for conventional compression molding. It also eliminates the manual insertion of rubber blanks. As rubber tends to stick in the mold, automatic demolding is unfortunately only possible in a few isolated cases. This means that the moldings themselves can usually be demolded, depending on their shape, but the gate runners and the skin have to be removed by hand (a different solution is offered by the cold-runner tool; refer to example 87).

Figures 6/18 to 6/20 show an 84-impression tool for the production of rings (wheels for toy cars). The mold is designed as a three plate tool. The moldings are pin-gate injected via a skin.

The operating sequence is as follows: The mold closes down to a gap of approximately 6 mm between (3) and (4). An accurately metered amount of material is injected into this empty space, forming a cake that is compressed to about 0.8 mm thickness during the subsequent final mold closing. The material is squeezed through the gate runners into the cavities in this way. Once the rubber has cured, the mold opens between plates (3) and (4). Due to the interspacing moldings plate (4) is dragged along until it contacts the collars on the guide rods (10). As the undercut in the bore of the moldings exceeds that on the exterior contour, the wheels remain suspended on the core pins (17) during further mold opening. Once the mold has opened completely, the stripper plate (5) is moved forward by the ejector bolt (16) and the parts are stripped off the core pins. The skin with the gates remaining in plate (4) has to be removed by hand. This procedure does not take long, as the skin is in one piece.

When processing elastomers, special care must be taken that the mold cavities are well vented, otherwise the moldings will be blotchy or short of material. In the case presented here this can be achieved by a play of 0.04 mm between core pin and stripper plate. One must advise against any larger play, however.

Approximately 2 mm wide and 0.1 mm deep air vents are ground between the stripper plate (5) and plate (6) straight across the drilled holes, in which the core pins move, to exhaust the air from the tool.

As there is no hollow space between ejector plate and bolster plate in this tool, heating has to be accomplished by heating plates, in the same way as it is done on compression molds. This has the advantage of uniform tool expansion, which is of particular importance in this instance.

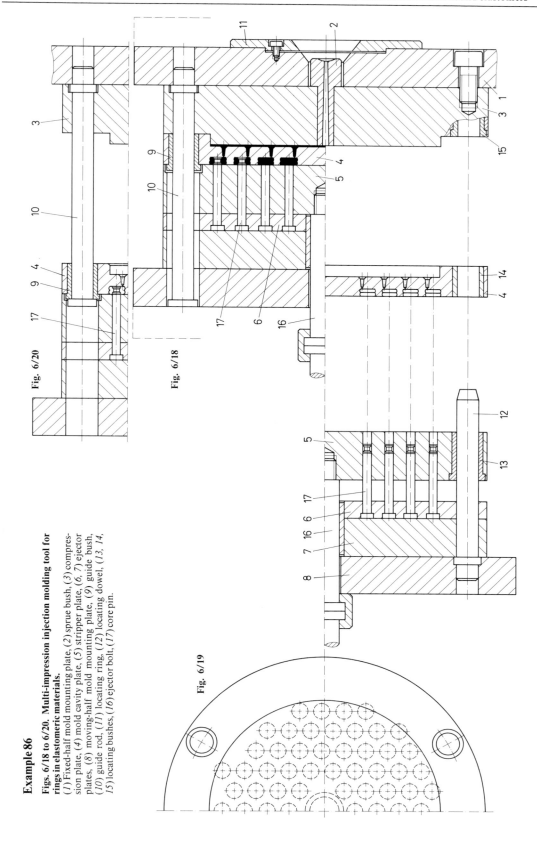

Example 86

Figs. 6/18 to 6/20. Multi-impression injection molding tool for rings in elastomeric materials.

(*1*) Fixed-half mold mounting plate, (*2*) sprue bush, (*3*) compression plate, (*4*) mold cavity plate, (*5*) stripper plate, (*6, 7*) ejector plates, (*8*) moving-half mold mounting plate, (*9*) guide bush, (*10*) guide rod, (*11*) locating ring, (*12*) locating dowel, (*13, 14, 15*) locating bushes, (*16*) ejector bolt, (*17*) core pin.

Fig. 6/20

Fig. 6/18

Fig. 6/19

Example 87. Rubber buffer injection molding tool with cold runner manifold

As it is not possible to regenerate vulcanized rubber, cold-runner molds are much preferred. They operate without gates and allow for a high degree of automation. The cold-runner system relies on intensive cooling within the sprue zone, and in this respect it represents the opposite of the well-known hot-runner system for thermoplastics molds. The cold runner consists of three parts: the main body (*1*), the insulating body (*2*) and the half-shell (*3*).

The insulating body is bolted to the half-shell by four M12 bolts, completely enclosing the main body. This contains the star-shaped runners into which the material is injected to be fed into the machined annular gate runner in parts (*2*) and (*3*). It is very important that the surface of these channels be well polished. The gates of 2 mm × 0.4 mm branch off this annular groove at chosen intervals to feed the individual mold cavities (refer to Fig. 6/22). The material that remains in the runner system is protected from heat transfer from the heated mold plates by effective cooling, which ought to be kept constant at 60°C to ensure that the material is of a homogeneity necessary for its flow characteristics. As shown in Fig. 6/21 the main body is surrounded by a labyrinth of cooling channels, relieved surfaces and machined grooves, the whole of which is sealed by O-rings. The locating of the cold runner insert is by conical surfaces, which hold it precisely in the parting line. The insert has been reliefed with machined slots to keep the contact area as small as possible against heat absorption. The cylindrical part should be a slight push-fit. When the mold is open, the cold runner is lifted off the mold mounting plate by about 10 mm through four springs (*4*). The movement is restricted by four bolts. This offers the advantage of the insert not contacting the hot mold mounting plate, preventing heat transfer during the opening and ejection period. When the mold closes, the insert is pushed back on its cone-shaped seatings again. The injected material flows through the runner manifold into the mold cavities. After curing, the tool opens and the sleeve ejectors (*5*) demold the parts. The play between sleeve (*5*) and core pin (*6*) should not exceed 0.05 mm, maximum.

In case the material nevertheless should cure in the cold runner, much time can be saved if a spare insert is available. An exchange of manifolds facilitates cleaning the blocked one outside the mold. Care must be taken that the mold is always closed when injecting, to counteract the pressure within the cold runner.

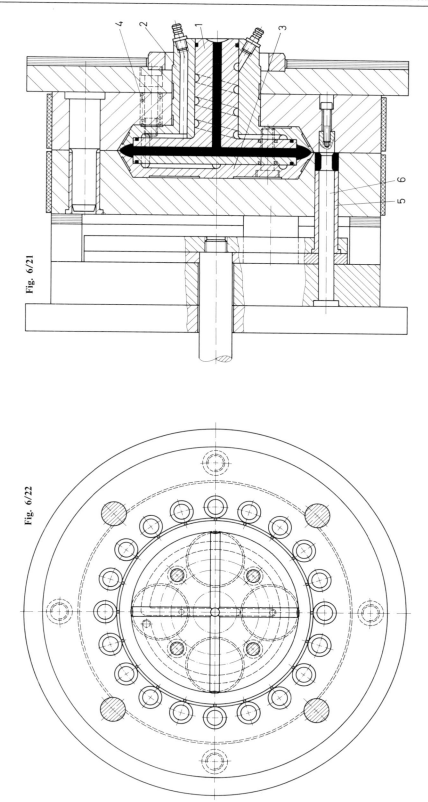

Fig. 6/21

Fig. 6/22

Example 87

Figs. 6/21 and 6/22. Rubber-buffer injection molding tool with cold-runner manifold.
(*1*) Main body of the cold runner manifold, (*2*) insulating body, (*3*) half shell, (*4*) compression spring, (*5*) sleeve ejector, (*6*) core pin.

7 Special Designs

Example 88. Injection molding tool for cord-fitted plugs

The satisfactory connection between the cord and plug remained a problem until continuity between plug pins and wiring by screw connections and the mechanical securing of the cable to the plug body by clamping between the two plug halves became standard procedure.

Since it has become permissible to employ thermoplastic materials as well for plug connections according to VDE 0346, a new type of mechanical possibility has arisen, of injection molding the plug directly onto the end of the cable, which already has the pins fitted to it. Where these plugs are produced in flexible PVC or low-density polyethylene, a soft, flexible transition from plug to cord results from skilled design, so that breaks at this danger spot can be prevented with some certainty.

The wiring can be secured to the pins without screw connections by either soldering or clamping. A reliable contact and mechanical connection of plug pins and wiring is established by complete embedding in plastic material.

For the economical production of these connecting plugs a minimum of molding effort should be necessary. It is uneconomical in any case to insert the cord and pins into the mold on the machine.

To avoid any shifting of the connecting wires within the mold cavity when the plastic melt is injected, the lead would have to be tensioned (pulled) against the clamping plug pins, which would lead to further time losses if this is to occur in the mold when the machine is open.

The two-impression tool subsequently described (Figs. 7/1 to 7/6) prevents this occurrence by inserting and tensioning the pins and lead in a frame outside the mold. This frame can quickly be inserted in the tool. Fairly long cooling times are necessary anyway for the relatively thick-walled plugs in the closed mold, so that the operator can fill the second frame during this idle time.

The engraved plates (a) and (b) are rigidly mounted in the tool and doweled with each other by the guide dowels (c) and (d). The point of injection lies immediately at the transition where the lead joins the plug, through two or more opposing gates to prevent one-sided displacement of the cable by the inflowing material mass.

The runner channel is led around the lead in the shape of an annulus, which enters the mold cavity through two or more gates of very small cross section. An angle dowel (e) has been provided on the moving half of the mold for demolding this ring channel, ejecting the molding itself on movement. The annulus is removed at the same time due to the tangential position of the angle dowel.

The demolding from the fixed half also takes place through an angle dowel (f), which is pushed forward by a leaf spring (g). A frame (h) and (i) is pushed onto the protruding cavity plate (b) of the moving half when the mold is open. The frame has been loaded outside the machine in the manner already described.

To ensure that all four plug pins in the two-impression tool are securely clamped by lever action, clamping pieces (k) have been provided in the mold. These are tightened with the clamping strip (l) by movement of the rotary lever (m) so that each plug pin is clamped individually. Each lead is clamped separately on the opposite side of the frame by a clamping strip (n).

This frame with the clamped and tensioned leads and pins is inserted into the machine to be encapsulated by injection molded material. The frame is pushed forward by about 10 mm when the ejector bolt (o) contacts the machine stop. However, it remains hanging on the cavity plate (b) and has to be removed manually. The second frame, which has been loaded in the meantime, is inserted and the next cycle can start.

Example 88 (page 216)

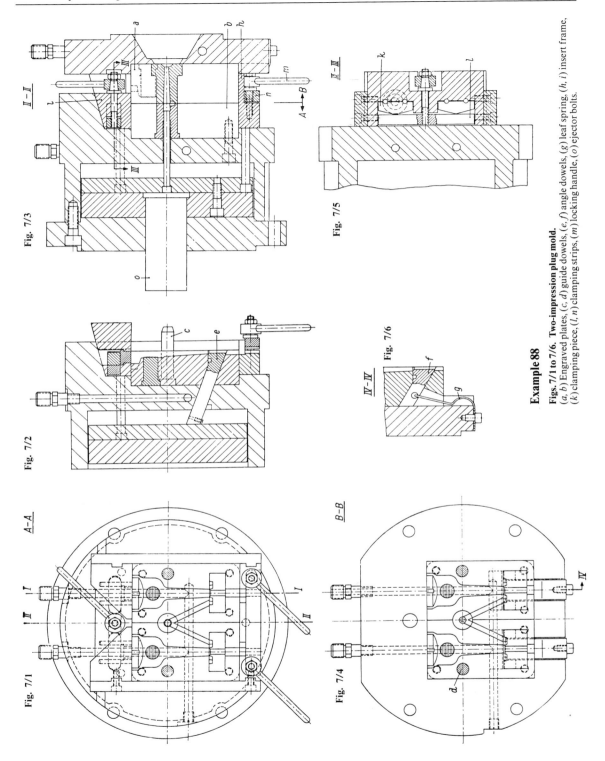

Fig. 7/3

I – I

Fig. 7/5

II – II

Fig. 7/2

Fig. 7/6

IV – IV

Fig. 7/1

A–A

Fig. 7/4

B–B

Example 88

Figs. 7/1 to 7/6. Two-impression plug mold.
(a, b) Engraved plates, (c, d) guide dowels, (e, f) angle dowels, (g) leaf spring, (h, i) insert frame, (k) clamping piece, (l, n) clamping strips, (m) locking handle, (o) ejector bolts.

Example 89. Injection molding tool for a spiral gear wheel

A spiral gear with external helical teeth at below 70° has to be produced in polyamide. There are two prominent problems: the production of the negative profile for the external tooth shape and the demolding of the 70° helical tooth profile.

Producing the mold cavity

The mold cavity can only be produced by electroplating, as it is of course possible to mill out a 70° helical gear but is impossible to reproduce the impression of that gear by mechanical means.

To produce a "negative" by electroplating poses no problems, however. For this purpose an exact pattern of the helical gear in plastics or metal is merely required, produced without difficulty on a lathe and a suitable gear-cutting machine of sufficient precision. Naturally, the shrinkage subject to the plastics material to be employed has to be allowed for when producing the model. A nickel-cobalt layer of 2 mm thickness is then deposited on the model by electroplating. This deposit is reinforced by a galvanic hard-copper layer

to such an extent that machining to the required mold dimensions becomes feasible.

Demolding the tooth profile

The second problem presenting itself is the demolding of the 70° tooth profile. Although the molding could be pushed out by an ejector supported on ball-bearings or an ejector sleeve in the present case with a relatively steep-angled helical gear, this method fails with a spiral gear of 70° or shallower pitch angle. The molding therefore has to be forcibly turned out of the mold profiles, corresponding to the pitch angle of the gear, when ejecting. So that the molding is gripped securely during ejection, flat grooves had to be machined into the face of the ejector sleeve to transmit the turning movement from the ejector sleeve to the molding.

As the number of units to be produced has not been very high, a single-impression tool only had to be provided.

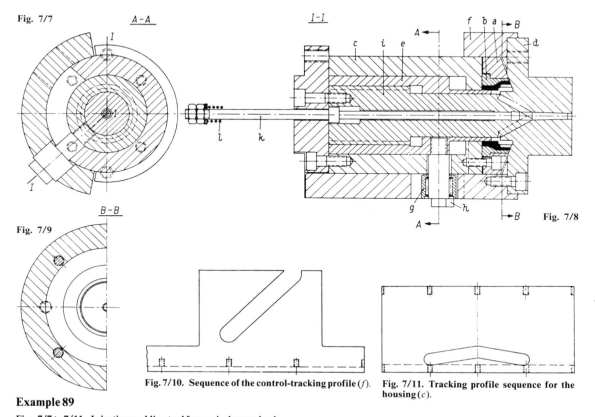

Fig. 7/7   A–A   I–I

Fig. 7/9   B–B

Fig. 7/8

Fig. 7/10. Sequence of the control-tracking profile (f).

Fig. 7/11. Tracking profile sequence for the housing (c).

Example 89

Figs. 7/7 to 7/11. Injection molding tool for a spiral gear wheel.
(a) Clamping lid, (b) electroformed insert, (c) housing, (d) mold mounting plate, (e) ejector sleeve, (f) control tracking profile, (g) needle bearing, (h) shaft, (i) fixed core, (k) ejector bar, (l) spring.

It is, however, possible to produce a multi-impression tool making use of the same principles as well. The mold (Figs. 7/7 to 7/11) is constructed in such a way that during the opening of the clamping lid (*a*), which connects the electroformed insert (*b*) with the housing (*c*), between the fixed mold mounting plate (*d*) the ejector sleeve (*e*) is forced forward, rotating at the same time according to the pitch of the gear teeth. To achieve this, the control tracking profile (*f*), which also serves to locate one mold half with the other, is bolted to the fixed mold half (*d*). Fig. 7/10 shows the sequence of this control tracking profile (*f*). Inside the control-slot profile, open toward the moving mold half, slides a needle bearing (*g*), whose shaft (*h*) is screwed into the ejector sleeve (*e*). With a rotating movement by the ejector sleeve of approximately 45° the helical teeth are demolded completely. A slot has been provided in the housing (*c*) to accommodate the shaft (*h*) (refer to the sequence in Fig. 7/11).

The mechanics described so far may result in a turning motion of the ejector sleeve (*e*) but do not determine the pitch of this turning movement as yet. In order to achieve this forcibly according to the helical profile of the gear wheel when the ejector sleeve (*e*) turns, that sleeve is meshed with the fixed core (*i*) through a lead thread of the same pitch angle as the gear wheel to be produced. When the ejector sleeve (*e*) is rotated by the cam track (*f*) the sleeve (*e*) follows the pitch of the gear wheel precisely. When the mold closes, the movement procedure takes place in the reverse order.

The helical gear is injected via three tunnel gates, which are automatically degated when the mold opens, and the sprue is retained by the undercut bore in the core (*i*). After mold opening the ejector bar (*k*) contacts the fixed machine stop and ejects the sprue. The ejector bar returns by the action of spring (*l*) when the mold closes.

Example 90.   Twelve-impression injection molding tool for blouse hangers

So-called disposable hangers are part of the purchase with men's shirts, women's blouses, etc. They are produced by the injection molding process exclusively, as any other manufacturing means would prove far too expensive. These hangers consist of as thin walled a carrier as possible, usually of T-section, with a central hole for the hook. In most cases the hole is arranged in the direction of the mold parting plane, which means that comparatively few hangers can be accommodated because the core pulling for the bore requires much space in the parting plane. As the hangers require relatively large tools due to their length and hence need correspondingly large machines, there is usually a striking disproportion between actual injection capacity required and the necessary machine size, which cannot even remotely be utilized.

The mold design according to Figs. 7/12 to 7/14 offers the advantage of incorporating as many hangers as possible in one tool, so that the injection capacity of the relatively large machine can be fully utilized. In this case hangers and hooks are produced in the same mold, resulting in considerable savings in mold-production costs.

The mold has been constructed as a three-plate tool, i.e., there are two opening planes. The manifold strip is housed in the split line facing the fixed half and the hangers are injected through pin gates on the inside of the boss. The hangers lie in the moving-half plane with the hole axis in the direction of the ejector. This arrangement makes it possible to accommodate 12

hangers at approximately 18 mm spacing within the place available between the tiebars of the machine.

The upper sides of the hangers are profiled into plate (*a*), which is displaceable on the guide strips (*b*) in the opening direction of the machine until stopped by registers on these strips. The hooks are partially profiled into the other side of plate (*a*). They are injected through their spheres by pin gates from the manifold strip situated in that plane. The gates must be substantial enough to demold the hooks withouth breaking when this parting plane opens and the sprue strip is forcibly ejected.

The other halves of the hooks are partially arranged in plate (*c*), which also accommodates the runner manifold. Conical bores from this manifold strip to the core inserts (*d*) lead right up to the bore of the hangers, where they enter the mold cavity through a pin gate of approximately 1.2 mm diameter at less than 45°.

Plate (*a*) is interlocked with the moving mold half, when the tool is closed, via the locking latches (*e*) and the leaf springs (*f*) riveted to them. The leaf springs are bolted together with the mounting plate (*g*) on the moving mold half. During opening the mold therefore initially opens in the sprue manifold plane. The gates on the hanger are severed and the sprues pulled out of their bores. The sprue strip is initially retained on the fixed half by undercut bores (*h*) in plate (*c*).

The center of the manifold strip is held captive by the sprue retainer (*i*) on the moving half. This retainer is allowed to move along for a distance approximately equal to the length of the gate runner before it contacts a register. The ejector bush (k) travels the same distance before it encounters its stop. The manifold plane continues opening for a distance of altogether approximately 150 mm, until the plate (a) contacts the registers of the guide strips (b). During this travel the main sprue is pulled from the sprue bush (l).

After an opening distance of 150 mm in the sprue manifold plane the latches (e) are released as the release pins (m) run onto the 45° cams on the guide strips (b) and the mold opens in the main opening plane, which houses the hangers. From that moment on the sprue retainer (i) pulls out from the undercut in the main sprue and the manifold strip is ejected by the forward propulsion of the ejector bush (k) under pressure of spring (n). Once the mold has opened sufficiently far in the main parting plane in which the hangers are positioned, the ejector plate (o) contacts the machine stop and the ejector plates (p) and (q) are pushed forward. The hangers are now ejected by tube ejector (r) and ejector (s).

Push-back pins return the ejector plates when the mold closes. With three cycles per minute, which is easily attainable on a machine with screw plasticizing facility, 2000 hangers and hooks per hour can be produced.

Example 90 (pages 220–221)

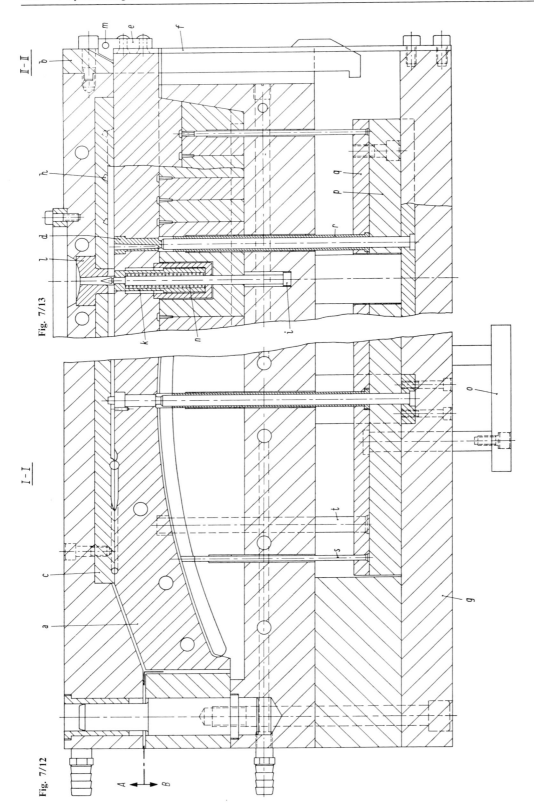

Fig. 7/12

Fig. 7/13

Example 90

Figs. 7/12 and 7/13. Twelve-impression injection molding tool for blouse hangers, secs. *I-I* and *II-II*.
For an explanation of terms refer to Fig. 7/14.

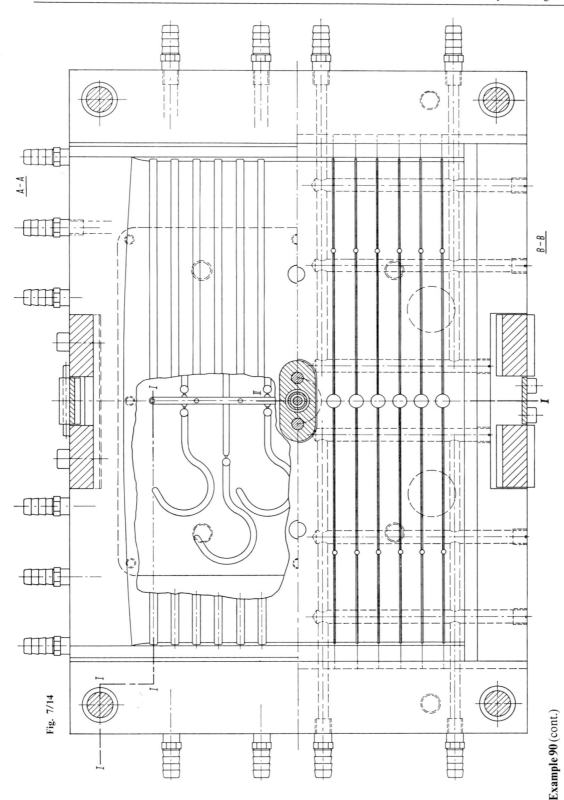

Fig. 7/14

A–A

B–B

Fig. 7/14. Secs. *A-A* and *B-B* of a 12-impression mold for blouse hangers.
(*a*) Cavity plate, (*b*) guide strips, (*c*) sprue plate, (*d*) core inserts, (*e*) interlocking latches, (*f*) leaf springs, (*g*) mounting plate, (*h*) undercut bores, (*i*) sprue retainer, (*k*) ejector bush, (*l*) sprue bush, (*m*) release pins, (*n*) spring, (*o*) ejector plate, (*p, q*) front and rear ejector plate, (*r*) tubular ejector, (*s*) ejector pins, (*t*) push-back pins.

Example 90 (cont.)

Fig. 7/15

Refer to Fig. 7/18

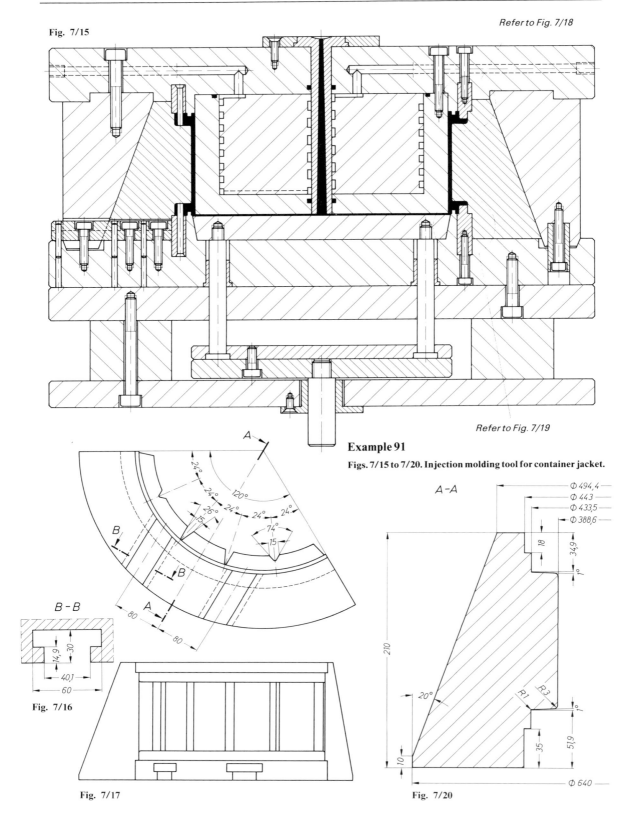

Refer to Fig. 7/19

Example 91

Figs. 7/15 to 7/20. Injection molding tool for container jacket.

A–A

$\emptyset$ 494,4
$\emptyset$ 443
$\emptyset$ 433,5
$\emptyset$ 388,6

B–B

Fig. 7/16

Fig. 7/17

Fig. 7/20

Example 91. Injection molding tool for container jacket with external rib reinforcement

The request had been for the production of tubular-section transparent containers (external dia. 425 mm, weight 2000 g) that would have the highest possible resistance to chemicals, resistance to heat reversion and dimensional stability at an internal pressure loading of 1.2 bar. The container jackets are equipped with lids of the same material for both openings. Light metal plates are fixed to the lids to absorb the internal pressure. They are held together by studs and nuts in noncorrosive material that are fitted through drilled holes in the flanges of the jacket.

A suitable thermoplastic material with fully adequate characteristics is polymethyl pentene. One of the peculiarities of this material is a certain unreliability in its shrinkage behavior. Variable processing conditions have a strong effect on the processing shrinkage with polymethyl pentene. Even the postshrinkage in warm air can vary. Processing shrinkage and postshrinkage can fluctuate independently of each other, and the sum of the two shrinkage magnitudes need not be constant at all every time.

The injection molding, however, must possess great dimensional stability, as the two sealing grooves on the flange faces are only 1 mm apart from similar grooves on the inside of the lids. A crossing of the two grooves must be avoided at all costs so that good sealing is not endangered.

It was therefore decided to equip the mold for the jacket (Fig. 7/15) with inserted rings on the fixed and the moving half. The proud parts on these rings for the sealing grooves were to be dimensioned by plenty of additional material from both sides, and these proud rings were then to be machined to the correct internal and external diameters on the first production-run-manufactured moldings once the jacket profile and the warm air treatment had been tested. It had also been determined that the sealing grooves should be molded 1 mm deeper than required, for it had been assumed that sinks would occur on the flange faces due to the rapidly changing wall thicknesses. This would mean that the face surfaces would probably have to be machined to make them flat. In fact, the flanges were molded without sinks. The ribs spaced axially around the outside area of the jacket led people to assume that the molding would not turn out rounded but many-cornered. A sprue system of radial runners to a certain number of gates would probably have increased this tendency even further. However, as the demand had been for the best possible roundness, a fully covering plate was employed as sprue runner (umbrella gate); this had to be subsequently removed by turning on a lathe. Estimating the effect of the internal pressure loading on the jacket under field conditions was not possible due to lack of experience. A symmetrically distributed larger number of well-dimensioned ribs would have meant a tool with a great many radially pulled splits, which would have increased the tool price considerably. As a compromise it was agreed to fit ribs positioned in a certain sequence of alternatively higher and lower dimensions, which decreased the number of splits to three (Figs. 7/17 and 7/18).

Finally, the question of ejection had to be resolved. Traditionally, tools for moldings of such shape are constructed so that the splits move immediately as the mold starts opening, with the ejector pins or a stripper plate to demold the article from the core at the end of the opening movement. But as it was feared that in this particular case the molding would adhere rather firmly to the only slightly tapered core and that cracks would occur in the flange on the ejector side due to the relatively small area for any ejector device to push against, it was decided to remove the molding from the core while the splits are still closed. The article is then removed from the mold by hand once the splits have

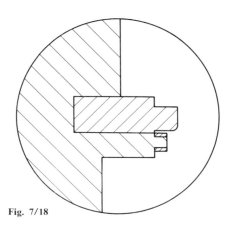

Fig. 7/18

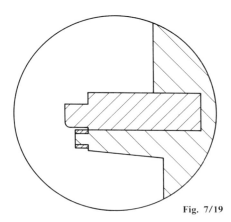

Fig. 7/19

been pulled radially by one hydraulic or pneumatic cylinder each at the end of the opening stroke.

It has been proved that this planning of molding and tool is correct. After the trial procedure and the correction to the insert rings laid down right at the beginning, production now runs so reliably according to fixed setting data for the injection molding machine and also fixed parameters for the posttreatment with hot air that the critical tolerances–outside diameter of the flanges and sealing groove diameters–are kept to within 0.2 mm on the end product.

It is worth mentioning that it has been observed that the container jackets stabilize within themselves slowly, contrary to the theory valid for thermoplastics materials, which holds that despite the internal pressure of 1.2 bar remaining uniform, no continuing "cold flow" occurs. The greater part of expansion takes place during the first hours, days or weeks at the most. After a few months of unchanged internal pressure the outside diameter of the jacket remains constant.

Mold designer: Nils Göran Niglöv, Fa. Rantil Plast AB, Karlskrona/Sweden.

Example 92. Three-impression injection molding tool for liquid-measuring cylinders

An injection molding tool had to be designed for manufacturing a measuring cylinder for liquids. Owing to the low wall thickness of 1.2 mm the wall-thickness tolerances were not to exceed 0.1 mm. This stipulation is very difficult to comply with for slim components.

To keep flexural stresses on the core that arise from the incoming plastic melt as low as possible, the sprue was directed onto it tangentially. This way the material is forced to flow around the central core (7) in Fig. 7/21 instead of flowing at it radially. For reasons of stability the core is fixed at both ends, at the top in the mold mounting plates (1) and (2) and at the bottom by a collar (8), which fits into a recess of the lower mold half (5) with a sliding fit (H7/h6).

At the start of injection the spring discs (9) push the collar (8) against the mold body (3). Once the plastic material has filled the cylinder jacket, it flows into the annular gap between the collar (8) and the mold body (3), pushing the collar away from the body. This removes the lower location of the core (7) by the collar (8), and the plastic material is allowed to fill out the bottom of the measuring cylinder. During mold opening the distance bolts (16) and (17) pull the three-plate tool apart. The spring (14) separates the sprue from the molding. Compressed air is admitted, which opens the mushroom valve (21), blowing the molding off the core (7).

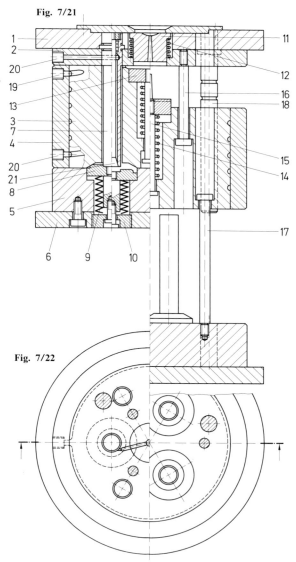

Fig. 7/21

Fig. 7/22

Example 92

Figs. 7/21 and 7/22. Injection molding tool for liquid-measuring cylinder.
(1, 2) Upper mold mounting plate, (3) mold body, (4) jacket, (5) lower mold half, (6) lower mold mounting plate, (7) core, (8) collars, (9) disc springs, (10) set screws, (11) sprue bush, (12) spring, (13) sprue ejector collar, (14) spring, (15, 16, 17) distance bolts, (18) guide dowels, (19) cooling water connection, (20) compressed air connection, (21) valve.

Injection molds for two-color plastics components

Example 93. Mold for a camping cup

Dichromatic plastics articles are often produced in two stages. An injection molding in one color is placed by hand in the second mold and the compound with the other color is injected around it. This procedure is uneconomical and incurs excessive production costs.

The camping utensils cup shown in Fig. 7/23 is a typical example of two-colored plastics parts. For aesthetic reasons, the cup should be white on the inside and a pastel shade on the outside. The aim is to design a mold that allows this dichromatic plastics article to be produced in one operation. The injection molding installation available for the purpose has two vertical injection units.

Fig. 7/23. Two-colored camping utensils cup.

Mold design and method of operation

The inner white lining of the cup is injection molded first along the lines indicated in Fig. 7/24. Afterward the clamping unit opens, and the springs (22) and (23) lift the core (13) together with the injection molding from the two-cavity mold. The springs (22) and (23) have the same constants. Thus the two half-shells (11) and (12) open simultaneously. Once the mold has opened to the extent that the core (13) together with the injection molding is exposed, the transverse pin (20) slides into the threaded groove of the sleeve (19), and the center of the mold (17) commences to rotate. After it has turned through 180°, the mold is completely open. A fresh closing stroke then begins. At the same time the sleeve (19) turns in the opposite direction, and the pawl (27) is disengaged. In other words, the central part (17) no longer rotates with the core (13). Once the mold is completely closed, the compound with the second color is injected from the second unit onto the first part while it is still warm. After the mold has opened, the finished cup is blown off from the core with compressed air, which is introduced through the connection (26). However, the mushroom-type valve (14) does not open until the position of the compressed-air inlet (21) coincides with that of the transverse groove (19) on the sleeve.

The two operations run in parallel, that is, when the second injection unit is injecting compound around the molding obtained in the first stage, the inner part is being injection molded in the first mold cavity.

Example 93 (right)

Figs. 7/24 to 7/26. Injection mold for two-color cups.
(A) Half of the thread pitch for the sleeve (19);
(B) turned through 105°.
(1) Upper clamping platen, (2) spacers, (3) upper cooling platen, (4) upper part of mold, (5) lower part of mold, (6) lower cooling platen, (7) lower clamping platen, (8) spring housing, (9) upper insert for the second color, (10) lower insert for the second color, (11) upper insert for the first color, (12) lower insert for the first color, (13) core, (14) mushroom-type valve, (15) plunger, (16) springs, (17) central part of the mold (rotatable), (18) screw, (19) sleeve, (20) transverse pin, (21) hole drilled to admit air (on one side only), (22, 23) springs, (24) sleeve, (25) guide bolts, (26) connections for compressed air, (27) pawl, (28) leaf spring, (29) screw to (27), (30) sprues for two parts each, (31) ball bearings in race, (32) washer, (33) bolts to arrest the stroke, (34) holes drilled for the cooling medium (upper and lower).

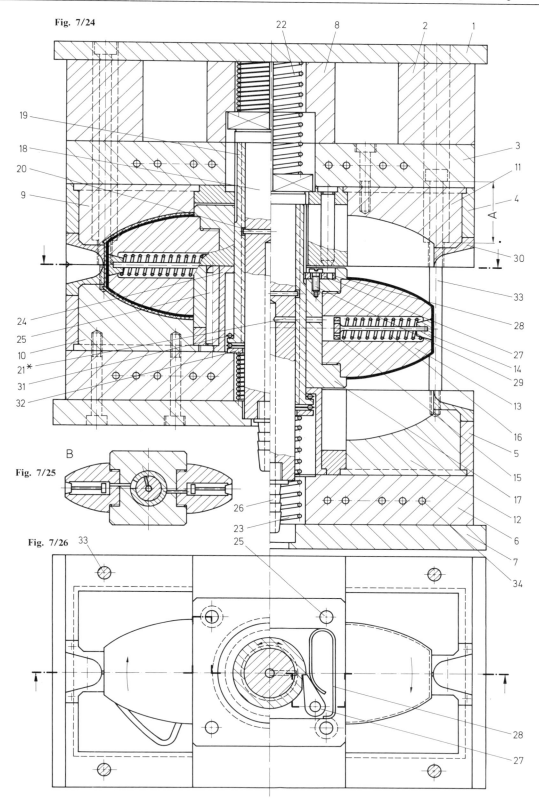

Fig. 7/24

Fig. 7/25

Fig. 7/26

Example 94. Mold for water tap handle

Decorative bathroom fittings are frequently made with transparent handles in which there is a second layer made from a nontransparent layer. The mold illustrated in Figs. 7/27 to 7/31 is designed for the production of this type of part. Both of the differently colored materials are injected one after the other at two stations on the mold, thus enabling the part to be produced in one operation. It is also necessary, however, to use an injection molding machine that has two plasticizing units arranged at right angles to each other.

The main view (Fig. 7/28) shows the mold in its closed position. At the left mold station the molding of the colored inner component of the handle is carried out by the injection unit on axis (*a*). At the same time the outer transparent part of the handle is molded over this part using the unit on axis (*b*) through the sprue bush (*22*). The wall thickness of the outer layer of the molding needs to be rapidly cooled and hence the

mold cavity bolster (*15*) is made with a narrowly machined cooling coil. On solidification the mold is opened and the part is ejected. This occurs in position II, as shown in the right-hand side of the drawing (Fig. 7/30), by advancing the ejector bar (*12*) with the help of the pneumatic cylinder (*20*). Only after this first step can plate (*4*) be freed, and held in the appropriate position by the limiting screw (*30*). The core carrier plates (*5*) and (*6*) with the cores (*11*), which carry the molded colored inner parts of the handle, run out of the plate (*4*) only so far as necessary to allow them to be turned through 180° under plate (*4*), so that on reclosing the mold the freed cores will reengage with the premolding station and the cores containing the inner part will engage the final molding station.

The turning movement is made by a four-cornered spindle (*16*), whose gear wheel (*17*) engages a pinion (*18*) moved by the pneumatic cylinder (*19*).

Example 94 (right)

Figs. 7/27 to 7/31. Injection mold for a transparent water tap handle containing a colored inner layer.
(*1, 2*) Fixed mounting plates, (*3*) mold cavity for interior molding, (*4*) mold cavity mounting plate, (*5, 6*) turnable discs, (*7*) guiding ring, (*8*) base plate, (*9*) distance ring, (*10*) movable mounting plate, (*11*) collars, (*12*) ejector pins, (*13*) spring, (*14*) mold cavity holding ring, (*15*) mold cavity insert, (*16*) spindle with four-sided head, (*17*) gear wheel, (*18*) pinion, (*19*) pneumatic cylinder for moving plates (*5, 6*), (*20*) pneumatic cylinder for ejector of finished moldings, (*21*) fitting disc, (*22*) sprue bush, (*23*) spring, (*24*) rod, (*25*) hook, (*26*) cross pin, (*27*) bearing housing, (*28*) spring, (*29*) cooling water connection, (*30, 31*) movement limiting screws, (*32*) guiding column, (*33*) cross bolts, (*34*) fitting rings, (*35*) disc, (*36*) bushes, (*37*) nuts for (*12*), (*38*) sealing discs, (*39*) O-rings, (*40*) telescopic shell for (*30*).

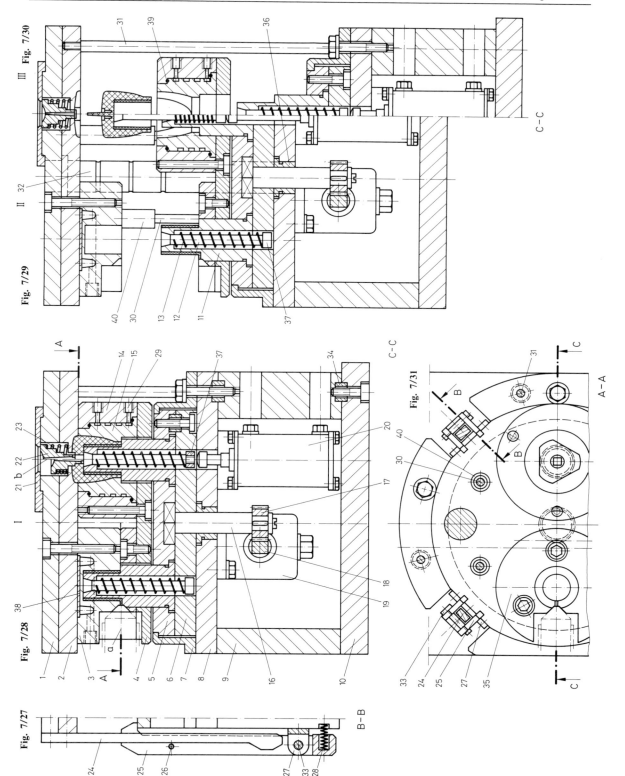

Fig. 7/30

Fig. 7/29

Fig. 7/28

Fig. 7/27

Fig. 7/31

C–C

A–A

B–B

Example 95. Six-impression injection molding tool for fixing-nuts with metal inserts

Fixing-nuts on electrical instruments are provided with a threaded copper insert part to ensure good contact. To prevent the thread from becoming contaminated with the plastics material injected into the mold cavity these inserts are usually screwed onto a core. This process requires a considerable amount of time during loading a well as demolding of the finished part. Although it would be expedient to employ a turntable injection molding machine, the loading and demolding time of a six-impression mold determines the cycle.

A slight alteration of the insert can change this. If the insert is provided with a collar on the bearing area that rests against the centralizing mandrel, this can prevent plastics material melt from entering the threads from below. In this case a smooth bolt can be used as a register at the upper end of the ejector (*13*), so that loading and demolding are greatly facilitated. That part of the insert which is not calibrated is equalized by the pressure bolt (*11*) acting on the disc springs (*12*). The pressure bolt seals off the thread from the top side.

Fig. 7/32

Fig. 7/34

Fig. 7/33

Fig. 7/35

Example 95

Figs. 7/32 to 7/35. Six-impression injection molding tool for fixing nuts with metal inserts.
(*1*) Upper fixing plate, (*2*) insert retaining plate, (*3*) mold bolster, (*4*) base plate, (*5*) distance plate, (*6, 7*) ejector plates, (*8*) lower fixing platen, (*9*) upper inserts, (*10 a, b*) cavity inserts, (*11*) pressure bolt, (*12*) spring discs, (*13*) ejector bolt, (*14*) sprue bush, (*15*) springs, (*16*) sprue ejector, (*17*) ejector rod, (*18*) guide bolt, (*19*) guide bush, (*20*) bolt, (*21*) cooling water connection, (*22*) centralizing disc, (*23*) connecting bolt, (*24*) slotted washer.

Example 96. Injection mold incorporating a device for continuously numbering the molded parts

Difficulties are encountered in the serial numbering of injection moldings directly in the mold. The molding compound enters the mold under pressure and rapidly fills the spaces that have to be maintained between the counter cylinders. As it solidifies, it restricts the rotary movement of the cylinders.

The following description of a mold for the production of 10 jetons, each carrying the same number, presents an example of how this difficulty can be overcome. The mold is fitted with a three-position rotary housing (see Figs. 7/36 to 7/46). The cavity is filled in position *I*. Before the compound finally solidifies, the housing is rotated into position *II*, where the number

is embossed. Simultaneously, another cavity is filled again in position *I*, and a third cavity is emptied in position *III* by ejecting the completed molding.

The details are as follows. After the mold has been filled in position *I*, it is opened by the machine. The cup springs (*16*) thus raise the plate (*8*), which can rotate around the shaft (*13*). In this position the hydraulic or pneumatic cylinder (*31*) forces the toothed rack (*29*) forward and rotates the shaft (*13*) through 120° by means of the gear (*15*). The three cavities in the plate (*8*) are brought into positions *I, II* and *III* by means of the ratchet gear (*14*) and the ratchet (*38*), which is connected to the plate (*8*).

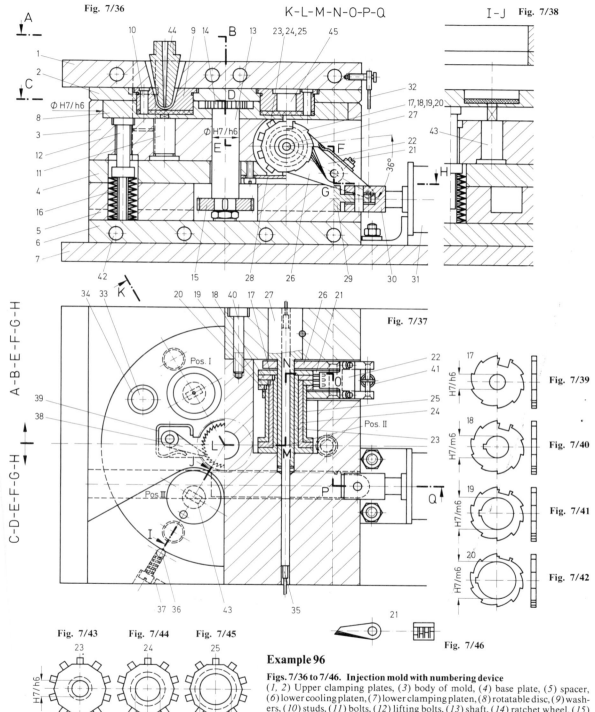

Fig. 7/36

K-L-M-N-O-P-Q

I-J   Fig. 7/38

Fig. 7/37

Fig. 7/39

Fig. 7/40

Fig. 7/41

Fig. 7/42

Fig. 7/43   Fig. 7/44   Fig. 7/45

Fig. 7/46

Example 96

Figs. 7/36 to 7/46. Injection mold with numbering device

(1, 2) Upper clamping plates, (3) body of mold, (4) base plate, (5) spacer, (6) lower cooling platen, (7) lower clamping platen, (8) rotatable disc, (9) washers, (10) studs, (11) bolts, (12) lifting bolts, (13) shaft, (14) ratchet wheel, (15) gear wheel, (16) cup springs, (17 to 20) ratchet wheels, (21) ratchet with four projections of different lengths, (22) leaf spring, (23 to 25) counter cylinders, (26) fork, (27) axis, (28) leaf spring, (29) threaded rack, (30) fork, (31) hydraulic or pneumatic cylinder, (32) steel cable, (33) guide bolts, (34) guide bolt sleeves, (35) cartridge heater, (36) stop, (37) spring, (38) ratchet, (39) leaf spring, (40) bolts, (41) spring, (42) cooling water channels, (43) ejectors, (44) nozzle, (45) insert for punching the name of the firm.

Toward the end of the mold opening stroke, the steel cable (*32*) pulls the fork (*26*). The ratchet (*21*) on the fork turns the ratchet wheel (*17*) through 36°. Depending on their positions, it may also rotate the other ratchet wheels (*18, 19, 20*). As a result, the counter cylinders (*23, 24, 25*) are brought consecutively into the correct positions. When the mold is closed, the number is punched onto the molding in position *II*. The completed molding in position *III* is simultaneously ejected by the ejectors (*43*). In this position a recess is exposed in the upper clamping platen, through which the molding can leave the mold. In position *I* the cavity is free for refilling.

Example 97. Injection molding tool for sealed electrical safety plugs

The mold (Figs. 7/48 to 7/51) that is described below is used for the production of electrical safety plugs, using the "insert molding" process, the plugs being used to fulfill the safety regulations applying to domestic appliances (Fig. 7/47). Two processing steps

Fig. 7/47. Preassembly (still without inserted cable) and the complete molded safety plug.

are used to prepare the moldings. The insert from a thermosetting plastic is made at first (e.g., type 31), into which the contacts are pressed, the earth contact inserted and the cable leads soldered on. This preassembly is then placed in an injection mold where it is covered with a thermoplastic material (e.g., PA).

The preassembly is placed in the mold by hand. It is therefore recommended to use a molding machine with a turntable into which two lower mold halves are placed, the one upper half being in the machine itself. This allows the finished molding to be removed and the preassembly to be inserted into one of the lower halves while the other lower half is closed in the machine for the molding cycle. In this process the side ejector plate (*11*) is run out upward. When the new preassembly is inserted the spring (*20*) draws by means of the ejector pin (*19*), the ejector plates (*6, 7*) and the ejector pins (*15*), and the plate (*11*) back into the mold. After the upper half is closed onto the lower half, three pieces of the plugs are injection molded while the other bottom half is ready for demolding and preassembly.

This simple tool allows a very high production rate.

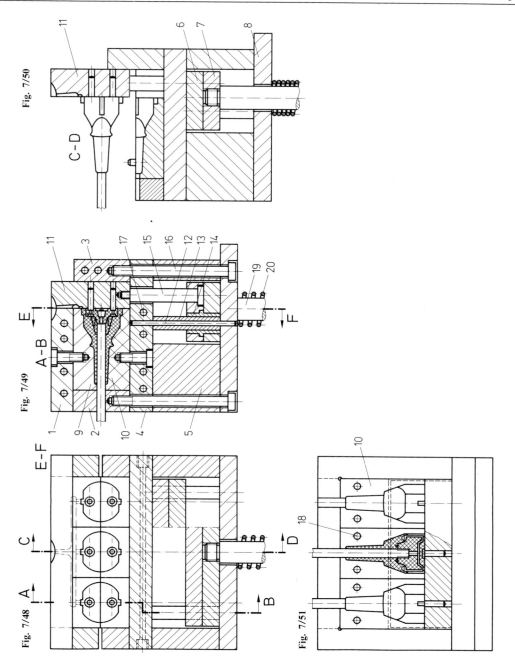

Fig. 7/50

Fig. 7/49

Fig. 7/48

Fig. 7/51

Example 97

Figs. 7/48 to 7/51. Three-part injection mold for molding safety plugs.
(*1*) Upper fixing plate, (*2*) upper cavity holding plate, (*3*) lower cavity holding plate, (*4*) base plate, (*5*) distance shells, (*6, 7*) ejector plates, (*8*) lower fixing plates, (*9*) upper cavities, (*10*) lower cavities, (*11*) side ejector plates, (*12*) dowel pins, (*13*) guiding bolts, (*14*) guiding sleeve, (*15*) ejector pins, (*16*) assembly screws, (*17*) cooling channels, (*18*) dowel pins, (*19*) ejector plate, (*20*) spring.

Example 98. Injection molding tool for the automatic molding of transport plates onto a wire cable

Such granular materials as plastics granulate or grain can be transported by pipe conveyor plant. A conveying cable fitted with transport plates at fixed intervals runs through the pipe. These plates match the inside diameter of the pipe (Fig. 7/52).

Fig. 7/52. Conveying cable with plastic transport plates for mechanical pipe conveyer plant.

The mold shown in Fig. 7/53 to 7/55 was developed for the production of these conveying cables. Plates are molded simultaneously onto two parallel cables to increase productivity. There is no problem guiding the cables through the mold if the mold parting line is in the horizontal plane and the plasticizing unit is mounted vertically on the machine.

To start production the two cables are pulled through the bores in part (8) and placed in the grooves in part (9). Automatic production can only commence once two discs each have been molded onto both cables. Up to that time the cables have to be advanced by hand. Thereafter the paddles (11) situated on the roll (10), which are rotated with each machine opening stroke, engage the molded plates and advance them by one division. To achieve this the

cable (19) fixed to the bolt (30) lifts the double lever (13) against the resistance of spring (17) on bolt (16). The pawl (14) rotates the wheel (27) by engaging in its ratchet teeth, advancing the paddles (11) fitted to shaft (12) by 90°. The turning movement must only be allowed to start when the newly molded discs have been demolded from the lower cavity half (7) by lifting the mold splits (8) and (9), followed with advancing mold opening by demolding the upper cavity half (6). Only then is the cable (19) put under tension. Therefore a total mold opening distance of at least 110 mm is required for demolding and cable advancement. The length of cable (19) must therefore be matched to the opening movement of the injection molding machine.

Fully automatic operation of the mold necessitates interlocking with the injection molding machine controls. The functions of the mold and the presence of melt are supervised by switches (K_1 to K_4). The siting of these switches is shown schematically in Figs. 7/53 and 7/54. Figure 7/56 shows the wiring diagram into which these switches have been integrated. With melt present, the switch K_3 is being actuated during each cycle by the mold plates, closing relay J_1. Subsequently K_4 is also being actuated (by the mold plates) as is K_1 (via the moving mold plate I), influencing a relay in the injection molding machine control to indicate the end of the cycle so that a new sequence can be started. Should switch K_2 not be actuated due to a lack of melt, a subsequent machine cycle cannot take place. During mold closing the parts (8) and (9) are pushed back into the frame (3) again. Switch K_2 is thereby opened, which in turn opens relay J_1 so that the switching sequence for the next cycle is set up. Figure 7/57 shows the time sequence of these functions.

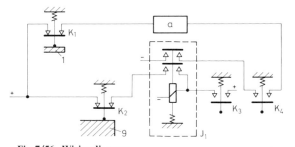

Fig. 7/56. Wiring diagram.
K_1 to K_4: switches, J_1: relay
(a) Injection molding machine controls
(1, 9) Splits (refer to Figs. 7/53 to 7/55)

Fig. 7/56

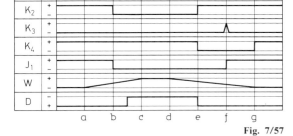

Fig. 7/57

Fig. 7/57. Functions diagram of the controls.
(a) Mold fully opened, start of mold closing movement; (b) mold halves are touching, so that K_2 and J_1 open; (c) mold closed; (d) start of mold opening; (e) mold halves separate, cable advance starts, K_4 opens, K_2 closes; (f) new plate temporarily closes K_3; (g) advanced plate closes K_4, mold is open; (h) wire cable; J_1: realy; K_1 to K_4: switches; W: mold
+ closed or tensioned; − open or relaxed.

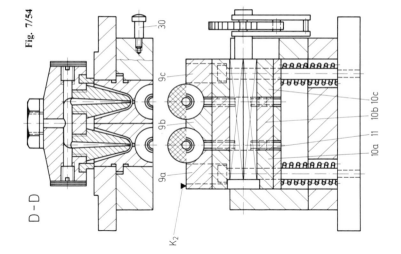

Fig. 7/54

D – D

C – C

Fig. 7/53

Fig. 7/55

A – A

B – B

Example 98

Figs. 7/53 to 7/55. Injection molding tool for the automatic mold-ing of transport plates onto conveying cables of mechanical pipe conveyors.

(*1*) Upper mold fixing platen, (*2*) upper mold cavity retaining plate, (*3*) lower mold bolster, (*4*) mold base plate, (*5*) lower mold fixing platen, (*6*) upper mold cavity half, (*7*) lower mold cavity half, (*8*) moving cable feed, (*9*) moving cable discharge, (*10*) rota-tion cylinder, (*11*) paddles, (*12*) square shaft, (*13*) double lever, (*14*) pawl, (*15*) pawl shaft, (*16*) cross pin, (*17*) spring, (*18*) eye on the draw cable, (*19*) draw cable, (*20*) screw, (*21*) spring, (*22*) injec-tion head, (*23*) beryllium copper nozzle, (*24*) pressure ring, (*25*) cooling water channels, (*26*) connecting bolt, (*27*) ratchet wheel with buttress teeth, (*28, 29*) connecting bolts, (*30*) bolts, (*31*) heat-ing element.

K_1 to K_4: electrical switches.

Example 99. Injection mold for spacer rings

Polyacetal spacer rings of 22 mm inside diameter, 24.9 mm outside diameter and 1.9 mm thickness were produced for years with an eighteen-cavity stripper plate mold (Fig. 7/58). Each cavity was connected individually to the sprue with a resultant adverse ratio for the weight of the moldings to the weight of the sprue. A two-daylight mold would allow the number of cavities to be increased, but the weight of the sprue would then also rise. It appears advisable to turn the mold through an additional angle of 90°; this arrangement allows 44 cavities to be accommodated (Fig. 7/59).

Design details

The fundamental design is for a two-daylight mold (Figs. 7/60 to 7/63). The first parting line (x) is for degating, and the second (y) for demolding. Since they are arranged vertically, their external contours must be contained in the wedge-shaped mold inserts (F). In other words, on the opening stroke of the mold the cavities are parted in the (y) plane. There are four inserts on each daylight, and each contains 11 cavities. The washers on the core plungers are stripped off by means of the levers (H), which are actuated by two compressed air cylinders (Z) and move the plungers (K) outward.

Opening stroke and demolding

During the opening stroke of the injection molding machine the mold is first opened in the x plane. The platen (a) is made to follow the movement by means of the actuating pin (b), which extends into the cone of the sprue and reaches the individual gates. A recess on the pin (b) ensures that the sprue carries the platen to the stop (A). The actuating pin is withdrawn from the cone of the sprue. The gates are removed from the moldings, and the action of the spring allows the ejec-

tor pin to degate the sprue. As the opening stroke proceeds further, the mold travels toward the stop pin MB on the machine. The transoms (T), which are connected to the ejector strip (L) through the sliding bar (S), are raised by about 10 mm. As a result the washers resting on the core plunger are moved out of the lower cavities. Compressed air is admitted through an electrically-pneumatically controlled valve to the cylinders (Z). It acts on the lever (H) to force the core plungers outward so that the washers are stripped from them.

Closing stroke

After the core plungers have been returned by the compressed air cylinders to original positions, the closing stroke of the machine forces the mold, one daylight after the other, into the filling position. An air gap on the upper and lower sides of the transom (T) allows the core plungers (K) to center in the mold inserts during the closing stroke.

Features

In designing the mold care was taken to ensure that standardized parts were used, whenever possible, for the guide bolts and bushings. The parts that actually form the molding compound are the core plungers (K) and the mold inserts (F), in which the mold cavities have been machined. They were designed so that they could be replaced to allow the production of washers of different dimensions without major retooling. Efficient cooling ensures economic cycling, and in this case particular attention was devoted to the core plungers. All the hose connections in the cooling system were fitted with quick-release couplings in order to reduce the time required for retooling.

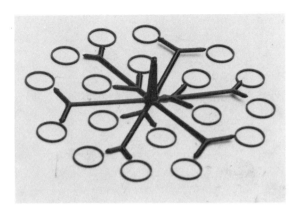

Fig. 7/58. Spacer rings with sprue runner produced in an 18-impression stripper plate mold.

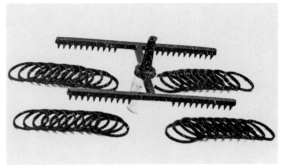

Fig. 7/59. Spacer rings with a sprue manifold produced in a three-plate mold.

Example 99

Figs. 7/60 to 7/63. Injection molding tool for spacer rings.
(*a*) Plate, (*b*) engaging bolt, (*x*) parting plane 1, (*y*) parting plane 2,
(*A*) register, (*B*) ejector bolt, (*F*) mold cavity inserts, (*H*) lever, (*K*) core plug, (*L*) ejector strip, (*MB*)
register bolt on machine, (*S*) split, (*T*) traverse, (*Z*) compressed air cylinder.

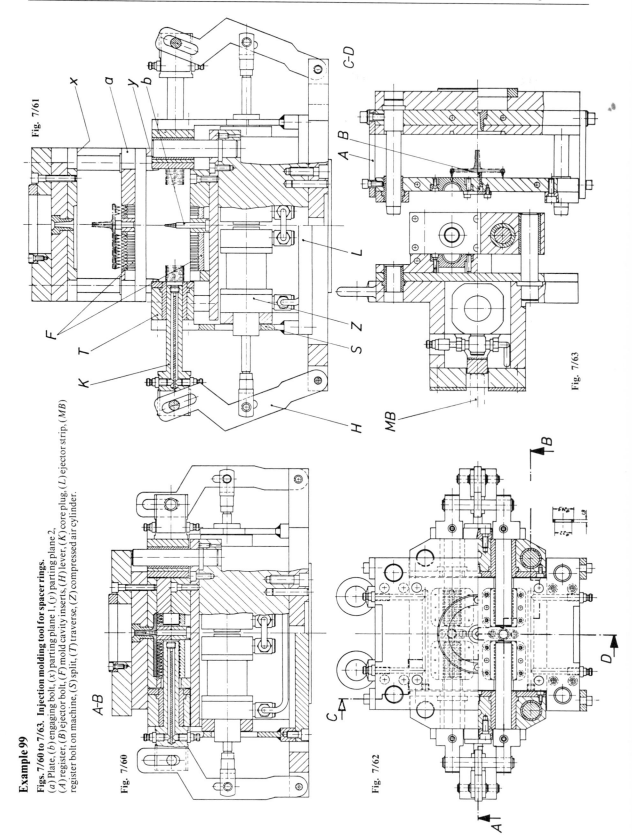

Fig. 7/61

Fig. 7/63

Fig. 7/60

Fig. 7/62

Economics

Apart from a few brief interruptions for maintenance and cleaning, the mold described above has been in continuous use for about a year. Its predecessor allowed the fully automatic production of about 40 000 washers in eight-hour shift. Under the same conditions 90 000 washers can be produced with the new mold. Thus the increase in production rate was 125 %. One of the advantages is that the ratio of the weight of the molding to that of sprue has been substantially improved from 1:1 to 2:1. Formerly two injection molding machines, each with the one mold, were required to achieve the production target. Hence the new mold has released a machine. Although the tooling costs for the new mold were 30 % higher than those of the old one, the production costs per article have been reduced by 50 %.

Example 100. Stack molds with a hot-runner system for sprueless molding of polystyrene container lids using direct lateral gating

In selecting a suitable injection molding machine, the necessary locking force, shot volume, mold height and mold opening stroke must be in a balanced ratio to each other. This, however, is achieved only partially in the production of relatively flat and thin-section parts unless the number of cavities in a mold is doubled by adopting the multidaylight design. This increases injection volume, mold height and necessary mold opening stroke while the necessary locking force remains unchanged[1].

Fig. 7/64   Polystyrene packaging container.

Fig. 7/65   Lid for the container shown in Fig. 7/64.

Stack molds for container lids

Stack molds became established to any extent only when it became possible to employ sprueless gating of the mold cavities lying in the two mold parting surfaces via hot runner systems. With few exceptions the systems used have a common feature, namely that the gate is always parallel to the longitudinal axis of the mold.

The task was to produce polystyrene lids (Fig. 7/65) for a polystyrene container (Fig. 7/64) using a stack mold (Figs. 7/66 to 7/68) so as to make better use of the machine. The outer surface of the lid must not, however, show any gate mark, so that the lids can only be gated on the inside or externally from the side.

Gating on the inside of the lid is not possible since it would be too difficult and complicated to design a hot runner system passing through the mold core and the necessary ejector system. This means that the only solution is to provide for direct edge gating of the lid, the gate being situated on an external side wall surface.

Although standard hot runner nozzles specially developed for the purpose are now on the market for sprueless, direct edge gating, the shape of the article will dictate whether such a hot runner nozzle can be used. As Fig. 7/69 shows, the space for hot runner nozzles used for direct edge gating should be far enough away from the mold cavity for the cavity wall lying in between to be able to absorb the stress produced during injection. On the other hand, the thinner the cavity wall and the shorter therefore the gate, the smaller will be the sprue remaining inside the gate until the next injection molding cycle. Under no circumstances must the sprue be longer than the component wall thickness.

In the present container lid this kind of sprueless edge gating of the article with a hot runner nozzle cannot be realized since this would make the gate dispro-

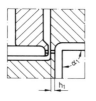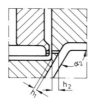

Fig. 7/69 and 7/70. Dependence of gate height on article wall thickness of the minimum distance of the antechamber from the cavity (governed by strength considerations) for hot runner nozzles used for direct edge gating.

h_1: gate height for right angled position of article side wall to base and minimum distance of mold cavity from the antechamber of the hot runner nozzle, h_2: gate height for non-rectangular position of article side wall to base ($\alpha_2 \geqq 95°$). In this case $h_2 > h_1$.

portionally long (Fig. 7/70) because of the slope of the side wall relative to the lid surface.

To gate the component direct on the side wall nevertheless, the hot runner system of the stack mold was equipped with Thermoplay hot runner nozzles, type 1[1] (Fig. 7/71). In contrast to the generally used direction of installation (along the longitudinal axis of the mold), installation in this case was at right angles to the longitudinal mold axis. This hot runner nozzle is of pointed conical shape at the front end, which fits into a conically shared gate so that the nozzle tip can be fused with the cavity wall. In this way the formation of a sprue, which could prevent demolding of the component, is prevented.

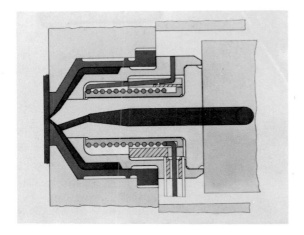

Fig. 7/71. Thermoplay hot runner nozzle with tip drawn forward, for smoothed out gate marks.

[1] System Enrietti/BASF.

Construction and mode of action of the stack mold

Two container lids (C) lie in each of the two parting surfaces (A) and (B) of the stack mold (Fig. 7/68). The mold consist of three plates ($1, 2, 3$), the cavities being in the center plate (2), formed by the cavity plates ($4a$, $4b$, $5a$, $5b$) and core inserts (7) and (8). The core inserts are attached to plates (9) and (10), which form part of the plate assemblies (1) and (3).

The plate assemblies (1) and (3) are guided via columns (11) and centering bushes (12) (Fig. 7/67). The position of the three plate assemblies relative to one another is balanced by means of further centering units (13), which lie in the parting surfaces (A) and (B).

The container lids (C) are injected via directly heated hot runner nozzles (14) in the center of a longitudinal side at a distance of 10 mm from the lid bottom. By use of these hot runner nozzles the lids are produced with a smoothed out gate mark so that there are no protruding sprues that could hamper the demolding operation (a risk in the present instance since the gate is at right angles to the direction of demolding) or that could interfere with the lid's appearance (Fig. 7/72). Each mold cavity is filled through the annular gap of about 0.3 mm between hot runner nozzle and gate.

To keep the heat requirements for the two heated hot runner nozzles as low as possible compared with those of the cooled mold, the nozzles are surrounded by thermally insulating antechamber bushes (15). These center the nozzles and at the same time support them relative to the cavity plates. Each antechamber bush lies centrally in an antechamber cavity and the gate linked to it. This ensures that the nozzles tip is exactly central in the gate.

At the center of the stack mold there is a hot runner (16). This is rectangular; only near the band heater (650 W) (17) and the centering collar is it round. In the rectangular part of the hot runner the cartridge heaters are accommodated by means of bars fixed to it (18). Two high-capacity cartridge heaters (19) are incorporated, each with a heating capacity of 800 W (Fig. 7/66).

On the outside of the mold there are compartments (20) that pull the cavity plates ($4a$) and ($4b$) as well as ($5a$) and ($5b$) toward the hot runner via the hot runner nozzle when the center plate assembly is being assem-

Fig. 7/72 Smoothed-out gate mark of container lid.

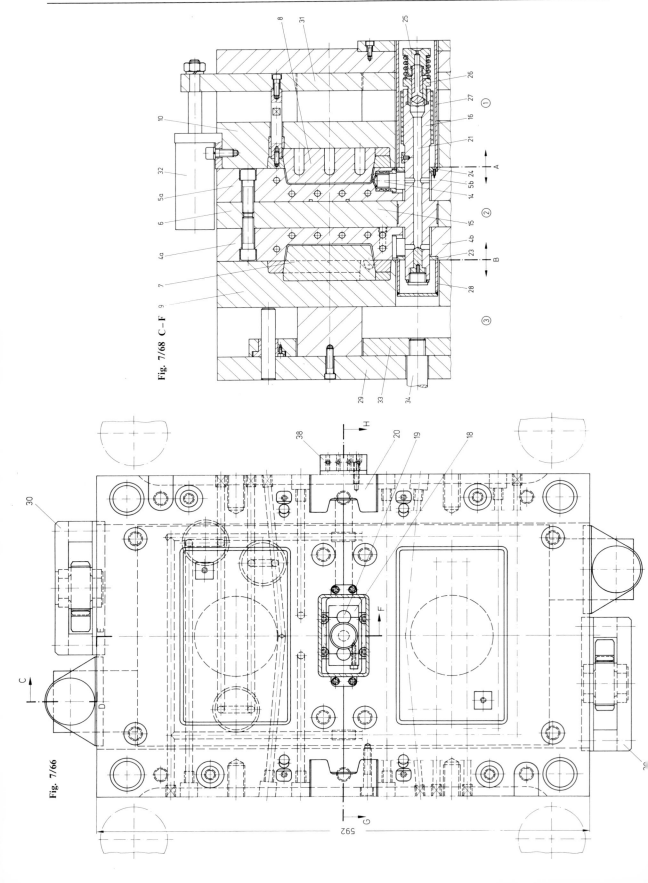

Fig. 7/68 C – F

Fig. 7/66

Example 100

Figs. 7/66 to 7/68. Multidaylight mold with hot runner system for sprueless lateral direct feed of polystyrene container lids.

(*1, 2, 3*) Plate assembly (*4a, 4b, 5a, 5b*) cavity plates, (*6*) intermediate plate, (*7, 8*) core inserts, (*9, 10*) support plates, (*11*) guide column, (*12*) centering bush, (*13*) centering unit, (*14*) hot runner nozzle, thermoplay type 1, (*15*) antechamber bush, (*16*) hot runner, (*17*) band heater (650 W), (*18*) cover strip, (*19*) high-capacity cartridge heater, (*20*) centering clamp, (*21*) principal hot runner, (*22*) secondary hot runner, (*23, 24*) centering piece, double-shell, (*25*) sliding shut-off nozzle unit, (*26*) torpedo, (*27, 28*) sheet metal cladding, (*29*) platen, (*30*) rack-and-pinion drive, (*31*) ejector device, (*32*) pneumatic cylinder, (*33*) ejector device, (*34*) ejector bolt, (*35*) core pin, (*36*) slide, (*37*) slanted column, (*38*) electrical connection block for thermoplay nozzles.

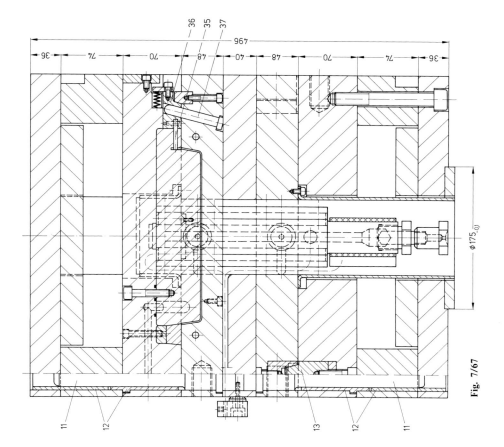

Fig. 7/67

bled. These parts are thus clamped in such a way that there is no risk of leakage and hot runner. The surface contact between nozzles and runners is further increased during operation because of thermal expansion.

A flangelike thickening at the hot runner is clamped between cavity plates (*4a, 4b*) and (*5a, 5b*), so that the injection unit's nozzle contact force acting axially on the runner is maintained. The runner is centered in the intermediate plate (*6*) as well as by the two two-part centering pieces (*23*) and (*24*).

The mold cavities are fed with melt through the central feed channel (*21*) and the four runners (*22*) lying at right angles to it and the four hot runner nozzles. At the front side the hot runner is closed by a sliding nozzle unit (*25*) when the machine nozzle moves away from the injection unit, so as to prevent molding compound escaping, which would inevitably cause production problems after cooling and solidifying. Because of the axial displacement of the torpedo (*26*) when the hot runner moves away from the machine nozzle, the melt compressed in the hot runner system during the injection process can expand in the resultant space of the channel (*21*). This prevents the melt escaping through the gates when the mold opens.

The claddings (*27*) and (*28*) protect the hot runner from major heat loss when the mold is opened and at the same time it serves to protect the operator against accidental contact with the hot runner.

When the mold is opened, the plate assembly (3) is pulled toward the left by the platen (*29*), which is fixed to the mold support plate of the injection molding machine, thereby exposing parting surface (*B*). During this operation, a synchronous opening movement of the two parting surfaces is achieved via a rack and pinion drive (*30*), which lies diagonally on the front and back surface of the mold (Fig. 7/66).

Ejection of the container lids takes place in the parting surface (*A*) via the ejector device (*31*), which is operated via two pneumatic cylinders (*32*). These lie on two opposite mold outer surfaces diagonally relative the each other. The ejector movement for the articles in parting surface (*B*) is carried out, as usual, via the ejector device (*33*), which is initiated via the ejector bolt (*34*).

The hinge holes on the component are produced by the core pins (*35*), which lie in the slides (*36*). The slides' movement at right angles to the direction of demolding is achieved by slanted columns (*37*) (Fig. 7/67).

Example 101 Two-by-eight-impression stack mold for lozenge box in polystyrene

A mold was to be designed for a transparent, thin-walled lozenge-box bottom in polystyrene. The manufacturing costs had to be kept in an acceptable relation to the production costs. An injection molding machine of sufficient daylight opening was available, hence the decision for a two-by-eight-impression stack mold (Figs. 7/73 to 7/77). This mold consisted of three plate assemblies with interspaced ejector plates (3) and (9). In the central plate assembly (4 to 8) are installed the hot runner (15) with the heated sprue bush (19), the hot runner nozzles (14) and the mold cavities in plates (4) and (8). The latter can be cooled intensively, as can be the cores (12) fixed in the outer plate assemblies.

The H-shaped hot runner manifold (15) is heated by four cartridge heaters (30). A cartridge heater (18) installed in the torpedo (16) ensures uniform tempering of the molding material in the sprue bush (19). The specially designed nozzle from the machine's plasticizing unit (dipping nozzle) dips into the sprue bush (20). The space envisaged for this purpose serves to absorb the expansion when the machine nozzle has been retracted by a few millimeters. The plasticized material is prevented from exuding from the melt-guiding system in this way. The hot runner nozzle (14) projects its tapered tip up to the shape-forming surface of the mold cavity, so that a "gateless" injection is feasible. The antechamber bush (21) required with indirectly heated thermal conduction nozzles for thermotechnical reasons had to be shortened, because a continuous antechamber bush would have left an unacceptable marking on the molding.

Opening and closing of the two mold parting planes is coordinated by two laterally fitted angle levers (32, 33) that are linked to the plate assemblies. When the mold opens, the central plate assembly (4 to 8) is held centrally between the two outer plate assemblies (1, 2) and (10, 11) by this lever arrangement. The ejector plates (3) and (9) are set in motion simultaneously by the levers (34), so that the moldings are pushed off the cores (12) by the ejector plates (13) during the continued opening movement.

Rack-and-pinion drives (Fig. 7/78) are increasingly employed nowadays for the coordinated movement sequence of stack molds. Rack-and-pinion drives make faster opening of the mold possible. In this case also the ejector plate movements can be initiated by the externally fitted drive mechanism to run synchronously. Lever drives (Fig. 7/76 and 7/77) have the advantage of the softer movement sequence, enabling the central plate assembly movement and the plate ejectors' movement to be accelerated over a longer period and therefore at lower forces and with less wear.

Fig. 7/78. Stack mold with rack-and-pinion drive for the stroke movements of the individual mold plates and the mechanical linkage for the displacement of the ejector plates [2].
(a) Mold mounting plate, (b) core carrier plate, (c) ejector plate, (d) plate containing mold cavities, (e) hot runner zone.

Example 101 (pages 244-245)

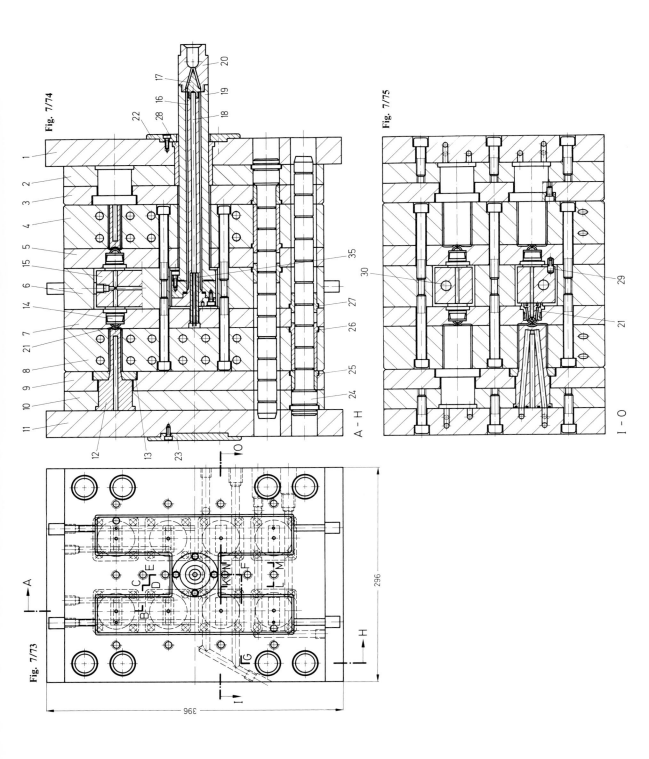

Fig. 7/73

Fig. 7/74

Fig. 7/75

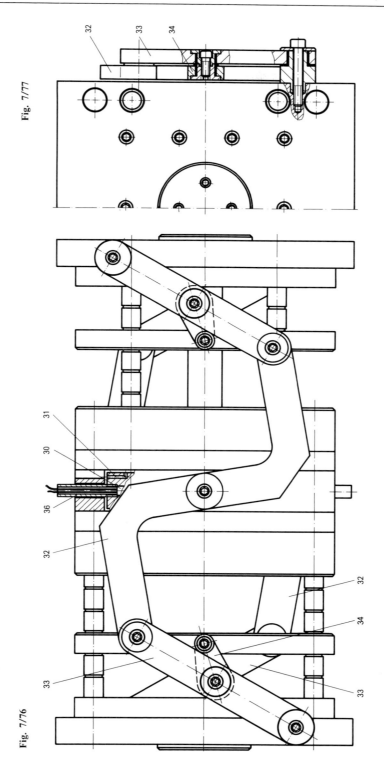

Fig. 7/76

Fig. 7/77

Example 101

Figs. 7/73 to 7/77. Two-by-eight-impression stack mold for lozenge-box bottoms in polystyrene.
(*1*) Fixed-half mold mounting plate, (*2*) fixed core retaining plate, (*3*) fixed-half ejector plate, (*4*) fixed-half mold cavity plate, (*5*) fixed-half nozzle plate, (*6*) hot runner plate, (*7*) moving-half nozzle plate, (*8*) moving-half mold cavity plate, (*9*) moving-half ejector plate, (*10*) moving core retaining plate, (*11*) moving-half mounting plate, (*12*) core, (*13*) ejector insert, (*14*) nozzle housing, (*15*) hot runner block, (*16*) torpedo, (*17*) torpedo tip, (*18*) cartridge heater, (*19*) heated sprue bush, (*20*) sprue bush, (*21*) hot runner antechamber bush, (*22, 23*) locating disc, (*24*) locating dowel, (*25, 26, 27*) locating bush, (*28*) guide bush, (*29*) locating pin, (*30*) cartridge heater, (*31*) thermocouple, (*32*) angle lever, (*33*) connecting lever, (*34*) pilot link, (*35, 36*) cartridge heater housing. The cores (*12*) are not shown in Fig. 7/76.

Example 102. Hot runner injection molding stack tool for trays

Flat moldings of large areas such as trays cannot be produced in customary design stack molds if only one cavity is to be provided in each one of the two parting planes. In this case the heated sprue cannot be located in the central longitudinal axis of the mold as connecting body between the injection unit of the machine and the hot runner manifold. If, however, an injection molding machine is available with the plasticizing unit at right angles to the axis of the clamping unit (L position), then the mold illustrated in Figs. 7/79 to 7/84 represents a simple solution for the above-named case of application. With this design the injection material is injected from the side immediately into the hot runner manifold (7), which is situated as usual in the center of the plate assembly. Each of the two injection moldings is injected "spruelessly" via four pin gates from the bottom. The injection molding material is fed into the

star-shaped hot runner manifold (7) from the center, so that the flow paths of the melt in the manifold to the gates are of equal length.

The mold is symmetrically constructed except for plates (4) and (5) which enclose the hot runner manifold (7). In the completely open position the central plate assembly (4, 5) with the hot runner manifold is placed at equal distance centrally between the two outer plate assemblies (1, 2, 3) due to the drag bolts (18). The moldings are ejected by the ejection device (18 to 21), which is actuated by spring pressure and pushes the ejector plate (22) forward when the drag bolts (18) make contact with plate (4) or (5). The moldings are then ejected by the ejector pins (24). This can take place in both stories of the mold independently of each other and at different times.

Bibliography for section 7

[1] E. Lindner, W. Hartmann, *Plastverarbeiter* vol. 28, 1977, pp. 351–353.
[2] T. Johnson, *Kunststoffe,* vol. 70, 1980, pp. 742–746.

Example 102 (right)

Figs. 7/79 to 7/84. Hot runner injection molding stack tool for trays.
(*1*) Mold mounting plate, (*2*) sandwich plate, (*3*) core plate, (*4, 5*) mold cavity plate, (*6*) sprue bush, (*7*) hot runner manifold, (*8*) clamping plate for hot runner manifold, (*9, 10*) spacer ring, (*11*) outer body of nozzle, (*12*) heat conducting insert for nozzle, (*13*) pressure ring, (*14*) locating ring, (*15*) pressure ring, (*16*) locating bolt, (*17*) locating sleeve, (*18*) drag bolt, (*19*) spring bolt, (*20*) pressure spring, (*21*) washer, (*22*) ejector plate, (*23*) clamping plate for ejector pin, (*24*) ejector pin, (*25*) locating plate, (*26*) cartridge heater.

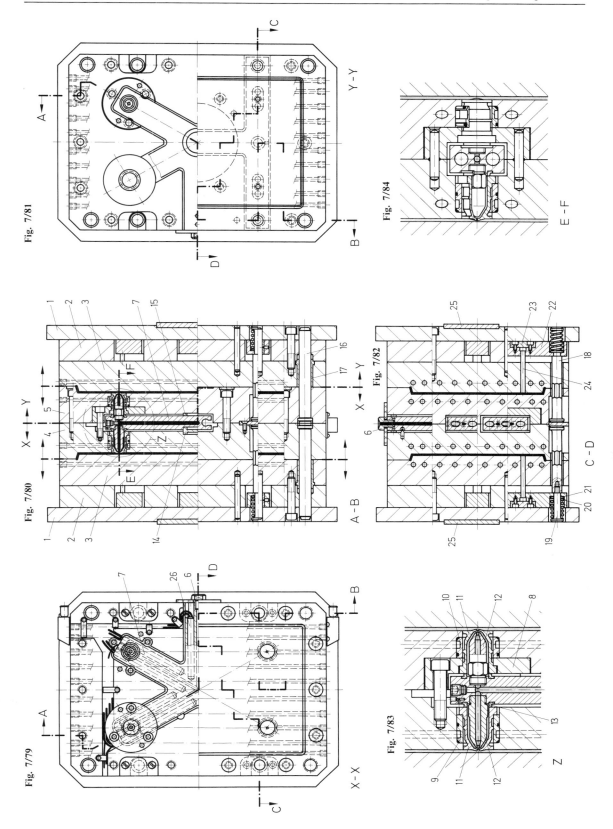

Fig. 7/81

Y – Y

Fig. 7/84

E – F

Fig. 7/80

A – B

Fig. 7/82

C – D

Fig. 7/79

X – X

Fig. 7/83

Z

Fast And Dedicated To Perfection

That Makes A Buyer 500 km Away Order His Tools And Moulds In Helmond.

Fast, which shows in the dashboard mould we manufactured in exactly nine months.

Dedicated to perfection, which shows in our proven ability to build medium-sized and large tools and moulds for the automotive, electronic and allied industries.

In fact any buyer in Europe, demanding high quality tools or moulds should not hesitate to contact us.

Make a good start and ask for our brochure. You'll get a fair impression of how you can benefit by our capability, expertise and reliability.

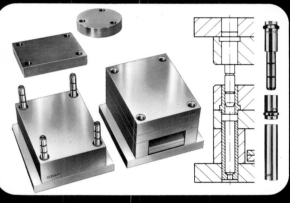
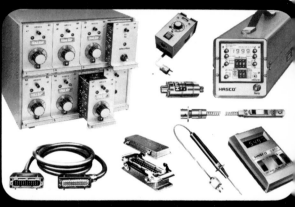
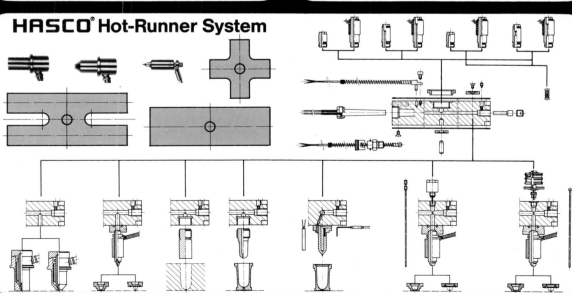

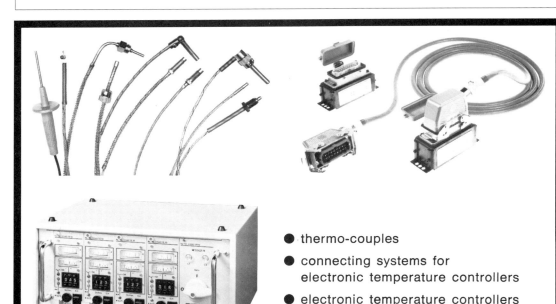

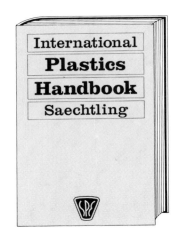

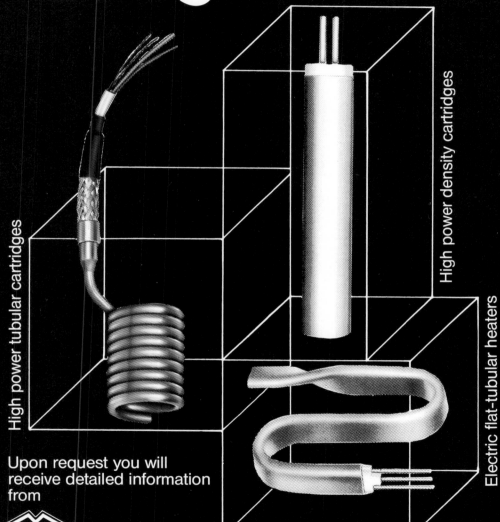

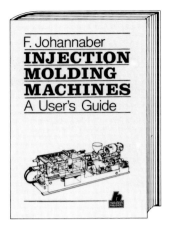
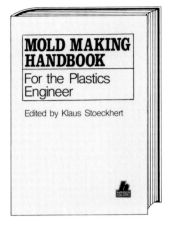

To find ways and means must not always be expensive.

Manufacturing injection moulding machines for components in the range between 0,1 - 180 g shot weight, we would not know of any problem our ALL-ROUNDERS® could not handle, no matter whether talking of thermoplastic, thermosetting or elastomeric materials, insert moulding, liquid silicone rubber two-colour or interval mouldings . . .

Both ALLROUNDER® with toggle clamp system and fully hydraulic ALL-ROUNDER®, New Generation type with computer comfort, are most versatile with up to 7 different working positions, offering easy working with different moulds.

The ARBURG Service also includes:
agencies all over the world, training, technical courses, expert advice, quick spare parts service, servicing centers, mould design and modern tooling department, as well as important technical information by distribution of the "ARBURG heute" review.

If you have the idea — ARBURG stands by with know-how and equipment.

ARBURG — a modern and dynamic private enterprise shows you the way to technological future.

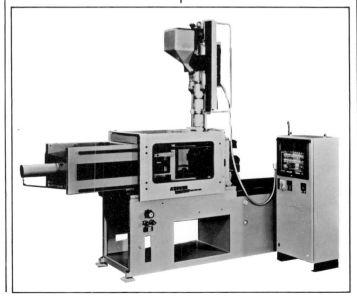

Maschinenfabrik Hehl & Soehne GmbH & Co. KG - D-7298 Lossburg Federal Republic of Germany Tel. 07446/190 - Telex 0764250

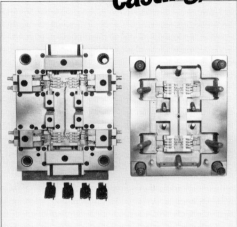

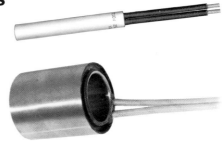
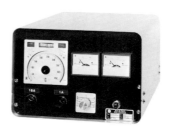

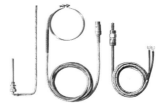

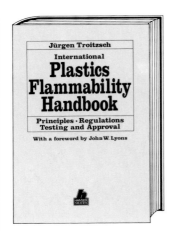
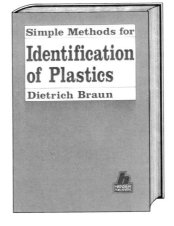

Pregnancy
DAY BY DAY

An illustrated daily countdown to motherhood,
from conception to childbirth and beyond

Pregnancy
DAY BY DAY

Canadian consultant **Elaine Herer, MD**
Sunnybrook Health Sciences Centre
Assistant Professor, Department of Obstetrics & Gynecology,
University of Toronto

Editor-In-Chief **Maggie Blott, MB BS**

Project Editors Dawn Bates, Claire Cross
Project Designers Emma Forge, Tom Forge, Peggy Sadler
Senior Editors Andrea Bagg, Anne Yelland, Emma Woolf
Canadian Editor Barbara Campbell
Senior Art Editors Sarah Ponder, Nicola Rodway, Liz Sephton
Production Editor Ben Marcus
Production Controller Alice Holloway
Creative Technical Support Sonia Charbonnier
Illustrators Debbie Maizels, Medi-Mation
New Photography Ruth Jenkinson
Art Direction for Photography Emma Forge
Picture Researcher Sarah Smithies
Managing Editors Esther Ripley, Penny Warren
Managing Art Editors Glenda Fisher, Marianne Markham
Publisher Peggy Vance

First Canadian Edition, 2009
Dorling Kindersley is represented in Canada by
Tourmaline Editions Inc.
662 King Street West, Suite 304
Toronto, Ontario M5V 1M7

09 10 11   10 9 8 7 6 5 4 3 2 1

Published in Great Britain by Dorling Kindersley Limited

Library and Archives Canada Cataloguing in Publication
Pregnancy day by day ; consultant editor: Elaine Herer ;
editor-in-chief: Maggie Blott. -- Canadian ed.
Includes index.
ISBN 978-1-55363-118-7
1. Pregnancy--Popular works. 2. Childbirth--Popular works.
I. Herer, Elaine II. Blott, Maggie
RG525.P72 2010   618.2   C2009-904107-3

Color reproduction by MDP, Bath, UK
Printed and bound by Star Standard, Singapore

Discover more at **www.dk.com**

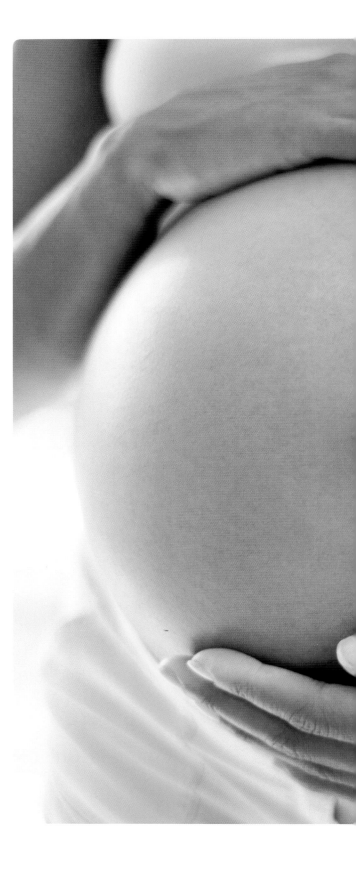

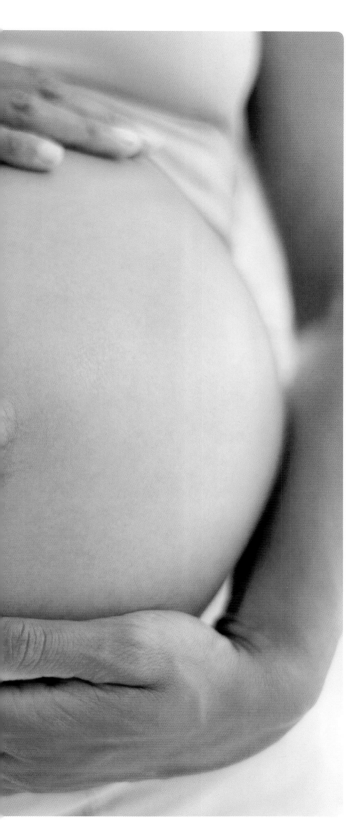

Canadian consultant

Dr. Elaine Herer is an obstetrician/gynecologist and an assistant professor at the University of Toronto in the Department of Obstetrics and Gynecology. She received her medical degree from the University of Calgary in 1982, and completed her residency in obstetrics and gynecology at the University of Toronto.

Dr. Herer is an active staff member at Sunnybrook Health Sciences Centre, and also chairs the Quality Assurance Committee and is a member of the Labor and Delivery Committee at the Centre. She has published numerous papers and also gives lectures in the community on topics covering pregnancy and birth, including a series for Motherisk at the Hospital for Sick Children in Toronto. She is currently researching gestational diabetes and iron deficiency in pregnancy. Dr. Herer was awarded the Chair's Award for Master Teacher in 2008, and the Chair's Award for Research Facilitation in 2003.

Editor-in-chief

Dr. Maggie Blott MB BS, FRCOG is Consultant Obstetrician at University College Hospital, London, where she jointly manages a multidisciplinary high-risk prenatal clinic and runs the labor ward. She is also spokesperson for The Royal College of Obstetricians and Gynaecologists, London. Dr. Blott is a regular columnist for *Top Santé* magazine and writes for a number of other pregnancy-related publications.

Contributors

Dr. Carol Cooper MA, MB, BChir (Cantab), MRCP General Practitioner, London; Tutor at Imperial College School of Medicine, London ■ **Ms. Friedericke Eben** FRCOG Consultant Obstetrician and Gynaecologist, Whittington NHS Trust and Portland Hospitals, London ■ **Dr. Katrina Erskine** MD, MRCP, MRCOG Consultant Obstetrician and Gynaecologist, The Homerton Hospital, London ■ **Dr. Laura Goetzl** MD, MPH Associate Professor, Department of Obstetrics and Gynecology, Division of Maternal Fetal Medicine, Medical University of South Carolina, Charleston, South Carolina ■ **Dr. Belinda Green** PhD Midwife, University College London Hospitals, NHS Foundation Trust, London ■ **Dr. Deirdre Guerin** MB BCh, BAO, LRCP and SI, FFA, or CSI Medical Director of Resident Obstetric Services and Consultant Anesthetist, The Portland Hospital for Women and Children, London ■ **Amanda Hutcherson** DipHeMid, RM, PGCert Ed, MA Midwife Practitioner, London ■ **Dr. Philippa Kaye** MD, MB BS Hons, MA Hons (Cantab), DCH, DRCOG, DFSRH Works in general practice ■ **Dr. Su Laurent** MRCP, FRCPCH Consultant Paediatrician, Barnet Hospital, London ■ **Mr. Andrew Loughney** PhD, MRCOG Consultant Obstetrician, Royal Victoria Infirmary, Newcastle upon Tyne ■ **Dr. Paul Moran** MD, MRCOG Consultant Obstetrician, Head of Fetal Medicine, Royal Victoria Infirmary, Newcastle upon Tyne ■ **Melinda Nicci** BA (Psych), HDipEd Fitness and lifestyle coach and founder of baby2body: pregnancy and post pregnancy health and fitness ■ **Catharine Parker-Littler** SRN, RSCN, SCM, DPSM (Advanced midwifery), BScMid (Hons) Practicing midwife; founder and midwifery director of midwivesonline.com, a website for midwives, health-care professionals, and parents-to-be ■ **Dr. Hope Ricciotti** MD Associate Professor of Obstetrics, Gynecology, and Reproductive Biology, Harvard Medical School, Beth Israel Deaconess Medical Center, Boston, Massachussetts ■ **Dr. Vincent M. Reid** PhD Lecturer in Developmental Psychology, Durham University ■ **Dr. Mary Steen** RGN, RM, BHSc PGCRM, PGDipHE, MCGI, PhD Reader in Midwifery and Reproductive Health, University of Chester ■ **Karen Sullivan** ASET, VTCT, BSc Developmental Psychology; Child-care expert and author ■ **Sally Watkin** Pregnancy and parenting author

Contents

Introduction

Pregnancy is an exceptional time when you enter one of your most significant life stages and need to quickly assimilate knowledge and understanding of the process of pregnancy and birth. In the past, when women traditionally gave birth at home, cared for by midwives and female relatives, pregnancy and birth was a familiar event. Today, it's unusual to have such firsthand experience and a woman's knowledge of pregnancy and birth is often nonexistent or limited to that which she gained in her first pregnancy. As a result, many, if not all, women contemplate pregnancy with a mixture of trepidation and curiosity. These feelings are often compounded by the recognition that their own lifestyle choices can have an enormous influence on their own and their baby's health. For all these reasons, there is a great need for women to be able to access information about pregnancy that is accurate, balanced, and accessible.

In *Pregnancy Day by Day*, information is gathered from a wide body of professionals, each with his or her own area of expertise. The midwives, doctors, obstetricians, and pediatricians who have contributed the core information in this book have between them cared for thousands of women at each stage of pregnancy and labor, delivered thousands of babies, and provided care and support for women and their babies after the birth. The exhaustive record of pregnancy, birth, and the postpartum period provided by their combined expertise is complemented by specialized knowledge on diet and exercise from a nutritionist and a lifestyle and exercise coach. The information presented—at once practical, detailed, and full of simple explanations and advice—will provide the vital tools women need to help them plan for pregnancy, negotiate the many changes they will experience, and develop a safe and appropriate birth plan.

Most pregnancy books are written for women. Today many men also want to follow closely the development of their unborn child, but have little information and often feel excluded. Within the book, there are reassuring explanations for partners about the changes that occur during pregnancy as well as advice for women on how to include partners during pregnancy and the early days of parenthood.

Margaret J. Blott

Dr. Maggie Blott

How this book is organized

This book starts with guidance on how to enjoy a healthy and safe pregnancy, with lifestyle advice that often applies to the preconceptual period too. The core section of the book gives a day-by-day account of pregnancy with detailed explanations of the physical and emotional changes that take place in your body along with fascinating insights into how your baby develops within the uterus. A labor and birth chapter takes you through the delivery of your baby, followed by a summary of the first two weeks with your new baby. A final chapter deals with concerns and complications in the mother and baby in pregnancy, labor, and the postpartum period.

A healthy pregnancy

This chapter provides the information you need to make lifestyle choices that will maximize your own health throughout pregnancy and give your baby the best possible start in life. It includes guidelines for exercising safely, eating healthily, avoiding hazards, and dealing with illnesses. It also addresses concerns you may have about how the emotional and physical changes of pregnancy may impact your relationships.

Pregnancy day by day

Here, the book takes you day by day through the extraordinary story of conception and pregnancy, counting down each of the 280 days until the onset of labor. Each day reveals how your baby is developing and the changes that are occurring in your body. The 280 days, or 40 weeks, of pregnancy are divided into three trimesters, each of which comprises around a third of the pregnancy. Beyond being a simple measure of time, each trimester represents a distinct phase in the development of the baby and in the pregnancy.

The first trimester The definition of the first trimester is given here as weeks 1–12, though you may also see weeks 13 and 14 included elsewhere. This trimester covers the time from the beginning of the menstrual period to the moment of conception, which is usually around two weeks. Because the exact moment of conception is unknown, pregnancy is counted from the one definite date, the beginning of the menstrual cycle. Although technically your pregnancy may not begin until two weeks into your menstrual cycle, these two weeks are very important in helping your body achieve a healthy pregnancy. Here, we explain day by day the changes that take place in your uterus to prepare it for conception and implantation of the early embryo, and offer dietary advice and recommendations from fertility experts to boost your chances of conceiving.

The first trimester is a period of extraordinary development, when all your baby's major organs form, and he or she will grow faster than at any other period in life. A day-by-day account is given of the changes that you and your baby undergo, and advice offered on how to cope with the exhausting changes that occur in early pregnancy. There's also an honest appraisal of the emotional feelings you're likely to experience, reassuring you that negative as well as positive emotions are normal. Practical information

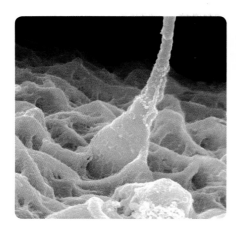

on accessing prenatal care and detailed explanations of the choices that are available help you begin to plan your pregnancy and think about your options for the birth.

The second trimester In the second trimester, which is designated as weeks 13–25, your baby's organs mature further and growth continues. This is an exciting time as your body starts to change shape to accommodate your growing baby and you feel your baby move for the first time. However, it is also a time when women can experience symptoms that are often due to quite normal pregnancy changes but that can occasionally indicate a problem. For example, abdominal pain can be due to ligaments being stretched or to constipation; however, it could also indicate a problem with the placenta. Symptoms such as these are discussed at the relevant point in pregnancy, with detailed explanations that will provide reassurance or alert you to the possibility of something more serious that should be brought to the attention of your doctor.

The third trimester In the third trimester, designated as weeks 26–40, your baby continues to grow and mature and, if born early, could survive life outside the uterus. During this time, your body starts to prepare itself for labor. We describe the changes taking place and explain why they occur, as well as providing pointers to what is normal and which symptoms need to be reported to your doctor. Women recount their experiences, and questions that are presented daily to doctors are reproduced to provide a bank of vital knowledge. Practical guidance on all matters, from maternity leave entitlement information to reassurance

that having sex won't harm the growing baby, helps you navigate your way through the final weeks of pregnancy.

Labor and birth

One of the best ways to cope with labor is to understand its stages. In the labor and birth chapter, a team of professionals covers in detail the progress of labor, each providing their own expert insight. A doctor writes about normal births and discusses natural pain relief. An anesthesiologist gives the options available for medical pain relief, including detailed descriptions of how epidurals are given and their pros and cons. While most women have a normal birth without complications, 30 percent have a cesarean section, and around 5 percent have an assisted delivery, with either forceps or vacuum extraction. An obstetrician writes about difficult births, describing complications and the medical interventions that may be required.

The first two weeks

Here, the early days as you adjust to life with your new baby are charted in the day-by-day format. A pediatrician addresses the practical issues of baby care. Also discussed are the emotional and physical renewal you undergo as your body recovers from the birth and you begin the new tasks of nurturing and feeding your baby.

Concerns and complications

This reference section is a concise guide to conditions in pregnancy and labor, and postpartum concerns in the mother and baby. Clear explanations enable you to digest medical information, understand which symptoms are not of concern, and feel reassured about how more serious conditions are managed in pregnancy, labor, and the postpartum period.

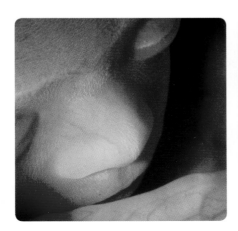

In pregnancy, feelings of awe and excitement are often mingled with concerns about your own and your baby's well-being. With an ever-growing body of knowledge on how a mother's behavior in pregnancy impacts her baby's short- and long-term health, women today have the opportunity to ensure that their lifestyle choices positively benefit their babies. Eating healthily, exercising regularly, and avoiding hazards will all help give your baby the best possible start in life.

A healthy pregnancy

Your pregnancy diet

You can optimize your own health and your baby's future health by eating a nutritious, balanced diet throughout pregnancy.

Eating regular nutritious meals and snacks throughout the day is vital during pregnancy to keep your energy levels up, and to provide your growing baby with all he needs to develop well.

In recent years, much has been learned about what constitutes a healthy diet in pregnancy. In addition to the importance of nutrients such as folic acid (see p.16), there is mounting evidence that a person's health may be influenced by the mother's diet in pregnancy, including whether particular nutrients were received at certain times. Current thinking is that good nutrition in pregnancy may reduce a baby's future risk of diseases such as obesity, diabetes, and heart disease.

In addition to influencing your baby's health, good nutrition in pregnancy also optimizes your health, helping you to deal with the demands of pregnancy.

A healthy diet

Getting the right balance of protein, carbohydrates, and fats in pregnancy is simple, since the ratios are the same in pregnancy as at other times: 45–65 percent of your calories should come from carbohydrates; 20–35 percent from fats; and 10–35 percent from protein. The components of these nutrients don't need to be in this exact ratio for each meal, or even every day, but you should aim to achieve this balance over the course of a week. A diet that includes plenty of vegetables, fruits, whole grains, and good proteins and fats will automatically contain the proper mix of nutrients.

Carbohydrates

Carbohydrates are an important source of fuel for you and for your baby since they are broken down into glucose, which passes easily across the placenta. Try to get six servings a day, a serving being equivalent to a slice of bread, 2 oz (60 g) of cereal, or five crackers.

Carbohydrates are divided into two subgroups: refined and unrefined. In general, white is bad when it comes to carbohydrates, since refined foods such as white rice and white breads are rapidly broken down and enter the bloodstream in the form of a spike of glucose. It is thought that this spike may have health risks for mother and baby, producing larger babies with a subsequent risk of obesity later in life.

Unrefined carbohydrates are less processed, so they break down more slowly in the bloodstream and release glucose steadily. They are also a good source of fiber, which helps prevent constipation. These are a healthier choice, and at least half, if not all, of your carbohydrates should come from unrefined (whole grain) sources. such as whole-wheat or multigrain bread; brown rice, whole-wheat pasta, and cereals.

Protein

Protein is essential for the growth of the baby and the placenta, as well as for your health. Pregnant women need around 6–6½ oz (170–185 g) each day. Aim for two to three servings of protein-rich foods a day, a typical serving being 3 oz (85 g) red meat, or 5 oz (150 g) fish. Since most adults get about 3½ oz (100 g) of protein daily, there is usually no need to increase your intake, especially if you have protein at each meal. If you're vegetarian, in addition to protein at each meal, you should have a protein-containing snack. If you're having twins or more, ask your doctor how much protein to consume and when breast-feeding, 6½ oz (185 g) daily.

Choose protein sources that contain less saturated fat, such as skinless chicken, lean beef and pork, tofu, low-fat cheese and yogurt, and skim milk. Fish, nuts, and seeds contain healthier unsaturated fats (see below), although your intake of some fish should be limited since they contain mercury, which could be harmful to your baby (see p.17).

Fats

Fats contain vitamins and contribute to the healthy development of cells. However, although fats make a useful contribution to overall nutrition, their intake needs to be limited. Choose healthier unsaturated fats, found in foods such as fish and some types of oil, over unhealthy saturated fats found in whole milk dairy products, meat, or trans fats found in processed foods.

Omega 3 fatty acids Studies suggest that the development of the baby's nervous system may be boosted by omega 3 fatty acids, the richest source of which is found in fatty fish. Avoid fish that are high in mercury (see p.17) and opt instead for salmon and anchovies, which are good, safe sources of omega 3 fatty acids. Wild salmon is very rich in omega 3, but farm-raised salmon is also a good source. Other sources include omega 3-enriched eggs, flaxseed, flaxseed oil, walnuts, canola oil, and omega 3 supplements and prenatal vitamins containing omega 3 fatty acids.

Dairy products

These are an important component of the diet since they provide a good supply of proteins and fats, as well as calcium and some vitamins. Calcium is essential for the healthy development of bones and teeth. Opt for low-fat dairy products and low-fat or skim milk. Aim for 2–3 servings each day, a typical serving being 1 oz (30 g) of hard cheese, or 1 cup (200 ml) milk.

Vitamins and minerals

In pregnancy, you need to ensure a rich supply of vitamins and minerals, since these are important for your own health and for your developing baby. They support the healthy functioning of body systems and contain antioxidants, which protect the body against the effects of

YOUR RECOMMENDED DAILY INTAKE

Eating a healthy, balanced diet is of paramount importance during pregnancy to help you deal with the additional demands on your body and to provide your developing baby with essential nutrients. By eating a wide variety of healthy foods, you will be ensuring that you and your baby are receiving the correct balance of nutrients. Try to include a range of foods each day from each of the major food groups (see opposite) and eat plenty of fresh fruit and vegetables.

Include 2–3 portions each day of protein-rich foods, such as fish, lean meat, chicken, legumes, cheese, and nuts to ensure the healthy growth of body structures.

Try to include 3 servings of dairy products each day. Ideally, these should be low-fat products, such as low-fat milk and low-fat cheese and yogurts.

Have 3 servings of whole grain carbohydrates, such as brown rice and whole-wheat breads and and pasta, to keep up energy levels and ensure a supply of fiber.

4–5 servings of vegetables each day will ensure a good supply of essential vitamins and minerals. Try to eat different colored produce and don't overcook vegetables.

3–4 portions of fresh fruit daily will also provide a wide range of vitamins and minerals, many of which contain important protective antioxidants.

1–2 servings daily of iron-rich foods such as eggs or dark leafy green vegetables will help maintain healthy iron levels during pregnancy when demands are increased.

Eating plenty of fresh fruit and vegetables will help optimize your health during pregnancy because your body will be equipped with all the essential vitamins and minerals.

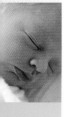

harmful chemicals called free radicals. Good sources of the most important vitamins and minerals are given below. As long as you eat a varied diet that includes plenty of fruits and vegetables, you should be getting all you need, with a couple of exceptions. It can be hard to get enough iron in your diet to meet the demands of pregnancy. Your iron levels will be checked during pregnancy and supplements may be recommended. You'll also need a folic acid supplement before conceiving and in early pregnancy (see right).

Vitamin A This is important for healthy eyes, skin, and hair; it's found in orange fruit and vegetables, such as apricots, peppers, carrots, and tomatoes.

Vitamin B This contributes to the healthy functioning of body systems, and helps the body fight infection. Good sources include bananas, milk, whole grains, cheese, and cabbage.

Vitamin C This aids the absorption of iron and helps fight infection. Rich sources include citrus fruits, kiwis, peppers, broccoli, and spinach.

Vitamin D This helps the absorption of calcium. Food sources include eggs and dark leafy green vegetables, and it is also obtained from sunlight. Women with limited exposure to sunlight, who are housebound, predominantly covered when outdoors, or from Africa, South Asia, the Middle East, or the Caribbean should take a 10 mg vitamin D supplement daily.

Vitamin E This vitamin contains antioxidants and keeps skin, hair, and muscles healthy. Good sources of vitamin E include nuts and seeds.

Folate and folic acid Studies have shown that sufficient amounts of the B vitamin folic acid, or its natural form folate, can help reduce the risk of neural tube defects, such as spina bifida, by up to 50 percent. In these defects, the embryonic neural tube fails to close properly during the first four weeks of pregnancy, leading to incomplete development of the brain and spinal cord. Folate helps the neural tube close and pregnant women are advised to eat a folate-rich diet. Foods high in folate include green leafy vegetables, legumes; and fortified cereals. It may not be possible to get sufficient folate through diet alone, so women are also advised to take a folic acid supplement of 0.4 milligrams before conception and during the first trimester.

Iron This is needed for hemoglobin production in red blood cells. Sources include meat, fish, chicken, eggs, dried apricots, spinach, and broccoli.

Calcium This is essential for healthy bones and teeth. Sources include dairy products, eggs, fortified cereals, and leafy green vegetables.

Zinc This helps maintain a healthy immune system. Sources include seafood and nuts.

A vegetarian diet

A vegetarian diet, and vegan diets where dairy products are excluded, can be safe and healthy during pregnancy as long as you ensure a good balance of nutrients and sufficient protein (see p.126). Babies born to vegetarians are in a healthy weight range, although vegans do need to be vigilant about obtaining adequate protein, as well as reliable sources of B12 and zinc. Vegans can discuss with their doctors whether they'll be able to meet their vitamin B12 needs through diet alone. Since vitamin B12 is found primarily in animal sources, a supplement may be required. Non-animal sources of B12 may be unreliable.

A low GI diet

Glucose, the product of carbohydrates, serves as the primary fuel for your growing baby. A new concept in nutrition is the glycemic index (GI), which looks at how much a food will raise the level of glucose in the bloodstream. Foods that release glucose gradually, such as unrefined carbohydrates (see p.14), and thus have a low GI, appear to be healthier.

Benefits of a low GI diet Evidence suggests that a low GI diet has health benefits for both the mother and baby. Maternal carbohydrate intake can affect glucose levels in the bloodstream, which in turn can affect the baby's growth. Higher glucose levels, even those in the normal range, can make for a bigger baby—above the 90th percentile (the top

end of a baby's growth chart, see p.284). There are health risks later in life linked to a high birth weight, such as obesity, diabetes, and heart disease. One study found that women who consumed a low GI diet had infants that were a normal size, but had less body fat than those from women who consumed a high GI diet.

A low GI diet can also help control glucose levels in mothers with gestational diabetes (see p.473), in turn reducing complications of labor and birth associated with this condition.

Your calorie intake

During pregnancy, most women need to increase their calorie intake by 100–300 calories a day for proper nutrition and weight gain. Your energy needs may vary depending on your pre-pregnancy weight and your activity levels.

Gaining the correct amount of weight in pregnancy has benefits for both mother and baby. You're more likely to return to your pre-pregnancy weight if you gain weight within the recommended guidelines (see p.99). Gaining too much weight is linked with bigger babies, which carries future risks to the baby's health (see above). Conversely, gaining too little weight is also not ideal for a baby's future health.

YOUR BODY MASS INDEX

At the start of pregnancy, your doctor may tell you your body mass index, or BMI. This is an estimate of your body fat based on your weight and height. By calculating your BMI, your doctor can establish whether you are a healthy weight for your height or whether your weight could cause problems during pregnancy.

Your BMI is calculated by dividing your weight in kilograms by the square of your height in meters. A BMI of 18.5–24.9 is considered normal; 25–29.9 is considered overweight; 30–39.9 is

classified as obese; and over 39 is very obese. If you have A BMI of below 18.5, you are thought to be underweight.

Being underweight in pregnancy can make you more likely to give birth prematurely, or have a "small-for-dates" baby. Being overweight means that you are at a higher risk of problems such as high blood pressure, preeclampsia (see p.474), and gestational diabetes (see p.473), and are more likely to have a larger baby. These factors increase the risk of complications at the time of delivery.

WHAT TO AVOID

Dietary precautions

Certain foods should be avoided or their intake limited since they may pose a risk to your unborn baby. Simple cooking and hygiene measures are also important to limit the risks.

Listeria is a food-borne bacteria to which pregnant women are more susceptible. It is found in unpasteurized dairy products, as well as refrigerated, ready-to-eat foods like meat, poultry, and seafood. To avoid it, thoroughly reheat hot dogs, lunch meats, or prepared deli foods and avoid unpasteurized dairy products and check soft cheeses labels to be sure they're made with pasteurized milk.

Nearly all seafood contains at least trace amounts of mercury which can affect the development of the fetal nervous system. Pregnant women should avoid swordfish, shark, king mackerel, and tilefish. To stay within safe limits, eat up to 12 ounces (340 g) per week of lower-mercury seafood like shrimp, salmon, pollock, catfish, and canned light tuna.

Toxoplasmosis is a parasite spread through cat feces or undercooked beef, pork, or lamb that can harm the fetus. Avoid changing cat litter and practice careful hygiene in the kitchen when preparing raw meat, being careful not to contaminate other foods such as lettuce or vegetables. Beef, pork, and lamb all need to be well cooked.

Salmonella bacteria are found in chicken and eggs. Infection with salmonella can cause severe vomiting, but doesn't directly affect the baby. Avoid any products containing raw or undercooked eggs, and make sure all poultry is thoroughly cooked through, since cooking kills the bacteria.

Exercising safely

Staying fit in pregnancy has many benefits for you and your baby and increases your stamina for labor and birth.

Stay well hydrated by drinking plenty of water before, during, and after your workout.

If you had an exercise program before you became pregnant, you can continue with this in the first trimester as long as you have the all clear from your doctor. As your pregnancy goes on, you may need to adapt your program.

If you didn't have a regular exercise program before, now is the ideal time to adopt a new, healthier way of life from which you will reap the rewards for years to come. If you do start exercising now, build up gently; listen to your body and do only what feels comfortable.

Regular gentle exercise is much better than intense irregular bouts of exercise (which aren't advisable in pregnancy), since your body responds more postively to consistent, moderate exercise.

How exercise helps

In addition to increasing your energy levels, exercise helps you maintain a positive outlook and feel confident about your changing body image. Exercise can also ease common pregnancy discomforts such as nausea, leg cramps, swollen feet, varicose veins, constipation, insomnia, and back pain. By keeping muscles strong and toned, exercise makes it easier for your body to deal with changes in posture during pregnancy. There is also evidence that increased fitness helps shorten labor and your postpartum recovery time and lessens your overall anxiety about the birth.

Food for fuel

A nutritious, balanced diet is vital in pregnancy. If you're exercising too, eating well to keep energy levels balanced is doubly important. Eat regular, nutritious meals, ensuring that your calories come from wholesome, fresh foods, and avoid high-calorie sugary snacks.

DO'S AND DON'TS

Exercise is safe in pregnancy as long as you follow the simple guidelines listed below. As your pregnancy progresses, you will probably need to adapt and moderate your exercise program.

Do:
■ Warm up and cool down properly.
■ Drink enough water before, during, and after exercising.
■ Wear comfortable clothes that don't restrict your rib cage.
■ Exercise regularly and consistently.
■ Adjust your expectations; pregnancy is not a time to go for personal bests.

■ Build your strength, but do this gradually. Focus on your back, shoulders, chest, and lower body.
■ Practice Kegel exercises (see p.69) daily to maintain the pelvic floor tone.
■ Breathe properly while exercising, especially when lifting weights.
■ Protect your back when getting up from a lying position: roll onto your left side and sit up using your legs.
■ Avoid exercises that feel awkward or uncomfortable.
■ Focus on posture and alignment.
■ Stop immediately and seek advice if you feel severe localized pain, vaginal bleeding, or general unwellness.
■ Eat frequent small meals and snacks

to maintain energy and avoid having your blood sugar levels fall.

Don't:
■ Exercise in a hot or humid environment.
■ Do jerky or bouncy moves or twist or rotate your abdomen.
■ Lift weights that are too heavy.
■ Do sports where you risk falling, such as skiing or horseback riding.
■ Overstretch: the pregnancy hormone relaxin can make you feel more supple than you are.
■ Exercise to exhaustion. If you're tired, decrease the intensity or duration. Get an hour's rest for each hour of exercise.

Sex and relationships

You may find that you and your partner need to adapt to the emotional and physical changes that accompany pregnancy.

In a low-risk pregnancy, sex is perfectly safe, although your levels of desire may fluctuate throughout pregnancy. Most women report that their interest in sex is the same or slightly reduced in the first trimester. In the second trimester, it varies from woman to woman, and in the third trimester libido often falls.

Sex during pregnancy

During the first trimester, the hormonal changes that cause nausea, vomiting, and fatigue can naturally result in a reduced interest in sex. However, other pregnancy changes may increase your desire, such as an increased blood flow, which produces swelling in the clitoris and labia and extra vaginal secretions. In the second trimester especially, vaginal lubrication and intensity of orgasm can increase, which may be accompanied by gentle contractions; these are normal and are nothing to worry about. Many women find that their libido falls toward the end of pregnancy since a bigger belly makes sex more awkward and uncomfortable, and they may also feel increasingly anxious about the birth.

How your partner feels As with women, men display a range of feelings toward sex in pregnancy. While some may find their partner's new, fuller shape particularly sensuous, others may feel apprehensive about sex, fearing that they may harm the baby. Some men may feel a combination of these emotions. Unless there are concerns about your pregnancy (see right), it's generally thought that sex won't cause harm, since your baby is well protected by the amniotic fluid and your uterus.

Spending time touching and caressing can help you and your partner maintain feelings of closeness and intimacy.

When to seek advice

Some women experience vaginal bleeding after sex in pregnancy. This is most likely to be harmless and is often caused by the increased blood flow to the cervix in pregnancy, which can cause it to bleed on contact with your partner's penis. If this is the cause, the bleeding should resolve after the birth. However, since there are other possible causes, report any bleeding to your doctor.

In addition to the size of your belly causing discomfort during sex, some women experience pain during sex toward the end of pregnancy as the baby moves farther into the pelvis; or they may find that the contractions that can accompany orgasm become increasingly uncomfortable. These symptoms are unlikely to be a cause for concern, but it's worth mentioning them to your doctor for reassurance.

There are some circumstances in late pregnancy when intercourse may not be safe. This can be the case if you've had a

WHAT TO DO

An intimate pregnancy

During pregnancy, fatigue, feelings of insecurity about your new shape, and concerns about the safety of sex can all take their toll on your relationship. Allowing yourself time to adjust and keeping the channels of communication open will help you and your partner enjoy this new stage in your relationship.

■ **Talk to each other about your feelings** and be aware that, for both of you, levels of interest may fluctuate.

■ **If your belly makes some positions uncomfortable,** experiment with alternative ones that accommodate your size, such as side-by-side, rear entry, or woman-on-top positions.

■ **Enjoy other ways to maintain intimacy** besides intercourse, such as touching and massage.

previous premature labor or risk factors for premature labor, such as a weak cervix, or if you have placenta previa (see p.473), or leakage of amniotic fluid, which can mean your water has broken.

If you have any concerns, don't be afraid to ask your doctor for advice. Being able to enjoy sex in pregnancy will help you and your partner feel close during this time of transition. Indeed, psychologists have found that couples who enjoy sex in pregnancy are more tender toward each other and communicate better after the birth.

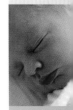

Illnesses and medication

Knowing how to manage illness and what medications are safe to take is important to protect your own and your baby's health.

Whether you have a preexisting medical condition, or acquire an illness or infection during pregnancy, always consult your doctor before taking medication or before stopping any prescribed medication.

Preexisting conditions

If you have a condition such as high blood pressure or diabetes prior to pregnancy, your pregnancy will be classified as high risk and you'll need to be monitored carefully. If you become pregnant while taking medication for a condition, don't stop taking the medication, but consult your doctor as soon as possible. You may find that your existing medication is safe, or you may need to change to another type of medication. The most important thing is to control your condition during pregnancy to minimize the risks to you and your baby, which will usually mean continuing with medication.

Diabetes If you have diabetes and are planning to conceive, you need to get advice on how to manage your condition. Meet with your doctor while you're thinking about conceiving to discuss the best way to control your blood sugar levels and talk about how diabetes will be managed in pregnancy. Women with diabetes are advised to take a prenatal vitamin with folic acid before trying to conceive and for the first three months of pregnancy. Diabetic women who are overweight may be advised to lose weight before getting pregnant, and they'll likely be told to monitor their blood sugar more frequently and take their medications on time during their pregnancy. Babies born to diabetic women also have a greater risk of other problems, such as having a large birth weight, respiratory problems at birth, jaundice, and low blood sugar at birth.

As soon as you're pregnant, you should be referred to an obstetrician who specializes in pregnancy and diabetes where you'll receive extra care. You will have more frequent prenatal visits, additional scans, and extra blood tests to monitor your blood sugars. You may need diabetes medication and/or insulin injections each day; the dose usually changes throughout pregnancy and needs to be monitored. The better your blood sugar control, the less likely you or your baby is to experience problems during pregnancy.

Since diabetic women have an increased risk of late pregnancy problems such as preeclampsia (see p.474) and premature labor (see p.431), you may be advised to have an induction of labor a week or so before your due date (see p.432).

Once in labor, your blood sugar levels will be closely monitored, and you will probably be given an insulin IV. After the birth, your baby's blood sugar levels will be closely monitored too for around 24 hours. If you're planning to breast-feed, which is recommended, your insulin dose may need to be changed after the birth.

Epilepsy If you have epilepsy, it's very important to discuss pregnancy with your doctor before you become pregnant, since certain drugs carry a small risk of causing harm to the developing baby. Nonetheless, it's also important that your epilepsy is controlled, so your doctor will try to ensure that you're on

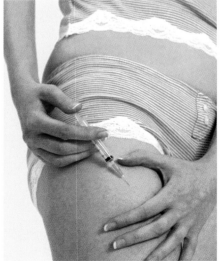 

Diabetes is controlled with daily insulin injections in pregnancy. As the skin on your abdomen becomes taut, you may find it easier to inject into the fatty tissue of the thigh (left). **Continuing with asthma medication** is important to keep symptoms under control in pregnancy (right).

the lowest possible dose of medication before you get pregnant. When you are pregnant, the fetal anatomical ultrasound at 18–20 weeks (see p.214) will check for problems such as cleft palate, which are slightly more common with certain medications. If your condition worsens in pregnancy, contact your doctor.

Systemic lupus erythematosus

This is an autoimmune disorder that can affect many parts of the body, including the kidneys, joints, skin, nervous system, heart, and lungs. The condition is more common in women, and particularly in those of childbearing age. Some women find that the symptoms for this condition ease during pregnancy, however for some they can worsen. It's important to control the condition during pregnancy since it can affect the developing baby, with an increased risk of miscarriage, poor growth, premature labor, and stillbirth. Most medications for lupus are safe to use during pregnancy, but some aren't, so you need to check with your doctor about whether you need to change your current medication. From around 32 weeks, your baby will be closely monitored and his growth and well-being will be checked. If there are concerns about you or your baby, labor may be induced early, or you may have a planned cesarean.

High blood pressure If you have high blood pressure that requires medication, check with your doctor that the medication you are on is safe to use during pregnancy. It's important to continue your medication so that your blood pressure is controlled, because high blood pressure can be dangerous both for you and your baby. Your doctor will frequently check your blood pressure, and will test your urine to check for the presence of protein, because high blood pressure and protein in the urine are symptoms of the condition preeclampsia (see p.474).

COMMON WORRIES

I'm asthmatic. Can I use my inhalers during pregnancy?

It's essential that you keep asthma under control in pregnancy, which means continuing to use your inhalers, since the risks from uncontrolled asthma are greater than any risk from taking asthma medication. If asthma is uncontrolled, it can mean that not enough oxygen gets to the baby, leading to a low birth weight or other problems. One of the best ways to control asthma, in addition to taking medication, is to avoid asthma triggers such as pet fur and dust mites. Use air filters, vacuum often, and damp dust, and use duvet, mattress, and pillow protectors. Sometimes, pregnancy reduces the severity of asthma, but if you feel wheezier than usual, talk to your doctor about reviewing your medication.

Homeopathy seems to be a popular form of therapy. How effective is it and is it safe?

Homeopathy works on the principle of treating like with like to stimulate the body's natural healing mechanisms.

There has been debate about the efficacy of homeopathy and the scientific opinion is that there is insufficient evidence to show that homeopathy has any effect beyond that of a placebo. But talk to your doctor before using any homeopathic products or remedies during pregnancy, since homeopathy is an area of complementary and alternative medicine that's associated with much debate and scientific controversy. If your doctor gives you the okay, a certified homeopath may be able to provide treatment.

What's the verdict on taking herbal remedies and teas during pregnancy?

Herbal remedies and teas are not necessarily safe just because they're 'natural.' There's not much research about the health effects of many herbs on pregnant women, so it's best to avoid them while you're pregnant. Decaffeinated black teas are your best bet, but if you want a fruit or ginger tea, read the ingredient label on the package carefully to be sure that no herbs are present. If you want to use an herbal remedy, talk to your doctor first.

Your doctor may also recommend additional scans to check that your baby is growing well.

Thyroid problems If you have an underactive thyroid gland for which you are taking a thyroid hormone replacement, you'll need to have a blood test to ensure that your thyroid is functioning well and that you're taking the correct dose, since sometimes the medication requirement increases in pregnancy. It's important that you are not lacking in thyroid hormone, because this may affect the baby. If you are being treated for an overactive thyroid gland, check with your doctor that you're taking a thyroid medication

that is safe in pregnancy. Your thyroid function will be monitored to check that your medication doesn't need to change.

Bowel disease Women with inflammatory bowel conditions, such as ulcerative colitis or Crohn's disease, usually find that their condition improves during pregnancy, although you may relapse after the baby is born. Although it's unusual for bowel conditions to cause major problems during pregnancy, it is important to check that you are not anemic, which can be a side effect of some bowel conditions, and your doctor may recommend extra scans to check that the baby is growing well.

Exposure to chickenpox or rubella

Chickenpox in pregnancy can cause problems for the baby and can be severe in a pregnant woman, possibly leading to pneumonia. If you contract rubella for the first time in early pregnancy, it can cause miscarriage or severe problems in the fetus.

If you encounter chickenpox, contact your doctor who can check your immunity. If you aren't immune, your doctor may advise an injection to protect you from severe chickenpox.

Your rubella status is checked at the start of pregnancy. If you aren't immune, you can be vaccinated after the birth. Meanwhile you need to be extra careful.

If you develop chickenpox or suspect rubella because of a rash, contact your doctor immediately, but don't go to the doctor's office, where you may spread the infection to other pregnant women.

Infections during pregnancy

When you're pregnant, your immune system is slightly suppressed. This is necessary to stop you from rejecting the baby, who is genetically half the father's! This means that you may be slightly more susceptible to common problems such as colds, coughs, a sore throat, or food poisoning, and that the illness may last longer.

Colds and coughs Most women get a cough or cold at some stage during their pregnancy. However, you should avoid taking cold medications since these can contain ingredients that are not safe in pregnancy, especially during the first three months (see opposite). Steam inhalations can ease congestion and hot honey drinks help to soothe a sore throat. Saline nasal sprays can also help relieve congestion.

Flu If you get the flu during pregnancy, call your doctor to get advice or make an appointment. Drink plenty of liquids and get plenty of rest. Don't take any flu or cold medications without talking to your doctor first. Flu complications can include dehydration and pneumonia, and complications are more common in pregnant women. The Public Health Agency of Canada recommends that all pregnant women should get flu vaccinations. However, pregnant women should not get the nasal-spray flu vaccine, which is currently available in the US but not in Canada.

Food poisoning and stomach upsets A severe episode of food poisoning can cause problems for you and your baby and could trigger an early miscarriage, so it's vital to practice good kitchen hygiene (see p.17). If you do develop food poisoning or a stomach upset, try to drink plenty of fluids, and if it continues for more than 24 hours, see your doctor (see also Gastroenteritis, p.468).

Yeast If you have an abnormal discharge, talk to your doctor since this may be yeast (candidiasis), which is common in pregnancy. A swab may be taken to confirm the diagnosis, and an appropriate local antifungal treatment prescribed (see opposite). Eating natural yogurt may help restore the bacterial balance in your vagina. Wearing cotton underwear and avoiding tight clothing is also recommended.

Urinary infections Many pregnant women get urinary infections because the hormone progesterone relaxes all of the smooth muscle, allowing the bacteria that normally live in your vagina to travel up the urethra (the tube that leads to the bladder) where they may cause an infection. The symptoms of an urinary infection may be slightly different in pregnancy. You may have the classic symptoms of burning when urinating and frequent passing of urine, or you may have different symptoms such as back pain, lower abdominal pain, nausea, or vomiting. These are usually easily treated with antibiotics, most of which are safe in pregnancy.

If you're laid low with an illness during pregnancy, take time to rest and recuperate since pregnancy can exacerbate everyday symptoms.

Taking medications during pregnancy

During the first three months of pregnancy, it's best to avoid all over-the-counter medications. Once you are past the first trimester, some other medications are considered safe, but always consult your doctor if you are in any doubt. The following provides guidance on medications used for treating common pregnancy complaints and minor illnesses.

Antacids Heartburn and indigestion are common problems in pregnancy, particularly during the third trimester when the increased size of the baby puts pressure on your stomach. Some antacids are safe to use during pregnancy, although you should avoid sodium bicarbonate because it may increase fluid retention. Consult your doctor or pharmacist about which ones are recommended.

Antibiotics Many antibiotics used to treat infection are safe for use during pregnancy. This includes antibiotics containing penicillin, although there are safe alternatives if you're allergic to penicillin. The following antibiotics should be avoided during pregnancy:
- Streptomycin. This can damage the ears of the fetus as it develops and may result in hearing loss in the baby.
- Sulphonamides. These can cause jaundice in the newborn baby.
- Tetracyclines. These drugs shouldn't be taken because they can affect the development of the baby's bone and teeth and can cause discoloration in the teeth.

Antiemetics If you have severe nausea and vomiting and natural remedies such as gingersnaps or ginger tea don't relieve the problem, your doctor may recommend an antiemetic medication that is safe to use during pregnancy, such as Gravol or Dilectin.

Antifungal remedies Consult your doctor or pharmacist, who can recommend an antifungal medication that is appropriate for use in pregnancy.

Cold remedies Remedies for coughs and colds often contain a range of ingredients, such as caffeine, antihistamines, and other decongestants, which may not be safe in pregnancy. Ideally, try relieving congestion with steam inhalations and soothing a sore throat with hot caffeine-free drinks. If you need still need relief, talk to your doctor or pharmacist before using any over-the-counter treatments.

Diuretics It's normal to experience some swelling in the hands and feet during pregnancy, and you shouldn't attempt to deal with this by taking diuretics, including herbal diuretics. If you have sudden swelling in the face, hands, or feet, you should consult your doctor immediately because this can be a sign of preeclampsia (see p.474).

Laxatives The first step in dealing with constipation is to take dietary measures by increasing your intake of fiber and drinking plenty of fluids. If this isn't enough to ease constipation, then some over-the-counter laxatives may be safe to take during pregnancy, including laxatives that contain bulking agents. Those containing castor oil may cause uterine contractions. Check with your doctor before taking any laxatives.

Analgesics Before using pain medication for a common problem, such as a headache or backache, first try natural remedies; massage or a warm bath are often effective in relieving aches and pains. If these aren't sufficient, call your doctor for advice. Tylenol (acetaminophen) is generally recommended; Aspirin (ASA) and anti-inflammatories such as Advil (ibuprofen) should be avoided throughout pregnancy. The pain medicine codeine can sometimes be used for a short period to treat specific pain, but should only be taken on the advice of a doctor.

Rehydration solutions If you have a stomach upset resulting in a severe bout of diarrhea that lasts for an extended period, your doctor may recommend a rehydration solution that is safe to use in pregnancy.

Steroids If you have eczema, or find that this condition develops or worsens during pregnancy, talk to your doctor about appropriate medications. Corticosteroids, which are used to treat eczema, aren't associated with birth defects, but they are known to cross the placenta, so discuss the risks with your doctor to see what is recommended in your situation.

Steroid inhalers used to treat asthma are safe in pregnancy, and it's important to control your asthma while your're pregnant.

Oral steroids may also be prescribed for certain other conditions, and these may be safe to continue with under the guidance of your doctor. Anabolic steroids should not be taken during pregnancy.

Lifestyle hazards

Pregnancy can be beset with anxiety about potential hazards. Being aware of exactly what to avoid will help to allay fears.

Whether you're pregnant or are planning to conceive, now is the time to do a safety check on your social habits and home and work environment. Anything that could affect your well-being could affect your baby too, especially in the first trimester. However, don't become overly anxious. Instead, arm yourself with the facts so that you can avoid hazards, but also relax and enjoy your pregnancy.

Your social habits
The decision to have a baby may inspire you to review your social habits and, if necessary, make changes.

Alcohol consumption You should stop drinking alcohol while trying to get pregnant and once you're pregnant, according to the Public Health Agency of Canada. There is no known safe consumption level for pregnant women, so abstaining from drinking is the safest option. What isn't in doubt is the damage caused to the fetus by excessive alcohol intake. Continuous heavy drinking in pregnancy can lead to a condition known as fetal alcohol syndrome. The effects of this include retarded growth, facial and joint abnormalities, and heart problems.

If you drank in the weeks before you knew you were pregnant, try not to worry, but stop now. Many women also decide to give up alcohol while they're trying to conceive to optimize fertility.

Smoking Ideally, you should stop smoking before you get pregnant. If you're still smoking once you conceive, try to stop right away. If your partner or friends smoke, ask them not to smoke in your home or anywhere near you. Inhaled cigarette smoke interferes

Wearing rubber gloves when using household cleaning products will reduce your exposure to chemicals (left). **Opt for "greener" paints** and keep rooms ventilated while decorating (right).

with the supply of oxygen to the baby, which can lead to a low birthweight and increases the risk of stillbirth or the death of a baby in the first month of life.

Recreational drug use In addition to damaging your own health, recreational drugs are contraindicated in pregnancy since some pose dangers for the fetus and others carry a range of possible hazards.

Heroin and cocaine are damaging both to a pregnant woman and her unborn baby. These drugs stunt fetal growth, affect the placenta, and can cause miscarriage or premature birth, as well as health problems in the newborn. Babies born to women who use heroin often show drug withdrawal symptoms. A report on ecstasy linked the use of this in pregnancy to a rise in birth defects, such as limb abnormalities. The specific effects on the fetus of amphetamines and LSD are unclear, but it's safest to avoid them.

The direct effects on the fetus of the active chemicals in marijuana are not

clear, but smoking the drug involves the same risks as tobacco smoking.

Hazards at home
Many of us use chemicals daily in and around the home. In addition to personal products, such as bath oils, deodorants, and hairsprays, we also keep dozens of other substances around the home, including cleaning fluids, detergents, bleach, and air fresheners.

When products are used in accordance with the manufacturers' instructions, there is little chance of them causing harm in pregnancy. However, minute traces of chemicals can enter the bloodstream, either through the skin or by inhalation, and cross the placenta. While there is no hard evidence to show that this has an ill effect, it makes sense to minimize the chances of chemicals from reaching a developing baby.

When using products, wear rubber gloves to prevent skin contact and ventilate rooms. To avoid inhaling mists

A healthy pregnancy

24

or vapors, choose nonaerosol products. Also, choose products recommended for their low environmental impact, which contain fewer chemicals. Where possible, use natural alternatives to chemicals.

Painting and decorating It's important to stay safe while doing home projects. Be careful on ladders or while standing on tables to reach high places since your belly alters your center of balance. Also avoid skin contact or inhalation if you use oil-based paints; spray paints; paint strippers; floor varnishes; and sealant adhesives. Make sure rooms are well ventilated while decorating, and, ideally, get someone else to do the decorating.

Pets and infections Certain infections that could harm the fetus can be picked up from pets. The parasitic infection toxoplasmosis is spread through contact with cat feces. It may produce flulike symptoms, or no symptoms at all, and many unknowingly acquire immunity through previous exposure. However, although it rarely happens, contracting toxoplasmosis for the first time in pregnancy can cause serious problems, such as miscarriage or birth defects. Other pets, such as dogs, caged birds, and turtles can carry salmonella bacteria. Salmonella infection doesn't directly harm the baby, but can make a pregnant woman ill.

Being scrupulous about hygiene helps you avoid such infections. Wear rubber gloves when handling a cat litter box, cleaning cages where animals are kept, or disposing of dog feces, then wash your hands (and the gloves) afterward. Wear gloves also for digging or weeding in case animals have defecated in the garden. Or get someone else to do these tasks.

Toxoplasmosis and salmonella can also be contracted from eating undercooked or raw meat or eggs, so be careful with kitchen hygiene and cooking (see p.17).

Workplace hazards
It's the legal responsibility of your employer to provide a safe environment.

In pregnancy, being aware of your rights can help protect you and your baby.

In recent decades, women worried about whether working at a computer screen put their babies at risk. It's now clear that using a VDT (as well as photocopiers and printers) is safe. Some environments do pose possible dangers. If you work in a health-care setting with ionizing radiation or cancer-treatment drugs, inform your department that you're pregnant, so that if necessary, you're given alternative duties.

Women employed in places such as hairdressers, manicure salons, labs, and craft workshops may be exposed to toxic chemicals. Working around some dry cleaning solvents has been linked to miscarriage. It's up to employers to ensure protection from hazards. If you're unhappy about conditions, talk to your boss or HR manager.

Standing on your feet all day and physical work that involves heavy lifting can be exhausting in pregnancy. If your work involves either of these, ask if it's possible to switch to less tiring tasks.

If your job involves handling chemicals, ensure that a risk assessment is done and that you are able to avoid harmful substances.

Is it safe to use a cell phone during pregnancy? I've read that phones emit radiation.
The radiation emitted by cell phones is "non-ionizing." This is not the same as the radiation received from X-rays, which can be harmful in large doses. There is no evidence to show that using a cell phone is a health risk to either you or your baby.

I go swimming twice a week and love the feeling of having the weight taken off my belly! But is the chlorine in the pool bad for my baby?
In the past there has been some debate about whether it's safe to swim in chlorinated pools during pregnancy. However, now most experts believe that swimming in chlorinated water does not pose any health risks for pregnant women and their developing babies. You may find that the smell of chlorine might add to your nausea if you are suffering from morning sickness, although this is less of a problem in an outdoor pool. Try not to swallow the water, and shower when you come out of the pool. Swimming has great benefits during pregnancy. It has a low risk of injury while providing a good cardiovascular workout and improving muscle tone, so don't be put off by unnecessary worries.

Is it OK to use nicotine patches or gum while I'm pregnant?
Nicotine is known to decrease the blood supply to the fetus. This could affect the baby's growth, especially in early pregnancy. Although tobacco substitutes such as patches, gum, and lozenges deliver less nicotine to your body than smoking, you should never use them without a doctor's advice. Ask your doctor for information on safer ways to beat cigarette and nicotine cravings.

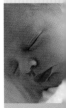

Skin, hair, and teeth

In addition to affecting what happens to you internally, hormonal changes in pregnancy can also affect your external appearance.

Many women look and feel better than ever during pregnany, while those less fortunate report that there is a downturn in their appearance. However pregnancy affects you, the changes will be temporary and you'll be back to your normal self soon after the birth.

Skin

You may find that your skin looks better in pregnancy due to hormonal changes, mild fluid retention, and increased blood flow. These can all result in smoother skin and are responsible for the famous "pregnancy glow." On the other hand, you may find that your skin gets drier and more pimply and you may need to take extra care of it during pregnancy.

Skin also tends to darken during pregnancy, although the cause for this is unknown. One possible explanation is the increased levels of estrogen and melanocyte-stimulating hormone, which stimulate skin pigmentation.

Stretch marks (striae gravidarum)

Many women develop stretch marks during pregnancy, which can occur on bellies, breasts, hips, or legs. These initially appear as pink or purple lines and may be quite itchy. After pregnancy they fade into pale wrinkles. Nobody knows for sure why these occur, but they probably result from a combination of pregnancy hormones and your skin stretching. You're more likely to get stretch marks if you're very young, if you gain a lot of weight in pregnancy, or if you have a very big baby. There is less agreement about the role of other factors such as a family history, being very overweight before pregnancy or belonging to a particular ethnic group.

Many creams, lotions, and oils have been marketed for the prevention or treatment of stretch marks but none has been proven to work. Studies have shown that some creams containing ingredients such as vitamin E, elastin, collagen-elastin hydrolysates, and menthol can reduce the development of stretch marks; but other trials have shown that creams containing vitamin E had no effect. If you want to use a commercially recommended cream, lotion, or oil, they are safe to use and may help prevent stretch marks, but unfortunately there is no guarantee.

Chloasma This describes the increased pigmentation of the cheeks, nose, and chin that affects around 50–70 percent of pregnant women. Using a protective sunscreen and avoiding the use of any photosensitizing skin-care products may reduce chloasma. A recent study found that using a highly protective sunscreen (SPF 50 and UVA-PF 28) prevented most pregnant women from developing chloasma.

Hair and nails

Hair stays longer in the growth phase during pregnancy, meaning that your scalp hair is likely to grow and thicken. Not so welcome is the fact that facial and body hair may also increase. After the birth, many women find that they suddenly lose a lot of hair as the growth phase stops. You should find that your hair is back to normal within six months.

Fingernails may also change, often becoming stronger, although some find that they become softer and brittle. Nails may develop white spots or

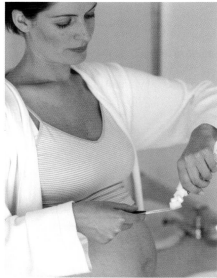

Applying moisturizing creams to relieve dry, itchy skin, or ones recommended to reduce stretch marks, is safe during pregnancy (left). **Taking good care of your teeth and gums** is important during pregnancy, when you're more susceptible to dental problems (right).

I am 18 weeks' pregnant and due to go on a beach vacation. My facial and body hair has grown and become very unsightly. How can I safely remove it?
You can safely tweeze, wax, and shave new stray hair. Skin bleaching and hair removal creams are probably safe during pregnancy, but there has been insufficient research to clear them since they can be absorbed through the skin and their effects on the baby are unknown. Permanent hair-removal techniques, such as laser and electrolysis, are thought to be safe in pregnancy. Both techniques penetrate the skin no deeper than a few millimeters. Consult your doctor to see if this is okay.

I've been using topical cream to treat acne and I've just found out that I'm pregnant. Will it harm my baby?
Tretinoin belongs to a group of medications called retinoids that contain vitamin A and may be associated with birth defects. Studies have looked at the effects of this cream in pregnancy and have found that babies whose mothers used it, even in the first trimester, had no increase in birth defects. However doctors recommend avoiding tretinoin cream in pregnancy.

Another similar medication, isotretinoin, which is taken orally, may increase the risk of birth defects and is therefore contraindicated in pregnancy.

I'm in the first trimester and will be going to my sister's wedding. Can I have highlights put in my hair?
Although the research into the safety of hair dyes if used in the first trimester may seem conflicting, the amount of chemicals used is small and it's unlikely that hair dyes cause harm. Also, if your hairdresser uses foil, the dye is kept off your skin.

I've heard that nail polish needs to be removed if you have a cesarean. Why is this?
Previously, women were encouraged to remove nail polish before surgery. One of the reasons was that the "pulse oximeter," a device attached to your finger to measure the oxygen in your blood during surgery, may give lower readings if placed over nail polish. However the device works as intended with nail polish or long nails if it's mounted sideways on a finger. Therefore there's no need to remove your polish.

transverse grooves, but these are rarely anything to worry about and don't mean that you're lacking in vitamins.

Teeth
Pregnant women are more prone to tooth decay (dental caries), bleeding gums, and chronic gum infection (periodontal disease). Poor dental health not only affects you, but can also have an impact on your baby. Studies have linked infection of the gums in pregnant women to premature birth, and if a woman has ongoing tooth decay after the birth, her baby may acquire bacteria directly from her saliva, leading to tooth decay in the child later on. It's therefore important that you take care of your

teeth during pregnancy and visit your dentist and dental hygienist regularly.
To keep your mouth healthy during pregnancy, brush twice a day with fluoride toothpaste and floss every day. Routine dental treatment and some local anesthetics are safe in pregnancy, although it's better to postpone elective dental treatments until after pregnancy or take care of them before pregnancy. Many women worry about having their teeth x-rayed in pregnancy. The radiation exposure from dental X-rays is minimal and the risk to your baby probably negligible. However, dentists will take every precaution to minimize your radiation exposure, covering you with a leaded apron before the X-rays.

Beauty treatments and cosmetics

The following advises which products and treatments are safe in pregnancy.

Hair and nail products Shampoos, conditioners, manicures, and pedicures are safe. Minute amounts of hair dye may be absorbed through the skin, but there's no evidence that this affects the baby. Chemical hair straighteners and curlers are also thought to be safe.

Piercing Facial piercing or piercing the belly button, nipples, or genitalia isn't advised since you're at a higher risk of infection. If you have a navel piercing already, you can change a metallic ring for a flexible plastic retainer made from PTFE (polytetrafluoroethylene). Nipple rings can affect breast-feeding, so remove a ring before birth so the skin can heal. Vaginal or vulval piercings are best removed to avoid damage at birth.

Tanning Tanning beds aren't advised because of harmful UV rays. Tanning beds can cause your body to overheat, which can harm your baby, and UV rays may break down folic acid. Tanning lotions are safe.

Body wraps/ Hot tubs These raise body temperature, which is unsafe for you and your baby. Heat exposure from a hot tub in the first three months can increase the risk of a baby developing spina bifida.

Facials The cosmetics used for facials are thought to be safe.

Botox It is generally recommended that women who are pregnant or breast-feeding should not use Botox. Although it's used for cosmetic reasons, it is a drug and should be considered as such. Doctors also advise avoiding Botox during pregnancy.

Traveling in pregnancy

Your growing belly shouldn't put a stop to travel plans. Just a bit of extra planning is required to help your vacation run smoothly.

Trimester-by-trimester travel guide

Think about the implications of traveling at different times in your pregnancy when planning a trip.

1st trimester (weeks 1–12)
- Period of highest risk for miscarriage and development problems in the baby. Be extra careful to avoid extremes of temperature and overly vigorous activities.
- Motion sickness could make morning sickness worse.
- Flying is allowed, provided you have no pregnancy complications.
- Insurance is unlikely to be a problem.

2nd trimester (weeks 13–25)
- You are likely to be feeling your best, and the chances of miscarriage or fetal development problems are greatly reduced.
- Flying is allowed, but check to see whether you need to carry a doctor's letter stating your due date.
- Check with individual travel insurance companies to see if you can get coverage—policies vary.

3rd trimester (weeks 26–40)
- Your belly is huge and travel may be very uncomfortable now.
- Some airlines may not allow you to fly after 36 weeks without a letter from your doctor written within 72 hours of your flight that includes your due date and confirms your fitness to fly.

Provided your pregnancy is normal, going to faraway places is perfectly possible. However, discomforts such as extreme heat, high altitude, and makeshift accommodations may be less tolerable, and in some cases may compromise the safety of your baby.

The best time to travel

In the first trimester, you may find that morning sickness and fatigue lessen your enthusiasm for travel. Most women feel at their best in the second trimester and this is also seen as the safest time to travel since your risk of miscarriage is low, energy levels are increased, and your due date is still some way off. After 28 weeks, the size of your belly, fatigue, and the looming birth date are likely to make home seem the best place to be.

You've found your passport and put the tickets in your bag. However, when you're pregnant you may also need to take the following items:
- A note from your doctor stating your due date and giving you the all-clear to travel (helpful if you're over 28 weeks).
- Any special medical records regarding your pregnancy or general health.
- A list of numbers for health-care facilities at your destination.
- Remedies for heartburn or other minor pregnancy problems, such as hemorrhoids. You may not be able to buy your usual products abroad.

Making plans

A little extra planning is the key to successful travel in pregnancy. However tempting brochures look, think carefully before you book. How will you get there and how long will it take? Pregnancy adds to the stress of a long-haul trip. If you want to fly, check with the airline about its policy. Some require a current letter from your doctor confirming your due date and your fitness to fly after 36 weeks. This is largely because of the possibility of going into labor mid-flight.

Taking precautions Unless you have no choice, avoid visiting countries where disease is a high risk factor. Many doctors agree that protective drugs, such as certain vaccines and antimalarial pills, are not advisable in pregnancy

The best time to travel is often during the second trimester when nausea has abated and your belly size is not yet uncomfortable.

or when trying to conceive. Check the internet for information about an area's health hazards and local hospitals. If you have a condition such as diabetes that could cause complications, make sure you can get treatment while away.

Before you leave, try to get travel insurance. Some companies consider pregnancy a preexisting condition and won't provide coverage for your trip.

Avoiding bugs

Pregnancy reduces the efficiency of your immune system, increasing your risk of an infection. When you're traveling, "stomach bugs" caused by contaminated food and water are more likely to strike.

If you're unsure about local tap water, buy bottled water (make sure the seal is unbroken) and use it when brushing your teeth as well as for drinking. Avoid drinks with ice and don't eat salads or fruit you can't peel since they may have been washed in contaminated water. A less obvious danger is fruit such as melon, which may have been injected with water to increase its weight.

Avoid outdoor stalls or cafés where food might have been prepared hours in advance. Try to find restaurants where food is freshly cooked and standards seem high. Be scrupulous about hygiene, and carry moist wipes in case hand-washing facilities are inadequate.

On the trip

Sitting in a cramped seat for hours can cause your ankles and feet to swell. If you're traveling by car, stop every hour to stretch your legs, have a snack, or find a bathroom. On a train or airplane, keep your circulation moving with foot and ankle exercises, and get up regularly to walk down the aisle when it's safe to do so. Stay hydrated by drinking lots of water or juice, even if you do need to empty your bladder frequently. A few comforts, such as a cushion to tuck behind your back or a cooling water spritzer, can make a trip more bearable.

I am five months pregnant and about to go on a beach vacation. I know that too much sunbathing causes skin damage, but can hot sun also harm my baby? Experts are investigating a link between prolonged exposure to the sun and damage to the fetus. There is a possibility that ultraviolet rays could cause a deficiency of folic acid—a vitamin that helps prevent defects in the baby's nervous system leading to spina bifida. Nothing is yet proven, but it's not worth taking the risk. Enjoy the sun in moderation but don't bake yourself or use tanning beds before you go on vacation.

I'm worried about flying, because someone told me there is a high risk of DVT in pregnancy. Is this true? Deep vein thrombosis (DVT), the formation of a blood clot in a vein (often in a leg), is sometimes caused by long periods of immobility, such as sitting on a plane (see p.186). Although the risk factor may be slightly increased in pregnant women, because their blood tends to clot more easily, the chance of your developing DVT is still very low. To minimize the risk even further, you could purchase some special support socks, which are designed to improve blood flow in the legs.

The position of your seatbelt may need adjusting to accommodate your belly.

Are car seatbelts and airbags safe to use in pregnancy? In the event of an accident, these appliances are far more likely to prevent injury than cause it—never travel without fastening your seatbelt. For comfort, position the straps above and below your belly rather than across it. Being hit by an inflated airbag will not hurt you or the baby, but to lessen the impact you should position your seat as far back as possible.

Vacation activities

There are some activities to forego in pregnancy, such as water skiing or horse riding, where a fall could harm your baby. Scuba diving is particularly dangerous because of the risk of air bubbles forming in the bloodstream. If you have children, ignore pleas to join them on amusement park rides.

If you're used to exercising, there is no reason not to go swimming or walking, just don't overdo it—hiking up hills under a blazing sun could send your temperature soaring, which is a bad thing in pregnancy. In the first trimester especially, extreme heat can affect fetal development. You might also become dehydrated, which later on can increase the risk of premature labor.

Be cautious also about less energetic activities. Hot tubs and saunas are best avoided since the heat could make you feel faint and may be harmful to your baby. An aromatherapy massage sounds like a treat, but some oils may be toxic to the baby, especially in the early months. If you want pampering, look for spas with treatments for pregnant moms.

In pregnancy, your skin becomes more sensitive to the sun, so whatever you're doing be careful to protect against overexposure to the sun.

The 40 weeks, or 280 days, of pregnancy are a time of constant change as your body continually adapts to accommodate the new life growing inside you. This extensive chapter guides you through the physical and emotional changes you'll experience and offers reassurance, advice, and practical tips. Your baby's progress is charted in fascinating detail with scans and day-by-day insights into how your baby grows and develops within your uterus.

Pregnancy
day by day

Welcome to your first trimester

WEEK		1	2	3	4	5

Pre-conception care A daily prenatal vitamin supplement before and during early pregnancy helps protect your baby from spinal cord defects.

Avoid alcohol Drinking soft drinks rather than alcohol may help you to conceive; add fruit to drinks for extra benefit.

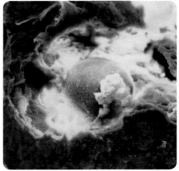

The release of an egg At ovulation, an enlarged follicle in the ovary ruptures to release the mature egg, ready to be fertilized in a fallopian tube by your partner's sperm.

It's official! By the time you discover you're pregnant, your baby has reached the embryonic period and the brain, heart, and other organs are starting to form.

Early growth In the crucial first weeks, the baby's vital organs begin to develop and the neural tube, which becomes the brain and spinal cord, is forming.

At first, only you are aware of subtle body changes. By three months, changes may be visible.

First trimester Your baby is developing rapidly and you may have a whole host of symptoms, but outwardly there's little sign that you're pregnant. **Starting to show** By the end of this trimester, your waistline may start to expand.

The path to conception Sexual intercourse timed to coincide with ovulation is most likely to lead to a successful pregnancy.

Facts and figures You have a 3.5 in 1000 chance of having identical twins.

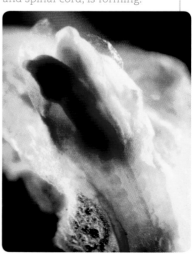

You're at the beginning of an incredible stage of life that will see your body undergo dramatic changes.

6	7	8	9	10	11	12

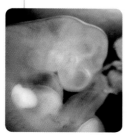

At 6 weeks, budlike structures can be seen on the embryo that will develop into your baby's limbs.

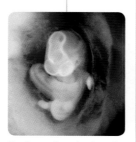

By 8 weeks, the head has grown rapidly, giving an unbalanced appearance, and the limbs are lengthening.

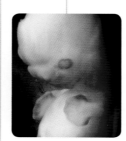

At 9 weeks, the fetus is starting to have a recognizable form, with facial features beginning to develop.

Feeling exhausted A classic symptom of early pregnancy is a feeling of complete exhaustion, thought to be due to rising hormone levels and the dramatic physiological changes your body undergoes as your baby grows rapidly.

Facts and figures At 7 weeks, your baby measures just ⅓ in (8 mm) crown to rump.

Dating the pregnancy Between 10 and 14 weeks, your first ultrasound will confirm the gestational age of your baby. Your original due date may be revised as a result of this scan and the timing of future tests will be based on its findings.

Parents-to-be As the realization sinks in that you're facing parenthood, you may discover a new dimension to your relationship and an enhanced sense of togetherness.

Soothing foods Early pregnancy can often be marred by nausea and vomiting, especially in the mornings; eating crackers or sipping a decaf tea can help quell the symptoms.

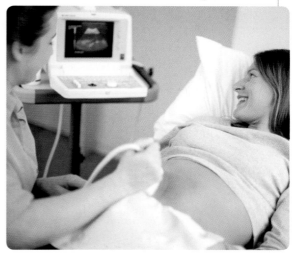

Your 1st week

It's business as usual for your body this week. You're having a period, so you know you're not pregnant. But if you conceive during this menstrual cycle, the first day of your period will count as the first day of pregnancy. It's a good idea to review your lifestyle and to make sure that you understand how everything works "inside." Knowing the facts may help to raise your chances of conceiving.

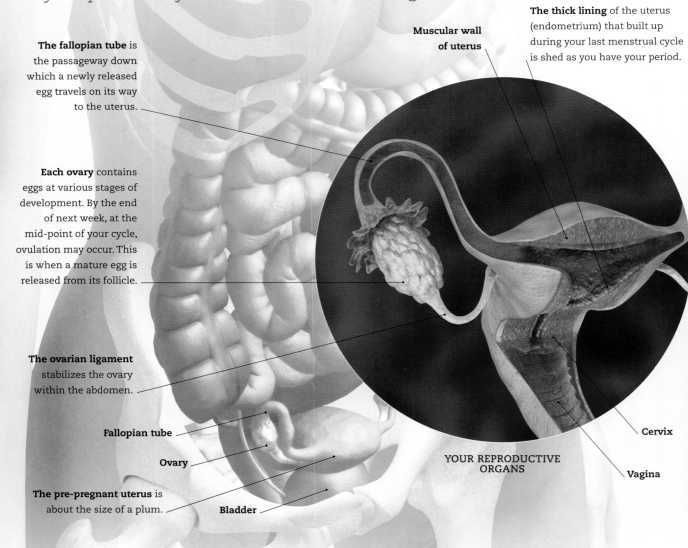

The fallopian tube is the passageway down which a newly released egg travels on its way to the uterus.

Each ovary contains eggs at various stages of development. By the end of next week, at the mid-point of your cycle, ovulation may occur. This is when a mature egg is released from its follicle.

The ovarian ligament stabilizes the ovary within the abdomen.

Muscular wall of uterus

The thick lining of the uterus (endometrium) that built up during your last menstrual cycle is shed as you have your period.

Fallopian tube

Ovary

The pre-pregnant uterus is about the size of a plum.

Bladder

YOUR REPRODUCTIVE ORGANS

Cervix

Vagina

279 days to go...

WHAT'S HAPPENING INSIDE

The lining of the uterus builds up in the first two weeks of the menstrual cycle to prepare for pregnancy. The yellow and blue areas seen here are cells and the pink area, secretions. If no pregnancy occurs, the lining breaks down and menstruation occurs.

This is day one of your period. If you are trying to conceive during this menstrual cycle, keep a note of this highly significant date.

Although this is officially the first day of your pregnancy, you won't conceive until around two weeks from now. This is classified as "day one" because once you conceive your pregnancy will be dated from the first day of your menstrual period. It would be more logical to date a pregnancy from the day of ovulation or conception, but, like most women, you're unlikely to know the day on which you ovulate, let alone conceive. You are, however, far more likely to remember when your last period started, especially if you're hoping to get pregnant and are keeping a record of your menstrual cycle.

While dating a pregnancy in this way is a handy, if slightly baffling, convention, it does mean that your body is getting geared up for pregnancy from today. In around 280 days, or nine months' time, you could be holding your newborn baby in your arms. Good luck and enjoy the journey!

FOCUS ON... NUTRITION

Take folic acid

Start taking this vital supplement now, from day one, if you haven't already. You should take folic acid as soon as you begin trying to conceive because it will be essential to your baby's development in the first few weeks of pregnancy (see p.16).

The amount of folic acid that has been shown to be effective is a daily supplement of 0.4 mg. A diet of foods rich in folate is also advisable so eat plenty of green vegetables, such as green beans, spinach, and broccoli; legumes, such as peas, beans, and chickpeas; fortified cereals; and wheat germ and other fortified grains.

TIME TO THINK ABOUT

Having a baby

There's no perfect time to become parents, but you might want to bear in mind the following:

■ **While practical matters** such as the state of your finances and the size of your house are considerations, remember that being parents is about more than what you are able to offer your baby materially.
■ **This is a decision** only you and your partner can make. Don't act on the advice of family members and friends.
■ **You might conceive** immediately or it could take several months, so relax and don't have a set date in mind.

AS A MATTER OF FACT

Just 20 percent of couples actively trying to conceive become pregnant in the first monthly cycle.

For 75 percent of couples it takes six months. So be patient and try not to get too stressed if you don't manage to conceive immediately.

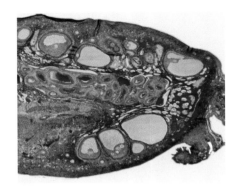

278 days to go...

WHAT'S HAPPENING INSIDE

Your eggs are already developing, as can be seen in this color-enhanced ovary. The small white structures are the immature follicles that contain the eggs at different stages of development. Once one of the follicles matures, the egg will burst out.

By tracking your menstrual cycle and understanding how it works, you may increase your chances of conceiving.

This is day two of your period and day two of your complete menstrual cycle, which starts on the first day of your period and ends on the first day of your next period. A full cycle is, on average, 28 days, but many women have a shorter or longer cycle.

This may be the time when your period is at its heaviest, since the tissue and blood that make up the lining of the uterus (the endometrium) is shed. The average blood loss during menstruation is around two tablespoons (30 ml). While the lining is being sloughed off,

the blood vessels in the uterus constrict, which can cause cramplike period pains. As soon as your period has finished, an egg begins to mature within its follicle in one of your ovaries, ready to be released around mid-cycle. This is called ovulation (see p.49).

Meanwhile, the lining of the uterus starts to build up again under the influence of the hormones progesterone and estrogen, ready to receive a fertilized egg. If the egg is not fertilized, hormone levels fall, the lining sheds, and the cycle begins again.

AS A MATTER OF FACT

Periods can synchronize in women who live or work together.

Scientists claim that pheromones (chemicals that trigger a biological response in someone) waft from one woman to another. Receptors in the nose detect these pheromones and a biological process takes place whereby one woman naturally adjusts her menstrual cycle.

CHANGES DURING THE MENSTRUAL CYCLE

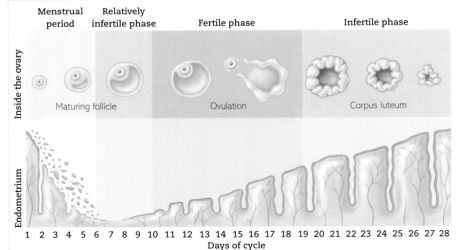

Menstrual period | Relatively infertile phase | Fertile phase | Infertile phase

Inside the ovary

Maturing follicle — Ovulation — Corpus luteum

Endometrium

1 2 3 4 5 6 7 8 9 10 11 12 13 14 15 16 17 18 19 20 21 22 23 24 25 26 27 28
Days of cycle

The monthly cycle of an egg as it grows to maturity inside an ovary is shown at the top of the chart. It is released from its follicle around day 14. The bottom of the chart shows the corresponding development of the lining of the uterus—shedding at the start of a period, then rebuilding in preparation for the fertilized egg.

The empty egg follicle (called the corpus luteum) secretes progesterone, which is a hormone that helps the endometrium reach a thickness of about 0.2 in (6 mm) over the 28 days of the menstrual cycle, ready to receive a fertilized egg.

277 days to go...

WHAT'S HAPPENING INSIDE

The lining of the uterus, known as the endometrium, can be seen here (pink structure) shedding during menstruation. This happens if a fertilized egg does not implant. The red dots are red blood cells, released when the blood vessels break down.

When you're trying to get pregnant, it helps to be aware of lifestyle and medical factors that can affect your menstrual cycle.

You may notice the timing and volume of your period differs. Your menstrual cycle can be affected by stress as well as by medical conditions, such as an overactive thyroid. In both these cases, periods can become lighter or less frequent. If your periods are erratic, it can be difficult to predict when you might ovulate. Unpredictable or missed periods may mean that ovulation isn't occurring at all. If you know this to be the case because you're monitoring the signs of ovulation (see p.43), or using ovulation predictor tests (see p.43), seek medical advice about your fertility.

You may be able to become pregnant naturally and easily despite problems related to your period, but some conditions that cause long, irregular, or heavy periods are linked to lower fertility. Heavy periods can be caused by conditions such as fibroids (see p.218), which can affect fertility. A higher than average level of blood loss can also make you anemic, which is not the best start for pregnancy for you or your baby, so you may want to look at boosting your iron intake (see p.154).

Painful periods can impact fertility. Endometriosis is a common disorder that can make periods painful and cause discomfort during sex. If you have these symptoms, see your doctor who might arrange a scan or refer you to a specialist. In endometriosis, cells resembling those that line the uterus come to lie outside the uterus on structures such as the ovaries, the fallopian tubes, and walls of the pelvis. There are treatments for endometriosis, including laser surgery, that can boost a woman's chances of conceiving.

ASK A... DOCTOR

Should I monitor my menstrual cycle? Yes, monitoring your cycle is an important part of planning for pregnancy because it can help you figure out roughly which day you're ovulating (see p.49) and thereby improve your chances of conceiving. It means you can ensure you have sexual intercourse at roughly the right time.

It's also helpful to note the length of your cycle, which may vary. The most important thing to note is that from ovulation to the start of your next period is always around 14 days so when you get your next period, you can figure out roughly when you ovulated.

FOCUS ON... IVF

Stimulating egg follicles

IVF (in vitro fertilization) may be an option if a woman is having trouble conceiving. The first stage with this procedure is to stimulate the ovaries to produce many follicles, so that multiple eggs can be fertilized outside the body.

Starting on around day three of your cycle, you will be given drugs to stimulate your ovaries. You will need to inject yourself (see right) or use a nasal spray to suppress the normal cycle, followed by injections of a follicle-stimulating-like hormone. Egg retrieval will then take place (see p.57).

276 days to go...

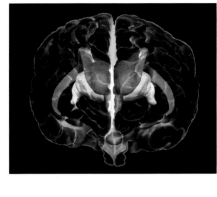

WHAT'S HAPPENING INSIDE

In this color 3-D scan of the human brain, the green central structure is the hypothalamus. This controls emotions and body temperature, and releases chemicals that regulate the release of hormones from the pituitary gland (green circle at bottom).

Like many women, you may sometimes feel ruled by your hormones, and it helps to understand why they fluctuate.

The hormone build-up to ovulation starts right now in week one of your menstrual cycle. Your pituitary gland, which lies in the base of your brain, produces follicle-stimulating hormone (FSH). During your period, the level of FSH rises steadily, triggering the development of the follicles (around 15–20 each month) in each ovary. As well as containing each egg, the follicles produce estrogen.

The hormone estrogen circulates, affecting the pituitary gland and causing it to produce luteinizing hormone (LH)—this triggers ovulation (see p.49). This week your estrogen levels are low and steady, but will rise dramatically later in your cycle.

Progesterone levels are low during your period, but start to rise several days afterward and stay high for the second part of the cycle. Under the influence of progesterone, the muscles in the cervix relax, easing open the cervical canal. Changes also affect the mucus, which becomes more fluid, so sperm find it easier to swim through. It is progesterone that enables the lining of the uterus to thicken in preparation for implantation of the fertilized egg.

AS A MATTER OF FACT

Men get PMS too!

Scientists have confirmed there's a male version of PMS—Irritable Male Syndrome. Mood swings, temper tantrums, and loss of libido in men were found to be caused by falling levels of testosterone due to stress.

THE LOWDOWN

Fertility rites

Rooted in folklore, these fertility tips require a leap of faith and a good sense of humor!

■ **Use the moon.** Exponents of "lunaception" believe that women whose menstrual cycle aligns with the lunar cycle—so they menstruate during the new moon and ovulate when the moon is full—have more chance of conceiving. It's based on the theory that women's cycles are influenced by natural light.

■ **Dance around the Maypole.** Maypoles are thought to herald the arrival of spring and celebrate fertility.

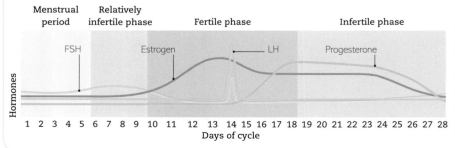

CHANGES DURING THE MENSTRUAL CYCLE

Menstrual period | Relatively infertile phase | Fertile phase | Infertile phase

FSH | Estrogen | LH | Progesterone

Hormones

1 2 3 4 5 6 7 8 9 10 11 12 13 14 15 16 17 18 19 20 21 22 23 24 25 26 27 28
Days of cycle

There are four hormones at work during the menstrual cycle: FSH (follicle-stimulating hormone) causes the egg follicles to start developing in the ovary; estrogen is produced by the developing egg and peaks just before ovulation; LH (luteinizing hormone) triggers ovulation; progesterone thickens the lining of the uterus.

275 days to go...

WHAT'S HAPPENING INSIDE

This cross section through the ovary shows several ovarian follicles. Between each follicle, the connective tissue can be seen. Each month about 15–20 follicles mature, but it is usually only one that will fully mature and release an egg.

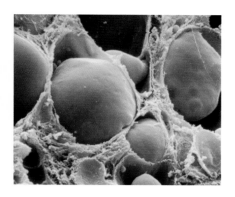

Making some lifestyle changes is essential when you're trying to get pregnant and cutting down on alcohol is a good start.

Even though it's still the week of your period, and some time before you ovulate, try to ensure you're in the best possible health to maximize fertility. One way is to cut down your alcohol intake.

Heavy drinking can reduce the chances of conceiving and, if you do get pregnant, it can also harm your unborn baby's development. There is plenty of evidence that drinking beyond the recommended amounts is harmful. What's lacking is evidence of the effects on conception and pregnancy of the occasional alcoholic drink. There is no known safe level of alcohol consumption for pregnant women. However, many women decide to err on the side of caution and stop drinking alcohol entirely while trying to conceive and in early pregnancy. Some find that morning sickness (see p.81) naturally reduces desire for alcohol.

Alcohol also affects male fertility. It has adverse effects on the quantity and quality of sperm produced, and drinking large amounts can cause impotence.

You may find a drink helps you and your partner relax and puts you in the mood for sex, thereby increasing your chances of conception, but you may want to rethink having the occasional glass of alcohol. The Public Health Agency of Canada recommends that women trying to get pregnant abstain from alcohol to eliminate potential problems.

Opt for nonalcoholic drinks if you're trying to get pregnant. A high intake of alcohol can adversely affect your chances of conceiving.

AS A MATTER OF FACT

Illicit or "street" drugs can harm your unborn baby.

You should try to stop using drugs before you conceive. However if you regularly use drugs, or find it hard to manage without them, it is essential to get medical support. Ask your doctor for advice. He or she will be able to help and put you in touch with a support group.

TIME TO THINK ABOUT

Medical checkups

Before you try to conceive, speak to your doctor about the following tests:

■ **Rubella:** have a blood test to check that you have antibodies against rubella (German measles). Being infected by the rubella virus for the first time in early pregnancy is associated with an increased risk of the baby developing an abnormality, and increasing the risk of miscarriage. If you were vaccinated against rubella as a child, your antibody level may be high enough to protect your baby. If it isn't high enough, you'll be offered a MMR (measles, mumps, rubella) vaccine booster and advised not to conceive for three months.

■ **Sexually transmitted infections:** go to your doctor for tests to rule out infections such as chlamydia, genital warts, and herpes. You may want to consider having an HIV test as well. Women with HIV can still bear children, but may be prescribed a medicine to reduce the chances of passing the infection to their child. A cesarean may be recommended for women with HIV or active genital herpes.

Your 1st week

274 days to go...

WHAT'S HAPPENING INSIDE

In this artwork of the uterus, the green central structure is the pear-shaped uterus itself; the red part is the cavity of the uterus. The blue structures to either side are the fallopian tubes, which each have an ovary, seen in pink here, at the end.

Eating well is an essential part of conception and pregnancy so you and your partner should get into good habits now.

FOCUS ON... NUTRITION

Vital B vitamins

Your diet should include foods containing B vitamins (see p.16). Take a pregnancy multivitamin if needed.

- **B1** deficiency has been linked to failed ovulation and implantation.
- **B2** deficiency has been linked to infertility and miscarriage.
- **B5** is important for conception and fetal development.
- **B6** is essential for the formation and functioning of sex hormones.
- **B12,** with folate (see p.16), is essential to fetal development.

Take the time in this first two weeks of your cycle, before you ovulate, to look at what you eat on a daily basis—if you and your partner (see p.44) make some simple changes to your diet, it might just improve your chances of conception.

Use this opportunity to check your weight ie. your Body Mass Index (BMI) (see p.17) since a BMI of under 19 or over 24 could adversely affect fertility.

If you're overweight, excess fat tissue may affect your metabolism and hormones and you may not ovulate as regularly, or at all. If you need fertility treatment, the chances of success are also lower if you're overweight, because you may respond less well to the drugs that stimulate ovulation. Once you're pregnant, being overweight can also cause an increased risk of complications, decreasing the chance of carrying the pregnancy to full term.

Weighing too little when you're trying to conceive isn't healthy either. Pregnancy takes its toll on a woman's reserves, so a little stored fat is a good thing for mother and baby. Being seriously underweight can affect ovulation and make periods irregular or absent, and conception unlikely.

Your BMI when you conceive is also a good indication of how much weight you should gain once you're pregnant (see p.99) so it's worth getting it checked at this point.

GET FIT AND FERTILE!

Regular exercise can increase your chances of conceiving by allowing your body to work at optimum levels. If you're fit and have a healthy lifestyle, you will reduce the level of toxins in your body and be less stressed, which makes it easier to conceive. Exercise will also regulate your energy and your blood-sugar levels, which assists the body in regulating the hormonal cycle—a key player in the reproductive process. Conversely, overexercising can adversely affect the ovulation process and make conception more difficult.

The guidelines for exercising at this crucial time of conception are to continue weight-bearing exercise, such as walking, running, or aerobics, for 30 minutes five times a week at a moderate intensity. It is important to listen to your body— moderate means exercising within a comfortable range, where the exercise isn't too hard but is pushing your body enough to feel the benefits.

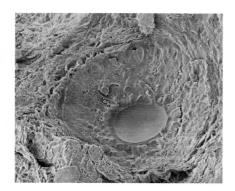

273 days to go...

WHAT'S HAPPENING INSIDE

Here an egg can be seen, in orange, developing in the ovary. The cells of the follicle, in which it is contained, can be seen surrounding the egg. At birth, baby girls have millions of follicles present in their ovaries.

When you're trying to get pregnant, you need to take your age into account because your fertility will change as you get older.

In about a week's time you are likely to ovulate. At the start of puberty, you had no more than about 400 eggs in your ovaries, and will have made no new eggs. Your lifetime of eggs were there when you were born. Given these facts, it's hardly a surprise that your fertility falls as you age.

Women 20–24 are generally at their most fertile and although, for most women, periods continue until their early fifties, the rate of fertility gradually lowers in the 30s, 40s, and 50s and the rate of chromosomal abnormalities and miscarriage increases. Nonetheless, every year thousands of babies are born to women in their late thirties and forties. Women can conceive beyond that age, which is why doctors advise menopausal women to use contraception for two years after their last period.

If, however, you're hoping to start a family, it's safe to assume that fertility begins to fall off sharply after age 35. Your age also affects the quality of your eggs. In women in their early 20s, around 17 percent of eggs have a chromosomal abnormality, but the figure rises to over 75 percent in women in their 40s. Chromosomal problems increase the chances of having a child with a disorder such as Down syndrome (see p.476).

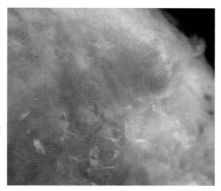

The follicle lies below the surface of the ovarian wall and protrudes just prior to ovulation. The follicle is most likely to rupture and release an egg mid-cycle, around days 13 and 14 of a 28-day cycle.

If you're concerned about your fertility, it is possible to have a blood test that can give an indication of your remaining ovary function so that you know how much reproductive time you have left. While some tests are based on levels of FSH (see p.38) and estrogen, newer tests use other markers found in the blood, such as anti-Mullerian hormone (AMH) and inhibin B.

But making a baby depends on more than releasing an egg; it must travel down the fallopian tube, be fertilized, implant, and the pregnancy be maintained. There's also the father's contribution to consider (see box, right).

THE MALE BIOLOGICAL CLOCK?

A man can continue to make sperm more or less throughout his life, so you might not expect male fertility to fall significantly. There are plenty of older fathers around that seemingly prove this.

Recent research from France, however, found that men over 35 took a lot longer to get their partner pregnant. For those who conceived, there was a slightly higher risk of miscarrying. This is because sperm from older men is more likely to contain damaged DNA. So although older couples do conceive, it's a fact that men, like women, pass their peak fertility.

AS A MATTER OF FACT

Sperm have a long and perilous journey of 12–16 in (30–40 cm) to reach the egg.

This is why nature is bountiful when it comes to sperm, producing many millions with each ejaculation. On average each ejaculation produces 2–8 ml of semen, with over 40 million sperm in each milliliter.

Your 2nd week

YOUR "FERTILE WINDOW" IS APPROACHING AND THIS COULD BE THE TIME YOU CONCEIVE

Toward the end of this week, one of the eggs in your ovaries is likely to have reached full maturity. Ovulation occurs as the egg, under the influence of hormones, bursts out of its follicle. If it meets a sperm, you may become pregnant. Now is the time to enjoy lots of sex with your partner, so go for it—as often as you like. If you have any anxieties about fertility, try to put them aside and relax.

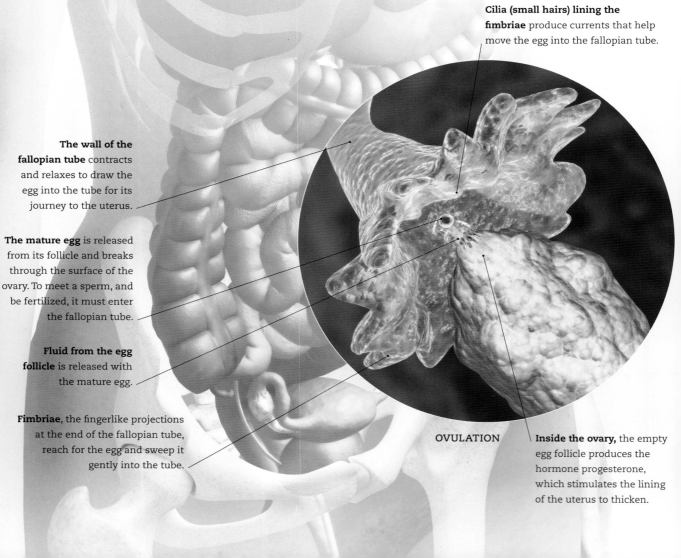

Cilia (small hairs) lining the fimbriae produce currents that help move the egg into the fallopian tube.

The wall of the fallopian tube contracts and relaxes to draw the egg into the tube for its journey to the uterus.

The mature egg is released from its follicle and breaks through the surface of the ovary. To meet a sperm, and be fertilized, it must enter the fallopian tube.

Fluid from the egg follicle is released with the mature egg.

Fimbriae, the fingerlike projections at the end of the fallopian tube, reach for the egg and sweep it gently into the tube.

OVULATION

Inside the ovary, the empty egg follicle produces the hormone progesterone, which stimulates the lining of the uterus to thicken.

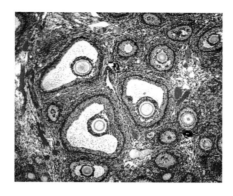

272 days to go...

WHAT'S HAPPENING INSIDE

Here, three developing ovarian follicles can be seen in white. The inner circle of each is the egg. Of the follicles shown, it is likely that only one will fully mature at ovulation (see p.49) and release an egg.

By the end of this week you're likely to have ovulated. It's a good idea to know the signs that indicate you're at your most fertile.

This is week two of your cycle. You will probably ovulate by the end of this week and will therefore be fertile. However, the fertile window can be from 5 days before ovulation to 12–24 hours after as sperm can survive for 5 days inside you. If your periods are regular, ovulation can be easier to track, but you may want to use other methods, such as looking out for natural signs (see box, right) or using an ovulation kit. Remember, however, the best way to conceive is to have sex regularly.

While they are useful, testing kits are expensive and can be counterproductive because they make sex more clinical and less enjoyable. They work by testing the urine to detect a surge in LH, the hormone that triggers egg release.

Always follow the instructions given. Testing between 10 am and 8 pm should be fine, but try to aim for roughly the same time every day. After a positive test, you should ovulate 12–36 hours later. Results are about 99 percent accurate but occasionally the result is a false positive. Results can occasionally give a false negative, especially if you've drunk a lot of water. If your test was negative, do another one the next day. Once you have a positive result, you can stop testing for that month.

ARE YOU OVULATING?

This week, look out for:
- **Lower abdominal pain** at ovulation, called mittelschmerz (the German for "pain in the middle").
- **Basal body temperature** (your temperature when you first wake in the morning) rising slightly.
- **Cervical mucus**—the cervix produces secretions, which become wetter, clearer in color, and stretchy, resembling raw egg white, just before ovulation. This indicates the start of your fertile phase.

CHANGES DURING THE MENSTRUAL CYCLE

Body temperature can be seen at the top of the chart, rising sharply right after ovulation. The bottom section shows cervical secretions. These begin in the days leading up to ovulation, starting off moist and sticky, then becoming wetter and stretchy at your most fertile time.

If you feel some of the cervical mucus with your fingers, you will find you can stretch it out. This is a sign that you are about to ovulate.

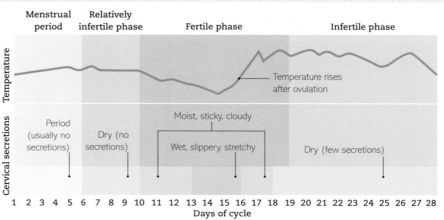

| Menstrual period | Relatively infertile phase | Fertile phase | Infertile phase |

Temperature

Temperature rises after ovulation

Cervical secretions

Period (usually no secretions) — Dry (no secretions) — Moist, sticky, cloudy / Wet, slippery, stretchy — Dry (few secretions)

1 2 3 4 5 6 7 8 9 10 11 12 13 14 15 16 17 18 19 20 21 22 23 24 25 26 27 28

Days of cycle

271 days to go...

WHAT'S HAPPENING INSIDE

In your partner's body, sperm is constantly being produced. Here the sperm cells can be seen: they consist of a head (green), which contains the genetic material, and fertilizes the egg, and a tail (blue), which propels the sperm along.

While you wait to ovulate, fascinating changes are occurring in your ovaries as your follicles mature to release an egg.

In the time leading up to ovulation, which will happen later this week, the most advanced follicle moves to the surface of the ovary, ready to release its precious cargo. While you were having your period, around 15–20 follicles were developing in your ovaries.

Both of your ovaries contribute to follicle growth, but usually only one ovary brings a follicle to ovulation. Which ovary it is seems to depend on chance since ovaries are not on a strict rotation. As the follicles grow, they enlarge greatly, filling with fluid secreted inside the follicle. Some women release more than one egg some months (see p.49) and if both are fertilized, it will mean nonidentical twins are conceived.

By the time of ovulation, the follicle will be about 1 in (2 cm) in diameter, while the egg is just about visible without a microscope.

To mature, follicles need FSH (follicle-stimulating hormone) produced by the brain's pituitary gland (see p.38), but their early growth doesn't appear to rely on it. It may, however, depend on other hormones and chemicals.

SPECIALIZED MEDICAL ADVICE

If you have any ongoing medical problems, go to see your doctor before you start trying to conceive. Conditions such as diabetes, asthma, high blood pressure, heart trouble, a previous bout of deep vein thrombosis (DVT) (see p.186), thyroid conditions, sickle-cell disease, and epilepsy can all impact a pregnancy.

The effect will depend on the individual condition and a specialist's advice and care will be needed. If you're in any doubt about how your own medical history may affect a pregnancy, check with your doctor before you start trying to conceive.

FOCUS ON... DADS

Dads: your diet counts too

It's never too late to start eating well if you want to become a dad. But because sperm take some weeks to mature, ideally start eating a healthy diet at least three months before conception. There are supplements, but most vitamins and minerals work better in the form of real food.

■ **Antioxidants** A diet rich in anti-oxidants, including vitamins A, C, and E, selenium, and zinc, helps prevent damage to sperm DNA.

■ **Selenium** may also help sperm penetrate the outer layer of the egg.

Eat tuna, wheatgerm, whole grains, and sesame seeds.

■ **Zinc** is present in large amounts in semen. Eat fish, lean meat, shellfish, turkey, chicken, eggs, whole grains, rye, and oats.

■ **Manganese** is another element that could help male fertility. Eat leafy vegetables (including broccoli) carrots, eggs, whole grains, and ginger.

■ **Essential fatty acids** may improve sperm motility. Eat oily fish, such as mackerel, salmon, and sardines, flaxseed and linseed, and kiwi fruit.

270 days to go...

WHAT'S HAPPENING INSIDE

As ovulation approaches, more cervical mucus is produced. Here it has crystallized to form a "fern leaf" pattern. Around the time of ovulation the mucus becomes clear, slippery, and stretchy, which makes it easier for sperm to swim through.

You may not care whether you have a boy or a girl, but according to some theories you can influence gender.

Conceiving is all about having sex at the right time this week, but if you're hoping to have a child of a specific gender, the timing could be even more important. Some experts claim there is a link between when you have sex and the baby's gender (see below).

Recent research suggests that women who have a high calorie intake (especially if they eat that most phallic of fruit, the banana) are marginally more likely to bear a boy. Those who skip breakfast or have a low calorie intake are more likely to have a girl. One reason for this is thought to be that the extra calories consumed affect vaginal secretions and help to give the Y sperm that makes baby boys a vital boost.

Research has found that women with high glucose levels, achieved by eating normally and not skipping breakfast, were more likely to conceive a boy.

AS A MATTER OF FACT

If you already have two same-sex children, you're 75 percent more likely to conceive a child of that sex again.

Although the sex of the baby conceived is random, conceiving children of the same sex could be due to the fact that some men produce better quality X sperm, which makes baby girls, or Y sperm, which makes baby boys.

Statistically, couples who have two children of different sexes are less likely to try for a third child.

MAKING BABIES... BOYS AND GIRLS

The Shettles method, devised by Dr. Landrum Shettles, is based on the fact that Y sperm (for boys) are smaller, faster, and less resilient than X sperm (for girls), and are less able to withstand an acidic environment in the vagina.

To conceive a boy, the Shettles method advises:
■ Timing sex as close to ovulation as possible and adopting positions such as rear-entry that promote deep penetration.
■ The woman should orgasm, ideally at the same time as the man to make the vagina less acidic and favor Y sperm.
■ Drinking a cup or two or strong coffee just before sex to give Y-sperm an added kick.

The Whelan method, devised by Dr. Elizabeth Whelan, suggests that having sex earlier on in the cycle, some four to six days before ovulation, is more likely to result in a boy. Sex nearer the time of ovulation is more likely to result in a girl. Curiously, the Whelan way is more or less the opposite of the advice given by Shettles.

But what works? The mainstream medical view, supported by reports in journals such as the *New England Journal of Medicine*, is that the timing of sex has little or no bearing on gender. The possible exception is that having sex two days before ovulation may be slightly more likely to favor a girl.

Your 2nd week

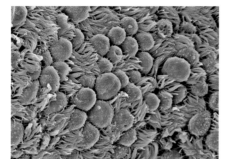

269 days to go...

WHAT'S HAPPENING INSIDE

The lining of the fallopian tube, seen here, has a moist mucous membrane. This contains cells (brown) that protect the tube's surface. The hairlike cilia (blue) move the eggs along the tubes following ovulation.

If this isn't the first month you've been trying to conceive, don't be too disappointed. It's normal for it to take some time.

Have you been trying for a baby for some time? It's hard to face the fact that we don't always conceive when we want to. This lack of success may be difficult to handle, especially if you're someone who has achieved in other areas of your life.

With reproduction, there's a large element of chance. Even for young women at their peak of fertility, the odds of conceiving in any one cycle are 50–50. It's not unusual to try for six months, or even 12 months, without success. Around 16 percent of couples take over a year to achieve a pregnancy. So plan for conception over a longer time frame, say 12 months, unless you have any specific reasons to be concerned about your fertility or your health in general.

The main exception is if you are over 35. In this case, see your doctor after trying for about six months. The first step is likely to be a blood test for you, and a semen analysis for your partner. However, be reassured that if you are over 35, you may still get pregnant in the old-fashioned way. The average time taken for a 39-year-old woman to conceive is 15 months. But the snag is that if you do end up needing assisted fertility techniques, it all takes time.

ASK A... NUTRITIONIST

I've heard that green tea will help me conceive. Is this true? So far, studies on green tea and fertility aren't conclusive one way or the other. Overall, it's likely to benefit your health without affecting your fertility. However, although green tea has a host of health benefits, it contains small amounts of caffeine and tannic acid, both of which have (at least in large quantities) been linked to fertility problems and an increased risk of miscarriage.

STOPPING CONTRACEPTION

You can get pregnant as soon as you stop using some contraception.
- **IUD (coil):** you can get pregnant if you have sex in the week before it's removed since sperm can live 3–5 days.
- **Pill:** assume you're fertile immediately. Some women seem to be extra fertile after stopping the Pill.
- **Implants:** fertility can return immediately after removal of the implant, but some women find it takes longer. Occasionally periods can take three to nine months to become regular. This suggests that the effects of the hormone are still lingering, but you may still conceive.
- **Injections:** irregular bleeding can continue for months, and you may not be able to conceive for several months either. However, as with implants, it's possible to get pregnant before your periods return properly.
- **Progesterone IUD:** you could get pregnant if you have sex in the week before removal of this system, but because the system contains progesterone, conception is less likely than with a regular coil (see left).

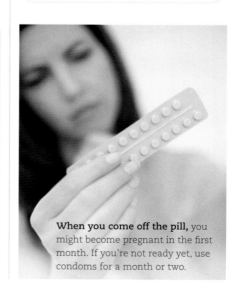

When you come off the pill, you might become pregnant in the first month. If you're not ready yet, use condoms for a month or two.

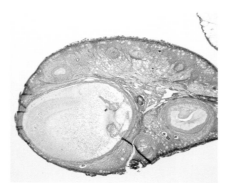

268 days to go...

WHAT'S HAPPENING INSIDE

This mature ovarian follicle contains a fluid-filled cavity (pale pink) known as the follicular antrum. At this stage, just prior to ovulation, one follicle has become much larger than the others, and it is this follicle that will rupture to release an egg.

As your hormone level rises around this stage of your cycle, so might your libido—it seems nature takes care of everything!

Estrogen levels are rising and reach their peak today, based on a 28-day menstrual cycle. The rise in estrogen from the follicles is what stimulates the release of the LH hormone (see p.38), which surges about 24 hours before ovulation. FSH (see p.38) from the pituitary gland starts rising later this week. Progesterone levels are low. There's no call for this hormone until the uterus lining needs to thicken. In fact, high levels would make the cervix hostile to sperm, so they would have trouble getting through to the uterus and the fallopian tubes to fertilize the egg.

Women also produce the male hormone testosterone and this reaches a peak around ovulation. This hormone is responsible for libido in both sexes so, hopefully, you and your partner should find you're both in the mood for making babies at this time.

ASK A... DOCTOR

I had a miscarriage four weeks ago. Is it safe to try for another baby right away? There is no exact advice on when you should try again following a miscarriage. As a general guide, wait until you've had one menstrual period. This will help to date the pregnancy should you conceive quickly. However, your doctor may advise otherwise, especially if your miscarriage was linked with an infection. If you are waiting for tests because you miscarried, it makes sense to have these first.

You and your partner may need time to grieve for the lost pregnancy, so it is unwise to rush into trying to conceive again. Be reassured that the vast majority of women who had a single miscarriage go on to have a baby.

AS A MATTER OF FACT

Being stressed can affect your ability to conceive.

Perhaps it's no surprise that nature makes it more difficult to conceive in stressful circumstances. One reason might be that it reduces the ovary's response to the hormone surge at mid-cycle (see left). There is also a link between stress and the failure of fertility treatments, although the exact reason for this isn't known.

It's a good idea to talk about and work through your grief together before trying to get pregnant again. Miscarrying can be extremely tough and may put a strain on your relationship.

Your 2nd week

47

267 days to go...

WHAT'S HAPPENING INSIDE

The sperm cell can be seen here inside the fallopian tube. Since sperm can stay active and alive inside you for up to 72 hours, it's possible to get pregnant even if you don't ovulate for two to three days from now.

This is an optimum time to conceive, but try not to think too much about when you might be ovulating and just enjoy sex!

AS A MATTER OF FACT

Having an orgasm could boost your chances of conception.

One theory is that the female orgasm is an evolutionary device designed to convey semen into the cervix as the uterus contracts. If the woman climaxes up to a minute before her partner, or she doesn't orgasm, she will retain less semen than if she comes at the same time or after him.

Use the time around ovulation to put some excitement and spontaneity back into your sex life. With all the recommendations and restrictions, not to mention old wives' tales, that supposedly maximize conception rates, it's easy to forget that sex is meant to be enjoyable. If you're hell bent on conceiving, then the fun can get forgotten. You might want to try different positions, times, or places for sex. If you and your partner aren't usually that adventurous, this is a good opportunity to try varying things a little.

Try to have sex every 24–48 hours. If your partner ejaculates regularly, it will encourage the production of quality sperm. The benefits of abstaining have been greatly overstated in the past. It is true that not having sex for up to seven days can boost the number of sperm, but research now shows that abstinence can impair the motility (swimming ability) of sperm, especially if the sperm were already borderline. The longer the period of abstinence, the more marked the effect will be. So have fun and if you conceive that's a bonus!

It may improve your chances of conception if you lie down for 15–20 minutes after having sex. Lying with your legs in the air will aid gravity further.

SEXUAL POSITIONS

It seems that how you have sex can help conception. Positions that maximize penetration, such as rear entry, may work best since sperm is then deposited as close to the cervix as possible—languishing too long in vaginal secretions can lead to a sperm's early death. If the man is on top, the woman could try placing a pillow under her buttocks to raise her pelvis and aid the movement of sperm toward the cervix. Woman-on-top positions may lead to leakage of sperm. Avoid using lubricants because they can adversely affect sperm.

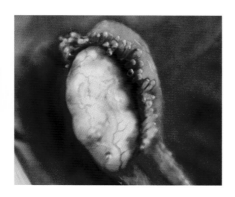

266 days to go...

WHAT'S HAPPENING INSIDE

The ovary can can be seen here at the end of the fallopian tube. At around this time of the menstrual cycle, a follicle at the surface of the ovary releases an egg, which is swept down the tube by clearly visible fingerlike projections called fimbriae.

You're highly likely to ovulate today, if you haven't already, and if egg meets sperm you may soon be pregnant.

Typically ovulation occurs around day 14 but it can occur earlier or later. Ovulation is when an egg is released from your ovaries (sometimes two eggs are released—see box, below). LH rises thanks to estrogen output from the growing follicles (see p.47), and it is this rise that triggers the events that now take place in the follicle. LH makes the egg inside the follicle become fully mature, ready for release and fertilization. This is the point at which the egg reduces its number of chromosomes (see p.55) from 46 to 23.

The follicle is rich with fluid by now. Just before ovulation, it is some 1 in (2 cm) or more in diameter. In position, it lies just below the surface of the ovary. If you could see the follicle, it would look like a blister about to burst. Next the follicle produces enzymes that digest its outer layer, releasing the egg on to the surface of the ovary.

Once the egg is released from the follicle, it's soon swept into the nearest fallopian tube by the fingerlike projections that form the end of the tube, where it will hopefully be fertilized.

AS A MATTER OF FACT

If you've had nonidentical twins already, your chance of having another set quadruples.

Nonidentical twins occur when more than one follicle ripens completely and the two eggs released at ovulation are both fertilized. The increased chance of having another set of twins is because most women who conceive nonidentical twins (without fertility drugs) show a pattern of releasing more than one egg per cycle. Your chance of having a second set of twins is about 1 in 3000.

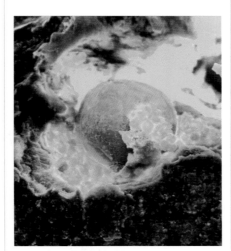

At ovulation, the follicle ruptures and the egg breaks through the surface of the ovary. Sometimes two follicles mature to this point, both releasing an egg.

FOCUS ON... RELATIONSHIPS

Pressure to conceive

If you're trying to conceive, you may have little else on your mind and this can put a strain on your relationship. With the goal of pregnancy in mind, it's easy to become clinical about sex. At this point, you and your partner may be regarding each other not so much as sex objects, but as components of a baby-making machine. Enjoyment can so easily get lost.

Understandably, you may find that your partner becomes aggrieved if he feels pressure to provide sperm; the distress may have an adverse effect on a man's willingness and even ability to have sex. If this happens, it can lead to a downward spiral, which naturally makes conception less likely, and may cause discord.

Make an effort to be loving and work together rather than against each other. Consider taking a break; couples often conceive when they're away on vacation and more relaxed. Make sure you also enjoy some stress-free sex outside of your fertile window.

Conception

Pregnancy begins with conception, a complex process that involves the release of one or more eggs from the ovary, successful fertilization by a sperm in a fallopian tube, and implantation in the lining of the uterus.

The release of an egg

Each woman is born with her full quota of follicles that contain immature eggs, some of which will mature and be released in her lifetime. Every month, follicle stimulating hormone (FSH), released from the pituitary gland, encourages a number of the follicles to ripen. These follicles in turn produce the hormone estrogen, rising levels of which encourage the uterus to thicken to prepare for the implantation of a fertilized egg. As the eggs mature, the level of estrogen rises and the pituitary gland receives a message to produce luteinizing hormone (LH). Every month, this surge in LH triggers one follicle (and sometimes more than one) to release a mature egg—the moment of ovulation.

Once the egg leaves the ovary, it enters the fallopian tube, which lies close by, and starts to travel through the tube to the uterus. The fallopian tube is just 4 in (10 cm) long and its lining has many tiny fronds that literally brush the egg in the direction of the uterus. Even so, the journey takes five days or more. In the course of this voyage, the fertilization of the egg takes place.

The journey of the sperm

During sex, the man releases an abundance of sperm—around 250 million at each ejaculation—into the vagina. Each sperm has a long tail to propel it, so it's well equipped to swim up to the fallopian tube, where fertilization of the egg takes place. The whole distance, from the vagina

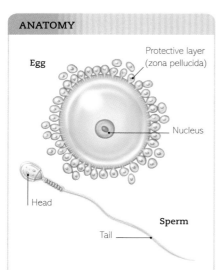

ANATOMY

Egg

Protective layer (zona pellucida)

Nucleus

Head

Tail

Sperm

The mature egg has a diameter of 0.1 mm and is surrounded by a protective outer layer known as the *zona pellucida*. The far smaller sperm consists of a head, which contains the male genetic material and enzymes to help break down the egg's outer layer, and a tail that propels the sperm up the vagina and uterus to the fallopian tube.

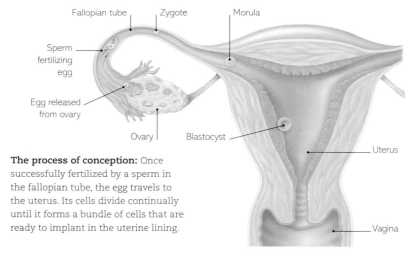

Fallopian tube Zygote Morula

Sperm fertilizing egg

Egg released from ovary

Ovary Blastocyst

Uterus

Vagina

The process of conception: Once successfully fertilized by a sperm in the fallopian tube, the egg travels to the uterus. Its cells divide continually until it forms a bundle of cells that are ready to implant in the uterine lining.

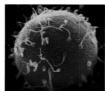

At fertilization, one sperm penetrates the egg. Once the egg and sperm have merged, they form a single cell called a zygote.

The zygote divides into two identical cells, and continues to divide as it travels down through the fallopian tube.

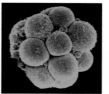

A morula—a bundle of around 16 cells—has formed by around three to four days after fertilization of the egg.

A blastocyst, a mass of up to 100 cells, hatches out of the egg's protective layer and prepares to implant in the uterus.

through the uterus and up into the fallopian tube can be accomplished in hours. However, the sperm can survive in the vagina and the uterus for 3–5 days, meaning there is a window of around 6 days in which fertilization can take place (an egg lives 12–24 hours after ovulation). Not all of the millions of sperm make it as far as the fallopian tube; in fact, most of them die, seep out of the vagina, or get lost along the way. Around just 200 sperm, only a tiny fraction of the number originally released, arrive at the site of the egg.

The moment of fertilization

Although many sperm cluster around the egg and try to penetrate its outer layer, only one of them will manage to burrow its way through the surface and fertilize the egg. Once this happens, the egg's outer layer thickens quickly to keep out other competing sperm, so that each egg can be fertilized by only one sperm.

Implantation in the uterus

By the time the fertilized egg reaches the uterus, it has grown from a single cell into a compact cluster of cells, called a blastocyst. This cluster attaches to the uterine lining very loosely at first, then more deeply and permanently. At this early stage, the blob of cells, which is more than just a fertilized egg, but not quite an embryo, is sometimes referred to as a "conceptus." Although its sex is already determined, it's not remotely baby-shaped yet. The cells produce enzymes that allow it to digest its way into the uterus lining, and lie snugly below the surface.

Assisting conception

Some couples find that conception takes longer than anticipated. If you haven't become pregnant after two years of trying, your doctor may suggest fertility testing to identify if your fertility or that of your partner is suboptimal. If this is the case, you may want to embark on

---

TWINS

How twins are conceived

Today in Canada, one in every 90 births is a twin birth. Twins are conceived in two ways that result in either identical or nonidentical twins.

Identical twins occur when one fertilized egg splits into two separate cells. This type of twin is half as common as nonidentical twins. Identical twins have the same genes and are the same sex, so they are very alike, although subtle differences in their environment can mean they're not always identical in every way. Identical twins are known as "monozygotic" twins, since they come from one "zygote," or fertilized egg. Triplets, quads, and higher multiples can be monozygotic too. However, triplets and more can arise from more

complex combinations. For example, there may have been two fertilized eggs, one of which split into two.

Nonidentical twins occur when two eggs are released at ovulation. Each twin's genes comes from the parents, but the twins don't share the same mix of genes. Nonidentical twins are also called "fraternal" twins, since they're no more alike than other siblings and can be of a different sex. They're also referred to as "dizygotic" twins, because they come from two separate "zygotes," or fertilized eggs. Nonidentical triplets arise when three eggs are released instead of one. This is more likely to occur when ovulation is induced with drugs during fertility treatment.

  A fertilized egg divides into two

  Two eggs are fertilized

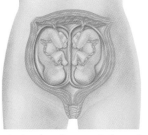

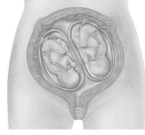

Identical twins that result from the division of one fertilized egg may share a placenta in the uterus. Occasionally, they also share an amniotic sac.

When two eggs are fertilized at the same time, nonidentical twins are formed, each with its own placenta and amniotic sac.

---

fertility treatment to assist conception. The most popular treatment is in vitro fertilization, or IVF. This involves taking fertility drugs to help you produce more eggs. The eggs are harvested and fertilized with your partner's sperm in a laboratory (hence the term "test-tube baby"), and you're given hormone treatment to prepare the uterus to receive the fertilized eggs. If the quality of sperm is poor, a

procedure called intracytoplasmic sperm injection, or ICSI may be used, whereby a single sperm is injected directly into an egg and the fertilized egg is transferred to the uterus. Intrauterine insemination, or IUI, involves putting sperm that have been selected for viability directly into the uterus. This is used where sperm has poor motility, or there are problems with ovulation.

Your 3rd week

THIS IS THE WEEK A MIRACLE TAKES PLACE—YOUR BABY IS CONCEIVED

If you ovulated and the egg met a sperm, amazing things will happen fast. It takes just three days from fertilization for a single egg to divide into a ball of 58 cells. By the end of the week, this ball, called the blastocyst, will have reached the uterus, where it will start to implant in the lining. It will be a couple of weeks before you know whether you've conceived, but special hormones kick in now to help maintain the pregnancy.

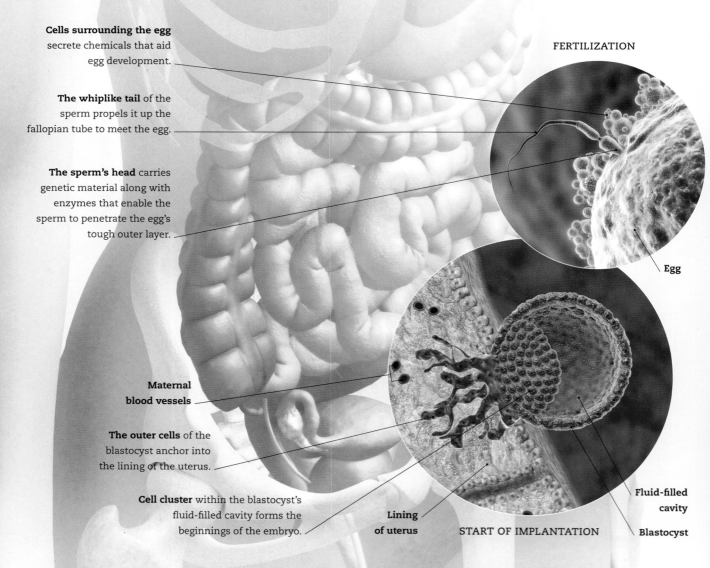

Cells surrounding the egg secrete chemicals that aid egg development.

The whiplike tail of the sperm propels it up the fallopian tube to meet the egg.

The sperm's head carries genetic material along with enzymes that enable the sperm to penetrate the egg's tough outer layer.

FERTILIZATION

Egg

Maternal blood vessels

The outer cells of the blastocyst anchor into the lining of the uterus.

Cell cluster within the blastocyst's fluid-filled cavity forms the beginnings of the embryo.

Lining of uterus

START OF IMPLANTATION

Fluid-filled cavity

Blastocyst

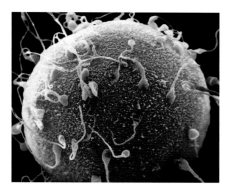

265 days to go...

WHAT'S HAPPENING INSIDE

Here the egg is shown surrounded by sperm. Although only one sperm will fertilize the egg, several hundred are thought to be necessary to break down its defensive layers and enable fertilization to take place.

Your newly released egg will only survive 24 hours, but hopefully in that time it will meet sperm and be fertilized.

You are likely to have ovulated and your unfertilized egg now begins its journey. Once it has been released by the ovary, the egg is swept up by one of your fallopian tubes and, moving in the direction of the uterus, comes to rest in the widest portion of the tube, awaiting fertilization.

It is no exaggeration to say that for each sperm released the chance of even reaching the site of fertilization is in the order of one in a million. Around 300 sperm reach the tube but only one will fertilize the egg. Once the sperm has penetrated, it triggers a reaction that

makes the surface impenetrable. Each sperm and egg contain 23 chromosomes, half of the total genetic material required. The egg will always contain an X chromosome but the sperm will carry either an X or Y chromosome and therefore determines the sex of the embryo. The sperm and egg chromosomes combine forming the "zygote" and fertilization is complete.

A few hundred sperm survive the journey and encounter the egg in the fallopian tube, but it is just one sperm that actually fertilizes the egg.

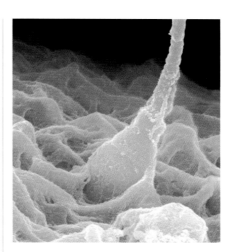

FOCUS ON... DADS

Fit but not fertile?

If you want to become a dad, there are many reasons why you should ensure you're in good shape, not least to support your partner as she prepares for pregnancy. However, while a couch potato lifestyle isn't desirable for men who want to conceive, it seems that pulling out all the stops at the gym might not be the best course of action either.

Researchers asked a group of fit young men to exercise intensively four times a week for two weeks.

Afterward, their semen was tested and found to contain fewer sperm and lower levels of the hormones essential for conception. These hormonal changes were temporary and returned to near normal within a few days of the men resuming previous levels of activity.

The concern is that recovery might not be so fast among older men, or in those who have poor sperm counts and/or low hormone levels. So stay in shape but don't overdo it.

AS A MATTER OF FACT

The hormones responsible for the production of sperm are released every 60 to 90 minutes. So a man is constantly producing sperm cells.

In theory, this means that a male is always fertile, but it takes sperm a 72-day period to fully develop. So leading an unhealthy lifestyle during that time will impinge on the quality. For this reason, if you're trying to conceive, your partner should embark on a healthy lifestyle for three months to produce good sperm.

YOU ARE 3 WEEKS AND 2 DAYS

257 days to go...

YOUR BABY TODAY

In this computer-generated image the entire blastocyst can be seen embedded in the lining of the uterus. The cells that will develop into the embryo are seen as the dark area in the 12 o'clock position.

Adopting a healthy lifestyle and improving your well-being are sensible measures now that you might be pregnant.

THE LOWDOWN

Cultural beliefs

Here's what some cultures believe:

■ **Hindu fathers** part the hair on their partner's head three times upward from the front to the back to boost the development of the growing baby.

■ **In some countries,** there is great emphasis placed on protecting the unborn baby. In Thailand, the pregnant woman's abdomen may be painted to ward off evil spirits. It is also believed that giving gifts before the birth will attract evil spirits.

AS A MATTER OF FACT

There are at least 30 chemicals in cigarette smoke that can adversely affect fertility.

Because smoking reduces the rate at which cells replicate, it may cause most damage during the first days and weeks of pregnancy. In addition to causing fertility problems in women, smoking can have negative effects on sperm and reduce testosterone in men.

Once your pregnancy is confirmed in the next week or so, you'll find you're bombarded with more health information than ever. Is your diet well balanced? Could you cut back on the amount of salt, sugar, and fast food you eat? Are you eating plenty of fruit and vegetables, particularly leafy green vegetables, which are a good

Get gentle exercise, such as walking or swimming, which are ideal before, during, and after pregnancy.

source of folic acid. Are you exercising enough and safely? Even though you don't know you're pregnant yet, it's worth being aware of the recommended advice and making some basic dietary and lifestyle changes. Turn to the section on pages 14–29 for some up-to-date information. It's also worth being aware of the early signs of pregnancy so you know what's normal.

If you have a preexisting medical condition or are taking medication, seek medical advice.

FOCUS ON... YOUR HEALTH

Lifestyle changes

If you smoke, you should quit (so should your partner) for health reasons. Once you're pregnant, not smoking will reduce the risk of miscarriage, stillbirth, premature birth, low birth weight, and sudden infant death.

You should also stop drinking alcohol. The current advice from the Public Health Agency of Canada is to avoid drinking alcohol completely while trying to get pregnant and once you are pregnant, since there is no known safe consumption level for pregnant women.

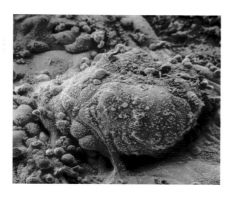

256 days to go...

YOUR BABY TODAY

The embryo is implanted and is 10 days old. The entry point at which the embryo buried into the lining of the uterus is now covered by a clot, and this prevents blood loss and protects the embryo.

Try to stay busy to distract yourself from constantly wondering whether you're pregnant, and think positively.

ASK A... DOCTOR

I did an early pregnancy test and have failed to conceive again, for the sixth month. Could it be because I have irregular periods?
Menstrual cycles that vary more than a few days in length from month to month are considered irregular. An irregular cycle can be troublesome when trying to conceive, but being aware of the signs of ovulation (see p.43) can help you determine when you are approaching your short window of fertility.

Irregular ovulation and menstruation account for around 30–40 percent of fertility problems. Many factors determine how fertile a woman is, such as her age, whether her cervical fluid is wet enough to sustain sperm, or whether her fallopian tubes are open, but the most important factor is whether she ovulates regularly. Sometimes, a condition called anovulation occurs, in which there is irregular menstrual bleeding but no ovulation. If you don't release an egg each month, you won't have as many chances to conceive. You may be given medication to stimulate egg production and boost ovulation.

Waiting for your period to start—or better yet, not start—can be quite stressful when you're trying to conceive. If your menstrual cycle is irregular you may not know when your period is due and therefore may not know if you're late and potentially pregnant or not. The uncertainty is likely to make you anxious and every time you go to the bathroom you dread seeing that your period has started.

Whether or not you know you have fertility problems, the wait can be difficult. If you do get your period, the disappointment can be hard. The cycle of having your period, waiting for ovulation, hoping you're pregnant, and then finding out you're not can become very wearing month after month.

If you have been trying to conceive for a year with no luck then you should go to your doctor for tests. Or go at six months if you are over 35 or know that you may have fertility problems, such as blocked fallopian tubes. Try confiding in a good friend about your problems so that you have someone to talk to, but try not to become obsessive and let it dominate all your relationships.

If you've only just started trying, remember there is a only a one in four or five chance that you will conceive each month, so you're unlikely to get pregnant in the first month of trying!

If you're over 35 and have been trying to conceive for six months, speak to your doctor about fertility tests. You should both be checked because your partner's sperm will need to be tested too. You will be given blood tests.

AS A MATTER OF FACT

Around half of pregnancies in Canada could be unplanned.

According to statistics, this accounts for approximately 200,000 unplanned pregnancies a year, either due to lack of birth control or birth control failure. The highest proportion of unplanned pregnancies falls in both the under-18 and over-40 age groups.

YOU ARE 3 WEEKS AND 4 DAYS

255 days to go...

YOUR BABY TODAY

To embed itself in the lining of the uterus, the embryo-to-be needs the help of progesterone, secreted after ovulation by the empty egg follicle, the corpus luteum (shown in pink in this cross section of an ovary). Progesterone helps the lining thicken.

Do you feel different? You'll find yourself analyzing every twinge in your body as you look for signs that you're pregnant.

FOCUS ON... NUTRITION

Diet ban

If you were dieting before you conceived, it can be tempting to continue once you find out you're pregnant. Don't diet: your baby may become undernourished and is more likely to be premature and underweight at birth. Do, however, eat a healthy, balanced diet (see p.15). Don't eat junk food when you're pregnant since this can increase the risk of your baby developing weight problems.

If you are overweight or obese, your doctor may recommend that you gain less weight than other pregnant women. The recommended weight gain for overweight women is 15–25 pounds (6.8–11.3 kg). And for obese women, the recommended weight gain is at least 15 pounds (6.8 kg). (By contrast, normal-weight women should gain 25–35 pounds/ 11.3–15.8 kg during pregnancy.)

In an ideal world, you should lose excess weight before conceiving, because obesity makes you more prone to diabetes and high blood pressure and means you're more likely to need a cesarean.

It's still very early and you're unlikely to have pregnancy symptoms yet—although you may have some light spotting (see opposite). Some women claim to "feel" pregnant, even before changes to their breasts are noticeable or before they start feeling sick. Some women say that they just "know." You may be very in tune with your body and may notice that your body is changing even before you are able to take a test. Unfortunately, sometimes our minds can play tricks on us: you may want to be pregnant so much that you can sometimes convince yourself that you're feeling different. If you don't feel any different, don't worry, this is also completely normal.

Either way the only definitive way to know whether or not you are pregnant is to take a pregnancy test (see p.71). You don't need to go to your doctor to confirm your pregnancy since the tests that they use are the same as those bought over the counter. If the test is positive, you're pregnant!

ASK A... NUTRITIONIST

Should I give up coffee in case I'm pregnant? Health Canada advises pregnant women or those trying to become pregnant to drink no more than 300 mg of caffeine a day (that's about two 8-oz/237-ml cups of coffee). Going without your caffeine fix is a good thing when you're pregnant, since research shows that, in high doses, it can increase the risk of miscarriage.

One study discovered that pregnant women who consumed more than 300 mg of caffeine a day were twice as likely to miscarry as those who gave up caffeine. Before switching to decaff, be aware that decaffeinated drinks may raise cholesterol. The

good news is that many women find they naturally stop wanting coffee in early pregnancy.

Your first trimester

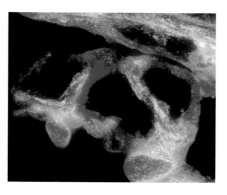

254 days to go...

YOUR BABY TODAY

The first stage of placental development—your baby's life support system—is shown here. The image shows nuclei (blue) within a continuous network of cells that will become the placental villi. At first the tiny villi are solid; later, they will contain blood vessels.

As the fertilized egg becomes completely embedded in your uterus, it may cause some light bleeding.

This computer-generated image shows the ball of cells—the blastocyst—as it appears situated within the uterus. The outer ring of interconnected cells that will eventually form the placenta are clearly seen.

AS A MATTER OF FACT

It is thought that around 50 percent of pregnancies might miscarry before implantation.

Up to a third of pregnancies miscarry up to the fifth week and around a quarter will end in miscarriage between the fifth and seventh week. Thankfully, the risk of miscarriage becomes much lower as the weeks go by, decreasing dramatically after the 12th week of pregnancy.

The ball of cells, known as the blastocyst, that will form the embryo has now completely embedded within the lining of the uterus and the lining has regenerated over it.

Unfortunately, in the complex process of conception, only about half of all fertilized eggs progress to become a blastocyst and only about half of these go on to become successfully implanted in the uterus.

When the blastocyst embeds, there may be some bleeding, known as "spotting." This often leads to confusion regarding the dating of the pregnancy, not least because it can occur around the time that you would normally start your period.

The color of the blood can vary. In most cases it is pinkish, although bright red blood (fresh blood) can occur, as can brownish, old blood. As long as it is not profuse, the color really doesn't matter. If the bleeding lasts for a short period, and you don't experience discomfort, it's likely that things are just fine, but do see your doctor for a checkup.

Around 25 percent of women will experience some bleeding in early pregnancy, but most go on to full term. However, in some cases, bleeding does mean a miscarriage is occurring so always report the fact that you've bled to your doctor.

DOUBLING UP

As with many parents, you probably thought long and hard about trying to conceive your second child. There's no ideal age gap between children, but consider:

The pros:

■ **You are in "baby mode"** and will be used to the routine and all aspects of baby care. You will have all the equipment you need from bottles to a carriage and crib.

■ **A two-year-old** might find it easier to accept his new sibling than a four-year-old who is much more conscious of having the sole attention of his parents.

■ **There will always be squabbles,** but children close in age tend to play better together.

The cons:

■ **It's tiring** caring for a one- or two-year-old while pregnant.

■ **It can put a strain on your body** to have pregnancies close together.

■ **If you have a second baby** before the first one can walk, you could be doing a lot of carrying, increasing the chance of backaches.

■ **You won't have as much time** to get to know your first child before your second is on the scene.

67

253 days to go...

YOUR BABY TODAY

This microscope view of an embedded blastocyst shows the amniotic cavity (semcircular white area at top), with the cells that will develop into the baby just below (dark oval at the 12 o'clock position). The yolk sac is the pink area below.

Complex changes are taking place inside your uterus to create a safe and nourishing environment for your unborn baby.

The ball of cells embedded in the uterus is already laying down the foundations for its future life as an embryo. At two layers thick, the germ cells form a flat disk that divides the fluid-filled inner part of the ball of cells into two chambers. The smaller of these fluid-filled chambers will become the amniotic sac. The larger chamber, lying closest to the future placenta, will become the yolk sac that supports the early embryo. The umbilical cord will eventually develop close to the smaller chamber. The inner germ cells have been developing at a slower rate than the rapidly expanding outer cell layers.

At first the umbilical cord is a simple stalk, containing no blood vessels but simply anchoring the embryo to the future placenta (see p.76), which will eventually become your unborn baby's lifeline.

(see p.76)

AS A MATTER OF FACT

Newborns are getting heavier.

This is mostly due to improved diet and living standards. However, obesity in the mother is another factor—if the mother is overweight, there is an increased risk of diabetes (see p.473), which can increase the baby's weight.

(see p.473)

ASK A... NUTRITIONIST

I'm hoping I'm pregnant, but I'm already worrying about the amount of weight I might put on, and am scared I'll never be slim again!
These days, it is almost impossible to pass a newspaper stand without seeing the latest celebrity who has not only fit right back into her clothes after having her baby, but who actually weighs less than she did before pregnancy. However, this is concerning for health professionals, since a dramatic weight loss after the birth is not good for mother or baby.

The recommended weight gain during pregnancy is 25–35 lb (11.3–15.8 kg), if you have a Body Mass Index (BMI) (see p.17) within the normal range. Your baby and her support system will make up a good proportion of this (see p.99), as will the increased pregnancy fluids, fats, and an enlarged uterus. Much of this extra weight will be lost as soon as your baby is born. Also, after the birth, some of this extra weight provides nutrients for breast-feeding, which uses up to 500 calories a day.

(see p.17)
(see p.99)

The most sensible approach to controlling your weight during pregnancy is to eat a healthy diet and get gentle exercise to ensure that weight gain is not too dramatic. You should be aiming to eat around 2,100–2,500 calories a day, increasing this by 200 calories in the last trimester of pregnancy—the equivalent of a banana and a glass of milk.

You'll gain weight in the months to come but not necessarily an excessive amount. Try not to become obsessive about weighing yourself.

252 days to go...

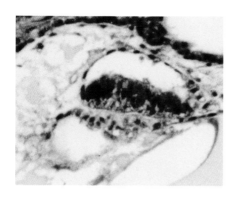

YOUR BABY TODAY

This highly magnetized image shows that the embryo consists of two layers of cells—those of the upper, darker layer are more rectangular in shape and lie on the side of the amniotic cavity, and those on the lower layer lie on the side of the yolk sac.

Are you feeling irritable and tired, and are your breasts tender? Well, you might just be pregnant!

Nature has a strange way of working. You might feel low if you have your usual PMS symptoms and think it means that you haven't conceived, but in fact, there are many similarities between the symptoms of premenstrual syndrome (PMS) and those of early pregnancy. This is because the hormones that cause PMS are raised in pregnancy and so can cause the same symptoms. In addition to this, you might be irritable and emotional even without having PMS, just due to the anxiety of wanting to be pregnant and waiting to see whether or not your period arrives.

While you are in the middle of this storm of hormones and raging emotions it can be difficult to remain calm. Talk to your partner about your emotions and anxieties—just expressing that you're finding things stressful can help you get through this tense time.

Alternatively, confide in a female relative or friend, who might be able to relate to how you're feeling.

Frustratingly, at this point it is still a waiting game; all you can do is try to be patient until you take your pregnancy test. If your period was due today—day 28 of your cycle—and hasn't made an appearance, you can take a test as early as today or tomorrow. Good luck!

FOCUS ON... YOUR BODY

Start squeezing!

It's never too early to start Kegel exercises and you'll be glad you did once you become pregnant. The pelvic floor is a broad sling of muscles that stretches between your legs and extends from the pubic bone in front to the spine at the rear. It holds and supports your bladder, uterus, and bowel in place and controls the muscles which hold closed the anus, urethra, and vagina.

Try these simple steps to tone your pelvic floor:

■ **First** try to locate your pelvic floor: sit on a chair and close your eyes—now visualize the sling of muscles stretching right across your body holding your uterus and bladder.

■ **Next** contract your pelvic floor muscles pulling inward and upward, hold for a count of five, then release. Repeat this exercise at least 10 times a day.

■ **Test:** if you're having trouble identifying the muscles, imagine that you are trying to stop the flow of urine; the muscles you feel contracting are those of the pelvic floor.

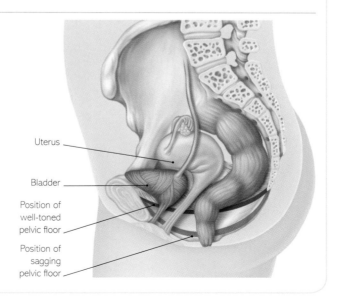

Uterus

Bladder

Position of well-toned pelvic floor

Position of sagging pelvic floor

Your 5th week

IF YOU HAVE NO PERIOD AND A POSITIVE TEST RESULT, YOU'RE GOING TO HAVE A BABY!

When your pregnancy is confirmed, it's natural to experience a mixed bag of emotions—excitement, disbelief, joy, and anxiety. Everything is about to change forever for you and your partner. Give yourselves time to take in the big news. You may not feel pregnant yet, but momentous changes are taking place in the hidden world of your uterus. Step by step, the building blocks of life are being set in place.

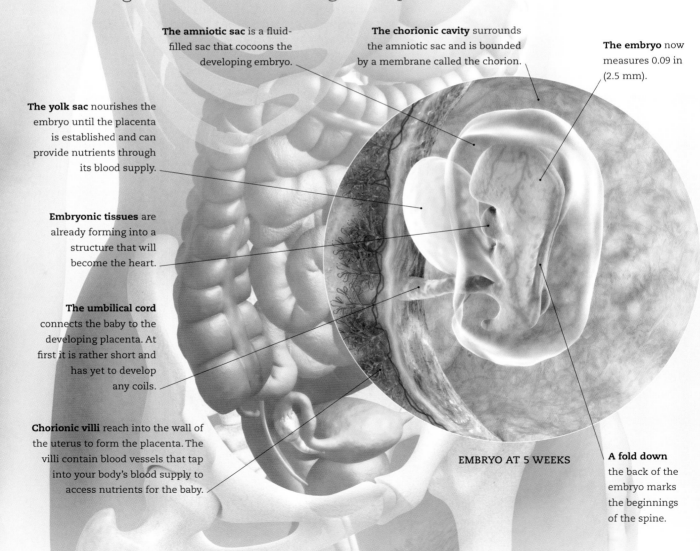

The amniotic sac is a fluid-filled sac that cocoons the developing embryo.

The chorionic cavity surrounds the amniotic sac and is bounded by a membrane called the chorion.

The embryo now measures 0.09 in (2.5 mm).

The yolk sac nourishes the embryo until the placenta is established and can provide nutrients through its blood supply.

Embryonic tissues are already forming into a structure that will become the heart.

The umbilical cord connects the baby to the developing placenta. At first it is rather short and has yet to develop any coils.

Chorionic villi reach into the wall of the uterus to form the placenta. The villi contain blood vessels that tap into your body's blood supply to access nutrients for the baby.

EMBRYO AT 5 WEEKS

A fold down the back of the embryo marks the beginnings of the spine.

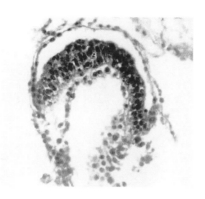

251 days to go...

YOUR BABY TODAY

This is a microscope view of the amniotic cavity with the cells that will become the baby in a close-up. These cells will repeatedly divide and multiply, becoming more and more specialized at each stage of their development.

The waiting is over. If your period hasn't started, take a home pregnancy test to find out whether you've conceived.

If you've missed your period

(assuming that your normal cycle is no more than 28 days and that your period is therefore late), you may want to do a home pregnancy test today.

A home pregnancy test, available at pharmacists and most supermarkets, contains a chemical that reacts if your urine contains the hormone hCG (human chorionic gonadotrophin). This is produced by an implanting embryo and will be found in your urine if you are pregnant. Levels of hCG are likely to be over 50 mIU/ml on the day your period is due. With between 97 and 99 percent accuracy, the majority of over-the-counter tests are sensitive enough to detect this amount, so they can be used on the first day of your missed period; some can be used earlier (see p.63).

The tests only turn positive once there is a certain level of the hCG hormone present in your urine: if you test too early, the result might be negative even though you are pregnant. Therefore, if you don't get your period but you had a negative result, test again after two to three days. If you are pregnant, the levels of hCG will have risen, giving a positive result.

If you get a positive result but your period starts anyway, it may be that you have suffered a very early miscarriage.

You can find out within minutes whether you are expecting a baby, but as you await this life-changing result it can seem like a lifetime for the symbol to appear.

HOW TO USE A HOME PREGNANCY TEST

Always read the instructions, but most tests work as follows:
- **You urinate on the stick** and leave it for a specified number of minutes.
- **A symbol will appear** in the control window to indicate the test is working (if this does not appear, the test is faulty). If a symbol then appears in the results window, you are pregnant.

- **It is advisable to do the test** first thing in the morning when your urine is most concentrated. By doing this, the hCG levels are likely to be detected more easily
- **The results symbol** gradually fades, so read it after the specified time, not later. Do another test the next morning if you're unsure of the result.

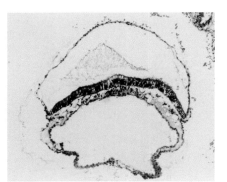

250 days to go...

YOUR BABY TODAY

The embryo until this stage of development has consisted of two layers of cells. Now, a third layer starts to become visible as a "bulge" between the two—this bulge can be seen in the center of this image.

In this third week since conception, the cells that will become the embryo move to form the basis of the central nervous system.

While you're busy coming to terms with being pregnant, there are incredible changes taking place inside you. The group of cells, that will become your baby is currently shaped as a flat disk and undergoing significant development. A narrow groove begins to form down the middle of the cells. The leading edge of the groove is slightly wider forming a circular "node." The outer edges of the node and groove are slightly raised. The cells move from the rolled edges of these structures downward into the groove to lie between the original two layers of cells. This creates three layers of cells, those on each outer disk surface and those sandwiched between them. The node and groove do not extend along the entire length of the disk.

At the head end, a separate groove forms. Called the neural groove, this ultimately forms the brain and spinal cord (the central nervous system). In four days time, the disk will lengthen and widen at the end that will form your baby's head. In six days time, the neural groove has folds on either side that will later meet to form the neural tube.

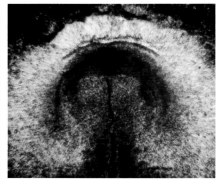

Shown here is the neural tube of an embryo in the early stages of pregnancy. The brain and spinal cord will develop from the neural tube. If the tube does not fully close, it can lead to birth defects, most commonly spina bifida.

ASK A... DOCTOR

I've been having difficulty getting pregnant and have now been diagnosed with polycystic ovary syndrome. What is this? This condition causes the ovaries to be bigger than normal and they produce a large number of small follicles that never grow to full maturity. Therefore an egg is not released to be fertilized and periods are very irregular.

The condition is a common cause of fertility problems and treatments are aimed at stimulating ovulation and also reducing some of the symptoms, such as increased body hair. Polycystic ovary syndrome appears to run in families.

FOCUS ON... RELATIONSHIPS

"You're going to be a dad!"

It's the positive result you've been waiting for—hopefully!—but how do you share it with your partner? You could present him with an envelope containing your positive pregnancy test, or explain that you have a "special gift" for him but it won't be ready until about, oh, nine months. It shouldn't take him long to figure it out! Ideally, choose a time when you are both alone and feeling relaxed so that it can be a special moment. You may want to do another test with your partner just to make sure and also so that he feels involved.

Even if you're excited, and even if you can't get in touch with your partner for a day, don't be tempted to tell your mom and close friends first Your partner may be upset, understandably, if others know he's going to be a dad before he does.

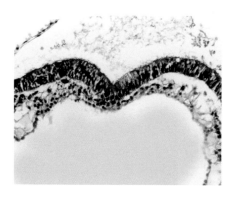

249 days to go...

YOUR BABY TODAY

As the embryo transforms from two cell layers into three, a groove develops along the back of the embryo. This groove (the dark area in the center of this image) will develop in the embryo's neural tube—the forerunner of the brain and spinal cord.

Happy? Excited? But a little nervous? There is no greater life-changing event than finding out you're going to be parents.

SURPRISED TO BE PREGNANT?

If you're one of the few women who has become pregnant while using contraception, it is unlikely to have done your baby any harm, but depending on what you were using, here's what you should do:

- **Contraceptive pill:** stop taking it.
- **Contraceptive patch:** remove it.
- **Contraceptive implant:** see your doctor to have it removed.
- **IUD (intrauterine device):** visit your doctor without delay if you're using an IUD since there's a small risk that the pregnancy could be ectopic (see p.93). Even if a scan shows that the pregnancy is not ectopic, the IUD should be removed: the risk of miscarriage is greater if it is left in place.
- **Contraceptive injection (Depo-Provera):** see your doctor if you conceive while using this. Research indicates that it won't affect the unborn baby, but you should not have any more injections.
- **Morning-after pill:** once an egg has implanted, the morning-after pill has no effect so it won't harm your baby. Do, however, see your doctor if you're concerned.

In the few days since you conceived, you may have experienced a whole host of different feelings. Even if you planned to get pregnant, it's perfectly normal for the initial elation to be replaced with some anxiety as the reality hits you that you are going to be a mom. You might also doubt the result of the test you've taken and not actually believe it until you begin to have some of the early symptoms of pregnancy.

Your partner may react differently than you. If he doesn't appear as excited, don't interpret this as meaning that he is not happy about the news; not everyone deals with big events in the same way, and it might be some time before the reality of becoming a dad hits him. Withdrawing into himself may be his way of giving himself some time to process the information. Conversely, you may find he's actually more excited about the news than you!

Handling your feelings might be made more difficult by trying to keep the pregnancy a secret, for the time being. Most couples decide not to tell people until after the 12-week scan when the miscarriage risk is significantly decreased, but you may find that confiding in a few close relatives and friends will give you a much-needed outlet to talk about your feelings.

Discovering that you're going to be parents is a momentous occasion, and you and your partner are likely to experience a renewed closeness as a result.

AS A MATTER OF FACT

Pregnant women often try to connect with their baby through dreams.

You may find it difficult to fully bond with your baby and believe you're actually pregnant. A common dream in pregnancy is that you're swimming; it is thought to be a way of trying to "reach" the baby, who will soon be bathed in water (fluid) inside you.

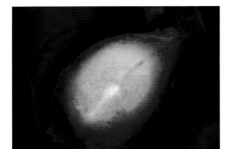

YOU ARE 4 WEEKS AND 4 DAYS

248 days to go...

YOUR BABY TODAY

The embryo seen from above now has a subtle groove (the primitive groove) and a small central depression (the primitive node), both seen here in white. These changes start at what will become the base of the spine and progress toward the head.

You're probably eager to know when your baby will be born. The chart below will tell you the expected date of delivery.

Until you have an ultrasound in a few weeks' time, your baby's due date will be calculated by counting 280 days from the first day of your last menstrual period—see chart, below. At the dating scan (see p.137), your baby will be measured and his age calculated. The scan date will then be used since it is considered to be accurate.

While you're bound to want to know the due date, try not to get too fixated on it. Most babies are born within about two weeks of their due dates but your baby will be considered to be born at term if you give birth between 37 and 42 weeks. So your estimated delivery date is just that, an estimate; your baby may be born earlier or later.

WHEN WILL YOUR BABY BE BORN?

To figure out your expected date of delivery (EDD)—also known as the due date—you need to know when you started your last menstrual period (LMP) (see p.35).

Find your LMP date on the chart below to discover when your baby is expected. For example, if your last LMP was January 13, then your baby will be due on October 20.

January Oct/Nov	1 8	2 9	3 10	4 11	5 12	6 13	7 14	8 15	9 16	10 17	11 18	12 19	13 20	14 21	15 22	16 23	17 24	18 25	19 26	20 27	21 28	22 29	23 30	24 31	25 1	26 2	27 3	28 4	29 5	30 6	31 7
February Nov/Dec	1 8	2 9	3 10	4 11	5 12	6 13	7 14	8 15	9 16	10 17	11 18	12 19	13 20	14 21	15 22	16 23	17 24	18 25	19 26	20 27	21 28	22 29	23 30	24 1	25 2	26 3	27 4	28 5			
March Dec/Jan	1 6	2 7	3 8	4 9	5 10	6 11	7 12	8 13	9 14	10 15	11 16	12 17	13 18	14 19	15 20	16 21	17 22	18 23	19 24	20 25	21 26	22 27	23 28	24 29	25 30	26 31	27 1	28 2	29 3	30 4	31 5
April Jan/Feb	1 6	2 7	3 8	4 9	5 10	6 11	7 12	8 13	9 14	10 15	11 16	12 17	13 18	14 19	15 20	16 21	17 22	18 23	19 24	20 25	21 26	22 27	23 28	24 29	25 30	26 31	27 1	28 2	29 3	30 4	
May Feb/Mar	1 5	2 6	3 7	4 8	5 9	6 10	7 11	8 12	9 13	10 14	11 15	12 16	13 17	14 18	15 19	16 20	17 21	18 22	19 23	20 24	21 25	22 26	23 27	24 28	25 1	26 2	27 3	28 4	29 5	30 6	31 7
June Mar/Apr	1 8	2 9	3 10	4 11	5 12	6 13	7 14	8 15	9 16	10 17	11 18	12 19	13 20	14 21	15 22	16 23	17 24	18 25	19 26	20 27	21 28	22 29	23 30	24 31	25 1	26 2	27 3	28 4	29 5	30 6	
July Apr/May	1 7	2 8	3 9	4 10	5 11	6 12	7 13	8 14	9 15	10 16	11 17	12 18	13 19	14 20	15 21	16 22	17 23	18 24	19 25	20 26	21 27	22 28	23 29	24 30	25 1	26 2	27 3	28 4	29 5	30 6	31 7
August May/June	1 8	2 9	3 10	4 11	5 12	6 13	7 14	8 15	9 16	10 17	11 18	12 19	13 20	14 21	15 22	16 23	17 24	18 25	19 26	20 27	21 28	22 29	23 30	24 31	25 1	26 2	27 3	28 4	29 5	30 6	31 7
September June/July	1 8	2 9	3 10	4 11	5 12	6 13	7 14	8 15	9 16	10 17	11 18	12 19	13 20	14 21	15 22	16 23	17 24	18 25	19 26	20 27	21 28	22 29	23 30	24 1	25 2	26 3	27 4	28 5	29 6	30 7	
October July/Aug	1 8	2 9	3 10	4 11	5 12	6 13	7 14	8 15	9 16	10 17	11 18	12 19	13 20	14 21	15 22	16 23	17 24	18 25	19 26	20 27	21 28	22 29	23 30	24 31	25 1	26 2	27 3	28 4	29 5	30 6	31 7
November Aug/Sept	1 8	2 9	3 10	4 11	5 12	6 13	7 14	8 15	9 16	10 17	11 18	12 19	13 20	14 21	15 22	16 23	17 24	18 25	19 26	20 27	21 28	22 29	23 30	24 31	25 1	26 2	27 3	28 4	29 5	30 6	
December Sept/Oct	1 7	2 8	3 9	4 10	5 11	6 12	7 13	8 14	9 15	10 16	11 17	12 18	13 19	14 20	15 21	16 22	17 23	18 24	19 25	20 26	21 27	22 28	23 29	24 30	25 1	26 2	27 3	28 4	29 5	30 6	31 7

247 days to go...

YOUR BABY TODAY

The embryo, still less than 3 mm long, now has a deep and narrow groove extending along its entire length. This groove will soon become so deep and its edges will curl over so much that it forms into a tube running along the length of the embryo.

Although there's lots of information to take in, try to enjoy this time and remember pregnancy is a natural process.

ASK A... DOCTOR

I'm 40 and in great shape. Will the doctors still see my pregnancy as potentially high-risk? Yes, any woman over 35 is categorized as high risk, regardless of her health status. Although this can be frustrating, the reason for the close monitoring is that, statistically, women over 35 are more likely to suffer from complications during pregnancy, such as high blood pressure, miscarriage, and gestational diabetes; there is also an increased risk of having a baby with a genetic disorder, such as Down syndrome.

Your doctor will simply want to keep an eye on you to be sure that your pregnancy progresses normally, and that both you and your baby remain healthy. By having regular monitoring, any potential problems can be addressed and hopefully rectified at an early stage.

Try not to see it as an intrusion. It's great that you're in good shape already, and if you continue to take care of your health and exercise regularly, you will reduce the risks of complications from occurring.

No sooner than you found out you were pregnant, like most expectant women, you may have begun to worry about all aspects of your lifestyle and your unborn baby's health. To put things in perspective, remember that in generations gone by pregnancy was considered to be a natural event, and few women made lifestyle changes to accommodate the condition. So in the past, pregnant women were likely to continue eating unhealthy foods, drinking alcohol, and smoking.

Furthermore, pregnancy tests tended to be much less accurate or sensitive, meaning that many pregnancies ended in early miscarriage without anyone being aware. For this reason, many of the problems now known to be risk factors for pregnancy complications or miscarriage were not analyzed or addressed, or worried about.

Today, with the benefit of a great deal of research, and precise monitoring of ovulation, conception, and pregnancy, women are very aware of what is happening inside their bodies, and are informed about the potential pitfalls. This is a mixed blessing: while it is important to avoid anything known to adversely affect your unborn baby, it is equally important to relax and enjoy the pregnancy, because stress is not good for you or your baby.

As an older expectant mom, you are likely to have more prenatal checkups. High blood pressure can be a sign of preeclampsia (see p.474), which is a more significant risk for first-time pregnant women over 40.

AS A MATTER OF FACT

Pregnant women used to be advised to drink dark beer because it's a good source of iron.

Sadly, this is an old wives' tale as the iron content of beer is negligible. So, even though they're not as interesting, stick to your leafy green vegetables!

246 days to go...

YOUR BABY TODAY

The upper part of the embryo is shown. There is still a wide opening along the back of the embryo that will gradually close over the next few days. The head and lower spine portions are the last to close.

The placenta—the structure that will become your unborn baby's lifeline—is forming.

Your pregnancy test result may be the only sign that you're pregnant, but there are many fascinating changes taking place inside you. The basic structures that will form the placenta (see p.127) are now in place. The outer layer of cells that originally entered the lining of the uterus are now coated with projections of placental tissue. It is the outer cells that are in direct contact with small lakes of your blood. The inner placental projections or fronds are termed "villi." Some villi anchor the pregnancy to your tissues and, from these, smaller free-floating villi arise. Later, more branches will appear and ultimately resemble the branching pattern of a fern leaf. The villi are still immature and have not established a blood supply of their own. It will be several weeks before the placenta is mature enough to supply all the oxygen and nutrients that your developing baby needs.

ASK A... MOM

I really wanted a baby, but now that I have a positive pregnancy test result, I'm suddenly not so sure. Is this normal? I felt exactly the same at first and after talking to friends discovered that lots of them had mixed feelings, especially at the beginning. I found a good way to overcome this was to focus on the reasons why I wanted the baby. I wrote these down. Then I tried to figure out what I was really worrying about. Was it the thought of giving up some freedom? Financial worries? Concerns that I wouldn't be a good parent? This helped me get things in perspective and realize I really did want the baby.

If you have any doubts while you're pregnant, try talking to a close female relative—perhaps your mom—or a friend. You're likely to find they, at times, had similar doubts, but went on to enjoy their pregnancy and being a mother.

TIME TO THINK ABOUT

Seeing your doctor

If you've had a positive pregnancy test, call your doctor's office to schedule your first prenatal visit, which will be between 8 and 12 weeks. The receptionist will likely ask the date of your last menstrual period to properly time the appointment.

■ **At the appointment,** your doctor will confirm your home pregnancy test results with urine and blood tests and possibly an ultrasound, as well. She will also determine your estimated due date based on the date of your last menstrual period.

■ **This first visit will typically be your longest appointment,** since the doctor will give you a thorough physical examination, take your family and personal health history, and answer any of your pregnancy-related questions or concerns.

■ **You will be weighed** and have your blood pressure checked.

■ **You'll also have blood drawn** for several tests, including your blood type, Rh status, and a variety of sexually transmitted diseases.

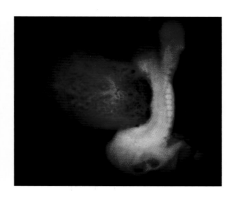

245 days to go...

YOUR BABY TODAY

The bulge at the lower part of this image will eventually become the baby's head. Segments called somites (seen as bright, round areas running down one side of the embryo), which will form the baby's spine, have started to develop.

At this important stage of development, the building blocks of your baby's spine are being laid down.

By the end of this 5th week, individual elements that will form the embryo have begun to develop.

Starting at what will become the head end, individual segments, called "somites," form. Roughly three new pairs of somites appear every day and each forms part of your baby's spine as well as the muscles associated with each segment of the body. Eventually there will be four somites at the head, eight in the region of the neck, 12 at chest level, five in the lumbar region, and five in the pelvic area.

More somites develop in the baby below the pelvis but most disappear. In other mammals, these develop to form the tail.

Doing moderate aerobic exercise during pregnancy—such as walking or running—regularly will burn excess fat, but won't affect your baby's development.

FOCUS ON... YOUR BODY

Your metabolism

Regular exercise will increase your base metabolic rate, which is the rate at which your body burns calories. During pregnancy your metabolism will already be slightly elevated. When exercising your body will be encouraged to use up excess energy and fat reserves, but will always keep enough reserve energy to facilitate the growth of your baby.

Exercise will also help your body regulate blood sugar (see p.92) and energy levels.

ASK A... NUTRITIONIST

I'm underweight. Could this affect my pregnancy? You may be more likely to suffer from nutritional deficiencies, which could affect the baby's health; you are also more likely to give birth prematurely, and have a smaller-than-usual baby, who is more vulnerable to health problems.

To gain weight, eat bigger portions and choose healthy foods that have plenty of protein, good-quality fats, and unrefined carbohydrates (see p.92). Opt for nutrient- and calorie-dense foods, such as avocados and whole-milk dairy products; eat lots of leafy greens to ensure you are getting key vitamins and minerals (see pp.15–16). Eat healthy snacks, such as nuts, fruit, and seeds, and don't skip breakfast. Your doctor will refer you to a dietician, if necessary.

ACTUAL SIZE OF YOUR BABY

At 5 weeks of pregnancy, the embryo is 0.09 in (2.5 mm) long.

5 weeks

Your 6th week

THIS WEEK YOU MAY NOTICE THE FIRST SYMPTOMS OF PREGNANCY—IF NOT, DON'T WORRY

Not all women start to feel pregnant this early on. Some experience a twinge of nausea or breast tenderness, while others notice no changes. Of course, it's natural to long for "proof" that your pregnancy is progressing, even if that happens to be morning sickness. But a lack of symptoms doesn't mean something is wrong; it's all really happening and your baby is going through some critical stages of development.

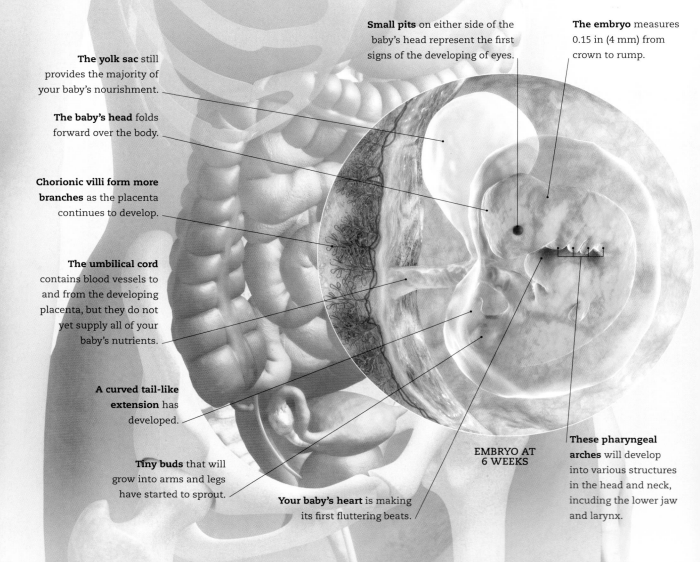

Small pits on either side of the baby's head represent the first signs of the developing of eyes.

The embryo measures 0.15 in (4 mm) from crown to rump.

The yolk sac still provides the majority of your baby's nourishment.

The baby's head folds forward over the body.

Chorionic villi form more branches as the placenta continues to develop.

The umbilical cord contains blood vessels to and from the developing placenta, but they do not yet supply all of your baby's nutrients.

A curved tail-like extension has developed.

Tiny buds that will grow into arms and legs have started to sprout.

Your baby's heart is making its first fluttering beats.

EMBRYO AT 6 WEEKS

These pharyngeal arches will develop into various structures in the head and neck, incuding the lower jaw and larynx.

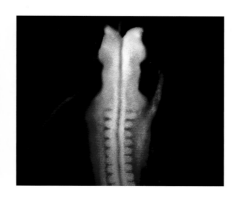

244 days to go...

YOUR BABY TODAY

The embryo now has 14 somites—the building blocks of your baby's muscular system. The first nine pairs are shown here. The upper part of the image shows the open end of the neural tube, which, along with the opening at the base of the spine, has closed.

If you've had no symptoms as you enter your 6th week, you may be on the lookout for signs that you are in fact pregnant.

You and your partner are probably the only people who know you're pregnant, and you may still be wondering if it's real. At this stage you may not have any symptoms at all, despite the rapidly changing and growing embryo inside you.

This absence of pregnancy signs is completely normal and is not a cause for concern. Try to remember that the majority of pregnancies are without any complications. It's normal for a healthy pregnant woman to have a wide range of side effects or none at all. So don't worry if you're feeling great—in fact count yourself lucky!

ASK A... NUTRITIONIST

Since being pregnant, I don't seem to have much of an appetite. Is this normal? It is common to not especially want food if you have morning sickness (see p.81). You may no longer be able to stomach your favorite foods. If you're not eating much, it's important that what you do eat is nutritious. Choose nutrient-rich dark green leafy vegetables and legumes, and fish (see p.96) since it contains essential fatty acids.

AS A MATTER OF FACT

Up to 90 percent of your supply of vitamin D depends on adequate exposure to sunlight.

Vitamin D helps your body absorb calcium, which is vital for the development of your unborn baby's skeleton. A daily 15-minute walk outside—with the sun on your skin—is sufficient; you can also boost your intake of vitamin D by eating oily fish, eggs, fortified cereals, and bread, and by taking supplements (see p.16).

EARLY ULTRASOUND SCANS

Some women will have an early ultrasound scan, but the majority of women will have one around the 12th week of pregnancy (see p.137). Early scans are usually done vaginally, with a scanning probe inserted gently into the vagina. They are performed for the following reasons:

■ **If there is a history of multiple births** in your family (or you have used IVF or another form of assisted pregnancy), your doctor may want to check the number of fetuses.

■ **If you've had a miscarriage in the past,** or show signs of cramping or spotting, or more profuse bleeding, a scan can be done to check that there is still a heartbeat.

■ **To establish the cause of vaginal bleeding.** Your baby may be healthy, but fibroids or other conditions may be causing you to bleed. This will be addressed by your doctor.

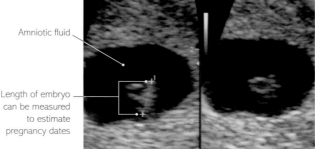

Amniotic fluid

Length of embryo can be measured to estimate pregnancy dates

Early vaginal scans do not show a great deal of detail. The sonographer waits until the embryo is in the correct position (left) to be measured.

Your 6th week

79

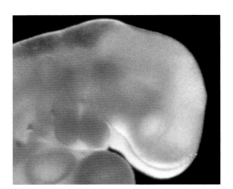

243 days to go...

YOUR BABY TODAY

The center of this image shows the baby's developing heart(darker gray), a very primitive structure at this stage. The baby's head is to the right of the image. The embryo is almost completely transparent.

There won't be any visible signs of pregnancy on the outside for some time, but there are many changes taking place inside.

At this early stage, all your unborn baby's needs will be met by the yolk sac. Attached to the embryo by a connecting stalk, this essential balloonlike structure indicates the site of your pregnancy and can usually be seen as early as this week as a sphere 0.1–0.2 in (3–4 mm) across. At first the yolk sac is as large as the disk of embryonic cells that will eventually become your baby.

Containing cells that perform a similar function to the liver, the yolk sac releases several pregnancy hormones and produces the embryo's first red blood cells. After week 9 the liver will take over these functions as the yolk sac gradually disappears and the placenta takes over, by around the 10th week of pregnancy.

Over the next seven days, a primitive circulatory system develops, well before any blood circulates to the placenta in the 10th week. And, by the end of this week, using the highest quality ultrasound equipment, it is just possible to see the embryo's heartbeat. At this early stage, the heart is simply a tube.

If you can't stomach big plates of food, try eating a combination of small portions at mealtimes and as snacks.

ASK A... NUTRITIONIST

Should I be eating for two?
Unfortunately, pregnancy is by no means a licence to eat anything and everything you'd like. "Eating for two" is a myth, and if you do so, you'll end up consuming too many calories and gaining too much weight. The best advice is to use your common sense. Studies show that pregnant women who eat according to their appetite naturally eat the proper amount and gain a healthy amount of weight.

Caloric needs in pregnancy vary greatly from woman to woman, depending upon pre-pregnancy weight and physical activity. In general, energy needs increase by approximately 300–500 calories per day during pregnancy. In the first trimester, caloric needs are a bit less, more at the lower end of the range.

In the first trimester, when up to 80 percent of women are nauseous or vomiting, getting enough calories can sometimes be a challenge. Like many pregnant women, you may feel most nauseous when your stomach is empty. One good trick is snacking. Eating five small meals rather than three large ones can be soothing to a nauseous stomach, while at the same time giving you the calories you need.

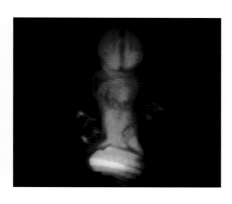

242 days to go...

YOUR BABY TODAY

A front view of the embryo: the head region is bent downward so that the central nervous system can be seen. The tubelike structure in the head region is the developing spinal cord. The tail of the embryo is curving upward.

Morning sickness is one of the most common and least welcome symptoms of pregnancy.

FOCUS ON... HEALTH

Ease the nausea

Unfortunately there is no definitive cure-all for morning sickness, though you could try the following natural remedies:

■ **Eat little and often**—having low blood-sugar levels may make the nausea worse so even if you feel sick, eating small snacks may help.

■ **Try eating a plain cookie or cracker** first thing in the morning before you get out of bed.

■ **Stick to bland foods** such as cereal or toast and avoid eating fatty and oily foods.

■ **Try having foods and drinks that contain ginger** (see right) such as gingersnaps or ginger tea.

■ **Drink plenty** if you are vomiting, to avoid becoming dehydrated. Put a bottle of water in the fridge and sip it gradually throughout the day. If you feel you are getting dehydrated, for example if your urine is getting very concentrated, you may need to see a doctor.

If the nausea or vomiting is too much to bear, then consult your doctor, who will be able to prescribe anti-nausea medications.

Feeling sick and vomiting are common symptoms of early pregnancy. There are various theories to explain why morning sickness occurs; one is that it's due to the rising levels of hCG (human chorionic gonadotrophin) hormone during the first trimester. Morning sickness, unfortunately, doesn't only happen before breakfast; in fact it can happen at any time of day and more than once in 24 hours.

One of the greatest challenges of early pregnancy is keeping it a secret from colleagues. If you have to keep rushing to the bathroom to vomit, people are likely to become suspicious.

Ginger contains properties that help to ease nausea. Put a plate of cookies on your bedside table, and nibble them before you get out of bed.

They may also notice that you look unwell or are more tired than usual. To help you handle this, you may want to tell one or two colleagues or your boss. You could ask them to keep it a secret for the time being. It's a good idea to keep some face wipes, toothpaste, and a toothbrush in your drawer, together with any snacks that you have found help to ease your nausea.

If you're finding it difficult to handle your vomiting, or are worried you are vomiting too much, seek advice from your doctor. Rarely, the sickness can become more serious and require medical treatment (see p.111).

AS A MATTER OF FACT

Ginger has been shown in studies to help with pregnancy-induced nausea.

One study found that the decrease in nausea happened four days after including ginger in the diet daily; so don't give up if you don't get relief right away. Try crystallized ginger chews or tasty ginger cookies; drink soothing ginger tea; and try cooking with fresh ginger. Be aware that most ginger ale does not contain real ginger, so is unlikely to ease nausea.

A changing world

The family is an ever-changing unit and has undergone some major shifts in the past two decades. Although times have changed, your role as a parent is the same as ever: to give your child consistent love, loyalty, and care.

THE STATISTICS

Changing family life

The statistics below reveal how family life has changed over decades.

■ In Canada, 65 percent of moms with children under the age of three work; in the UK, 55 percent of mothers of children under five work (compared with around 25 percent in 1975).

■ About 13 percent of children with working moms are cared for full-time by dad.

■ About 25 percent of moms with partners stay at home full time with the children.

■ Today, around 18 percent of children live in one-parent families; about 20 percent of one-parent families have a single dad at the helm.

■ Around 25 percent of babies in the UK are born to immigrant moms, and in some parts of the country up to a third of all babies are born to ethnic minority families—a figure that is similar in New Zealand and Australia. In Canada, about 20 percent of children under age 18 are immigrants or children of immigrants.

■ More than 41 percent of babies in the UK are born to unmarried women; in Canada, approximately 26 percent of babies are born out of wedlock. This trend is echoed throughout the West, and the numbers are steadily rising.

The family today

Today, there are many varieties of family life. Although studies report on the problems of modern childhood, children are familiar with and tolerant of different cultures, and living and working practices.

Mature moms The bulk of births now occur to women aged 25–34, accounting for 62 percent of all births in 2004, up from 55 percent in 1979. Births to mothers older than 35 account for 17 percent of all births, up from 4.5 percent in 1979. Benefits are that older women are more likely to be settled, financially stable, and mature.

Single parenting Single moms in Canada headed up 80 percent of all one-parent families in 2006. There's no doubt that children in single-parent families can be disadvantaged, but it's thought that much of this is due to financial constraints, and that those who have adequate socioeconomic resources do well.

Stepfamilies Stepfamilies are the fastest-growing family type, and account for more than 12 percent of families in Canada. Siblings may be of wildly different ages, or of the same age; these are unique and beneficial relationships for all children.

Modern dads

Dads today are more involved in family life. Dads taking leave from work, either paid or unpaid, to care for their newborns rose from 38 percent in 2001 to 55 percent in 2006. Research shows that children whose dads spend

THE GENDER GAP

Boys versus girls

Historically, about 106 boys have been born for every 100 girls—a phenomenon believed to be nature's way of compensating for the fact that males are more likely to be killed through conflicts. But ratios are changing with girls outnumbering boys. One factor may be increased stress (women under stress produce more girls than boys). However, the most important contributor is now thought to be the number of gender-bending chemicals in our environment, such as synthetic estrogens, PCBs (polychlorinated biphenyls), and pesticides.

considerable time with them do well educationally and at work.

Child care

This is a necessity in most families. Studies show that good care outside the family has a positive impact on social skills, intellect, and language. Grandparents care for about 30 percent of North American babies. A good grandparent relationship provides stability, family values, and may improve cognitive development.

Multiple cultures

Your baby will live in a multicultural society. This affects educational experience and friendships, and there's a strong chance a child will be cared for by someone from another culture at some point in her childhood.

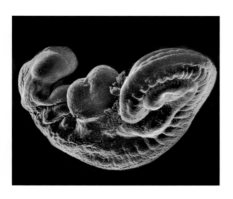

241 days to go...

YOUR BABY TODAY

This image shows just how curled up the embryo is at this stage. The head end of the embryo is on the left. The embryo now has 22 pairs of somites (building blocks of the musculoskeletal system) running along the back.

This is a crucial time for your developing baby as the neural tube, which will become the brain and spinal cord, is forming.

TIME TO THINK ABOUT

Whether to tell

You're excited to be pregnant, but should you tell people yet?

■ **Most parents-to-be** wait to share their exciting news until after week 12 when the risk of miscarriage falls. You, may, however, decide you want to confide in family and close friends. If they are people whom you would tell if you miscarried, then there is no harm in sharing your news.

■ **Most women don't tell** their employers yet, unless severe morning sickness interferes with their ability to keep up with work responsibilities. Most wait until after the first trimester or when they start to show. If you want time off for prenatal appointments before this, you'll need to explain why.

■ **Similarly, if your job** involves anything that could be a health and safety risk (for example, heavy lifting or working with chemicals), you should inform your employer early so your role can be adapted. It's also sensible to tell your boss the good news before office gossip about your expanding girth snowballs.

This week your baby begins to grow rapidly and will become much more recognizable as a baby over the next five weeks. There are three types of cell, each committed to a separate function. The first will form the skin and nervous system; the second forms blood vessels, muscles, and bones; the third forms the entire digestive system.

At this stage, it is the cells responsible for the spine and nervous system that are at work. Changing shape from a flat disk, the embryo starts to curl up. The edges of the groove that has already partially formed along the back gradually start to meet, closing and fusing to form a tube, which will become the brain and spinal cord. The last parts of the tube to close are at the very top of the head and then the base of the spine, two days later.

Being careful to get an adequate intake of folic acid (see p.35) in early pregnancy is essential to ensure the neural tube closes completely, with no gaps.

Not telling many people, if anyone, in the first few weeks will give you both time to come to terms with the news.

FOCUS ON... DADS

Keeping quiet

Your first reaction to finding out that your partner is pregnant might be to tell the world. After all, you may be excited or nervous and may want to confide in people who you can trust. Think twice before telling lots of people (see box, left) and don't do so without talking to your partner. Of course your partner may find it hard to hide some aspects of pregnancy, such as morning sickness.

Most importantly, make sure that you are both in agreement that it is the right time to tell others.

YOU ARE 5 WEEKS AND 5 DAYS

240 days to go...

YOUR BABY TODAY

This is a view of the right side of an embryo with the fronds of the chorionic villi in the background. The curled shape of the embryo is clearly demonstrated. The umbilical cord attachment to the early placenta can just be seen.

Are you feeling up one minute and down the next? Be reassured that this is a perfectly normal response to pregnancy hormones.

It may not happen quite yet, but be forewarned that you may become very emotional or irrational during pregnancy and suffer from mood swings. You may cry at things that had previously not affected you. This is due to a combination of your rapidly fluctuating hormones and the fact that pregnancy is a major life change.

Mood swings can be difficult for both you and your partner—try to keep communicating with each other and explain how you are feeling, no matter how irrational it may seem.

MORE VEGGIES PLEASE!

Be creative to stimulate your appetite and get essential nutrients:
- **Try raw veggies** with a dip.
- **Throw in a few vegetables** when you make your morning smoothie (see p.135)—cucumber, celery, peppers, and carrots are mild in flavor, but deliciously nutritious.
- **Try grating** zucchini or carrots into soups, pasta sauces, and stews, or throwing a handful of squash, frozen peas, broccoli, asparagus, or green beans into a risotto.
- **Add vegetables** to a cheese sauce. If you cook them in the sauce, it will absorb all of the nutrients that would normally make their way into the cooking water.
- **Make your own pizza** topped with crunchy and colorful vegetables.
- **Choose vegetarian** dishes when you get takeout.

FOCUS ON...YOUR HEALTH

Tackling fatigue

Fatigue is a common pregnancy complaint and you might find you have a sudden loss of energy in the early stages as your body adapts to the changes caused by pregnancy. This often lasts throughout the first trimester, but after about week 13 you should start to feel more energized. When you're not resting, try to stay active.

Another cause of fatigue is anemia. When you see your doctor you will be offered a blood test to check your iron levels, and if these are found to be low you will be offered supplements. To avoid anemia, eat iron-rich foods, such as dark green leafy vegetables, red meat, whole-grain cereals, and legumes, and drink prune juice. Vitamin C helps your body absorb iron so try drinking fresh orange juice with meals. Limit caffeine intake (see p.66) since it inhibits iron absorption.

The embryo is developing rapidly, although still only 4 mm long. The spinal column is in place and the eyes have formed. The yellow yolk sac on the left is larger than the embryo which it is nourishing.

YOU ARE 5 WEEKS AND 6 DAYS

239 days to go...

YOUR BABY TODAY

Development in the upper body usually precedes that in the lower body—this image shows the bulge containing the heart and liver, and the very earliest sign of development of the upper limb buds, but as yet there is no sign of the lower limb buds.

You may notice a marked increase in your breast size, even at this early stage of pregnancy.

The first part of your body to change shape is likely to be your chest. Your breasts may increase in size quite rapidly, looking bigger and feeling heavier. They may become quite tender to touch.

The nipples will change, the areola (the darker skin around the nipple) may become darker in color and your nipples may tingle. As your breasts get bigger, you might notice blue veins appearing. All these breast changes are due to the hormone estrogen.

AS A MATTER OF FACT

Each breast will increase, on average, by 2 in (5 cm) and 3 lb (1.4 kg) during pregnancy.

That is why it is important to wear the right bra, even in the early stages of pregnancy.

Read the labels on cleaning products carefully to make sure they are not toxic, and always wear rubber gloves. Pregnancy can be a good time to ask your partner to clean the bathroom!

ASK A... DOCTOR

How can I ease the soreness in my breasts? Wearing a supportive bra can help with both the feelings of heaviness and soreness in your breasts, which are common in pregnancy. If your breasts are very tender at night, try wearing your bra at night while you sleep which may help. Try to avoid sleeping on your front if this causes discomfort. You may find that rubbing in a cream containing aloe vera is soothing.

FOCUS ON... SAFETY

Detox yourself

Once you know you're pregnant, it's only natural to want to keep your baby safe, so...

Be careful when you're cleaning. Studies suggest there may be a link between pregnant women using bleach and spray air fresheners, and babies developing asthma. Plus, commercial oven cleaners contain toxic chemicals that experts believe could damage unborn babies.
■ Don't use "toxic" products.
■ Keep rooms well ventilated.
■ Steer clear of fumes.
■ Wear gloves.
■ Make your home sparkle with a solution made of bicarbonate of soda, distilled white vinegar, lemon juice, and essential oils.

Get someone else to clean your cat's litter box (or if that's not possible, wear rubber gloves and wash your hands afterward). Cat feces may contain parasites that can cause toxoplasmosis (see p.101), an infection that could harm your unborn baby.

238 days to go...

YOUR BABY TODAY

Here the back of the embryo can be seen lying over the yolk sac. The opening overlying the developing brain has now closed (left side of image) and this will be followed two days later by closure of the opening at the base of the spine (out of view).

By the end of this sixth week, one of your baby's major organs—the heart—is rapidly developing and circulating blood.

Your developing embryo may still be tiny, but is undergoing rapid and complex development.

The heartbeat is now more easily recognized on an ultrasound scan. The heart continues to form from a simple smooth tube which, as it becomes more muscular, loops, folds, and divides to form four chambers. On the left side the upper chamber (left atrium) takes in blood from the lungs. From here blood passes through a one-way valve (the mitral valve) into the main left pumping chamber (the left ventricle). This then pumps blood out of the heart to the body along the main artery (the aorta). On the right-hand side of the heart, the upper chamber (right atrium) collects blood returning from the body and passes it through a one-way valve (tricuspid valve) into the right main pumping chamber (right ventricle). This pumps blood to the lungs and the cycle continues.

At this stage of development, the circulation is very basic with the heart tube simply sending blood around the length of your baby. No blood travels from your baby's circulation to the placenta (see p.127).

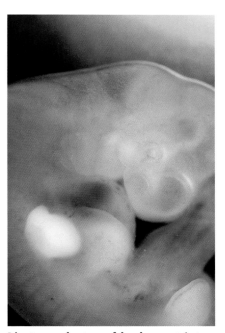

It's at an early stage of development, but the developing heart can be seen here as the dark red area. It lies just above the larger, slightly paler red area, which is the liver. Below the liver is the umbilicial cord.

TYPES OF SPONTANEOUS ABORTION, OR MISCARRIAGE

At this early stage, a common concern is that the pregnancy will spontaneously abort, or miscarry. This is the spontaneous loss of a pregnancy at any time up until the 20th week. After 20 weeks the loss is referred to as a stillbirth. The signs of a spontaneous abortion are vaginal bleeding and periodlike cramps.

Unfortunately, there is nothing that you can do to prevent a spontaneous abortion. In around 60 percent of cases, it is caused by a one-time genetic problem. Bleeding does not always mean that the pregnancy is being miscarried. Since not all spontaneous abortions follow the same pattern, there are various terms to describe what happens:

- **A threatened abortion** occurs when the pregnant woman experiences bleeding and possibly pain, but the baby survives.
- **An inevitable abortion** occurs when there is bleeding and pain due to the pregnant woman's uterus contracting. The cervix opens, and the fetus is expelled.
- **A missed abortion** is when the fetus dies but is not expelled. Surgery may be needed to remove it.

ACTUAL SIZE OF YOUR BABY

At 6 weeks, your baby's crown to rump length is 0.15 in (4 mm).

5 weeks   6 weeks

Your 7th week

SET YOURSELF SOME FITNESS STANDARDS TO SEE YOU THROUGH YOUR PREGNANCY

Getting in shape now will stand you in good stead as your pregnancy continues. Keeping active is important, so work up a daily exercise routine to strengthen your muscles and reduce fatigue—but listen to your body and don't exhaust yourself. This week your baby's vital organs, including the lungs and gut, start to develop. Your baby's head already looks too big for his body as the brain rapidly enlarges.

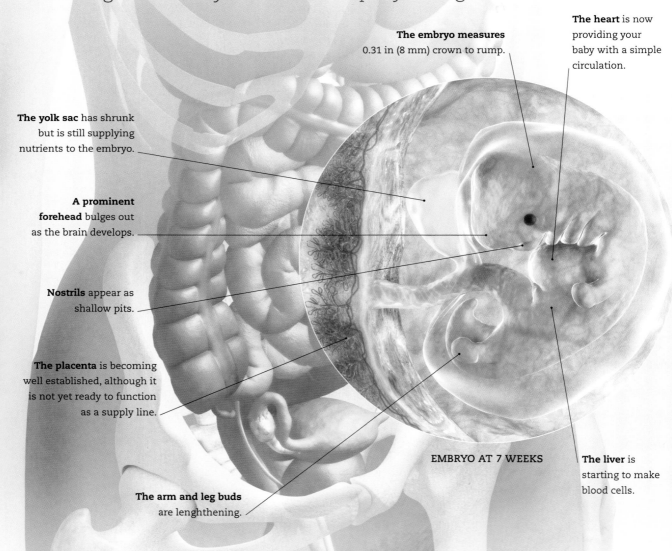

The embryo measures 0.31 in (8 mm) crown to rump.

The heart is now providing your baby with a simple circulation.

The yolk sac has shrunk but is still supplying nutrients to the embryo.

A prominent forehead bulges out as the brain develops.

Nostrils appear as shallow pits.

The placenta is becoming well established, although it is not yet ready to function as a supply line.

EMBRYO AT 7 WEEKS

The liver is starting to make blood cells.

The arm and leg buds are lenghthening.

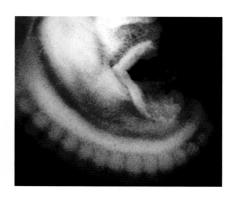

237 days to go...

YOUR BABY TODAY

In this side view of the embryo the spinal cord is clearly curved as it begins to develop. The pale-yellow ridgelike structures along the back are somites—your baby's developing muscular system.

You may be spending a lot of time in front of the mirror trying to spot your "bump," but it could be weeks yet before you show.

Like most newly pregnant women, you're probably on the lookout for a rounded belly, but it's unlikely to make an appearance just yet. On average, the fourth month marks the greatest period of growth, with your pregnancy most definitely appearing as a rounded abdomen.

If it's not your first pregnancy, you might show earlier, possibly as early as eight to 10 weeks, since your abdominal muscles will be more relaxed. Conversely, women who have firm abdominal muscles may show later. If you are expecting twins or triplets, you can expect to show even earlier.

ASK A... DOCTOR

Can having sex in pregnancy harm the baby? Unless you have been told by your doctor to avoid sex because of specific problems, such as a history of miscarriage or unexplained bleeding, then sex is safe at any stage. Enjoying intimacy with your partner is beneficial to your relationship.

Your baby is cushioned in fluid in the amniotic sac inside your uterus and protected by a plug of mucus at the cervix. Even deep penetration isn't harmful.

STRENGTHEN YOUR ABDOMINALS

It's safe to do abdominal exercises lying on your back during your first trimester. Toward the end of the first trimester, or when you start "showing" (see left), you should stop doing abdominal exercises on your back (see p.250 for other exercises you can do at this point).

When you are doing abdominal exercises, it's important to breathe correctly: remember to inhale to start and exhale on each effort.

The purpose of abdominal exercises is to strengthen core muscles. The deeper transverse abdominis muscle that runs horizontally across your body is vital for core stability and strength as your baby develops. The rectus abdominis muscle that runs vertically down your body is the muscle that will stretch during pregnancy and weaken, so it's vital to keep the transverse muscle strong to help your posture and support your spine.

The sooner you begin to strengthen the transverse abdominis, the better. In the first trimester, one of the exercises you can do to strengthen this muscle is shown below.

Knees bent

Feet flat on the floor

Feel your abdominal muscles tightening

Lie on your back, feet flat on the floor and arms at your sides. Inhale to begin and as you slowly exhale, push your lower back flat on to the floor. Hold this position for 3–5 seconds and repeat.

Your 7th week

Strengthening and toning exercises

Exercises that strengthen your muscles will help you deal with the additional demands of pregnancy and to manage better during labor and birth.

The exercises shown are sometimes called "functional movement enhancers" because they increase the strength of the muscles that you use for everyday functions such as walking, carrying, lifting, sitting, and standing. The workout can be used alongside walking, swimming, or other cardiovascular exercises and can be done around 2–3 times a week.

Warm up Walk in place, swinging your arms back and forth. Continue for 3–5 minutes until your muscles are warm.

Side lunges (left) These (and the foward lunges, right) strengthen the abdominal and thigh muscles. Start with hands on hips, legs hip-width apart. Step one leg out to the side, bending the knee. Keep the other leg straight. Step back to the starting position, keeping the tummy pulled in and torso straight. Do 10 lunges on each leg. **Forward lunges** (right) Start with hands on hips, feet hip-width apart. Step one leg forward; bend the opposite knee toward the floor, allowing the heel to lift off the floor. Return to the starting position. Do 10 lunges on each leg.

Biceps curl The biceps is an important muscle for carrying and lifting. You can use 3–5 lb (1–2 kg) weights for this sequence if you're a regular exerciser. Stand with feet hip-width apart, knees slightly bent, back straight, and arms at your sides. Breathe in, then exhale as you bend one elbow, raising your hand to shoulder level. Alternate arms until you've done 20 curls each side (40 in total). If you find this easy, try doing a total of 60 curls.

The bridge This exercise works your bottom, hamstrings, and inner thighs, and builds strength in your lower body to support your growing belly. Lie on your back with your feet flat on the floor and knees slightly apart. Raise your hips (this relieves pressure on your back and is safe in the second and third trimesters). Keep your hands on the floor next to you, arms straight. Slowly bring your knees together while clenching your bottom; open and close your knees 10 times. Slowly lower your hips and roll onto your left side to end.

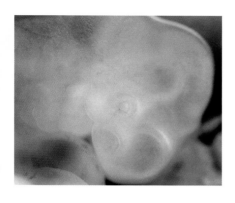

236 days to go...

YOUR BABY TODAY

The first recognizable facial feature to be formed is the eye, visible as a black dot in the center of this image. The gray areas are the fluid-filled chambers of the underlying brain.

Try not to dwell on your lifestyle before you realized you were pregnant, but start making changes now.

Have you only just discovered you're pregnant? Not all women realize they are pregnant immediately, especially if it wasn't planned. If you've only just found out, it's natural to be concerned about things that you did before you knew, such as drinking alcohol or taking drugs. You may be worried that you've harmed your unborn baby. Use your pregnancy as an opportunity to assess your lifestyle and improve your health.

Because of how pregnancy is dated (see p.35), your baby is still only a little over four weeks old. If you have not been taking folic acid (see p.35), start taking supplements starting today.

If you're single and pregnant, don't be alone—share the highs and the lows with those close to you.

TIME TO THINK ABOUT

Prenatal care

The options for prenatal care in Canada are outlined on p.102, but they do vary from area to area. Whatever your type of prenatal care, any ultrasound scans, tests, and investigations may also take place at a hospital. Your options are likely to be:

- Group medical practice (OB or GP)
- Solo medical practice
- Midwifery care
- Doula care

GOING SOLO

The prospect of being pregnant and single, especially if it wasn't your choice, can be tough. Make sure you:
- **Take care of yourself:** plan a healthy diet, and an exercise routine. Get as much rest and restful sleep as you can. Ask a friend to spur you on or get online and seek support from other single pregnant women in your area—you will have a ready-made support network after the birth.
- **Ask for help** from family and friends. You will probably find they

are delighted to be involved in your pregnancy and are willing to come to prenatal appointments and classes with you: you may want to consider asking one of these people to be your birth partner.
- **Discuss support and access** with your baby's father (if appropriate), and if you can't agree, seek legal advice. You and your baby will benefit if an amicable arrangement is reached, and the sooner you start talking, the easier it will be after the birth.

- **Arrange support** for after the birth. A survey found that grandparents who are actively involved in their grandchildren's lives contribute positively to their well-being. If you don't have family close by, try to build a network of other support that will see you through the early weeks.
- **Start thinking early** about your career options for after the birth. You don't have to make any decisions, but it helps to know some of the choices you may have to make later.

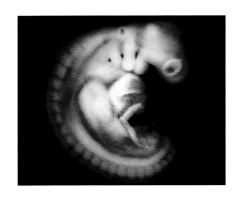

235 days to go...

YOUR BABY TODAY

The eyes begin life as shallow depressions, one on each side of the developing face. This image shows an early eye in the center right, together with the curve of the pale yellow somites of the developing musculoskeletal system.

Needing to urinate frequently is, unfortunately, one of the unwanted side effects of pregnancy.

ASK A... DOCTOR

Why do I have so much saliva in my mouth now that I'm pregnant? Called pytalism, excess saliva is caused by increased hormone levels. Don't try to keep the saliva in your mouth; if you find yourself drooling, spit into a tissue or small cup. Place a towel on your pillow. Sucking lemon wedges or ice cubes may help. Pytalism usually subsides in later pregnancy.

Are you spending a lot of time in the bathroom? In addition to dealing with symptoms such as nausea and vomiting (see p.81), if you're like the majority of pregnant women, you'll need to urinate more frequently. It means you're unlikely to want to be too far away from the nearest bathroom.

It can feel as though your bladder cannot hold much urine so you may feel the need to go to the bathroom not long after you've just been, during the day and at night. This is because there is more blood being pumped through the kidneys so you produce more urine. As your uterus grows, it puts pressure on your bladder so it cannot expand as much as normal and will feel uncomfortably full earlier than usual. This can last throughout pregnancy, though you're most likely to experience it in the first and third trimesters.

If, however, you're concerned about the amount of urine you're passing, and/or develop pain or stinging while passing urine, you may have developed a urinary tract infection and should see your doctor immediately.

FOCUS ON... NUTRITION

Get carb loading

Make carbohydrates part of your balanced diet, but make sure you choose the right ones. Refined carbohydrates, such as white bread and white rice, are very quickly broken down, releasing a large amount of glucose into the bloodstream. This is quickly used up and then glucose levels fall rapidly. This fluctuation in glucose levels has been associated with diabetes, obesity, and heart disease, and recent data suggests it is not the optimal environment for adult or fetal health.

Unrefined carbohydrates, such as whole-wheat bread and brown rice, break down more slowly, releasing glucose steadily leaving you fuller. This can prevent the hunger signals that follow a rapidly digested meal and help with weight control. Your baby is constantly drawing glucose from your bloodstream, so a steady release of glucose leaves you both with plenty of fuel on an ongoing basis. New research has found that babies exposed to a diet based upon unrefined carbs may have more lean body mass and less body fat, though still a healthy birthweight. This will make them less likely to be overweight later in life.

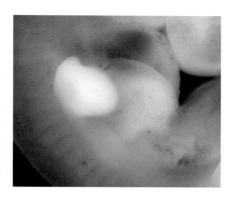

234 days to go...

YOUR BABY TODAY

The early limb bud that will form your baby's arm can be seen here (white area). The upper limb buds appear before the lower limb buds. At this early stage, the hands and fingers are not yet developed.

Your baby's lungs won't be fully developed until late in pregnancy, but the foundations are being laid down right now.

ECTOPIC PREGNANCY

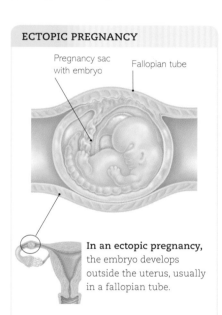

Pregnancy sac with embryo

Fallopian tube

In an ectopic pregnancy, the embryo develops outside the uterus, usually in a fallopian tube.

An ectopic pregnancy can cause abdominal pain on one side and irregular vaginal bleeding. Some women get shoulder-tip pain, thought to be caused by internal bleeding. An ectopic pregnancy can rupture the fallopian tube causing severe pain. Emergency medical attention is essential.

If an ectopic pregnancy is suspected, you will be given a scan. Sometimes the pregnancy will naturally regress; if not medication or surgery will be necessary.

In this 7th week of pregnancy, your baby's lungs are starting to develop. This begins with a small lung bud branching out from the upper part of the tube (esophagus) between your baby's mouth and stomach. This lung bud forms the main windpipe or "trachea," which then divides into two main branches (bronchi) that will eventually form your baby's right and left lungs. These bronchi continue to branch into smaller tubes, a process that will be repeated many times.

Your baby's gut is also starting to develop, from the mouth downward. At the beginning of this week, his future digestive system consisted of a simple tube that lay along the length of the embryo; this tube was closed at each end. The tube remains closed but the esophagus has now started to separate from the trachea and connect to the stomach. The swelling that will become your baby's stomach forms around the center of his body, but undergoes a 90-degree rotation to lie more on the left-hand side.

Buds arise from the duodenum (the first part of the bowel that leaves the stomach) that will form the pancreas and bile duct to the gall bladder.

In just a couple of weeks, your baby will have all its major organs and body systems.

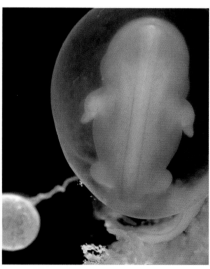

The embryo is safely cocooned in the fluid-filled amniotic sac. The yolk sac can be seen in the bottom left-hand corner, attached by what is now a very fine thread; its function is gradually replaced by the placenta.

AS A MATTER OF FACT

Music therapy is a highly effective way to reduce stress.

A study found that pregnant women who listened to music that mimicked the human heartbeat had reduced stress levels compared to those who did not receive the treatment.

Your 7th week

Miscarriage, or spontaneous abortion

Miscarriage is the spontaneous loss of a pregnancy before the fetus is mature enough to survive outside the uterus. Miscarriage is common, affecting 15–20 percent of pregnancies, with the majority occurring in the first 12 weeks. Late miscarriage, after the first trimester, occurs in about 1 percent of pregnancies.

DIAGNOSIS

Types of miscarriage

Different terms are used to describe miscarriage, depending on what is found during an ultrasound scan or an internal examination. The medical term used is 'spontaneous abortion.'

■ **Threatened abortion** is the term given to bleeding early in pregnancy, but in which the cervix remains closed. In this case, the bleeding stops after a few days, and the pregnancy is likely to continue.

■ **Inevitable abortion** occurs when there is bleeding and the cervix is open, meaning that the fetus will be lost. If the pregnancy is less than eight weeks, the bleeding may be like a heavy, painful period. After eight weeks, the bleeding may be considerably heavier.

■ **Incomplete abortion** occurs when there is bleeding and the cervix opens, but the uterus doesn't expel its entire contents and some pregnancy tissue is left behind.

■ **Complete abortion** is when there is bleeding, the cervix opens, and the uterus expels all the pregnancy tissues.

■ **Missed abortion** is less usual. There may be no miscarriage symptoms, but the pregnancy stops developing and the miscarriage isn't diagnosed until the routine scan at around 12 weeks.

Why miscarriage happens

An early miscarriage is usually due to a problem such as a chromosomal or structural abnormality in the fetus. It may also be caused by a fibroid (a non-cancerous growth in the uterus), an infection, or an immune system disorder. Miscarriage occurs more commonly in older women, in smokers, and in multiple pregnancies.

If you miscarry, it's important to know that it wasn't linked to anything you did, such as exercise, sex, or travel. Also, there is no evidence that rest reduces the risk of a threatened abortion going on to become inevitable (see box, left).

What will be done

If you bleed in early pregnancy, contact your doctor immediately who will arrange for you to have a pelvic exam and/or ultrasound scan. If a scan shows a healthy fetal heart, the chance of miscarriage is reduced. If there is no heartbeat, or no developing baby, the doctor will assess if you've had a complete or incomplete miscarriage (see box, left). A complete miscarriage doesn't require treatment. If it is incomplete, you may be offered medication to hasten the miscarriage, or a procedure to scrape the uterus, although your doctor may recommend expectant management—monitoring the situation while letting your uterus expel its contents. Expectant management means that you avoid risks such as infection from an invasive medical procedure, but its disadvantage is that you may bleed longer. Discuss the options with your doctor.

If you have two or more miscarriages in a row, known as "repeated abortion,"
your doctor may arrange tests to see if there is a cause. About half the time, no cause will be found but sometimes testing will find fetal chromosomal problems, uncommon uterine problems, or blood disorders or other medical conditions.

After a miscarriage

Your period may be delayed by 6–12 weeks. Once the bleeding stops, there is no medical reason to not try to get pregnant again. The only problem is that you may not know if your period is late since your cycle is readjusting after the miscarriage, or whether you are pregnant again. It's wise to wait until you both feel mentally ready to try again. Talking to a close friend, family member, or a counselor, can help you come to terms with your loss.

LATE MISCARRIAGE

Pregnancy loss after the first trimester

Losing a pregnancy after the first trimester is much more unusual than an early miscarriage. After 20 weeks, a pregnancy loss is referred to as a stillbirth. There are several reasons why late pregnancy loss may occur, including infection; uterine abnormalities or abnormalities in the baby; and a weak cervix. If you have a late miscarriage, your doctor will discuss the possible causes with you and, if a cause is identified, whether anything needs to be done in a future pregnancy.

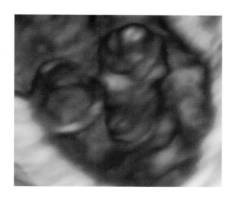

233 days to go...

YOUR BABY TODAY

This 3D ultrasound scan shows the embryo and its yolk sac, attached to the wall of the uterus. The yolk sac provides nourishment for the embryo until the placenta is fully functional, and produces blood cells until the liver can take over this role.

By this stage, you may have experienced bouts of dizziness. It's all part of your body and brain adjusting to the pregnancy.

THE LOWDOWN

Being a teetotaler

Your baby's health is the most important consideration, so before you've announced your pregnancy, you may need to take steps to discreetly avoid drinking alcohol.

■ **Buy the first round** and get yourself a carbonated mixer and ice and a slice without the alcohol. Once everyone else has had one drink, they're less likely to notice that you're on the wagon. For the next round, say you're pacing yourself and ask for a mixer.
■ **Claim you're detoxing** or hungover and order a juice or a Virgin Mary.
■ **Discreetly swap your full glass** with your partner's empty one.

AS A MATTER OF FACT

Exercising regularly can help you sleep more deeply.

Insomnia is common in pregnancy, due to anxiety or difficulty in getting comfortable. Exercise is a destresser and will tire you out, increasing your chance of a good night's sleep.

If you feel lightheaded, especially when you get up from lying down, be extra careful. Dizzy spells are common, especially as your pregnancy progresses and you get bigger, since your heart has to work harder against the forces of gravity to get blood to the brain.

Try to stand up very gradually, in stages, from lying to sitting to standing. Dizziness can also occur if you have been standing for a long period of time, since blood may collect in your legs.

Keep moving to encourage the blood to be pumped back to your heart.

Alternatively, you may feel dizzy due to low blood-sugar levels. Other symptoms of low blood sugar include feeling sweaty, shaky, and hungry. Even if you're feeling or being sick, try to eat little and often to ensure that your blood-sugar levels remain stable.

If you regularly feel dizzy, speak to your doctor, who will carry out some basic health checks.

KEEP ON MOVING

The last thing you may feel like doing is exercising, but it can play a significant role in alleviating and preventing pregnancy symptoms. Although a run through the park or a walk downtown may not sound as inviting as a cozy nap on the sofa, exercise is invigorating and the effects will last. Try to think of it as being active, rather than "exercising."

If after completing a physical activity you feel even more fatigued, decrease how hard and long you exercise. Always listen to your body. As you become more fit and your pregnancy progresses, these feelings of fatigue should diminish, usually by weeks 12–14.

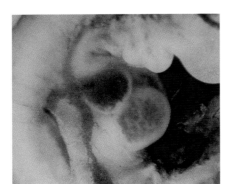

232 days to go...

YOUR BABY TODAY

At this stage of your baby's development, the heart is a tubular structure, visible in the center of this image. It is, however, already providing your baby with a very simple circulation.

What will become your baby's tiny arms and legs are beginning to develop during this seventh week of pregnancy.

It's still some weeks before your baby—still an embryo—will become recognizable as a human fetus. At the end of this seventh week, however, there are four simple limb buds, each slightly flattened at the end where, over the next two weeks, a hand or foot will form.

With the exception of muscle tone, which comes much later on, all stages of your baby's upper limb development precede any developments in his lower limbs.

The eyes are the first recognizable landmarks to form on the face. At this stage, the eyes consist of two simple surface indentations, which then develop a second indentation within the first; the inner one will become the lens and the outer the eyeball. Your baby's eyes are wide apart at this stage and his ears and nose have yet to form.

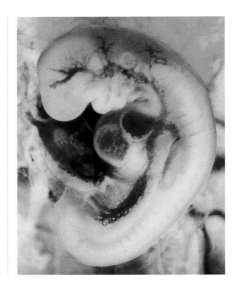

At this stage of an unborn baby's development, the circulatory system is at a very primitive stage. The upper dark bulge shown here is the heart and beneath it lies the liver, where blood cells are starting to be made.

ASK A... DOCTOR

Can exercising increase the risk of miscarriage? There is no evidence to suggest that, as long as you're healthy and have been given the all-clear from your doctor, exercise will put you at a greater risk of having a miscarriage. In fact, the benefits of getting regular moderate exercise while you're pregnant far outweigh the risks to you and your baby.

The most important factors at this stage of your pregnancy are to exercise at the same level you did prior to being pregnant. Do not attempt any new high-impact and strenuous activity or take up a new sport. Follow the guidelines that are set out on page 18.

FOCUS ON... NUTRITION

Know your fish

Fish is packed with essential nutrients that are good for your baby's development, so try to eat at least two portions a week.

You do, however, need to be careful of consuming high levels of mercury, present in trace amounts in nearly all fish and shellfish, since it can harm an unborn baby's nervous system. Health Canada recommends the following for pregnant women:

- **Don't eat fish** that are highest in mercury, including shark and swordfish.
- **Eat up to** 12 ounces (340 g) per week of lower-mercury seafood like shrimp, salmon, pollock, catfish, and canned light tuna.
- **For fish caught locally** check local advisories regarding mercury content. If no guidance is available, eat up to 6 ounces (170 g) and consume no other fish that week.

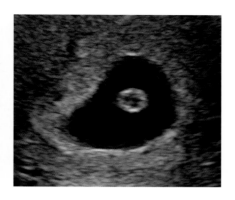

231 days to go...

YOUR BABY TODAY

This early vaginal ultrasound scan shows the first signs of pregnancy: the black central area is the fluid-filled cavity in which your baby (not visible) is developing. Within this is a small circular area, which is the yolk sac.

As your baby's body continues to develop, it won't be long before some very general movements will be visible on a scan.

While you're dealing with early pregnancy symptoms, your tiny embryo is tightly curled in your uterus. There is a short portion at the lower end of the spine that in other species goes on to develop into a tail. This portion now starts to disappear as more recognizably human features appear.

The ends of your baby's limb buds flatten, like paddles, and begin to form short digits that will become your baby's tiny fingers and toes. At first these are fused together—then, like the remainder of the skeleton, the digits grow around a soft framework of cartilage that will gradually harden into bone. As the upper limb buds lengthen, your baby's elbows begin to form.

Your baby's eyes continue to develop but won't be fully formed until around week 20; his nostrils now appear as two shallow nasal pits.

ASK A... DOCTOR

Help! I'm pregnant again and my little boy is only 12 months old. How will I cope? Pregnancy can be exhausting, particularly in the first trimester, when your body is adjusting to the new demands placed upon it. Having a toddler to contend with at this time makes it even harder.

Find quiet activities to enjoy with your toddler and leave the rough and tumble play to someone else. Take time to nurture yourself, sleeping when your toddler naps, or just settling down on the sofa while he watches a DVD. Don't feel guilty about putting your feet up: it's important to take a step back at this stage and remember that your most important job right now is "growing" your baby.

THE LOWDOWN

Good friends

Keeping your pregnancy quiet in these early weeks is difficult. Whether you want to tell people you're expecting is a matter of personal choice, but there's a good reason to keep it quiet for the time being (see p.83).

You may, however, need to talk to someone (other than your partner), so confide in a friend. Choose someone who will indulge your need to discuss everything—from pregnancy symptoms to birth fears and baby names. The ideal candidate will find your food cravings and 4 am trips to the bathroom riveting... and provide bowls of ice cream and pickles, and advice around the clock.

ACTUAL SIZE OF YOUR BABY

At 7 weeks, your baby's crown to rump length is 0.31 in (8 mm).

5 weeks	6 weeks	7 weeks

Your 8th week

YOUR MOOD MAY SWING FROM HIGH TO LOW AS HORMONES AND EMOTIONS TAKE HOLD

You're probably beginning to feel different, even though you don't look pregnant. You may feel a bit low and irritable at times; this is largely due to the changing levels of hormones in your body. You may sometimes have mixed feelings about being pregnant, however much you long for a baby. If the idea of going on vacation appeals to you, opt for short trips and a safe climate, and take extra care of yourself.

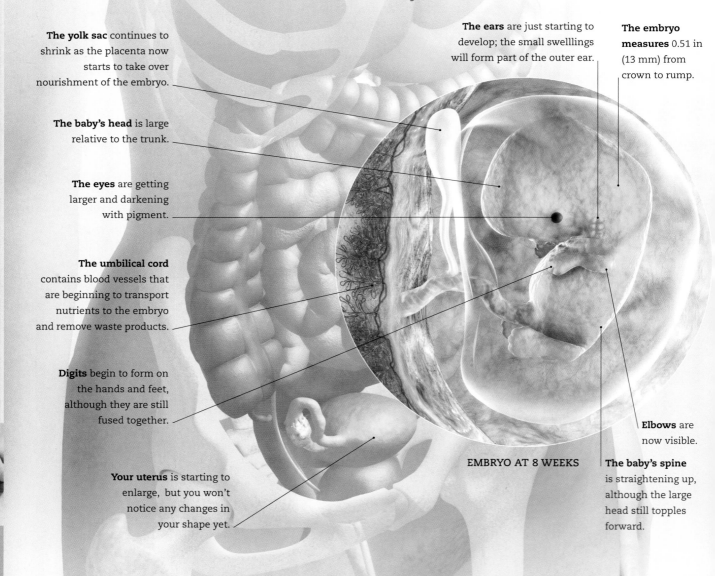

The yolk sac continues to shrink as the placenta now starts to take over nourishment of the embryo.

The baby's head is large relative to the trunk.

The eyes are getting larger and darkening with pigment.

The umbilical cord contains blood vessels that are beginning to transport nutrients to the embryo and remove waste products.

Digits begin to form on the hands and feet, although they are still fused together.

Your uterus is starting to enlarge, but you won't notice any changes in your shape yet.

The ears are just starting to develop; the small swellings will form part of the outer ear.

The embryo measures 0.51 in (13 mm) from crown to rump.

Elbows are now visible.

EMBRYO AT 8 WEEKS

The baby's spine is straightening up, although the large head still topples forward.

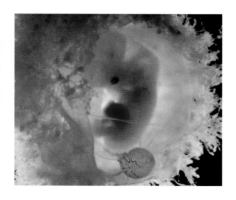

230 days to go...

YOUR BABY TODAY

The fronds that will form the early placenta can be clearly seen on the right here. At the bottom and separate from the embryo is the yolk sac, which is becoming ever smaller as its role is taken over by the placenta.

As your body begins to change shape, you may begin to worry about gaining too much weight.

You're supposed to put on weight during pregnancy and while this is not a time to overeat, neither is it a time for fad or restrictive diets. By eating sensibly and exercising moderately, you should gain a healthy amount of weight during pregnancy.

How much weight you should gain depends on your starting weight. If you are underweight when you become pregnant, you should put on more weight than someone who's overweight.

This starting weight is calculated by working out your BMI (see p.17), which is a measure of weight in relation to height. It's a useful tool to figure out approximately how much weight you should gain during your pregnancy.

If your BMI falls within the normal range, then your recommended pregnancy weight gain is 25–35 lb (11–14.5 kg). If your BMI is in the underweight category, you should gain 28–40 lb (12.5–18 kg). If you're overweight, your

pregnancy weight gain should be 15–25 lb (7–11 kg). Women in the obese category should gain at least 15 lb (7 kg). Women carrying twins should plan to gain about 35–45 lb (16–20 kg).

As a rough guide, an ideal weight gain is no more than 5 lb (2.2 kg) in the first trimester; no more than 12–19 lb (5.5–9 kg) in the second trimester; and no more than 8–11 lb (3.5–5 kg) in the third trimester. Remember not all of this weight gain is fat (see box, below).

HOW MUCH WEIGHT WILL YOU GAIN?

Over the 40 weeks of pregnancy, you are likely to gain very little weight in the first trimester and then experience a steady weight gain of around 1½–2 lb (0.7–1 kg) a week.

In the final few weeks of pregnancy, it's normal to gain a few more pounds. Remember that all figures given are averages and the amount you gain will depend on many individual factors;

where weight is gained can also differ from woman to woman. Always consult your doctor if you're concerned about any aspect of your weight gain or diet.

Weight gain chart

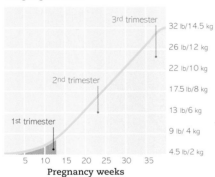

3rd trimester

32 lb/14.5 kg

26 lb/12 kg

22 lb/10 kg

17.5 lb/8 kg

2nd trimester

13 lb/6 kg

9 lb/ 4 kg

1st trimester

4.5 lb/2 kg

5 10 15 20 25 30 35

Pregnancy weeks

Components of weight gain

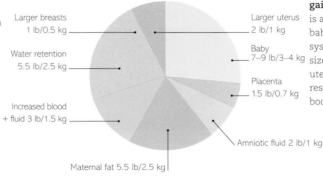

Larger breasts 1 lb/0.5 kg

Water retention 5.5 lb/2.5 kg

Increased blood + fluid 3 lb/1.5 kg

Maternal fat 5.5 lb/2.5 kg

Larger uterus 2 lb/1 kg

Baby 7–9 lb/3–4 kg

Placenta 1.5 lb/0.7 kg

Amniotic fluid 2 lb/1 kg

The weight you'll gain during pregnancy is a combination of your baby and her support system, the increased size of your breasts and uterus, essential fat reserves, and additional bodily fluids and blood.

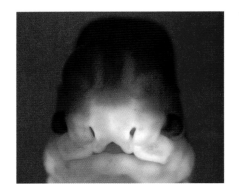

229 days to go...

YOUR BABY TODAY

Your baby won't look recognizably human yet, but the lower lip and jaw are formed; the upper lip is not yet complete, and the mouth appears very wide. The external ears are developing low down at the jaw line and the eyes are wide apart.

Although your baby's brain is still very simply formed, it's undergoing some remarkable changes.

This is a really important stage of development for your baby.

At this time, her brain is a hollow structure, which is joined to the spinal cord, but it's now starting to fold and form five distinct areas.

The lowest part, or hindbrain, is the first part to grow rapidly and will become structures known as the pons, medulla, and cerebellum. These structures are the most primitive areas of the brain and determine many basic actions that we do without conscious effort, such as breathing and keeping our balance.

Above this is the midbrain that conveys signals from the hindbrain, peripheral nerves, and spinal cord to the forebrain. This part of the brain consists of the thalamus—involved with emotions and sensory perception— and the two cerebral hemispheres, both

quite smooth at this point. Each hemisphere contains a fluid-filled chamber and within that the cerebrospinal fluid is produced.

At the 11–14 week scan (see p.139), brain development checkups will be done to confirm that the baby has normal early cerebral development.

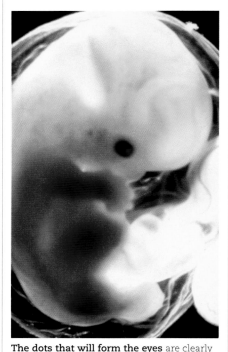

The dots that will form the eyes are clearly visible now. At the side of the head, the deep cleft can be seen between the front and back of the brain; this is normal at this stage.

AS A MATTER OF FACT

Fish really is brain food!

Research found that six-month-olds whose mothers had consumed high amounts of fish during pregnancy scored better in mental development tests. But only varieties low in mercury should be eaten (see p.96).

ASK A... DOCTOR

I'm eight weeks pregnant and have had some bleeding. Should I be concerned? Bleeding in early pregnancy is common. If the bleeding is light, and not accompanied by abdominal cramping or pain, then it's unlikely that there is anything wrong. However, always consult your doctor if you have bleeding at any stage of pregnancy to rule out any complications.

Bleeding in early pregnancy can sometimes be due to a cervical ectropian, which is when the surface of the cervix becomes "raw." This results from hormonal changes and is not harmful to the baby. Sexual intercourse can aggravate a cervical ectropian, causing bleeding.

Bleeding in late pregnancy may be more serious since it can be due to the placenta partially, or totally, detaching from the wall of the uterus, known as placental abruption, or to a low-lying placenta (see p.212). If you have a mucus discharge tinged with blood in late pregnancy, this may be a "bloody show" (see p.391).

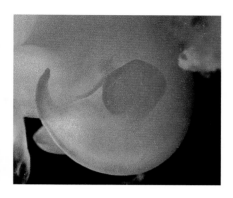

228 days to go...

YOUR BABY TODAY

At this stage, the embryo's "tail," shown curving up on the left, is starting to disappear. The somites of this area of the musculoskeletal system will eventually form the four fused bones of your baby's coccyx—the lowest part of the spine.

Even if you're happy about having a baby, it's natural to have mixed emotions at times.

Your emotions may fluctuate— one minute you're laughing and the next you're irritable and yelling, or crying. You might be confused that at a time when you should be happy, you often feel tense and tearful. Be reassured that this is a normal and temporary part of pregnancy.

Don't be too hard on yourself since these changing moods are caused mainly by pregnancy hormones, which is something out of your control. They are the same hormones that cause the symptoms of PMS—rapid mood swings, crying, and irritability—that you might have experienced before.

Be kind to yourself during these down times and do what works best for you, whether it's taking time out to be alone or sharing your feelings with others.

AS A MATTER OF FACT

Up to 70 percent of pregnant women sometimes have symptoms of depression.

While one woman hardly has any mood swings, another could suffer for weeks, especially in the first trimester.

FOCUS ON... SAFETY

Protect yourself

Toxoplasmosis is a disorder caused by a parasite that can harm a developing fetus. The symptoms may resemble those of mononucleosis with a fever and/or swollen glands in the neck.

It can be spread through cat feces. However, it can also be spread from undercooked meat. Thus, in addition to avoiding changing cat litter, use some caution in the kitchen. Beef, pork, and lamb need to be cooked well. Avoid cross-contamination in the kitchen when preparing foods. Be certain to clean chopping boards and utensils well with hot soapy water after preparing meat.

When you're having a down day, remember that these negative feelings will pass; mood swings are a normal part of pregnancy.

ASK A... DOCTOR

I'm struggling to deal with my wife's mood swings. Are these normal? Yes, your partner will be emotional and all you can do is be as supportive, patient, and understanding as you can.

At this early stage of pregnancy, her changing hormone levels may cause mood swings and unexpected emotional responses. Sometimes things that have never been a problem, such as hearing a particular piece of music, might make her cry, or she may snap at you over something trivial. With her emotions out of kilter, she's likely to be as frustrated and confused by this behavior as you are. Until it passes, just bide your time, bite your tongue, and give her a hug.

Your 8th week

Prenatal care options

Throughout your pregnancy, you may be cared for by a family-practice doctor, obstetrician, midwife, or a combination. The goal of your prenatal care is to monitor you and your baby so that problems can be identified and managed.

Your care during pregnancy

Early in pregnancy, you will need to think about who you would like to care for you during pregnancy, labor, and the postpartum period. You will also need to consider where you want to give birth since this will have an influence on your choice of care provider. The main options are set out below, although these may vary depending on where you live. When you attend your first prenatal appointment at 8–12 weeks (see pp.122–3), you will be given information about the prenatal services you can access in your area. The medical checkups that are done during this appointment will also help establish the best choice for your prenatal care.

Types of prenatal care

The majority of your care will usually be provided by an ob/gyn or a GP. At your first appointment, she will outline the prenatal services you will receive.

Group medical practice With this type of care, you will see two or more doctors (typically ob/gyns and/or family practitioners) throughout your pregnancy on a rotating basis. One of these doctors will be present at the hospital when you deliver.

Solo medical practice You'll only have one doctor, and you will see her at every prenatal visit. She will attend your birth at the hospital, unless she's unavailable and arranges for another doctor who covers for her to be present for your delivery.

Midwifery care If your pregnancy is low-risk, you can see registered midwives for most of your appointments throughout pregnancy. Midwives will provide total care, antenatal visits, labor and delivery care, and postpartum care, including help with breastfeeding. Ob/gyns are available for consultations as required. If you choose this option, you'll deliver your baby at the maternity or birthing center or at home, unless complications arise, in which case your care would be transferred to the affiliated hospital.

Doula care Doulas are women who provide emotional and physical support before, during, and after childbirth; they do not have medical training and will not deliver your baby. A doula will help you get ready for birth by making sure you have the information that you need, helping with the preparation of a birth plan, and with practicing relaxation techniques. When you go into labor, a doula will support you and your partner, providing massages and liaising with your care team if needed. After the birth, she can assist you with breastfeeding and other aspects of newborn care in your home. Doulas are not required to be certified, however certification is available through different organizations, and their fees are not covered by your health plan.

Where you give birth

This important decision doesn't have to be made at your initial appointment, but your midwife or doctor may discuss the options at this time. It's wise to be aware of the risks, benefits, and consequences of your choice. If you have a preexisting problem, or one that develops during pregnancy, this must be factored into your decision on where you will give birth.

In the hospital Some women prefer to give birth in a hospital with doctors and medical equipment close by. Also, some women need specialized care and input from obstetricians because of existing conditions or problems that develop in labor. In this case, the obstetrician and the family doctor will work closely together. Other specialists may also need to be involved during labor, for example if a woman has diabetes or a heart condition.

YOUR OPTIONS

Informed choice

Being able to choose the type of care you receive is one of the most important aspects of pregnancy and childbirth. Make sure that you have the most up-to-date, evidence-based information available so that you can make informed decisions. The care you receive should take into account any special needs you have, such as a disability, or cultural or religious beliefs. You should be able to discuss the options with your doctor or midwife and feel free to ask her whatever you want, change your mind, and know that your preferences will be taken into consideration by your doctor or midwife.

In a birthing center Currently not widely available in Canada, these units provide a homelike setting. They are led by midwives with no obstetric input and have facilities such as birthing tubs and pools. The goal at a birthing center is to make labor and birth more natural, with less monitoring and fewer routine medical procedures. Some pain medication may be available, but epidurals are not. Some birthing centers are next to or affiliated with hospitals so that, if necessary, you can be transferred quickly. Birthing centers are an option for low-risk pregnancies.

At home A home birth attended by midwives and perhaps a doula is an option for women who want to give birth in familiar surroundings. However, a home birth is only advised for women who have low-risk pregnancies and for those with no preexisting medical problems. In Canada, home births are still controversial in some medical communities. However, the Society of Obstetricians and Gynecologists of Canada supports the rights of women to choose where to give birth, and the integration of midwives into the maternity care team.

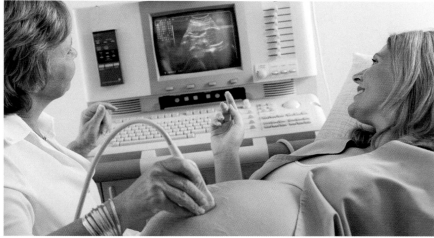

Hospitals have clinics where you may go for routine scans; (top). **Midwives** provide care at doctors' offices, maternity centers, or their own practices (bottom left). **Ob/gyns** see patients in their offices and may share care with midwives or family doctors.

Your care providers

Several different health-care professionals will care for you during pregnancy and labor, and in the postpartum period:

Ob/gyns provide the vast majority of care for women in pregnancy, labor, and the postpartum period. They're specially trained to handle all phases of pregnancy and postpartum recovery. If you have a preexisting condition that could complicate your pregnancy, like diabetes or high blood pressure, or if you're pregnant with twins, you should see an ob/gyn. Special doctors known as high-risk obstetricians, or maternal-fetal medicine specialists, may see you for some appointments if you have a very high-risk pregnancy, such as a baby diagnosed with a serious medical condition or a history of pregnancy complications or repeated loss.

General practitioners (GPs) may also provide antenatal, labor, and postpartum care.

Midwives can provide care for women with low-risk pregnancies throughout all phases of pregnancy and the postpartum period. Registered midwives may work in a practice with ob/gyns but primarily practice on their own. They are accredited by the College of Midwives in their province or territory.

Pediatricians are doctors with special training in the health of babies and children. All babies born in a hospital have a newborn checkup by a pediatrician or family doctor before being discharged.

Neonatologists specialize in the care of newborns with problems.

Prenatal care options

103

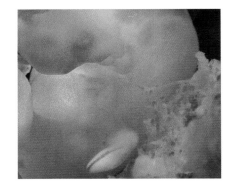

227 days to go...

YOUR BABY TODAY

The upper and lower limb buds that will form the legs and arms are clearly visible by now. The baby's head is still curled over the chest, but the beginnings of ears can just be detected as raised areas at the base of the head.

Your baby's facial features are beginning to develop and over the next few weeks will become much more defined.

AS A MATTER OF FACT

According to one study, eating apples during pregnancy could reduce the risk of your child developing asthma.

Following a Mediterranean diet may have the same effect. Researchers found that the babies of mothers who ate plenty of fish, olive oil, fruit, and vegetables were up to 30 percent less likely to wheeze as well as 50 percent less likely to develop skin allergies.

Your baby has ears! Low down, near the jaw line, the ears form, each arising from six small mounds, fusing together to give your baby his unique and individual ear shape. As the face and jaw forms and your baby's neck extends moving away from the chest wall, the ears migrate upward; they will come to lie at the same level as his eyes by 11 weeks.

The lips and nose are now beginning to take shape. To form the upper lip, two separate ridges of tissue grow from each side of your baby's face to fuse with the small piece of tissue in the midline extending downward beneath the nose (the grooved part of the upper lip).

At around this stage, your baby's small and large bowel lengthen. Because they have insufficient room to expand inside the still very curled-up embryo, the intestines appear as a bulge on the surface of the abdominal wall. This bulge is covered by a membrane, into which the umbilical cord becomes attached. The bowel will continue to grow in this embryonic sac until 11–12 weeks when it will be reabsorbed into the abdominal cavity, leaving just the surface attachment of the cord.

FOCUS ON... SAFETY

Cooking with care

Scrupulous food hygiene is important in pregnancy for a number of reasons. Firstly, your immune system is under extra pressure during pregnancy, making you more susceptible to food poisoning. Secondly, there's a risk that food-borne illnesses can affect the health of your baby, so it pays to be cautious. Do the following:

■ **Wash your hands carefully** and regularly, with hot water and soap. Make sure they are completely dry before preparing food, since bacteria spread more easily on damp skin.

■ **Keep food in your fridge** until you plan to prepare it, and cook it thoroughly before serving.

■ **Serve food piping hot,** since germs can multiply in lukewarm conditions.

■ **Refrigerate leftovers** immediately, and reheat them well, only once.

■ **Thoroughly clean your hands,** implements, and work surfaces.

■ **Set the correct temperature** on your fridge and freezer.

Make time for preparation and take the precaution of washing all fruit and vegetables. Keep raw foods away from cooked foods.

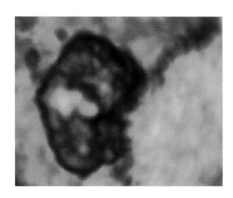

226 days to go...

YOUR BABY TODAY

This ultrasound scan of the baby in side view shows that the head (at top) is relatively large compared to the rest of the body. The lighter, elongated area at the center of the baby's darker body is an upper arm bud.

Life goes on even though you're pregnant, but make sure you seek the right help if you're becoming overly tired.

ASK A... DOCTOR

I'm going on an overseas, pre-paid vacation to a tropical climate. Can I have vaccinations now that I'm pregnant? In principle, it's a good idea to avoid traveling to parts of the world where there is a high risk of disease unless you really need to. Local health care might not be adequate and food and water may be contaminated, which poses dangerous risks.

If it isn't possible to change your destination or postpone your vacation, be aware of the following:

■ **Oral vaccines** to protect against yellow fever, typhoid, polio, and anthrax, for example, are contraindicated during pregnancy, although your doctor may decide that if you need to travel, the risk of having the vaccine is lower than the risks associated with contracting the disease.

■ **Some vaccines** (polio and typhoid) are safe when given by injection. Mefloquine tablets, taken to prevent malaria, are considered safe after week 16.

■ **It's safe to have a tetanus** vaccination if you're pregnant; check whether yours is up-to-date.

You may find work a strain at times. If you have symptoms, such as fatigue, and still haven't told colleagues you're pregnant, it can make for a stressful and day. If you've told some colleagues, or your boss, you're expecting it may be easier but you might feel you have to prove you can still do your job as efficiently as before.

Traveling can be tiring so explore the possibility of doing more flexible hours, so that you can commute when it's less busy. Be reassured that even though you aren't feeling your best, your unborn baby is unlikely to be affected. Do, however, take care of yourself.

If you find that you're struggling to deal with your workload, consider speaking to your boss (you can ask him or her to keep your pregnancy a secret until you are ready to tell), or someone in the human resources department, to give yourself a little breathing space. If you have colleagues who are close friends, lean on them for support in these early weeks.

ARE YOU NESTING ALREADY?

There's nothing like a new arrival to inspire you to get all those do-it-yourself (DIY) jobs done around the home. For most women, the nesting bug occurs in the later weeks of pregnancy, but if you're itching to get your house in order before then, make sure you exercise a little caution.

First of all, avoid putting yourself and your baby at risk: don't stand on tall ladders, and don't bend and crouch for long periods since this may affect your circulation. Avoid contact with oil-based paints, polyurethane (used for flooring), spray paints, turpentine, and other paint removers, and avoid inhaling plaster dust.

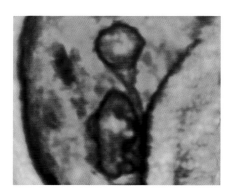

225 days to go...

YOUR BABY TODAY

The yolk sac can be seen floating like a balloon in the amniotic cavity on its fine stalk. As the embryo has drawn nutrition from the yolk sac it has gradually reduced in both size and importance. Meanwhile the placenta (on the right) is becoming established.

If you're planning a vacation, take into account that you may not feel up to a long trip.

BREATHE EASY

Exercise can help keep breathlessness at bay, and increase the efficiency of your heart and lungs (cardiovascular system), helping you to deal with the physical demands of pregnancy now and in later months.

A cardiovascular workout involves increasing your heart rate for at least 20–30 minutes. However, pregnancy is not a time to start training for a marathon; stick to moderate-intensity workouts. A way to test if you are exercising at the right level is to talk while you are working out (see p.161)—if you can't, lower the intensity.

Try doing interval training, which involves alternating five minutes of cardiovascular workouts with five minutes of toning for the upper body (see p.196). Breathe out as you lift the weights, and in as you relax.

Breathing deeply allows oxygen to travel to your vital organs and helps the cardiovascular system to function effectively. During pregnancy, it's important to avoid taking short, shallow breaths and to focus on expanding your rib cage and filling your lungs with air.

You may have planned a vacation before you found out you were pregnant, or just feel like getting away. If you're feeling tired and have morning sickness, however, you may not feel up to traveling too far.

One advantage of going away is being able to spend quality time with your partner and fully embrace the fact that you're going to be parents.

When going on vacation, check with travel insurance companies to see if you can get coverage during pregnancy and check the medical facilities at your destination. If you have prenatal records, take them with you. Some airlines may not accept pregnant women on flights after 36 weeks without a doctor's lettter written within 72 hours of the flight confirming your due date and your fitness to fly.

Relax and take the opportunity for a snooze on the plane trip, but make sure you get up regularly to stretch your legs. It's even more important to keep the blood circulating when you're pregnant.

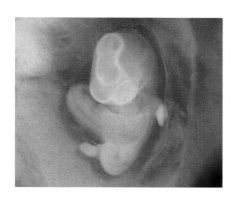

224 days to go...

YOUR BABY TODAY

The head is disproportionately large at this stage. In the center of this image, the underlying structures of the brain can be seen: the forebrain has divided into two and these two halves will become the two cerebral hemispheres of your baby's brain.

You're probably already wondering if you're carrying a boy or a girl, but the physical signs of gender aren't apparent yet.

Although the sex of your baby was determined at the moment of fertilization, it will not yet be apparent whether the embryo is male or female.

At this stage of development, the external genitalia have exactly the same appearance (almost nonexistent). In a girl, no uterus or tubes have formed internally. The ovary in a female embryo and testes in a male embryo are currently just ridges of tissue, without any of the characteristics of either reproductive organ.

Incredibly, your baby's heart has already developed, with four chambers beating at about 160 beats per minute. The common tube leaving the heart has divided into the two main blood vessels: the aorta takes your baby's oxygen-carrying blood to his body and the pulmonary trunk takes his blood to the lungs. Valves within the heart ensure that the blood only travels one way and all of the major blood vessels are now established.

Your baby's eyes appear open because the eyelids have just started to appear and have yet to fuse. In reality, they won't properly open until week 26. Pigment is just starting to accumulate within the retina of the eye. The developing lens is supplied by a single blood vessel in the optic nerve, which will later disappear.

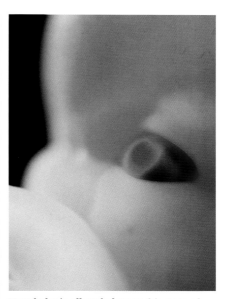

Your baby is all curled up at this stage of development, with her chin on her chest. Her head is quite large due to rapid underlying brain expansion giving the impression of an overhanging forehead.

ASK A... DOCTOR

I'm eight weeks pregnant and have an ear and throat infection. Will I be allowed to take antibiotics? You may be prescribed antibiotics by your doctor since there are some that can be taken during pregnancy. Penicillin-based antibiotics are usually prescribed, or if you are allergic to these your doctor will be able to offer other safe alternatives.

Never take antibiotics that have not been prescribed for you specifically. The following antibiotics should not be taken during pregnancy:

■ **Tetracylines** taken during pregnancy can adversely affect the development of an unborn baby's bones, and may cause some discoloration of the enamel on the baby's teeth.

■ **Streptomycin** can cause damage to the ears of the developing baby and result in hearing loss.

■ **Sulphonamides** can cause jaundice in the baby.

ACTUAL SIZE OF YOUR BABY

At 8 weeks, your baby's crown to rump length is 0.51 in (13 mm).

6 weeks

7 weeks

8 weeks

Your 9th week

YOUR BABY HAS HANDS AND FEET, AND HIS BONES ARE GROWING

During this week, your baby starts to make tiny movements. You won't be aware of this, but it's exciting to think about. On the downside, you could be in the throes of nausea and sickness. However, many women find that the nausea starts to lessen from now on. There are various self-help measures you can take to relieve the sickness, but if it's making life miserable, talk to your doctor.

Your first trimester

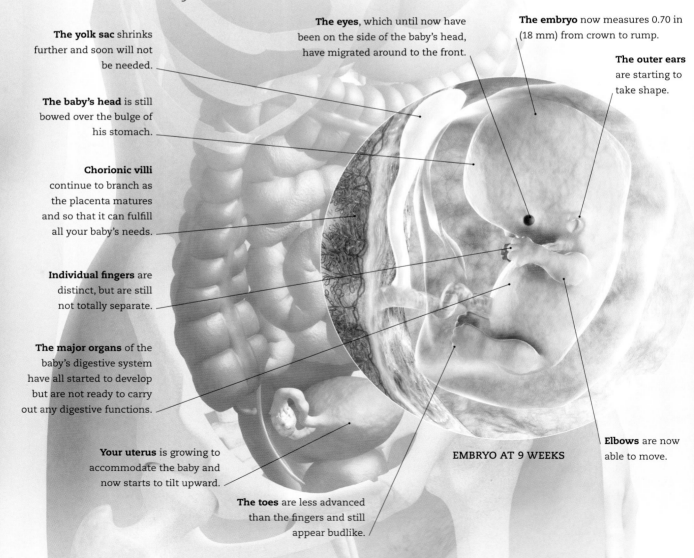

The yolk sac shrinks further and soon will not be needed.

The baby's head is still bowed over the bulge of his stomach.

Chorionic villi continue to branch as the placenta matures and so that it can fulfill all your baby's needs.

Individual fingers are distinct, but are still not totally separate.

The major organs of the baby's digestive system have all started to develop but are not ready to carry out any digestive functions.

Your uterus is growing to accommodate the baby and now starts to tilt upward.

The toes are less advanced than the fingers and still appear budlike.

The eyes, which until now have been on the side of the baby's head, have migrated around to the front.

The embryo now measures 0.70 in (18 mm) from crown to rump.

The outer ears are starting to take shape.

EMBRYO AT 9 WEEKS

Elbows are now able to move.

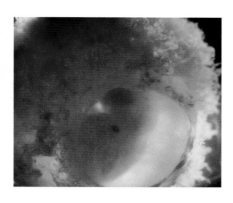

223 days to go...

YOUR BABY TODAY

At this early stage in the pregnancy the placenta is much larger than the fetus. The fetus can just be seen within the amniotic sac. The fronds (white area) on the surface of the sac make up the placenta and at this stage surround nearly all of the amniotic sac.

Not all pregnant women have cravings, but many women do experience a change in their food preferences.

When it comes to being pregnant, it seems your body instinctively knows what you like to eat. Experts are not sure how this can happen but it seems your body has natural protective mechanisms; certain foods are not good for the developing baby so your body turns you away from them; or your body is deficient in certain nutrients, so craves foods that will provide them.

Suddenly you can't stand the thought of food and drinks that you have always loved and find yourself craving things you never previously liked, or you long for bizarre combinations of foods. Aversions and cravings are often associated with nausea. It's common to be turned off by fatty foods since the smell alone can make you feel sick. You may start to dislike the taste or the smell of coffee or tea, cigarettes, and alcohol.

It is common to crave strong-tasting foods such as pickles, which may be due to the fact your taste buds change during pregnancy. What's termed "pica" is an unhealthy craving for bizzare items (see p.121).

You should try to eat healthily, but there are a few foods which should be avoided (see p.17). Otherwise eat whatever combinations you desire—and don't worry about the strange looks you might get in the sandwich shop!

ASK A... NUTRITIONIST

Should I stop adding salt to my food? There is no need to limit salt intake but don't have in excess of the recommended 0.2 oz (6 g) a day.

During pregnancy, your blood and other bodily fluids expand almost 50 percent, an expansion that requires extra water and salt. The majority of salt in the diet comes from processed foods, not from the salt shaker or the salt you add in cooking. To manage your intake, eat whole foods you cook yourself and add your own salt to taste.

FOCUS ON... DADS

Satisfy her cravings

If it's a mom-to-be's responsibility to play host to baby for nine months, it most definitely falls within your dad-to-be's job description to see that your partner gets everything she needs. A word of warning: cravings usually occur the minute the local store has closed, or in the evening when you're relaxing. Forget the pickles and ice cream you've been told to expect. Instead, be prepared for a last-minute dash to the local pizza place, a trek to a 24-hour supermarket that carries organic sour cream-flavored potato chips, beets, or a chocolate doughnut.

You can help by preparing meals and snacks some of the time: if your partner is presented with healthy food lovingly prepared by you, she may be less likely to reach for any unhealthy food she craves.

If an ice cream craving strikes, try to have one spoonful, not the whole container. Pair it with fresh fruit for a healthy combination.

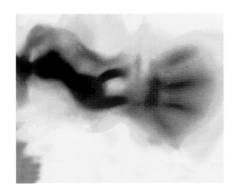

222 days to go...

YOUR BABY TODAY

The baby's hands (seen here) and feet are gradually developing and they are formed of cartilage, not bone at this early stage. In the center left, the fused rays of the hand plate that will become the fingers can be seen. The ribs are in the background.

Who will your baby look like? His unique facial features are beginning to take shape this week.

If you were to have an ultrasound scan this week, it would be possible to recognize several of your baby's facial features.

His eyelids fuse and will remain closed until around the 26th week. The lips have already formed and with the surrounding skin will have the greatest concentration of nerves. The muscular tongue arises from the base of your baby's mouth, but it will be two weeks before the first taste buds appear. The hard palate that forms the roof of the mouth arises from two "shelves" that start to grow, one each side, beneath the tongue; these shelves will lift upward to connect horizontally, allowing the tongue to drop down in to the mouth. Once they have joined together, the septum of the nose grows downward to meet them.

Your baby's tiny tooth buds are in place and this is critical to adequate jaw development. One branch of tooth buds will form the first milk teeth and a separate branch will eventually form the permanent teeth. The milk teeth develop slowly and it will not be until the six month of pregnancy that they acquire their hard enamel coating.

The embryo is still very curled up, with the head resting on the chest. Over the next two weeks as the jaw and neck grow, the head will gradually lift.

If you are in regular contact with young children while you're pregnant, it's even more important that you check your immunity to childhood illnesses.

CHILDHOOD ILLNESSES

Having immunity against common infectious illnesses will protect your unborn baby. You may have natural immunity from having conditions such as chicken pox and fifth disease as a child. You will almost certainly have been vaccinated against mumps and measles, so your unborn baby will be protected from these.

If you are unsure about your immunity or medical history, or think you may have been in contact with any of these infections, contact your doctor immediately for further advice. He or she will be able to do a checkup and provide reassurance.

ASK A... DOCTOR

I work for a dry cleaner. Could the chemicals harm my unborn baby? Concerns about dry-cleaning chemicals stem from research showing that women who operated dry-cleaning machines had a higher risk of miscarriage. If touched or inhaled, some organic (carbon-containing) solvents used in dry-cleaning machines can pass through the placenta and some are thought to increase the risk of miscarriage or birth defects.

Talk to your employer to find out how your duties can be changed for the duration of your pregnancy to limit your contact with organic solvents and industrial chemicals.

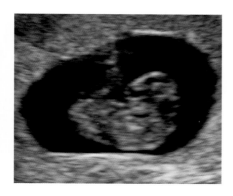

221 days to go...

YOUR BABY TODAY

In a matter of days, your baby's eyes have developed from slight ridges to clear depressions, on each side of the face. The face is developing rapidly at this stage, and your baby's heartbeat would be seen on an ultrasound scan.

It's a few weeks before the hormone responsible for morning sickness subsides, but the nausea will pass soon.

You may be wondering when you'll wake up and no longer feel sick. HCG (human chorionic gonadotrophin) levels, which may be responsible for feelings of nausea will begin to fall in about three weeks' time and most women begin to feel better then. For some women the sickness may continue beyond this time.

You may have just started to feel nauseous or your sickness may have begun weeks ago and now be worse, but by around week 12 you should be over the worst. Nausea that happens daily, especially if it is associated with fatigue, can be very wearing so try to remember that it's temporary.

It's normal to have some morning sickness and you should be able to keep some foods and fluids down. However, for a small minority of pregnant women—about 1 percent—the vomiting is severe, occurring regularly and lasting over a period of weeks. This more serious form of morning sickness is called hyperemesis gravidarum and can lead to dehydration. Hospital treatment with intravenous fluids and anti-nausea drugs may be required to rehydrate you.

Seek advice from your doctor if you're concerned about the amount of times you're vomiting or if you're struggling to keep fluids and food down.

FOCUS ON... HEALTH

Fit—not sick

If you're feeling particularly nauseous, try going for a brisk walk in the fresh air while concentrating on your breathing and posture. Sometimes frequent sips of water help these feelings, and will allow you to exercise longer. Regular exercisers may find that nausea is absent during exercise, although it may resume after the session.

Extreme nausea and vomiting can be a sign of overexercising. Always drink water before, during, and after any physical activity.

ACUPRESSURE WRISTBANDS

A simple solution to help relieve feelings of nausea is to wear acupressure wristbands. Available from pharmacists, these bands have been clinically tested in the treatment of pregnancy-induced nausea. Unlike anti-nausea drugs, they don't have any side effects and are easy to use.

The elastic bands, one worn on each arm, work by applying pressure on the Nei Kuan acupressure point (known as P6). They can be washed and reused as necessary.

AS A MATTER OF FACT

About 70–80 percent of pregnant women suffer from morning sickness.

If you are one of the 20–30 percent who don't, be thankful. You may get anxious if you're not feeling sick because it is such a common symptom, but don't worry and just count yourself lucky.

Your baby's life support system

The placenta links your baby's blood supply to your own and carries out all the functions that your baby can't perform for himself. The placenta is rooted to the lining of your uterus and linked to the baby by the umbilical cord.

HOW SUBSTANCES ARE EXCHANGED IN THE PLACENTA

Inside the placenta

The placenta contains a huge network of tiny projections called chorionic villi that branch out from a thin membrane, the chorion, and contain fetal blood vessels. The chorionic villi are bathed in maternal blood within the intervillous space. Each villus is only one or two cells thick, which allows the transfer of gases and nutrients between the mother and the baby, while ensuring that the two circulations never come into direct contact. Through the process of diffusion, oxygen and nutrients such as glucose, your baby's primary source of energy, from the mother pass into the fetal circulation, and waste products from the baby are picked up and carried away in the mother's bloodstream. The chorionic membrane also acts as a protective barrier, preventing many harmful substances and infections from reaching the baby.

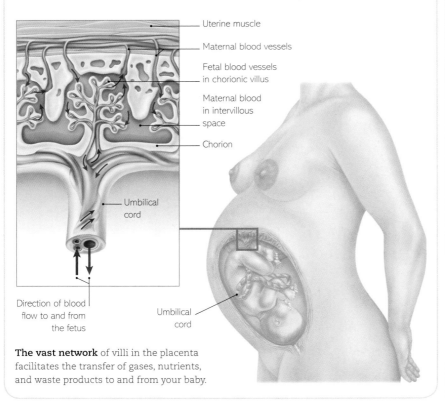

Uterine muscle

Maternal blood vessels

Fetal blood vessels in chorionic villus

Maternal blood in intervillous space

Chorion

Umbilical cord

Direction of blood flow to and from the fetus

Umbilical cord

The vast network of villi in the placenta facilitates the transfer of gases, nutrients, and waste products to and from your baby.

How the placenta develops

The placenta forms from cells in the embryo shortly after the egg implants in the lining of the uterus. Early placental growth is rapid, and at the beginning of the first trimester, the placenta is larger than the baby. However, the baby's growth catches up by 16 weeks, and by the end of pregnancy the baby is almost six times heavier. The final weight of the placenta is between 12 oz (350 g) and 1 lb 5 oz (600 g). Once its structure is complete at the end of the first trimester, it takes on many important functions for the rest of the pregnancy (see opposite).

Growth after the first trimester The placenta grows throughout the second trimester. By the third trimester, growth slows, but placental efficiency continually improves as extra villi (through which substances are exchanged; see left) grow and increase the available surface area of the placenta by nearly fourfold. Cell layers also become thinner so that substances can be exchanged efficiently.

Placental blood flow is massive and many of the changes in your circulation are designed to meet its needs. By term, a tenfold increase in placental blood supply results in a fifth of your circulation supplying the placenta with up to half a liter of blood (almost a pint) each minute.

The aging placenta The placenta ages towards the end of pregnancy, especially after 40 weeks. However, at least 60–80 percent of its function would need to be lost before there were any signs of problems with blood flow in the umbilical cord.

The role of the placenta

The placenta fulfills many essential roles that help sustain your pregnancy and enable your baby to grow and develop.

The exchange of substances. The placenta transports substances to and from your baby, acting as your baby's lungs, kidneys, and digestive system.

To obtain oxygen, the baby's blood cells grab oxygen molecules from your own hemoglobin (the oxygen-carrying subtance in blood). Fetal hemoglobin has a modified structure that makes it bind readily to oxygen. Your baby requires twice as much oxygen weight for weight as your own needs so the transfer of oxygen needs to be efficient. The placenta's enhanced blood supply, large surface area, and the characteristics of fetal hemoglobin all ensure the efficient transfer of oxygen from mother to baby.

As your hemoglobin gives up oxygen, it accepts carbon dioxide molecules. Your lungs breathe out air rich with the baby's carbon dioxide as well as your own and the cycle begins again.

To grow and develop your baby also needs amino acids, the building blocks for proteins, and minerals like calcium and iron and these all pass from your own circulation via the placenta to the baby.

Protecting your baby The placenta protects your baby from infections and harmful substances. Since your baby hasn't encountered any external threats he doesn't yet make protective antibodies known as immunoglobulins that can identify threats, such as viruses or bacteria. Instead he is reliant on the transfer of immunoglobulins from your circulation via the placenta and into his circulation. This means that you are able to protect your baby in the uterus from illnesses such as chickenpox. After your baby is born, the immunglobulins he acquired from you will eventually be lost, which means that later as a child he becomes susceptible to chickenpox.

The umbilical cord

The umbilical cord, which connects your baby to the placenta, contains three vessels: two arteries, which carry blood from the baby to the placenta, and one vein, which carries blood back to the baby. The blood in the arteries contains waste products, such as carbon dioxide, from the baby's metabolism. Carbon dioxide is transferred across the placenta to your bloodstream and then to your lungs, where it's breathed out. Oxygen is transported from red bloods cells in your circulation, across the placenta to the baby in the umbilical vein. In addition to oxygen, the umbilical vein transports nutrients from the placenta to your baby.

The vessels in the umbilical cord have a protective coating called Wharton's jelly, and the cord is coiled like a spring so that the baby is free to move around. The coiling pattern of the cord has usually established itself by week nine and is usually in a counterclockwise direction. However, the cord can coil later, and sometimes isn't established until 20 weeks. The baby's movements seem to encourage the cord to coil.

The cord is usually attached to the center of the placenta, although sometimes it's attached near the edge. Very occasionally, it divides into its separate vessels before finally entering the placenta. The cord is usually under 1 in (1–2 cm) in diameter and 23 in (60 cm) long, which is twice the length needed to ensure that there are no problems at delivery.

After delivery, the cord vessels close by themselves. The arteries close first, helped by their thicker muscular walls. This prevents blood loss to the placenta from your baby. The umbilical vein closes slightly later (starting at 15 seconds, but only completed by 3 or 4 minutes). This allows blood to continue to return to your baby during the first few minutes of life. As a result, many feel that a slight delay before clamping the cord can be beneficial to the baby. There are no nerves within the cord, so cutting the cord after delivery is a painless procedure for your baby.

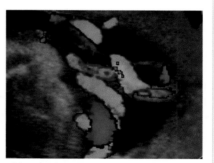

This Doppler scan shows the blood vessels in the umbilical cord. Blood flows through a single vein (blue) and two arteries (red).

Hormone production The placenta produces hormones, such as estrogen and progesterone, that are vital to your baby's well-being and lead to many of the changes in your body during pregnancy.

Heat transfer A baby's high metabolic rate generates heat. The placenta's big surface area and high blood flow disperses heat, controlling the baby's temperature.

Some harmful substances can cross the placenta

For this reason, it's important that you protect your baby by taking medical advice before you use any type of medication during pregnancy.

Your baby's life support system

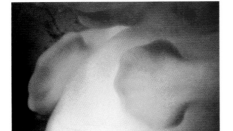

220 days to go...

YOUR BABY TODAY

In the upper limb bud, the flat expansion that will form the hand can be identified. The fingers are becoming more distinct and there will now be the first signs of movement at the elbows.

Your baby's bones are beginning to develop—and they will continue to lengthen from now until his teenage years.

FOCUS ON... NUTRITION

Good mood foods

If being pregnant gets you down at times, try a dietary boost. Happy, relaxed people tend to have high levels of serotonin, a brain chemical that is produced when you consume protein-rich foods. So eat meat (especially turkey), fish (see p.96), legumes, and well-cooked eggs (see p.17).

Eating foods that are rich in vitamin B, such as bananas and avocados, can also help increase your serotonin levels.

You won't be aware of your developing baby's activities

inside the uterus for some months yet, but the fact that his elbows are forming allows him to make some small movements; the wrists do not yet move.

Your baby is looking more human by the day. His vertebrae and ribs are now in place, and his fingers are gradually lengthening. His body is less curled up than it was a few weeks ago.

The skeleton will gradually calcify and harden. With the exception of the cranial skull bones, all your baby's bones have a soft cartilage core that will later be reabsorbed as it is converted into hard bone. This process of hardening, known as ossification, starts in so-called primary ossification centers during the next five weeks of your pregnancy. Within these primary centers, specialized cells form spongy then hard bone as calcium salts are laid down. Within the hard bone is red bone marrow, which in later weeks will become the main producer of the baby's red blood cells.

Secondary ossification centers develop in the second trimester at the ends of each of your baby's bones.

The portion of bone between the hardening primary and secondary centers is known as the growth plate. This plate is responsible for the continued lengthening of your unborn baby's bones.

MORE CHEESE PLEASE

Tired of being told what you can't eat? It is a common myth that eating cheese harms the unborn baby. Only unpasteurized cheeses are potentially dangerous because they increase the risk of listeria (a rare bacterium that can attack the baby). These products may be produced at local cheese stores or dairy farms.

All other types of cheeses pose no danger and are regarded as a good source of calcium.

So, while there are some cheeses you should avoid eating, you can enjoy all of the following, if they're pasteurized:
- Hard cheese, such as Cheddar and Parmesan
- Feta
- Ricotta
- Mascarpone
- Cream cheese
- Mozzarella
- Cottage cheese
- Processed cheese, such as spreads.

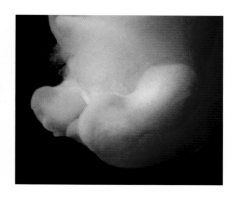

219 days to go...

YOUR BABY TODAY

The development of the baby's lower limbs always lags slightly behind that of the upper limbs. At this stage, the toes are not distinct and the legs are not yet bending at the knee.

It's understandable that your pregnancy will be on your mind. Try to find ways to communicate this to your partner.

At a time when you want to feel close to your partner, you may find that your relationship is changing, and it may be quite fraught with issues. Often men say that their pregnant partners are more sensitive or now react to things differently and that this can be difficult for them to handle.

Your relationship will inevitably change—going through pregnancy together is momentous—but as long as you keep communicating, you will be able to support each other. Being united now will stand you in good stead for the first year of parenting.

During the early stages of pregnancy, your partner may find it hard to relate to the fact that you're expecting a baby; the physical changes to your body won't be that visible at this stage and he is yet to see his baby on a scan. Conversely, you will be very aware of the pregnancy and undergoing many physical and emotional changes.

Your partner may need more time than you to adjust to the idea of becoming a parent. He may be concerned about practical issues, such as the changes to your lifestyle and the financial implications of having a baby. Talking openly to each other can help ease anxieties for you both. Remember, that although many changes are happening to your body, your partner does have feelings and this is a big life change for him too. If you've told your family and close friends about the pregnancy, all the attention may be on you. Your partner may be feeling left out and this is something that often gets worse as the pregnancy progresses and after the baby arrives.

Take time to find out your partner's concerns and look for ways to involve him more in the pregnancy, if that's what he wants. If you have a good support network of friends, encourage him to spend time with male friends who have been through the expectant dad experience.

Support each other as you both go through the different emotions attached to becoming parents. Don't lose sight of your relationship and be understanding of each other's needs.

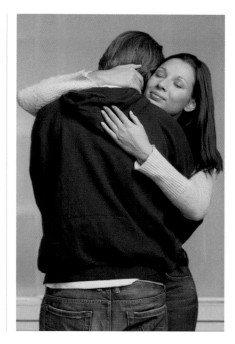

ASK A... MOM

I'm worried we won't have space in our small apartment, but is a house move inadvisable while I'm pregnant? We started the process but thankfully it fell through since it was proving quite stressful, and it's not advisable to deal with those kinds of pressures while you're pregnant. We stayed in our apartment until our baby was one and it was fine. Remember that small babies have very few needs, other than being fed, loved, changed, and stimulated, and much of the paraphernalia that you think you need is unnecessary. If you have room for a crib, a stroller, a drawer for your baby's clothes, and a corner for toys, you'll be fine in a small space for the time being.

115

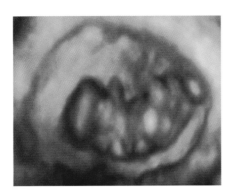

YOU ARE 8 WEEKS AND 6 DAYS

218 days to go...

YOUR BABY TODAY

This 3D ultrasound scan shows a baby lying on its back, in exactly the same orientation as the image opposite. It is just possible to pick out the limb buds on an ultrasound scan taken at this stage.

It's not long until you have your first prenatal appointment and will see your doctor.

In a couple of weeks' time, you will have your initial appointment (see p.129) with the doctor. If you haven't made an appointment for this yet, contact your doctor now to arrange it. You may or may not have a choice of hospitals. If you do have options, talk to women you know locally who have had their babies at those hospitals to find out about their experience. For example, some hospitals may have a birth center attached, and have a less medically managed approach to childbirth.

Start thinking now about the kind of questions you want to ask your doctor. It's a good idea to write these down. Also make a note, in advance, of the key details of your medical history and any pregnancy symptoms.

TACKLING COLDS

Cold medicines contain a variety of ingredients, including antihistamines, that are best avoided in pregnancy. Check the label and talk to your doctor or pharmacist before taking any medications.

Try natural remedies, such as steam inhalations or saline nasal sprays before resorting to medication.

ASK A... PANEL ABOUT HOME BIRTH

It's my first pregnancy. Can I have a home birth?

Midwife: if you're in good health with no complications, giving birth at home is an option. Many women enjoy the experience of giving birth at home, because they may feel more comfortable with familiar surroundings and people. Some women find labor easier when they get into water, either a familiar bathtub at home or a birthing pool that has been purchased or rented.

Find out from your doctor if a home birth is a possibility for you.

Obstetrician: there is no problem with this in general, but take advice from your doctor. You should avoid taking risks. If there is a history of long or complicated labors in your family, your baby is breech or very small, there are issues about the location of the cord or the placenta, you are very overweight or unhealthy, or you suffer from conditions such as diabetes, it might be worth erring on the side of caution. If you have your baby in a hospital, quick and early intervention can take place if needed. You may want to have a home birth; however, it is sensible to listen to the experts. Delivery of a healthy baby is the most important thing.

Mom: I had my first baby at home, and it was wonderful. I was nervous about what might go wrong, but my midwife reassured me that she would be monitoring me, and would get me to the hospital if there was a problem. She also explained I could change my mind if I didn't think things were going well, and go to the hospital for the birth (and some pain relief!).

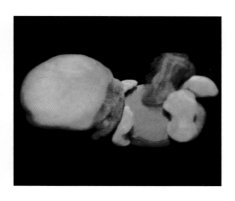

217 days to go...

YOUR BABY TODAY

The baby's hands can be clearly seen here but the fingers are still fused at this stage. The fingers will be completely separate in just one week's time and wrist movement is just about to begin.

By the end of this ninth week, your baby's digestive system is rapidly developing but won't function properly for some time.

Your baby is developing quickly inside the uterus. The simple tube forming along his gut has undergone most changes at the upper end. Now the lower part dilates as the single tube then divides into what will become the rectum at the back and then the bladder and urethra at the front.

Although the mouth is open to the amniotic fluid, there is still a membrane in place, which will disappear in one to two weeks' time. The lower bowel is not yet mature and does not move material along its length.

The remainder of the large bowel and small bowel is still lengthening. The duodenum is the first part of the small bowel and it is still a solid tube. The pancreas, gall bladder, and liver have all formed buds leading off from the upper small bowel, but none are yet contributing any digestive function.

Looking at a computer screen for long periods of time can make headaches—a common side effect of pregnancy—even worse. Take regular breaks and drink plenty of water since being dehydrated can exacerbate headaches.

ASK A... DOCTOR

Since I've been pregnant, I've had terrible headaches. Could computer work be the cause?
Tension headaches and migraines are common in pregnancy, probably due to fluctuating hormones, and it is not uncommon to have severe headaches with prolonged computer use. This could be due to eye strain and the fact that you are immobile, which can cause tension.

Take even more breaks from your computer screen now that you're pregnant. You'll probably find you need more bathroom breaks anyway. If this doesn't help, ask if you can do tasks that don't require computer use for a short time. Headaches are often worse in the first trimester.

ACTUAL SIZE OF YOUR BABY

At 9 weeks your baby's crown to rump length is 0.70 in (18 mm).

7 weeks   8 weeks   9 weeks

Your 10th week

NO LONGER AN EMBRYO, YOUR UNBORN BABY ENTERS A NEW PHASE

This is your baby's last week as an embryo; next week she'll be known as a fetus. Her major organs are in place, although by no means in full working order. There's a long way to go yet and her body systems will continue to mature for the rest of pregnancy, and beyond. The most noticeable difference to your body will be in your breasts. You may well have gone up a cup size—or more.

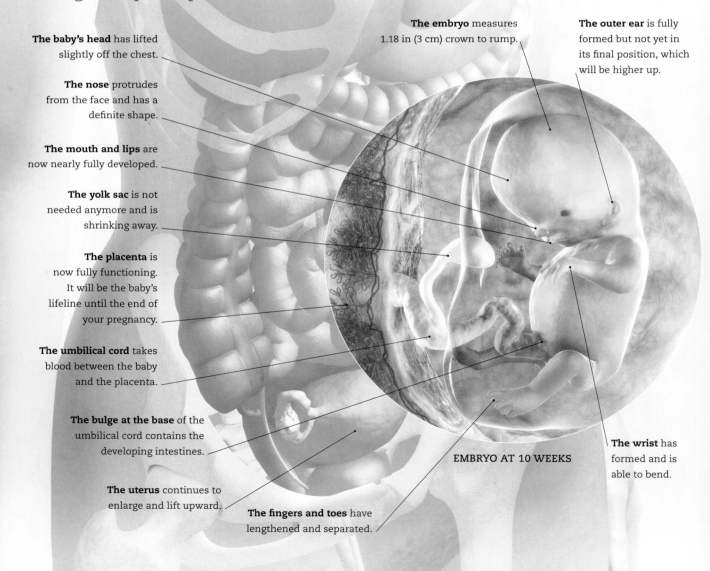

The baby's head has lifted slightly off the chest.

The nose protrudes from the face and has a definite shape.

The mouth and lips are now nearly fully developed.

The yolk sac is not needed anymore and is shrinking away.

The placenta is now fully functioning. It will be the baby's lifeline until the end of your pregnancy.

The umbilical cord takes blood between the baby and the placenta.

The bulge at the base of the umbilical cord contains the developing intestines.

The uterus continues to enlarge and lift upward.

The fingers and toes have lengthened and separated.

The embryo measures 1.18 in (3 cm) crown to rump.

The outer ear is fully formed but not yet in its final position, which will be higher up.

The wrist has formed and is able to bend.

EMBRYO AT 10 WEEKS

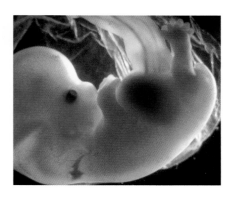

216 days to go...

YOUR BABY TODAY

At about seven weeks, the human embryo measures about 1.2 in (3 cm). Most of the primitive organ systems are formed: the arms and legs have budded; the retina of the eye, and the nose, can be seen. The large dark mass is the enlarged liver.

Your baby's welfare will be your main concern, but be reassured that, however you're feeling, she'll be getting sustenance.

You may be very conscious of your health and well-being at this time but be reassured that even if you've felt unwell during this first trimester, your baby will have been taking what she needs from you: you have internal reserves of various minerals and substances, such as iron, and will still be absorbing some nutrients from what you eat. However, if you're concerned about the amount of vitamins and minerals you're consuming through your diet, for the sake of your own health you could take a prenatal vitamin supplement. Remember, you should still be taking folic acid supplements and eating folate-rich foods (see p.35).

There is no cause for concern if you do not put on any weight in the first trimester, or even if you lose a bit of weight. The majority of weight gain takes place in the second and third trimesters (see p.99).

If you're vomiting a lot and struggling to keep food down (see p.111), don't hesitate to see your health care provider.

FOCUS ON... YOUR BODY

Your changing breasts

The changes to your breasts you will be noticing are caused by both an increased blood supply and a rise in pregnancy hormones, particularly in the first 12 weeks.

Before your pregnancy was confirmed you may have felt tingling sensations (especially in the nipple area) as the blood supply increased.

- **As early as 6–8 weeks,** your breasts will have become larger and more tender and may have begun to look different on the surface, with threadlike veins starting to appear.
- **At around 8–12 weeks,** the nipples darken and can become more erect.
- **As early as the 16th week** of pregnancy, colostrum, the first milk, may leak from your breasts.

THE LOWDOWN

He's "pregnant" too

Can your partner ever really understand what you're going through? According to a recent study, some dads don't need a fake pregnancy belly to empathize. Known as Couvade syndrome, symptoms experienced by expectant fathers ranged from morning sickness to backaches, mood swings, and food cravings. Although, interestingly, often it was the woman claiming her partner had these symptoms.

Couvade is thought to happen because men are so deeply involved in the pregnancy. Others believe it could be jealousy (you're getting all the attention) or guilt that he's responsible for your condition and therefore your symptoms.

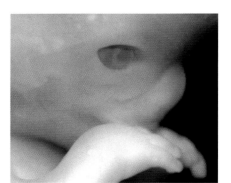

215 days to go...

YOUR BABY TODAY

The baby now begins to bend her wrists. The natural position is for the limbs to be slightly bent at all joints, especially in the early stages. There is a more distinct neck area as the baby's head is now slightly lifted off the chest.

The muscular diaphragm that will eventually enable your baby to breathe—and hiccup—is developing now.

As your baby's lungs develop in the chest, there is nothing to separate them from the stomach, liver, and bowel in what will later become her abdominal cavity.

In adults, the chest is separated from the abdomen by the muscular diaphragm. When we breathe, the diaphragm moves downward and the ribs expand outward. This process allows air to enter the lungs.

Your baby's diaphragm forms from four in-folds of tissue. First seen at around this week of pregnancy, these folds gradually expand inward, fusing together and closing the space by the end of this week.

In the center of the diaphragm there are openings for the esophagus to the stomach, main artery to the body—the aorta, and main vein returning blood from the lower body, the inferior vena cava. As your pregnancy progresses, muscle fibers gradually strengthen your baby's diaphragm, which later allows her to make breathing movements.

The nuchal translucency screening is a scan. It measures the width of the skin behind the baby's neck to assess if excess fluid has collected there—if a high level is found, it may indicate a greater risk of Down syndrome. Nuchal translucency is the most accurate way to screen for Down syndrome.

FOCUS ON... TWINS

Twin tests

If you're expecting twins or more, blood-based screening tests for Down syndrome can mislead, since they rely on measuring the amounts of circulating AFP (alfa-fetoprotein) and other markers, which are present in much higher levels when there's more than one baby. That's why your best bet for screening is the nuchal translucency test from 11–14 weeks (see right).

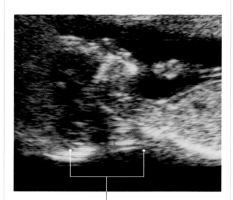

Red area shows the fluid under the skin at the back of the baby's neck.

TIME TO THINK ABOUT

Screening and diagnostic tests

It's useful to be aware of the screening tests (see pp.142–3) and diagnostic tests (see pp.152–3) that will be available in the weeks to come. Your doctor will talk through the pros and cons of having each test. Some abnormalities may be detected at the 18–22 week scan.

■ **Screening tests:** these tests identify the "risk factor" for a particular condition, but do not confirm that your baby definitely has a condition. For example, a screening test for Down syndrome may give your baby a risk factor of 1:200. This means that your baby has a 1 in 200 chance of being affected by Down syndrome, but it does not mean that he actually has the condition.
■ **Diagnostic tests:** if screening tests reveal your baby has a high risk factor for a chromosomal abnormality, you will be offered a diagnostic test, such as amniocentesis or chorionic villus sampling (see pp.152–3), which gives a definite result as to whether or not a condition is present.

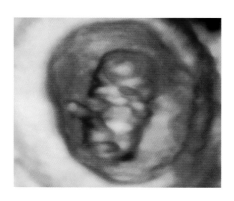

214 days to go...

YOUR BABY TODAY

The shoulders, elbows, and wrists are flexed leaving the hands in front of the face. It's far too early to be aware of them but several fetal movements will start to become apparent on an ultrasound scan at this stage.

You don't need to shop for a maternity wardrobe just yet, but it might be time to purchase some bigger bras.

If your normal bras are starting to feel a little uncomfortable, it's time to go for a fitting. If you have not done so already, get yourself measured professionally. Wearing a good and supportive bra during pregnancy is essential to prevent backaches and sagging breasts.

Whenever you feel you need a new bra, get measured properly to ensure that you're wearing the right size. Although your breasts may be growing very quickly at this time, you should find that by the end of the first trimester the growth has stabilized. There is then unlikely to be much more breast growth until you're in your third trimester and after the baby is born.

Wearing underwire bras during pregnancy is not recommended because they can dig into the developing breast tissue and damage it, and may even cause problems with milk production; the wires digging into the skin can also be uncomfortable. Non-underwire bras with wide supportive straps, such as sports bras, are good in pregnancy.

Look for maternity bras that double as nursing bras, which unhook at the front, for after the birth. There are some very pretty and feminine styles available.

AS A MATTER OF FACT

Pica means craving inedible substances and comes from the Latin for magpie, a bird that scavenges indiscriminately.

If you like crunching coal or sniffing your hot-water bottle, you have pica. While licking the toothpaste is fairly harmless, you should resist eating toxic items such as chalk, glue, and soap. Pica could be a sign that your diet is deficient in some way, so seek advice. Taking an iron or vitamin supplement could help.

FOCUS ON... NUTRITION

Vegan needs

If you are a vegan and pregnant, you may have to work a little harder than most women to get the right nutrients. You need to make sure you obtain adequate B12 and since there are no natural sources of vitamin B12, it needs to be obtained from fortified foods such as:
- Yeast extracts
- Vegetable stock
- Veggie burgers
- Textured vegetable protein.

You also need zinc, an important nutrient in pregnancy—necessary for growth and energy and supporting the immune system. Zinc can be found in the following foods:
- Beans
- Legumes
- Nuts
- Seeds—pumpkin seeds are a particularly rich source.

Like most vegans, you probably already eat many of these foods.

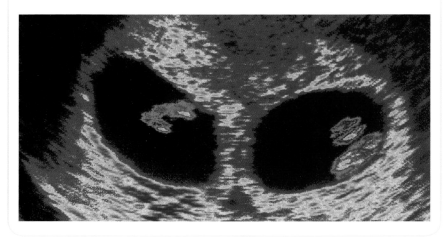

213 days to go...

YOUR BABY TODAY

The baby's facial features are becoming more distinctive by this stage. The very fine eyelids have now completely fused over the developing eye and will remain closed until approximately the 26th week of pregnancy.

Just as you've become used to the idea you're pregnant, you may discover that you're carrying more than one baby.

Do you have an instinct that you're having twins? Some women, even very early in pregnancy, suspect they're carrying more than one baby simply because they feel "more pregnant." Signs of a multiple pregnancy include highly sensitive breasts, and extreme morning sickness and fatigue. In a multiple pregnancy, your uterus might also be larger than expected. Your doctor may be able to feel it rising into your lower belly from this week, instead of from 12 weeks.

Whether or not you suspect anything, the first ultrasound scan (see p.137) will show definitely if you are carrying more than one baby.

FOCUS ON... TWINS

The shocking news

The news that you're having two or more babies may not always be delivered with the greatest tact. For instance, the sonographer may look at the scan and say that "something needs checking." This sounds worrying, of course, but remember, he or she is only being cautious before giving you the life-changing news. The sonographer may also be checking your twins for size, to rule out any major problems. Once this is done, however, there are likely to be hearty congratulations.

ASK A... MOM

I'm delighted we're having twins but how will I manage? I felt the same when I was expecting and had so many worries—"Will I be able to breast-feed two babies? How many cribs will I need?" At first, your head is likely to be spinning with these thoughts, as you get used to the idea of your twin pregnancy.

To give yourself time to come to terms with the news, you may prefer to keep it to yourselves for a few weeks. What you'll find is that family and friends react differently. Responses can range from pure joy (usually from thrilled grandparents) to envy or a bit of scaremongering (from friends and strangers).

We found it helpful to talk to others who were expecting twins or who were already parents to twins. Visit the website of Multiple Births Canada to find a local group.

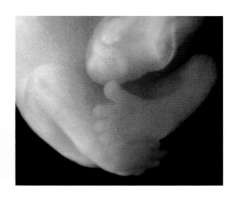

212 days to go...

YOUR BABY TODAY

The lower limbs are now held flexed at the hip and knee joints, leading to a slightly crossed-legs position. The separate toes can be distinguished. Further growth of the thigh and shin bones will bring the foot length into proportion with the rest of the leg.

One of the downsides of pregnancy is being at greater risk of urinary tract infections, so you need to be aware of the signs.

It's important to be on the lookout for any signs of a urinary tract infection while you're pregnant. While it's not very serious, and can be easily treated, it's a complication you can do without.

An infection may cause you to urinate more frequently, but this is also a symptom of early pregnancy so can be hard to spot. If, however, you also have stinging or discomfort when you actually urinate, lower abdominal pain, or even blood in the urine you may have developed a urinary tract infection. These infections are very common in women in general, because the urethra (tube which carries urine from the bladder to the outside) is very close to the anus and so bacteria do not have far to travel to create an infection.

In pregnancy, there are high levels of the hormone progesterone; this relaxes the tubes of the urinary system making it even easier for bacteria to enter and infect the bladder or even the kidneys. It is very important that if you have the symptoms of a urinary tract infection that your doctor tests your urine. In general, urinary tract infections are easily treatable in pregnancy. If there is an infection, you will be prescribed antibiotics that are safe to take in pregnancy. The infection must be treated because, if left, it may cause damage to your kidneys.

STAYING IN SHAPE

If you were a regular exerciser prior to becoming pregnant, it is important to continue with some form of exercise. Stopping entirely, just because you're pregnant, would be a shock to your fit body.

There are some contraindications to exercising (see p.18), but if you have clearance from your doctor, take the following steps to ensure that you are continuing to exercise safely and effectively, and getting all the benefits from your program without putting you or your baby at risk.

■ **Continue with activities,** such as jogging, and swimming, as long as you feel comfortable.

■ **Listen to your body** very carefully—look for signs that you should slow down or take a break.

■ **Get adequate rest** between workouts, and drink water before, during, and after all forms of exercise.

■ **Exercise at a moderate level—** you should be able to do the talk test (see page 161).

■ **Keep to low-impact** and low-risk activities (avoid sports that involve contact and the risk of falling).

■ **Wear the right clothing:** cotton will enable your body to dissipate heat, and a supportive sports bra is vital for your growing breasts, especially if you're jogging.

If you're used to bicycling, switch to a stationary bike at the gym during pregnancy. It's best to avoid activities that can lead to falls, such as biking outside.

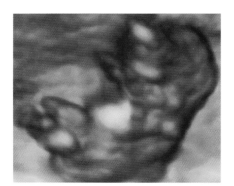

211 days to go...

YOUR BABY TODAY

The umbilical cord widens where it enters the baby's abdomen. This bulge is necessary to accommodate the bowel that is forming underneath at this stage of development. The bones of the head are not yet fully formed.

Your baby's organ systems are now present, in a basic form, so at this point she changes from being an embryo to a fetus.

The early embryonic period is complete at the end of this week, and it is the start of the fetal period. The development of the embryo was characterized by the three cell lines each developing into their own types of tissues and organs, as it grew from a flat disk of cells into a human shape. Many of the changes took place concurrently, but it was the heart, circulation, and nervous systems that developed initially with the gut, limbs, and face development following.

During next week (your 11th week), your baby's kidneys and genital system will undergo their most rapid development. All your baby's organs need to mature fully, and many of them, such as the brain, lungs, and kidneys, will continue to mature throughout pregnancy and after birth.

During this ninth week, your baby's facial features are becoming more recognizable. The ears will take on their final shape, although they are still positioned low.

The eyes which started on the side of the face start to move more centrally, the nose is visible, and the head achieves a more rounded contour.

FOCUS ON... NUTRITION

Vegetarian mom-to-be

A vegetarian diet can be safe and healthy in pregnancy. Lacto-ovo vegetarians, those who consume dairy products, usually have no trouble getting enough nutrients, though they should be careful to eat a varied diet rich in whole grains, beans, legumes, fruit, and vegetables, in order to obtain the proper mix of amino acids, vitamins, and minerals.

Vegetarians also need to obtain enough, as well as complete, protein since vegetarian sources tend to be lower than animal proteins. An intake of 2 oz (60 g) of protein is needed daily in pregnancy, which for vegetarians usually means that a protein source be included in all three meals, as well as a protein-containing snack.

In addition, vegetarians need to obtain all 23 essential amino acids, since vegetarian proteins don't usually have all of these in any one source. To obtain all 23 amino acids, eating a variety of protein types at several meals will usually do the trick. It is not necessary for each meal to contain all 23, since the body can store them over several meals. If you're vegan, see p.121.

AS A MATTER OF FACT

A new noninvasive test to detect chromosomal disorders could soon be available.

This could require simply a sample of blood from the pregnant woman, unlike current tests that require a needle to be inserted into the uterus.

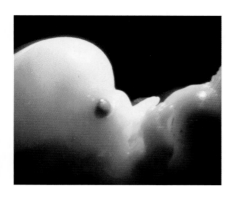

210 days to go...

YOUR BABY TODAY

The bones of the front of the skull are starting to grow over the baby's forehead and harden from cartilage to bone. The forehead is still very prominent and the top of the head still very flexible to accommodate the baby's rapidly developing brain.

The placenta is rapidly developing and once it's fully formed, will supply all your baby's needs.

FOCUS ON... NUTRITION

Refreshing melons

Staying hydrated is essential throughout pregnancy. A good tip is to eat fruit that is high in water. Water contained in fruit is easily absorbed into the body, because fruit contains natural sugars that draw water into the bloodstream. Melons—watermelon, cantaloupe, and honeydew—are naturally high in water. In addition, their mellow and less acidic nature make them well tolerated in pregnancy.

In addition to staying hydrated, by eating melons you will get some extra folate, as well as other vitamins and nutrients. Try combining melons with cottage cheese or yogurt, sprinkled with granola, for a light meal, or blend them into a nutritious smoothie.

A milestone in your baby's development—the placenta takes over from the yolk sac to provide your baby with nutrients. Just like your baby, the placenta has needed to grow and develop a circulation to support the ever-increasing demands that are being placed on it.

One week into the pregnancy, the placenta formed a distinct inner and outer layer of cells that gradually

ASK A... DOCTOR

What is meant by Rhesus negative? Red blood carries a positive or negative Rhesus factor (Rh-factor). Problems arise if a Rh-negative woman carries a Rh-positive baby who has inherited the Rh-positive status from the father. If the mother's blood comes into contact with the baby's during delivery, she may produce antibodies against it.

This may cause problems in subsequent pregnancies when a mother's antibodies attack the cells of another Rh-positive baby, which can lead to severe anemia and heart failure in the baby after the birth. You will be given Rh immune-globulin to combat this.

penetrated the lining of the uterus, with fingerlike fronds. You may have noticed a very slight bleed at this implantation stage (see pp.67). More and more fronds spread out into the lining of the uterus, which itself undergoes a transformation process that enables each frond or villus to be bathed by small pools of maternal blood, enabling oxygen and nutrient transfer to take place.

Up until now, this blood flow has been limited by plugs of tissue, but at this stage of pregnancy these plugs begin to disappear. This means the placenta is sufficiently developed to withstand the pressure of maternal blood on each delicate villous. Villi will continue to branch out until around 30 weeks of pregnancy.

ACTUAL SIZE OF YOUR BABY

After 10 weeks your baby's crown to rump length is 1.2 in (3 cm).

9 weeks

10 weeks

Your 11th week

YOU'LL NOW BE SETTING UP THE HEALTH CARE THAT WILL SUPPORT YOU OVER THE COMING MONTHS

Your baby is now unmistakeably human and is undergoing many sophisticated changes, such as development of the sense organs. To mark his new status, he's now called a fetus. If pregnancy hasn't seemed quite real to you so far, it soon will. It's time to get down to such practicalities as your first prenatal checkup. Procedures such as ultrasound scans and blood tests are about to become part of your normal pregnancy routine.

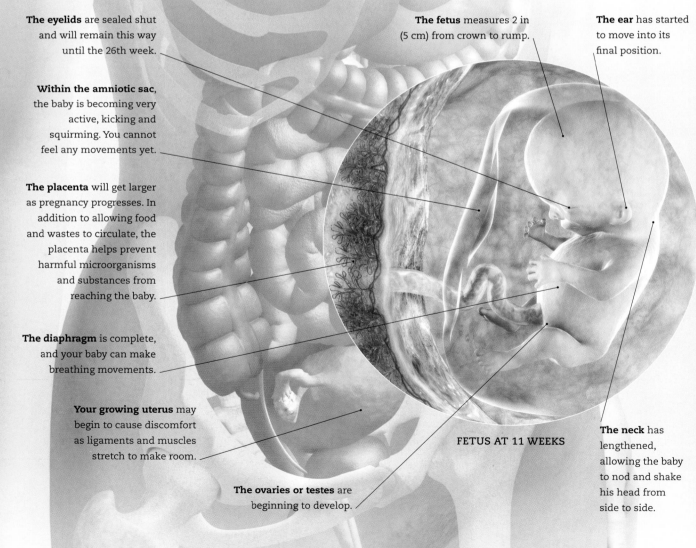

The eyelids are sealed shut and will remain this way until the 26th week.

Within the amniotic sac, the baby is becoming very active, kicking and squirming. You cannot feel any movements yet.

The placenta will get larger as pregnancy progresses. In addition to allowing food and wastes to circulate, the placenta helps prevent harmful microorganisms and substances from reaching the baby.

The diaphragm is complete, and your baby can make breathing movements.

Your growing uterus may begin to cause discomfort as ligaments and muscles stretch to make room.

The fetus measures 2 in (5 cm) from crown to rump.

The ear has started to move into its final position.

The neck has lengthened, allowing the baby to nod and shake his head from side to side.

The ovaries or testes are beginning to develop.

FETUS AT 11 WEEKS

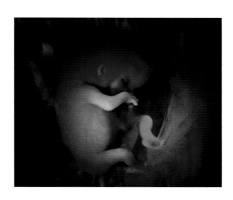

209 days to go...

YOUR BABY TODAY

In this side view of a fetus, the right ear and eye are just visible and the right hand and leg can be seen in characteristically bent positions. The reddish, tubelike structure, to the right of the image, is the umbilical cord.

Your prenatal care begins with your first appointment, where you will get to talk with your ob/gyn about your pregnancy care.

You should have your first prenatal appointment around now. The exact timing of it will vary depending on when your doctor sees pregnant patients for the first time. This is the first time you will see your ob/gyn during pregnancy. Unless your doctor has a solo practice (see p.91), your prenatal team is likely to consist of several doctors who will take care of you throughout your pregnancy.

The purpose of this appointment is for a doctor to obtain your medical history, provide information, and plan your care for pregnancy and the birth. It's also an opportunity for you to ask any questions you may have and discuss the schedule for appointments, blood tests, scans, and prenatal classes. You will be given booklets, information leaflets, and important contact telephone numbers.

AS A MATTER OF FACT

Midwife comes from the anglo-saxon word "mit wif," meaning "with woman."

A midwife's role is to respect the ability of a woman to give birth independently, and to only intervene when it is essential to do so.

The doctor will ask you about your medical history; your family's medical history; your partner and your partner's family's medical history; about any previous pregnancies you have had; and how this pregnancy has been so far.

Your answers will help the doctor identify factors that may affect your pregnancy, for example if there is a family history of preeclampsia (see p.474). The doctor will also do some health tests, such as urine tests, at this and other prenatal appointments.

At your prenatal appointments you will have routine checks, including taking your blood pressure. It's the doctor's job to take care of your health throughout pregnancy.

ASK A... DOCTOR

How should I decide which tests I want? Your doctor will give you lots of information regarding tests and it is up to you to decide whether you want them. There are two different types: screening tests (see pp.142–3) and diagnostic tests (see pp.152–3). The goal of screening tests is to figure out the risk of there being a problem—based on the result, you may be advised to have a follow-up diagnostic test.

Most women opt to have the screening tests, but it's worth considering how far you would continue with the process. For example, if you had a high-risk result from the screening test, would you opt to have a diagnostic test? If you did, and the results of that were positive, would you want to continue with the pregnancy?

Such considerations are difficult but important. For example, if you know that, no matter what, you and your partner would want to continue with the pregnancy then you may decide not to have a test, or decide to have the test so that you can prepare yourself for a baby with potential problems.

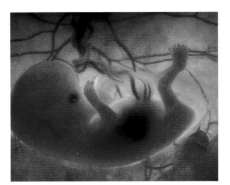

206 days to go...

YOUR BABY TODAY

The umbilical cord gradually becomes more coiled as the pregnancy progresses—as seen here on the left of the image. This coiling is thought to occur because of the many movements the embryo makes.

Your baby's limbs are more developed now, enabling him to move, and his hands and fingers can be clearly seen on a scan.

Your baby takes on a more human form as his neck lengthens and his head is seen as separate from his body. The head is still about half the total length of your baby. The length of your baby can be measured on an ultrasound by measuring the distance between your baby's head (crown) and his bottom (rump). This is noted as the CRL (crown-rump length) measurement. The head is also measured: this is the biparietal diameter (BPD), which is the distance between the two parietal bones on each side of the baby's head.

Now that the neck is more developed and all the limb joints have formed, your baby can begin to make several movements. The completed diaphragm allows for breathing movements. In the gut, your baby's duodenum now opens up along its length, the small bowel starts to rotate and prepares to re-enter the abdominal cavity.

Within your baby's mouth, the hard palate has formed; the relatively large tongue makes it easier for your baby to move amniotic fluid through the nostrils rather than through his mouth with each breath.

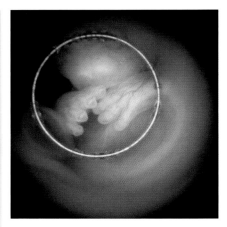

This endoscopic image, obtained by passing a fine light-emitting tube into the uterus, shows the hands obscuring the fetus's face.

TIME TO THINK ABOUT

Nuchal fold screening

At around 11 weeks of pregnancy, you may be offered a nuchal translucency screening. This test assesses the risk of Down syndrome by measuring the width of the fold of skin behind your baby's neck to see if any excess fluid has collected there.

■ **The nuchal fold scan** is considered to be at least 60 percent accurate. If your doctor offers you a blood test (PAPP-A—see p.142) with the scan, it becomes 85–90 percent accurate. When the nasal bone is measured, the accuracy rises to 95 percent.
■ **If the results** show a high risk, another test (see pp.152–3) is offered.

FOCUS ON... TWINS

Double the trouble

Since your body is growing two or more babies, there will be physical effects. But there is a positive side: Since your growing size and hormones are the cause, these symptoms are often worse if the babies are doing well.
■ **In the first three months,** your heart has to work harder to pump more fluid around your body, which can lead to a greater feeling of fatigue.
■ **Morning sickness** can be more severe because you have higher amounts of pregnancy hormones.

Mention severe symptoms if you're suffering, but remember these symptoms are not serious. You may be seen earlier if you suspect you're having twins, and will go on to have more prenatal appointments and ultrasound scans. You may be asked to limit activities like travel and exercise as your pregnancy progresses.

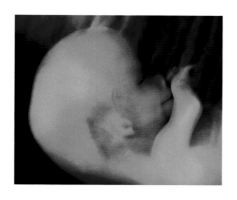

205 days to go...

YOUR BABY TODAY

The external ear is now more clearly seen as it makes its way to its final position. The eyes are also much closer to their final position and the neck continues to lengthen. The baby will often bring his hands up to his mouth, providing important sensory feedback.

Healthy teeth and gums are essential in pregnancy, so brush thoroughly and make regular dental appointments.

Make sure you're taking care of your teeth and gums. The hormone progesterone causes gum tissue to soften and it's therefore more likely to bleed when brushed and to become infected. Unfortunately, there may be a link between gum disease and premature birth. The bacteria caused by periodontal disease release toxins into the mother's bloodstream, which reach the placenta and can affect the baby's growth. The infection can also lead to the production of inflammatory chemicals that can cause the cervix to dilate and trigger contractions.

To keep your mouth healthy during your pregnancy, brush your teeth twice a day with a fluoride toothpaste and floss your teeth every day. Be sure to see your dentist regularly for cleanings as recommended. If you need antibiotics to treat an infection, make sure to remind your dentist you are pregnant so that medications that are safe in pregnancy are prescribed.

If your dentist needs to take X-rays of your mouth, he or she will protect your baby by covering your abdomen with a lead apron.

Make sure that you brush your teeth regularly, or even more often than usual, and ensure that you floss well. This will reduce the risk of your gums being infected.

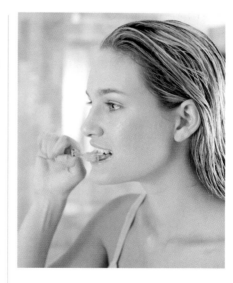

ASK A... DOCTOR

Why am I getting more vaginal discharge since being pregnant? In pregnancy, the layer of muscle in the vagina thickens, and cells lining the vagina multiply in response to an increase in the pregnancy hormone estrogen. These changes prepare the vagina for childbirth. As a side effect, the extra cells mean that there is an increase in vaginal discharge, known as leucorrhea.

If you feel sore or itchy in the vaginal area and the discharge is anything other than cream or white, or smells, your doctor will need to take a swab to rule out infection.

Some infections, such as yeast, cause an abnormal discharge. They are common in pregnancy and are easily treated. Even if you've self-treated yeast infections before, call your doctor for advice this time. She'll likely recommend medication that's applied vaginally, but if she determines that you have bacterial vaginosis, oral medication may be required.

AS A MATTER OF FACT

A US study found that, on average, those with one child were missing two or three teeth, and those with four or more children were missing between four and eight teeth.

So the old wives' tale that "You will lose a tooth for every child" could have some basis in truth. It might be because of the hormonal changes that occur during pregnancy that can cause gum disease (see above).

Your 11th week

204 days to go...

YOUR BABY TODAY

This is the umbilical cord of an 11-week-old fetus. The cord is a strand of tissue that contains the two spiraling arteries that carry blood to the placenta and a vein that returns blood to the developing baby.

Has sex been the last thing on your mind, or have you noticed an increase in your libido? It seems all women are different.

ASK A... NUTRITIONIST

Is it safe to drink herbal teas?

Herbal teas do not contain caffeine, but there isn't sufficient scientific research data available to date about the effects of many herbs during the course of a pregnancy.

Stick to decaffeinated black teas. If you want to drink fruit or ginger teas, read the ingredient label carefully to make sure that no herbs are present. Also, limit green tea intake, because it may interefere with fetal growth.

Being expectant parents can bring you emotionally closer as a couple, but not necessarily physically. While some women find that their libido increases during pregnancy, often much to their partner's surprise, the majority find that their sex drive diminishes in the early weeks.

In the first trimester many women are affected by fatigue and nausea, and so the last thing they want to do is have sex. If this is the case then make sure you explain how you feel to your partner, so that he doesn't feel rejected.

Try to find other ways to stay physically connected with each other: perhaps you can still enjoy some aspects of foreplay, if not penetrative sex. If not, at least try to be affectionate to each other.

It may be your partner who's anxious about having sex. Many men worry about harming the baby through penetrative sex, although there is no chance of this happening.

Remember, if you do want to have sex, then unless a doctor tells you otherwise, it's safe to do so while you are pregnant.

FOCUS ON... YOUR BODY

Tackling spider veins

Spider veins (or spider nevi) are tiny, red blood vessels that branch outward, just under the skin. They are caused by an increase in the level of estrogen during pregnancy. They usually appear on the face, upper chest, neck, arms, and legs. Often disappearing soon after birth, spider veins are not a cause for concern and can usually be covered with makeup. You can discourage spider veins by:

■ **Upping your intake of vitamin C,** which helps to strengthen your veins and capillaries.

■ **Avoiding crossing your legs,** which can exacerbate the problem.

■ **Getting regular exercise** because it keeps your blood circulating around your body.

■ **Avoiding standing or sitting** for long periods, and elevating your feet when you do sit down.

■ **Avoid eating spicy food** since some women have found that this helps reduce spider veins.

If you suddenly notice lots of broken veins appearing on your skin, see your doctor.

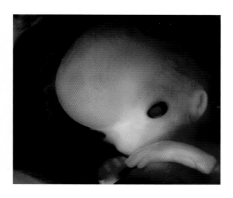

203 days to go...

YOUR BABY TODAY

The hands can now be easily brought up to the face and the baby's neck has lengthened, which will enable him to flex it and make side-to-side movements. The baby's ear and eye are clearly visible.

The key organs that enable your baby to see, hear, and taste are developing rapidly now, and he's starting to move around.

SUPERNUTRITIOUS SMOOTHIES

Smoothies are a simple way to stay hydrated, and at the same time obtain some nutrients. The basic recipe for making smoothies includes frozen fruit, a banana, yogurt, and juice to help blend it. Here are a few ideas:

- **Strawberry/banana**—frozen strawberries, banana, nonfat vanilla yogurt, and orange juice.
- **Raspberry/orange**—frozen raspberries, orange sorbet, nonfat vanilla yogurt, and orange juice.
- **Blueberry/banana**—frozen blueberries, banana, nonfat vanilla yogurt, and orange juice.

Your baby will rely to a great extent on his senses inside the uterus (and once he's born) and key development is taking place now.

The ears continue to move up toward their final destination, but your baby can't hear at this stage. Hearing requires the middle and inner ear to structurally mature and the inner ear to complete nerve connections to the brain. Hearing will, however, be one of the first senses to develop and can be tested by seeing if the baby responds to the sound waves that reach him in the uterus. Judging when taste is established is harder, but taste buds have started to appear on the tongue.

Your baby's eyes have a lens and early retina but even if the eyelids were open the eyes would not yet be able to see light signals. The lens is solid and the optic nerve is not yet responding to signals from the retina.

More signs of bodily movement appear but although your baby is quite active he is too light for you to feel the kicks. But you'll be fully aware of him in about two months (see p.213).

ASK A... DOCTOR

I had some bleeding after I exercised. Should I be worried?
If you experience vaginal bleeding during exercise with or without cramping, stop immediately and seek medical advice. It's unlikely that exercise is the cause, but you should be checked before doing any more exercise.

Bleeding in the first trimester may be due to a number of issues completely unrelated to exercise, but it's important to rule out any problems at the outset. Once you have the all-clear from your doctor, you can begin exercising again.

ACTUAL SIZE OF YOUR BABY

After 11 weeks your baby's crown to rump length is 2 in (50 mm).

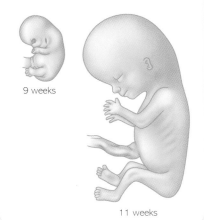

9 weeks

11 weeks

Your 12th week

AN IMPORTANT MILESTONE IS PASSED AS THE FIRST TRIMESTER ENDS

Yawning, arms and legs waving—your baby is on the go and you can actually see it happening. Most women have their first scan this week, and it's the big thrill of the first trimester. Up until now, you may have preferred to keep your pregnancy a precious secret. After the scan, you'll probably feel more confident about making an announcement, especially when you have the photos to prove there's really something happening!

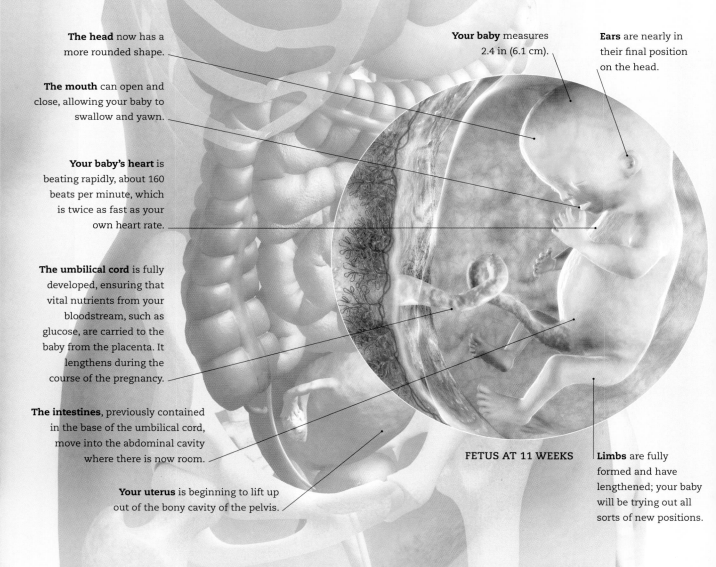

The head now has a more rounded shape.

The mouth can open and close, allowing your baby to swallow and yawn.

Your baby's heart is beating rapidly, about 160 beats per minute, which is twice as fast as your own heart rate.

The umbilical cord is fully developed, ensuring that vital nutrients from your bloodstream, such as glucose, are carried to the baby from the placenta. It lengthens during the course of the pregnancy.

The intestines, previously contained in the base of the umbilical cord, move into the abdominal cavity where there is now room.

Your uterus is beginning to lift up out of the bony cavity of the pelvis.

Your baby measures 2.4 in (6.1 cm).

Ears are nearly in their final position on the head.

FETUS AT 11 WEEKS

Limbs are fully formed and have lengthened; your baby will be trying out all sorts of new positions.

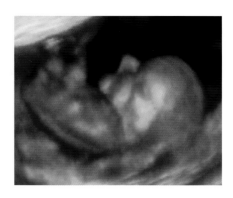

202 days to go...

YOUR BABY TODAY

Although on a scan it might look as though the baby is resting on her back, the fluid in the amniotic sac means that she is floating in a near weightless environment and can easily move into any position within the uterus.

In this final week of your first trimester, you'll probably have your first ultrasound scan and see your baby for the first time.

You and your partner have reached an exciting milestone.
You'll have your first ultrasound around now and see your baby; this may help you feel closer to her. For many men, seeing the baby on the scan may be the first time the pregnancy becomes a reality.

At this scan, your baby's length will be measured (see p.139) and this will be used to figure out her age. Up until about 12 weeks of pregnancy, all babies grow at around the same rate so irrespective of whether you and your partner are tall or short, at this time your baby will be the same size as others at this stage of development.

Figuring out your due date (see p.74) using the first day of your period, isn't always accurate, especially if your menstrual cycle is long or irregular. The dating scan can give a more accurate expected date of delivery, but it by no means tells you for certain—less than 5% of babies arrive on their actual due date.

You may be given a printout of your baby. Don't be surprised to find yourself looking at it again, and again, and again! It's also a great way to share the news with others.

It's really happening!

As a dad-to-be, going to your first scan will be a time of great excitement, but you may be anxious too. It's normal for you and your partner to wonder if your baby is okay and be desperate to hear that all is well.

The first scan may seem quite technical since it is used to detect your baby's heartbeat and take some measurements, but it's also very emotional. In reality, the first scan gives you the first look at this new life. It lets you see your baby moving around, with legs kicking and arms flailing, even though your partner can't feel these movements yet.

Perhaps, as a man, the biggest shock of the scan is the fact that it confronts you for the first time with the physical evidence that your baby really exists. Your partner is likely to be more used to the idea of pregnancy, because she's carrying the baby, but the scan will make the pregnancy much more real to you, and you may be surprised at how emotional you feel.

Your 12th week

First ultrasound scan

Your first scan at 8–14 weeks can pinpoint the length of your pregnancy to within a five to seven day window. Such accurate dating helps to estimate your due date and determine the right time to perform tests later in pregnancy.

Your first scan

This ultrasound helps to accurately establish your baby's gestational age. This is particularly useful if you are not sure when your last menstrual period was, if you have irregular periods, or you became pregnant immediately after you stopped using contraception such as the pill. At this stage of pregnancy, your baby can be measured from crown to rump (from the top of the baby's head to its bottom). In addition to establishing your due date and the timing of other screening and diagnostic tests, accurate dating of your pregnancy is important since it helps avoid misdiagnosis of problems such as poor fetal growth (see p.284). Your due date will usually be changed at this scan if there is more than a five day difference between your menstrual dates and the dates based on the crown–rump length.

A scan may be given before 10 weeks if you have bleeding or pain to rule out the possibility of a miscarriage or ectopic pregnancy (see p.93).

How the scan is done During an ultrasound scan, high-frequency sound waves are emitted through the abdomen via a handheld device called a transducer. As the sound waves hit solid tissue, they translate into an image that is viewed on a computer screen and interpreted by the sonographer.

At this scan, you will need to drink plenty of water to raise the uterus and provide a clearer image. The sonographer will put some cold gel on your abdomen to maximize contact with the skin and will then move the transducer gently over the area.

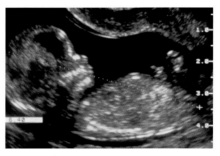

By 12 weeks the fetus has taken on a human appearance. The forehead, eye sockets, and small button nose are all visible in profile.

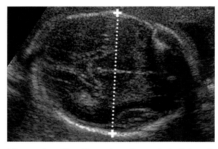

Measuring the diameter of your baby's head (the biparietal diameter) helps assess your baby's growth and date your pregnancy.

WHAT THE SCAN SHOWS

What can be seen on a first scan?

In addition to confirming your dates, your first scan may reveal some other useful information.

■ **This scan usually confirms whether** you have a single or multiple pregnancy (twins, triplets, or more).

■ **Uterine anomalies** can be seen, such as a double uterus, although this is rare. Uterine fibroids (benign tumors) will also be identified.

■ **The scan may reveal an ovarian cyst** (corpus luteum) on the ovary that produced the egg. These are common and can persist in the first trimester.

■ **Major anomalies** may be seen, but most are diagnosed at the 20-week scan when the organs are seen (see p.214).

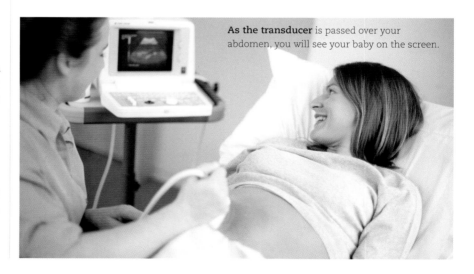

As the transducer is passed over your abdomen, you will see your baby on the screen.

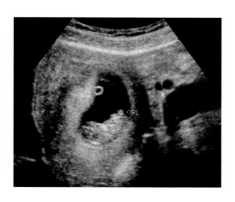

201 days to go...

YOUR BABY TODAY

This image shows the yolk sac at the 12 o'clock position with the placenta seen as a thickening to the lining of the uterus on the left. The baby is in the lower part of the uterus and is positioned lying on her back.

The dating scan is reassuring because it's an opportunity for your baby's progress and development to be thoroughly checked.

At your ultrasound scan, the pregnancy is dated according to your baby's length from crown (head) to rump (bottom) because he is—and will remain—quite curled up. This is known as the CRL (crown–rump length).

Since your baby can flex his spine and stretch his neck, this measurement needs to be taken with your baby in a specific position so it can take some time to achieve. The measurement is used to estimate your baby's date of delivery and this may be different than the EDD you calculated (see p.74)

This first ultrasound scan should be able to recognize all four limbs, your baby's hands and feet, the spine, some aspects of brain development, the fluid-filled stomach, and the bladder. From now on your baby's kidneys will be producing small amounts of very dilute urine and the bladder will start to fill.

AS A MATTER OF FACT

Dating scans are only an estimate. The chance of delivering on your due date is only around 5 percent.

So keep the estimated due date in mind but don't expect your baby to abide by it!

ASK A... DOCTOR

I've had quite a few pregnancy symptoms and don't feel as though my body is my own. How can I relax and enjoy being pregnant?
Not all women adapt well to pregnancy and for some dealing with the symptoms and worrying about issues such as weight gain, makes them feel out of control. The best way to cope with these feelings is to embrace the changes and remain in touch with your body by exercising and taking time to focus on what is happening inside you. We spend most of our lives listening to all the things that happen on the outside, but very little time focusing on the inside.

Take a few minutes each day to practice deep breathing and relaxation and consider learning some pregnancy yoga and meditation techniques (see right).

The dramatic changes happening to your body may be mirrored in the wide swings of emotions and feelings you experience throughout your pregnancy. Some days you may feel excited and elated at the prospect of becoming a parent, and on others you may feel overwhelmed and anxious.

Perhaps the nine months' gestation period is nature's way of giving us time to get used to the idea of becoming a parent, and allowing us time to deal with our emotions and prepare for the birth. So try to relax but if you're feeling really anxious, speak to your doctor.

This simple yoga pose allows you to fully relax your body and mind. Consider joining a pregnancy yoga class since it's a great way to learn techniques and also an opportunity meet other moms-to-be.

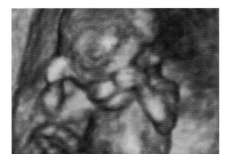

YOU ARE 11 WEEKS AND 3 DAYS

200 days to go...

YOUR BABY TODAY

As the baby floats in the amniotic fluid, her limbs are now more fully developed, allowing her to make many movements. The lips and fingers—which are now completely separated—stimulate sensory feelings.

Does your face resemble the pimply complexion of your teenage years? Don't worry, it's those hormones again and it will pass.

Your skin is likely to change during pregnancy. Some women find that they develop pimples or acne, due to the high levels of progesterone. Conversely, you may get dry skin, also due to pregnancy hormones. The dryness may become worse over your abdomen as your belly grows and the skin is stretched.

Freckles and moles may get darker. You may also notice tiny red lines on your chest or legs: these are called spider nevi (see p.134) and are due to the increased blood supply to the skin which makes the vessels dilate and become more visible.

Other women find that the high levels of estrogen mean that their skin is in a better condition than before they were pregnant. The "glow" of pregnancy is due to the increased blood supply that occurs in pregnancy, which gives you a rosy healthy looking complexion.

Your skin may become dry and flaky, on your face, as well as elsewhere on your body. Using a good moisturizer should help.

TIME TO THINK ABOUT

Telling your employer

As soon as your employer knows you're pregnant, you should be protected by human rights laws, which say that pregnant employees must be treated the same as other employees with disabilities or limitations. Most parents-to-be wait until 12 weeks when the risk of miscarriage is lower. Some wait longer.

■ **Each company has its own policy** on maternity leave. Some offer paid or unpaid leave for a set period. Others let employees use sick leave or vacation days. Meet with a human resources representative to learn your options.

■ **You can discuss** when your maternity leave will start. If your baby is born early or your maternity leave starts earlier than planned due to illness, the arrangements can be altered at short notice.

■ **Your employer** should respect your right to confidentiality. If you want the news of your pregnancy to remain under wraps until a certain date, make this known.

ASK A... DOCTOR

Since going to the scan my partner is very overprotective. Is this normal?
Your partner is now realizing his responsibilities and affection for the baby, and is showing these feelings by taking care of you. If you're finding that his pampering of you is a little too much, you might want to discuss other ways he can feel involved in the pregnancy and prepare for the baby. Try to embrace his involvement and enthusiasm—it's a great way for you to strengthen your relationship and prepare for parenthood together.

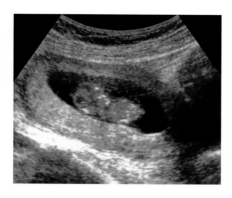

199 days to go...

YOUR BABY TODAY

The fetus can be seen inside the uterus on this color ultrasound scan. At this stage of development, the fetus measures approximately 2.4 in (6 cm) crown to rump and weighs around 0.3 oz (10 g).

At around 12 weeks, the doctor might be able to hear your baby's heartbeat with a handheld monitor.

At this stage your baby's heart beats at approximately 140 beats per minute, so at least twice as fast as your own. The heart and its internal electrical conducting system are structurally complete but its external nerve supply is still quite immature. The nerves to the heart influence its rhythm, gradually slowing the rate as the pregnancy advances.

The heart is tiny and to maintain an adequate output the heart is unable to increase the amount of blood it pumps with each beat (as we can), but instead increases the number of times it beats each minute.

The abdominal cavity is large enough to hold the intestines. Whereas before they were bulging outside of your baby's body, they now fit into her abdominal cavity. Having started to rotate while outside the body, the bowel completes its final rotation in the abdominal cavity. Once inside, the bowel position remains fixed, and its diameter increases as the loops of bowel become hollow.

SMOKING: THE FACTS

If you've only cut down, rather than quitting, read on. Many smokers inhale more deeply when smoking less and their intake of damaging toxins increases. Here's how smoking affects your baby:

■ **The carbon monoxide,** nicotine, and other substances that you inhale pass from your lungs, into your blood-stream, and cross the placenta.

■ **Nicotine** makes your baby's heart beat faster as she struggles for oxygen, which can affect her growth rate.

■ **Smoking increases the risk** of miscarriage, premature birth, and low birth weight, and exposure to tobacco chemicals makes your baby more likely to suffer from conditions such as asthma and chest infections after the birth, which may be bad enough to warrant a hospital stay.

■ **There is also a higher risk** of crib death if you or your partner smokes. Your partner should stop too.

■ **If you live with a smoker,** you will be inhaling thousands of toxic carcinogenic chemicals that are released into the air around you from the burning end of the cigarette and the exhaled smoke.

■ **Several studies** have confirmed that passive smoking can damage the baby's health and increase the risk of miscarriage and premature birth.

FOCUS ON... TWINS

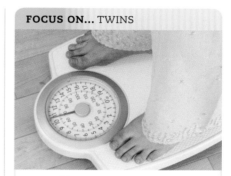

Feeding two?

If you're carrying twins, you're likely to have put on some weight by now, perhaps around 11 lb (5 kg). Early weight gain is usually a good thing, especially in your case, since this is a vital time for the formation and development for your babies organs. As a rough guide, a good recommended weight gain is:

■ **For twins,** total weight gain of 35–45 lb (16–20 kg), preferably 24 lb (11 kg) by week 24, then a gradual increase until the birth.

■ **For triplets,** a total weight gain of 50–60 lb (23–27 kg), preferably 35 lb (16 kg) by week 24, then a gradual increase until the birth.

■ **For quads,** total weight gain of 65–80 lb (31–36 kg), ideally 50 lb (22.5 kg) of it by week 24.

Screening tests

Optional routine screening tests in the first trimester assess the risk of your baby having a chromosomal disorder such as Down syndrome. If your risk is high, you will be offered a diagnostic test (see pp.152–3) for a definite result.

Your doctor will discuss in advance the available screening tests so you are fully informed before agreeing to a test.

What is screened for

In addition to Down syndrome, screening tests also assess the risk of another chromosomal abnormality called trisomy 18. Babies with this condition have more severe mental and physical abnormalities than babies with Down syndrome and seldom survive beyond a year. The condition is rare, with each year around 1 in 6000 babies born with trisomy 18, compared to 1 in 800 babies born with Down. Screening can also detect neural tube defects like spina bifida and anencephaly, which occur in about 1 in 1000 pregnancies.

The first trimester screen (FTS)

The recommended screening test, and the one most commonly offered, for Down is the "nuchal translucency screening," performed between 11 and 14 weeks. This test has a high accuracy rate and the results are produced quickly.

The test uses a combination of a maternal blood test and an ultrasound of your baby. The ultrasound measures the thickness of the skin at the back of your baby's neck, called the nuchal fold (see box, opposite). The blood test looks at the levels of two chemicals: pregnancy associated plasma protein A (PAPP-A) and one of the pregnancy hormones, human chorionic gonadotrophin (hCG). The results of the blood test is combined with your age, and the measurement of the nuchal fold. A mathematical formula is then used to calculate your baby's risk of Down syndrome.

If you have your blood test before your ultrasound, you will usually receive your results immediately following your ultrasound. If you have your blood drawn at the time of the ultrasound you will receive your results a few days later. Your risk based on the combined test may be higher than your risk based on your age alone, lower, or stay the same.

The integrated prenatal screen (IPS)

This test is done in two stages using results from a range of screening tests done in the first and second trimesters. Your age will also be taken into account when calculating your risk. In the first trimester, a blood test at 12 weeks measures the PAPP-A. You will also have a nuchal translucency screening. Between 15 and 20 weeks, another blood test measures the levels of hCG, AFP, and estriol. IPS is the most sensitive screening test, but it has the disadvantage that the results are not available until later in pregnancy. It is not available everywhere.

UNDERSTANDING TESTS

Accuracy of screening tests

As more screening tests have become available, the detection rate for Down syndrome, which used to be assessed on maternal age alone, has significantly increased. The aim of screening tests is to provide a high detection rate for Down syndrome and a low "false positive" rate. A false positive means the screening test indicated a high risk of Down syndrome, but subsequent diagnostic tests gave the all clear, which means the mother would be exposed to unnecessary testing.

Tests	Timing (weeks)	Detection rate	False positive rate
FTS	11–14	85%	5%
IPS	11–13/15–20	85%	2%
MSS	15–20	80%	8%

Maternal serum screen (MSS)

This screening test is done in the second trimester, usually between 15 and 20 weeks' gestation, and assesses your baby's risks of Down syndrome, trisomy 18, and neural tube defects such as spina bifida from blood tests alone. The maternal serum screen measures levels of the hormones hCG, AFP and estriol, and results are available within about one week. This test is available for women who have not had either the first trimester or the integrated prenatal screen.

A positive screen

It's important to remember that a positive result does not mean your baby has Down syndrome. For example, if you have a 1 in 100 risk of Down syndrome, your test will be positive. However, the chance that your baby has Down syndrome is low since your baby will be normal 99 times out of 100. Talking to your doctor or a genetic counselor can help you understand your actual risk and decide if you want to have a diagnostic test such as amniocentesis (see p.153) for a definite result. Since diagnostic tests carry a risk of miscarriage, you need to weigh the risks before deciding to go ahead.

Some research suggests that women are more likely to enjoy their pregnancy and birth and come to terms with the diagnosis if they know in advance that their baby has Down syndrome. So don't assume therefore that you should only have a diagnostic test to decide whether or not to continue your pregnancy.

If you have a positive screening test for another more severe chromosomal disorder, such as trisomy 18, your doctor will talk to you about the outlook for babies with these conditions—the majority of whom die early in life, sometimes within the first week—to help you decide what to do. In some cases these disorders are associated with abnormalities detected during the dating scan (see p.138), and the presence of these abnormalities

Nuchal translucency screening

An ultrasound scan, known as the nuchal translucency screening, is done between 11 and 14 weeks of pregnancy and is used to help assess your baby's risk of Down syndrome. During this test, the sonographer measures the depth of fluid under the skin at the back of the baby's neck, known as the nuchal fold. If this measurement is high, it indicates that excess fluid is present, which means that the baby has a higher risk of Down syndrome. The measurement is then combined with the results of blood tests and the average risk based on your age to give your baby's individual risk for Down syndrome. If your risk is higher than 1 in 250, you will be counseled and offered a diagnostic test, such as amniocentesis or chorionic villus sampling, to give a definitive result (see p.152).

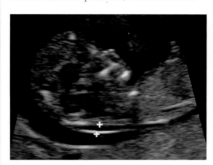

The small depth of fluid seen in the neck's nuchal fold in this scan means that the fetus has a low risk of developing Down syndrome.

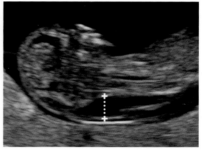

The thicker nuchal fold seen here indicates an increased risk of Down syndrome in this fetus and a diagnostic test will be recommended.

combined with a positive test may confirm the diagnosis. Nevertheless, many women opt to have a diagnostic test before deciding whether or not to terminate their pregnancy.

Further screening Another option is to have a specialized ultrasound scan to look for Down syndrome markers between 17 and 22 weeks. If the ultrasound doesn't show any signs of Down syndrome, the risk of your baby being affected is reduced. However, a second trimester ultrasound is not such an accurate test for Down syndrome as other screening tests and so you should only consider this path if you are strongly against having a diagnostic test such as amniocentesis and feel that you don't need a definite diagnosis.

Should I have a diagnostic test?

Deciding on whether or not to go ahead with genetic or diagnostic testing (see pp.152–3) is a personal choice. Factors that may affect your decision-making process include:

- **Your anxiety level** without knowing for sure, and how this will affect your enjoyment of pregnancy.

- **Your fears about** pregnancy loss.

- **What you would do if** you found out your baby had Down syndrome or another condition such as Trisomy 18.

Screening tests

143

198 days to go...

YOUR BABY TODAY

At this stage the eye—not yet in its final position—still dominates the appearance of the face. The eye is not yet responsive to light and remains well protected behind the covering eyelid.

Having your first scan this week and knowing your risk of miscarriage is reduced now, should mean you can start to relax.

This can be a very positive time for you, especially if you've been anxious from day one of your pregnancy. The risk of miscarriage falls as your pregnancy progresses and by the end of this 12th week, it's no more than 1 percent.

As you enter the second trimester, you should begin to feel better (see opposite), and this, combined with the knowledge that you have passed the most risky time, may help you relax. If you've been keeping your pregnancy a secret, you can also enjoy telling others.

FOCUS ON... SAFETY

Safe scans

Ultrasound has been used for years and is thought to be safe. Children who've been exposed to prenatal ultrasound do not have differences in speech, hearing, vision, or school performance, or an increased risk of cancer. However, ultrasound should only be done when necessary.

AS A MATTER OF FACT

Medical ultrasound has been used since the early 1960s.

However, the first discovery of high-frequency echo-sounding techniques, on which ultrasound is based, was as long ago as 1880 in Paris. In the early 20th century, ultrasound was used as a therapy tool and it was not until the 1940s that research began into its use as a diagnostic tool.

ASK A... NUTRITIONIST

I have a really sweet tooth. Is it okay to indulge this while I'm pregnancy? While occasional treats of cookies or chocolate are fine, processed foods usually contain hidden fats and sugars and provide few nutrients, so it's best to try to find healthier sweet alternatives to snack on, such as fresh fruit.

Always read food labels and look for alternative foods containing less fat and less added sugars. Just as you would consider carefully how you feed your child, you should take care of yourself in the same way while you're pregnant.

One of the best ways to curb your sweet tooth is to eat regular meals. This helps to steady your blood-sugar level and reduce sweet cravings. Try not to go longer than three hours without eating and, if you're hungry, have a healthy snack between meals, such as a chicken sandwich, a low-fat yogurt, or fruit, which can be fresh, canned, or dried, such as raisins or apricots.

Try to drink about two quarts (1.8 L) of water a day, since perceived hunger is often really dehydration. Drinking a glass or two of water may stop you from reaching for the cookie jar.

It's possible to satisfy sweet cravings with refreshing fruit. You may find that you feel better after eating a fruit salad than if you eat a bar of chocolate.

197 days to go...

YOUR BABY TODAY

The bones of the front of the skull have continued to expand and cover the head, protecting the delicate brain structures beneath. The soft spot in between the skull bones (center) remains through pregnancy and into babyhood.

If you're finding you're out of breath when you get to the top of the stairs, accept this as a normal side effect of pregnancy.

By the end of the first trimester it's normal to begin feeling a little breathless. This is because your heart and lungs are having to work much harder to supply your body with oxygen due to all the changes that are taking place to allow the baby to grow.

The amount of oxygen you need in pregnancy is about 20 percent more than normal; some of this goes to the placenta (see p.127) and baby and the rest to your other organs. To get this increased amount of oxygen you breathe faster and deeper, almost hyperventilating so you feel short of breath, especially when you exercise.

As your pregnancy continues, you may find that this shortness of breath or feeling that you are not breathing very deeply continues, or worsens. As the baby grows, your uterus will expand upward and your other abdominal organs will rearrange themselves to create more room. Your organs and uterus push up against your diaphragm so it becomes more difficult to take a deep breath, so in order to get all the oxygen you need, you then have to breathe much faster. The hormone progesterone may also affect the rate at which you breathe.

If you have any concerns about breathlessness, don't hesitate to speak to your doctor.

FOCUS ON... HEALTH

Feeling better?

By the end of this trimester, many of the early pregnancy symptoms are likely to have passed.

■ **Nausea** may have begun to lessen and it can be a complete relief to wake up in the morning without feeling sick. Your loss of appetite will return, and you can stop worrying about whether your baby is being properly nourished, which is often a common concern for women who suffer from morning sickness.

■ **You won't need to urinate** quite so often, which will be good news if you've spent an inordinate amount of time in the bathroom. This is because your uterus is now moving up the abdominal cavity and therefore is placing less pressure on your bladder.

■ **The fatigue** that you may have felt in these early months is likely to have lifted by now, and you may be sleeping more deeply now that you're relaxing into your pregnancy.

If your sickness hasn't passed yet, don't worry—for some women, it does last longer (see p.159).

Some of your usual vitality should begin to return toward the end of the first trimester.

ASK A... DOCTOR

I've gone from an A cup to D cup. Will this increase in size last forever? The majority of women who have had babies do report a permanent increase in breast size but it's unlikely to be to this extent! The effects of estrogen cause fat to be deposited in the breasts and when your milk comes in after the birth your breasts will get bigger, but reduce again once you have stopped breast-feeding.

Your 12th week

145

196 days to go...

YOUR BABY TODAY

Here the legs are crossed and the arms outstretched. The umbilical cord is short and thick at this stage, but will lengthen as the baby grows, and become much thinner with many coils.

You've reached the end of the first trimester and in this time your baby has developed from a ball of cells to an active fetus.

YOUR DOCTOR

Most women develop a good relationship with their doctor, who can be a fountain of fantastic information, and a wonderful source of comfort and reassurance.

It's important that you are as honest as you can be with your doctor. Like many women, you may be reluctant to reveal concerns, or to admit to unhealthy habits for fear of being embarrassed or scolded. It's very likely that your doctor will have heard it all before, and will be able to help and advise—with a few tried-and-tested tricks up her sleeve.

Your amazing baby can do so many things already, including being able to open his mouth and yawn, hiccup, and swallow. Swallowing develops earlier than sucking. Your baby will be swallowing the amniotic fluid regularly but the more complex sucking movements cannot be identified until 18–20 weeks. Swallowing will encourage gut development. The amniotic fluid enters into the stomach not the lungs, which are protected now by the vocal cords and the higher pressure of the lung's own fluid. The amniotic fluid will later be excreted as urine when the fetal kidneys start to function.

After the stomach, the amniotic fluid will enter the small bowel. The intestinal walls are developing muscular layers but these do not yet contract in a coordinated way to move the fluid along the digestive tract. It will be 20 weeks before the structural organization of the gut is finally complete. Many digestive enzymes are starting to be released into the gut but these currently act as a stimulus to development rather than for the absorption of nutrients.

Your baby is reliant on a steady stream of glucose, which is stored as glycogen in the liver. This continues throughout pregnancy and at birth your baby will, for her size, have significantly larger glycogen reserves than adults do.

The correct level of glucose is controlled by insulin secreted by the pancreas. The placenta, however, has little control over the amount it takes from your bloodstream and passes on. For this reason if your glucose level is very high, for example in poorly controlled diabetes, the baby will be presented with high levels of glucose. He will maintain a normal glucose level but the insulin released leads to increased fat deposition and weight gain.

ACTUAL SIZE OF YOUR BABY

At 12 weeks your baby's crown to rump length is 2.4 in (6.1 cm).

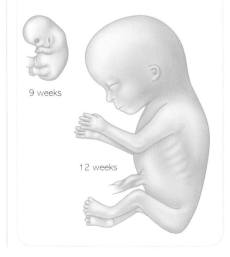

9 weeks

12 weeks

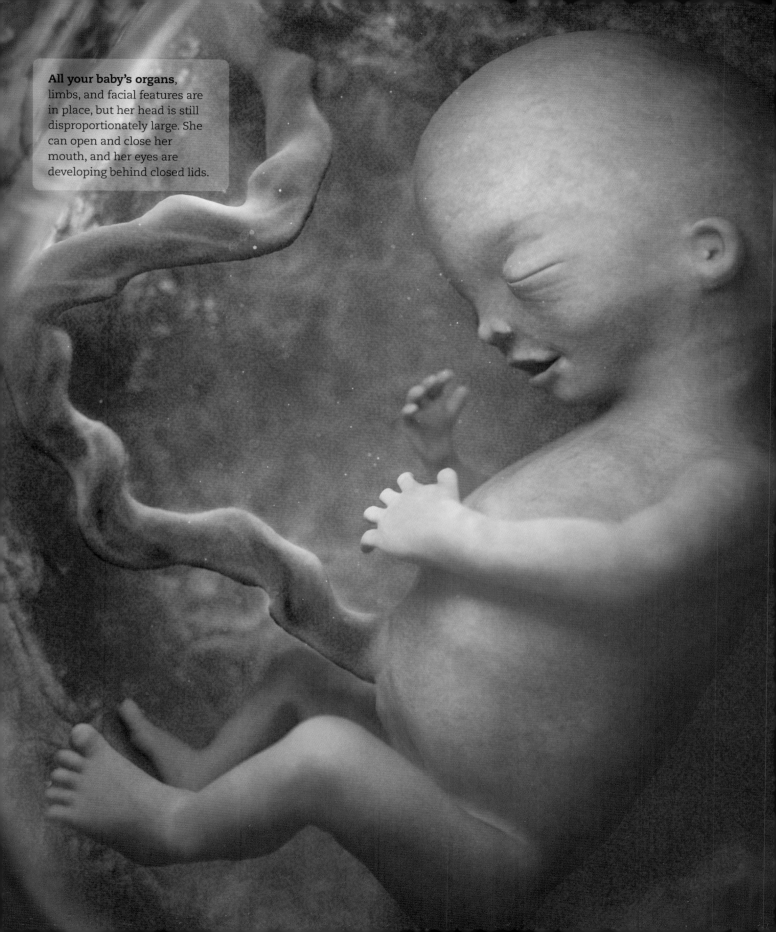

All your baby's organs, limbs, and facial features are in place, but her head is still disproportionately large. She can open and close her mouth, and her eyes are developing behind closed lids.

Welcome to your second trimester

| WEEK | 13 | 14 | 15 | 16 | 17 | 18 |

Spreading the word Safely past the first trimester, you will probably want to tell people your good news.

Visibly pregnant As your belly expands and your waistline disappears, you'll start to look as well as feel pregnant.

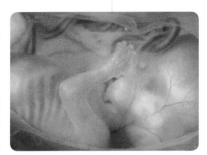

At 16 weeks your baby has taken on a definite human form. The body and limbs have grown substantially and a translucent layer of skin reveals underlying blood vessels.

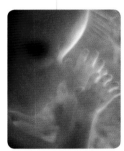

By 17 weeks the arms and hands are well developed; the fingers now move freely and start to grasp.

At three months your pregnancy becomes noticeable. By five months, there's no mistaking it.

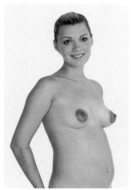

Second trimester As your pregnancy starts to show, you may feel renewed energy as the fatigue and nausea of early pregnancy fade.
Looking good By the end of this trimester, you'll look clearly pregnant as your baby steadily grows.

Feeling energized Regular exercise throughout pregnancy will positively benefit you and your baby in the months ahead and help prepare your body for labor.

Time for a vacation The second trimester is the ideal time to get away from it all as your hormones settle down, energy levels lift, and labor is still a safe distance away.

Facts and figures Even in the uterus, rhythmic movements such as walking send your baby to sleep.

Now your pregnancy starts to feel "real" as your body changes rapidly and you feel your baby move.

| 19 | 20 | 21 | 22 | 23 | 24 | 25 |

The 20-week ultrasound Your baby's major organs are now clearly visible and will be studied in detail to ensure they're developing normally.

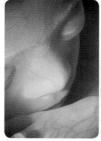

By 23 weeks your baby's facial features are distinct, with eyebrows and eyelashes visible. On the hands, fingernails start to grow.

Facts and figures At 21 weeks, your baby measures about 10 in (25 cm) from crown to heel.

Loud and clear By 24 weeks, your baby is able to hear sounds from the outside world and becomes familiar with your voice.

Exercise classes Prenatal exercise classes are tailored to meet your requirements in pregnancy and are also a great way to get acquainted with other moms-to-be.

First flutters As your baby's movements increase and strengthen, your partner can begin to share in your pregnancy experience.

Nutritious bites A varied diet with plenty of vegetables benefits your own and your baby's health.

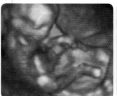
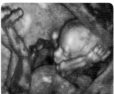
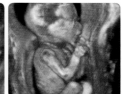

Your active baby Surrounded and cushioned by amniotic fluid, your baby is free to move around in the uterus without risk of being bumped or hurt.

Your 13th week

AS YOU ENTER THIS SECOND TRIMESTER, YOUR BODY WILL SETTLE DOWN TO PREGNANCY

For most women, any discomforts of early pregnancy start to disappear this trimester. The high levels of pregnancy hormones, which are thought to contribute to sickness, are subsiding, and fatigue should begin to diminish. Meanwhile, your baby floats peacefully in the amniotic sac. As he goes on growing, so the sac will expand to give him plenty of room to kick and stretch. His brain is developing at a rapid rate.

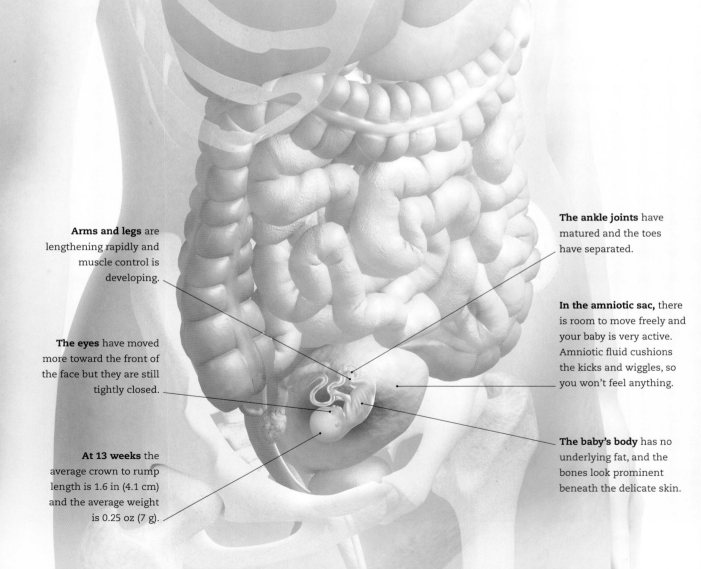

Arms and legs are lengthening rapidly and muscle control is developing.

The eyes have moved more toward the front of the face but they are still tightly closed.

At 13 weeks the average crown to rump length is 1.6 in (4.1 cm) and the average weight is 0.25 oz (7 g).

The ankle joints have matured and the toes have separated.

In the amniotic sac, there is room to move freely and your baby is very active. Amniotic fluid cushions the kicks and wiggles, so you won't feel anything.

The baby's body has no underlying fat, and the bones look prominent beneath the delicate skin.

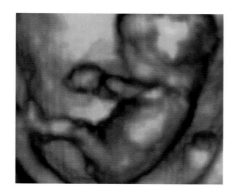

195 days to go...

YOUR BABY TODAY

This 3D ultrasound scan clearly demonstrates that the baby's arms and legs are now fully formed and much more in proportion with the trunk. All of the baby's joints are now formed, enabling a full range of movement.

This is a good time to start telling the important people in your life your exciting news—before they guess for themselves.

Now that you're in your second trimester and have had your dating scan (see p.138), you may want to start telling a wider circle of people that you're pregnant. You can feel confident doing this, knowing that the risk of miscarriage is reduced to no more than 1 percent after the 12th week. Besides this, your belly will begin to show in a few weeks, if it hasn't already, so hiding the pregnancy will become difficult.

If you and your partner have been keeping the pregnancy a secret for the past three months, announcing it will be a huge release and it can be a positive experience to share the news with others. However, be prepared for an onslaught of advice and people's tales of their pregnancy and birth experiences!

Sometimes letting others know that you're pregnant can be difficult. Be sensitive to other people's feelings: friends who also want to be parents, but are having difficulty conceiving, may find it difficult to share your happiness right away. It's preferable to tell these people face to face rather than them hearing it through the grapevine. Even if they don't react positively, and don't want to talk about your pregnancy all the time, give them time to come to terms with it at their own pace. Remember they can be sad for themselves while being happy for you.

TIME TO THINK ABOUT

Second trimester tests

If you haven't had a nuchal translucency scan (see p.143), blood tests will be offered this trimester to screen for Down (see pp.142–3).

■ **The maternal serum screen** is done at 15–20 weeks. It measures levels of the hormones hCG, AFP, and estriol. Results are available within about one week; the screen will also assess the risks of trisomy 18 and neural tube defects such as spina bifida.

FOCUS ON... YOUR BODY

Become a clothes cheat!

Although your clothes may be feeling a little tight by this stage, you probably aren't ready to wear voluminous maternity clothing just yet, so it's time to get creative! Simply bridge the gap between your button and button-hole with an rubber band (see right) or by sewing in an elastic panel. Assuming he's bigger than you, try raiding your partner's wardrobe—his T-shirts, shirts, and sweaters can be ruched in with a low-slung belt.

Check what's in your wardrobe already: empire-cut dresses will see you through most of your pregnancy; looser smock tops can be layered over tight-fitting T-shirts; low-slung pants can sit neatly under your belly, topped with an oversized shirt. The one item you might want to purchase is a pair of maternity pants—something stretchy with an adjustable waist.

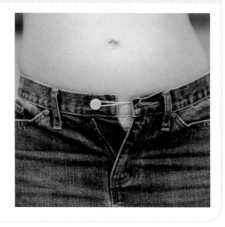

Diagnostic tests

If you've had a positive screening test for Down syndrome or another genetic abnormality, you will be offered a diagnostic test, which gives a definitive answer as to whether or not your baby has an abnormality.

What are diagnostic tests?

Diagnostic tests are tests that involve taking a sample of either the placenta, the amniotic fluid, or fetal blood. The samples are then sent away and examined in a laboratory for chromosomal or genetic abnormalities. The two main diagnostic tests are amniocentesis and chorionic villus sampling, or CVS. Since both of these tests carry a small risk of miscarriage (see right), you will need to carefully consider the advantages and disadvantages of the tests before going ahead with either of them.

Chorionic villus sampling (CVS)

Chorionic villi are fragments of placental tissue. Because the placenta originates from the fertilized egg, the chromosomes in the cells that make up the placenta are representative of your baby's chromosomes. During CVS, a small amount of tissue from your placenta is removed and tested in a laboratory to reveal if your baby has a chromosomal disorder such as Down syndrome or another trisomy disorder, such as trisomy 18. CVS is done between 11½ and 13 weeks' gestation and the preliminary results are usually available in 2 days. The procedure can also definitely identify your baby's sex, if you want to know. If you don't want to have this information, make your wishes clear before the test. In rare cases, the doctor will be unable to perform CVS due to the placenta's position. In this case, you may be asked to return for an amniocentesis at 15 weeks.

Amniocentesis This is the most common diagnostic test, done at around 15 to 19 weeks of pregnancy. The amniotic fluid around your baby mainly consists of your baby's urine and contains cells from your baby's skin and urinary tract. During amniocentesis, a number of cells are collected from the amniotic fluid. They are then sent to a laboratory and grown in a cell culture, until there is a sufficient number of cells to examine your baby's chromosomes and identify whether your baby has a chromosomal abnormality such as Down syndrome. Amniotic fluid can also be tested for high levels of the substance alpha-fetoprotein (AFP), which could mean that your baby has a neural tube defect such as spina bifida or anencephaly. Other DNA testing can also be done during amniocentesis to check for congenital conditions that may run in either parent's family. (see p.431).

HOW THE TEST IS DONE

Chorionic villus sampling

There are two ways of doing chorionic villus sampling. In the transabdominal method, a fine needle is placed through the abdomen to collect placental fragments. In the transcervical procedure, a thin tube (catheter) is inserted into the cervix. The method used depends on the position of the placenta and the doctor's training and expertise. During the procedure, ultrasound guidance is used so that the doctor can see the placenta's position.

CVS can also be done in a multiple pregnancy; in this case both the transabdominal and transcervical methods of collection may be used.

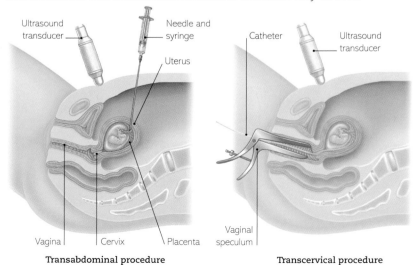

Transabdominal procedure: Ultrasound transducer, Needle and syringe, Uterus, Vagina, Cervix, Placenta

Transcervical procedure: Catheter, Ultrasound transducer, Vaginal speculum

Transabdominal procedure   **Transcervical procedure**

WHEN TO WORRY

If, following the procedure, you experience severe abdominal pain, fever greater than 100.5° F (38° C), vaginal bleeding, or a large gush of clear fluid from your vagina you should call your doctor immediately.

How you might feel

You may be concerned about the idea of a needle going through your abdomen, or a catheter into your cervix; however, the majority of women find that these procedures are not particularly painful. If you are having a transabdominal procedure, the needle usually doesn't hurt any more than it does when you are having a blood test. Some doctors use a small amount of local anesthetic before the transabdominal procedure to numb the area, although the anesthetic itself can occasionally sting. Although afterward it's common to experience uterine cramps, similar to the cramps you feel during menstruation, rest assured that these cramps alone do not mean that you have an increased risk of miscarriage.

If your blood type is Rh negative (see p.127) you should receive an injection of anti-Rh after the procedure to prevent complications from occurring during this and future pregnancies.

After the procedure

It's generally thought that being active after CVS or amniocentesis does not increase your risk of miscarriage. However, you may feel better if you don't exercise heavily right away; it's not necessary to remain in bed. In most cases, you should be physically able to return to work within a day or so after a diagnostic procedure, although some women may feel emotionally fragile and may not feel up to returning to work right away.

Getting the results

Usually, final chromosomal results from diagnostic tests take around 2–4 weeks to return. If you have had your AFP level tested with amniocentesis (see left), the results for this are usually available fairly quickly, after around 1–3 days. If you are considering terminating your pregnancy based on the results of a diagnostic test, opt for testing earlier in the time frame during which it is offered, rather than later, to reduce risks of complications.

RISKS AND BENEFITS

Comparison of CVS and amniocentesis

Before deciding on a diagnostic test, you may want to weigh their pros and cons. Consider too that the risks may be reduced with a doctor who has expertise in a particular test.

CVS: the pros

- CVS can be done up to five weeks earlier than amniocentesis, so if an abnormality is found and you decide to terminate, this can be done in a safer, less traumatic way.
- Since more genetic material is collected, the results may arrive sooner, decreasing the anxious wait.
- If you're nervous about a needle going into the abdomen, transcervical CVS means that you can avoid this but still have a prenatal diagnosis.

CVS: the cons

- The risk of miscarriage after CVS is greater than amniocentesis, but less than 1%. The miscarriage rate is the same whether it's done transabdominally or transvaginally.
- In the past, some women had CVS then had babies with limb abnormalities. It's now thought that most of these cases occurred when CVS was done before 11 weeks when the limbs were starting to form.

Amniocentesis: the pros

- Amniocentesis is highly accurate and has the lowest risk of miscarriage at around 1 in 600 to 1 in 900.

Amniocentesis: the cons

- Since this is done later than CVS and the results take longer, if you terminate you may be offered an induction for vaginal delivery, but most doctors can perform D&E until 20 to 24 weeks depending on their facilities.

HOW THE TEST IS DONE

Amniocentesis

During amniocentesis, the doctor uses ultrasound to locate an open pocket of amniotic fluid. Under continued ultrasound guidance, a thin needle is placed through the skin of the abdomen and then through the uterus and into the amniotic fluid. A small amount of the fluid is drawn up into the needle and an attached syringe. A local anesthetic may be applied to your abdomen before the procedure to ease any discomfort.

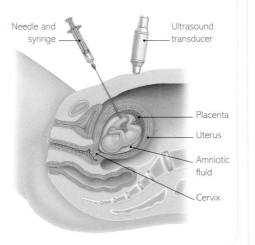

Needle and syringe
Ultrasound transducer
Placenta
Uterus
Amniotic fluid
Cervix

194 days to go...

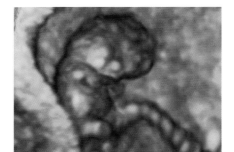

YOUR BABY TODAY

In this ultrasound scan, the baby is seen floating in amniotic fluid, which provides plenty of space for him to move around in. Later in pregnancy, your baby will excrete waste products into the fluid, but his bladder is still tiny and kidney function not yet established.

The bag of amniotic fluid is your baby's home—it will keep him safe and free from infection until he is ready to be born.

Your baby is safely cushioned in the amniotic fluid. This surrounds him, gives him space to move and grow, and helps him maintain a constant temperature.

The volume of fluid is only 1 ml at seven weeks but is 25 ml by this stage of your pregnancy. In about six weeks' time there will be around 60 ml, with plenty of room for your baby to do lots of somersaults.

The amniotic fluid increases steadily until around 32 weeks of pregnancy, then stays constant until 37 weeks. It begins to reduce slightly thereafter by about 8 percent per week.

Further on in the pregnancy, waste products excreted in your baby's urine will be absorbed from the fluid back into your bloodstream. At 37 weeks, your baby will urinate an astonishing one quarter to one third of his body weight every day. Compare this with your own production of 2–3 percent body weight as urine.

Your temperature directly influences your baby's temperature. Temperature control is not an important requirement until later in pregnancy when your baby's high metabolic rate means that he needs to transfer heat to you in order to cool himself down.

FOCUS ON... NUTRITION

Iron-rich foods

If you're suffering from pregnancy fatigue, try boosting your intake of foods that are rich in iron. Eat plenty of:
- Dark leafy green vegetables
- Red meat
- Whole-grain cereals
- Legumes
- Prune juice.

Vitamin C helps your body absorb more iron from your diet, so try drinking fresh orange juice with meals, and limit your intake of coffee and other caffeinated drinks: caffeine inhibits your body's ability to absorb iron.

ASK A... NUTRITIONIST

My appetite has come back, but how many calories should I be eating at this stage of my pregnancy? Like many women, you're finding that the second trimester has brought relief from the discomforts of early pregnancy. As a result, you may have noticed you're less nauseous and have more of an appetite.

Caloric needs in the second trimester are approximately 2,100–2,500 calories per day, depending upon your level of physical activity. You

shouldn't eat unlimited snacks, and when you do snack, opt for foods with nutritional value. For example, one banana has about 100 calories, and a handful (1 oz/28 g) of nuts about 170 calories. For a light 200-calorie snack, you can eat two pieces of whole-wheat toast spread with a small amount of butter and jam; a small bowl of cereal with skim milk; or a small can of soup with a slice of bread and butter.

If you're exercising regularly, you can of course increase your calorie intake without gaining excess weight.

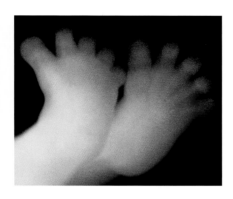

YOU ARE 12 WEEKS AND 3 DAYS

193 days to go...

YOUR BABY TODAY

The toes are now separate and are all the same length. The ankle joints are now mature enough to be working, although it will still be many weeks before you are likely to be conscious of any kicks.

As your uterus grows to accommodate your baby, you may begin to notice a few twinges around your pelvis.

There's a strong band of connective tissue in your pelvis, supporting your uterus. Known as the round ligament, this band has to stretch as your uterus expands, which can cause some discomfort. The pain is generally felt in the groin or lower abdomen and can be on either side. Although the pain starts in the pelvis, it may travel up to your hips. You may feel a short, sharp stabbing pain or a more prolonged, dull ache.

You will soon adapt and find sitting and lying positions that cause you the least discomfort and which may relieve discomfort. Also, try other common methods of pain relief, too, such as

taking a warm bath or resting comfortably with your feet up.

Round ligament pain is common in pregnancy and isn't a cause for concern. See your doctor, however, if you have sharp abdominal or pelvic pains don't resolve quickly or if your pain becomes crampy; if there is any bleeding; if there is a burning sensation when you urinate; or if you're feverish. If you're in any doubt, always seek medical advice.

The round ligaments, which help support the uterus, stretch as the uterus enlarges and pull on nearby nerve fibers and sensitive structures, causing discomfort.

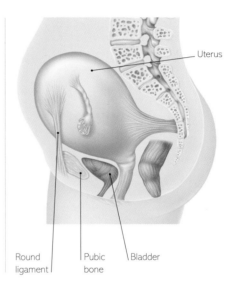

Uterus

Round ligament | Pubic bone | Bladder

FOCUS ON... TWINS

Carrying twins

If you're expecting twins, or more, it's good to know that most multiple pregnancies are straightforward and without complications. However, being pregnant with multiple babies is going to be more challenging for your body to handle than if you were carrying just one baby.

It's wise to know about the slightly higher risk of certain conditions that can occur. These include:

- Placenta previa (see p.212)
- Polyhydramnios (see p.473)
- Poor growth of one or more babies, which may be caused by twin-to-twin transfusion syndrome (see p.130)
- Premature labor (see p.431).

The fact that any of these conditions can develop is the reason why you'll have more prenatal checkups to preempt problems and minimize their effects.

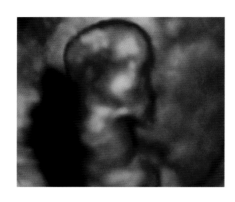

YOU ARE 12 WEEKS AND 4 DAYS

192 days to go...

YOUR BABY TODAY

By now the fetus's forehead is high and bulging, with visible joins in the plates of bone that comprise the skull. The eyes have migrated from the sides of the head at this stage of development.

Complex brain development is gradually enabling your unborn baby to become more responsive and mobile.

Your baby's brain is undergoing rapid development. The right and left cerebral hemispheres begin to connect. Each hemisphere controls the opposite side of the body, so the right side of the brain controls muscles on the left side of the body and the left side controls muscles on the right side of the body.

Motor fibers (those that control movement) mature first, so your baby can make increasingly complex limb movements. Sensory nerves (those that control feeding) mature later and are first present on your baby's hands and in his mouth. The brain matures quickly over the next three weeks and will be complete in around 10 weeks' time, as the rest of the upper and lower limbs and trunk achieve adult levels of sensitivity to stimuli. All your baby's nerves are very immature at this stage and he doesn't have any perception of position, pain, temperature, or touch.

As your baby's brain develops, he is able to make larger movements with his arms and legs, but this activity won't be well coordinated at this stage.

ASK A... DOCTOR

I've been diagnosed with diabetes. How will this affect my pregnancy? Whether you develop diabetes in pregnancy (known as gestational diabetes), or have pre-existing diabetes, you will require special care from a diabetic health-care team and a obstetrician. This is because diabetes poses risks in pregnancy, particularly if there is poor control of blood-glucose levels.

All this can be managed with close prenatal care: your blood glucose needs to be well controlled since your insulin requirements will increase during pregnancy. You will also need to adapt your diet and may need insulin injections.

Pregnant women who are diabetic are at a greater risk of high blood pressure, blood clots, and preeclampsia (see p.474). If you have diabetic kidney disease, and diabetic retinopathy, a condition that affects the retina in the eye, there's a chance it will worsen during pregnancy. For your baby, there is an increased risk of congenital abnormalities and growth may be too fast or too slow.

FOCUS ON... NUTRITION

Yummy yogurt

For a calcium-packed snack, stock up on yogurt. Those with so-called friendly bacteria are okay to eat during pregnancy and may help your digestion. Just make sure that the milk ingredients in your yogurts have been pasteurized to reduce the risk of infection with listeria (see p.17).

Your second trimester

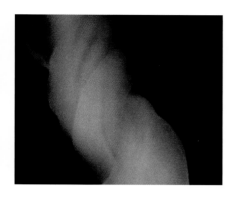

191 days to go...

YOUR BABY TODAY

This image is a close-up of your baby's umbilical cord. The umbilical arteries can be seen as they carry blood from the baby to the placenta. Since there are no nerve fibers in the cord, your baby is unaware that this is happening—or even that the cord is there.

You and your partner will be developing your own special relationship with your baby.

At this point in your pregnancy, you won't be able to feel your baby move but it is still possible to interact and bond with him. Some women feel comfortable talking to their babies, while others don't; do what feels natural for you, whether that is talking out loud or in your head.

Very soon, your baby will be able to hear (see. p.171) and recognize your voice and that of your partner, and hear other sounds, such as music.

You might want to think of an interim name for your baby. This might be "the bump" or "the bun" or an in-joke between you and your partner. It can be helpful to give your baby an identity because it's difficult to talk about him or her at this relatively early stage, and when you don't know the gender.

If you're still keeping the pregnancy a secret in some quarters, using a code phrase to refer to the pregnancy may be useful in some circumstances.

AS A MATTER OF FACT

At this stage, your baby may squirm if your abdomen is pressed.

He will gradually develop more reflexes: his eye muscles will clench if his eyelids are touched; touching the soles of his feet makes his toes curl; his fingers curl if you touch his palm.

ACTIVITIES TO AVOID IN THE SECOND TRIMESTER

The second trimester is generally when fatigue lifts, and you begin to feel more energetic. This is a great time to continue your exercise program, making good use of your increased energy levels before you are too big and too uncomfortable to move and enjoy being fully active.

While you're encouraged to continue to exercise during the second trimester, there are some high-risk exercises that should be avoided. You should avoid any activity that potentially could cause you to fall, activities that involve a high degree of balance and agility, and specifically exercises that require lying on your back for extended periods, or twisting of the upper body. Changes in your center of gravity can increase the chances of stumbling and falling, risking injury to you and your baby.

The following activities are best avoided during your second (and third) trimesters:
- Vigorous exercise at a high altitude (unless you are used to it)
- Diving and scuba diving
- Road or mountain bicycling
- Rock climbing
- Skiing, snow boarding, and waterskiing
- Ice skating/ice hockey
- Horse riding
- Bungee-jumping!

Racquet sports You should curtail activities such as tennis and badminton since your changing balance can be affected by quick movements and turns, increasing your risk of falling.

Your 13th week

157

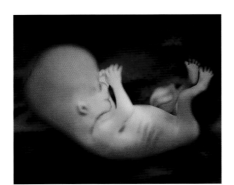

190 days to go...

YOUR BABY TODAY

The developing eyes are now facing forward and the baby's right ear can also be seen here. Your baby spends most of the time in a curled position, often with legs crossed, and hands close to the face.

It's never too early to start planning what you'll need to buy for your baby, even if you don't want to start shopping just yet.

Now that you're in your safer second trimester, you may be tempted to start buying a few baby items, unless you're superstitious and would prefer to wait. A good reason to start shopping in this trimester is that your energy levels should be at their pregnancy peak. In later months, you will find it too tiring to carry your belly, as well as your bags, around the stores and a shopping trip may not be your favorite pastime.

Even if you're not shopping yet, start planning. Ask friends to recommend their favorite strollers, cribs, slings, and car seats, then check prices so you can plan your budget. You might also find that family and friends offer used goods you can buy or borrow.

If you purchase new baby clothes, leave the tags on and check the store's return policy in case you have a baby who's too big for the newborn clothes or you decide against the items you've bought.

FOCUS ON... YOUR BODY

Managing hair growth

Changing hormones can play havoc with hair growth. To deal with any new unwanted hair:
- **Shave larger areas** and pluck out the odd stray hair.
- **Depilatory creams and hair-lightening bleaches** may be absorbed through the skin so shaving and tweezing are safer. If you feel you must use depilatory creams and bleaches, do a patch test first and keep the room well ventilated to avoid fumes.
- **If you're waxing,** be aware that your skin may be more sensitive during pregnancy.

ASK A... DOCTOR

I've just told my parents I'm pregnant but they reacted very negatively because they don't approve of my partner. What can I do? First, give them time to come to terms with the news. Creating a baby with someone is the ultimate commitment, and marks an important life-changing event. For your parents, it is a signal that your partner isn't going anywhere, however much they might disapprove of him.

Once things have calmed down, suggest that your parents take the pregnancy as an opportunity to reestablish their relationship with your partner and wipe the slate clean. Reassure them that you and your partner very much want them to be a part of their grandchild's life, and that you'd rather clear the air now, so that there aren't any negative feelings and tension once your baby is born.

Remember that all is likely to be forgotten when your parents hold a much-loved grandchild in their arms, and since part of that baby will be your partner's that should help them to feel warmer toward him.

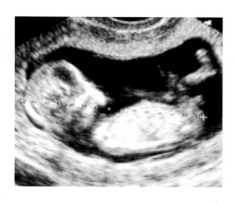

189 days to go...

YOUR BABY TODAY

This 2D black-and-white ultrasound scan is similar to the scan you may see and may be given. The baby is the white area, and the amniotic fluid is black. This type of scan is the best way to measure your baby's length at this stage.

Your hormones have done all the hard work to establish your pregnancy and as they settle down, so should your nausea.

AS A MATTER OF FACT

Your immune system weakens during pregnancy to stop your body from rejecting your developing baby.

This, unfortunately, makes you more prone to colds and bugs. As an added burden, pregnancy hormones can worsen a stuffed nose and nausea.

Morning sickness usually subsides around the start of the second trimester. It's believed that the rapid hormonal changes required to establish and maintain the pregnancy in the early stages may cause the sickness. By this stage your pregnancy is well established and your baby's major internal organs and support system are fully formed, so these hormone levels start to stabilize. This may be why the nausea passes.

Furthermore, there is a theory that nausea is the body's way of protecting your baby from harmful substances in the early crucial stages of development, so you become naturally adverse to alcohol and junk food, for example.

If your nausea and sickness hasn't begun to subside by this stage, don't worry since for some women it does continue into the second trimester. See your doctor if you are concerned about your level of sickness.

There doesn't have to be a loss of intimacy, even if you and your partner are having less sex. Take the time to be affectionate and show your partner you want to be physically close.

ASK A... MOM

My partner hasn't wanted sex at all since I've become pregnant. Will he ever desire me again? Yes! Although it's difficult, try not to take his reluctance to have sex personally. When I was pregnant, my husband didn't want to have penetrative sex, and most of his fears centered around harming the baby or me. This was made worse by the fact that I'd taken a long time to get pregnant, and was also having a difficult pregnancy, with lots of nausea and sickness.

We spoke to our doctor and she was able to reassure my partner that he couldn't harm the baby in any way by having penetrative sex. She also told us that it wasn't uncommon for either partner to experience a reduced sexual desire in pregnancy for a variety of reasons. Although many women experience an increased libido at this stage of pregnancy, the same may not be true for their partner.

It's important that you talk to your partner to find out his fears and explain your own thoughts and feelings. Don't let this issue cause an argument between you. Each couple is different and you will need to talk to each other to find your way through this problem.

You may also find it helpful to talk to someone who isn't so closely involved, such as your doctor or a trusted friend.

Your 14th week

THERE ARE SUBTLE CHANGES HAPPENING TO YOUR SHAPE THAT ONLY YOU WILL NOTICE

Your baby isn't big enough to give you an obvious pregnancy belly, but you'll definitely notice your waistline become thicker. At this stage of pregnancy, many women feel re-energized and have a strong sense of well-being. Healthy eating is very important, so be clued in about the best food choices. In particular, your body needs plenty of protein; and your baby needs it, too, to sustain her rapid growth.

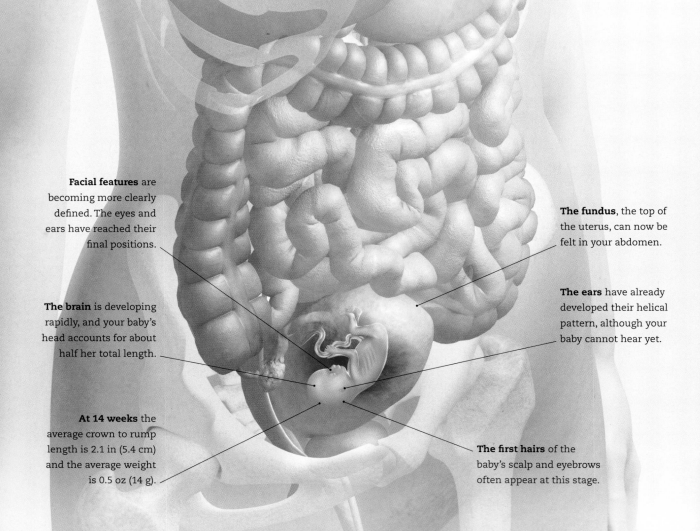

Facial features are becoming more clearly defined. The eyes and ears have reached their final positions.

The brain is developing rapidly, and your baby's head accounts for about half her total length.

At 14 weeks the average crown to rump length is 2.1 in (5.4 cm) and the average weight is 0.5 oz (14 g).

The fundus, the top of the uterus, can now be felt in your abdomen.

The ears have already developed their helical pattern, although your baby cannot hear yet.

The first hairs of the baby's scalp and eyebrows often appear at this stage.

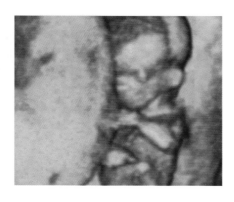

188 days to go...

YOUR BABY TODAY

It's easy to see where your baby's bones are on an ultrasound as they show up as brighter areas. Other features may be harder to see. If you have a scan and are unsure what you are looking at, ask your doctor to interpret it for you.

Relief, excitement, apprehension... it's normal to feel all this and more at this stage of your pregnancy.

While you're undoubtedly feeling better physically, and probably have lots more energy, you may still be up and down emotionally. This is completely normal.

This stage of pregnancy can be a very emotional time: reaching the second trimester is a pregnancy milestone and coincides with seeing your baby on the scan (see p.138). You know that, with the chances of miscarrying now being so minimal, you're really going to have a baby. However, like many pregnant women, you may find that the feeling of relief at reaching this stage is followed by occasional anxieties.

One good outlet for all this emotional energy is exercising, which you may find easier now that you're over the first trimester fatigue. Exercise releases endorphins, the feel-good hormones, and so can improve your emotional as well as physical well-being, but always exercise safely (see box, below).

AS A MATTER OF FACT

Exercising may reduce the time you are in labor.

Research has shown that women who exercise at a moderate to high intensity can cut their time in labor by up to three hours, and they tend to have less complicated deliveries than those who don't exercise.

LISTENING TO YOUR BODY

Check with your doctor or midwife whether there's any reason why you shouldn't be exercising; there are certain pregnancy conditions, such as placenta previa (see p.212) and the risk of premature labor, that may preclude you from exercising.

When exercising during pregnancy, always use your common sense and look out for symptoms that may indicate you are exercising too hard. Aerobic exercise is often tracked by measuring the heart rate, but this is difficult during pregnancy since there is a natural increase in your heart rate, even at rest. So the most effective way to keep your exercise at a safe level is the talk test: you should be able to carry on a conversation while exercising. This will indicate that you are not exercising to exhaustion and potentially restricting the oxygen flow to your baby.

There are other symptoms that indicate you're exercising too hard or should not be exercising at all:
- Vaginal bleeding
- Dizziness and headaches
- Chest pain
- Extreme and sudden muscle weakness
- Calf pain and leg swelling
- Leakage of amniotic fluid.

If you suffer from any of the above symptoms, even momentarily, stop exercising and seek medical advice.

Rather than taking a gentle stroll, try walking at a brisk pace, but make sure you can still talk. This will ensure you're exercising at a moderate aerobic level.

187 days to go...

YOUR BABY TODAY

This scan shows a cross section of your baby's brain, with the two hemispheres clearly seen. From this point on, your baby's brain measurement from one side to the other, taken just above the ear, is used as a reliable indicator of her growth and development.

Even at this early stage of development, your baby has started to urinate, although in very small quantities.

Your baby's bladder now fills and empties every 30 minutes; she swallows the amniotic fluid, filters it through her kidneys, and then passes it as urine. The bladder volume is tiny at this stage, and even by 32 weeks it will only be 10 ml, reaching 40 ml by 40 weeks. Your baby produces very dilute urine, having only a limited capacity to reabsorb water in the kidney to concentrate the urine. However, the placenta performs most of the kidney functions until birth.

Your baby's blood system can now make and break down blood clots. The placenta has been able to form clots for some time, reducing the risk of bleeding.

A small number of white blood cells are now being produced by your baby but she is still relying on yours to fight infection. Her red blood cells contain hemoglobin that transfers oxygen to all the cells of the body. Before birth she has several forms of hemoglobin that differ from yours. These are more stable at a lower acidity and bind more easily to oxygen. This allows your baby's body to extract the oxygen in your hemoglobin for her own use.

The toes are now fully formed and separated, and their individual bones can be clearly discerned on an ultrasound.

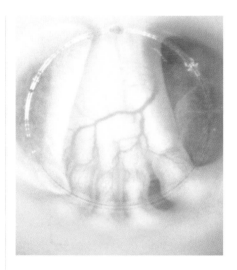

ASK A... DOCTOR

I'm expecting triplets. How will my prenatal care differ? All the usual risks of pregnancy are increased for women having more than one baby. This is partly because hormone levels are higher when there is more than one baby, and, in your case, it will be hard work for your body to carry and nourish three fetuses.

You can expect to be referred to an obstetrician, who will plan your prenatal care with you. You'll have more frequent checkups and scans to check the health and progress of your babies. Although many of the risks are outside your control, if you go to all your appointments and take care of your health, it is likely that you will have three healthy babies.

With triplets, you will probably need to give birth by cesarean section. The average pregnancy length for triplets is 34 weeks.

For more information about multiple pregnancy and details of local support groups, visit the website of Multiple Births Canada at www.multiplebirthscanada.org.

TIME TO THINK ABOUT

Amniocentesis

This involves testing the amniotic fluid and is normally done at 16–18 weeks (see pp.152–3) It may be offered:

■ **When there's** a family or pregnancy history of a genetic problem.
■ **To older women** who are more at risk of having a baby with a chromosomal abnormality.
■ **When a screening test** (see pp. 142–3) has shown there is a high risk of a chromosomal abnormality.

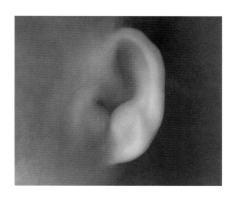

186 days to go...

YOUR BABY TODAY

It is surprising how much detail is already present in your baby's body. This closeup of an ear shows that its helical pattern of folds is nearly fully developed, although it is still too soon for your baby to hear anything.

Your waistline will be increasing and your body shape changing but your belly is unlikely to be very prominent for several weeks.

By week 14, if you stand in your underwear in front of the mirror, you will see a change in your body shape, but to the outside world you may not look very different. Women who have previously been pregnant tend to show earlier than those who are pregnant for the first time, because their stomach muscles have already been stretched once and so stretch much more quickly.

Women often say that this is the time when they look as though they have put on weight and feel fat, not pregnant! But it won't be long before your belly will be visible for the world to see.

If you're feeling uncomfortable and heavy, make sure you choose the right clothes. See page 151 for some tips on how to adapt your wardrobe without having to spend any money yet.

See page 151

ASK A... DOCTOR

Is it safe to use complementary therapies? Check with your doctor before opting for complementary and alternative medicine. This umbrella term covers medical practices and products that are not considered part of conventional medicine, and studies of their effects on pregnancy may not have been done. "Natural" doesn't mean "safe."

SLEEP PROBLEMS

Now that you're in the second trimester, you may be sleeping better, since the urge to go to the bathroom frequently may have subsided, allowing you to stay in bed all night long once again. Or maybe not, since sleep-related problems can affect women during the entire pregnancy. Here are some common problems and solutions:

■ **Heartburn** Lying down soon after a big meal can cause acid reflux, known as heartburn, which can make it uncomfortable for you to sleep. To lessen the possibility of disrupted sleep due to heartburn, avoid eating big meals 2–3 hours before bed. If your heartburn is severe, discuss over-the-counter medication options with your doctor.

■ **Restless leg syndrome** This condition, which makes you feel the need to move your legs around to relieve a creepy-crawly feeling while you're lying in bed, is fairly common in pregnancy. It's a good idea to mention it to your doctor, since it can sometimes be caused by a deficiency (like anemia) that can be treated by taking supplements.

■ **Napping** If pregnancy makes you tired, you may want to grab 40 winks in the afternoon. But for some pregnant women, this extra shut-eye makes it more difficult to fall asleep at night. If this happens to you, skip the afternoon nap and go to bed at night a little earlier than you usually do.

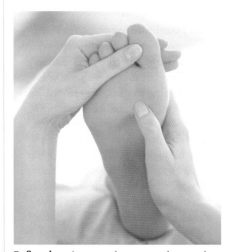

Reflexology is a complementary therapy that involves applying pressure to reflexes on the hands and feet. It's believed to help with morning sickness, backaches, fluid retention, and swelling during pregnancy.

Your 14th week

163

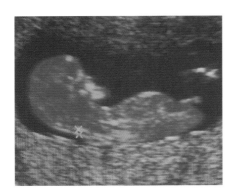

183 days to go...

YOUR BABY TODAY

In this color ultrasound image the baby is red and the placenta green. It is just possible to see the two crosses that measure the depth of fluid in the nuchal fold at the back of the neck (see p.143). Now is the last opportunity to measure this reliably.

Your baby is growing and getting stronger every day, and it's all thanks to her life support system—the placenta.

Your baby's rapid growth

continues and she'll nearly double in size from 2.25 in (5.5 cm) to 4 in (10 cm) during the next three weeks. Muscle and bone growth advances, but, although all joints are present, it will be three weeks before the skeleton begins to harden.

Your baby is now totally dependent on the placenta for her nourishment. Environmental factors have almost no influence on your baby's size at this stage; all babies up until around 20 weeks' gestation are the same size.

The placenta is larger than your baby and supplies all the nutrients she needs. To aid her growth, the placenta extracts amino acids from your circulation, giving her high levels. Amino acids are the building blocks of protein, from which muscles and organs develop.

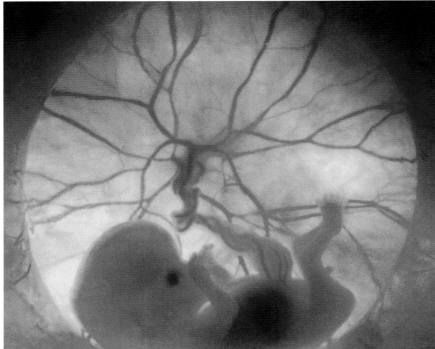

FOCUS ON... NUTRITION

Protein plus

Protein is required for the development of the baby and placenta, as well as to fuel changes taking place in your body (see p.14). The protein requirement for pregnancy is 6 or 6.5 oz (170–184 g) daily, instead of the usual 5 or 5.5 oz (142–156 g). Include a source in all three meals daily. Protein sources include meat, poultry, fish, milk, cheese, beans, nuts, and seeds.

The best protein foods are those that are lower in saturated fat and cholesterol. Trim the fat off meat and eat one or two servings of fish (see p.96) or seafood. When choosing dairy products, pick skim milk and low-fat cheeses. These retain all the protein benefits of the whole milk versions. Nuts and seeds are rich in heart-healthy oils. Vegetarians need to eat a wide range of plant proteins to ensure they are getting adequate amino acids (see p.126).

The umbilical cord can be seen connecting this 13-week-old fetus with the placenta, which nourishes your baby. The incredible blood vessels of the placenta are clearly visible in the background.

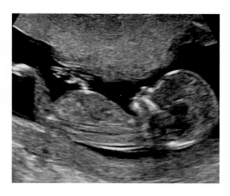

182 days to go...

YOUR BABY TODAY

This 2D ultrasound shows the profile of the baby particularly well. The nasal bone can just be seen at the bridge of the nose, as can bright echoes from the lower and upper jaws; the umbilical cord is rising from the center of the abdomen.

It can be difficult to avoid information overload—everyone, it seems, will have advice to share with you.

ASK A... DOCTOR

Why are varicose veins common in pregnancy and what can I do to avoid getting them? Your blood volume increases up to 30 percent during pregnancy, due to the added needs of your baby and your expanding body. In addition, the hormone relaxin (which is produced to soften ligaments and joints) also softens the walls of your blood vessels. The blood vessels relax and the increased blood and extra weight of the baby make you susceptible to varicose veins.

To reduce the likelihood of getting varicose veins:
- **Avoid sitting or standing in one position** for prolonged periods: walk around regularly, moving your arms as you do so to increase the blood flow in your body.
- **Exercise daily:** most forms of cardiovascular exercise will help increase blood flow. Water aerobics is a good choice since the pressure of the water helps increase blood circulation.
- **Sleep with your legs slightly elevated** by placing a pillow under your bottom sheet at the end of your bed.

One side effect of pregnancy all women have to deal with is conflicting information and advice. One article says to do something, while a friend says the exact opposite. It can be confusing and irritating. While you can choose to stop reading a newspaper or turn to a different television channel, it's more difficult to avoid the unwanted advice of other women. Even more difficult is the advice from close relatives, such as your mother and mother-in-law. You'll need the support of your family and friends,

The second trimester is a great time to pamper yourself with a new haircut and color. Your new hairstyle will complement your glowing skin.

so won't want to alienate them, but don't feel pressured to act in a certain way. Also don't reject everything immediately—some of the advice may in fact be useful and accurate.

If someone is persistently advising you explain that you're overwhelmed by information and would rather not talk about the pregnancy at this time. Or listen to the person's advice, smile politely, and then do what you want. You could subtly hint that you will ask for advice as and when you need it.

FOCUS ON... YOUR BODY

Style challenge

Give yourself a hair makeover.
- **There is no evidence** that the chemicals in hair dyes are harmful for your baby although only a limited amount of research has been done on pregnant women. If you're cautious, skip the chemicals and get a new cut.
- **If you're worried** stick to highlights, which don't expose the whole scalp to dye and make sure the room is well ventilated.
- **When coloring your own hair,** do so in a well-ventilated space and always wear the gloves provided.

Your 15th week

START TALKING TO YOUR BABY—HE CAN HEAR YOUR VOICE

Like many pregnant women in the second trimester, you may now be reaping the benefits of the pregnancy "glow," as hormones improve the appearance of your skin and hair. Enjoy this time and the attention that often comes with it. Amazingly, your baby's ears have formed enough for him to hear you speaking. He'll recognize your voice—and your partner's—when he comes out into the world.

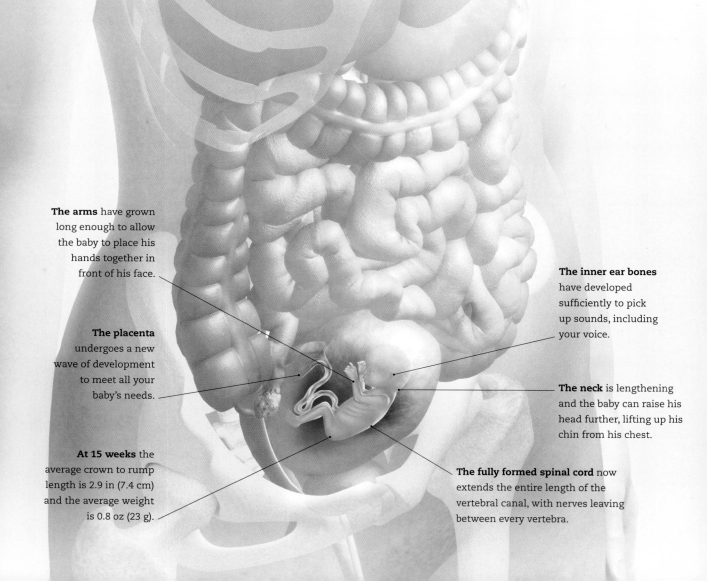

The arms have grown long enough to allow the baby to place his hands together in front of his face.

The placenta undergoes a new wave of development to meet all your baby's needs.

At 15 weeks the average crown to rump length is 2.9 in (7.4 cm) and the average weight is 0.8 oz (23 g).

The inner ear bones have developed sufficiently to pick up sounds, including your voice.

The neck is lengthening and the baby can raise his head further, lifting up his chin from his chest.

The fully formed spinal cord now extends the entire length of the vertebral canal, with nerves leaving between every vertebra.

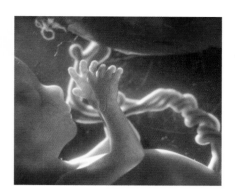

181 days to go...

YOUR BABY TODAY

At this stage, the fetus's forearms, wrists, hands, and fingers are all well differentiated. The eyes, which are visible as dark areas behind the sealed eyelids, have migrated inward from the sides of the head,

Now that some pregnancy discomforts have passed and while you await your belly "bump," you may feel strangely "normal."

You may not feel as though you are pregnant at the moment. The beginning of the second trimester is an interesting transition period: you know you're expecting a baby—you've seen the ultrasound scan—but you may not look or feel that pregnant, and you won't feel the baby move for several weeks yet (see p.213).

The physical reminders that were common in the first trimester—such as nausea and fatigue—may have greatly lessened or passed entirely.

Many women say they feel completely ordinary and find this strange because they think that they "should" be feeling something. Try to enjoy this time and keep looking at that scan picture if you need a reminder that your baby is there. You may long to feel normal once you hit the third trimester and some of that fatigue returns.

FOCUS ON... DADS

The two of you

Make the effort to set aside time for you and your partner to be alone together while she's pregnant. Whether it's an evening out once a week, or that weekend away you've been promising yourselves for ages, do it now! Remember, the second trimester is also a good time to go on vacation (see p.185).

It's common for there to be fundamental changes to a relationship when a baby arrives; some new fathers feel a bit pushed out, especially in the early weeks. By spending time together now, you will build a greater bond for when the baby is born and feel satisfied that you enjoyed lots of pleasurable time together during the pregnancy.

THE POWER OF OMEGA 3

It's a fact that what you eat could make your baby's brain and nervous system work better. Recent studies suggest that women who eat a diet enriched in omega-3 fatty acids during pregnancy and breast-feeding may enhance their baby's language development, IQ, and cognitive development. These essential fatty acids may also decrease allergies in children of mothers who eat them during pregnancy and breast-feeding, and decrease postpartum depression although more research is needed.

Omega-3 fatty acids are found in oily fish. In fact, only seafood contains two essential omega-3 fatty acids; essential because the body can't manufacture them.

Although fish is a main source of omega 3, you need to ensure you don't consume varieties that are high in mercury (see p.96). Salmon and anchovies are two oily fish that are low in mercury yet rich in omega-3 fatty acids. Wild salmon is a particularly rich, and delicious, source of these healthy fatty acids.

Other nonseafood sources of omega-3 fatty acids are canola oil, walnuts, flaxseed, and omega-3 enriched eggs. These sources contain only one essential omega-3 fatty acid, but it is still worth eating them. Note that flaxseed, which is also a great source of fiber, must be ground for the body to absorb it. Sprinkle it on cereal or yogurt.

Your 15th week

169

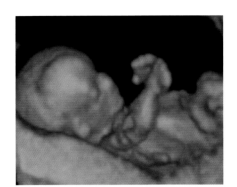

YOU ARE 14 WEEKS AND 2 DAYS

180 days to go...

YOUR BABY TODAY

In this 3D ultrasound scan, the baby is lying on his back. The arms and legs have lengthened and the baby is able to move them freely. His head is still relatively large compared to the trunk and the forehead bulges out.

He's well-developed on the outside, but complex changes are taking place as your baby's internal organs continue to mature.

WORKING DURING PREGNANCY

The majority of employers are supportive when they find out an employee is pregnant, and hopefully this will be the case for you. However, should a problem arise, there is employment law in place to protect pregnant women:

■ **You can't be fired** during pregnancy, unless you breach the terms of your agreement.

■ **You can't be laid off** because you're pregnant or on maternity leave. However, if the reason for the lay off is a legitimate one, unconnected with your pregnancy, it is allowed.

■ **Your employer** has extra responsibilities when you're pregnant, and these include ensuring that your workplace is safe. For example, you should be protected from handling or lifting heavy loads, standing for long periods of time, or handling toxic substances.

■ **If you need time off** for a pregnancy-related absence, your employer must hold your job for you the same length of time that jobs are held for employees on sick or disability leave.

Your baby's neck is growing, and he's now looking more and more like a human being. Internally, the thyroid gland first develops at the base of the tongue but gradually moves down to lie in the neck, overlying the trachea (windpipe). The thyroid gland is producing the hormone thyroxine, using iodine transported from your body across the placenta.

ASK A... DOCTOR

I've developed a dark vertical line down the middle of my belly. What is this? This line is called the linea nigra, which occurs due to changes in

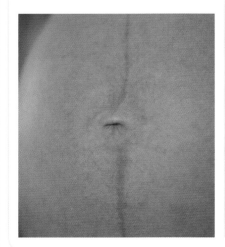

skin pigmentation. It's extremely common, affecting 90 percent of all pregnant women in some way or another, and is often more noticeable if you are darker skinned.

You may also notice a darkening of the skin around your nipples and a darkening of freckles, moles, or birthmarks. A few women may also experience brown patches on their face called chloasma or the "mask of pregnancy" (see pp.190 and 467). These changes are caused by the extra amounts of the hormone estrogen during pregnancy, which affects the melanin-producing cells of the skin—these cells produce the pigment that darkens the skin. These color changes are normal and will usually fade once the baby is born.

The baby's kidneys are starting to function. The nephrons in the kidneys are lengthening and maturing: these essential units enable the kidney to function by filtering the blood and eliminating waste from the body.

New nephrons will be produced up until the 37th week and the kidneys continue to lengthen by around 1 mm a week during the entire pregnancy.

Your second trimester

170

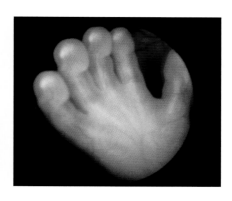

179 days to go...

YOUR BABY TODAY

The hands are well developed at this stage, but, as can be seen here, the skin is very thin and transparent, which means the developing bones of the fingers and the blood vessels can be seen.

Feel free to talk to your baby. His ears have now developed to the point where he can hear your voice.

ANIMAL MAGIC

Do you share your home with a pet? Recent research shows that living with a cat or dog in early childhood may reduce the risk of your child developing asthmatic symptoms. The study found that children residing with cats were more likely to have allergy-related antibodies to felines. Never leave your baby alone with a dog or cat.

Around this point in the second trimester, the bones of your baby's inner ear have formed and he starts to hear. Previously, your baby would have been able to feel the vibrations created by noise, especially when you talked, even though he couldn't hear sounds. Research has found that when an unborn baby hears something, his heart rate might change or he might move. You may be able to feel your baby move in response to a certain noise or type of music.

Your baby can now hear you when you talk to him, or when your partner talks to him (in fact, babies are thought to be able to hear deeper male voices more clearly than female ones), and when you give birth he will already be familiar with the sound of your voices.

ASK A... DOCTOR

How can I relieve my constipation? Constipation is a common symptom of pregnancy, mainly because the hormone progesterone slows down your bowel function, making everything more sluggish. Many women exercise less than usual during pregnancy, which can also cause things to become blocked. Finally, iron pills, which may be prescribed for anemia, are notorious for causing constipation.

There are, thankfully, many ways to relieve the problem:
- **Eat more fiber:** ensure that you are getting plenty of fiber in your diet, in the form of fresh fruit and vegetables, and whole grains, and drink plenty of water to aid the passing of stools.
- **Go natural:** Psyllium (or ispaghula), a common ingredient in some laxatives, appears to be safe during pregnancy, although studies in pregnant women have not been done.
- **Exercise regularly:** Exercise during pregnancy helps to reduce constipation.
- **Constipation during pregnancy can lead to itchy or painful hemorrhoids:** If this happens to you, ask your doctor what medicines you can use for soothing relief.
- **Don't ignore the urge to go:** Ignoring the urge too often can lead to constipation. Take care of your needs, even if you think you're too busy to stop what you're doing or if it means that you'll have to use a public toilet.

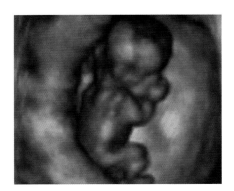

178 days to go…

YOUR BABY TODAY

In this image the placenta can be seen to the left of the baby. The placenta is still very much larger than your baby and is growing at a faster rate, preparing to meet the demands of your baby, who will later overtake it in size and weight.

To function successfully, the placenta needs a good maternal blood supply to the arteries in the wall of the uterus.

The placenta now starts a second wave of growth that will take almost six weeks. The outer layer of cells in the placenta move into the coiled, or spiral, arteries in the uterus, destroying their muscular wall. This causes the arteries to dilate, resulting in a low resistance to blood flow. Only those arteries beneath the placenta (80–100 vessels) are invaded by the placental cells in this way. If these cells move too deeply, they can fuse too tightly with the muscle of the uterus and have difficulty separating after delivery. If the wave of invading cells is inadequate, however, the low resistance to blood flow doesn't develop. This can increase the risk of the mother developing preeclampsia (see p.474), and cause the baby growth problems.

AS A MATTER OF FACT

It is a native Hawaiian belief that the placenta is part of the child.

It is a tradition to plant the placenta with a tree, which then grows alongside the child.

ASK A… DOCTOR

I'm trying to stay out of the sun but is it okay to use fake tanning lotions? Sunless tanning lotions are safer than sunbathing or tanning beds but they have not been tested on pregnant women so their effects aren't known. It may be better to err on the side of caution and go without a tan while you're pregnant. Bear in mind that a fake tan does not protect your skin so, if you do wear it, you'll need to wear additional protection when you are in the sun.

No tanning pills of any kind have been approved by Health Canada. They may contain canthaxanthin and can be toxic to your unborn baby, and also have been known to cause hepatitis and eye damage.

SLEEP REMEDIES

Even though you may not need to go to the bathroom as much at night as you did in the first trimester, and may not yet be suffering from too many aches and pains, sleep may still escape you in the second trimester.

You may find that during this life-changing time you may be having especially vivid dreams, which can disrupt your sleep. Even if you're feeling well, it's essential to get adequate sleep: after all, your body is working hard to create another life. To get more sleep:
- **Eat a late-night snack** containing the amino acid tryptophan (see p.177), which is sleep inducing.
- **Don't watch TV in bed** for an easier time falling asleep.
- **Cut down on caffeine** (see p.66)

and make non-herbal fruit tea your bedtime drink instead.
- **Take a bath before bedtime,** with soft music or candlelight (see below). Make sure the water isn't hot since because this can stimulate rather than relax.

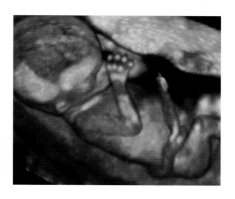

177 days to go...

YOUR BABY TODAY

This 3D ultrasound shows the hands held up in front of the face. The knees seem "knobby" with every bone clearly seen on the scan. The soft spot on the baby's head can also be seen: this protects the brain while still allowing for its rapid growth.

You might receive some compliments, because at this stage of pregnancy you're likely to look glowing with good health.

The terms "blooming" or "glowing" are often used to describe pregnant women, especially during the second trimester. The ideal image is a woman with thick shiny hair and perfect skin that has a healthy blush.

The improved condition of your skin is thanks to the hormone estrogen (pregnancy hormones can have positive effects, too!) and the increased blood supply to the skin; the many blood vessels just below the skin's surface give you a healthy glow, or at least stop you from looking pale and tired. The glands also secrete more oil, giving your skin a healthy-looking sheen.

Again due to hormonal changes, your hair may look thicker. Less hair than normal falls out during pregnancy and hair grows more quickly. After the birth you may find that your hair appears to be falling out more than normal as you lose the hair that's built up during the nine months. Normal hair loss is about 100–125 hairs a day; after the birth you might lose 500 hairs a day.

If you don't feel you match this picture of good health, it may just be that you can't see it yourself, especially if you're still adapting to your pregnancy. If you're looking pale and feeling tired, speak to your doctor because you may be anemic and need to boost your iron intake (see p.154).

In the second trimester, the combination of thick, luscious hair, rosy cheeks, and fewer pregnancy discomforts may make you look as though you're glowing.

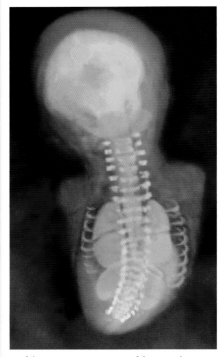

176 days to go...

YOUR BABY TODAY

Your baby is starting to swallow amniotic fluid more regularly: this enters the stomach (seen here as a dark circle in the center of the abdomen). The tiny bladder is also visible as a black fluid-filled structure within the lower pelvis.

The neural tube, the basis of your baby's spinal cord, developed in the very early weeks; now the spinal cord is fully formed.

Nerves from your baby's spinal cord are linked to each set of vertebrae, but as your baby lengthens the spinal cord does not grow at the same rate, and the lower tip ends up lying at the mid-lumbar level, half way between the hips and lowest rib.

Below the mid-lumbar level, the nerves leaving the spinal cord have lengthened so that they still exit between the lowest vertebrae. In adult life, the cord will end slightly higher than in the newborn baby. Because the spinal cord does not extend the entire length of the vertebral canal, a fluid-filled space fills the lower portion.

By the end of this week, your baby is able to use fat as a source of energy. This isn't, however, an important source of energy because that need is met largely by glucose crossing the placenta from your bloodstream. Free fatty acids in your circulation easily cross the placenta to your baby and are used for organ growth, forming cell walls, making myelin

In this computer-generated image, the internal organs of the fetus can be seen. The skull, spine, and rib cage are also clearly visible. The lungs (pink) are protected by the rib cage; the kidneys (red) are below.

sheaths around nerves to insulate them, and for many other functions.

Cholesterol is not only supplied to your unborn baby via the placenta, but he is also forming it within his own body. For this reason, your cholesterol level bears little relation to your baby's, which needs to be high for your baby to produce fat, especially in the first few months of pregnancy.

ASK A... DOCTOR

When can my baby first suck his thumb? Ultrasound scans have shown unborn babies sucking their thumbs from as early as 12–14 weeks of pregnancy. However, this is likely to be a reflex at this stage as the brain does not have any conscious control over movement until the fetus is much more developed later on in pregnancy.

Some research has suggested that if an unborn baby shows a preference for sucking, for example, his right thumb, then he will prefer to lie with his head turned to the right after the birth. The same research suggested that this preference could be used to predict right- or left-handedness in the baby as he grows older.

AS A MATTER OF FACT

Your baby could be tuning in to your favorite TV show!

Research examined babies of mothers who watched the Australian show, *Neighbours*, while pregnant alongside women who didn't. After the birth those babies who had heard the music in the uterus became quiet and "paid attention" to the tune, while the other group of babies ignored it.

Your second trimester

175 days to go...

YOUR BABY TODAY

This profile view shows that the bridge of the nose is shallow and the eyes are still dominating the face. The jaw is lengthening and the chin held away from the chest. The hands (with outstretched fingers) are in a common position—close to the face.

It's worthwhile finding comfortable sleeping positions now; these will stand you in good stead throughout pregnancy.

FOCUS ON... YOUR BABY

Quiet times

Times when you can focus quietly on your baby are precious bonding opportunities and a great way to relax. You may want to visualize your baby floating in the amniotic fluid.

Try this "butterfly" pose with the soles of your feet together. Place your hands on your abdomen and massage your baby using different strokes. Think of your baby and shed your preoccupations with each out-breath.

Your belly will be getting bigger by the day and, as a result, you may find it increasingly difficult to get comfortable when you're lying down, especially during the night.

You should avoid sleeping on your back in the second half of your pregnancy, so start practicing some new positions now. This is because the weight of your uterus will press on the major veins that return blood to your heart, which may result in dizziness, low blood pressure, and possibly a reduction in blood flow to the uterus.

Ideally, lie on your left side (although it will do you or your baby no harm to lie on your right side) since this is actually good for you and the baby. It improves blood flow to the placenta and helps your kidneys eliminate fluids and waste products. Don't worry if you wake to find you're lying on your back: just roll onto your side and support yourself with pillows if necessary.

It's fine to lie on your front if you prefer (your baby is safely cushioned in the amniotic fluid), but the bigger you get, the more difficult this will become.

ASK A... DOCTOR

My doctor is great but she's always in a hurry. How can I get her to answer my questions? This is a common problem. Doctors' practices are often very busy, with lots of women for the doctor to see. As a result, many doctors allow only a certain amount of time for each appointment—sometimes barely enough time to go through the basic physical checkup. However, it is important that your questions are addressed and it may be helpful to write them down so that you remember what you want to ask. If your doctor doesn't have time to discuss the issues during your appointment, ask her to arrange to talk to you at a mutually convenient time. This could be in the form of a phone call, or another appointment at her office. Or she may be able to direct you to other sources of information such as books, websites, or other health-care professionals.

It's a crucial part of your prenatal care that you feel comfortable with your caregivers and are given the opportunity to discuss any questions you have or issues that arise since they will be involved with your labor and delivery, which is a very important time for you.

175

Your 16th week

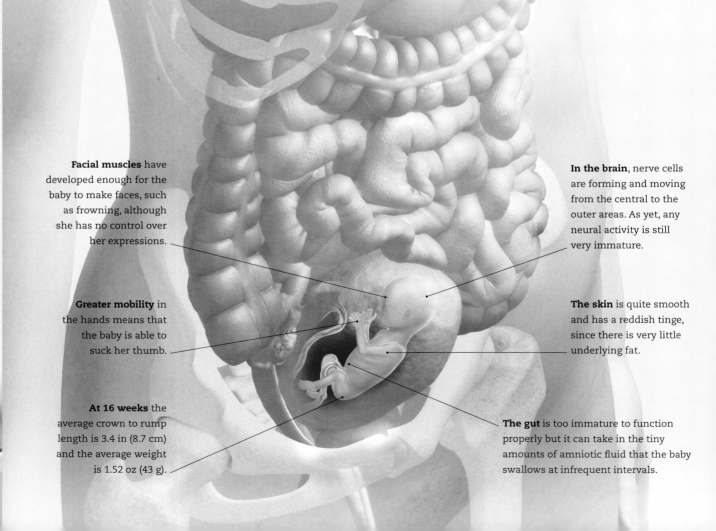

THE BELLY STARTS HERE, ANNOUNCING YOUR PREGNANCY TO THE WORLD

Some days, you'll take huge pride in your emerging belly, on other days you may sigh for the loss of a trim figure. Enjoy your changing shape— you'll probably find that your partner loves it, too. For many couples, this can be a time of increased interest in sex. If you have any emotional or physical worries, there'll be an opportunity to discuss them with your doctor. Another prenatal checkup is likely to take place this week.

Facial muscles have developed enough for the baby to make faces, such as frowning, although she has no control over her expressions.

Greater mobility in the hands means that the baby is able to suck her thumb.

At 16 weeks the average crown to rump length is 3.4 in (8.7 cm) and the average weight is 1.52 oz (43 g).

In the brain, nerve cells are forming and moving from the central to the outer areas. As yet, any neural activity is still very immature.

The skin is quite smooth and has a reddish tinge, since there is very little underlying fat.

The gut is too immature to function properly but it can take in the tiny amounts of amniotic fluid that the baby swallows at infrequent intervals.

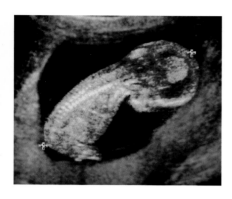

174 days to go...

YOUR BABY TODAY

In this artificially colored ultrasound scan of the baby within the uterus, the spine shows up especially clearly. The two blue crosses, at the top of the baby's head and at his bottom, indicate where the rump to crown measurement is taken.

Your belly "bump" may be clearly visible by this 16th week of pregnancy, and you'll be amazed at how quickly it grows.

At around this stage you may begin to "show," that is, instead of having a slightly bigger waist you develop a definite "bump" and start to look pregnant. You may begin to notice people's eyes are drawn toward your abdomen. If you'd rather keep the pregnancy quiet in some circles—for example, at work—wear baggy clothes.

While some women have neat little bellies positioned more to the front, others have bellies that are more spread out. The size and shape of yours will be individual to you, so try not to compare. There are old wives' tales that if you're carrying in front you're having a boy, and if you're carrying spread out over your hips you're carrying a girl, though this hasn't been proved.

If you haven't bought any maternity clothes, you may want to shop for some or adapt your clothes (see p.179).

(see p.179)

AS A MATTER OF FACT

Twin bonding occurs well before the babies are born.

Advanced video technology has captured the special relationship between twins in the uterus. They have been seen to interact and even grasp each other's hands.

Your belly may not be obvious to others when you're wearing baggy clothes, but in tight-fitting ones it will be quite prominent. Although your shape changes gradually, some women find that their belly gets larger more quickly during some weeks than others.

ASK A... NUTRITIONIST

I keep waking up hungry at night—what should I do? It is normal to get the nighttime munchies during pregnancy, but annoying, especially if you're already having difficulties sleeping. Try to preempt nighttime hunger by snacking on the right foods before you go to bed:

■ **Eggs, milk** (and therefore cheese, and yogurt, too), and turkey are good sources of the amino acid tryptophan, which encourages the body to produce the B vitamin niacin. This helps the production of serotonin, a brain chemical that has a calming effect and aids sleep.

■ **Eat slow-release carbohydrates,** such as whole-wheat bread or pasta. So, for example, half a cheese or turkey sandwich, a small amount of whole-wheat pasta with some cheese, or a bowl of good-quality whole-grain breakfast cereal with some warm milk and honey will fill you up, while also helping you sleep better.

■ **A handful of nuts and seeds,** or some plain yogurt with honey and fruit, are high in protein and will stop your stomach from rumbling.

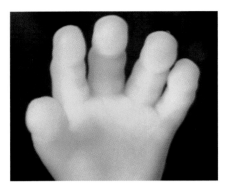

173 days to go...

YOUR BABY TODAY

The fingertips are prominent and the fingers still quite short. Each finger is separate and moves independently of the rest. This is the most comfortable position for the hand, with the thumb and fingers outstretched rather than curled into a fist.

You're unlikely to feel her move yet, but your baby is becoming increasingly active inside your uterus.

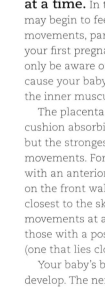

By now, your baby may be active for up to five minutes at a time. In the next few weeks, you may begin to feel some slight fluttering movements, particularly if this is not your first pregnancy (see p.193). You'll only be aware of those movements that cause your baby to make contact with the inner muscular wall of your uterus.

The placenta itself can act like a cushion absorbing the impact of all but the strongest of the baby's movements. For this reason, women with an anterior placenta (one lying on the front wall of the uterus—that closest to the skin) often feel the movements at a much later stage than those with a posteriorly sited placenta (one that lies closer to the back).

Your baby's brain is continuing to develop. The nerve cells that will form the outer gray matter start centrally within the brain, and need to move outward to their final position. This process takes place in waves that occur from 8 to 16 weeks. The migration process is not complete until 25 weeks and electrical activity cannot be detected until 29 weeks. Even after this point, gray matter continues to mature and organize neural connections in the brain throughout the pregnancy. Your baby's body is now longer than her head for the first time.

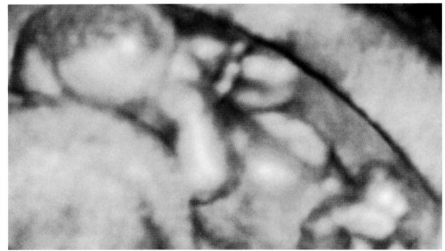

3D ultrasound scanning uses computer technology to produce more detailed images than conventional 2D scans. This scan shows a 15-week-old fetus in the uterus. At this stage all of the organs are formed, as are the vocal cords.

ASK A... DOCTOR

Can using tanning beds and hot tubs harm my unborn baby?
Tanning beds expose you to ultraviolet light which can prevent you from absorbing folic acid, which the baby needs for development. Also, it's been reported that a rise in the mother's temperature, which can happen on a tanning bed, in a hot tub or sauna, may increase the fetus's temperature. A temperature above 102° F (39° C) has been associated with spinal malformations in developing babies, and if a rise in temperature is maintained long enough, it may cause brain damage. The temperature of the amniotic fluid can also increase and it's thought that an extreme rise in your temperature can cause problems with the flow of blood to the baby. So avoid tanning beds and hot tubs while you're pregnant.

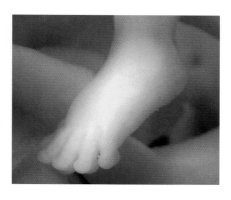

172 days to go...

YOUR BABY TODAY

Now the toes are lengthening and a gentle arch to the foot is beginning to take shape. Your baby can grasp her feet at will but has difficulty bringing them up to her mouth: this is not a problem a little later in pregnancy.

It's time for another routine prenatal appointment to ensure everything is progressing well with you and your baby.

You may have another prenatal appointment at around 16 weeks, if you had your last appointment at around 12 weeks. You'll be weighed.

Your urine will be tested, and your blood pressure measured, as well as the baby's heart rate monitored. Furthermore, the doctor should be able to hear your baby's heartbeat (see p.188), which can be very reassuring.

Women who do not have the nuchal translucency scan (see p.143) at around 11–14 weeks, may be offered a blood test, known as the maternal serum screen (see p.143), which is a screening test for Down syndrome.

This appointment also offers you an opportunity to discuss any concerns you may have, and your doctor will report the results of the routine tests (see pp.122–3) you had at your first prenatal appointment, or shortly thereafter.

If your blood test results show that your hemoglobin levels were low, you may be offered a prescription for iron.

AS A MATTER OF FACT

Maternity wear first appeared around the middle of the 19th century.

At this time a prudish society felt that pregnancy should be hidden. For this same reason, and for the well-being of mother and child, women were encouraged to stay in bed in the weeks leading up to the birth.

FOCUS ON... YOUR BODY

Does my belly look big in this?

You'll need to choose clothes that accommodate your growing belly, but that doesn't have to mean investing in a whole new maternity wardrobe just yet.

The following innovations will help keep you comfortable and extend the life of your normal clothes for a few weeks at least:

■ **Pregnancy support pants:** these stretch with you and ease the strain on your lower back, while giving you a smoother outline.

■ **Pants expander:** an elastic belt that enables you to wear your jeans with a burgeoning belly. Alternatively, loop a hairband—or, for extra girth, a slice cut from a pair of tights—around the button, through the buttonhole and back.

■ **Belly band:** a wide band of stretchy fabric that you wear on your belly, to conceal the gap between your top and waistband.

■ **Bra extenders:** hook on to the fastening at the back of your bra to add up to 3 in (8 cm).

■ **Borrowing:** you can borrow clothes from your partner or friends who are slightly larger than you.

A belly band is a versatile item that covers your belly, enabling you to continue wearing some of your favorite tops.

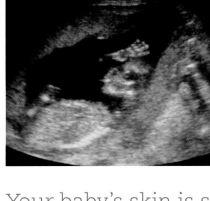

171 days to go...

YOUR BABY TODAY

In this 2D ultrasound, the top of the baby's head is in shadow, although the hand can be seen in front of the face. All the bones are growing and maturing at this stage of pregnancy.

Your baby's skin is still transparent and there is little fat lying beneath it at this stage of the pregnancy.

Your baby's skin is made from three layers. The outer layer is the epidermis, and beneath this lie the dermis layer, and the subcutaneous layer. The epidermis started as a single layer of cells but is now three or four cells thick. The most superficial layer of epidermal cells flatten but do not harden until much later.

The dermis is made from connective tissue comprising collagen (90 percent) and elastin fibers that allow for stretch and resistance. Within the dermis are blood vessels and nerves that support the epidermis and provide sensory feedback. At first, the junction between the dermis and epidermis is smooth, but increasingly dermal ridges form and it becomes irregular.

At the same time your baby starts to develop hair follicles. There is no significant subcutaneous fat present at this stage and the skin is almost transparent. Fat plays a part in temperature control and acts as a barrier to the passage of water. These barriers are not yet in place so the skin is still very permeable.

AS A MATTER OF FACT

Low-dose aspirin may reduce the risk of preeclampsia in women at the highest-risk.

Some research has shown that mothers who previously had severe early preeclampsia who take low-dose aspirin (81 mg daily) can lower their risk of getting it again. But don't use aspirin unless directed by your doctor, since it can cause serious side effects.

FOCUS ON... DADS

The "goddess" within

Your partner may have mixed feelings about her changing shape. She may at times appear to be a "pregnant goddess" who enjoys the fact that she's carrying a child. After all, there is nothing more female than being able to conceive and give birth. When she feels positive about this, she may seem strong and content.

However, at other times, rather than loving her belly she may feel down about gaining weight and losing her body shape. When some fashion magazines show extremely thin women as a symbol of "beauty," it is little wonder that the arrival of the belly can trigger a number of conflicting feelings in a pregnant woman, making her sometimes doubt her looks and knocking her self-esteem.

You can help your partner by steering her toward her more positive "goddess" side and reassuring her about her looks. It helps to remind her that what she's doing is amazing and that you think she's absolutely gorgeous.

Boost her self-esteem: as her body changes shape, make her feel beautiful and wanted.

170 days to go...

YOUR BABY TODAY

Here the baby is seen within the amniotic sac. For the first time, her head is smaller than her body, marking another developmental milestone. Having a large, heavy head is not a problem in the nearly weightless environment of the uterus.

Your doctor may speak to you about writing a birth plan so she can get an idea of the type of labor and birth you want.

The purpose of a birth plan is to communicate your wishes for labor and birth to those who are caring for you. Writing a plan will help you to address different aspects of the labor, such as methods of pain relief and who you'd like to attend the birth. It also gives you a chance to ask questions about procedures such as induction and other types of medical intervention. Filling in a plan is also a useful way for your birth partner to be made aware of

your wishes so that he or she can communicate these to the doctor while you're in labor.

Bear in mind that circumstances may dictate that not all of your preferences are met, but there's more chance of you getting the labor and birth you want if you've thought it through and written down your views. Being as informed as possible about labor and your choices (see pp.302–3) will help you to prepare in advance.

ASK A... DOCTOR

I have dry eyes and am finding it hard to wear my contact lenses. What can I do? During pregnancy, hormonal changes may cause your eyes to feel dry, and you may experience burning, itching, and a feeling that there is a foreign object under your eyelid. This is common in pregnancy. Dry eyes can also occur after menopause, when there are similar hormonal fluctuations.

The condition appears to be caused by a change in the composition and quantity of tears, leaving the eye dry and inadequately lubricated. The discomfort can be remedied with "artificial tears" (see right), available from an optician or pharmacist, and

it usually disappears once the baby is born. In the meantime, limit the time you wear your lenses and wear your glasses more often, especially if you are looking at a computer screen for long periods of time.

TIME TO THINK ABOUT

Your birth plan

Scented candles, womb music, and beanbags... or serious pain relief from the first contraction? Writing a birth plan is an opportunity for you to think about how you'd like your labor and delivery to go. Discuss your birth plan with your doctor and birth partner as early as this week, so you're all clear about your objectives (see pp.302–3).

■ **Write everything down:** your birth partner(s), pain-relief preferences, whether you'd like an active labor, and the environment you'd prefer to give birth in. You might know you want to give birth in the hospital or at home, or in a birth center, which offers a home-style setting with the backup of medical technology.

■ **Be specific:** for example, you might want to use a birthing pool to labor in or want to give birth in an upright position. You might want minimal medical intervention.

■ **Be flexible:** labor doesn't always go according to plan and your baby's safe delivery is the most important thing.

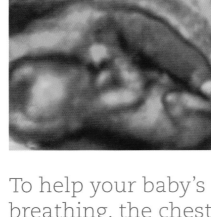

169 days to go...

YOUR BABY TODAY

The upper limbs are well differentiated into forearms, wrists, hands, and fingers; these develop at a faster rate than the lower limbs, a feature that continues even after the birth.

To help your baby's lungs expand and develop in preparation for breathing, the chest wall must be fully bathed in amniotic fluid.

FOCUS ON... RELATIONSHIPS

Surprisingly sexy

You may be taken aback by a sudden increase in your libido. Often, in the second trimester, women find that they feel far more energetic and sexy. The increased blood flow to the pelvic area combined with an increased lubrication of the vagina means that, in theory, having sex can be better than ever.

High levels of progesterone and estrogen make your breasts and vagina super sensitive so expect to become more easily aroused during foreplay. You may also find that you orgasm more quickly than usual. The uterus tightens when you orgasm, so be prepared for this.

Your partner may be delighted by this up-turn in events, as well as approving of a beautiful rounded body to explore, but if he isn't responding positively, talk to him about how he's feeling.

In this close-up the baby's left arm and chest wall can be seen. Because the skin is almost transparent the ribs are easy to see. They are very soft at this stage and still predominantly made of cartilage.

Your baby's lungs continue to branch and divide. The cells lining the airways constantly produce fluid that leaves the lungs when your baby makes breathing movements. The release of this fluid is regulated by the vocal cords within the larynx.

In addition to fluid, the lungs have glands that produce mucus. Cells with tiny hairlike structures, known as cilia, have appeared that help move the mucus. This production of mucus is important once the baby is born to prevent the constant flow of air from drying the lining of the lungs, to trap dust particles, and to act as a barrier to infection.

Because the gut is still very immature, the gradual increase in amniotic fluid is due to the relatively low frequency of fetal swallowing. By 37 weeks your baby will be swallowing 1.75 pints (almost a liter), half of the total amniotic fluid volume, each day.

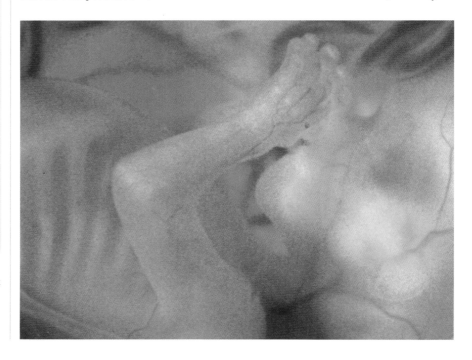

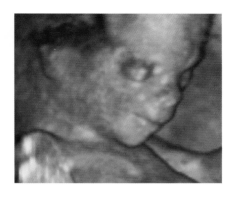

168 days to go...

YOUR BABY TODAY

As your baby's skin starts to become more waterproof, the amniotic fluid is increasingly made from urine produced by your baby's kidneys and bladder. This urine does not contain waste products, since these are transported across the placenta.

It's natural that your partner will want to protect you and his baby, but you may need to help him get the balance right.

AS A MATTER OF FACT

Dads-to-be tend to have more vivid dreams than usual.

Pending fatherhood can make a man think about his own background and roots, and trigger dreams of parents and grandparents. As he becomes more protective and nurturing, he may even dream that he's pregnant.

Is your partner worried about you having a sip of wine or eating a tad too much chocolate, or is he constantly checking that you're getting enough rest? You may find that your partner becomes very protective of you and his baby and while some women enjoy the attention, others find it irritating. If it bothers you, ask your partner why he feels the need to be so protective. If you can understand his feelings and concerns, it can help.

Take the time to explain to him how you feel, and if everything is going well and you're feeling great, let him know. Explain that pregnancy is not an illness and is a natural process, and reassure him that you're being well looked after by the doctor. For further reassurance, you could get him some reading material and involve him by inviting him along to a prenatal appointment. He may have particular questions he wants to ask the doctor.

STRENGTHENING YOUR LEGS

A strong and toned lower body can be achieved by doing the exercises shown below. Strengthening these muscles will make day-to-day tasks, such as walking and climbing the stairs, a lot easier as your baby grows. Strengthening your leg muscles can also help prepare you for labor positions, such as squatting.

Lie on your side. Place both legs in front of your body, bent at the knee at a 90-degree angle. Slowly lift your top leg up and lower it to the starting position. Repeat 30 times, if comfortable. If you need to, you can place a pillow under your belly for support.

Flex your foot

Place your hand on your hip

Support your head

Lie on your side, with your lower leg slightly bent at the knee and top leg positioned at a 45-degree angle. Lift your leg slightly (about 4 in/10 cm), hold for 10 seconds, and then lower back to 45 degrees. Repeat 30 times, if comfortable.

Raise your upper leg

Lower leg slightly bent

Your 17th week

YOUR BABY IS INCREASING HIS MOVEMENTS AND EVEN DOING SOMERSAULTS

Things are becoming lively in your uterus. Your baby has plenty of room to move around and he's making the most of it, stretching and turning. All the activity is good for his future physical and mental development. You might feel like some relaxation, so think about taking a break. The second trimester is usually regarded as the best time in pregnancy for traveling and getting out and about.

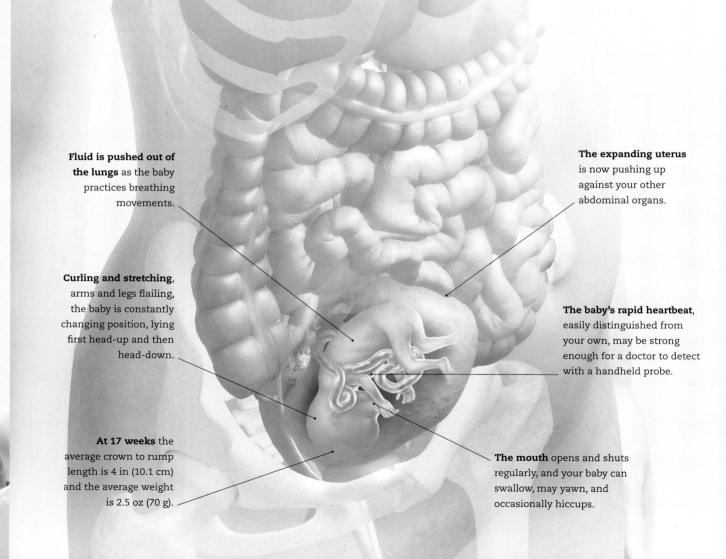

Fluid is pushed out of the lungs as the baby practices breathing movements.

The expanding uterus is now pushing up against your other abdominal organs.

Curling and stretching, arms and legs flailing, the baby is constantly changing position, lying first head-up and then head-down.

The baby's rapid heartbeat, easily distinguished from your own, may be strong enough for a doctor to detect with a handheld probe.

At 17 weeks the average crown to rump length is 4 in (10.1 cm) and the average weight is 2.5 oz (70 g).

The mouth opens and shuts regularly, and your baby can swallow, may yawn, and occasionally hiccups.

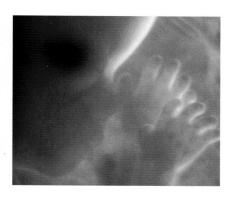

YOU ARE 16 WEEKS AND 1 DAY

167 days to go...

YOUR BABY TODAY

At this stage of development, your baby's lips and mouth are well formed, and she can open and close her mouth and swallow. Inside her mouth, her taste buds are now mature, but she cannot taste anything yet because nerve connections are immature.

Since this is considered a safe stage of pregnancy, with no, or few, symptoms to contend with, it's a great time to go on vacation.

At this time, you're likely to be over the sickness and fatigue of the first trimester and not overburdened by, or uncomfortable from, a large belly yet. You can also rest easy knowing that your baby is developing well, with very little chance of a miscarriage occurring. Going on vacation is a great opportunity to spend quality time with your partner and pamper yourselves.

Relax and enjoy yourself, but be aware of the extra health precautions you need to take during pregnancy (see below and pp.28–9). If you've had any complications, check with your doctor that it is safe to go on vacation.

You can enjoy hot climates but you may feel more comfortable sitting in the shade. If you're exposed to the sun, wear a high SPF sunscreen because your skin is likely to be more sensitive to the sun while you're pregnant.

FOCUS ON... SAFETY

Enjoy a healthy vacation

If you go on vacation while you're pregnant, there are a few additional factors to consider, not least the fact that you might not have as much energy as you had before:

■ **Give yourself plenty of time** when you're trying to finish all those pre-vacation preparations at home and at work; getting ready for a vacation can be stressful. Pack hand luggage for a flight sensibly so that you won't have to carry heavy bags with you.

■ **Plan a car trip carefully,** bearing in mind that you may need more bathroom stops or snack breaks than usual.

■ **Be aware that sightseeing** will be more tiring than usual, so pace yourself and allow yourself to spend time in a café, just watching the world go by.

■ **If you're abroad,** drink bottled water —lots of it, especially if you're in a hot climate. Avoid having ice in your drinks since this tends to be made using tap water.

■ **Peel fruit** or wash fruit and vegetables with bottled water.

■ **If you get diarrhea,** it's even more important than usual to drink plenty of water to replace the fluid you've lost. Don't take diarrhea medication and check with your doctor before taking any type of treatment for diarrhea. If your urine is very concentrated and you can't keep fluid down, see a doctor.

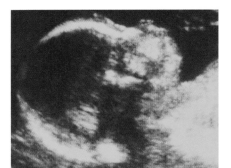

166 days to go...

YOUR BABY TODAY

In this color 2D ultrasound scan the baby is facing upward. The skull bones reflect the ultrasound beam most effectively and show as bright areas. The curved frontal bone of the forehead is seen just above the short nasal bone forming the bridge of the nose.

Your baby is at his most mobile about now, and he may even be doing somersaults in your uterus.

ASK A... DOCTOR

What is DVT and am I at increased risk of it when I fly?

DVT stands for deep vein thrombosis, a condition in which a blood clot forms in a deep leg vein. DVT partially or completely blocks the blood flow in the vein, causing pain and discomfort. The most serious form of DVT is a pulmonary embolism, when part of the clot breaks off and travels to the lungs, blocking a pulmonary artery. This can cause chest pain, shortness of breath, and blood-tinged phlegm to be coughed up. In severe cases, a pulmonary embolism can be fatal.

Pregnancy is considered to be a thrombotic condition, meaning it can lead to clots forming in blood vessels, so you are at increased risk of DVT even when you're not traveling by plane. Women who have previously had DVT or who are obese are more at risk of getting the condition.

Wearing support stockings (see p.225), drinking plenty of fluids, and moving around while flying can help prevent DVT. If you've had blood-clotting issues in the past, avoid flying at all during pregnancy.

There are several ways in which your baby can now move: he can curl and stretch his trunk, move his head up and down and from side to side, and move his arms and legs independently. Regular chest wall breathing movements occur, along with occasional hiccups. The mouth can open and shut, and your baby can yawn and swallow amniotic fluid. He'll bring his hands up to the face and prefer lying on his side rather than back. He has plenty of space in which to move.

Your baby's taste buds first appeared at 10 weeks and by now have an appearance very close to that of a mature taste bud. They also have their own nerve supply, connected to a branch of the facial nerve. Because these neural connections have not yet matured, it is too early for your baby to be able to taste anything.

FOCUS ON... TWINS

How your babies interact

By now, you may be starting to feel your twin babies move. Contact between them probably began a few weeks ago, long before you knew

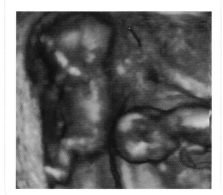

about it, and it becomes more complex as their brains develop. By this stage of pregnancy, a baby has the elementary brain circuits that help him feel the parts of his body and appreciate their position, so it's no wonder that your babies can now interact at a basic level.

Your babies will move around 50 times an hour and can touch each other, even though in all but a tiny percentage of cases they're in separate amniotic sacs so there's a membrane between them. Ultrasound studies show that twin babies make physical contact and sometimes react to each other's touch and pressure.

165 days to go...

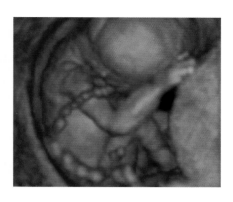

YOUR BABY TODAY

This 3D scan is taken from a viewpoint above the baby's head and looking over the shoulder, but since the baby is curled up the face cannot be seen. The placenta is to the right of the image, with the umbilical cord over the baby's arm.

While you're pregnant, it's even more important to find ways to relieve stress and keep any worries in perspective.

RELIEVING STRESS

Learn to recognize the signs that you're stressed: you may feel your heart racing or a rise in your body temperature. When you know you're stressed, take action.

■ **Identify the cause** and try to keep it in perspective. Let go of the stress by breathing deeply and relaxing your muscles. Imagine blowing the stress away as you exhale.

■ **Stay busy**—sometimes having too much time to think can make you more stressed.

■ **Go swimming:** it's a great stress reliever and a fantastic way to stay in shape, too.

■ **Take time to relax,** especially if you have a lot on your mind or are juggling lots of things. Put your feet up, watch TV, read a book, or think about your growing baby.

■ **Talk through your problems** with your partner or a close friend. If you're worrying about any aspect of your health or how your baby is developing, seek reassurance from your doctor.

■ **If work is an issue,** be honest with your boss or the human resources department and they may be able to help. Your most important job right now is to nurture your baby.

You may be pregnant and happy, but life goes on: you might still be working full time, as well as running a home, and you're bound to have stressful days and times when you feel you can't cope. And, of course, you're still contending with those challenging pregnancy hormones that can cause some emotional ups and downs.

Like many women, you may become stressed about the big changes that are going to happen, and worry about factors such as finances, whether you'll be a good mother, and how your relationship will change. It's important to keep worries in perspective and maintain an emotional balance because being stressed isn't good for your health or that of your baby.

Find ways to destress (see left), as well as talking to others—your partner, friends, and doctor—about any concerns.

AS A MATTER OF FACT

A mother's stress can be transmitted to the fetus.

The level of the stress hormone cortisol in the amniotic fluid matches that in the mother's blood. Cortisol is thought to adversely affect fetal development.

Your 17th week

187

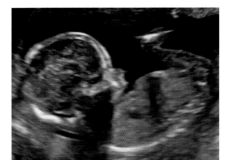

164 days to go...

YOUR BABY TODAY

In this 2D ultrasound, the baby's head is to the left, with the arms not visible, although the knee and lower leg can be seen. At this stage, details of the brain developing under the skull are becoming much more apparent.

Until you feel your baby move, hearing his heartbeat is the next best way for you to bond with him.

ASK A PANEL ABOUT... MONITORING YOUR BABY'S HEARTBEAT AT HOME

My partner is eager to rent a handheld Doppler so we can listen to our baby's heartbeat. Do you think this is a good idea?

Doctor: Handheld ultrasound Doppler devices, which allow parents-to-be to listen to the fetal heartbeat at home, are currently sold over the counter in Canada. Parents are told they can listen to their baby "in complete safety as early as 10 weeks of pregnancy" and "any time they want," implying there is no limit on frequency of exposure.

However, there has been no research into the effects of frequent scanning, which would be more than the baby receives during prenatal care. A Doppler is not a toy and using it in this way is an unnecessary risk.

Midwife: Using your own Doppler may help reassure you if you are very anxious about your baby's well-being, but it is just as likely to have the opposite effect if you can't pick up the heartbeat. Identifying different sounds takes practice and if you have difficulty finding the heartbeat (this happens to midwives, too!), it could be distressing. If you're worried about your baby for any reason, help and advice is only a phone call away.

Mom: I used a Doppler because I am a worrier and it really gave me peace of mind. I didn't use it very often and only when there was a good reason to. For example, at one stage of my pregnancy, I had an episode of bleeding and clots. After this, I was very worried about my baby's health and hearing his heartbeat really helped to calm me down, so it had benefits for the baby, too. I don't think a Doppler is a substitute for medical advice but it's a useful addition.

At this stage of pregnancy, your doctor may be able to hear your baby's heartbeat using a handheld Doppler ultrasound machine. Because ultrasound waves do not travel well in air, gel is applied to the end of the probe or "transducer" as it is placed on your abdomen. This then detects the heartbeat and converts it into a sound that we can hear.

It's quite easy to distinguish your baby's heartbeat from your own since it beats almost twice as fast. However, your baby's heart rate peaked around five weeks ago and, since then, has slowed down as the nerves controlling the heart's rhythm have matured.

During the second half of pregnancy, the range of the heartbeat is between 120 and 160 beats per minute and will be responsive to many stimuli, as well as to your baby's activity.

AS A MATTER OF FACT

The baby's heart rate is not an indication of gender.

A study in the mid-1990s, using over 10,000 measurements, dispelled the theory that the speed of a baby's heartbeat predicted whether it would be a boy or a girl.

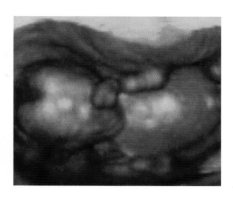

163 days to go...

YOUR BABY TODAY

The baby's face is partially obscured by the hand in this 3D image. Babies at this stage are small enough to fit onto the ultrasound screen, but beyond 20 weeks it is increasingly only possible to see a smaller part of the baby at any one time.

Ensuring you drink enough fluids is essential to good health in pregnancy, so carry your bottle of water everywhere.

Staying hydrated in pregnancy can be a challenge. Because of the hormonal changes taking place, some of the fluid you take in leaks into your body tissues, rather than staying within the bloodstream.

It's difficult to recommend an exact amount of fluid that should be drunk to keep you hydrated, since this depends on many factors, such as the foods you eat (some naturally contain water), your size, the amount you exercise, and the heat and humidity in the environment. Therefore, you need to listen to your own body to determine if you're adequately hydrated. One of the best ways to do this is to look at your urine. If it's clear to light yellow, you're adequately hydrated. If it's bright yellow or orange, you're likely to be dehydrated.

Drinking plenty of water is important. Sometimes, though, if you are nauseous, or just plain tired of drinking water, you may want to try other options for hydration, such as drinking juice or eating more fruit (see box, below). Remember that caffeinated beverages, such as coffee, are not hydrating; caffeine has a diuretic effect, which means that you will want to urinate more often.

In the second and third trimester, dehydration in pregnancy can lead to premature contractions. This is because an anti-diuretic hormone is produced to help your body hold on to water. This hormone acts a lot like oxytocin, the hormone that triggers labor, causing contractions. Staying hydrated will prevent this from happening.

FOCUS ON... NUTRITION

Fabulous fruit

One great way to stay hydrated is to eat fruit. Many fruits are very high in water, especially melons, grapes, and strawberries. The water in fruit is very well absorbed in your body, because it comes partnered with sugar, which helps the water stay in your bloodstream.

In addition, fruit is highly nutritious and contains many of the vitamins and electrolytes that your body needs to stay in balance.

ASK A... DOCTOR

Should I stop picking up my toddler while I'm pregnant? You may be experiencing some back pain and discomfort as your hormones begin to soften your ligaments. This means that your joints are less stable than usual, and injury is more likely.

Lifting your toddler will not harm your baby, but it may cause you discomfort, and you may be more likely to lose your balance. Ask your toddler to climb onto a chair so that you don't need to lift from bending position. To lift from floor level, squat down and use your legs to bear the weight. Avoid bending, which strains your back. Encourage your toddler to get onto your lap for a hug.

162 days to go...

YOUR BABY TODAY

Your baby often brings his hands to his face and sometimes sucks his thumb at this stage; however, the sucking action is not well coordinated and the thumb is more likely to enter the mouth by luck than design. The arms are now in proportion with the rest of the body.

Your baby is practicing his breathing movements, which are vital to develop his chest muscles and enable his lungs to grow.

While he's in the uterus, your baby is practicing his breathing movements and this also aids his lung development. When he breathes in, the diaphragm moves downward and the chest wall moves inward.

Each "breath" the baby takes lasts less than a second. Breathing might only happen occasionally at this stage and when it does it can be either regular or irregular.

Your baby might also open his jaw and swallow at the same time as making a breathing movement.

A single breathing movement with a large movement of the diaphragm may resemble a sigh.

For the chest wall movements to be effective, there must be adequate amniotic fluid (see p.182). This is especially true for the critical time of lung development, from 16–26 weeks.

By the 24th week of pregnancy, your baby will spend approximately three hours in a 24-hour period practicing breathing movements, and around eight hours in a 24-hour period in the last eight weeks of pregnancy.

AS A MATTER OF FACT

When a pregnant woman smokes, it reduces the number of times her baby practices breathing movements.

In a *British Medical Journal* research study, the proportion of time that the baby practiced breathing movements was found to fall within five minutes of the mother beginning to smoke her cigarette.

FOCUS ON... TWINS

Growth rate

While most unborn twins grow at much the same pace, from now on some don't.

Your babies are almost certainly developing all the right organs at the right time, even when there's a size discrepancy. If, however, a scan detects a growth difference between your twins, you'll have additional scans to monitor growth. Lesser degrees aren't usually a problem. Doctors aren't usually concerned unless there's a growth difference of more than 15 percent.

ASK A... DOCTOR

Why am I beginning to get brown patches on my face? As many as 70 percent of pregnant women find the color of their skin changes. You may notice brown patches appearing on your forehead, cheeks, and neck, known as chloasma or the "mask of pregnancy." Darker-skinned women may develop lighter-colored patches.

Chloasma is caused by an increase in the production of melanin, the pigment that gives the skin and hair its natural color. It will gradually fade after the birth. To minimize the patches, stay out of the sun as much as possible, use a high protection sunscreen, and wear a hat outdoors. Try covering larger patches with a tinted moisturizer or foundation and use concealer on smaller patches.

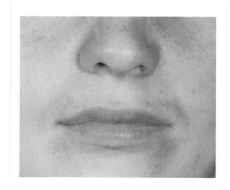

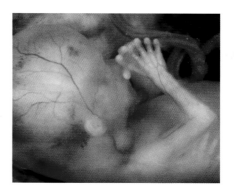

161 days to go...

YOUR BABY TODAY

Every part of your baby has an enhanced blood supply bringing nutrients for growth. Blood vessels are easy to see on scans because the skin is still quite transparent, with little fat yet deposited beneath the skin.

While your energy levels are at a peak, make the most of eating out but choose your meals wisely.

STRONGER NAILS

Your nails are likely to be stronger and healthier than ever, due to the hormonal changes that occur during pregnancy.

Since your nails are in good condition, you can simply file them and they'll look nice even without nail polish. If you do decide to have a manicure, make sure it takes place in a well-ventilated room. Avoid using nail polishes that contain dibutyl phthalate (DBP), an ingredient that is linked to birth defects in animals.

Being pregnant doesn't have to cramp your lifestyle, and it's perfectly possible to eat out safely. You may, however, have to ask what's in particular dishes to avoid eating foods that aren't recommended during pregnancy, such as soft cheeses, shellfish, and raw eggs (see p.17).

Don't be afraid to ask questions about what exactly is in a dish and always request that your meat and fish are cooked to well done, to avoid any possible contamination. Check that all cheese and milk products, including yogurts, included in recipes, have been pasteurized.

You may find that fatty foods upset your stomach and cause heartburn (see p.194), and, if so, stick with foods that have been grilled or steamed, rather than fried. Beware of accompaniments such as pickles and chutneys that may not be entirely fresh. Pâtés and terrines should also be avoided.

ASK A... NUTRITIONIST

I'm a vegetarian but keep craving meat. Is this normal? When you're pregnant, it's common for your body to crave things that might be missing from your diet. You may be craving meat because you are low in iron or protein, for example, both of which are required in higher quantities during pregnancy.

When you're pregnant, it's particularly important to ensure that you're getting the nutrients you need. If you don't eat meat, you can get iron from whole-grain cereals and flours, leafy green vegetables, molasses, legumes, such as lentils and kidney beans, and dried fruit, such as raisins, and apricots.

It helps to have a glass of orange juice, or another drink or food high in vitamin C, such as peppers and other citrus fruit, with your meals, since this encourages the absorption of iron.

Protein is also crucial to your baby's development. Legumes, whole grains, nuts, seeds, eggs, and dairy produce all contain good quantities of protein. Try adding some quinoa—a protein-packed grain—to your diet. Quinoa is a great alternative to rice and is one of the few plant sources of protein that contains all the essential amino acids. It's also high in omega oils, which will encourage the development of your baby's nervous system and brain.

Your 18th week

YOU'LL FIND YOU'RE GAINING WEIGHT WEEK BY WEEK, WHICH IS PERFECTLY NORMAL

Not all the weight you're gaining is your baby. In fact, most of the increase is because parts of your body, such as your breasts, are getting bigger and your blood volume is increasing. You might want to think about signing up for prenatal classes now because they fill up quickly. They are a great source of information, as well as a good way to make friends and compare notes with other pregnant women.

Your second trimester

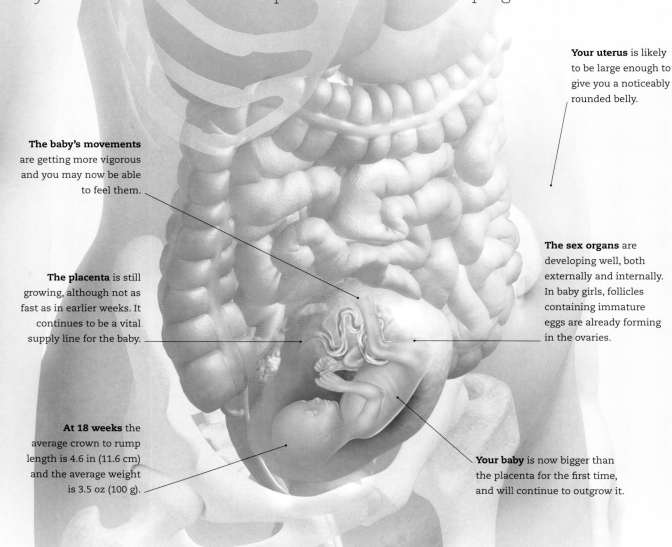

Your uterus is likely to be large enough to give you a noticeably rounded belly.

The baby's movements are getting more vigorous and you may now be able to feel them.

The placenta is still growing, although not as fast as in earlier weeks. It continues to be a vital supply line for the baby.

The sex organs are developing well, both externally and internally. In baby girls, follicles containing immature eggs are already forming in the ovaries.

At 18 weeks the average crown to rump length is 4.6 in (11.6 cm) and the average weight is 3.5 oz (100 g).

Your baby is now bigger than the placenta for the first time, and will continue to outgrow it.

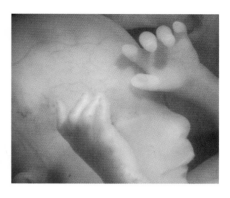

160 days to go...

YOUR BABY TODAY

Your baby's jaw continues to grow throughout the pregnancy, but at this time it can still appear to be quite short. The early tooth buds are hardening within both jaws and, just as with the other bones, calcium is being laid down to strengthen their structure.

Around this time, you may become aware of your baby moving, although for some women first movements are felt much later.

Although your baby is very active, she's not big enough for you to feel any but the strongest kicks on the walls of your uterus. "Quickening" is the term used to describe these first movements, which feel like tiny flutterings or bubbles in your lower abdomen. You may not notice them or not realize that they are the baby at first, since they feel similar to having gas.

If you've been pregnant before, you will be more familiar with the sensation and able to recognize it. First-time moms generally don't feel movements until a bit later, at about 18 to 20 weeks (see p.213), so don't worry if you haven't felt anything yet. The flutterings become more persistent and definite over time, and there will eventually be recognizable kicks and nudges.

Once you can feel the activity, you will become very conscious of them and may become aware of a pattern to them.

At around this time, you may begin to feel some slight sensations when your baby moves around.

THE LOWDOWN

That funny feeling

Was it gas, or did your baby move?
The first time you notice your baby moving marks the start of a new chapter in the bonding process, and it seems it has always been the case, even in ancient times.

In many cultures, until the advent of pregnancy tests, "quickening" was the first conclusive evidence of pregnancy, and was viewed as the point at which human life began.

According to ancient Egyptian, Greek, American, and Indian beliefs, the first movement marked the moment when the soul entered the fetus. Aboriginals regard the location where the first quickening is felt as highly significant for the baby.

FOCUS ON... DADS

Being patient

It will be exciting when your partner tells you she can feel the baby move and a great milestone of the pregnancy, but when you touch your partner's belly, you won't feel anything at all. Just be a little patient since there will be plenty of opportunities later on in the pregnancy to feel the movements. Meanwhile, keep talking to your baby—she can hear you!

AS A MATTER OF FACT

Babies are rocked to sleep by their mother's movements.

This is why you're less likely to feel your baby move when you're active. You're also likely to be distracted yourself and miss some movement.

159 days to go...

YOUR BABY TODAY

Here, the baby's legs are in the typical crossed-legs position. The right arm is on the right side of the image. The limbs and umbilical cord appear to be in a tangle, but the umbilical cord is filled with a jellylike fluid and does not become compressed.

The tiny embryo was once dwarfed by the placenta but now your baby has outgrown it and will continue to do so.

In the early stages of pregnancy, the placenta grew at a far greater rate than your baby. Your baby has now caught up and from now on will be larger than the placenta.

The structure of the placenta will change over the course of the next few weeks as the second wave of cells move into the spiral arteries in the uterus

(see p.172). The placenta is currently at its thickest but as it continues to grow, albeit at a slower rate for a time, it thins out.

Your baby's more rapid growth means that at 2.5 oz (70 g) she is now heavier than the placenta and by the time she is full term she will be six or seven times its weight. Nutrients supplied across the

placenta provide your baby with energy for growth, but growth is in part regulated by her own insulin production and insulin-like growth factors.

Although your baby has relatively high concentrations of growth hormone, which is responsible for growth after birth, this does not seem to play an important role in her growth during pregnancy.

FOCUS ON... HEALTH

Tackling heartburn

If you're battling with the burning sensation and sour taste of heartburn, try these solutions:

■ Eat smaller meals, and ensure you chew your food well
■ Avoid foods that aggravate your symptoms, such as spicy, rich, and fatty dishes
■ Don't smoke or drink alcohol
■ Drink milk
■ Wear loose-fitting clothing
■ Chew gum after eating, except for mint varieties
■ Remain upright after meals; bending can increase discomfort
■ Don't eat 2 to 3 hours before going to bed
■ Raise the head of your bed by 6 in and lie on your left side.

The baby is in a typical position, curled with feet and elbows bent. The well-developed ear is still a little low on the side of the head at this point, and the baby's blood vessels show up well.

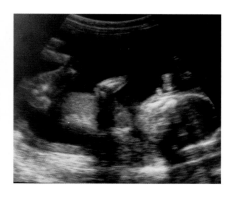

158 days to go...

YOUR BABY TODAY

Although the baby is lying on her side and the face cannot be seen, this image does show the leg and foot particularly well. Because 2D ultrasound only shows a "slice" of the baby, parts may appear to be missing, such as the arm here which stops midway.

It's normal and healthy for you to gain more weight in the second trimester than in the early months of pregnancy.

While you may have gained little weight in the first trimester, from the second trimester onward you will gain weight each week. On average, women should put on 3–4 lb (1.5–1.8 kg) per month from the second trimester to the end of pregnancy, though the weight gain tends to slow down in the last few weeks.

The amount of weight you should be gaining depends on many factors, not least your starting Body Mass Index (BMI) (see p.17). The target weight gains are detailed below.

Not all of the weight gained is the baby; in fact, the fetus makes up only a small part. The rest of the weight is accounted for by your growing uterus, amniotic fluid, breasts, and increased blood volume and fat (see p.99).

If you have any concerns about your weight, seek advice from your doctor. Your weight may not be checked routinely at your prenatal checkups, but your doctor will weigh you if she's concerned about the amount of weight you're gaining.

ASK A... DOCTOR

I keep having hot flashes. Is this normal? Many women experience hot flushes during pregnancy as a result of increased levels of the hormone estrogen. This encourages the blood vessels to dilate—suffusing them with blood, and heat. What's more, when you're pregnant, your metabolism increases, causing extra heat to be produced. That's not to mention the little heater that you have growing inside you.

Wear layers that can be speedily removed and avoid eating spicy foods, and drinking alcohol and caffeine, all of which can encourage hot flashes. Exercise can help by improving circulation, and yoga, and other relaxation exercises, can help you to keep cool and calm.

WEIGHT GAIN

Your target weight gain for the second trimester (as well as the third trimester) is 9–16 lb (4–7 kg), which is considerably more than that the recommended 2–4 lb (1–1.8 lg) for the first trimester. If, due to pregnancy discomforts, such as morning sickness, you had a difficult first trimester and

Weight gain chart

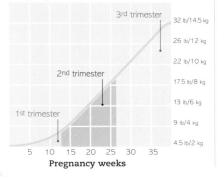

did not gain much weight, this is a good time to increase your calories to try to make up some of the weight gain. If you gained too much weight in the first trimester, focus on staying active, and filling your plate with lower-calorie yet nutrient-rich fruits and vegetables.

Keep your target goal weight gain in mind. The recommended total pregnancy weight gain is 25–35 lb (11–16 kg) for women whose Body Mass Index (BMI) (see p.17) is in the normal range, between 20 and 25.

If you were overweight at the start of pregnancy, your recommended weight gain is 15–25 lb (7–11 kg). Obese women should gain at least 15 lb (7 kg). If you started underweight, the recommended weight gain is 28–40 lb (12.5–18 kg). If you're expecting twins, you should gain about 35–45 lb (16–20 kg).

A safe workout

Alternating upper and lower body exercises keeps your heart rate up. Remember to get your health care provider's approval before starting exercise programs.

The following workout is effective and safe in the second trimester and can be done around three times a week to maintain tone and fitness. For exercises with weights, use 5 lb (2 kg) weights.

Warm up Begin by moving your legs side to side in a step and touch movement for one minute. Continue for another minute but add the arms: each time you step-touch, lift your arms to shoulder height then down. Next, with hands on hips lift your knees up to your stomach. Alternate the left and right legs for two minutes. Finally, take your left arm in a circle across the body and back to the side; repeat with the other arm. continue this movement for a minute.

Forward pull ups Stand with your left leg in front of you and both knees slightly bent; slowly lower your upper body toward your left knee and rest your left hand on the knee for support. Start with your right arm straight down, then lift your arm up, keeping your elbow close to your body. Your elbow should end pointing toward the ceiling. Repeat 20 times on each arm.

Forward lunge Stand with your hands on your hips. Step your right leg forward, then with the left foot in place, bend your left knee toward the floor until the right knee is nearly at a right angle. Alternate each side until you've done around 30 repetitions. (After the second trimester, you might need to hold the back of a chair.) Keep your stomach pulled in, your back straight, head up, and shoulders relaxed.

Squats Stand with your feet shoulder-width apart. With your arms stretched out in front of you at shoulder level, squat down, keeping your abdominal muscles pulled in and your feet firmly on the floor. Lower your bottom toward the floor then lift up to the starting point. Breathe out as you lower and in as you lift. Make sure your knees do not go over the end of your toes.

Upright row Sit on an upright chair or stand with legs slightly bent, feet hip-width apart. Hold the weights with your arms down in front of your body. Exhaling, slowly lift the weights to chest height, stopping under the chin. Then inhale and lower the weights to the starting point. Repeat 20 times.

Shoulder press Stand or sit as in the previous exercise. Holding a weight in each hand, slightly bend your arms at the elbows and hold your hands above your shoulders. Then, while breathing out, slowly lift your arms toward the sky until they are straight. Repeat around 30 times.

Pectoral lift Sit or stand as before. Hold your arms in front of you at shoulder height while holding a weight. Bend your elbows at a right angle, keeping the upper arms parallel to the floor. Bring your elbows together and then gently lift your arms up and down. Repeat 20 times.

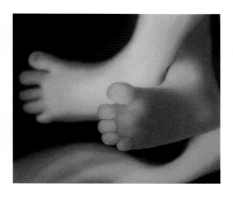

YOU ARE 17 WEEKS AND 4 DAYS

157 days to go...

YOUR BABY TODAY

The skin of your baby is extremely soft and smooth. The soles of the feet and toes are shown in this image and it is clear they are free from wrinkles. During the next week evidence of fingerprint and toeprint patterns will appear on the skin.

Although changes are taking place, your baby's lungs are still fairly immature and won't be fully developed until week 35.

Your baby's complex lung development is continuing.
To picture their growth and development, imagine the whole lungs as a tree: the trunk has developed (the trachea or windpipe), and this has branched into smaller and medium-sized branches (bronchi), but the twigs (bronchioles) holding the leaves (alveoli) have not yet formed. It is the alveoli that have walls so thin that they allow oxygen to be absorbed from the air in them and carbon dioxide to leave via the bloodstream.

From now until 28 weeks the "twigs" are forming that will hold the alveoli that will become filled with air after birth. These "twigs" will have a limited ability to transfer gases but the lungs will not be fully effective until the alveoli develop. The growth of the blood vessels that support the lungs closely matches the growth of the lungs themselves. These blood vessels will be essential for the transfer of oxygen after your baby is born.

After birth, all the blood that is leaving the right side of the heart will enter the lung circulation, but before birth, with the lungs filled with fluid and not used for breathing, only a small amount of blood (approximately 10–15 percent) is directed to them.

STRETCHING SAFELY

Relaxin is one of the most important pregnancy-related hormones. As its name implies, relaxin relaxes the connective tissue, tendons, and ligaments in your body to allow the diaphragm to expand and create space for your baby to grow. It also loosens the ligaments and tendons enough to facilitate the opening of the birth canal for a vaginal delivery.

Relaxin affects most parts of your body and, as a result, your spine and pelvis will also feel less stable, so be aware of your posture and alignment when exercising.

■ **When standing,** always keep your hips in a neutral position. Don't move your hips to one side.

■ **Beware of hyperextending** (arching) your lower back and rounding your shoulders.

■ **Keep all your movements slow** and controlled, and do not stretch beyond your comfort zone. The increased flexibility of your muscles and tendons could potentially result in overstretching during activities such as yoga or Pilates.

Relaxin is also responsible for the relaxation of the circulatory system: the walls of the veins are relaxed, which sometimes results in varicose veins (see p.167). Doing cardiovascular exercise will help increase blood flow and can reduce the occurrence of varicose veins.

Only stretch as far as is comfortable because during pregnancy you're more vulnerable to damaging muscles and tendons.

Your 18th week

197

156 days to go...

YOUR BABY TODAY

This image shows how much less obvious the soft spot on the top has become by now. The fingers show up well here, and as your baby increases in size, it becomes easier and easier for ultrasound to show this level of detail.

As your belly begins to grow and is more obvious, your pregnancy will become the main focus of people's attention.

Are you getting a little more attention than you would like?

Once your belly becomes very obvious, you may begin to feel that it and you are public property. Fascinated by your ever-increasing abdomen, some friends and family, or even strangers, may want to see your belly, touch it, or even kiss it. This can feel very strange because, as a rule, people tend not to go around touching each other's abdomens!

If you're uncomfortable about being touched, then you could politely ask people not to touch the belly, or simply move away. There are, however, some advantages to having people notice that you are pregnant: your belly acts as a warning for people not to jostle you in crowds and people tend to give you a seat on public transportation.

AS A MATTER OF FACT

It's not forbidden to eat salt while you're pregnant.

It was once thought that salt increased swelling and the risk of high blood pressure. But your body needs salt to expand your volume of blood and body fluids. Use sea salt (it contains less sodium) and don't have in excess of 0.25 oz (6 g) a day.

Another unwanted intrusion might be that people feel entitled to ask you intimate questions regarding your medical history and about the baby. This may make you uncomfortable, especially if you tend to be a private

Be prepared for some people to look at, comment on, and want to feel your wonderful belly as it becomes more noticeable. If you're a tactile person by nature, this attention can be easier to handle than if you're not.

person. People you have never met before might comment on your figure, and discuss whether you're having a girl or a boy.

Some pregnant women enjoy the attention, while others feel that people are intruding on a personal experience. If you feel uncomfortable, answer questions vaguely or try to change the subject; ask the person about themself instead. Another way of avoiding the unwanted attention is to wear loose clothing that makes your belly look less prominent and attractive to touch.

ASK A... DOCTOR

I'm so itchy that I'm scratching to the point of bleeding. What can I do? Most itching in pregnancy, especially on your belly, is due to stretching of the skin (see p.255), hormonal changes, and heat. Applying moisturizing cream should help.

If you have significant itching, see your doctor to determine whether you have obstetric cholestasis (see p.473), a serious but rare condition that affects the liver and occurs in about 1 percent of pregnancies.

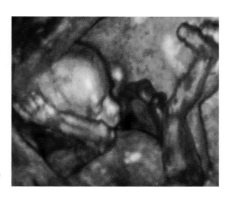

155 days to go...

YOUR BABY TODAY

In this image the whole baby is seen in one view. The legs, held straight, will now be kicking more strongly and, especially if you have had a baby before, you will be increasingly aware of these movements over the next few weeks.

You might want to think about signing up for prenatal classes now since in many areas they get filled up well in advance.

Prenatal classes help to prepare you for the birth of your baby. They usually start in the sixth or seventh month. You'll learn about the signs that you're in labor; breathing and relaxation techniques; pain-relief options; and medical interventions. You'll also be given practical advice on caring for your newborn baby, which can be invaluable if you're a first-time parent.

Depending on where you live, there are various types of classes. These range from classes run by a nurse or other certified instructor at the hospital or classes run by organizations like Lamaze International (lamaze.org) or the Bradley Method (bradleybirth.com). Classes are a great way to meet other expectant parents, and by doing so you'll gain an invaluable mutual support system through the rest of your pregnancy and the early weeks of parenting.

By attending prenatal classes with you, your partner can help to prepare for the labor and early weeks of parenting. Classes are also a good way for your partner to meet other dads-to-be. The significant role fathers can play during labor and in the early weeks of parenting is widely acknowledged, and as a result prenatal classes have become much more father-friendly.

By going to classes, you and your partner can practice and feel more confident about the techniques you'll use in labor.

FOCUS ON... TWINS

Classes for two

Since twins are likely to arrive ahead of schedule, you should definitely look into signing up for prenatal classes now so that you can start them early. Besides, your belly could be very large toward the end, and you may feel less mobile and inclined to go. Because twins sometimes need special care, you should arrange a tour of the Neonatal Intensive Care Unit too.

In some areas, there are special prenatal sessions for those having twins or more, often in the evenings. If your hospital doesn't provide these, a neighboring hospital might. Ask your doctor.

FIND A CLASSMATE

If you're single, you don't have to go it alone. There's no reason why you can't go to a class with a friend or relative—preferably the person who will be attending the birth. If you'd prefer not to do this, you could find out if there are any classes in your area for single expectant moms. You may feel more comfortable in this environment and you will get the opportunity to meet other women who are in the same position as you.

Don't skip classes just because you're single: they're an invaluable way of learning about pregnancy, labor, and parenting.

Your 18th week

199

154 days to go...

YOUR BABY TODAY

Like your own ear, your baby's ear is made of soft and flexible cartilage. Although the outer ear is well developed at this stage, inner ear structures will not be mature enough to enable your baby to hear for about another five weeks.

Is it a boy or a girl? You and your partner may want to start thinking about whether you would like to find out.

The sex of your baby should now be apparent on an ultrasound scan, but you may not have this for a couple of weeks yet (see p.211).

Whether your baby develops into a boy or a girl depends on the presence or absence of a Y chromosome. Males are

Some pregnant women will want to delay buying a complete set of clothes for the baby until they know the sex, but not everyone wants to settle for either pink or blue.

XY and the Y chromosome instructs the reproductive glands (gonads) to become testes. These then produce testosterone and other hormones that inhibit the development of the female organs and in turn stimulate the normal development of the external male genitalia.

If there is no Y chromosome, the gonad becomes an ovary and the internal genitals are female by default; it's not the ovary that dictates that the female reproductive organs will develop but the lack of testosterone. In the female the uterus is formed first and the vagina lengthens upward to meet it.

THINK ABOUT: GENDER

Many women have a strong opinion about whether or not they want to find out the sex of their baby at the 20-week ultrasound, but others are ambivalent. If your partner has strong feelings one way or the other, you can choose to follow his lead. Otherwise, try to figure out your feelings by deciding if you want to choose two names (boy and girl) and get mostly yellow and green baby clothing at your shower, or if identifying with the baby's gender will make these upcoming baby tasks more enjoyable for you.

ASK A... MOM

Our 20-week scan is fast approaching. I want to know the baby's sex but my husband doesn't. What should we do? When one person in a relationship wants something that is at odds with what his or her partner wants, tensions can arise.

Like you, I wanted to find out the sex of my baby but my partner didn't. We both explained our reasons: I felt that knowing the sex would better help me prepare for the birth, both emotionally and practically; my partner said he wanted the surprise element of discovering the sex of the baby at the actual birth.

Talk to each other openly and hopefully you'll be able to reach an agreement. Try not to let the issue get out of hand and consider backing down if necessary. It's important that you feel united at this special time.

You may find either one of you doesn't feel as strongly once you start talking. You could agree to find out but not tell anyone else. If you do find out, don't forget the result is not 100 percent accurate.

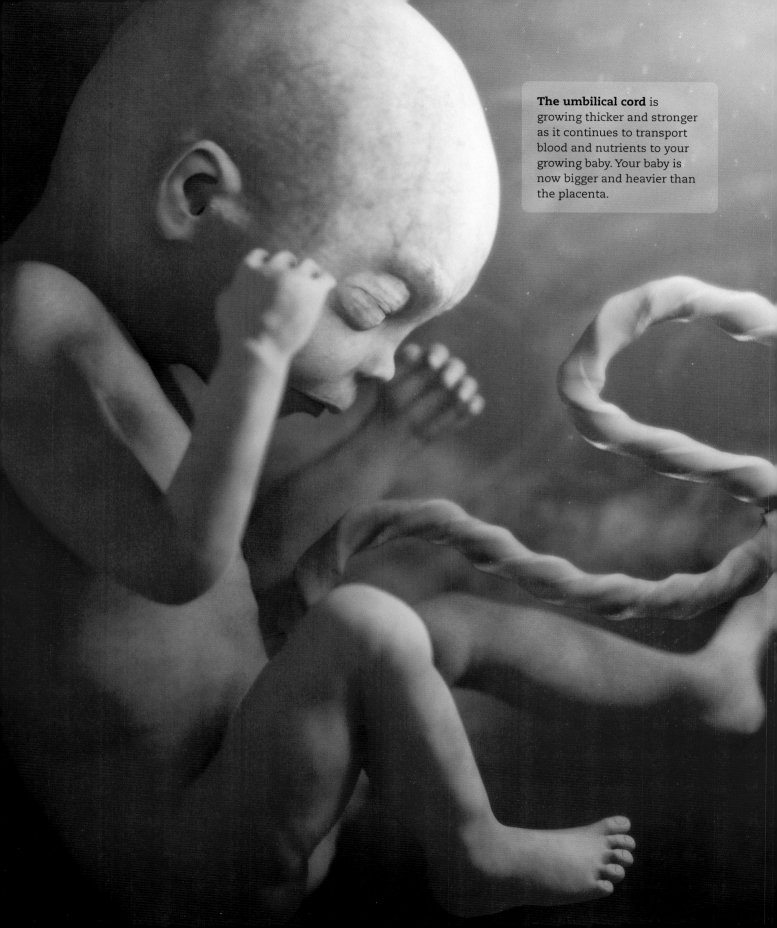

The umbilical cord is growing thicker and stronger as it continues to transport blood and nutrients to your growing baby. Your baby is now bigger and heavier than the placenta.

Your 19th week

YOU'LL PROBABLY FIND YOU'RE BECOMING MORE ATTACHED TO YOUR BABY EACH DAY

It's easier now to think of your baby as a real person, especially if you see him on another scan around this time. He's almost fully formed and the function of his organs is well advanced. You'll be taking your maternal responsibilities very seriously, but don't let anxieties build up. Talk over any worries you may have with your partner and your doctor; many pregnant women also seek comfort and advice from their own mothers.

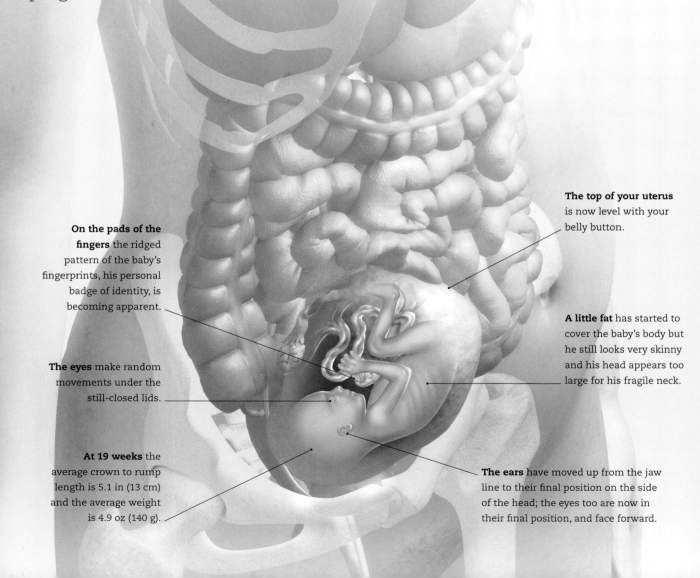

On the pads of the fingers the ridged pattern of the baby's fingerprints, his personal badge of identity, is becoming apparent.

The eyes make random movements under the still-closed lids.

At 19 weeks the average crown to rump length is 5.1 in (13 cm) and the average weight is 4.9 oz (140 g).

The top of your uterus is now level with your belly button.

A little fat has started to cover the baby's body but he still looks very skinny and his head appears too large for his fragile neck.

The ears have moved up from the jaw line to their final position on the side of the head; the eyes too are now in their final position, and face forward.

202

153 days to go...

YOUR BABY TODAY

Anchored to the placenta by the umbilical cord, your baby floats in amniotic fluid. Your uterus provides a warm, protective environment for your baby with lots of room to move in near weightless conditions.

As you approach the halfway mark of your pregnancy, you'll continue to be astounded that there's a baby growing inside you!

The further along the path of pregnancy you are, the more attached and protective you're likely to feel toward your baby. What was once a tiny bundle of cells now looks like an almost fully formed baby—and you will continue to be amazed that you and your partner have made that baby and that this incredible process is happening inside your body.

Once you feel your baby move (see p.213) within the next few weeks, the attachment to him is likely to grow even stronger. While you may have some anxieties at times, try to relax and enjoy your pregnancy—it will be over before you know it.

It's never too early for you and your partner to get to know your baby.

ASK A... DOCTOR

I have a high-powered career and have hardly had any time to think about the baby since I've been pregnant. Will this stop us from bonding? Even if you work full time while you're pregnant, this doesn't have to have a negative effect on your relationship with your baby. As your baby grows, you will probably find that you start to develop a relationship with your "belly" as you anticipate your baby's movements and perhaps talk to him. Make sure you plan enough maternity leave before your due date since this gives you time for practical and emotional preparations, as well as time to rest.

There's some evidence to suggest that too much stress in a mother can affect her unborn baby's brain development (see p.187). This highlights the importance of ensuring you have regular opportunities to relax during pregnancy and so, if your work is stressful, maybe this would be a good time to look at your priorities.

FOCUS ON... HEALTH

It's all a blur

Water retention in pregnancy can affect the eyes. Both the lens and cornea can become thicker, and there can be an increase in fluid in the eyeball, causing pressure and blurred vision. This usually resolves itself after the birth. Exercising to keep the fluid moving, and avoiding wearing contact lenses can help. Notify your doctor if you have vision problems.

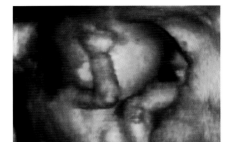

152 days to go...

YOUR BABY TODAY

The sound of your baby's rapidly moving heart muscle can be detected using a simple handheld listening device—the frequency change it produces is converted into a sound that is easy for you and your doctor to hear.

Although you won't feel it yet, your baby may start to have hiccups at this stage of his development.

FOCUS ON... NUTRITION

Not all fat is bad

Many fats are healthy, and should be consumed as part of a heart-healthy diet. The key is to choose healthy fat. For example unsaturated fats, such as those found in olive oil, canola oil, and in nuts and avocados, are good for you and your baby.

Saturated fats, such as those found in butter and whole milk, and trans fats (chemically altered vegetable oils) found in many processed foods, should be kept to a minimum. Substitute good fats for bad fats in your diet:

■ **When making a salad dressing** or in cooking, choose olive oil or canola oil. Store-bought salad dressings are often high in saturated fat.

■ **Eat nuts and avocados,** which are full of healthy fats.

■ **Eat white meat** since it is lower in saturated fat than red meat.

Your baby is looking more human and fully formed every day, with well-developed facial features and limbs—and he may even get the hiccups.

At around this time, your baby may start to hiccup. Just like your own, his hiccup is a short, powerful, jerky contraction of his diaphragm, which will last for less than a second.

Hiccups frequently follow each other in rapid succession and are often followed by gentle limb-stretching movements. No one is certain why babies hiccup. Perhaps it's due to the immaturity of the nerves supplying the diaphragm, or else to your baby's small stomach quickly becoming overdistended.

Your baby's ears and eyes are now in their final position on his face. The ears have moved up from the jaw line and the eyes have moved from the side of the head to lie closer together, looking forward. The eyes move beneath the lids but not yet in a coordinated way. He will open them at around 26 weeks.

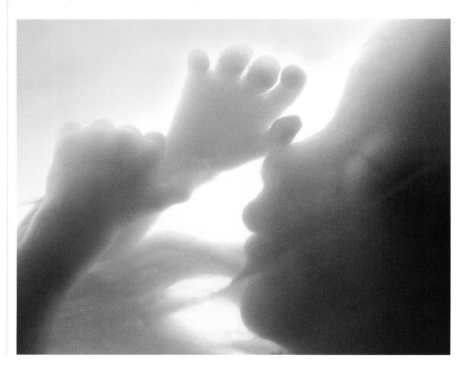

YOU ARE 18 WEEKS AND 3 DAYS

151 days to go...

YOUR BABY TODAY

Coiling is now well established in the umbilical cord. This coiling protects the cord from kinking and from pressing on the umbilical arteries and vein. The coils help ensure that there is a continuous flow of blood both to the placenta and also back to the baby.

Wanting to protect your baby is a natural maternal instinct and it's likely to have started already.

It's understandable that you want your baby to have the best start in life, but this may lead you to unnecessary anxiety about his health and well-being.

You may find yourself worried about things that previously did not bother you. For example, you may use a computer regularly and only now become concerned about the radiation it might produce (see box, right).

Try to relax and keep concerns in perspective; remember that your baby is very resilient and well-protected inside the uterus. If you have concerns about lifestyle issues or how your baby is developing, your doctor can provide information and reassurance.

Meanwhile, you can take good care of yourself by eating well, exercising regularly, and attending all your prenatal appointments.

ASK A... DOCTOR

What are the risks if I gain too much weight? Pregnant women who overeat tend to have larger babies, which can make the delivery more difficult (the baby is more likely to get stuck during the birth) and increase the likelihood of having a cesarean section.

Pregnant women who are overweight are also more likely to experience health complications, such as gestational diabetes (see p.473) and preeclampsia (see p.474). Their children may be at greater risk of becoming diabetic and being obese in later life.

Most of the research seems to focus on pregnant women who have gained more than 40 lb (18 kg).

Taking care of your baby will become your main concern and there's unlikely to be a day that goes by where you don't consider your baby's well-being.

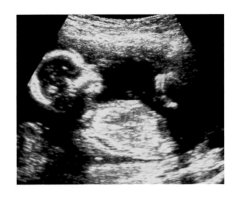

150 days to go...

YOUR BABY TODAY

This is a side view ultrasound scan with the baby's head in the top left. Your baby appears completely human with all fingers and toes fully developed. The skin is now covered with lanugo, fine protective hair.

There's no harm in encouraging your baby to move to increase the likelihood of you feeling his wiggles.

If you're waiting to feel your baby's first movements, be patient. Although it's reassuring to feel him wiggling around, becoming stressed about it won't be good for either of you. Remember, many pregnant women—first-time moms especially—don't feel those first flutterings until 18 to 20 weeks or later. Also remember that while you're awake, your baby spends a lot of time sleeping.

There are a few ways you can try to stimulate your baby into action—the more he moves, the more chance there is that you'll feel it. First of all, stop and relax. If you've been busy all day, you

may have been distracted and not felt your baby's movements. Keeping still may also waken him, since he isn't being "rocked" within your uterus.

Try playing loud music to him, which will not only wake him, but also encourage him to respond. Some women report that their unborn babies "kicked" to a rhythm!

It may also help to lie down on your side, with your belly supported. Doing this may stimulate your baby to move, as he changes his position to accommodate yours. If all else fails, have a sweet, icy cold drink, which may do the trick.

> **ASK A... DOCTOR**
>
> **My baby seems to "jump" when he hears loud noises—is this likely or am I imagining it?**
> Yes, this is common. Research has shown that a baby can react to sounds in the uterus from as early as nine weeks' gestation.
>
> Premature babies react to sounds with a "startle reflex," so this provides strong evidence that babies in the uterus will hear and react to loud sounds, too, possibly with sudden movements.

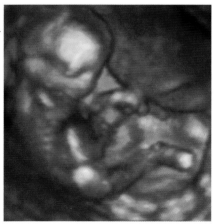

You will probably not be able to feel your baby move yet, but he is incredibly active inside your uterus. Somersaults and stretches

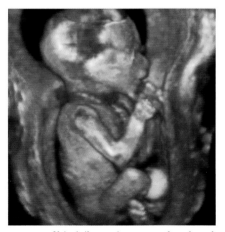

are part of his daily routine, as are thumb and toe sucking. Your baby moves when awake and asleep: he has no control over his

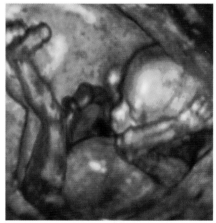

movements at this stage. Ultrasound scans reveal a huge range of movement in between inactive periods.

149 days to go...

YOUR BABY TODAY

Your baby's hands—and feet—look quite large at this stage in pregnancy: it is as if your baby needs time to grow into them. The past few weeks have seen rapid changes in the hands and feet and it's now time for the limbs to catch up.

Your baby's fingers and toes are fully developed and their unique prints are beginning to form.

Your baby will be a unique individual and his fingerprints will be proof of this. The ridge patterns in the dermis that will eventually form fingerprints (and "toeprints") are fully developed by this stage of pregnancy. These skin ridges are genetically determined and, as with most developments, are seen about a week earlier in the hands than the feet.

Your baby's sweat glands appeared in his skin in the eighth week, and will continue to increase up to 28 weeks; but they do not function until after birth. The color of your baby's skin is due to melanin, a pigment produced by "melanocytes," specialized skin cells that have now migrated into the skin. Different skin tones are not due to differing numbers of these cells but due to the amount and shade of pigment that each cell produces. Melanin protects the skin from ultraviolet light which damages DNA.

Although unborn babies produce melanin pigment, they do not achieve their final amount of skin pigment until well into childhood. For this reason it follows that all newborn babies are particularly vulnerable to sunburn. Dark-skinned babies are likely to have a light skin tone when they're born.

AS A MATTER OF FACT

Eating plenty of foods that are rich in vitamin E could reduce the risk of your baby developing allergies, including asthma.

Researchers believe that low levels of vitamin E during pregnancy could adversely affect your baby's lung development or immune system. To boost your intake, improve your diet rather than taking supplements. If you eat more than you need, vitamin E is stored in the body for future use.

ACUPUNCTURE

In acupuncture, certain points on the body associated with energy channels or meridians are stimulated by the insertion of fine needles. The belief is that these conduct vital energy or "qi" around the body. Illness or symptoms are associated with an imbalance of this vital energy.

Acupuncture has been widely and successfully used in pregnancy and regular treatments can help to treat a number of health problems:
■ Pain and nausea—a recent study has shown it to be effective in relieving nausea and vomiting or the potentially more dangerous hyperemesis gravidarum (see p.111).
■ Heartburn (see p.194)
■ Hemorrhoids (see p.468)
■ Stress (see p.187)
■ Headaches and backaches
■ Carpal tunnel syndrome (see p.471).

Acupuncture may be effective in "turning" breech babies (see p.433), and can also be used during labor to boost energy and relieve pain.

Use a registered practitioner with experience treating pregnant women.

Boost your intake of vitamin E by eating salad greens, green leafy vegetables, nuts, avocados, eggs, and wheatgerm.

Your 19th week

207

148 days to go...

YOUR BABY TODAY

Your baby appears to be quite thin on early scans. Fat reserves are not yet laid down underneath the skin, which can seem quite thin and almost transparent. An ultrasound image also highlights the underlying bony skeleton, enhancing this effect.

At around this time you'll have another scan, and your baby will get a thorough health checkup.

From 18–20 weeks most doctors' offices or hospitals offer a detailed ultrasound scan, which is termed an "anatomy" scan. The scan is used to check the baby's overall development and examine his organs and body systems (see pp.214–5) to check for signs of problems. For most women and their partners, this scan will reassure them that all is progressing well with the baby's development.

The scan can take some time to perform because of the detailed measurements and investigations taking place. The sonographer can only do the checks when the baby is in the correct position—this can be a challenge, given that the baby is likely to be moving around a lot. If the position of your baby makes it difficult to do all the checks, you may be asked to walk around for a little while and then return, or even to come back in a week or two for another attempt.

EXERCISING IN WATER

Water is a great environment to work out in during pregnancy: the added support for your belly and extra resistance will enable you to maintain your fitness.

When standing, the water should be just above your waist—too deep and you will not be stable enough and too shallow and you won't get enough support from the water.

You are likely to find pregnancy water aerobics classes at your local gym, but here are a few simple exercises you can do yourself:

■ **Running in place:** bring your knees up and push your arms forward and back in a pumping motion. Run for 3–4 minutes, if possible, but always stop if you feel tired. This exercise has cardiovascular benefits, and will help tone your legs and arms.

■ **Bicycle exercise:** stand in the water and place a float under each arm. Once you're comfortable, lean back slightly and move your legs in front of you as if you are rotating the pedals on a bicycle. Continue the cycling motion for 3–4 minutes, if possible, but always stop if you feel tired. This exercise will help you maintain your fitness and help tone your legs. It's also a good way to strengthen your back and arms.
■ **Arm exercises:** stand with your feet apart and knees slightly bent, then crouch to submerge your shoulders in the water. Lift your arms from your sides to the height of your shoulders and back down again. Pull your arms down in the water toward you and push up as hard as you can (see right). This exercise will help tone and strengthen the muscles in your arms, back, and abdomen.

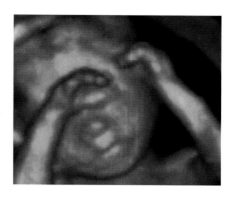

147 days to go...

YOUR BABY TODAY

Your baby has highly flexible joints, enabling her to raise her arms high. This is because her bones are first made of cartilage, which is soft and flexible. Gradually, the cartilage is being replaced by calcium-containing bone.

You'll be getting advice from all quarters, but there's one person you might want to listen to—your mother.

FOCUS ON... YOUR BODY

Taking the strain

There are a number of changes in your body during pregnancy that impact how you can exercise and how your body moves:

■ **The increased weight** of your baby, placenta, extra blood, enlarged uterus, and breast tissue can cause stress on your body, and most notably on your skeleton.

■ **Postural changes** due to changes in the center of gravity can increase your chances of developing hip, back, and knee problems.

■ **Relaxin** (see p.197), a pregnancy-related hormone that affects the ligaments, can increase flexibility and result in improper alignment of the spine and pelvis.

Effective and safe exercises are the most efficient way of maintaining and improving your posture and minimizing the stress on your body (see p.196 for a great second trimester workout).

Regular exercise (especially weight bearing exercise such as walking, and using weights—see p.196) generally improves the bone density of your skeleton.

Whether or not you're already close to your mother, being pregnant is likely to affect your relationship with each other. Many women feel naturally closer to their mothers as they go through this significant life event, turning to them for help and reassurance during the course of pregnancy and wanting them to be there in the days and weeks following the birth of the baby.

It's normal for a mother to respond to her daughter being pregnant by being very protective, so expect a few more phone calls than usual. Your mother is bound to offer lots of advice. Whether or not you take it all in, listen—you may just find some of it useful.

Your pregnancy is bound to trigger lots of memories for your mother of her own pregnancies, so expect to hear many stories of when you were a baby.

Your 20th week

THOSE BUTTERFLIES IN YOUR STOMACH MAY BE MORE THAN JUST GAS

In the next few days, you might feel your baby's movements for the first time. The little flutter can be such a tiny sensation that many women write it off as gas. But what a wonderful moment when you realize the truth! If you want to find out the sex of your baby, it could be revealed on the ultrasound scan you have this week.

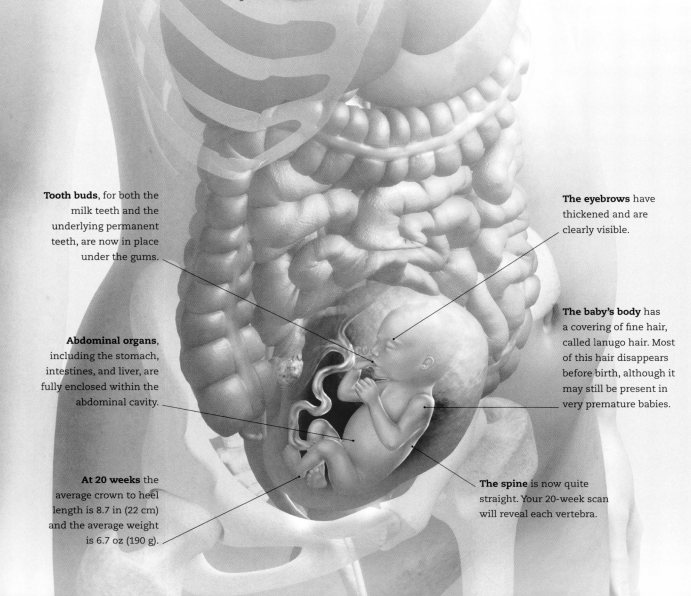

Tooth buds, for both the milk teeth and the underlying permanent teeth, are now in place under the gums.

Abdominal organs, including the stomach, intestines, and liver, are fully enclosed within the abdominal cavity.

At 20 weeks the average crown to heel length is 8.7 in (22 cm) and the average weight is 6.7 oz (190 g).

The eyebrows have thickened and are clearly visible.

The baby's body has a covering of fine hair, called lanugo hair. Most of this hair disappears before birth, although it may still be present in very premature babies.

The spine is now quite straight. Your 20-week scan will reveal each vertebra.

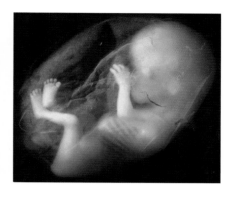

146 days to go...

YOUR BABY TODAY

This image shows the entire baby lying within the amniotic sac. Every finger and toe, and even the lower ribs in the chest, can be seen. Although the head is still quite large, the limbs are much more in proportion with the body.

If you want to know whether you're having a boy or a girl, this is the week you might be able to find out.

You'll have a scan this week and may be given the opportunity to find out the sex of your baby. Identifying the gender is dependent on a number of factors, including the expertise of the sonographer, the quality of the equipment being used, the position of the baby and, specifically, of the legs, which could obstruct the genitals. Even if all of these factors are favorable and the genitals can be seen, there is an error factor, so the information given is never 100 percent accurate. You may be able to identify the genitals yourself as you're watching the screen, so if you don't want to know, it's advisable to look away.

If you have an amniocentesis test (see pp.152–3) and want to know the sex of your baby, it can be identified with close to 100 percent accuracy.

This 2D scan is a close-up of the baby's profile, showing the bright frontal bone of the forehead, the nose, lips, and chin. The nasal bone appears as a bright area at the top of the bridge of the nose.

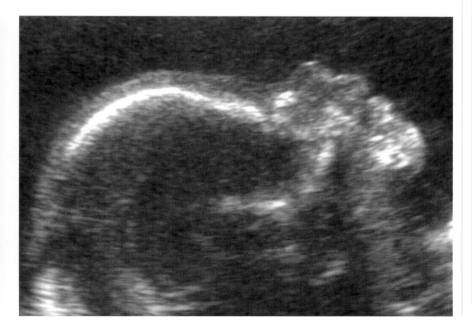

TIME TO THINK ABOUT

Finding out the sex of your baby

Is it a good idea to find out the sex of your baby before he (or she) is born?

Yes...
■ **Being able to call your baby** "he" or "she" rather than "it" or "the baby" may help you and your partner to bond with him or her.
■ **Knowing the sex** means you can choose a name before the big day, although bear in mind that it's not guaranteed to suit him or her.
■ **Decorating the nursery** and buying baby clothes may be simpler.

No...
■ **Not knowing is a huge motivator** during labor and birth for many women, and the excitement of finding out right at the end can help keep you focused through all the stages of labor and delivery.
■ **Remember that unless you had** an amniocentesis test or CVS test (see pp.152–3), there's no way of knowing your baby's sex for certain. Sonographers can (and do) get it wrong, so don't get too attached just yet to the name you've chosen.

Your 20th week

211

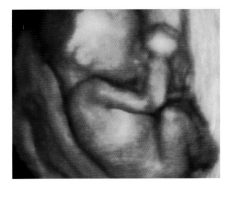

YOU ARE 19 WEEKS AND 2 DAYS

145 days to go...

YOUR BABY TODAY

Your baby is increasingly using her hands and feet to explore her surroundings. All limbs have a full and unobstructed range of movements and the fingertips especially are extremely sensitive. Most of her movements are reflex responses at this stage.

Comfortably floating in her fluid-filled amniotic sac, your baby is made up almost completely of water.

AS A MATTER OF FACT

Pregnant women used to believe that not drinking enough water would make the baby dirty!

While it is important to stay hydrated during pregnancy, the amniotic fluid is not affected by what you drink.

Because water can travel through the skin and the baby is floating in amniotic fluid, her water content is really high, nearly 90 percent. As your baby's skin thickens and becomes less permeable, and her kidneys better regulate the amount of water lost in the urine, her proportion of water will reduce to 70 percent at delivery and again to about 60 percent

by the age of 10 as kidney function continues to improve.

Fluids conduct sound waves but the inner ear is still immature and it will be three weeks before a startle response to sounds can be reliably seen on a scan. As both the uterine wall and the ear drums become thinner, she will gradually respond to higher frequencies and quieter sounds.

FOCUS ON... YOUR BABY

Low-lying placenta

Placenta previa is when the placenta is either partially covering (minor) or completely covering (major) the cervix. In major placenta previa, the baby cannot be born vaginally. Major/complete placenta previa poses a high risk of heavy bleeding, either in the later stages of pregnancy or during the actual labor, which is treated as an emergency.

If a low-lying placenta is detected at your 20-week scan, you may be offered another scan at about 34 weeks; the placenta may "move up" as the uterus grows, and by about 34 weeks no longer be low. With major placenta previa, you may be admitted to the hospital for bed rest in late pregnancy.

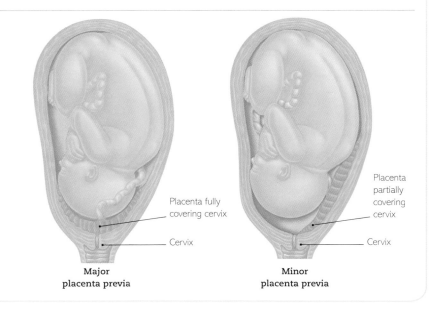

Placenta fully covering cervix

Cervix

Major placenta previa

Placenta partially covering cervix

Cervix

Minor placenta previa

Your second trimester

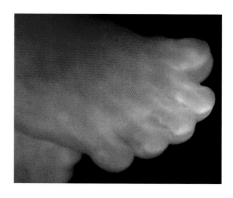

144 days to go...

YOUR BABY TODAY

The toes will wiggle and stretch just as much as the hands and fingers. Your baby is extremely flexible at this time and as likely to bring one or both feet up to her mouth as she is her hands in order to explore them with her sensitive mouth and lips.

Are you feeling your baby kicking? She's letting you know she's definitely in there—a wonderful pregnancy milestone.

At around this time, you're likely to feel that awe-inspiring first kick. While your baby has been moving in your uterus since around the sixth week of gestation, it's only at this stage that she'll make her movements so definitely felt (although some women do feel movements from around 15 to 16 weeks). When exactly you feel that movement can be affected by your body weight, your baby's position, the location of your placenta, and whether it's your first pregnancy.

Experiencing the first sensation of movement, whether it's a feeling of bubbles, butterflies, flipping goldfish, or even a resounding kick, is likely to be an emotionally charged moment. After all, this is the first time your baby has communicated with you, even though she's not aware of what she's doing.

Once you've felt your baby move, you may want her to do it again—just to make sure you didn't imagine it. You may, however, not feel another movement for a few days. Your partner may want to rest his hand on your belly when your baby is most active (usually when you're resting so that your baby isn't being rocked to sleep by movement) to experience those first thumps himself. It won't hurt your baby to play with her, so gently press on your abdomen when she kicks.

MATERNITY SWIMWEAR

Swimming is fantastic exercise during pregnancy, but you may need to invest in new swimwear as your breasts and abdomen grow.
- **Comfort and support:** maternity swimsuits have additional support. These swimsuits are designed to be higher at the back and have more support in the cups. Maternity swimwear is made with stretchy fabric that is comfortable and will give as you grow.
- **Try a tankini:** this is a two-piece swimsuit that has a tank-style, rather than bra, top. It will flash your belly without revealing too much.
- **If you're self-conscious** about your belly, wear a sarong. If you prefer to bare your belly to females only, go to women's sessions at your local pool.

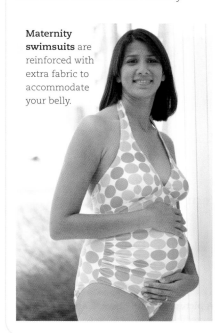

Maternity swimsuits are reinforced with extra fabric to accommodate your belly.

Maternity bikinis are designed with a generous cup size, and the bottoms fit neatly under your belly.

Your 20th week

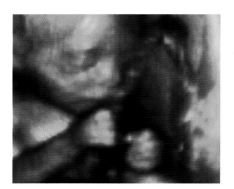

143 days to go...

YOUR BABY TODAY

The appearance of your baby's head is still dominated by a prominent forehead due to the rapidly growing brain. The jaw can seem small but as the toothbuds grow and expand within the jaw, it lengthens and changes proportion.

The foundations are already laid for your baby's teeth—both the milk teeth and the permanent ones that will follow.

Although it's very rare for any teeth to have come through by birth (only a 1 in 3,000 chance), your baby's tooth buds that will form her teeth are already in place within the jawbone.

All of your baby's teeth—both her baby "milk" teeth and her underlying permanent teeth—start their development beneath the gums while she is developing in your uterus. The milk teeth buds began to develop at eight weeks of pregnancy and by this week all of the buds are formed.

The first milk teeth to harden, as calcium builds up, are the central incisor teeth and the last are the back molars, at around 19 weeks. The crown of each milk tooth does not complete development until after birth and root completion takes until your child is more than three years old.

Buds for the permanent teeth begin to form between the 14th and 20th weeks. These lie deeper than those for the milk teeth and closer to the inner edge of the jaw and gum. They remain dormant until it is time for the milk teeth to be lost.

Your baby's milk teeth will start coming through at around six to eight months and she'll have a complete set of milk teeth by the age of 2½.

AS A MATTER OF FACT

Fetal alcohol syndrome leads to serious oral and dental problems in the baby.

Smaller teeth that have weak enamel is just one of the many unfortunate consequences of this condition.

To stretch your calf, lean against a solid support. Keep your front leg bent and straighten the other leg behind you for 20 seconds. Repeat with the other leg.

FEELING FLEXIBLE

Stretching and flexibility exercises should be a regular part of your fitness program at all times, but especially during pregnancy. Being flexible enables your muscles to work more efficiently, alleviates tightness, helps prevent cramping, and leads to improved balance and posture. Stretching can also help you feel confident and calm, especially if the exercises are combined with deep breathing.

Flexibility can be maintained or improved during pregnancy by doing a series of exercises that stretch your muscles in a safe and effective way.

■ **Do not stretch further** than feels comfortable or you risk injuring the ligaments and stressing your joints.

■ **Ensure that you're stretching** when the muscles are warm, at the end of a workout or after a warm bath.

During the second and third trimester you should avoid any exercises—stretching or otherwise—that require you to lie on your back for extended periods.

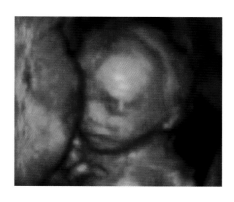

YOU ARE 19 WEEKS AND 5 DAYS

142 days to go...

YOUR BABY TODAY

Your baby often rests against the placenta. This has no effect on the placenta since its surface is protected by the amniotic sac and its composition and blood flow maintain its circulation at all times, leaving your baby free to explore her environment.

As the weeks go by, you'll find that you'll need to rest more and limit the amount of time you are on your feet.

By this stage, you may find it tiring to be on your feet for long periods of time. For one thing, the growing weight of your baby and uterus will lead to discomfort, and potentially to muscle strain. Because your center of gravity is shifting, too, you may find that you stand awkwardly, putting pressure on your ligaments, which are, themselves, softened due to hormonal

changes (see p.197). What's more, prolonged standing can cause blood and other fluids to pool in your legs, which can cause pain and dizziness.

If possible, take short, frequent breaks, so that you can put your feet up. If you do have to stand for long periods, you may find that resting one foot on a stool or box from time to time can help. Make sure your shoes offer good

support (see p.257), and consider wearing maternity hose (see p.225).

It's important not to stand for more than three hours at a time, so if your work involves standing make sure you are given adequate breaks.

(see p.197)

(see p.257)
(see p.225)

ASK A... DOCTOR

The bigger I get, the more difficult it's becoming to have sex. What should we do? As your pregnancy continues, you will have no choice but to try new sexual positions that will more easily accommodate your growing belly.

You can still use the missionary position but your partner may have to support his weight on his hands instead of lying on you; that way he won't press on your belly. However, you'll find that positioning yourself on top is a better alternative, and as your belly gets bigger you can squat or kneel over your partner. Side-by-side or rear-entry positions are also comfortable during pregnancy. Have fun experimenting to find out what's right for you.

FOCUS ON... YOUR BABY

That's tasty!

The flavors from the foods you eat will be transferred to the amniotic fluid, which is swallowed by your baby in the uterus. Therefore the types of food you eat can influence your baby before her first exposure to solid foods.

Studies show that prenatal and postpartum (through breast milk) exposure to a flavor enhances a baby's enjoyment of it in solid foods. These early flavor experiences may provide the foundation for healthy choices, as well as explain the cultural and ethnic differences in cuisine. So get your baby started on the road to good food choices by making healthy selections now.

Being out and about will make you tired. When you're going out for the day, plan lots of breaks so you can sit and rest.

141 days to go...

YOUR BABY TODAY

You will become much more aware of your baby moving as her size and strength increase. You will not be aware of the more gentle movements, or those movements that do not hit the side of the uterus.

You're likely to experience some backaches as your baby grows in size and your body continually adapts to accommodate her.

The increasing weight of your developing baby, and the fact that your joints and ligaments soften in pregnancy, can cause backaches, but thankfully you don't just have to put up with this pain. There are many simple ways in which you can ease a backache or even prevent it (see below).

See your doctor to make sure that the problem and its exact location is properly diagnosed. This way you'll have more chance of stopping it from becoming worse. A common problem, often in later pregnancy, is sciatica (see p.470)—a sharp pain that travels down the back and leg.

BANISH BACKACHES

To nip backaches in the bud, try the following:
- **Take a warm bath** or use a hot-water bottle on the painful area.
- **Ask your partner** to give you a nice back rub, or get yourself a massage with an experienced prenatal practitioner.
- **Go to yoga or Pilates classes** to strengthen your back muscles.
- **Watch your posture** (see p.249), and raise your legs when seated.
- **Ensure your car seat** is properly positioned to support your back.

FOCUS ON... YOUR HEALTH

Fibroids during pregnancy

In the second trimester, fibroids—a benign mass of muscle fiber within the uterine wall, or occasionally attached to it—can become problematic. Increased levels of the hormones estrogen and progesterone during pregnancy encourage them to grow along with the uterus.

In some circumstances, the rapid growth of the fibroid causes feelings of pressure, discomfort, or pain. Fibroids may increase a woman's risk of miscarriage, preterm birth, or having a baby in the breech position

which usually resolves the problem. Fibroids that do not cause discomfort do not require treatment.

The fibroid will not usually affect the developing baby, but if a large fibroid is positioned low down in the uterus or near to the cervix it can prevent the baby from descending into the pelvis, and a cesarean delivery will be necessary.

Once the baby is born and the uterus shrinks, the fibroids will also usually shrink to their pre-pregnancy size.

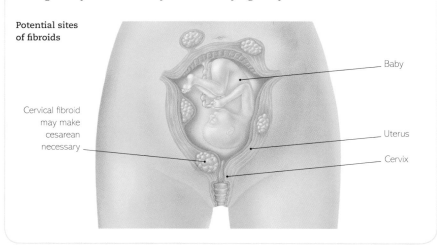

Potential sites of fibroids

Cervical fibroid may make cesarean necessary

Baby

Uterus

Cervix

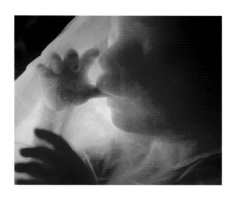

140 days to go...

YOUR BABY TODAY

Although your baby may be sucking her thumb, this is a very complex action that is not fully developed at this stage. For this reason, your baby is as likely to put her fingers or toes in her mouth as her thumb.

Congratulations—you're now halfway through your pregnancy. In around 20 weeks' time, you'll be a mom.

Does it seem like a lifetime, or has it flown by? At least from now on, you really will be counting down. Hopefully, at this halfway point you are feeling fine physically. You're not yet encumbered by a large belly and probably have a reasonable amount of energy. Psychologically, you may still be very emotional, although you will no doubt have gotten used to any mood swings by now (as will your partner).

At this stage you will continue going to prenatal appointments around every four weeks. Remember, your doctor or midwife is there to monitor your health and your baby's progress, but also to help, so get her advice on how to deal with some of the discomforts you might experience as you grow bigger.

AS A MATTER OF FACT

The gestation period for an elephant is an incredible 22 months, making it the longest of any land animal.

In addition to this, the common birth weight for elephants is 260 lb (120 kg). So, if your pregnancy is already starting to feel long, and your baby a tad heavy, spare a thought for our large-eared friends!

ASK A... DOCTOR

I haven't felt my baby move yet. Should I be worried? While you understandably want to feel your baby's movements, there is no cause for concern yet since your recent scan should have shown you that all is well with your baby.

If it's your first baby, you may not notice the early movements since you won't know what to expect. Also, if you're an active person, these slight flutters may be missed. Women with a placenta lying at the front of the uterus may feel movements later, as may larger women since the movement may not be detected through the flesh.

Once you do feel movements, don't become too focused on every one. It's not until around 28 weeks that it becomes important to monitor the pattern. From this stage, the amount your baby moves, as well as the type of movement and when it happens, are relevant since these indicate that the placenta is sustaining the pregnancy and your baby's muscles are developing.

If you're concerned about lack of movement from your baby at any stage, speak to your doctor.

SITTING CORRECTLY

Sit upright on a chair with your legs wide apart and your feet firmly on the floor to align your spine. Make sure your lower back is resting against the chair.

Good posture can help to minimize pregnancy discomforts, including backaches (see opposite page). When seated, make sure your lower back is supported by the back of the chair and keep your feet flat on the floor (see above).

Yoga is a great way to learn to hold your body correctly, including how to keep your spine aligned and your lower back supported.

Your 21st week

YOU'RE HALFWAY THROUGH YOUR PREGNANCY ALREADY—IT'S ALL HAPPENING SO FAST

Not all women happily accept their changing body shape, even though they're overjoyed to be pregnant. But a belly "bump" doesn't have to mean frump. You've got a good excuse to treat yourself to a few attractive maternity clothes or to indulge in some pampering, perhaps by having a gentle massage. Keep up your exercise routine, because you'll feel energized and all the better for it.

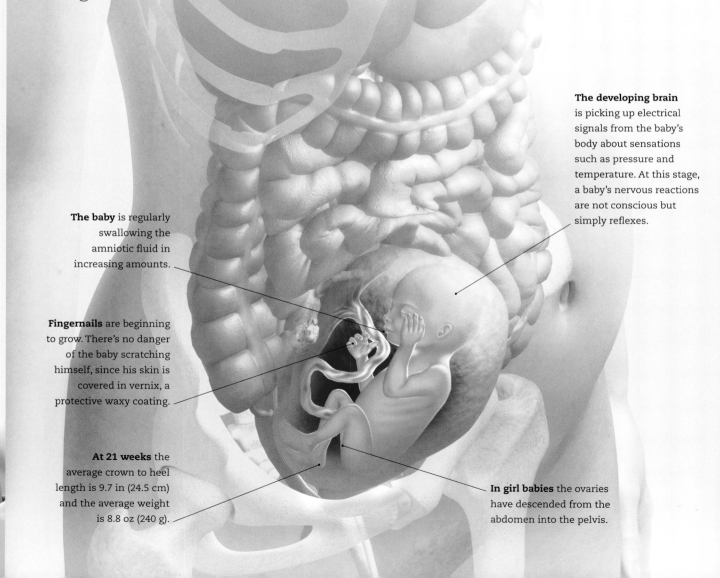

The developing brain is picking up electrical signals from the baby's body about sensations such as pressure and temperature. At this stage, a baby's nervous reactions are not conscious but simply reflexes.

The baby is regularly swallowing the amniotic fluid in increasing amounts.

Fingernails are beginning to grow. There's no danger of the baby scratching himself, since his skin is covered in vernix, a protective waxy coating.

At 21 weeks the average crown to heel length is 9.7 in (24.5 cm) and the average weight is 8.8 oz (240 g).

In girl babies the ovaries have descended from the abdomen into the pelvis.

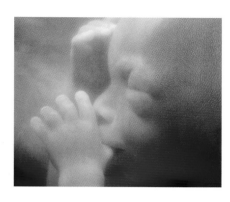

139 days to go...

YOUR BABY TODAY

Your baby's movements are still based on a set of reflex actions but this is now beginning to change. As the nerve pathways develop, expand, and mature, your baby gains greater and greater control of his actions.

You're in the second half of your pregnancy and in the months that follow you'll have more regular contact with your doctor.

Your prenatal appointments will become more frequent in the second half of your pregnancy. Even if you are in good health, and your baby has been thoroughly assessed at the 20-week ultrasound scan (see pp.214–5), it can be reassuring to have these regular checkups with the doctor.

The number of appointments you have will differ depending on whether you've had any complications, or whether you are having a high-risk pregnancy for another reason, such as a preexisting medical condition like diabetes. If it's a low-risk pregnancy, you can expect around 14 appointments unless there are complications. As a general rule you can expect to have prenatal appointments from now on: every 4 weeks until you reach 30 weeks' gestation, then appointments at 2-week intervals until you reach 36 weeks' gestation. From then on, you'll have appointments weekly. And if you pass your due date (see p.139), you'll need to see your doctor once or twice weekly.

However, you can contact your doctor if you have any concerns.

If you're expecting twins, appointments will be more frequent and will depend on the type of twins you're having: non-identical or identical. If identical, care will depend on whether they share any of their support system (see p.130).

The wide range of maternity clothes that is now available means you can still look good at work. Look for items that you can also wear after the birth.

FOCUS ON... YOUR BODY

Dressing well

With your usual office clothing straining at the seams, you might have to rethink your work wardrobe. The good news is that, unlike in years gone by, there is now a wealth of beautiful maternity clothing available and much at affordable everyday prices. These are often designed as coordinated sets, which makes putting them together easy.

Remember that you'll be wearing maternity clothing for a few months, and it's easy to become bored by the same items. If possible, designate a little of your wardrobe budget to buy yourself one or two items every month. If you're tired of your black elastic pants, sleeveless top, and smock dress, buy a pretty new shirt or jacket to jazz them up; you can wear them unbuttoned if necessary.

Don't hesitate to accept hand-me-downs; even if they are not right for your office dress code, wearing them at home will enable you to spend a little more on work clothing. And don't forget your shoes; if you were a stiletto girl before becoming pregnant, you'll need to rethink this (see p.257).

221

138 days to go...

YOUR BABY TODAY

This close-up of the fingertips shows that the nail beds have formed and the nails are starting to grow. The nails have not yet hardened: this prevents your baby from scratching himself accidentally while he has no control over hand movements.

Twin babies have been sharing a home in the uterus for a while now, but how are they relating to each other?

At 21 weeks, a baby's eyes are still closed, but he'll still be aware of light and dark. Because of this, twins can probably make out their sibling changing position and they're increasingly becoming aware of each other. It's thought that because memory starts developing around now, twin babies may begin to bond at this stage.

As ultrasound scanning has proven, there's plenty of contact between twin babies in the uterus, especially as the amount of space decreases. They have been seen to touch often, kick, and try to grab. Each twin reacts to the other's movements.

They may not act in the same way, with one twin favoring different movements than the other one. For instance, one baby may prefer sucking his thumb, while the other likes clutching his cord. Nor do they necessarily have the same body clock, so they may be active at different times. This proves that, even in the uterus, twin babies are already individuals.

ASK A... DOCTOR

Can my baby feel anything when we have sex? He may be aware of some movements when you have sex and of a change in your heart rate, but he won't be harmed by either. You may find that your baby responds to these sensations by moving a lot while you're having sex, or just afterward. Some women find this inhibiting, but remember that it doesn't mean the baby is uncomfortable and, of course, he doesn't understand what you're doing! If you have an orgasm, your uterus will feel tight and you may have Braxton-Hicks contractions (see p.410) but, again, this is not harmful to your baby.

Be reassured that your baby is well protected by the pool of amniotic fluid. Also, the cervix is closed by a plug of mucus during pregnancy so no semen can enter the uterus; this helps to guard against infection.

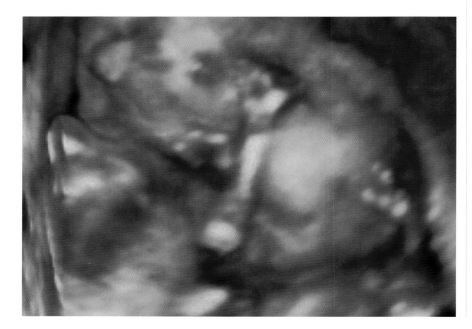

As the pregnancy progresses, contact between your twin babies will increase. Because you'll have more ultrasound scans in a twin pregnancy, you'll have plenty of opportunities to see them interacting with each other.

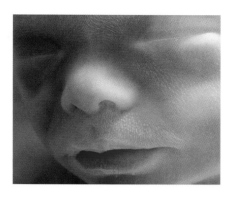

137 days to go...

YOUR BABY TODAY

The eyelids are still fused shut to protect your baby's developing eyes from prying fingers and toes. Deep within the brain, connections are starting to form to link the senses to those areas within the brain that are able to process information.

Part of the fun of not knowing your baby's sex is anticipating what it might be, but be prepared for others to do the same.

If you and your partner decided against finding out the sex of your baby at the 20-week scan, the guessing games will begin and you won't be short of people telling you what they think you're having.

Perhaps your own instinct is the best of all: in one study that asked women to guess the sex of their baby, 71 percent of the expectant moms surveyed guessed correctly.

THE LOWDOWN

It's definitely a...

If you like testing a few old wives' tales on gender, consider these:

■ **Ask someone to tie a gold ring** on to a piece of string and dangle it over your belly to "dowse" for the sex. If it swings from side to side or back and forth, it's a boy; if it spins around in a circular motion, you're having a girl.
■ **Hairier than usual?** Apparently, according to the "old wives," you're more likely to be carrying a boy.
■ **If your baby's heart rate** is faster than 140 beats per minute, you're having a girl (but see p.188!).
■ **Craving sugar, spice,** and all things sweet: girl. Sour or salty foods: boy.

ASK A... MOM

I've found out at the 20-week scan that I'm having my third girl, but I so wanted a boy. How can I feel better about this? It can be enormously disappointing to find out that your baby's sex is different than what you wanted, and perhaps even expected. I felt that I'd let my husband down in some way, especially since I knew he wanted a son.

The good news is that by the time our daughter was born, we were both over the disappointment, and were able to focus on being parents. We always said that if we'd waited until the birth to find out, it would have been hard to come to terms with it at the same time as trying to bond with our newborn baby.

Remember that you haven't met your new daughter yet, and it may be difficult to imagine loving another daughter, but you will do, in time. Try to focus on the fact that she is healthy and that you're having a beautiful baby.

Although you may prefer to have a child of a different gender, you might find that your children are delighted to be having another same-sex playmate.

223

136 days to go...

YOUR BABY TODAY

Shown here is a Doppler ultrasound scan. Your doctor may use a handheld Doppler ultrasound machine to identify your baby's heartbeat; Doppler scanning can also pick up sudden movements and the whoosh of blood through the placenta.

There are few better ways to relieve those pregnancy aches and pains, and to wind down, than to have a soothing massage.

When you book a massage, make sure you do so with a therapist who is experienced in prenatal massage. Although it's unlikely to occur at this stage, massaging the wrong areas or certain acupressure points can trigger uterine contractions (this can actually make a massage beneficial during labor when you want to speed things up).

Before making an appointment for a massage, check with your doctor or midwife that it's OK to have one. Massage may not be recommended if you've had complications such as high blood pressure or diabetes.

Comfort is crucial and most therapists will position you lying on your side with your head supported by a pillow (see right). Don't hesitate to tell the therapist if you're uncomfortable or if any aspect of the massage hurts. An experienced therapist should check that you're comfortable throughout the massage and stop if you're not.

If you don't want to book a professional massage, you can always call on your partner or a willing friend. It is, however, important that the person who is massaging you is careful and does not attempt to work on the abdominal area.

In addition to making a world of difference to those aches and pains and helping you to relax, a massage from your partner is a good way to be intimate with him at times when you might not feel like having sex.

If you don't feel up to having a full massage, a foot, hand, or head massage can be very soothing.

Having a professional massage during pregnancy can be a real treat. Besides feeling blissful, research shows that it eases aches and pains, helps you sleep, and can reduce stress.

ASK A... DOCTOR

I can't look in the mirror because I'm feeling so down about my size. Will things get better? You're not alone in battling with your self-image in pregnancy. For some women, their changing body shape can create negative feelings. Eating a healthy diet and getting some exercise helps prevent excessive weight gain, and exercising will also lift your spirits and improve your sense of well-being.

There's no set emotional response to pregnancy, but in addition to coming to terms with a momentous life and body change, you are also under the influence of fluctuating hormones, all of which affects your mood and can add to feelings of negativity.

Mild depression in pregnancy is often helped by reassurance and support from your partner, family, or friends. Talking over your fears and concerns may help relieve your anxieties—you'll probably find that other pregnant women are experiencing the same feelings.

If you are feeling very low and desperate, don't hesitate to consult your doctor.

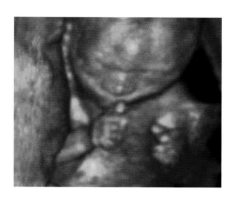

135 days to go...

YOUR BABY TODAY

The skin is less translucent now as your baby is starting to lay down fat reserves, which after the birth will help with temperature control and provide an energy reservoir for your baby to call upon when necessary.

Your developing baby is becoming more responsive and aware every day as his nervous system begins to work more effectively.

By this stage, your baby can use his senses and recognize the sensations of light, pressure, pain, and temperature. Sound is thought to be the first sense to develop, although taste buds are at least present on the tongue from as early as 10 weeks. Nerves carrying the sensations of pain, temperature, and light touch from your baby's body reach his spinal cord and then travel to the hypothalamus, which lies in the center of the brain. This then sends signals to another part of your baby's brain so that the stimuli can be recognized and also evoke an emotional response. Many, but not all, of these nerves require insulation around them to conduct signals effectively. Known as myelin sheaths, these do not develop until much later, after 29 weeks in the spine and 37 weeks in the brain.

Painful stimuli result in a reflex action (such as pulling your hand away from a hot object). Reflexes don't have to involve the brain and for these sensations to be recognized at a conscious level, rather than as a simple reflex, the nerves need to connect the hypothalamus to the gray matter in the brain. These connections are thought to function after 26 weeks of pregnancy, but it may be 34 weeks before their electrical activity can be clearly seen on an electroencephalogram (EEG).

ASK A... MOM

This is my second baby—does it make sense to go to prenatal classes again? I think so. There were three years between my pregnancies and it helped to have a refresher course; I even found that some of the advice had changed in that time. My partner found it helpful, too.

One reason to go is to meet some pregnant moms again; it's always useful to share the experience with others and, as with your first pregnancy, you'll probably find you make some great friends.

WEARING MATERNITY HOSE

You probably can't imagine wearing maternity hose, but they have their uses. They work by promoting circulation and the return of blood back to the heart and may be recommended to prevent vein-related problems, particularly if you suffer from varicose veins (see p.167) or spider veins (see p.134).

They also help to relieve aching feet, mild swelling in the feet, ankles, and legs, as well as fluid retention. They may be particularly helpful if your work means that you must be on your feet for long periods of time.

Thankfully, an element of fashion has been introduced and many brands are sheer and pretty. There is a variety available: some are thigh- or knee-high (see right) and others cover the whole leg. There are also some that provide support for your baby and uterus, taking the pressure off your back. You'll find lighter stockings for summer wear, when the hot weather can lead to further swelling.

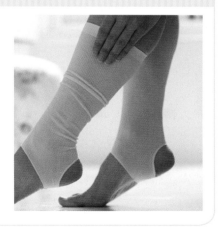

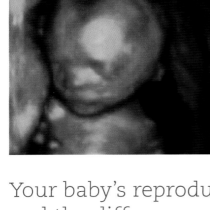

134 days to go...

YOUR BABY TODAY

Your baby is now developing periods of movement and activity and periods of rest and quiet. Soon these periods will become definite cycles of activity, providing something of a daily (and nightly) routine to his movement.

Your baby's reproductive organs are gradually developing and the differences in the genitals are increasingly obvious.

In the absence of high levels of testosterone in a female baby, the reproductive glands become ovaries, which contain 6–8 million follicles at this stage, of which about 1–2 million will remain at birth. The ovaries have now descended from the abdomen into the pelvis. The testes also undergo a similar descent, but have not yet reached the

scrotum. Under the influence of the hormone estrogen you produce, your baby of either sex may develop breast buds, although these will disappear after birth. Whether your baby is a boy or a girl has very little impact on the pregnancy. Later in pregnancy, there is a slight weight difference, with boys being slightly heavier than girls on average.

ASK A... DOCTOR

I fell recently. Could I have harmed my baby? Falling during pregnancy is extremely common, as your increasingly protruding abdomen, softening ligaments and joints, and changing center of gravity can cause you to lose your balance. The good news is that your baby is safely cocooned in amniotic fluid, which protects and cushions him when you fall. Your injuries would have to be quite severe to cause any harm to your baby.

The best thing you can do is to monitor your baby's movements after a fall. If he's moving as much as normal all should be fine, but if you want reassurance, pay a visit to your doctor or hospital. If you do experience any discomfort, or unusual discharge or bleeding from your vagina, seek medical help. If you pass water, this is likely to be urine caused by stress incontinence (see opposite), not amniotic fluid.

The amniotic sac is sometimes referred to as a "bubble" because of its appearance. It may be transparent, but it's tough and extremely difficult to pierce, so your baby is very well protected in this safe environment.

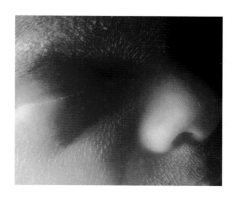

133 days to go...

YOUR BABY TODAY

This image shows just how large the developing eyes are underneath the lids. At birth, your baby's eyes will be large and blue. There are no eyebrows or eyelashes yet, but this will be the first adult type of hair to grow.

Try to find ways to fit in small amounts of energizing exercise every day—you'll feel much better for it.

ASK A... DOCTOR

I seem to have a lot of vaginal discharge. Is this normal? Yes, in the second trimester you may find that you have more discharge than normal. This is usually clear, stringy, or full of mucus and shouldn't smell offensive. If the discharge changes, becoming thick, white, and causes itching, you may have developed a yeast infection, which is common in pregnancy and easily treated (see p.133).

You should see your doctor or midwife if the vaginal discharge becomes green, or offensive in smell; see your doctor or midwife too if you have burning when you urinate, or your external genitals become sore. This may be a sign that you have an infection that must be treated. Don't ignore any abnormal discharge since, although it won't directly affect your developing baby, an infection can increase the risk of you going in to premature labor.

You may find that you leak urine, especially when you cough, laugh, or run. This is called stress incontinence (see p.471).

Maintaining your exercise routine while you're still working can be challenging. The last thing you may feel like doing is exercising after a day at work, especially as your pregnancy progresses. There are ways of exercising without a visit to the gym; it will just take some thought and planning. For example, every now and then, take the stairs, carefully, instead of the elevator, or get off the bus or train at a different stop, so that you walk some of the way.

OFFICE WORKOUT

If your job involves sitting down all day, it's even more important to find ways to keep on the move.
- **Get up from your desk** at least once every hour. Walk to speak to your colleagues instead of phoning or emailing them. Volunteer to get coffee for people—this will also make you very popular!
- **Try this exercise while seated:** straighten your leg out in front of you (see right), keeping your thigh parallel to the floor. Then repeatedly bend and straighten your leg to help your circulation. Follow with flexing and pointing your foot from the ankle. Do each of these exercises at least 10 times with each leg.

If there's a pool close to work, try to fit in an invigorating lunchtime swim. You'll feel much better in the afternoon.

Walk wherever you can, but be prepared: wear comfortable sneakers and take your work shoes in a bag with you. Remember to take some water with you when exercising, and keep hydrated throughout the day.

At night before you go to bed, try to fit in some abdominal exercises (see p.250) to strengthen those muscles.

Your 22nd week

DECIDING ON A NAME FOR YOUR BABY CAN BE TRICKY, SO START MAKING THAT LIST

You may not know the sex of your baby but you and your partner can still have fun choosing names. This is a discussion that can run on and on. Some couples don't make up their minds until the baby is born. With such matters to preoccupy you, it's probably hard to stay focused at work. Try to pace yourself without letting standards slip. Eating little and often, and drinking lots of water, will help you stay alert.

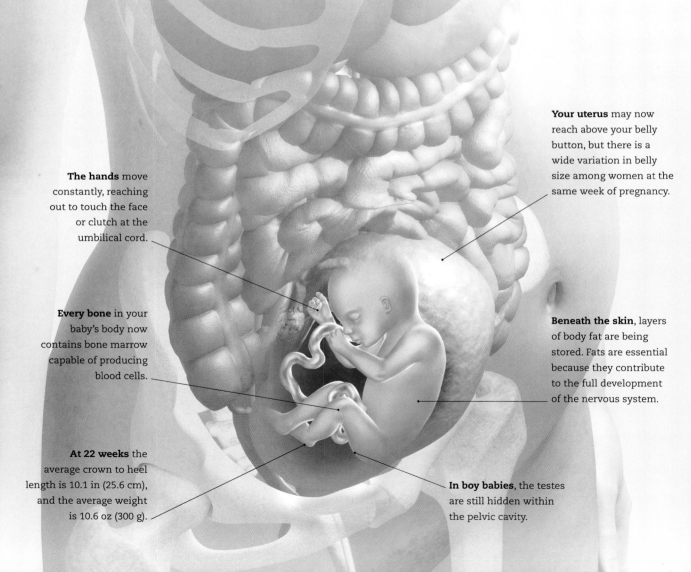

Your uterus may now reach above your belly button, but there is a wide variation in belly size among women at the same week of pregnancy.

The hands move constantly, reaching out to touch the face or clutch at the umbilical cord.

Every bone in your baby's body now contains bone marrow capable of producing blood cells.

Beneath the skin, layers of body fat are being stored. Fats are essential because they contribute to the full development of the nervous system.

At 22 weeks the average crown to heel length is 10.1 in (25.6 cm), and the average weight is 10.6 oz (300 g).

In boy babies, the testes are still hidden within the pelvic cavity.

YOU ARE 21 WEEKS AND 1 DAY

132 days to go...

YOUR BABY TODAY

Fine capillaries carrying blood underneath the skin lend a pinkish tone to your baby. Fat deposits are still sparse so the skin is still quite thin. Within the capillaries red blood cells are carrying oxygen to every part of your baby's body.

If you often walk into a room and forget why you're there, don't be concerned—you've simply developed "pregnancy brain"!

ASK A... DOCTOR

I've always been an enthusiastic walker, but should I cut down on the number of miles now that I'm over halfway through my pregnancy? No, you shouldn't need to, but you might want to take extra precautions. Walking is ideal since it is low-impact exercise that can be maintained throughout pregnancy. In fact, it's a great exercise in the later months because it doesn't jar your knees and ankles.

If you plan to continue lengthy walks and like to walk briskly, try combining this with a slower, more leisurely pace. It's important to control your body temperature so that you don't overheat and feel uncomfortable. To do this, drink plenty of water to avoid dehydration and wear layers that you can take on and off as required.
As your belly grows, you may find hill climbing causes physical instability, as may trekking over uneven terrain, so stick to level paths. If you find yourself getting breathless, take frequent breaks. Of course always make sure you wear good, sturdy footwear, and avoid carrying heavy loads.

Is your mind not feeling quite as sharp these days? Many women find themselves very frustrated by the onset of "pregnancy brain," which makes them so forgetful that they might not remember what they're talking about halfway through a sentence. Your ability to concentrate and pay attention to tasks may also be affected. Doctors are not sure

If you're finding you're more forgetful these days, write things down and prioritize so that you aren't overwhelmed with tasks.

why this happens, but it's likely to be a result of hormonal changes. It may also happen because during pregnancy you're focused internally: you're going through such a major life event, and there are so many changes happening to your body and lifestyle, that you simply pay less attention to other things.

As frustrating as it is, this tendency to forgetfulness is only temporary (although it may last into the first year of motherhood—see below). In the meantime, try making lists at the beginning of each day and check off tasks as you go. Delegate at home and work when you can and, for once in your life, don't try to multitask. Focusing on one thing at a time will help you remember and achieve more.

AS A MATTER OF FACT

"Pregnancy brain" might last until your child's first birthday.

This finding is based on research done around the world. After in-depth analysis of the results, the experts concluded that sleep deprivation in the first year of parenting may be a factor.

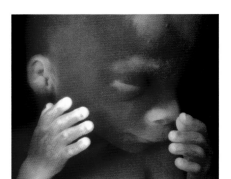

131 days to go...

YOUR BABY TODAY

The next three months are a time of particularly rapid growth for your baby. Cells are dividing, expanding, and maturing in every part of her body. The placenta too is growing and maturing, but this is far less important than your baby's growth from now on.

What's in a name? Well, quite a lot actually, as you'll discover when you start trying to choose one for your baby.

Deciding on a name for your baby is fun but not necessarily an easy task. In addition to finding one that you and your partner agree on, it can feel as though everyone has an opinion. Friends may tell you that they have already chosen a name, that it is "theirs" so you can't use it! Your family may have traditions that they want upheld, such as passing on a name that has been in the family for generations.

It's a good idea for you and your partner individually to write down a list of names that you like. Then look at each other's list and talk about which ones you do and don't like. If you're lucky, there will be one or more names on both lists that match.

Factors to consider include: does the name sound right with your last name? Does the middle name go well with the first name? What will the initials be? For example, Robert Anthony Taylor will become RAT! Are the meanings of the names important to you? If so, find out what the meaning is of your favorite names—it can be fun to tell your child what her name means when she's older. Is there a short version of the name that you can use informally or, conversely, do you hate names being shortened? If so, avoid those. If you're feeling obligated to use a family name, perhaps make it a middle name.

It's advisable to come up with a few alternative choices, since you may find that the name you have decided upon just doesn't seem to suit your newborn baby when you finally see her.

Researching in books or on the internet is a good way to find less popular names, and to discover interesting facts about the origin of names.

POPULAR NAMES

Do you want your child to have an original name, or are you influenced by what's in fashion? Bear in mind that opting for a popular name may mean your child is in a class full of namesakes.

Below is the list of the top 20 most popular girls' and boys' names in Canada in 2008.

Girls' names	Boys' names
1. Emma	1. Ethan
2. Mikayla	2. Aiden
3. Sarah	3. Lucas
4. Sophia	4. Kaden
5. Maya	5. Jayden
6. Danica	6. Nathan
7. Emily	7. Logan
8. Ava	8. Noah
9. Isabella	9. Liam
10. Lily	10. Jack
11. Madison	11. Jacob
12. Chloe	12. Nicholas
13. Hannah	13. Owen
14. Sophie	14. Alexander
15. Olivia	15. Matthew
16. Abigail	16. Benjamin
17. Hailey	17. Connor
18. Payton	18. Jackson
19. Claire	19. Evan
20. Alexis	20. James

Your second trimester

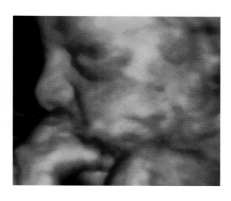

130 days to go...

YOUR BABY TODAY

In this 3D scan the baby's skin looks quite lumpy in parts. This isn't really the case. If the baby suddenly moves during a scan, the image can have difficulty "keeping up" and creates this unusual effect.

In addition to using fat for essential growth and development, your baby is now beginning to store it.

Up until this time, your baby has had little opportunity to store fat, because growth has been the most important priority. But now your baby starts to lay down a layer of fat beneath her skin and it becomes less translucent. The placenta is responsible for supplying fats to your baby.

Fat circulates in your bloodstream and within the placenta it is broken down into three free fatty acids, as well as cholesterol, which are passed into your baby's circulation. These fatty acids then recombine to form fats for storage or growth.

Fats are important for adequate nerve and brain development. A layer of fat covers each nerve cell, insulating it from adjacent nerves and improving its connections with other nerve cells.

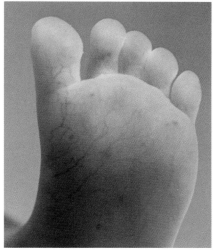

Your baby's veins will become less visible as she gains a layer of fat beneath the skin, making it less transparent than it was in the earlier stages of pregnancy.

ASK A... MOM

Should we tell people the name that we've chosen? I would advise you not to. We told people at first and found it upsetting to find we had so many negative reactions. People freely told us how they had negative associations with the name or that they knew a cat or gerbil called that—a fact that we didn't need to know! Older relatives told us it was "odd" and went on to give us a list of alternatives.

So I would say keep it to yourself until the baby is born and it's all a fait accompli. It takes a bold person to question your choice once your baby has been named.

FOCUS ON... TWINS

Bill and Ben?

Choosing one name can be difficult enough, so if you're expecting twins, start thinking now. If you want to avoid people making jokes at your twins' expense, avoid obvious pairs such as Jack and Jill, and Holly and Ivy. Consider how the names might sound when abbreviated (William and Benjamin, for instance, becomes Bill and Ben).

Finally, it might be a good idea to opt for names of similar length and complexity. For example, young Christopher may be discouraged as he struggles to spell his name, while his twin Jack has no trouble.

AS A MATTER OF FACT

In Hawaii parents often choose names that are associated with beauty.

Some examples of these are: Nohea— "loveliness"; Leia—"child of heaven"; Maka Nani—"beautiful eyes"; Hiwalani—"the attractive one"; Pualani— "heaven's flower"; and Nani, meaning "beautiful, pretty one."

129 days to go...

YOUR BABY TODAY

When looking down on the baby, the nose can look quite wide because the nasal bridge is not yet fully developed. This gives the characteristic "button nose" shape that many babies keep throughout the pregnancy.

Your baby is producing essential red and white blood cells at a rate that is greater than your own.

Stem cells in your baby's bone marrow produce red and white blood cells, and platelets—the cells that clump together to form a blood clot. Earlier in pregnancy all of these were produced in the yolk sac (see p.80), then the liver and spleen. Now every bone inside your baby contains red bone marrow capable of producing blood cells. Red blood cells do not last forever and after about 80 days are removed from the baby's circulation. This turnover is higher than your own, where a red blood cell will last for 120 days.

Bilirubin is a breakdown product from red blood cells. It's produced in the liver and removed from your baby's circulation by the placenta. Because your baby's liver takes a few days to efficiently process bilirubin, high levels may lead to jaundice at birth (see p.477). If jaundice does develop after birth then light phototherapy treatment is capable of breaking down bilirubin into a form that can be more easily excreted in your baby's urine.

As a newborn, your baby will be protected against infection by white blood cells and by antibodies from breast milk, especially the colostrum (see p.446). Because of this, breast-fed babies are at a lower risk of conditions such as asthma, cow's milk intolerance, and food allergies.

MAKING SENSE OF MEDICAL LINGO

Since your prenatal appointments are more regular now, it can be useful to get a handle on the medical jargon used in your pregnancy records:

- **Primagravida:** first pregnancy
- **Multigravida:** subsequent pregnancy
- **Hb:** hemoglobin levels
- **BP:** blood pressure

- **Urine tests:** NAD or nil means that no abnormalities have been detected; P or alb means it contains protein; Tr or + indicates a trace of sugar or protein; G stands for glucose; and "other" is anything else.

- **Heart rate:** FHH is fetal heart heard; FHHR is heard and regular; FMF or FMNF—fetal movements felt or not felt.

Your baby's position in the uterus is usually referred to as the presenting part or lie and there are several terms and abbreviations used to describe this. Occiput is the term used for the back of the baby's head.
- **LOT**—left-occipito-transverse. The baby's back and occiput are

If you're unclear about anything written in your pregnancy records or test results, don't hesitate to ask your doctor to explain.

positioned on the left side of the uterus at right angles to your spine.
- **LOA**—left-occipito-anterior. The back and occiput are closer to the front of your uterus on the left.
- **LOP**—left-occipito-posterior. The back and occiput are toward your spine on the left side of your uterus.
- **ROT**—right-occipito-transverse. The baby's back and occiput are at right angles to your spine on the right-hand side of your uterus.
- **ROA**—right-occipito-anterior. The back and occiput are toward the front of your uterus on the right-hand side.
- **ROP**—right occipito-posterior. The back and occiput are toward your spine on the right-hand side.

128 days to go...

YOUR BABY TODAY

There is still plenty of room for your baby to move around. Your baby is able to perform complete somersaults and change position several times a day or even several times in a few minutes.

Bellies come in all shapes and sizes and your doctor will keep track of how your baby is growing.

If, like some pregnant women, you are feeling big for this halfway stage, it doesn't necessarily mean that you'll have a big baby. Being large doesn't mean that all your weight is in your belly and from your baby; you may have put on weight on the rest of your body that doesn't affect your baby's size. Women who are carrying twins or triplets do, of course, show earlier and have much larger bellies than those expecting one baby.

The size of your belly is, however, a good indicator of your baby's growth, so it will be measured by your doctor (see pp.284–5). She will measure from a point on your pubic bone in your pelvis to the top, or fundus, of the uterus. This measurement should correlate with the number of weeks you're pregnant, with an accuracy of within ¾ in (2 cm). So, if you're 28 weeks pregnant your belly should measure 10¼–11¾ in (26–30 cm). This symphysis fundal height (SFH) will be written in your notes.

If your belly is found to be significantly larger or smaller than it should be for your dates, you're likely

While it's good to spend time with women who are at the same stage of pregnancy as you, try not to make comparisons. Your belly may be bigger than your friend's, but you may end up having a smaller baby.

to be referred for an ultrasound scan since this can give a much more accurate measurement of your baby's size.

Remember, though, what you think of as huge and what your caregiver feels is too large can be two very different things! You are used to your body being a certain size and shape and you are much bigger than you used to be, even though to doctors and midwives you are a normal and healthy size. This can feel particularly the case if you're someone who has always been slim.

ASK A... NUTRITIONIST

I've been told to rest but will I gain too much weight? It's important that you follow this advice, even though it can be frustrating. Ask your doctor if you're allowed to do gentle walking or swimming because this will help keep you fit and burn some calories.

If you're eating a healthy, nutritious diet that includes plenty of fresh fruits and vegetables, complex carbohydrates, and lean protein, you shouldn't gain too much weight.

Never be tempted to diet, or go hungry just because you're less active at the moment. Regular meals and snacks are important. Listen to your body; if you're hungry, it needs fuel.

If full bed rest has been prescribed, light exercise will be out of the question, but make sure you establish at the outset what is and isn't allowed. If you aren't active you are likely to gain some weight, but the goal of bed rest is to ensure that you deliver a healthy baby at full-term, and that's worth a few extra pounds.

Your 22nd week

233

127 days to go...

YOUR BABY TODAY

This is a close-up of the baby's skin just behind the ear. Every part of the skin's surface has small ridges and hollows in a unique pattern. During this week the dermal ridges—the deeper layers of skin—start to mature, giving rise to finger- and toeprints.

Your baby has been filtering amniotic fluid and storing the waste as a substance called meconium.

At the end of this week, your baby's anal sphincter muscle is fully functional. This should prevent any small particles of meconium from being passed into the amniotic fluid. Meconium is first produced at 12 weeks. It is the somewhat greenish/black first poop that nine out of 10 newborn babies pass in the first 24 hours.

Meconium is formed mainly from cells discarded from the lining of the gut as it lengthens and expands, and the waste of any nutrients which have been absorbed from the swallowed amniotic fluid. It is continuously produced, slowly moving down the gut to enter the large bowel (colon) by 16 weeks. Meconium is sterile since there are no organisms inside the gut and no bowel gas is produced.

AS A MATTER OF FACT

The unborn baby will move her hand to her mouth and even suck her thumb.

Research has shown that the baby may even open her mouth in anticipation. Anything that the hands encounter is firmly grasped and this grip is strong enough to support all of the baby's body weight.

KEEP TONED

Effective strength training during pregnancy, using free weights (see right) or a machine at your gym, will help your body deal with the demands of pregnancy. Being stronger will help you carry the increase in body weight and also help you recover after the baby is born. Having more toned limbs will help you look and feel better, too.

Like all aspects of exercise during pregnancy, there are guidelines that should be followed:
- **If you've been doing regular weight training,** continue with your program, but do not increase the weight loads or repetitions.
- **If you're new to using weights,** begin with very light ones and few repetitions and build up slowly. Do not increase the weight load until you are confident that you are able to manage the increase.
- **Take a deep breath** to start and breathe out as you lift the weight.
- **Free weights,** rather than machines, are safer to use during pregnancy. If you're using a machine, make sure a trainer has shown you how to use it correctly.

- **If you find standing up while doing strength training too tiring,** sit on a chair to lift your weights (see below).

If you're sitting and using weights, keep your back straight and relax your shoulders. When standing, make sure that you have your legs hip-width apart and your knees slightly bent.

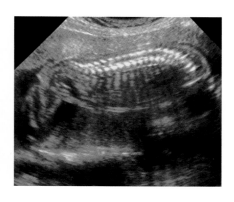

126 days to go...

YOUR BABY TODAY

The vertebrae that make up your baby's spinal column encircle and protect the spinal cord. The vertebrae are seen here on an ultrasound scan, forming a long chain (white areas) that narrows at the base of the spine and ends with a slight outward curve.

Maintaining a professional manner at work will set the standard for how colleagues treat you during pregnancy.

Chances are that everyone in your office will be aware that you are expecting a baby by this stage, even if you haven't told them personally. Good news does have a habit of traveling fast, and you may have that pregnancy "glow" that makes your condition pretty clear—as well as a fairly prominent belly.

If word of your pregnancy is getting around the office, it might be best to tell your boss now. It's always better and more professional if your boss hears this news before other people in your company.

You may need to adapt your working day a little, but play it carefully. Try to keep up with your work, and act professionally. Your colleagues are, hopefully, thrilled that you're pregnant, but try not to expect special favors or extra attention.

While being pregnant isn't an illness, do take adequate breaks to recharge your batteries, or work flexible hours, if that's an option, so that you can avoid traveling at the busiest times.

Try to go for a short walk on your lunch hour for fresh air and to get some gentle exercise. Drink plenty of water to keep you hydrated and alert, and eat little and often to keep your energy levels high.

Make sure people judge you on your work and not on the fact that you're pregnant.

FOCUS ON... HEALTH

Vaginal bleeding

If you have any vaginal bleeding, always see your doctor or midwife immediately. Growths on your cervix, or some inflammation, can produce light bleeding from time to time.

Heavy bleeding in the second trimester may suggest a problem with your placenta, such as placenta previa (see p.212). Similarly, the placenta may pull away from the wall of the uterus, causing some bleeding, or, very rarely, uterine rupture can occur, usually only in women who have had a cesarean section in the past.

ASK A... DOCTOR

My manager said I can't have time off to go to my prenatal appointments. What should I do? You'll be spending a lot of time at your caregiver's office for prenatal care during the next several months—every 4 weeks now, but as frequently as once a week at the end of your pregnancy. If you also work full-time, it's a good idea to schedule your prenatal appointments for the early morning, before you begin work, or during your lunch hour. If your appointments tend to run long or your caregiver's office is fair distance from work and your boss isn't understanding, ask if you should use your sick leave or your vacation time for the hours that you'll be away from the office.

235

Your 23rd week

YOU COULD BE FEELING A LITTLE OFF-BALANCE, BOTH PHYSICALLY AND EMOTIONALLY

Being pregnant can have all kinds of unexpected effects. There will probably be days when you just don't feel in control of your emotions and they get the better of you, making you cry for no reason. Or your body feels clumsy and uncoordinated, and you keep walking into the furniture. Just talk to some other moms-to-be and you'll find that these side effects are all a normal part of the pregnancy experience!

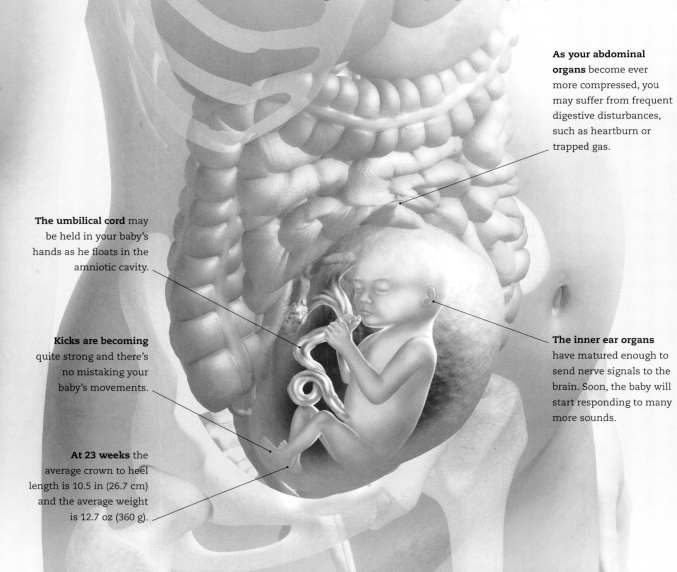

As your abdominal organs become ever more compressed, you may suffer from frequent digestive disturbances, such as heartburn or trapped gas.

The umbilical cord may be held in your baby's hands as he floats in the amniotic cavity.

Kicks are becoming quite strong and there's no mistaking your baby's movements.

At 23 weeks the average crown to heel length is 10.5 in (26.7 cm) and the average weight is 12.7 oz (360 g).

The inner ear organs have matured enough to send nerve signals to the brain. Soon, the baby will start responding to many more sounds.

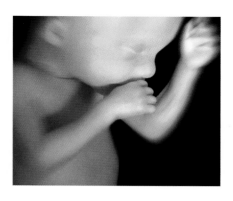

125 days to go...

YOUR BABY TODAY

This is a landmark week for your baby's senses: hearing and balance, both controlled by the inner ear, start to mature now. As this image shows, the ears are still not in their final position at the side of the head.

If your emotions are all over the place, try having a good cry, preferably on someone's shoulder. You'll feel a whole lot better.

It's normal to feel a bit up and down emotionally. The best way to manage is to give yourself some time out and the low points will soon pass. If you find yourself crying at a commerical yet again, try to see the funny side! Sharing this fact with someone else may also help, especially a pregnant friend or new mom—she more than anyone else will be able to relate to how you're feeling and reassure you.

The good news is you don't need to worry about your baby—he won't be affected by your occasional mood swings. However, it might not be good for him if you get too stressed since this causes your body to produce more cortisol, a hormone which can have adverse effects on your baby (see p.187). So, when you're feeling stressed, make adequate time to relax and take care of yourself, for your baby's sake.

FOCUS ON... TWINS

Maternity matters

If you're having twins, now is the time to discuss your maternity leave with your employers. Some women start their leave toward the end of their pregnancy, while others wait for their babies to be born. Ask your doctor for advice.

You may also want to take off as much time as possible after the babies are born, and your partner will want to take the maximum amount of leave he's eligible for (see p.349). Aside from help from family and friends, which will be essential, consider what you can afford in terms of additional child care.

ASK A... DOCTOR

I think I may have food poisoning. Will this harm my baby? Some food-borne illnesses, such as salmonella, campylobacter, and E. coli will not directly harm your baby but can make you very ill, causing profuse vomiting and diarrhea that could lead to extreme dehydration. It's important to keep your fluid intake up both to flush out the offending pathogens, and to ensure you're sufficiently hydrated. If the vomiting is so serious that you can't keep any fluid down, ask for an emergency appointment with your doctor.

Infection with listeria bacteria is the most serious since it can infect the baby and may cause a miscarriage or premature labor. It is, therefore, essential that you contact your doctor if you believe that you've eaten a contaminated food (see p.17).

Always be especially careful when choosing food and follow hygiene rules when preparing it. Avoid eating foods that are commonly associated with food poisoning (see p.17).

124 days to go...

YOUR BABY TODAY

The hands and fingers are clearly visible and the nail beds have been laid down. The baby's fingers will close if the palm of his hand is touched. The tips of the two bones in the forearm, the radius and the ulna, can just be seen in the lower part of this image.

Now that your baby's ears are sufficiently well developed to process sounds, his hearing will gradually improve.

Your baby's external ears have been developed for some time but for him to hear, the internal ear structures also need to mature. In the middle ear, three bones—the malleus ("hammer"), incus ("anvil"), and stapes ("stirrup")—conduct sound into the inner ear. These bones are formed initially from soft cartilage and embedded within connective tissue. The bones begin to harden and the connective tissue gradually dissolves. This allows the ear drum to vibrate onto the hammer, which passes the movement on to the anvil, and then the stirrup. The vibrations are then passed to the cochlea, a cavity of the inner ear, where they are translated into nerve impulses to be sent to the brain.

At 22 weeks, your baby's inner ear has matured adequately for sound to be processed into neural signals to the brain. The first part of the cochlea to develop is responsible for receiving lower-sound frequencies. As your baby develops, he will gradually be able to recognize and respond to higher sound frequencies. Over the next three weeks, your baby's responsiveness to sounds will gradually increase. At first the responses are slow and sluggish, but by 25 weeks he will react to a range of sounds by moving around.

In addition to being responsible for your baby's hearing, the inner ear also controls his balance. Small fibers within three semicircular canals of the inner ear are able to sense acceleration in any direction, providing the sense of motion and balance. Floating in the amniotic fluid is similar to weightlessness and, although your baby is very active, he has no sense yet of moving up and down.

AS A MATTER OF FACT

Men are faster than women at changing diapers.

Research shows that the average time a woman takes is 2 minutes and 5 seconds, whereas the average man takes 1 minute and 36 seconds! So that's a job for him, then.

Gardening is great exercise and will also ensure you get some fresh air. Make sure you wear gloves because the soil may contain toxoplasmosis parasites (see pp.25 and 86).

RARING TO GO

If, like many pregnant women at this stage, you feel incredibly energized, make the most of it. Here are some ways to direct that energy:
- **Get some exercise,** including doing some gardening (see left).
- **Organize your paperwork** and get your finances in order.
- **Clear out any clothes** that you know you won't wear again.
- **Learn to knit** or, if you already can, get going on some baby clothes.
- **Make time to see all the friends** you haven't been in touch with for a while—you may not feel up to socializing in later months.

However good you're feeling, always make time to relax and recharge your batteries.

123 days to go...

YOUR BABY TODAY

The baby's mouth and nose are well developed. The nervous and muscular systems are now mature enough for the baby to suck in amniotic fluid, which the kidneys slowly process. Waste is eliminated via the placenta.

During your pregnancy you'll probably make some new friends, but you may find that some old friendships are affected.

One thing you may not have anticipated before you were pregnant is how your friendships might change. It's normal to be drawn to other women who are pregnant or who have recently had a baby, and common to make friends at prenatal classes (see p.199). It's natural to want to surround yourself with people who are going through or who have been through the same experience as you, not least because you will have so many questions they can answer. You might also feel closer to female relatives, especially your mother (see p.209).

You may find that friends who are not pregnant or who don't have children may not be as interested in all the details of your pregnancy. It may be difficult for them to comprehend how all-encompassing pregnancy and then having a child is; it may be literally all you can think about. If these are friendships you value, make an effort to have some "nonpregnancy" chats. It will be good for you not to be 100 percent focused on the pregnancy.

If you find you drift apart from these friends for a while, don't worry. Good friends will always remain just that, whether or not your lives temporarily go in different directions.

By spending time with women who are also expecting a baby, you can share the ups and downs of your pregnancy experiences. It can also be fun to do activities together, such as going swimming or to water aerobics classes.

ASK A... DOCTOR

My fingers are tingling and I've been told I have carpal tunnel syndrome. What is it? This condition occurs when swollen tissues in the wrist compress the nerves and cause pins and needles and numbness in your fingers. There may also be difficulty grasping and a weakness in the hands. In pregnancy, it's caused by an increase in blood volume and fluid, especially in the second and third trimesters. There are ways to reduce the symptoms, such as circling and stretching exercises to improve circulation and increase wrist mobility. A physiotherapist will be able to demonstrate these exercises. Wearing wrist splints and elevating your hands on a pillow at night can also help.

Carpal tunnel syndrome usually disappears after the birth, once there is no longer excess fluid.

AS A MATTER OF FACT

The number of women over 35 becoming pregnant in Canada is at its highest level ever.

According to a Canadian census report, the birth rate for women aged 35 and older has almost quadrupled from 4.6 percent in 1979 to 17.2 percent in 2004. The mean age for Canadian moms giving birth is 29.3.

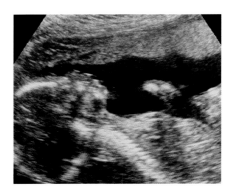

122 days to go...

YOUR BABY TODAY

Seeing your baby on a 3D or 4D scan gives you a better view, but most of the information that enables doctors to plan your care comes from looking inside your baby using 2D ultrasound, which provides the clearest images of internal structures.

Now that he can hear, your amazing baby is starting to develop the ability to remember things, too.

As your baby's nervous system develops, and especially once his sense of hearing evolves, he has the opportunity to learn and remember from experience. How this process develops is not fully understood, but experts believe that the first signs of learning coincide with the unborn baby's ability to hear, at around this mid-stage of pregnancy.

In later months, more sound will reach your baby as the walls of the uterus become thinner. Although babies have been seen to be startled by a noise at this stage, they seem to learn not to react to the sound if it is repeated again and again, gradually adapting to it as it's repeated over time, and eventually ignoring it.

This simple test demonstrates that a fetus can adapt to a repeated stimulus. If, however, the sound pattern is not repeated for some time, your baby will have forgotten it and become startled by it if it occurs again.

Retaining a memory for events is a much more complex function and relies on pathways in the gray matter of the brain. It will be weeks before learning and memory are linked in the last stages of your pregnancy.

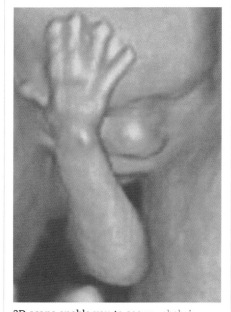

3D scans enable you to see your baby's face and features, such as the hands, in incredible detail. As these images are so real, they often improve the feeling of bonding a mother has for her baby.

AS A MATTER OF FACT

Your baby is likely to be increasingly more active and predictable in his movements.

At around this time you're likely to start feeling regular, more definite movements, and become accustomed to your baby's activities.

UP CLOSE AND PERSONAL

State-of-the-art technology means it's possible to see what your baby will look like before you give birth. Some ultrasound scans enable parents to see their unborn baby close up either in 3D, as a still image, or 4D as a moving picture.

Clear scans of the facial features can be seen from around this week. However, the optimum time to have one of these scans is between 26 and 34 weeks, when your baby still has room to move around easily. You will be able to see an amazing level of detail that won't be visible on a standard prenatal scan. Remember to inform the sonographer if you don't want to discover the sex of your baby.

Health Canada cautions against keepsake ultrasound images, since the ultrasonography may be done by someone not well-trained, using higher levels of energy for a longer time which could be harmful.

Be aware that it's expensive to have these scans and if your baby is in the wrong position, you may not get a great result. The position of the placenta, amount of amniotic fluid, and your size can also affect the quality of the picture.

121 days to go...

YOUR BABY TODAY

Extremely fine hairs called lanugo hairs cover your baby's entire skin surface. These are constantly shed and replaced but, during the final few weeks of pregnancy, will be replaced by thicker, permanent hairs. Lanugo cells help insulate the skin.

The occasional dizzy spell is common in pregnancy and not a sign that anything is wrong.

As your body works hard to nourish your baby, you may find yourself feeling dizzy from time to time. It's common to feel dizzy when you stand up suddenly; this is because, although your blood supply has increased during pregnancy, getting up quickly causes the blood to rush into your legs. This reduces the supply of blood to your brain, making you feel light-headed.

Dizziness can also be a symptom of anemia. Although you produce more red blood cells in pregnancy than before, your volume of blood also increases. This means that proportionally there are fewer red blood cells and your blood count will drop.

You may also become short of iron and, if this is the case, you will be prescribed iron supplements. In addition to dizziness, symptoms of anemia include fatigue and shortness of breath. Low blood-sugar levels (see p.92) can also cause dizziness and can be prevented by eating snacks regularly.

If you're feeling dizzy, although it's likely to be due to the physiological changes in pregnancy, inform your doctor so you can be examined and any relevant blood tests taken. If you feel dizzy when you're out and about, or if you need a seat on a bus or train, always tell someone—the majority of people will be understanding.

AS A MATTER OF FACT

Not all pregnant women toe the good health line.

Healthy-eating messages abound so pregnant women are well informed, especially about calcium-rich foods needed for strong bones among other things. A recent study found that pregnant women who rarely drank milk gave birth to smaller babies than those who drank the recommended three 8-oz (237-ml) glasses per day.

If you can't face crowds, see one friend at a time in a home environment. Be selective and prioritize those people who really matter to you, rather than trying to fit everyone in.

ASK A... MOM

I don't feel up to socializing but should I force myself to go out?
I remember that feeling well! When you're pregnant, it's normal to feel like battening down the hatches sometimes because you're too tired to socialize. It's worth, however, trying to make the most of your leisure time before the baby arrives. You may not feel like getting out and about, but once you do you'll probably be glad you made the effort and it will help you maintain friendships.

I chose my activities carefully, opting for early evening or weekend get togethers, and went to cafés rather than bars. I also had friends over for lunch and dinner but asked everyone to bring a dish. I realized I might not get to the movies or theater for a while once the baby was born, so planned lots of great trips. You can always go to weekend matinées if you're too tired in the evening. When I was really too tired to go out, I'd catch up with a friend on the phone.

120 days to go...

YOUR BABY TODAY

Your baby's nervous system and muscular coordination are now much more developed. He has a grasping reflex—when his palm is touched his fingers will close—and he is able to suck his thumb purposefully, rather than through random movements.

When clumsiness strikes, something as simple as walking in a straight line may prove difficult!

If you find that you're often bumping into things and tripping over, it sounds as though you've been hit by clumsiness, a common side effect of being pregnant.

Clumsiness in pregnancy has physical causes: the hormone relaxin causes your joints to loosen, your center of gravity changes as your abdomen expands, and your extra weight shifts you off balance. There are, however, also emotional reasons: if you're preoccupied by being pregnant, your concentration is bound to slip now and then, making you less likely to notice potential hazards in your path.

The good news is that your usual grace will return once you're no longer pregnant, but until that time it's important to avoid situations that might put you at risk of injury. So wear flat shoes rather than heels, avoid wet or slippery surfaces, and be careful on steep staircases. Tape down the edges of loose rugs, and keep the stairs and hallways clear of things that might trip you up. Be particularly careful when you're lifting something because it's very easy to lose your balance if you're leaning forward. Be careful also, getting into and out of the bath or shower, since these are notorious hotspots for pregnancy-related injuries.

It's worth noting that normal clumsiness in pregnancy is not accompanied by visual disturbances, headaches, or dizziness, so if you have any of these symptoms, you should see your doctor.

TIME TO THINK ABOUT

Preparing your home

If your partner's nesting instinct has kicked in, make the most of it by figuring out what needs to be done around your home.

■ **Decorate the room** your baby will eventually sleep in once you move him out of your bedroom.
■ **Take the opportunity** to have a look around and take any unwanted clutter to the dump or charity shop.
■ **Make storage space** by putting up some extra shelves and cupboards where you can. Figure out where you'll store large items, such as the carriage.

Let your partner do the majority of the decorating and don't attempt to climb a step ladder yourself. Be aware of which paints are safe to use during pregnancy (see pp.24–5).

119 days to go...

YOUR BABY TODAY

External appearances are deceptive: although your baby seems very well developed, it's still early in the pregnancy—the state of the cervix and progesterone produced by the placenta both play a part in ensuring that labor does not start for some months yet.

You may be surprised by the strength of feeling you have for your baby, and this maternal instinct will grow stronger each day.

Do you feel as though you're a mom yet? Whether or not you're a maternal person, you'll already have started, instinctively, the process of becoming a mother. You may be taking better care of yourself, eating better, and making lifestyle changes, not necessarily to benefit your own health but for your baby. You're likely to find yourself being very protective and nurturing toward your growing belly, wanting the best for your baby, and being worried about anything happening to him. It's nothing to worry about if you don't feel this bond: all women are different and it may not be until you're holding and caring for your baby that you experience strong maternal feelings.

Your partner may not have this strong parental instinct, but the more you involve him in the pregnancy, the greater the chance of him getting close to his unborn child. By reading books or on the internet about how the baby is developing at every stage, and attending some or all of the prenatal appointments with you, he will be able to picture the baby and follow his progress as closely as possible.

You'll find that your baby occupies your thoughts a lot of the time. Being pregnant makes most women act selflessly in the best interests of their baby.

Your 24th week

YOUR BABY'S BODY SYSTEMS ARE BECOMING MORE AND MORE EFFICIENT

A baby getting prepared for independent life needs all the help you can give her. Keep up your good habits by nourishing the two of you with healthy food; and make sure your own body is in peak physical condition to support your pregnancy. Some minor discomforts, such as feeling too hot, leg cramps, and hemorrhoids may be plaguing you. These annoying problems are only temporary and will disappear once your baby is born.

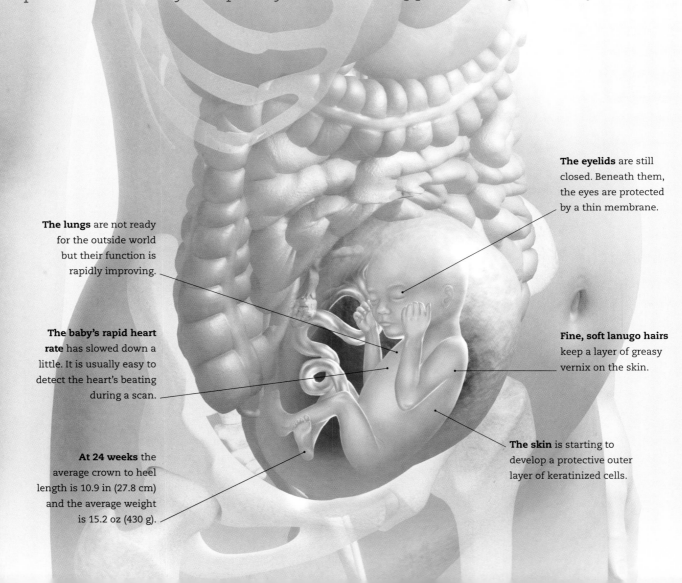

The lungs are not ready for the outside world but their function is rapidly improving.

The baby's rapid heart rate has slowed down a little. It is usually easy to detect the heart's beating during a scan.

At 24 weeks the average crown to heel length is 10.9 in (27.8 cm) and the average weight is 15.2 oz (430 g).

The eyelids are still closed. Beneath them, the eyes are protected by a thin membrane.

Fine, soft lanugo hairs keep a layer of greasy vernix on the skin.

The skin is starting to develop a protective outer layer of keratinized cells.

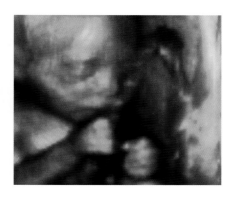

118 days to go…

YOUR BABY TODAY

There is no light in the uterus, but 3D ultrasound is designed to produce highlights and shadows to give the same effect as if you shone a flashlight into the uterus. Now your baby may be holding her hands flexed into a fist.

From this point onward, your baby is considered "viable" and would receive life-saving treatment were she born early.

Week 24 is considered the age of viability for your baby, and therefore an important pregnancy milestone. Like many women, you may feel relieved to get past this point.

If you went into labor and delivered your baby before this week, she would be unlikely to survive and you would be considered to have had a miscarriage, or spontaneous abortion. After 24 weeks, the doctors will do everything they can to save the baby, although babies delivered this early have an increased risk of long-term disability. The more advanced you are in your pregnancy before you deliver, the less likely it is that your baby will face the problems associated with being born prematurely.

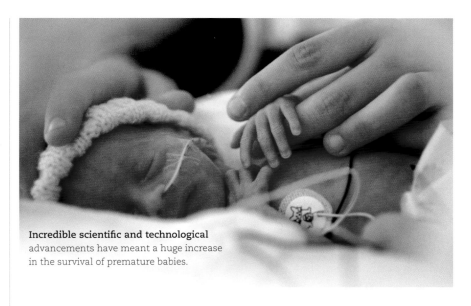

Incredible scientific and technological advancements have meant a huge increase in the survival of premature babies.

AS A MATTER OF FACT

The world's youngest surviving premature baby was born in Florida in October, 2006 at just 21 weeks and six days.

The baby weighed only 10 oz (283 g) and measured 9.5 in (24 cm). Her feet were the size of an adult's fingernail. It was the first time a baby born before 23 weeks had survived.

NEONATAL INTENSIVE CARE UNITS

Babies who are born prematurely, or newborns who are sick, will receive specialized round-the-clock care in a neonatal intensive care unit (NICU) (see pp.452–3). The earlier the baby is born, the more chance there is of complications, such as infections, occurring. If your baby is born several weeks prematurely, she may need to be cared for in a level 3 NICU—this may not be in the hospital where your baby was born.

Your baby may be put in an incubator with monitors attached and receive oxygen through a special ventilator. Some of the equipment looks very frightening, but remember it is there to help your baby stay warm and nourished and improve her health.

The staff will readily explain what is going on, and they will be eager for you to be involved as closely as possible in your baby's care and encourage bonding.

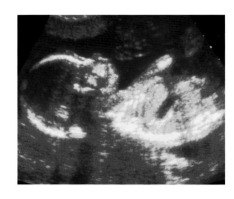

117 days to go...

YOUR BABY TODAY

You will probably be aware of your baby's movements by now: the number of movements and their nature will vary during the day and night and you may notice that they start to form into a particular pattern or respond to your own activity.

With a layer of fat and a tough layer of cells, your baby's skin is now becoming more resilient.

Your baby's skin is continuing to develop and has now started to "keratinize." Keratin is the substance that transforms the skin's outer layer into a protective layer of dead cells. Hair and nails also form from keratin.

The outer keratinized layer of skin cells, plus a layer of fat laid down between the skin cells, gives the skin a waterproof covering. This process of keratanization reduces the amount of water your baby loses into the amniotic fluid. Each new skin cell, made in the deepest part of the skin, matures as it gradually moves up toward the surface and, now keratinized, becomes part of the outer protective layer before it is eventually shed. The cycle takes approximately 30 days.

The thickest layers of keratinized cells are on the palms of the hands and the soles of the feet. The keratinizing process has only just begun. Since the fat layer is very thin at this stage, your baby's skin will still appear translucent, but less so than it did in earlier weeks.

At this stage of pregnancy, your baby still has plenty of room to maneuver inside the uterus, and although you're likely to be feeling lots of movements by now this will only be a fraction of the total. This is because the only movements you'll feel are those that cause your baby to kick or bump into the wall of your uterus. You will be unaware of many of the finer movements that are performed close to the baby's body since they won't make any contact with your uterus.

COPING WITH LEG CRAMPS

Getting painful spasms in the leg muscles is common in pregnancy, particularly at night. You may find that you wake up due to the sudden and severe localized pain in your legs or feet. This is thought to be due to the pressure of the uterus on the pelvic nerves.

Some experts believe that cramps during pregnancy may be caused by a lack of calcium or salt or an excess of phosphorus, but these theories are as yet unproven.

When you get a spasm, relieve it by flexing your foot or leg (see far right), and gently massaging the affected area. The cramp should resolve itself once you are out of bed and using the muscle. However, if the pain doesn't recede and there is any reddening or swelling in the leg, you should seek medical advice immediately to eliminate the possibility of a clot (see p.186), since this can be dangerous.

To reduce the incidence of cramps or its severity, drink lots of water to prevent dehydration and regularly do leg stretches (see right) and ankle exercises, circling your heel and wiggling your toes.

Getting gentle exercise, such as walking or swimming, can also help, as can regularly massaging the calf muscle to improve circulation.

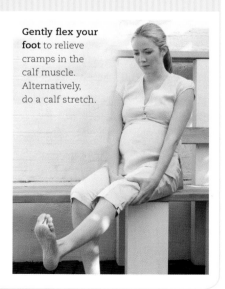

Gently flex your foot to relieve cramps in the calf muscle. Alternatively, do a calf stretch.

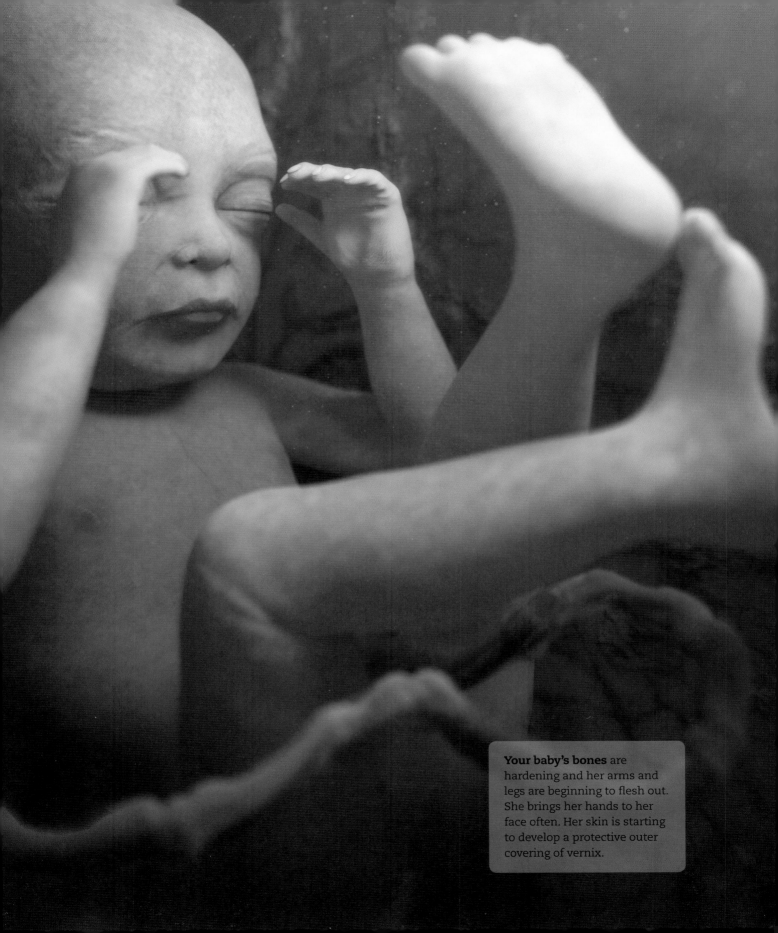

Your baby's bones are hardening and her arms and legs are beginning to flesh out. She brings her hands to her face often. Her skin is starting to develop a protective outer covering of vernix.

116 days to go...

YOUR BABY TODAY

Ultrasound uses sound waves of a very high frequency, well beyond the audible range of the human ear, so your baby's hearing will be completely unaffected by the sound waves transmitted during these scans that check her growth and development.

Are you feeling hot? Being pregnant can sometimes feel as though you have your own personal radiator strapped to you.

You may find that you're much hotter and sweating more than normal during pregnancy. This is because you're carrying more weight than usual and you have more blood pumping around your body.

If you're pregnant during the summer, this can be difficult to bear, so find ways to stay cool (see p.324). If you're pregnant in the winter, you may find yourself walking down the street in a light sweater while other people are all bundled up in coats and scarves. You might get into debates with your partner if he wants the heat on and you want the windows open!

Make sure you drink enough fluid throughout the day. You might find that the increased sweat causes a rash in the creases under your breasts or in your groin, so wash frequently and make sure that you dry these areas well.

Hot flashes can be worse at night, so pack away your pajamas for a few months and get naked.

AS A MATTER OF FACT

It's common to dream that you give birth to an older baby, who is born walking and talking!

This is thought to reflect a mother-to-be's insecurities about caring for a tiny, helpless baby. The older the baby, the more self-sufficient she appears.

ASK A... DOCTOR

I keep having really strange and vivid dreams. Is this normal in pregnancy? Yes, when you're pregnant, it's common to dream more and to remember your dreams. Experts attribute the vividness of these dreams to all the emotional and physical changes a pregnant woman is going through.

The vivid dreams may be a way for your unconscious to deal with all the hopes and fears you may have about your unborn baby and impending motherhood.

The increase is also believed to be due to hormonal changes: increased levels of estrogen are thought to cause longer periods of REM (rapid eye movement) sleep—the phase of sleep in which we are most likely to dream.

If your dreams are disturbing, try writing them down to get them off your mind.

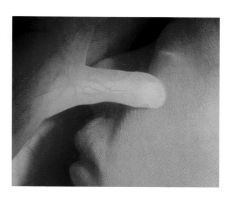

115 days to go...

YOUR BABY TODAY

The joints and bones of the hand are still very soft, although the cartilage skeleton is now gradually being replaced by bone. This image shows well the numerous capillaries supplying blood to the hands, right down to the fingertips.

Over the next few weeks, your baby will take on more of the appearance of a newborn.

Your baby's eyelids and eyebrows are well developed by this week of pregnancy, but the eyelids remain fused. The cells that are destined to become your baby's fingernails were present at 10 weeks, and the cells for the toenails were present four weeks later.

Now, at 23 weeks, the nails are just beginning to make an appearance at the base of the nail bed. The nails will grow continuously throughout life, but it will be several weeks before they have reached the tips of the fingers and then the toes.

Your baby's skin is developing quickly and often appears wrinkled at this stage; it is as if the baby has yet to grow into it. Your baby is now covered in extremely fine and short hairs, known as "lanugo." This layer of hair will be almost completely lost before birth. The hairs help trap vernix onto the surface of the skin; this is the white, greasy layer that you often see in patches on a baby's skin at birth. It collects in the skin folds and creases and helps protect the baby's skin not only from the water content of the amniotic fluid, but also the waste products within it.

As your pregnancy advances, your baby's kidney function is improving and the amniotic fluid produced becomes increasingly similar to urine in its composition.

PREGNANCY POSTURE

Your posture will naturally change as a result of pregnancy; this is due to the extra weight you're carrying and the softening of your joints.

Prior to pregnancy, your center of gravity was directly over your hips; during later pregnancy it shifts forward to your enlarged abdomen. This dramatic shift in your center of gravity increases the curve of your lower spine, and can result in lower back pain (see p.218). The weight you gain during pregnancy can also put strain on the back.

Exercises can help balance your body and alleviate the muscular aches associated with changes in your posture (see right for one example).

It's important to adapt to these postural changes in pregnancy:
- **Do abdominal exercises** (see p.250), to strengthen the core muscles, as well as back stretches. These help maintain good posture and avoid back pain later in pregnancy.
- **Be aware of** the way you're walking and standing: pull your shoulders down and back, do not arch your lower back and keep your pelvis in a neutral position.
- **Avoid balancing anything** on your hip, because this can affect your hip and back alignment.
- **Don't hold a phone between** your head and shoulder because this can result in neck pain.

Your growing abdomen affects the curvature of your spine. Practice tilting your pelvis to lengthen your spine.

Pull your shoulders back

Roll your pelvis under

Bend your knees slightly

Support your lower back

Abdominal exercises

Strong abdominal muscles are beneficial during pregnancy because they will help you carry the weight of your baby and assist you during labor and birth.

Abdominal exercises done while lying on your back aren't recommended after the first trimester. The reason for this is that when you lie on your back, your enlarged uterus presses on one of your major blood vessels, reducing the amount of blood pumped around the body and to the baby. However, you can strengthen abdominal muscles without lying on your back by using gravity and your body to strengthen and tone the torso. In pregnancy, you can tone your abdomen with exercises where you adopt an all-fours position or an upright sitting position. Try to do the exercises below around 2–3 times a week.

Benefits of abdominal exercises

Strong abdominal muscles enable your body to work more efficiently in labor. They also help support the weight of the baby, which takes pressure off the spine, reducing the likelihood of backaches. In addition, keeping your abdominal muscles strong means that you may be less likely to get a condition called *diastasis recti*, in which the abdominal wall muscles separate, often following childbirth, making it harder to regain your figure.

The sling Get down on all fours with your hands on the floor, feet apart, and arms straight. Keep your back flat in a neutral position, being careful not to arch your back. Imagine your abdominal muscles as a sling holding your baby. Take a deep breath, then slowly pull your abdominal muscles (the sling) in toward your back, pulling the baby closer to you, and gently release, returning to the starting position. Repeat at least 20 times. Remember to breathe properly while doing this exercise, breathing in to start and breathing out as you pull in your belly.

The abdominal pull This can be done anywhere and at any time. It's advisable to start by doing it sitting in an upright chair with your shoulders relaxed and back straight. Put your hands around your belly below your navel. Breathe in slowly and pull in your abdominal muscles for two seconds and then release; repeat 10 times. Take a short break, then start again. Once you've mastered this, move on to the next level. In the same position, pull in your muscles and release quickly, almost every second. Breathe properly and do not hold your breath.

The superman pose This exercise will strengthen your core muscles, keeping your abdomen and back strong, and helping prevent lower back pain. It also stretches your leg and arm muscles. Start from an all-fours position. Keeping your back in a neutral position, lift your left arm in front of you and your right leg up behind you. Be careful not to arch your back or lift your leg higher than the hips. Hold for a count of five and slowly lower. Then repeat with your right arm and left leg. Do around 10 repetitions for each arm and leg.

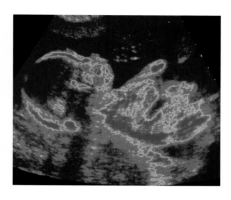

YOU ARE 23 WEEKS AND 5 DAYS

114 days to go...

YOUR BABY TODAY

In this color 2D ultrasound scan the baby is lying face upward. it is now increasingly difficult to show the whole baby using this type of ultrasound because it only shows a thin slice at any one time. Here, only the upper part of the baby can be seen.

Practicing yoga in pregnancy can be hugely beneficial, both physically and emotionally.

In addition to strengthening and toning muscles, yoga aims to bring about a greater awareness of your breathing. Learning to control your breathing is a great way to relax during pregnancy and an invaluable way to prepare to breathe through the contractions when you're in labor.

Standing poses in yoga focus on achieving core stability, thereby strengthening the back and abdominal muscles. This is beneficial during pregnancy when the additional weight you're carrying can affect your balance and cause unsteadiness. Calm sitting poses that concentrate on aligning your spine help you focus on steadying your breathing and centering yourself. If you feel unsteady doing yoga poses, you can simply lean against a wall.

Pilates is also a good exercise to do in pregnancy because it heightens your bodily awareness, giving you greater control of—and confidence in—your body. Pilates also incorporates Kegel exercises (see p.69).

Whatever classes you're doing, it's important to find an accredited instructor who is experienced in teaching pregnant women. There are now many specialized pregnancy yoga and Pilates classes.

AS A MATTER OF FACT

Practicing prenatal yoga under expert supervision can be safe and may reduce the risk of complications.

A recent study found that pregnant women who practiced yoga had a reduced risk of developing pregnancy-induced high blood pressure and of going into premature labor.

Going to pregnancy yoga classes is a great way to exercise gently, while also meeting other pregnant women.

ASK A... DOCTOR

Why are hemorrhoids common in pregnancy? Hemorrhoids are, like varicose veins (see p.167), dilated veins, but they occur around your anus. The weight of your baby pushes down on your back passage, restricting blood flow and causing the veins to dilate.

Hemorrhoids can be itchy and sore, and may cause a throbbing sensation. The discomfort can be relieved with cold packs and creams containing lubricants to help the passage of stools, and/or local anesthetics to relieve soreness. Hemorrhoids can bleed— you may notice bright red blood on the toilet paper after you pass a stool.

If you have hemorrhoids, it is important to try not to get constipated (see p.468) since this means you have to strain and push to pass stools, which increases the pressure on the hemorrhoids and makes them worse. Ensure that you drink lots of water and eat sufficient fiber.

If your hemorrhoids are becoming very problematic and uncomfortable, seek your doctor's or midwife's advice.

Your 24th week

251

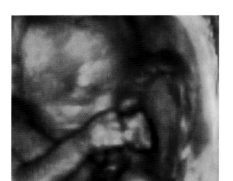

113 days to go...

YOUR BABY TODAY

Your baby is now making regular deep breathing movements. These have been present for some weeks, but not in a sustained and coordinated fashion. These breathing movements are critical for the development and expansion of your baby's lungs.

Although the lungs are the last of your baby's organs to be fully functional, they are undergoing rapid development now.

ASK A... DOCTOR

Is it true that playing music to my unborn baby will enhance her development? Some research into this claim finds that playing music to an unborn baby will lead to a shorter labor and easier birth, and to the newborn baby crying less, being more relaxed, and, overall, being in better health. At the moment, there doesn't seem to be any significant research to suggest that babies who listen to music in the uterus are more intelligent, or develop at a greater speed.

The jury is still out on these findings, but there is anecdotal evidence from pregnant women that their babies move to the rhythm of music. It makes sense that as you relax to gentle music or are invigorated by livelier music, your baby will respond in kind. Many moms say that music played frequently during pregnancy seems to be familiar to their newborns, and soothes them.

So whether your baby is simply experiencing the benefits of your happy state as you listen, or responding to the rhythm, playing music is a good idea.

At this stage, your baby's lungs are starting to mature, as the barrier between the bloodstream and what will become air-containing sacs gradually starts to thin. The thinner this barrier, the more easily oxygen and carbon dioxide will transfer into and out of the baby's bloodstream.

The lungs remain filled with fluid during your pregnancy and when your baby practices breathing, the fluid moves out of her lungs into the amniotic fluid.

At 23 weeks, cells begin to line the smallest branches within the lung and start to produce surfactant, a substance that greatly assists lung function. This substance enables the smallest air sacs to remain open when the newborn baby breathes in and out so that gas transfer can continually take place. Without it, the tiny air sacs would collapse after each breath and it would take much more effort to move air in and out of the lungs. The cells that produce surfactant are not, however, fully functional yet.

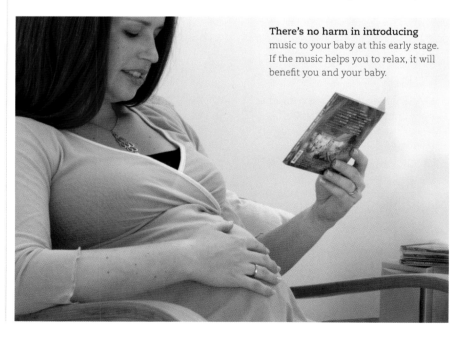

There's no harm in introducing music to your baby at this early stage. If the music helps you to relax, it will benefit you and your baby.

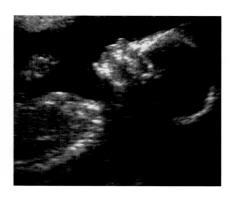

112 days to go...

YOUR BABY TODAY

As your pregnancy advances your baby's skeleton starts to harden, reflecting more of the ultrasound beam and casting black shadows. In this scan, the forehead casts a shadow, and it is no longer allowing the brain beneath to be easily seen.

Even though you're well settled into your pregnancy, ensure you maintain all those healthy lifestyle habits you've established.

You've been pregnant for almost six months and are, hopefully, feeling great in yourself. Don't, however, let this make you complacent. Even though your baby is well developed by this stage, it's important to maximize her health, and your own, by continuing to eat well and taking care of yourself. Changes, such as not smoking or drinking alcohol, will probably be part of your normal lifestyle now as opposed to something that you have to think about and work hard at.

If you have not managed to change your lifestyle to become more healthy, then it is never too late to start. Any changes you make now will benefit both you and your baby.

While you'll need to adapt your exercise routine, if you have one, in these later stages, ensure you continue to be active and, ideally, do something physical every day, even if it's just a 20-minute stroll. Also keep up your daily Kegel exercises (see p.69)—once the baby is born, you'll be thankful you did.

(see p.69)

A correctly worn seat belt reduces the risk of injury to the unborn baby by 70 percent.

In recent research, over half of pregnant women did not wear their seat belt correctly, positioning it too high across the abdomen and putting the torso strap behind them rather than over the shoulder.

FOCUS ON... DADS

Hello, it's Daddy

Don't be afraid to talk to your baby. To begin with, she will recognize lower-pitched sounds, such as deep male voices, more than higher-pitched sounds, like your partner's voice. This is good for you since it means that there is plenty of time for your baby to get to know your voice before she is born. After birth, your baby will recognize your voice and this will have a calming effect when she is distressed. So tell her about your day and even read to her—it helps create a bond.

For maximum safety and comfort, wear the seat belt positioned between your breasts and under your belly.

HOW TO WEAR A SEAT BELT

It may feel cumbersome to wear a seat belt while you're pregnant, but it is essential, and a legal requirement. The good news is it's possible to buckle up comfortably.
- **Fasten the belt** over your shoulder, as normal, and between your breasts (see left).
- **Position the lower part** of the belt below your belly, and flat over your hips (see left).

If an emergency stop is necessary, be reassured that your baby is very safely cushioned by the amniotic fluid that surrounds her and your strong uterine muscles.

Your 25th week

IT'S THE END OF THE SECOND TRIMESTER, SO YOU MIGHT WANT TO START LOOKING AHEAD

The rest of your pregnancy will pass before you know it. Make sure you have all the practicalities in hand, such as deciding what date to stop work, and you might want to give some thought to the birth. Meanwhile, friends and family will no doubt be monitoring your growing belly with interest. Try to be patient if they bombard you with advice and don't listen to too many "tall tales" about pregnancy and childbirth.

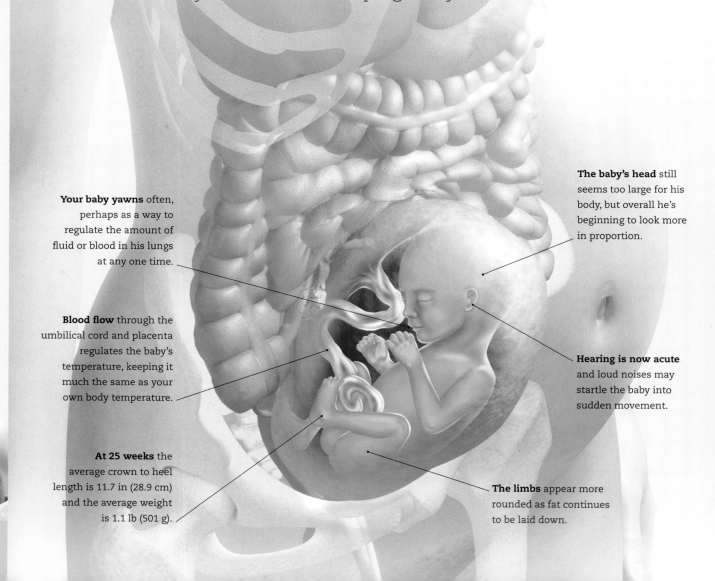

Your baby yawns often, perhaps as a way to regulate the amount of fluid or blood in his lungs at any one time.

Blood flow through the umbilical cord and placenta regulates the baby's temperature, keeping it much the same as your own body temperature.

At 25 weeks the average crown to heel length is 11.7 in (28.9 cm) and the average weight is 1.1 lb (501 g).

The baby's head still seems too large for his body, but overall he's beginning to look more in proportion.

Hearing is now acute and loud noises may startle the baby into sudden movement.

The limbs appear more rounded as fat continues to be laid down.

111 days to go...

YOUR BABY TODAY

From this week, brown fat is laid down in your baby's neck, chest, and back to be used after birth to produce heat and energy. At the moment he has no control over his temperature, which is efficiently maintained at a perfect level by the placenta.

This week, think about starting discussions with your employer about your upcoming maternity leave.

Since you're more than halfway through your pregnancy by now and are likely showing, you've probably already told your boss that you're pregnant. But just informing your company isn't enough—you need to know all the details that pertain to your upcoming maternity leave and what will happen if you decide to stop working before the baby is born.

Every company has different guidelines; some include paid maternity leave while others do not. Talk with a human resources representative to discuss your company's policies on maternity leave and time off. If paid time off isn't available, your company may allow you to use paid vacation days or sick leave, and you may be eligible for federal maternity benefits.

FOCUS ON... YOUR BODY

Stretchy skin

You may have developed stretch marks due to your skin stretching rapidly as you gain pregnancy weight. Initially, these marks are pinky/red and can be itchy. After pregnancy, stretch marks fade to a lighter, silvery color and become less obvious. They generally occur on the breasts, belly, hips, and thighs, and affect the majority of pregnant women.

Stretch marks can be genetic and are more likely to occur the older you are because older skin is less elastic. Moisturizing the skin won't prevent stretch marks but it may help to keep it smooth. A combination of exercising and eating healthily can minimize the rate at which you gain weight and "stretch."

ASK A... DOCTOR

My doctor measured me and said I seem small for dates. What does this mean? It means your baby appears to be small for your stage of pregnancy, but it doesn't necessarily mean there's a problem. You'll be given a scan for an accurate measurement so that your baby's development can be thoroughly checked.

Sometimes slow growth is due to a condition called intrauterine growth restriction (IUGR). It can be due to a problem with the placenta, multiple babies, or heart disease in the mother, affecting the nutrients reaching the baby. Preeclampsia (see p.474) can cause IUGR, as can smoking, alcohol, and recreational drugs.

AS A MATTER OF FACT

You may be eligible for maternity and parental leave.

This is job-protected unpaid time off work. Length of leave varies depending on your province or territory, so check with your local goverment and your human resources department.

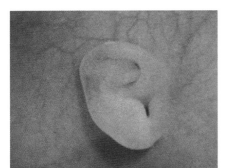

110 days to go...

YOUR BABY TODAY

In the uterus, your baby's ears not only have fluid around them but also inside. This is part of the reason that he can only hear certain lower sound frequencies. Yawning may be a way to unblock the ears, and from now on your baby spends a lot of time yawning.

If you're feeling tired, you're not alone. Your developing baby has been yawning for some weeks now.

All babies are known to yawn in the uterus, although the reason why they do this remains unclear. Yawning is often accompanied by shrugging of the shoulders or stretching, exactly as you would do when tired. Unborn babies have even been seen to rub their eyes!

Your baby first started yawning at around 15 weeks and has gradually yawned more and more frequently. The precise function of yawning for the baby remains in doubt and there are several hypotheses. While it's difficult to imagine that an unborn baby is actually tired, it has been found that babies who are anemic yawn much more frequently than others. Another theory is that

yawning may help the unborn baby to regulate the amount of fluid or blood flow he has within his lungs. Or yawning may simply be a primitive reflex, a remnant from an earlier evolutionary stage, with no current function.

Whatever the reason for yawning, the early stage at which this develops in the unborn baby, and the fact that all mammals are known to yawn in the uterus, does suggest that it plays an important, though unknown, role in fetal development.

AS A MATTER OF FACT

Women aged over 40 are more than twice as likely to have left-handed babies.

This is according to a Canadian study and may be related to the fact that older women are more likely to experience complications in pregnancy and have more arduous deliveries. Several studies show a correlation between left-handedness and birth stress.

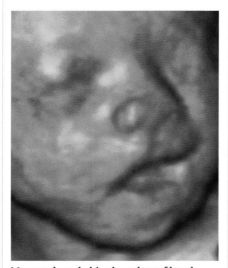

Many unborn babies have been filmed yawning on 4D scans, which give a very up close view of fetal behavior.

FOCUS ON... YOUR BABY

Listen to Mommy

Your developing baby's ears are structurally complete, and studies show that he can hear clearly now. Far from cushioning him against noise, the amniotic fluid that surrounds your baby has excellent sound-conducting properties. Your heartbeat and digestive system provide a constant background rhythm, but he's also aware of other sounds.

Talking to your baby will help you to bond: research indicates that newborns recognize—and turn toward—the sound of their mother's voice in preference to other female voices. To begin with he'll hear deeper voices more clearly, but later he'll register higher-pitched sounds. He will, of course, become more familiar with his mother's voice because this is what he will hear most often.

You may have noticed that sudden noises make your baby startle. In one study, ultrasound scans of fetuses showed that they had a "blink-startle" response to loud noises from around 26 weeks.

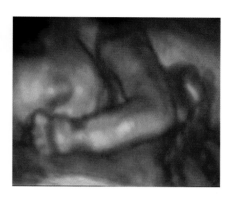

109 days to go...

YOUR BABY TODAY

Here the baby is lying with an arm up to the face and the face lying on the placenta. The eyes are shut at this time and it will be a couple of weeks before they start to open. The hand is held in the most relaxed position, with the fingers slightly curled.

Your body is working hard to grow your baby, so take care of it by enjoying some pampering.

Think of your pregnancy as a time to focus on yourself and your body; once your baby is born, the majority of your focus will be on baby care.

If you have the time and money, treat yourself to a day at a spa. Most spas will have special packages for pregnant women. Spending time at a spa, where you can go for a gentle swim, have some pampering treatments, and enjoy being in a tranquil environment, is a great way to relax and unwind. If a spa day is out of the question, create your own at home. Run a bath, add some relaxing music (for a background soundtrack), light some candles, and relax. If you don't want to be disturbed, let your partner know and turn off the phone.

Pregnancy massage (see p.224) either from a professional or your partner, can be very therapeutic, both physically and emotionally. Another great treatment to have at this stage is a pedicure; you'll increasingly be unable to see your toes, let alone reach them, so it's a treat for someone else to take care of them for you.

Now is the time to indulge yourself in a little pampering. When booking beauty treatments, always make it known that you're pregnant.

> **ASK A... DOCTOR**
>
> **I haven't felt my baby move for four hours. Should I be worried?**
> Contact your caregiver and explain your baby's usual pattern of movements. She may ask you to drink something sugary and come to the hospital if you don't feel any movement within four hours.
>
> If you're not familiar with your baby's movements, lie down—he is more likely to sleep if you're active.

> **ON YOUR FEET**
>
> **You may now find it more of a struggle** to be on your feet, especially for long periods of time. Weight gain, changes in your center of gravity (particularly during the second and third trimesters), and hormones can cause foot pain and swelling (see p.225 and p.466). The pregnancy hormones that relax your joints ready for childbirth can also work to loosen the ligaments in your feet and hips, which can cause some discomfort.
>
> To minimize foot discomfort:
> ■ **Wear sports shoes** that have a good arch support to help reduce strain on your spine. They may also prevent a condition called *plantar fasciitis*—this is where the large ligament that connects the heel to the ball of the foot becomes inflamed.
> ■ **Avoid wearing high-heeled shoes.** In addition to being uncomfortable, they may make you unsteady on your feet and cause you to fall.
> ■ **Ensure that your shoes fit** correctly and invest in new ones if not. Some pregnant women's feet expand by a size, and never return to their normal size after pregnancy.
> ■ **Get regular exercise,** and avoid standing for long periods. Take regular breaks if your job involves standing.

Your 25th week

257

108 days to go...

YOUR BABY TODAY

This 3D scan shows the baby thumb sucking. The 3D technique uses several routine 2D images, linked together to give the 3D effect. In a 4D scan, a series of 3D images are shown in quick succession to give almost real-time movements: the 4th dimension is time.

A natural temperature-regulating mechanism within the uterus means your baby never gets cold.

The temperature inside the uterus is between a third and half a degree higher than yours. Because your body temperature is so closely controlled, your baby never becomes cold so never needs to shiver. He has started to lay down a special form of brown fat, particularly around the neck, chest, and back. After birth, metabolism of this fat produces both energy and heat. In the uterus, however, the baby cannot use this fat to raise his temperature. Some temperature control occurs as heat is lost from the baby's skin into the amniotic fluid through the uterine wall and then into your body tissues. However, the regulation of temperature is predominantly achieved by means of the blood flow to the placenta. The large surface area of the placenta allows it to act as a heat exchange, keeping the temperature of the blood leaving the baby in the umbilical arteries constant with that of the oxygenated blood returning to the baby through the umbilical vein.

After birth, babies lose heat quickly. They are still unable to shiver and cannot maintain their temperature, cooling rapidly if they're not wrapped up warmly or held skin-to-skin shortly after the birth.

SENSIBLE SNACKING

In addition to eating three meals a day, you may find you need to snack throughout the day, too. There's nothing wrong with that as long as you're choosing the right foods, and not reaching for the cookies and chips all the time. These tempting foods might satisfy a hunger pang, but the lack of nutrients and empty calories won't serve you any real purpose. Healthy snacking can be accomplished with a bit of planning before you go shopping:

■ **Dried fruits** should be a mainstay of your snacking, since they can easily be stored and carried. Enjoy a wide variety of dried fruits, since the more variety you consume, the more likely you are to obtain the nutrients you need. Try dried apricots, raisins, cranberries, cherries, and peaches.

■ **Lightly salted mixed nuts** will satisfy any salt craving you may have in a healthy way.

■ **Opt for pretzels, oatcakes,** or crackers, rather than potato chips.

■ **Fresh fruit** is a convenient and nutrient-rich snack; always carry one or two pieces with you when you're out and about, and make fruit salads that you can keep in the fridge. Keep frozen fruit on hand, and along with some vanilla yogurt, you can whip up a smoothie in no time at all.

■ **Frozen yogurt and low-fat ice cream** both make good snacks and desserts. Stock up on a variety of low-fat yogurt brands.

Always take a healthy snack with you when you leave the house.

107 days to go...

YOUR BABY TODAY

Here the skin looks almost loose around the neck as the baby has turned his head slightly. This is normal at this stage: the lack of fat beneath the skin and the need to grow rapidly can make your baby appear as if he needs time to "grow into" his own skin.

Some meals may be followed by an uncomfortable bout of indigestion, but you can take steps to prevent and relieve this.

THINK ABOUT GAS

I seem to be gassier than usual lately. Is the pregnancy to blame?
Yes, pregnancy slows down your digestive tract, which can lead to unpleasant burping, bloating, passing gas, and an uncomfortable feeling in the stomach. Symptoms can be worse after you eat a large meal. To minimize problems:

■ **Steer clear of foods that make you gassy.** For many women, this may include cabbage, beans, and other foods rich in fiber. Some women have trouble with large amounts of dairy products.

■ **Eat smaller meals more frequently** rather than a couple of large meals.

■ **Avoid swallowing air.** This means you shouldn't hurry when you eat, you should chew every mouthful thoroughly, and you should avoid drinking through straws. Also, skip carbonated beverages and chewing gum.

■ **Reduce your intake of fatty, fried foods** which can contribute to bloating and discomfort.

■ **Don't take any OTC indigestion remedies** without first checking with your pharmacist or caregiver.

While you may be enjoying your food, you could be paying the price with indigestion. The pregnancy hormone progesterone relaxes the muscles in the entire digestive tract. This slows digestion and the sphincters, or rings of muscles, at each end of the stomach become less effective. This can cause heartburn and indigestion as acidic juices from the stomach leak back into the esophagus. In addition, as your pregnancy progresses, your growing baby is squashing your stomach so that you have a smaller space to digest food.

To relieve indigestion, eat little and often, eat slowly, don't eat late at night, and cut down on fatty or spicy foods. Make sure to talk to your doctor about any natural remedies, including peppermint tea. Rather than lie flat, prop yourself up with pillows. Check with your pharmacist before taking over-the-counter medicine.

Make your own peppermint tea by steeping fresh leaves in hot water. Drink it after you've eaten for the best results.

FOCUS ON... DADS

Arranging parental leave and benefits

You may qualify for parental leave, which is job-protected unpaid time off work and regulated by your provincial or territorial government. You may also be entitled to parental benefits through the federal Employment Insurance Act (EI), which will replace a portion of your salary while you aren't working, provided you fulfill certain requirements (see pp.348–9). Talk to your human resources department about your specific situation.

106 days to go...

YOUR BABY TODAY

The nose is well defined and in addition to regularly swallowing the amniotic fluid your baby is breathing it in and out through each nostril. Just as adults do, your baby will tend to favor breathing more through one nostril than the other.

From this point onward, babies grow at an individual rate, which is largely influenced by their genes.

The proportions of your baby's body are becoming much closer to those of a newborn baby. Up until the third month, his head accounted for almost half of his overall length. Now his head, trunk, and legs each account for a third. At birth your baby's head will still be large in proportion compared to an adult's, but it will be just a quarter of his overall length.

Still very skinny, your baby is now starting to fill out more as fat reserves continue to be laid down.

Up until this point most babies are approximately the same size and weight. Genetic and especially environmental forces increasingly come into play, influencing how quickly your baby can grow and whether his full growth potential is eventually reached.

Because different babies increasingly vary in size from this stage of pregnancy, ultrasound dating becomes less accurate at determining the number of weeks you are into your pregnancy. The best time to date the

pregnancy is between 11 and 14 weeks, simply measuring top to bottom (the crown rump length) (see p.138). The 20-week scan (see pp.214–15) also dates the pregnancy very accurately from the head and abdominal circumferences and the bone measurement in the leg.

If your first scan is at this late stage, it is only possible to estimate roughly the stage of pregnancy and age of the baby. It is never appropriate to change your due date if an earlier, more accurate scan has been performed.

IT'S ALL IN THE BELLY

The general story goes that if you're carrying your baby low, you're having a boy, if you're carrying high, then you're having a girl. The truth is, the way you carry is probably determined by the tone of your abdominal and uterine muscles as well as the position of your baby.

According to those "old wives," there are other physical clues: if you've gained weight on your face and it's round and full, you're having a girl. If your right breast is larger than your left, it's a boy—and if your partner gains weight, you're "definitely" having a girl!

Small-framed woman carrying baby to the front

Medium-framed woman carrying baby low

Larger-framed woman carrying baby high

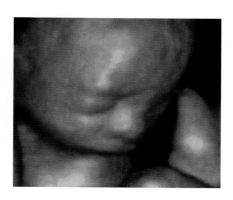

105 days to go...

YOUR BABY TODAY

Here the baby's head is looking down toward the chest. The right arm is bent at the elbow to lie across the neck, the left arm is only just visible as it is partly in shadow, and finally the tip of a knee can be seen tucked up just below the right forearm.

You can expect to be subjected to a few unwelcome birth stories, whether you want to hear them or not!

TIME TO THINK ABOUT

Birth partners

The benefits of having a supportive birth partner are indisputable, so it's a good idea to think about it now.

■ **Research shows that** women who receive continuous emotional and physical encouragement during labor are less likely to need pain relief or medical intervention such as an epidural (see pp.404–5), assisted delivery (see pp.436–7), or cesarean (see pp.438–9), and should experience a shorter labor.

■ **Women who feel their birth partner** was supportive are more likely to view their birth in a positive light, and to take to motherhood and breast-feeding easily, and are less prone to postpartum depression.

■ **Your birth partner** doesn't have to be the baby's father (although he may be there as well); in fact, studies indicate that a woman may do the job better. A close female friend who's had her own children could be ideal; your mom is another option.

■ **You could consider** hiring a doula (see right).

It appears to be a rite of passage for some women to describe the birth of their babies in minute detail, literally giving an hour-by-hour account. For these women, it appears to be part of the recovery process and they like nothing better than a new audience, and, especially, a woman who is pregnant for the first time. So you'll no doubt find yourself on the receiving end of a few birth horror stories—sometimes from complete strangers!

These women may feel it's their duty to "warn" you about the "reality" of childbirth, and what you should and shouldn't do—for example, "definitely

Having a close female friend or relative with you during labor, even if it's only at home in the early stages, may prove to be a great help to you and your partner.

have an epidural, otherwise the pain is horrendous." Remember that every woman's experience is different and stay focused on your own birth plan. Childbirth is undoubtedly difficult for some women, while others have straightforward deliveries, without complications. Tell the story-teller you'd rather not hear the gory details but promise to book a date for a joint debrief once your baby is born!

MOTHER'S HELP

The prospect of giving birth and then taking care of a newborn can be daunting. For some moms, hiring a doula is the perfect way to ensure a gentle progression from pregnancy to motherhood.

Doulas are women who "mother the mother" by providing emotional and physical (but nonmedical) support before, during, and after childbirth. Widespread research shows that the presence of a doula can help you have a shorter, easier birth, making it less likely that you'll need pain relief or medical intervention (including an epidural or cesarean). To find out more about hiring a doula, visit dona.org/mothers/find_a_doula.php.

Welcome to your third trimester

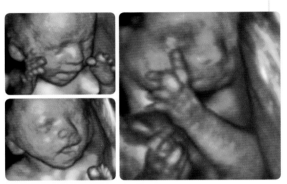

A new person emerges Your baby is close to being a fully functioning individual. His major organs are almost ready to work in the outside world, but he would need medical help if he were born now.

From weeks 26 to 40, your baby will probably grow by about 5½ lb (2.5 kg) and 8 in (20 cm).

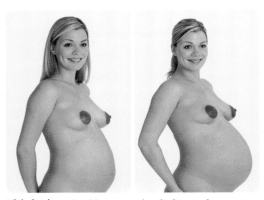

Third trimester Your growing baby pushes out your lower ribs and fills up most of the space in the uterus. **Ready for birth** Your belly is huge and you're tired and breathless, but excited too.

Monitoring growth By measuring your growing abdomen, your baby's rate of growth is assessed and any concerns addressed with further tests.

A new brother or sister Include older children as you prepare for your new baby. They can help you choose clothes and think about names.

Sleeping comfortably You need to take the weight off your belly, but relaxing is easier said than done. Use lots of pillows to cushion you when you rest in bed.

Preparing for labor Going to prenatal classes and exercise sessions will help you prepare both mentally and physically for the approaching labor and birth, and feel confident about how you'll manage.

You're in the home stretch now and your thoughts turn increasingly to the birth of your baby.

33	34	35	36	37	38	39	40

Fiber fit An adequate fiber intake is especially important in late pregnancy when a sluggish digestion makes constipation more likely.

Ready to go Delivery date is on the horizon. Before you go to the hospital, pack your bags some time in advance. Start gathering essential items.

Nearing the end As you reach the end of your pregnancy, you'll marvel at the size of your belly.

38 weeks It's a tight fit now for your baby, so he doesn't have much room to turn and kick. You should still feel him moving, though—so it's important to be aware of any change in activity.

Facts and figures By week 38, the placenta's role is nearly over and it starts to age.

Bringing on labor If you've reached 40 weeks with no sign of labor, you may be starting to think about ways to trigger its onset—making love is one of several methods to try.

Taking the weight It's worthwhile to continue swimming as long as you feel able since the water supports all your additional weight, bringing welcome relief.

Facts and figures By 33 weeks, your baby is rapidly putting down fat deposits and is starting to look more like a newborn baby.

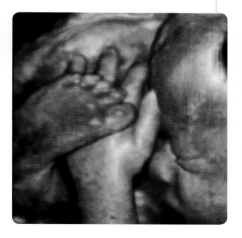

Hello, baby Here at last, and worth all the waiting. Immediate skin-to-skin contact has significant benefits for your baby.

Your 26th week

YOU'VE REACHED THE THIRD AND FINAL TRIMESTER AND WILL BE HEAVILY PREGNANT BY NOW

You're in the last lap and, although your belly is probably big, you've still got a lot more expanding to do. Your baby will be moving around quite vigorously and may even respond to loud noises and music. Nerve cells in her brain are beginning to connect and her coordination is improving. Keep your own brain stimulated by going to prenatal classes for fun, company, and information.

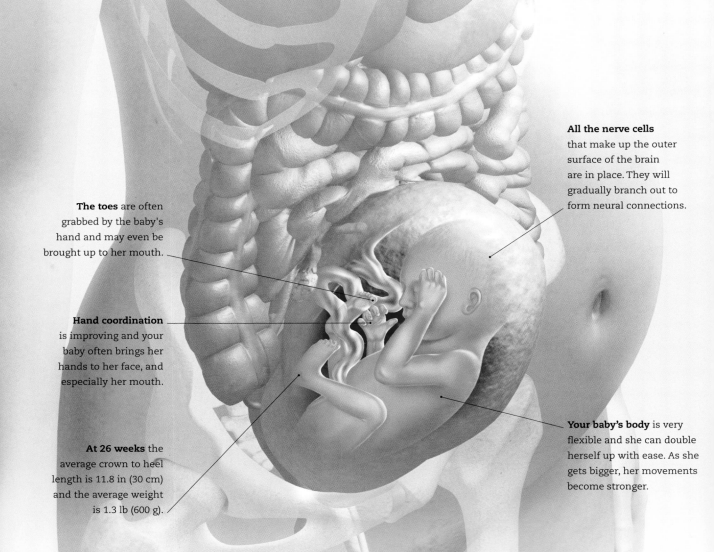

All the nerve cells that make up the outer surface of the brain are in place. They will gradually branch out to form neural connections.

The toes are often grabbed by the baby's hand and may even be brought up to her mouth.

Hand coordination is improving and your baby often brings her hands to her face, and especially her mouth.

At 26 weeks the average crown to heel length is 11.8 in (30 cm) and the average weight is 1.3 lb (600 g).

Your baby's body is very flexible and she can double herself up with ease. As she gets bigger, her movements become stronger.

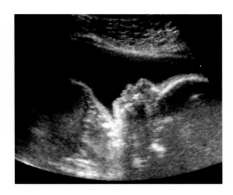

104 days to go...

YOUR BABY TODAY

Here the baby is looking directly upward. The profile is nicely detailed with the nose, lips, and chin clearly outlined. The neck is still quite short so, as this image shows, the head is still held quite close to the chest.

Your prenatal classes will give you a chance to learn about labor, birth, and life with a newborn, and make new friends.

If you arranged them earlier in your pregnancy (see p.199), you may be starting prenatal classes, also called childbirth education classes, about now. The Lamaze Method and The Bradley Method are common classes. Ask your health-care provider, friends, and staff at the hospital where you're giving birth about where to find a class near you. In the class, you may be taught, for example, relaxation or breathing techniques, or be told about the different types of pain relief available. Some hospitals also offer newborn care classes, where you'll learn all the basics: How to diaper, dress, feed, carry, and generally take care of your baby when she is brought home from the hospital.

It's common to feel excited about the classes and eager to learn about what's going to happen and to meet other people going through the same experience. But prenatal classes are not just about gathering information, they're also about meeting others, which is difficult for some people. However, since you're all parents-to-be, you're likely to find things to talk about. Just talking with others about your symptoms or worries can help, especially if they're going through the same emotions as you. It can be reassuring to know that you're not the only person to feel a certain way.

If you do make friends in your prenatal class, this support group can also be very helpful after you all have your babies.

FOCUS ON... YOUR BODY

Rib pain

As the uterus expands, the rib cage is pushed outward to make room for it, and this can lead to rib pain or discomfort. This is not inevitable, but it is more likely if you have a smaller than average body frame or you're carrying twins or more. It can be worse if your baby kicks a lot or if she spends a lot of time in the breech position since her head will push against your diaphragm and rib cage.

Sitting down may make the pain worse since being seated compresses your internal organs more. If you have a sedentary job, get up and move around as often as you can, and if you're forced to sit for long periods, keep adjusting your position until you find one that's comfortable.

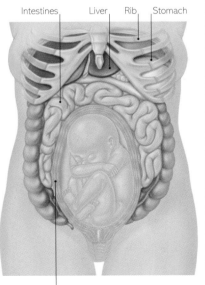

Intestines   Liver   Rib   Stomach

Expanding uterus reduces space for stomach and intestines

ASK A... DOCTOR

I think I have a vaginal infection. Will this harm my baby? A vaginal infection is very unlikely to harm your baby since the mucus plug around the cervix stops infection from reaching her. The symptoms of an infection—itching, irritation, and a discharge with an unpleasant odor—are uncomfortable. Your caregiver may prescribe medication to clear it up.

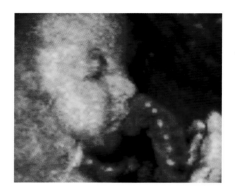

103 days to go...

YOUR BABY TODAY

This image shows the baby in profile, this time in 3D. The coils of the umbilical cord are just seen in the background passing behind the baby's head. The eyelids can be seen, still firmly closed. Fat reserves are now giving the face a much more rounded contour.

Two tiny glands control your baby's growth and development now, and give her the ability to face life's stresses later.

Relative to body size, your baby's adrenal glands are 20 times larger than your own. The adrenal glands are roughly triangular in shape, with their base wrapped over the top of each kidney. They have an outer layer, or cortex, which releases steroid hormones such as cortisol, and an inner layer, or medulla. Adrenaline and the related hormone noradrenaline are secreted from the medulla in response to stress.

Adrenaline prepares the body for a "fight or flight" response, increasing the availability of glucose, speeding up the heart rate, and maintaining or raising blood pressure. These are vital adaptive responses for your baby that will help to maintain a stable environment

within the uterus and prepare her for the stresses of life later on in the outside world.

It is the outer cortex, however, that needs to work hard, producing many hormones that help to coordinate your baby's growth and development. The cortex produces three types of hormones: mineralocorticoids that

regulate salt balance; glucocorticoids that help to control the availability of sugars, fat, and amino acids in the bloodstream; and androgens, male-type sex hormones, such as testosterone. It is the cortex that accounts for the large size of your baby's adrenal glands. After birth, in the first couple of weeks, the adrenal glands rapidly reduce in size.

FOCUS ON... TWINS

How identical are identical twins?

Twins from the same egg have the same DNA. In a way, they're natural clones, so you might expect them to

be identical in every way. They will certainly look very alike, and have the same hair color, eye color, and skin color. They will also have the same blood group and tissue type.

However, the environment isn't the same for each baby, even pre-birth. Small differences in blood flow, and in location in the uterus, can have far-reaching effects.

■ **There may be recognizable differences** in the weight, height, and head shape of identical twins.
■ **Each twin** has unique fingerprints and iris patterns.
■ **Identical twins** can have different personalities too, partly because of subtle dissimilarities in their very early environment.

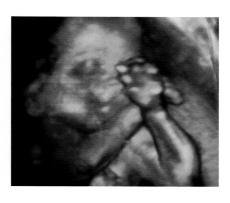

102 days to go...

YOUR BABY TODAY

This baby has her hands held up in front of her face. In the top right-hand corner, the curved inner lining of the uterus can be seen. Shadows in the image give the impression of hair but ultrasound is not detailed enough to show hair—even if there was any to see at this stage.

Going to prenatal classes together is a good way for your partner to stay closely involved with your pregnancy.

Not all dads-to-be are eager to go to prenatal classes. They might not feel the classes apply to them, and may fear that they will be asked to do exercises that they find embarrassing.

If your partner is reluctant, discuss it with him, pointing out what the classes are for and why you feel that you need his support. You could explain that you want him to be informed about labor so that he is not anxious in the delivery room. He might find it useful to talk to male friends who went to classes when they were expectant dads.

Classes may include some sessions with men and women together and others where the women go on their own, for example to practice breathing techniques, while the men have a separate session where they can share any concerns. If time off work is an issue for your partner, ask for a list of what topics will be covered each week and pick those sessions that you think are the most relevant for him. If your partner is well informed, he'll feel more involved in the pregnancy and more confident in helping you during labor and birth.

What you learn at prenatal classes may bring you closer. Try to stay in touch with each other at home, spending time relaxing together and feeling your baby moving.

TIME TO THINK ABOUT
Maternity benefits

You may be eligible for maternity benefits through the federal Employment Insurance Act (EI), which will pay for a part of your salary while you aren't working. EI also offers parental benefits, which can be taken by either parent, or split between them. If a mother chooses to take both maternity and the complete parental benefits together, she could receive a total of 50 weeks' benefits. Your employer may "top up" what you receive from EI, so talk to your human resources department.

FOCUS ON... RELATIONSHIPS
Anticipating changes in your relationship

It might seem obvious, but once your baby is born your relationship won't just be about you and your partner any more. Suddenly there is a tiny new person around, who wakes during the night and who has her own needs. By necessity, after your baby is born you and your partner will pay less attention to each other. There

may also be less physical intimacy between the two of you, not least because you both will be very tired.

It's best to talk about, and acknowledge, these issues before the birth. This way, you and your partner will better accept that these factors are a normal part of making the life change from coupledom to being a family.

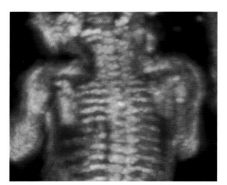

101 days to go...

YOUR BABY TODAY

This 3D image shows the back of the baby, taken using a scanner setting that enhances the reflections from the skeleton. The back of the spine, ribs, and shoulder blades are clear: this technique has opened up many new possibilities for visualizing your baby's development.

All the nerve cells are now on the surface of your baby's brain; what they need to do next is make connections with each other.

Your baby's brain is so complex that it needs the entire length of your pregnancy not only to grow, but also to mature. It is continually forming new connections and sensory pathways.

The nerves that make up the brain's gray matter started in the center of the brain on the outer surface of the lateral ventricles (there is one ventricle in each hemisphere of the brain). The lateral ventricles contain the part of the brain known as the choroid plexus, a loose, seaweedlike structure that produces the fluid that bathes your baby's brain and spinal cord. Constantly circulating around the brain, this fluid protects and buffers the brain from the harder structure of the bones of the surrounding skull.

The gradual, wavelike, outward movement of nerve cells in the gray matter, which started more than 12 weeks ago, is now complete. Coming to rest close to the brain's surface, these cells need to mature, branching out to make multiple connections, or "synapses," with other nerve cells.

The surface of your baby's brain is very smooth at this stage but as the cortex matures, beginning to form six clear layers, it takes on its familiar wrinkled appearance.

FOCUS ON... YOUR BELLY

Your belly: to show or not to show?

Whether you want to clothe your belly in figure-hugging fabrics and proudly show it off, or choose looser styles that may fit you longer and obscure just how pregnant you are, is a personal choice.

■ **If you're fine showing your belly,** you may feel comfortable in stretchy fabrics that can expand as your belly does. The downside to wearing tight clothing is that your skin may be sensitive to anything snug-fitting. Tight tops will also bring attention to your breasts.

■ **If you feel more comfortable** not showing the profile of your belly, choose baggier clothes, such as tunics, smocks, and overshirts. These may be more comfortable and will cloak your belly longer.

■ **If you want to bare your belly,** do so when the weather is warm enough. One advantage is you may find you can wear some pre-pregnancy tops.

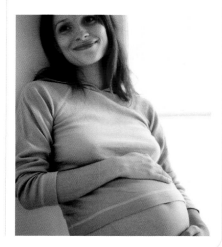

ASK A... DOCTOR

I'm getting quite big—should I adapt my swimming style?
You may find that in these final couple of months, you need to change your swimming style to one that is more comfortable; many women opt for breaststroke, which can also help to get the baby in to an optimum position (see p.329).

If you don't feel up to swimming laps, just relax in the pool instead. Being in the water will relieve pressure on your abdomen and help to ease lower back pain.

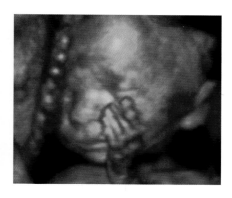

100 days to go...

YOUR BABY TODAY

With fingers held up to the cheek, eyes closed, and the ear just visible in the background, this image shows a very peaceful baby. To the left, the umbilical cord is visible on its way to the placenta, seen further to the left.

It will be some years before you'll know your child's personality, but even in the uterus she has some likes and dislikes.

As your baby continues to grow you may find yourself wondering what she is going to be like: easy going or demanding? Funny or serious? Happy playing alone or social? Boisterous or quiet? You may believe that babies are born with their personalities already developed, or that they are born with a personality that is further shaped and developed as they grow. The nature versus nurture debate rages on and, in all likelihood, it's a combination of the two: some aspects of your child's personality may already be decided before birth, some may be developed later in childhood, or even adulthood.

You may already have noticed that your baby has certain likes or dislikes, for example she may kick or move in response to loud music or to a certain genre of music, though it's difficult to tell whether the increased movements mean your baby is enjoying it or not.

Your baby is very stimulated inside the uterus. By this third trimester, she can feel vibrations, and hear not just sounds from inside your body, such as your heartbeat, but also sounds from outside, such as people talking. Your baby is aware of when you're moving or are still and you may have noticed a pattern of movements from her, not least that she "communicates" more when you're resting.

As part of her activity, she will continue practicing for life after the birth, with breathing movements and swallowing—and she may even suck her thumb.

(see p.291)

BUYING FOR YOUR BABY

Preparing for your baby's arrival doesn't have to break the bank.
What your baby needs:
■ **Milk:** breast milk is free (and best for your baby). For bottle-feeding, you'll need bottles, nipples, formula, and a sterilizing system.
■ **Diapers:** you'll need to decide between disposables, reusables, or a combination of the two (see p.291). Whichever type you choose, you'll also need to use diaper wipes.
■ **Somewhere to sleep:** she can sleep in a crib from birth if you don't want to buy a bassinet. If you buy a used crib, make sure it was made after 1986 to ensure that it meets safety standards, and buy a new mattress.
■ **Lots of onesies:** don't buy too many newborn size.
■ **Transportation:** a stroller (with a lie-option until your baby can sit up), or a sling or frontpack to carry your baby.
■ **Car seat:** this is a legal requirement for car travel. Don't buy used.
What your baby can live without:
■ **Changing station:** a mat (or towel) on the floor is cheaper and safer.
■ **Bottle warmer:** heat in a jug instead.
■ **Pack-n-Play:** borrow one if necessary. Save money by shopping online. Scour second-hand shops and yard sales. Swap clothes and toys with friends, family members, and other parents.

Babies soon outgrow onesies and get little wear out of them so you may be offered some from friends. You can cut the feet off the onesies if they're too tight.

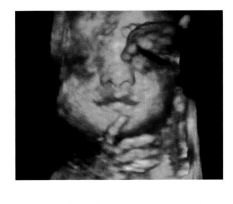

99 days to go...

YOUR BABY TODAY

A 3D scan can be colored in different ways: this image demonstrates that by this stage your baby's lip shape is clearly defined. The lips are the most sensitive part of the entire body and your baby's hands are often held up toward them.

Your baby can make coordinated movements with her hands and feet, make a fist, and grab hold of her toes.

Your baby's hand coordination dramatically improves now and she constantly brings her hands up to her face, particularly her mouth. The face, and especially the lips, are extremely sensitive, and this heightened sensitivity provides strong positive feedback as your baby successfully coordinates smooth, purposeful movements between hand (and foot) and mouth.

There is still plenty of room in the uterus for all sorts of movements and your baby is extremely flexible. It is quite easy for her to adopt a doubled-up position, with her feet up by her mouth or even on top of her head, and to do full somersaults.

Your baby's bones are hardening from the center out so their outer edges are still formed of soft cartilage.

ASK A... DOCTOR

Why do I get so hot when I'm exercising? During pregnancy, your core body temperature rises due to the effects of the hormone progesterone, your increased weight, and the greater demands on your body. Exercise generates heat and raises your core temperature even further, which is why you're likely to feel extra hot when you exercise during pregnancy.

You'll also sweat more easily while you are pregnant. This is because pregnancy-related hormones cause dilation of blood vessels and thus blood flow to your skin (this explains the rosy "glow" some women get), allowing your body to lose heat through the skin more readily. This means that, although you

get hotter while you're exercising, you'll cool down more quickly than usual. When you're exercising, always remember to:

- **Drink water** before, during, and after a workout.
- **Wear appropriate clothing** that will allow your skin to breathe.
- **Avoid exercising** when conditions are hot and humid.

FOCUS ON... YOUR BABY

Birth weight

A woman's weight gain during pregnancy influences her baby's birth weight, which in turn influences the future health of the baby. Birth weights that are too high or too low have been associated with an increased chance of health problems in the baby's future. Thus, pregnancy is a balancing act, in which women need to take in enough, but not too many, calories and gain the right amount of weight (see p.99).

Health experts are increasingly concerned about the fact that fetal over-nutrition is resulting in high birth weight. Being overweight, or putting on excessive amounts of weight during pregnancy, increases the chances of gestational diabetes in the mother (see p.473), a cesarean delivery, complications during delivery, large newborns, and childhood obesity. If a child is obese, there's an increased risk of a lifetime of being overweight or obese, which increases the chances of diabetes, high blood pressure, cancer, and heart disease.

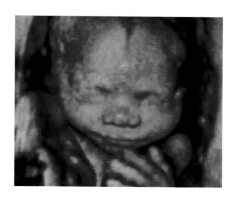

98 days to go...

YOUR BABY TODAY

The space between the two frontal bones of the forehead (the dark line) has now nearly closed. The bones on the left and right sides come to lie very close to each other with a small gap to allow for further growth of the head and brain.

Dreaming is a natural and healthy part of your sleep cycle, but at this stage of pregnancy unsettling dreams can be common.

Vivid dreams are common among women in the third trimester. You may, in fact, not be dreaming more than usual, but difficulty in finding a comfortable sleeping position and waking often to go to the bathroom may mean that you remember your dreams more than usual (you normally would not wake during the dreaming phase of your sleep cycle, so often do not recall your dreams in the morning).

It is common to dream about babies and small children in distress or danger. It is not uncommon for women to feel anxious about such dreams, but you should know that they are in no way insights into what is in store for you. Dreaming is a way of filtering any negative emotions so that you do not have to experience them first hand. Rest assured that, although disturbing, these dreams will help you cope with your natural concern for your baby's welfare.

GOING ON A HOSPITAL TOUR

As part of the build up to your baby's birth, you may be offered a tour of the hospital. Not only will you be able to see first hand where you'll be delivering your baby and what the units are like, but you can also figure out the practical details, such as parking, admission procedures, what you'll need to bring, and what facilities there are, such as cafés and shops for visiting friends and family.

Ultimately, a hospital tour offers you a reassuring chance for you and your partner to prepare yourself mentally for the big day and what will follow your baby's birth.

Use the opportunity as a fact-finding mission. Ask how the hospital uses birth plans (see p.303), and when and why they might have to be adapted. Ask how many other moms there will be in the unit, and, if you want, how you can arrange a private room. There may be a fee for this. Find out what support you'll have in the first 24 hours. Most hospitals now expect the mother to keep the baby with her during the night. Ask about visiting hours, and the number of visitors you can have at any one time. You could also ask how many babies are born at the hospital each year, and how many of these are born by cesarean (emergency or otherwise). Request information about how long the shifts are and what nurses and doctors do to provide continuity of care during labor and birth. Ask to see a delivery room and the nursery.

Are there birthing pools or baths available? Do they have TENS machines or any other form of pain relief you may be considering? What support is there for breast-feeding, and are there breast pumps available?

Finally, although you probably won't need to use it, you may want to see the neonatal intensive care unit (NICU) (see pp.452–3). If your baby needs this type of care, it can help to have seen the equipment and gained a basic understanding of what it's used for.

Your 27th week

YOU MAY FIND IT DIFFICULT TO SLEEP DUE TO YOUR BABY'S ACTIVITIES

Space is now getting tight in your uterus. The baby is likely to give you a few sharp jabs with his feet and fists as he stretches and turns. However uncomfortable the kicks may be, you'll find them a welcome reassurance that the baby is thriving. Relax in bed or in the bath and watch your belly—you'll be amazed and amused at how it pops up and down and moves around.

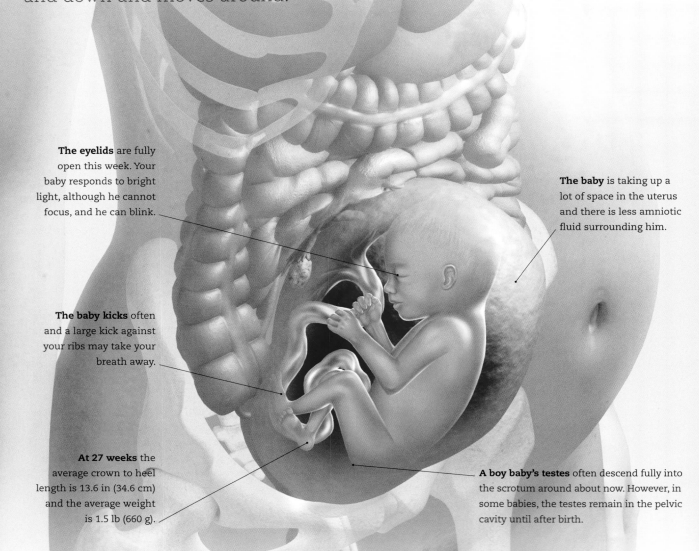

The eyelids are fully open this week. Your baby responds to bright light, although he cannot focus, and he can blink.

The baby is taking up a lot of space in the uterus and there is less amniotic fluid surrounding him.

The baby kicks often and a large kick against your ribs may take your breath away.

At 27 weeks the average crown to heel length is 13.6 in (34.6 cm) and the average weight is 1.5 lb (660 g).

A boy baby's testes often descend fully into the scrotum around about now. However, in some babies, the testes remain in the pelvic cavity until after birth.

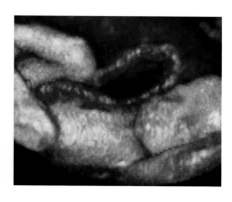

97 days to go...

YOUR BABY TODAY

The coiling umbilical cord is very clearly seen in this image. The umbilical cord grows as your baby grows and will be about the same length as your baby at this stage of your pregnancy: about 13.6 in (34.6 cm).

When you settle down for a nap it can be frustrating if your baby starts exercising, but take this as a sign that all is well.

You may have noticed that your baby is more active at some times than at others, often when you're trying to relax or sleep! This is likely to be because when you're busy or distracted, you're less aware of your baby moving because you're not paying much attention to him as at other times. The moment you stop and sit down to put your feet up or go to bed will be the time your baby starts to do his somersaults.

Remember that, like newborns, babies still in the uterus spend a lot of time sleeping, so there will be periods when you don't feel your baby being very active—it's fine for him not to be moving all the time. Every baby has a different cycle of waking and sleeping, and there are no rules as to when your baby should be kicking and when he should be still.

If you're familiar with your baby's pattern of movements and are concerned that you haven't felt him move, try lying down on your side and relaxing or playing music to see if your baby responds. If you're concerned, contact your doctor or midwife, who may recommend that you have a sugary drink—and if there's no movement in four hours you should go to the hospital. Some women count their baby's kicks using a chart, noting down when they feel the baby move. Kick charts are not often used now, because they are thought to cause unnecessary concern. Babies have an individual pattern of movements, and it is this, rather than the number of kicks, that's important.

ASK A... MOM

I've never taken care of a baby and I don't even know how to put a diaper on one! What can I do?
You're not alone: I had never been around babies much and was full of questions. How do diapers work? What do babies do all day? What if I drop my baby? Luckily a friend had a three-month-old who we "borrowed." As you'll soon realize, there are plenty of weary moms and dads out there, and almost certainly someone among your family and friends will be only too happy to take a break. But before you remove the baby from his comfort zone, spend time with him and his parent(s). Feed him and change diapers under his mother's watchful eye. If she's confident that you're up to the job, offer to take charge, perhaps just for a few hours at first.

If all goes well, you could build up to a day—or even overnight. It'll work wonders for your confidence and eliminate any fears you have about baby care. When it comes to taking care of your newborn, you'll have some idea of what to expect and feel more sure about what you're doing.

AS A MATTER OF FACT

During pregnancy your total volume of blood is 50 percent higher than normal.

The amount of blood pumped with each heartbeat increases by about 40 percent and you make around 20 percent more red blood cells than normal.

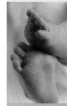

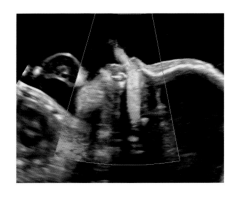

96 days to go...

YOUR BABY TODAY

This color ultrasound shows the baby breathing the amniotic fluid (red, flowing toward the ultrasound beam) in and out. The baby is breathing a stream of fluid out through the nostrils and, at the same time, a smaller amount through the mouth.

As the development of your baby's eyes and sense of sight continues, he reaches another milestone: the eyelids open.

Although your baby's eyelids formed at nine weeks of pregnancy, they have remained fused together until this week. Your baby is not in complete darkness, however, because as the uterus grows its wall thins allowing in increasing amounts of light. Now, your baby's eyes have reached a stage of development where they can open.

Even with the eyelids open, the delicate structures of the eyeballs are protected by a fine membrane that will completely disappear during the final month of pregnancy.

It's too early for your baby to respond to light in a fully coordinated way, but he may turn toward very strong lights or, if startled by a sudden loud noise, he will often respond with a blink, just as children and adults do.

The retina has just started to be lined by light-receptive rods and cones. The cones are responsible for color vision and develop later than the more numerous rods. The rods transmit an image in black and white and are used for nighttime vision and for peripheral vision. Connections form between the retina and the optic nerve, that then transmits the information it receives to be decoded in the visual cortex at the back of the brain.

Your baby will often bring his hands up to his face. However, because his limb movements are now so well coordinated, he won't touch his eyes.

ASK A... DOCTOR

I've got inverted nipples. Will I be able to breast-feed? Babies breast-feed rather than "nipple feed" and if your baby latches onto your breast correctly (see p.448), inverted nipples shouldn't cause difficulties. About 10 percent of women have flat or inverted nipples. The best way to find out whether you can breast-feed is simply to try once your baby is born. There are various techniques that may help: consult your caregiver if you're having problems or contact a lactation consultant. Your caregiver may recommend one or the La Leche League can help (see p.480).

FOCUS ON... TWINS

Growth of twins in the last trimester

In these last three months, you're likely to get very big. As you'd expect, the more babies inside, the greater the challenge for your body to provide enough space as well as the perfect conditions for growth. You'll probably be advised to gain just under 1 lb (0.5 kg) a week for the first half of your pregnancy and slightly more each week in the second half.

From around 28–29 weeks, the growth of twins and other multiples slows down compared with that of singletons. But they still move and kick as much as possible, cushioned by amniotic fluid, which continues to increase in volume until 36 weeks.

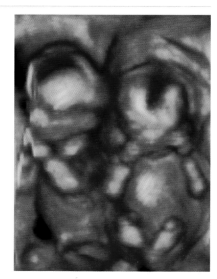

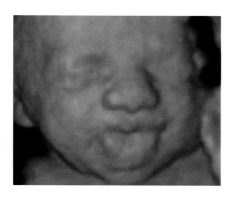

95 days to go...

YOUR BABY TODAY

Your baby sticks his tongue out often especially before or after a particularly large gulp of amniotic fluid. Fluid doesn't enter the lungs but is swallowed into the stomach. Your baby would be completely unaware of the ultrasound scan, so is not reacting to the scanner.

It's a natural instinct that parents are fiercely protective of their children, and not unusual for this to start well before the birth.

You may be feeling very protective of your belly and baby. The belly almost acts as a beacon to other people, making them aware that you're pregnant. It's not unusual to feel quite vulnerable, for example in a jostling crowd or when you're out shopping. When this happens, make it clear to people that you're pregnant and, hopefully, they'll give you more space and give up their seat, if necessary.

When you're driving, you may find you're doing so even more carefully than normal, or becoming a very nervous or critical passenger. You may become more irritated than usual by people who you feel are driving without concern for your safety.

This protective instinct is a natural part of becoming a mother. It's the desire to protect and nurture your child, even before yourself. Rest assured, though, that your baby is in the safest possible environment inside your uterus. Your body is providing your baby with warmth, food, and oxygen. The baby is cushioned and protected by the amniotic fluid in which he floats, and this acts as a buffer to any shoving or bumping by crowds of people.

ASK A... DOCTOR

Why am I being told I need a glucose tolerance test?

In pregnancy some women develop a form of diabetes known as gestational diabetes (see p.473), which disappears when the baby is born. Most women have no symptoms, but it may be suspected if you have signs such as fatigue and thirst. A doctor will confirm whether or not you have this by testing your blood glucose levels. If it's found, you'll be advised to have an oral glucose tolerance test (OGTT) between 24 and 28 weeks.

HypnoBirthing is a great idea but it's important that you are taught the various relaxation and visualization techniques and practice them regularly during pregnancy.

THE LOWDOWN

HypnoBirthing

The idea of hypnoBirthing—giving birth in such a relaxed state that you barely feel pain—sounds too good to be true. But the research extolling its benefits is impressive. Several studies have shown that self-hypnosis helps women feel less anxious about labor and birth. They also tend to require minimal pain relief and medical intervention: many women succeed in giving birth at home.

■ You learn a series of self-hypnosis, relaxation, visualization, and breathing techniques, which over time become second nature, enabling you to approach childbirth in a calm, positive frame of mind.
■ By practicing hypnoBirthing, you should feel in control of your body and able to manage the pain during labor and delivery.
■ The key is to practice frequently, and a supportive birth partner is invaluable for helping you perfect the techniques, and use them in labor.
■ Visit HypnoBirthing.com to find out more about this procedure and a course that is near you.

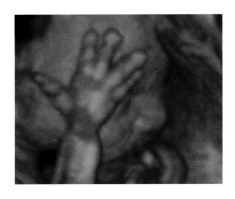

94 days to go...

YOUR BABY TODAY

On this 3D image each finger is held outstretched in front of the face. Holding the fingers in this way for any length of time is tiring so most of the time the hands are held with the wrists slightly flexed and the fingers bent, ready to grasp any object that floats into reach.

Your baby's reproductive organs are now in place; a boy's testes have descended and a girl's ovaries have all their follicles.

ASK A... MOM

Is it normal to argue all the time when we should be happily looking forward to our baby's arrival? Expecting a baby puts pressure on even the strongest of relationships. Concerns about having a healthy baby and adjusting to parenthood were at the heart of most of our arguments. And when we started to talk about it, we found we had conflicting opinions about big child-rearing issues. I was sensitive, irritable, and moody, and often snapped when I didn't mean to.

We sat down and talked calmly and agreed not to "sweat the small stuff," avoiding areas of contention, and compromising when it didn't really matter. In the throes of a disagreement, I'd stop and think: I love this man, we're having a baby together, is this really important in the long run? We also made time to do positive things together that we had enjoyed before I was pregnant, and tried to find opportunities to laugh, to reduce stress, and to put things into perspective. By the time the baby arrived, we were both much more relaxed.

If your baby is a boy, it's at about this time that the testes complete their descent into the scrotum. This is often associated with a small amount of fluid around each testis called a "hydrocele." This fluid will disappear naturally either before or after birth.

The cremaster muscle, part of the spermatic cord, is able to raise the testes back into the groin. This helps to regulate the temperature within the testes after birth, relaxing when cooling is needed. If your baby is slightly cool when examined, the cremaster muscle retracts the testes giving the impression of an undescended testis in your newborn baby.

Temperature control is not required in the uterus and the testes slowly move down into the scrotum. It is by no means unusual for one testis (or both) not to have descended at birth. Your doctor will check for this as part of the routine baby development checkup and confirm that both testes can be brought down into the scrotum.

Unlike the ovary, which already contains all of the egg-producing follicles that it will ever make, the testes do not start to make sperm until puberty.

Differences in the speed of growth and weight gain become more apparent now, and boys tend to be slightly heavier than girls at birth.

WEIGHT GAIN IN THE THIRD TRIMESTER

In your third trimester gaining weight steadily is important. If you were a healthy weight before your pregnancy, you should gain 3–5 lb (1.3–2.2 kg) in the first trimester and 1–2 lb (0.5–1 kg) a week the rest of your pregnancy, for a total of 25–37 lb (11–17 kg). The largest contributing factor to your overall weight gain will be your baby, followed by extra fat, which you will need to sustain your pregnancy and when breast-feeding. Your doctor will monitor your weight gain to ensure it's healthy.

Weight gain chart

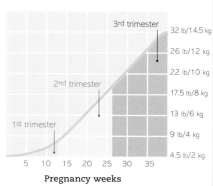

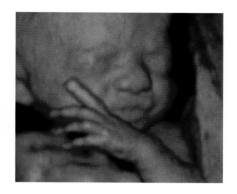

93 days to go...

YOUR BABY TODAY

This week, some babies open their eyes for the first time but this is a brief event, difficult to capture on ultrasound, so you may not see it on a scan. Some light is reaching your baby but he hasn't developed a sleep–wake cycle that corresponds in any way with day and night.

As each day passes, your baby is getting bigger and bigger and you will be more conscious of his body and movement.

As wonderful as it is to feel your baby move inside you, sometimes it can be uncomfortable. As your baby grows there is less and less room for him to move around, especially as he kicks or stretches against the walls of your uterus. These movements can vary from gentle paddling motions to feeling as though the baby has hiccups. Sometimes the baby will kick hard; if it's under the ribs it can take your breath away and leave you feeling quite sore. The kicking can also wake you when you're sleeping, and many women say that their babies are more active at night. If you're sitting or lying in a position that the baby doesn't like— for example, if you spend too much time on one side—your baby may well kick until you move.

Although sometimes these movements can be uncomfortable or take you by surprise, most of the time they're just a gentle reminder of your growing baby and, as such, are something to look forward to feeling.

ASK A... DOCTOR

If I went into labor now, would my baby survive? Until relatively recently, babies born before 28 weeks' gestation often did not survive. Today, with medical advances in neonatal intensive care units (NICU), babies of 22 weeks' gestation have survived outside the uterus, although this is still very rare. At many hospitals, doctors won't resuscitate a baby under 24 weeks, because there is little chance of survival.

Extremely premature babies have an increased risk of disability, even with the best medical care, and often the delivery itself can put an enormous strain on the baby. Very experienced doctors and nurses are involved in the care of extremely premature babies.

If possible, the delivery should take place in a hospital with a neonatal intensive care unit (NICU) (see pp.452–3). If this isn't possible, babies are often transferred to a special center when they are stable enough to be moved. Very premature babies take a long time to "catch up" and meet developmental milestones.

Each day and week of pregnancy is a milestone, and the closer to full term (37–42 weeks) you deliver, the better it is for your baby.

FOCUS ON... SAFETY

Buying bedding

Your baby doesn't need a blanket or pillow—in fact, experts advise against them. To reduce your baby's risk of sudden infant death syndrome (SIDS), put a fitted sheet on a firm crib mattress (don't use a second-hand mattress), and keep blankets, pillows and stuffed animals out of the crib. If your baby sleeps in a Moses basket or bassinet, you should buy sheets designed specifically for these. Keep the room at a temperature that feels good to you. If you're concerned that your baby is chilly, consider a sleep sack. Many parents find them to be comfortable for their baby.

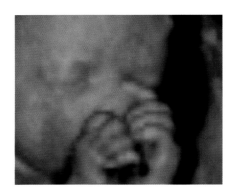

92 days to go...

YOUR BABY TODAY

At this stage, thumb sucking is becoming much more coordinated as the sensitive lips and fingers meet. On scans most babies look as if they enjoy it, and there's no doubt that it provides important sensory feedback and perhaps reassurance to your developing baby.

The thought of being off work in the last months of pregnancy is tempting, but it will give you less time off with your baby.

As long as you're feeling in good health, try to work into the last month of your pregnancy. It can be particularly frustrating if you finish two months before, only to find that your baby is born later than expected. Working as late as possible may also allow you to spend some time with your replacement. If you're finding work tiring, try to adapt your working day and avoid traveling during rush hour, if possible. Whenever you start your leave, colleagues may hold a party and want to buy gifts for your newborn. If you're asked what you want, suggest gift certificates since these will allow you to purchase some of the more expensive baby equipment, and prevent duplication of gifts. Many stores also offer baby registries, which are a good way to choose the items you want.

BACK PAIN IN THE THIRD TRIMESTER

One of the most common pregnancy complaints, back pain is generally a reaction to your increased weight and the laxity of the joints that are an integral part of pregnancy. There are some ways to alleviate this, and anecdotal evidence suggests that women who exercise are far less likely to suffer from extreme back pain than those who don't.

It is best to try to avoid back pain by exercising your abdominal muscles which will give your back support, and keep your legs and arms strong too. See page 250 for an effective abdominal workout.

Carrying does not end when you have had your baby. You will have a car seat, baby bag, and perhaps groceries to carry, as well as your newborn. So it's best to keep your muscles strong throughout your pregnancy to prepare for this. Here are five top tips to avoid back pain in the third trimester:

■ **Stay strong:** strength training for all parts of your body (see p.196) will help you deal with the increased weight you gain during pregnancy.
■ **Support:** invest in a support belt that will give your back a break from bearing the load of your belly. It will also support your sagging stomach and may relieve discomfort in your legs. This can be particularly useful if you're carrying twins or more.
■ **Sleep:** while sleeping, place a pillow between your legs to ease the stress on your back. Buy or borrow a shaped pillow that gives your belly and back support at the same time.
■ **Stretch:** flexibility will help your back to relax and prevent your muscles from getting too tense.
■ **Sit:** keep your back supported by the back of a chair (see p.219). Use a pillow to increase the support in your lower back, if necessary. If you work at a desk, make sure your chair adequately supports your back.

Stretching helps prevent your muscles from tightening, so you feel less tense and more relaxed. Put on some comfortable clothes and stretch as often as you can, and always stretch before and after exercise.

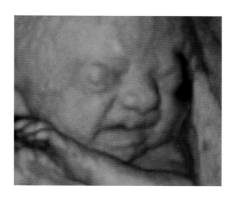

91 days to go...

YOUR BABY TODAY

This baby looks quite upset. Your baby often makes strange and funny faces in the uterus. It's as if he is practicing every type of facial expression in preparation for after the birth when these will be one of the tools he uses to communicate his needs and emotions.

As you soak in a relaxing bath, it's an amazing sight to look at your baby moving and stretching your belly.

Your belly is a marvelous thing. It's already changed so much over the last 27 weeks and will continue to grow until you give birth.

Inside that belly your growing baby is moving around. When your baby is kicking and turning around, take the time to look down, and you may be able to see him move or even see the imprint of a foot as it kicks you.

While you're taking a bath is a good time to watch your belly—you may find that your baby is more active around this time because you're relaxed—and you can take the time to observe his movements. Keep your partner involved when your baby is active by encouraging him to touch your belly.

Watching your baby move is wonderful. You may even miss your ever-expanding and active belly once you're no longer pregnant.

ASK A... DOCTOR

My belly measurement has been the same for three weeks. Why isn't my baby growing? In pregnancy your abdomen is measured to establish the height of the top of the uterus, which indicates how the baby is growing. It is important to know whether the same person is measuring you since there is an element of subjectivity depending on the technique your caregiver uses. In early pregnancy, it is not necessary to measure you because this doesn't give an indication of fetal growth, but after 26 weeks, growth can be assessed this way However, even with your own growth chart and with the same person measuring you, the estimation of your baby's growth may still not be 100 percent accurate. If there are any concerns, your doctor or midwife may order an ultrasound to figure out why your measurement, called your fundal height, hasn't changed.

FOCUS ON... DADS

Are you tired too?

Being pregnant is more tiring than most women anticipate. In the third trimester, your partner's bladder is under pressure and this can cause her to wake during the night to use the bathroom. The size of the belly starts to become uncomfortable, and it can be difficult for her to find a relaxing sleeping position. The other changes she's going through, from shifting internal organs through to altered hormone levels, can contribute to her restlessness. And if she's having trouble sleeping, you are likely to be disturbed too. The end result is that both of you feel constantly tired.

Unfortunately there is no answer. Going to bed earlier can help, but having some time to relax together before bed is just as important. The bottom line is that disrupted sleeping patterns will now become part of the norm for both of you. There is no quick fix to this problem, but it may help to cut back on your social life in the evenings.

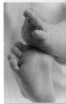

279

Your 28th week

EVEN BEFORE BIRTH, YOUR BABY IS ESTABLISHING A PATTERN OF BEHAVIOR

Your baby is beginning to have regular sleep–wake cycles and her breathing, yawning, and swallowing are taking on a more definite pattern. However, your own life may seem less rhythmical. You may find things are slightly different at work and, perhaps, be seeing less of some friends because you don't always feel up to socializing. Don't become isolated, though—if nothing else, stay in touch by phone and email.

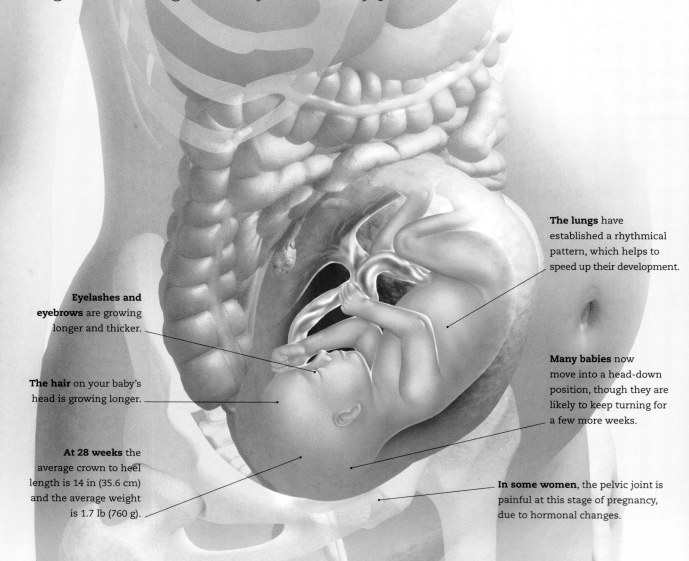

The lungs have established a rhythmical pattern, which helps to speed up their development.

Eyelashes and eyebrows are growing longer and thicker.

The hair on your baby's head is growing longer.

Many babies now move into a head-down position, though they are likely to keep turning for a few more weeks.

At 28 weeks the average crown to heel length is 14 in (35.6 cm) and the average weight is 1.7 lb (760 g).

In some women, the pelvic joint is painful at this stage of pregnancy, due to hormonal changes.

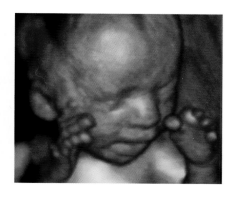

90 days to go...

YOUR BABY TODAY

On a scan the space between the frontal bones of the forehead appears as a dark line on the soft spot at the top of your baby's head. This is not a line on the skin: instead where there is no underlying bone, more of the ultrasound beam passes through rather than being reflected.

Do all you can to stay involved with medium- and long-term plans at work so that you continue to feel part of the team.

The difficulty of balancing motherhood and a career can crop up even while you're still pregnant. Depending on your career, you may find yourself excluded from long-term planning discussions as colleagues assume that you won't be around, or won't come back after your maternity leave. Some colleagues may simply treat you differently just because you're pregnant, assuming you can no longer do your job in the same way. You may feel left out of future planning, or feel that your opinions are disregarded since you will not be there to implement them. This can be compounded by the fact that it can be difficult to motivate yourself if you know you won't be there to see a project through to the end.

No one can be certain of being in a job in six months' or a year's time, but you have the advantage of knowing how much longer you're going to work and you may even have a reasonable idea of when you're intending to return to work. Continue to do your job and make it clear by your actions that you want to provide input on all projects, even though you may not be there to see them through to the end. If at this point in time you're intending to return to work after the baby is born, make this clear to any colleagues who may doubt your long-term commitment.

You can also help plan for your maternity leave by, perhaps, dividing up your workload or helping to search for a replacement to cover your role. Being organized now will make the countdown to going on maternity leave much easier in the coming weeks.

ASK A... MOM

Should we buy a baby bath or can the baby use our bath? I thought a baby bath was an optional extra, but having bought one found it really useful. A huge advantage is that you can use it in any room (though if the room doesn't have a water supply, you'll need to transport water).

I was a bit apprehensive the first few times we bathed the baby, then experienced parents told me even they found it tricky to hold a wiggling baby safely in a bath of water. Using a smaller baby bath is less daunting and helps you develop confidence. However, a baby outgrows a baby bath by around six months and, once not in use, the bath can take up a lot of storage space (unless you can recycle

it to a pregnant friend). Many parents choose a bath seat designed for newborns in the family bath. Alternatively, enjoy a bath together, although you must keep the water tepid for the baby and you may find this too cold for you.

AS A MATTER OF FACT

As your uterus grows, your diaphragm is compressed with the result that you may find it difficult to breathe deeply.

In fact, you're actually taking in more air. It's important not to fight the natural tendency to hollow your back. This opens up your rib cage to let in more air, and also helps balance the excess weight of your belly.

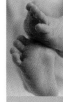

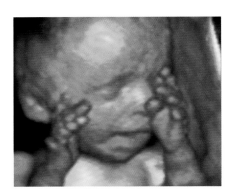

89 days to go...

YOUR BABY TODAY

Your baby may be looking happy today. Babies smile and grimace, wrinkle their foreheads, and stick their tongues out. Many of these behaviors are only becoming more apparent now as 3D ultrasound has provided a unique opportunity for their study.

Your baby has developed a sleep–wake cycle very similar to the one she will have in the days and weeks after birth.

Your baby's yawns have, until this point occurred only occasionally as a single event, but they are now becoming more repetitive, with several yawns following one another. Your baby's swallowing reflexes were developed at 25 weeks but still need to become much better coordinated.

The baby's breathing movements are vital for the normal development of the lung tissue. Your baby does not breathe amniotic fluid into her lungs; the lungs are filled with fluid produced by the lung tissue itself, and as breathing movements are practiced, small amounts are expelled. With each breath, the diaphragm pushes down, and the chest wall moves in as the larynx relaxes, allowing fluid to escape. Only a tiny proportion (0.5 percent) of the fluid in the lung escapes with each breath. This compares to a fifth (20 percent) of the air in the lungs moving in and out with each breathing movement.

Your baby has been breathing for some weeks, but the pattern up until now has been somewhat random. Now, the baby's breathing patterns start to reflect her better developed sleep–wake and becomes more rhythmical.

FOCUS ON... NUTRITION

Burning calories

During pregnancy your body will store fat—mainly in the hips, thighs, and abdomen—to ensure there is enough energy for your baby to grow. Usually, the body relies on glucose for energy but in mid and late pregnancy, hormonal and metabolic changes facilitate the use of fat as an energy source. If you exercise regularly without adding on calories, you could be reducing the amount of stored fat. In addition, doing cardiovascular and weight-bearing exercise regularly tends to increase your metabolic rate slightly; therefore even when you're not exercising, your body will burn more calories.

It's important that you do exercise regularly during pregnancy but you need to make sure that you're taking in enough calories to meet the demands of your growing baby and your body. A simple guideline is that during your third trimester you should be taking in an extra 200 calories a day, with an extra 150 calories on the days that you exercise.

TIME TO THINK ABOUT

Prenatal care

As your pregnancy progresses, you'll have appointments every two weeks.

At each one, your blood pressure will be measured, and your urine tested for protein. The doctor or midwife will also check the size of your baby by measuring the height of your uterus, and she will listen to any concerns and offer you advice.

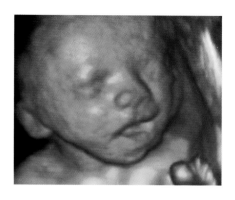

88 days to go...

YOUR BABY TODAY

This baby is at the end of a yawn. Your baby is yawning in a more coordinated way now with one yawn often following another. It may look as if this image shows the fingertips in the bottom right but in fact it is a foot, nearly brought up to the mouth.

Pregnancy is a subject about which everybody has an opinion they want to share with you, whether you like it or not.

Although you may have become very proud and protective of your belly, it can be extremely irritating if other people become overprotective of you. You may find that everyone has an opinion on your pregnancy, and what you should and should not be doing to stay healthy. Some women find all the attention comforting, but others find it frustrating or suffocating. If you're someone who finds all the advice difficult to handle, try to remember that people mean well.

Of course, it's your body, and you'll do what is best for you and your baby. If it's all getting too much, then try talking to the main offenders, often a partner, mother, or mother-in-law. Explain that you're trying your best and that you're aware of what you should and shouldn't do while you're

pregnant and are following the advice of your doctors. Politely thank them for their input and reassure them that you're taking good care of yourself and your baby.

Choose the perfume you put on carefully since you may find that some scents, even one you're used to wearing, make you feel nauseous or light-headed during pregnancy.

(see p.474)

FOCUS ON... YOUR HEALTH

Blood pressure checks

About 8 percent of women have problems with high blood pressure in pregnancy. High blood pressure can be caused by preeclampsia (see p.474), a serious condition that also leads to protein in the urine. Preeclampsia can affect the liver and kidneys and, if

untreated, lead to eclampsia or seizures. If you have preeclampsia, your doctor will closely monitor your blood pressure. High blood pressure can also affect your baby, so medication may be advised. Don't stop the medication without your doctor's consent.

THE LOWDOWN

On smelling good

Are you wafting through pregnancy feeling fresh as a daisy? It's rarely discussed, but being pregnant may make you feel less fragrant than usual, not least because you will sweat more than before—although it's unlikely that anyone else will have noticed. An increase in vaginal discharge is also nothing to worry about, but if it smells offensive or is yellowish or greenish in color, you could have an infection so see your doctor. To stay smelling sweet:

■ **Shower or bath regularly** and apply deodorant every time. Take handy wipes with you to stay fresh all day.

■ **Use body sprays** and lotions if your usual fragrance doesn't smell "right": they tend to be lighter and are less likely to cause headaches.

■ **Avoid wearing tight clothing:** wear loose clothes in natural fabrics, which absorb sweat and allow your skin to breathe.

■ **Wear cotton underwear,** and change it more often, if necessary.

■ **Use disposable panty liners,** if needed, to stay feeling fresh.

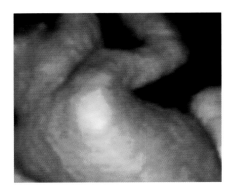

87 days to go...

YOUR BABY TODAY

This baby's back is turned and she's facing away from the ultrasound scanner. The skin is much less transparent than before since your baby is constantly laying down fat reserves beneath it. This fat accounts, in part, for much of your baby's weight gain from now on.

Your baby is growing eyebrows and eyelashes—and hair on her head—and making good use of all the space in your uterus.

Your baby's eyes are now open, and both the eyebrows and the eyelashes have grown. The hair on your baby's head continues to get longer.

It's quite likely that your baby is making use of all the space available and may well be in a breech position (bottom down), at least some of the time. This is the case in a third of pregnancies at this stage but your baby's position is unlikely to stablize until after 36 or 37 weeks.

Because the shape of your uterus naturally favors a head-down position, only 3 to 4 percent of babies remain in the breech position after 37 weeks. It may be quite difficult for you (and your caregiver) to tell the position of your baby at this stage. For example, just because the feet kick you in one particular place doesn't tell you much about your baby's position. She is very flexible and an ultrasound might show that she is doubled up with her feet on her head.

BLOOD TESTS

Some time between 26 and 30 weeks your blood will be tested to check that you aren't anemic. If you are found to be anemic your doctor may prescribe iron pills for you. Because of an increase in the fluid content of your blood, your hemoglobin count is likely to fall later on in your pregnancy, so it's a good idea to address this issue now. Iron pills can cause digestive problems, such as constipation or diarrhea, so if this happens to you, ask your doctor if your prescription can be changed. The liquid medications available over the counter are kinder on the digestive system than pills, so ask

your doctor if one of these is appropriate for you. If a previous blood test has shown that you're Rh negative, you'll receive an injection of Rh immunoglobulin (RhIg) at around 28–34 weeks. You'll get another shot after the baby is born.

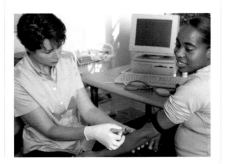

Pelvic girdle pain

You know you've got pelvic girdle pain—or PGP—when sneezing hurts, you're waddling like an old woman, and turning over in bed is a major task (see p.470). Formerly known as SPD, or symphysis pubis dysfunction, PGP affects one in five pregnant women. It's caused by hormonal changes that change the way the pelvic joint functions and it can be extremely painful. Try the following if you have PGP:

■ Keep your legs together when getting in and out of bed or the car (place a plastic bag on the seat to help you swivel).
■ Sleep on your side with a pillow between your legs.
■ Wear comfortable shoes.
■ Avoid doing tasks that hurt, such as housework or pushing a supermarket cart.
■ Relax in warm water.
■ Ask your doctor for a support belt to help ease the pain.
■ Get some therapy: studies show that physical therapy and acupuncture may help symphysis pubis dysfunction.

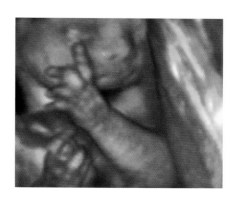

86 days to go...

YOUR BABY TODAY

A finger is held close to the eye in this image. The eyes are shut for most of the time but also a simple reflex action will prevent a stray finger (or toe) from touching the eye. Furthermore, the fingernails are still well away from the fingertips at this time.

Deciding to go it alone is never an easy option, but with the right support, you can look forward happily to your baby's birth.

It's reassuring to know that many women have babies on their own and do not find life an endless struggle. Although it would be wrong to pretend that parenting alone is as easy as it is when you share the care, with additional support it is possible. Even if you are in a relationship, you may feel you are going it alone at times. You may have very strong reasons why you want a baby, for example your increasing age, and this determination will give you strength and focus.

It is helpful for all pregnant women to find someone to talk to and confide in. This could be your mother or a close friend or relative. As you are making far-reaching decisions about your future, it's important that you have support, accurate information, and time to think things through without fear, panic, or pressure from others. Finding somebody you really trust and whom you know can give you support when you need it—especially in labor and in the first days and weeks with your baby—may help relieve any pressure you are under. It will also enable you to think more calmly and clearly about your situation and make plans.

It's worth, even at this early stage, starting to think about who you would like to ask to be your birth partner: this is a big decision that should not be rushed.

BUILDING A SUPPORT NETWORK

It's important for all pregnant women to have emotional and practical support, and this is especially true if you're single.

- **Go to all your prenatal appointments** and build a relationship with your doctor; she is an invaluable source of information.
- **Sign up for for prenatal classes.** If you're single, you may find that daytime courses are less populated by "couples"; this gives you a chance to build up a network of female friends. Also try to go to classes, such as yoga and water aerobics.
- **Give plenty of thought** to choosing your birth partner: a trusted friend, or perhaps your own mother, who is likely to be thrilled to be asked to share this experience with you.
- **Don't be too proud to accept offers of help** from friends and family—most will genuinely want to be involved now and after the birth.

You may find an added bonus of having a baby on your own is that it reshapes your relationship with your own mother, and you may talk together more often.

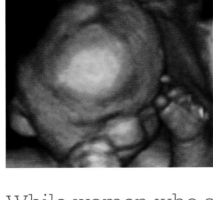

YOU ARE 27 WEEKS AND 6 DAYS

85 days to go...

YOUR BABY TODAY

Although ultrasound cannot show it, there is now some hair on your baby's head and her eyelashes and eyebrows have grown. The pattern and color of hair growth has a significant impact on the overall look of your baby but this is not apparent on a scan.

While women who are pregnant in the summer may find it hard to stay cool, being pregnant in the winter is also challenging.

Most women are understandably reluctant to buy a winter coat that will see them all the way through pregnancy and may well never be worn again. The good news is that you probably won't need one at all! You are likely to feel very warm toward the end of your pregnancy, and may find it more comfortable to wear plenty of layered knits rather than one warm coat or jacket. Layers can also be easily discarded if you become overheated while you're traveling.

You can also probably hijack some of your partner's wardrobe, and borrow a coat or jacket that will fasten over your belly if you're planning to be outside for extended periods. Alternatively, go to a local second-hand shop—you may well find a larger coat or jacket for a bargain price that will last the few weeks of your pregnancy.

Another thing to consider is wearing your own coat unfastened, with a long scarf hanging down to fill the gap.

Think about purchasing a large shawl or wrap, which will see you through the winter months, and keep you and your baby warm after the birth. Shawls and wraps are ideal for keeping you warm when your baby is in a sling, and also for unexpected breast-feeding sessions outdoors.

You'll need to be extra careful in the winter, when you're in icy conditions. Make sure you wear sensible flat shoes when you're out and about to reduce the risk of slipping and falling.

FOCUS ON... TWINS

Practical adjustments

If you're having two or more babies, you'll need to consider making some adjustments to your living space. To reduce the risk of crib death, it's best for babies to sleep in the same room as their parents but you don't need two cribs. You can put both your newborn babies to sleep in one crib (see p.335), but this isn't recommended after they're three months old.

It's a legal requirement for each baby to have an individual car seat if you plan to drive them anywhere, including home from the hospital.

ASK A... NUTRITIONIST

My doctor has told me I'm anemic. Can I improve my iron levels through my diet? All pregnant women should be offered screening for anemia, which is done early in pregnancy (at the first appointment), and again between 26–30 weeks (see p.286). Generally, an iron-rich diet is advised in pregnancy and this is enough to prevent or improve anemia. Eat plenty of lean red meat, beans, dried fruits, dark green vegetables, fortified cereals, and bread. Try including a vitamin C-enriched food or drink in your diet, since vitamin C helps the body absorb iron more efficiently. Vegetarians need to eat plenty of eggs, legumes, beans, and nuts to boost iron supplies.

Taking iron supplements may be recommended depending on how low your iron levels have become.

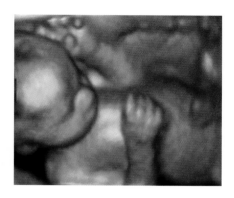

84 days to go...

YOUR BABY TODAY

The amniotic fluid is approaching its maximum amount at this time and your baby will have plenty of space in which to move. Here the baby is down toward the level of the umbilical cord. Your baby is still likely to change position several times a day.

If you're the first among your friends to have a baby, be prepared for friendships to evolve and change.

Some friendships change as you go through different life stages. You'll probably have had different groups of friends through school, college, and different jobs, with one or two close friends throughout. Friendships often develop with people when you're at a similar stage in your lives. This means that during your pregnancy and when you have young children you may feel most comfortable with other women in similar situations. You'll meet new friends at postpartum classes or postpartum groups, or in situations such as toddler swimming or music classes.

As you make new friends, you may find your old relationships begin to change. Friends without children may find it difficult to understand your new role as a mother, and the intense love that you have for your child, and you may start to drift apart. Of course this is not always the case; some friendships are unchanging, irrespective of whether your lives go along different paths.

ASK A... DOCTOR

I've seen a second-hand car seat advertised. Is there any reason why I shouldn't buy it? Don't use a second-hand car seat unless you can be absolutely certain of its history because it may have been in an accident or damaged.

If you must use a second-hand seat, only accept one if you are absolutely certain that it hasn't been in a bad accident. Don't use a seat that is cracked, that doesn't come with the original instructions, is missing parts, was recalled, or is past its expiration date. Don't purchase a car seat for your baby at a second-hand store or through classified ads, or on the internet.

FOCUS ON... NUTRITION

Choosing organic

Eating organic food is one way to eat more healthily during pregnancy. Organic fruit and vegetables are grown without any chemical pesticides or fertilizers. Organic meat, poultry, eggs, and dairy products come from animals that are not given growth hormones or antibiotics. For these reasons, organic foods are free from pesticide residues, additives, and preservatives. They are also usually higher in nutrients. Organic farming also promotes the use of environmentally friendly practices. Most additives are safe during pregnancy, but eating organic is a second step that can add to a healthy foundation of food choices.

The downside of eating organic food is that it tends to cost more than regular groceries. Given the price of food, many families cannot afford the extra that goes with eating organic. If you can't afford organic foods, eating whole foods in their least processed, most natural form, and plenty of fresh fruit and vegetables is the next best thing, and is still a very healthy diet.

Your 29th week

You may feel a little bored and back-achey at this stage of pregnancy, but there are plenty of positive ways to take your mind off things. For example, you could start to make enquiries about breast-feeding classes, plan your maternity leave, and draw up shopping lists of baby essentials, such as diapers, a changing mat, onesies, bibs, and baby wipes, and perhaps buy a couple of items each week.

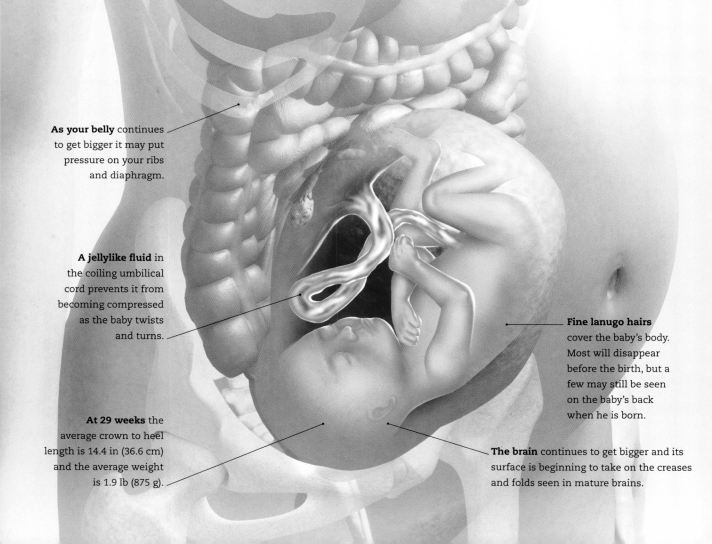

As your belly continues to get bigger it may put pressure on your ribs and diaphragm.

A jellylike fluid in the coiling umbilical cord prevents it from becoming compressed as the baby twists and turns.

Fine lanugo hairs cover the baby's body. Most will disappear before the birth, but a few may still be seen on the baby's back when he is born.

At 29 weeks the average crown to heel length is 14.4 in (36.6 cm) and the average weight is 1.9 lb (875 g).

The brain continues to get bigger and its surface is beginning to take on the creases and folds seen in mature brains.

Your third trimester

290

83 days to go...

YOUR BABY TODAY

This week is something of a landmark in your baby's development. Although a baby born at this stage would still need help with breathing, the lungs have matured to an extent that survival chances outside the uterus are significantly better than earlier in the pregnancy.

It's never too early to start thinking about the financial implications of maternity leave, and whether to return to work.

When you're on maternity leave, it may be the first occasion that you haven't worked for a long time. This change can be quite daunting, even though you know you'll soon be busy taking care of a baby. Maternity leave is regulated by each province and territory, and your employer isn't required to pay you, but some do. Every company has a different maternity leave policy, and you may be able to use sick days or vacation days. Depending on your situation, you may also be entitled to receive maternity benefits from the federal Employment Insurance Act (EI). Ask a human resources representative about your options. Depending on your partner's situation, he may be eligible for parental benefits from EI. Some companies are more generous than others, and will top up what you receive from EI during your maternity or parental leave. Going on maternity leave may cause a significant drop in your income. You should talk to your partner about how much money will be coming in and going out and how you will manage a change in your finances.

Even though it's a long way in the future, you might also start thinking about plans for working after the baby is born. You may think that you have no real option financially and have to return full time, but explore the possibilities of working more flexibly, or working part time, or from home one or two days a week. You may also want to start thinking about your child-care options (see p.332).

CHOOSING DIAPERS

Should you opt for disposables (use once, then throw away) or cloth (wash, dry, and use again)?

■ **Disposable diapers** are slim fitting, super absorbent, and will keep your baby dry, even overnight. However, they cost more (by some estimates, around $2,000 per child by the time you start potty training) and there's the landfill factor to consider. Eco-friendly diapers, however, are now available—they use no polluting bleaching agents and fewer chemicals are used to produce them.

■ **Cloth** costs less—although the initial investment is greater. They also provide a softer landing for toddlers who topple over. However, all that soaking, washing, and drying could get you down (plus this has an environmental impact). You may opt to use a diaper-laundering service each week (at a cost). Cloth diapers need changing more often than disposables. They are slightly more difficult to put on and take off, but modern cloth diapers are fastened with Velcro, not pins.

■ **Using a combination** of reusable and disposable diapers can work well: buy the occasional package of disposables for when you're out and about or for if you leave your baby with a babysitter, but opt for cloth the rest of the time.

Disposable diapers are easy to use and ideal for when you're out and about. But they cost more than cloth diapers, which can be washed and used over and over, even for your next baby.

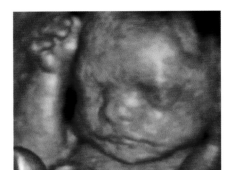

82 days to go...

YOUR BABY TODAY

This image shows a typical chin-on-the-chest position with an arm held up to the side of the face. A knee is just visible to the left of the image with a loop of umbilical cord above it. Your baby now is likely to be in a head down position but there's still time to change.

The coiled umbilical cord connects your baby to the placenta, his life-support system until birth.

Most umbilical cords finally grow to be about the same length as the baby (although there are exceptions), reaching a final length of 20–23.5 in (50–60 cm). The umbilical cord has up to 40 turns along its length and these turns are seven times more likely to twist to the left than the right. The coiling pattern was in place nine weeks after conception, with more coils at the baby's end than the placental end; this may be a response to your baby's movements. The cord contains three blood vessels: two arteries taking deoxygenated blood and waste from your baby to the placenta and one vein carrying oxygen-rich blood from the placenta to the baby. The cord diameter is usually less than ¾ in (2 cm) and the blood vessels are embedded in and protected by a layer of jelly. The watery composition of the jelly, together with the cord's coiling pattern, prevents compression of the cord.

After the birth, your doctor will check the number of vessels in the cord since in 1 percent of singleton pregnancies the cord contains only one umbilical artery.

ASK A... DOCTOR

If my baby has a low birthweight, will he have health problems?
A low birthweight is less than 5½ lb (2.5 kg) and although the majority of small babies thrive, some do have difficulties. Most low birthweight babies are small because they are premature. There are many ways you can reduce the risk of your baby being a low birthweight: eating adequate amounts of healthy food to gain the right amount of weight (see p.99), not smoking or drinking alcohol, reducing stress, and keeping all prenatal appointments so that your health— and your baby—can be monitored.

FOCUS ON... YOUR BODY

Restless legs

Some pregnant women experience restless legs syndrome (RLS), whereby they have an irresistible urge to move their legs. It most commonly happens while resting, so can be very disruptive to sleep. The exact cause isn't known but it may be related to an imbalance of a brain chemical called dopamine. The level of dopamine can be affected by a lack of iron. Restless legs syndrome will pass once you're no longer pregnant. To minimize the effects of restless legs syndrome:

■ **Ensure your diet** includes an adequate intake of iron (see p.154).

■ **Taking steps to get a good night's sleep** may help you fall asleep—and stay that way. Keep your bedroom cool, quiet, comfortable, and dark. Don't watch television, use a laptop, talk on the phone, or do any work in bed, and keep a consistent sleep schedule. Also, try doing something to challenge your brain before bed (a crossword puzzle, word jumble, or Sudoku puzzle). This may help ease your restless legs.

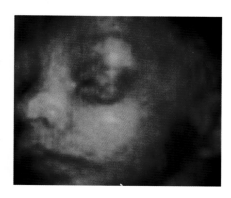

81 days to go...

YOUR BABY TODAY

This image offers the first view of the eye opening. The lids have separated and the dark pupil can be seen. There is no true reflection of color on ultrasound so the white of the eye is colored the same as the eyelids and face. The "eyebrows" are in fact shadow.

If you're starting to feel that you've been eclipsed by your belly, it's time to do something just for you.

Like many pregnant women, you may feel that you've disappeared behind your belly; that the essence of who you are has been lost in the guise of "pregnant woman." People may no longer ask about how you're feeling, or what's going on in your life. Instead of "How are you?", they might ask, "Is everything OK with the baby?"

It can be difficult for people, and even for you, to remember that you still exist in a role that is separate from pregnant woman or mother. If during your pregnancy you are feeling very frustrated by this, consider doing something just for you, maybe some pampering or a dinner for two, to make you feel special again.

FOCUS ON... NUTRITION

Grazing through the day

You need to eat plenty of good-quality protein to encourage your baby's growth and keep you in glowing good health, so try to eat either eggs, cheese, lean meats, fish, legumes, or grains at every meal. Add to that lots of fruits and vegetables, nuts, seeds, and some unrefined carbohydrates (see p.92).

Break the food down into a plan of five to seven small meals and snacks each day. If you usually have soup and a sandwich for lunch, try a vegetable soup mid-morning, and have the sandwich later; prepare snacks such as raw vegetables, cheese, nuts, and fruit and graze on them through the afternoon. Perhaps have a bowl of oatmeal early evening, followed by fruit later.

There are no "rules" about when food needs to be eaten, so eat these "mini-meals" when you're hungry. As long as you get the nutrients you need and don't overeat, you can graze as often as you like.

ASK A... DOCTOR

I have a sharp pain in my lower back and leg. What causes this?

This sounds like sciatica, a sharp pain that travels down the back and leg when the sciatic nerve—the longest nerve in the body—is trapped in a joint in the lower back. This is not related to your pregnancy, although it can get worse in pregnancy. For lower back pain, warm baths and a warm compress can help, as can gentle massage by an experienced practitioner. Exercise such as yoga or water aerobics classes can help strengthen back muscles, but check with your caregiver before embarking on a new exercise regimen. Watch your posture (see p.249) and wear comfortable, supportive shoes.

If you have sciatica, ask your caregiver to refer you to a physical therapist. You'll be shown exercises to help relieve the pain and minimize the risk of it recurring.

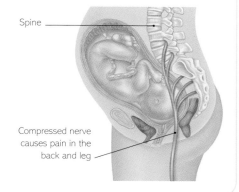

Spine

Compressed nerve causes pain in the back and leg

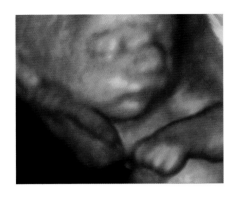

80 days to go...

YOUR BABY TODAY

The sleep–wake cycle is now more established, however just because your baby is moving you cannot assume that he is awake. He spends little time fully active with his eyes open, so many of the movements you are feeling are happening while he is asleep.

Your baby's growth depends on many factors and its rate varies through the course of your pregnancy.

The growth of your baby relies on a steady stream of nutrients. Most nutrients are transferred unaltered across the placenta, but some substances are made by the placenta itself and a few are produced from scratch by your baby. These include the hormone thyroxine, the production of which depends on iodine from the mother crossing the placenta. Thyroxine has several functions and its level needs to be controlled very precisely. The placenta forms a nearly perfect barrier to thyroxine, enabling you and your baby to adjust thyroxine levels independently of each other.

In the early stages of pregnancy, genetic factors largely determined the size of your baby, but by now environmental factors are becoming more important. Overall, your baby's final birthweight is determined about 40 percent by genetic factors and 60 percent by environmental factors. Your baby grows at a steady rate from 24 weeks until the last 2–3 weeks, when growth continues but more slowly. (If you're expecting twins, your babies grow as if alone in the uterus up until 28 weeks but from this point there is a reduction in their growth rate.) Your baby's internal organs account for much of his current growth.

The liver and brain, in particular, continue to enlarge and muscle mass increases. Later, fat will be deposited under the skin, rounding out your baby's contours.

AS A MATTER OF FACT

The number of twin births has jumped significantly in the last 10 years.

Between 1997 and 2006, the rate of multiple births increased by about 35 percent. Over 11,000 multiple birth babies are born every year in Canada.

FOCUS ON... TWINS

Buying for your twins

The clothes you buy for your twins should be easy to put on and take off, and, of course, machine washable. You'll probably be given outfits as presents, so just buy the basics.

For each baby, you're likely to need at least:
- Six undershirts
- Six onesies
- Two jackets
- One or two hats (sun hat for summer)
- Several burp cloths and bibs.

Keep in mind when choosing diapers that twins are often smaller on arrival than a single baby, and you may therefore get through a wide range of sizes in the first few months.

It's advisable to buy a good-quality double stroller, since it will be used for quite a while. When choosing a stroller, a side-by-side model is preferable to a tandem stroller, so that your babies can see each other and communicate as they grow older.

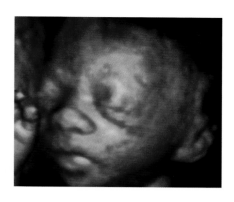

79 days to go...

YOUR BABY TODAY

Although many babies look similar on 3D ultrasound, particularly strong features, such as those affecting the shape of the ears, lips, or nose, are easy to see. From now on these features will become more and more individualized and recognizable.

Breast-feeding may be natural but it can be tricky to get started, so try to go to a class or two now while you have the time.

There is a lot of pressure on women to breast-feed: breast-feeding has health benefits for both you and your baby and it helps with bonding. People may already be asking you whether you intend to breast-feed or not, and it's reasonable that you don't yet know the answer. After all, you haven't tried!

Most women want to try breast-feeding, but some feel uncomfortable with the thought of doing it, especially in public. There will likely be a lactation consultant in the hospital or you may be able to hire one. In some areas you can go to classes during pregnancy, which will explain the benefits of breast-feeding and aspects such as positioning the baby so that you're both comfortable and the baby is latched on (see p.449).

The expectation of breast-feeding is that, because it's natural, it's easy. The reality is that until you get the hang of it, it can be a little more difficult. Ask your delivery nurse to show you how to position the baby. Most importantly, keep an open mind and try it. Once breast-feeding is established, it's beneficial to your baby's health, great for your figure, and a wonderful way to be close to your baby.

On leakages

Some pregnant women experience some leakage of breast milk, perhaps when their breasts are massaged or sexually stimulated, and sometimes for no apparent reason. Some discharge in pregnancy does mean that things are working properly, but women who don't experience this symptom are perfectly able to produce and provide milk for their baby.

FOCUS ON... NUTRITION

Cultured foods

Probiotics—such as some yogurts, miso (a Japanese paste, often used in soups), and some juices and soy products—contain enzymes and bacteria that help your body digest food, and build up friendly bacteria in the intestines. If your digestion is sluggish and you're finding constipation a problem, ask your doctor about whether eating more probiotic foods could help.

Talk to pregnant friends about breast-feeding now, and you can support each other once you start feeding your babies. Also get your partner involved: research shows that partners who are aware of the benefits of breast-feeding are more likely to be supportive.

295

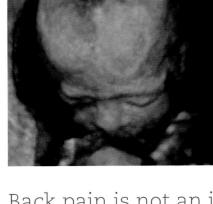

78 days to go...

YOUR BABY TODAY

Your baby's external appearance is fully formed but inside there is still a great deal of activity as many of the organs are continuing to mature. Even after pregnancy further development occurs, especially of the brain and lungs.

Back pain is not an inevitable part of being pregnant: there are lots of things you can do to help prevent and relieve it.

Yoga and other stretching exercises are great during pregnancy, since they strengthen key ligaments while relaxing areas that are tight and painful. Although it may seem easier to rest when you experience pain (especially back pain) and to avoid exercise, gentle stretching and movement often decreases muscle spasm and improves the function of the spine, resulting in less pain. Exercise also boosts energy levels and contributes to an easier labor, delivery, and postpartum recovery. Try stretching and relaxation techniques as a first resort for back pain.

If the pain is severe, ask your partner to massage the area. Ask your doctor or midwife if you can safely take any painkillers or if acupuncture might help ease your pain. If the area feels inflamed and painful, try placing a cold pack on the affected area for 5–10 minutes, several times a day.

ASK A... MOM

I'm bored of being pregnant! How will I get through the next couple of months? I felt the same at about six months but found the last three months went quite fast just because more was happening. Along with more prenatal visits and classes, there was planning when to start maternity leave, then finishing work, then getting the nursery ready, and buying things for the baby. And I made an effort to see all my girlfriends—it all made the time pass quickly.

FOCUS ON... YOUR BODY

Minimizing strain on your back

Your growing belly shifts your center of gravity to the front of your body. As the baby strains your abdominal muscles, and pregnancy hormones soften your ligaments, your abdominals give less support to your spine, which can result in back pain. Lifting and bending can exacerbate back pain, so try these strategies to help avoid added strain.

■ **To lift something from the floor,** stand close to the object with one foot in front of the other. Bend your knees, then straighten them, so that you use your thigh muscles to lift. Avoid locking your knees: always bend from the waist with your knees bent. If you need to pick something up, consider sitting, kneeling, or squatting to reach it to avoid putting your lower back under stress.

■ **If you have to move a heavy object** (try to avoid this if you possibly can), push it rather than pull it: that way, your legs, not your back, take the strain.

■ **To get into and out of a car,** or bed, keep your hips, pelvis, and back aligned in the same direction. To get out of bed, roll on to your side, and use your arms to push yourself up.

Always bend your knees to lift any weight—to prevent putting strain on your back.

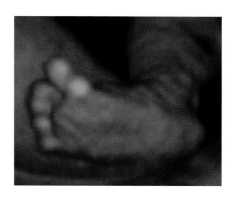

YOU ARE 29 WEEKS EXACTLY

77 days to go...

YOUR BABY TODAY

This is a close-up of how your baby's foot is looking now. Your baby will easily put his feet on top of his head one minute only to bring them down the next, so just because your baby is kicking you at one end it doesn't mean the head is at the other.

Pregnancy can be a time of information overload, and sometimes it's difficult to know which sources are reliable.

In today's society women are simply overloaded with information about pregnancy, from newspapers, magazines, books, and the internet. Photographs of glamorous pregnant celebrities, who look as if they don't have a care in the world, abound in the media. Two sources on the same topic can offer conflicting opinions. Although the internet can be a wonderful source of useful information, it has drawbacks: you don't know who has written an article on a website, it may not have been written by a health professional, and some recommendations may even contradict standard medical advice.

This means that constantly scouring the internet and reading everything you find can be confusing and scary.

Articles telling you that you risk the health and well-being of your baby by doing something can make you feel inadequate. Keep telling yourself that women have been having children for centuries without the aid of the internet! If reading lots of information makes you feel empowered and better able to make informed choices, then read away, but if it makes you feel confused then don't. A sensible course might be to pick just one reliable book or information source to read instead.

Use the internet to gather information about your pregnancy, using reputable health sites. However, if too much information makes you anxious or stressed, get your caregiver's advice.

ASK A... DOCTOR

I plan to bottle-feed. What do I need to buy in advance? You'll need plastic bottles (nipples are included), a sterilizing unit or kit (see p.449), which often has everything you need, and your preferred formula. Each comes in a range of options, so you need to decide what works best for you.

As you get to know your newborn baby, you may have to change the type of nipple and/or formula, so it's not advisable to buy too many before the birth.

FOCUS ON... NUTRITION

Immunity-boosting blueberries

According to a US study, blueberries topped a list of more than 40 fruits in terms of antioxidant activity. They are also a source of fiber, which is great during pregnancy, especially if—like many women—you suffer from constipation. Blueberries also contain nutrients that can prevent or repair damage to the body's cells. This may strengthen the body's immune system and your ability to fight infections.

Your 29th week

297

Your 30th week

YOU'RE GETTING TIRED MORE EASILY BUT THAT PROBABLY WON'T STOP YOUR NESTING PLANS

The nest-building instinct often kicks in as a woman approaches her due date. You may be overwhelmed with the urge to clean and decorate, but although it's natural to want a perfect home for your baby don't wear yourself out. Work, traveling, and a constant round of prenatal appointments are probably all much more of an effort these days. If you need to keep stopping to rest, listen to your body and do just that.

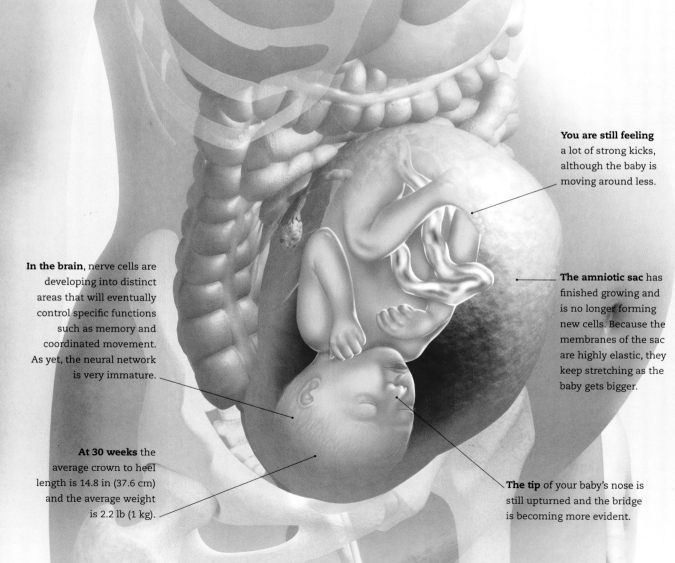

You are still feeling a lot of strong kicks, although the baby is moving around less.

In the brain, nerve cells are developing into distinct areas that will eventually control specific functions such as memory and coordinated movement. As yet, the neural network is very immature.

The amniotic sac has finished growing and is no longer forming new cells. Because the membranes of the sac are highly elastic, they keep stretching as the baby gets bigger.

At 30 weeks the average crown to heel length is 14.8 in (37.6 cm) and the average weight is 2.2 lb (1 kg).

The tip of your baby's nose is still upturned and the bridge is becoming more evident.

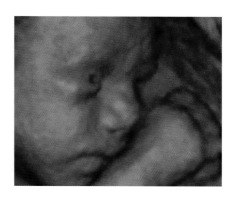

76 days to go...

YOUR BABY TODAY

The image shows the eyes are open once more for a brief look around. It's not completely dark within the uterus and the more advanced your pregnancy, the more light can penetrate inside. Your baby will gradually be assimilating this information.

Be prepared to spend more time in waiting rooms from now on, as your care providers ask to see you more often.

It's important to remember that your pregnancy is a natural, healthy process, but with more regular prenatal appointments, and a lot of time spent sitting in a waiting room at the doctor's office, sometimes surrounded by people with various medical conditions, you may start to feel that you have a medical problem. Even though you're visiting the hospital so often, you are fit and well; you just also happen to be pregnant.

At every prenatal appointment you will be asked for a urine sample, which is checked for protein. If you find it's getting increasingly difficult to catch your sample in the tiny, difficult to hold bottle you're given, don't worry. Only a small amount of urine is needed, so if you can't see anything just start to urinate and then move the bottle underneath the flow to catch some.

Urine is sterile (unless you have a urinary tract infection) so don't worry about getting some on your hands — just wash them thoroughly afterward.

Regular appointments with your caregiver take time out of your day, but they offer reassurance that all is well with your baby.

ASK A... DOCTOR

We know our baby has Down syndrome. How can we prepare ourselves? Knowing now will give you time to come to terms with the fact that your baby will have Down syndrome. You won't need any special equipment or toys when your baby is born, but you will need emotional support, so turn to the people now who you think will best give you this.

Contact the Canadian Down Syndrome Society (see p.480) for information and support, including getting in touch with parents of children with Down syndrome through your local support group.

THE LOWDOWN

Freebirthing

Giving birth without any medical assistance from a midwife or doctor might seem a little crazy, but a small minority of women believe that so-called freebirthing is the ultimate way to welcome their baby into the world. Some moms-to-be plan an unassisted home birth after having a negative experience during a previous labor; others want their birth to be natural, private, and devoid of medical intervention.

■ **Freebirthing is not against the law,** but it is radical. The Society of Obstetricians and Gynecologists of Canada recommend against freebirths because of the potential for complications, even in low-risk pregnancies. Complications such as the baby needing oxygen can and do happen.

■ **Some women have an unplanned "do-it-yourself" delivery**—usually because of a short labor—and in these instances the mothers and babies are usually fine. But actually choosing to go it alone is definitely not something that should be considered lightly.

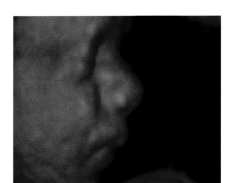

75 days to go...

YOUR BABY TODAY

Now the bridge of the nose is more apparent than earlier in the pregnancy. The tip of the nose can still look slightly upturned at this stage adding to the "button nose" appearance. As the face lengthens, the tip of the nose does move downward slightly.

Your baby's nerve cells are developing, but they are still not mature enough for her to feel pain, temperature, or touch.

Electrical activity can now be detected in the increasingly convoluted folds of gray matter, the part of your baby's brain that controls the higher functions, such as memory and consciousness, as well as muscle control and sensory perceptions, such as seeing and hearing.

The neurons of the cortex—the outer layer of gray matter—have started to develop into six distinct layers with separate functions, a process that will be completed in about about five weeks, although further maturing will be

needed. Your baby is born with almost a full complement of neurons, but there is further growth in early childhood.

For nerves to function effectively and signals to pass along them faster, they need insulating. In a process known as myelination, the nerves are insulated with myelin sheaths of fat. Although all of the components of the nervous system are present from an early stage of development, the peripheral sensory and motor nerves, spinal cord, and brain need the entire pregnancy to develop and function as a unit.

The nerves of the brain and spinal cord carry the sensations of pain, temperature, and touch. However, the process of myelination is ongoing and will not be complete until the final few weeks of pregnancy, so your baby does not register or recognize pain, temperature, and touch at this stage.

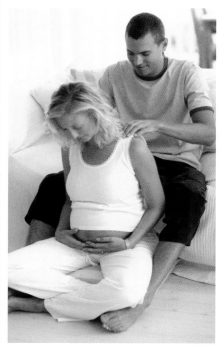

A massage is soothing and relaxing and can be very welcome attention as you wind down toward the birth of your baby.

ASK A... DOCTOR

The reality of having to give birth is hitting me now! How can I avoid getting too anxious? A little way into your third trimester, the reality of childbirth may sink in. You may be experiencing some pregnancy discomforts, including Braxton Hicks' contractions (see p.410), which give an indication of what is to come.

First of all, remember that the calmer and more relaxed you are, the easier your birth will be. Try to use a little positive visualization—your baby coming out easily in a "whoosh" of fluid, and focus on contractions being "positive pain" to bring your baby into

the world. Remember that your baby will be fine, however long she takes to arrive, and that your pain and discomfort are all controllable. In other words, even if you decide on a natural birth now, you can get help and relief when you need it.

Try to relax and enjoy the last months of your pregnancy. Treat yourself to a massage, and keep yourself busy—perhaps undertaking a creative project for your new baby. Above all, don't worry. Think about childbirth as welcoming your baby into the world, and focus on this rather than any concerns.

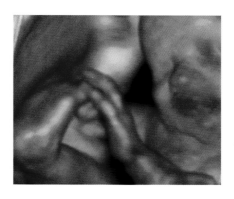

74 days to go...

YOUR BABY TODAY

Your baby often grasps one hand with the other or, as this image shows, grasps a foot. This helps with important sensory feedback to the brain as the nerves within the brain start to mature and become insulated along their length to carry signals more effectively.

Start getting your baby's room ready now, while you still have the energy for shopping and helping with decorating.

It's recommended that your baby sleeps in the same room as you for the first six months, but many parents-to-be still like to prepare the baby's bedroom. This room can still be used for the baby's clothes and any newborn gifts you're given. You might also want to breast-feed, and set up a diaper-changing area in there.

Check out garage sales and eBay for second-hand baby equipment. This can be a good opportunity to buy some bigger items at a reduced price. If you do buy a second-hand crib, make sure it was made after 1986 to ensure that it

meets safety standards, and that the slats are no more than 2 ⅜ inches (6 cm) apart. Hand-me down clothes, sheets, and towels also save money. If this isn't your first baby you may find that you have more or less everything you need, except for disposables, such as diapers (unless you are using cloth diapers—see p.291).

Although it's good to be prepared (and sometimes babies do arrive early), remember you won't be trapped in your house forever so you don't need to prepare as if for a siege. If you don't have something you need or you run out, you can always get it after your baby is born.

ASK A... DOCTOR

Do I need a carriage/travel system/stroller? Most parents-to-be are unsure about the type of stroller they'll need for their baby and, since there are a number of options and types available, this can make choosing the right item difficult. You will need to buy some type of travel equipment for your baby and what you choose will vary depending on your circumstances.

If you mostly drive a car, you may want to consider a car seat that attaches to a carriage, or a car seat and separate travel crib. If you intend to walk a lot, you may find a lightweight stroller more appropriate than a carriage. Keep in mind how long your baby will be in the stroller: it must be comfortable, have a lie-flat option for the first six months, and adjustable seat options as your baby grows. The stroller must also be weatherproof.

If you do a lot of "around town" travel, you might consider a lightweight option in addition to your main system. It's a good idea to take a look around in stores and online to compare different models and get the best price.

If you don't know the sex of your baby, opt for a neutral color scheme for your baby's room. If you do know, then you can decorate accordingly.

Planning for your birth

As your due date approaches, you may start to think in greater detail about how you would like to manage your labor and birth. Being informed will help you feel more confident about the choices you make.

Your choices for birth

When planning the type of birth experience you would like to have, you'll need to consider a number of factors. One of the most important decisions is where you would like to give birth. You may also want to think about the details of your birth, such as which positions you would like to adopt during the birth, and what type of pain relief you might choose to use (see pp.396–407).

It's important to be flexible. You may have preferences as to the type of birth you want, but accepting that your choice may be limited or advised against because of a preexisting medical problem, or because a problem arises in labor, will help you prepare mentally and curb disappointment if events don't go as planned. It is generally accepted that the care of healthy women in labor who have had a straightforward pregnancy should be monitored and managed by their doctors or midwives at the hospital, with support given by the nursing staff throughout the process.

The place of birth Earlier in pregnancy, you'll probably have thought about where you would like to give birth and discussed the options with your doctor. Although you may have already stated a preference, it's important to know that you can review your choice and change your mind toward the end of pregnancy.

Where you give birth may be influenced by factors such as whether you've had complications in pregnancy, such as gestational diabetes (see p.473) or high blood pressure, that would make a hospital birth preferable. On the other hand, if your pregnancy has been straightforward and you have become more informed about labor and birth over the course of your pregnancy, your confidence may have grown and you may decide to look into a home birth in familiar surroundings, or to investigate midwife-run birthing centers in your area.

Sometime in the third trimester you may have a hospital tour, which gives you a chance to see the labor and postpartum wards in your hospital, and to ask questions about hospital policies and what facilities are available. Ask your doctor for details of tours.

An active labor In prenatal classes, you'll learn a range of techniques to help you cope with pain during labor. Most methods center around breathing and relaxation techniques that help you focus during labor and birth and don't inhibit movement. Maintaining mobility and an upright position during labor is thought to help you deal with

NEW PROCEDURES

Stem cell collection

The collection of stem cells, which are found in the umbilical cord, is a relatively new private service. Stem cells develop into many different types of cell in the body and can be used to treat diseases such as leukemia by replacing diseased cells (see p.310). Stem cells are collected from the umbilical cord immediately after birth and sent to a laboratory where they are frozen and stored, acting as health insurance for the baby in future life. If you want to have this done, you must make arrangements with a private company and check that the hospital has procedures to allow the collection to be done.

Focusing on your birth preferences helps you to consider your options and feel mentally prepared for labor.

contractions and to use gravity to help push your baby down the birth canal.

If you want an active birth, this may influence how you feel about the type of pain relief you want to use (see below) and about monitoring in labor. For example, continuous monitoring (see p.418) can limit your movement. If your caregiver wants to monitor your labor continuously, talk to her about how you can maintain some mobility; for example, by sitting on a birthing ball, or adopting an all-fours position on the bed or on a mattress on the floor.

Your pain relief options Factors that may influence the type of pain relief you would like include how active you want to be (see above); what effect different drugs may have on how you experience labor; and how drugs can affect the baby.

Natural methods, such as breathing techniques, laboring in water, and TENS (see p.399), and some medical pain-relief options, such as analgesics (see pp.402–3)

allow an active birth because you won't lose all feeling or muscle movement. However systemic (IV) analgesics cross the placenta and can affect the baby's breathing at birth. Regional anesthetics, such as epidurals (see p.404), limit movement and can mean that you won't feel when you're pushing.

Making a birth plan

Writing your preferences in a birth plan helps you to consolidate your thoughts and to pass this information on to your doctor. Or your caregiver may discuss a birth plan with you. A birth plan is useful too for your birthing partner, who may need to advocate on your behalf in labor. Birth plans also allow you to state any special needs you may have, such as whether you have a disability.

Make your birth plan straightforward and accessible. Working with your caregivers as a team will help you deal well with labor and be involved in decision making, whatever the outcome.

(see p.418)

THINKING ABOUT THE BIRTH

Questions to consider

When planning where and how you ideally want to give birth, you need to consider both what you would prefer and what the hospital or birthing centers can offer. The following questions may act as helpful prompts.

Questions to ask yourself
- Who would you like to have with you during the labor and birth?
- Do you want an active labor?
- What pain relief do you want?
- If you have an assisted birth, would you prefer vacuum or forceps?
- Do you want your partner to be present if you have a cesarean?
- Do you want the third stage of labor to be managed naturally or assisted with drugs?
- How do you want to feed your baby?

Questions to ask the hospital
- What is the policy on induction? Will the hospital monitor your baby before labor if you don't want to be induced?
- Will the choice of pain relief and the place of birth change if you're induced?
- Are there tubs or birthing pool facilities?
- Will you be able to bring in aids such as massage oils or music?
- How much privacy will you have?
- How many people will you be allowed to invite into your labor and delivery room?
- Will your baby remain with you throughout your stay in the hospital?
- Does the hospital have facilities for sick babies, or are babies transferred?
- Can you go home when you feel ready, or is there a set discharge time?

Birth ideologies

In the mid-20th century, labor and childbirth in the West became highly medicalized. In reaction, several childbirth philosophies emerged that focused on empowering women and viewed childbirth as a natural rather than a medical experience. Many of these approaches are now integral to the way childbirth is managed today.

Dr. Grantley Dick-Read, an American obstetrician, linked labor pain to fear when he was working during the 1950s. He promoted breathing and relaxation to help cope with pain, and his methods are now commonplace.

Dr. Ferdinand Lamaze was inspired by the Russian scientist Dr. Pavlov, who trained dogs to have a set response to stimulus. In the 1950s, Lamaze extended this idea to childbirth, believing that women could be trained to respond positively to labor pain.

Sheila Kitzinger, a well-known birth practitioner who became prominent in the 1960s, believes in a woman's right to choose how to give birth.

Frederick Leboyer, a French obstetrician, came to prominence in the 1970s with his book *Birth without Violence.* Focusing on the baby, he believed a traumatic birth could impact negatively later in life. He promoted "gentle birthing" where the baby has skin-to-skin contact and is immersed in warm water.

Michael Odent, a birth practitioner, advocates active birthing, believing women act on instincts in labor. His birthing center in Pithiviers, France has the lowest national rates of intervention.

Janet Balaskas founded the Active Birth Movement in 1981. At her Active Birth Centre in London, she teaches relaxation, breathing, and yoga.

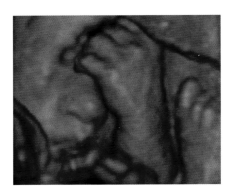

73 days to go...

YOUR BABY TODAY

In this image a hand is held up to the forehead and, to the right, part of a foot can be seen. The groove between the nose and the upper lip is visible and the nose has the characteristic "button" shape. It looks cramped in there but there is still room to move.

Your baby is cushioned in a sac of amniotic fluid, which surrounds her until your water breaks and you go into labor.

As your uterus has enlarged throughout your pregnancy, the amniotic sac has expanded to accommodate both your baby and the amniotic fluid. From now on, however, the sac will grow by simply stretching rather than forming new cells.

The amniotic sac is formed from two distinct layers or membranes, an inner "amnion" and outer "chorion." The chorion originally had a blood supply of its own, but this has now been lost. The thinner amnion is able to slide over the chorion as your baby pushes against it. Neither layer contains nerve cells: this explains why it's not painful when your membranes rupture or "water breaks."

Combined, the layers are only 0.5 mm thick. Collagen fibers in each layer allow for a great deal of stretch—this is vital in these final months to avoid early rupture of the membranes. Indeed, the membranes may be so resistant to rupture that they don't break until the final stages of your labor (see p.411).

In addition to holding in the amniotic fluid and providing a barrier to possible infection through the cervix, the membranes contain substances that form prostaglandins. Prostaglandins play an important part in the initiation of labor. This is one of the reasons why labor often starts when the membranes have ruptured.

Your baby may have several episodes of hiccuping in a day, or only one or two—you will both be able to feel these as a series of light, rhythmic movements.

Your third trimester

AS A MATTER OF FACT

The only reliable way to discover the sex of your baby is to have a diagnostic test (see pp.152–3), such as amniocentesis or chorionic villus sampling.

Even ultrasound can be wrong. And despite the common belief that the size and shape of your belly indicate gender, these are in fact determined by your muscle tone, your baby 's position, and your weight gain.

FOCUS ON... DADS

Kicks and hiccups

By now, it's possible to see and feel your baby moving, often with kicks and punches. This may happen more often in the evenings, when your partner finally gets to sit down and relax. Watching your baby's movements can be a great way to bond with her, and with your partner.

Your baby will respond to your voice, to music, and may even jump at unexpected noises (see p.206);

it's impossible to say whether this is because these noises are enjoyed or because they're irritating.

Your baby will also hiccup sometimes (see p.204) and you have a better chance of feeling her moving while she's hiccuping than any other form of movement. This is because hiccups occur over prolonged periods of time, while kicks and punches can be fairly random.

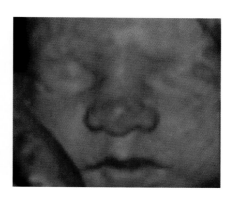

72 days to go...

YOUR BABY TODAY

The lip shape and groove between the nose and upper lip are particularly well shown here. If you or your partner has a prominent groove, or philtrum, above the upper lip, your baby may too, or she may inherit characteristics that are somewhere in between.

Having large hips is not a guarantee that you'll have an easy birth, nor are slender hips a guarantee of a difficult delivery.

Your body shape isn't an indication of whether you'll have an easy birth. The size of your hips is not always a good indication of the size of your pelvis so having slender hips doesn't mean you'll have a difficult birth, and having larger "child-bearing" hips doesn't mean you'll have an easier birth.

What is known is that, although how big your child will be is determined genetically, women have an extra influence on the size of their babies while they are in the uterus. So, even if your child ends up growing to 6 ft (1.80 m) tall, if you're small you'll limit how big she gets in the uterus. This makes sense—if you're small, you wouldn't be able to deliver a hefty 12 lb (5.5 kg) baby, so your body limits the baby's size at delivery. Your baby will then catch up on her expected growth after the birth.

There's a condition called cephalo-pelvic disproportion in which the baby is too big or the pelvis is too small for the baby to engage. If this is the case, you will need a cesarian section.

ASK A... DOCTOR

What will happen when I go for a gestational diabetes screening? You'll be given a very sugary drink and asked to wait for an hour, after which your blood will be tested. If your levels are high, you'll have to take a glucose tolerance test, which is similar, but longer. If you do have gestational diabetes, you will be taught how to test your blood sugar at home. You'll likely be able to control your condition with diet and exercise.

It's reassuring to know that most women who have sugar in their urine have normal blood-sugar levels in the glucose test.

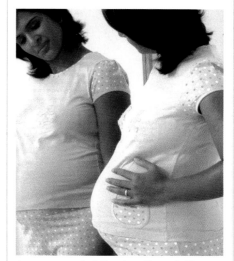

As you marvel at the size of your belly, you may be concerned about how you'll ever deliver your baby. But don't worry—nature is on your side.

TIME TO THINK ABOUT

A support network

After giving birth, your body will spring back into shape overnight; you'll be bursting with energy and raring to go. That's one scenario! The other—more realistic—possibility is that you'll find yourself struggling to get breast-feeding established and to brush your teeth before lunch time. If you don't like living in a mess, act now to prevent resentment (and the laundry) from building up in a few months' time.

■ **Talk to your partner now** about how you're going to split the chores once you're parents.
■ **Your "job" will be to nurture your newborn,** so you'll need domestic backup, if possible, particularly during the first few weeks. Recruit helpers (family and friends; or pay professionals if needed). Delegate so that you won't have to think about shopping, cooking, or cleaning.
■ **New parents need their own space,** so it's never too early to arrange for some babysitters for a few weeks after the birth. If you're breast-feeding, you'll need to express your milk.

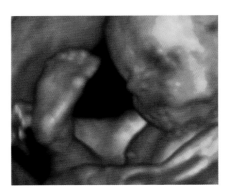

71 days to go...

YOUR BABY TODAY

Increasingly sounds enter the uterus and your baby will respond to some of the loudest. The fluid all around her can have quite an effect on the sounds that your baby can hear: the effect is similar to how you might feel when you swim with your head under water.

Your maximum blood volume won't be reached for a few weeks yet, but your circulation is working harder than ever at this stage.

Your blood volume is likely to be nearly a gallon and a half (5.5 L) between weeks 25 and 35—an increase of about 25 percent. This increased blood volume means that your heart is pumping harder and faster. Your blood vessels are as relaxed as they can be by this stage of pregnancy, and will not stretch any further to accommodate this extra blood flow. You may notice that you sweat more, and that your skin feels hotter (this is the rosy glow that many women experience).

In addition to this extra blood, there is also a lot more fluid circulating around your body. This makes all your body tissues thicker. It's common and normal for your face, fingers, and ankles to be puffy or swollen (see pp.466–7). However, since puffiness is also a sign of preeclampsia (see p.474), it's important to have your doctor or midwife to check this out.

Your face shape may change this trimester as you retain more fluid and gain weight.

ASK A... DOCTOR

I've noticed that I get short of breath very easily. Should I be concerned? No, when you're pregnant, your lungs have to work much harder to meet your body's increased oxygen needs. To help you take in more air, your ribs spread sideways and your lung capacity increases dramatically. This can make you feel breathless, particularly from mid-pregnancy.

In the last three months of pregnancy, most women find they get breathless even during mild exertion, which happens as the expanding uterus pushes up against the lungs. However, being breathless can also be a sign of anemia (see p.472), which may need to be treated. Your breathing may start to get easier when your baby engages (moves down into your pelvis ready to be born) (see p.361).

FOCUS ON... TWINS

Exercising safely

If you're pregnant with twins, it's recommended that you don't do any vigorous or aerobic exercise in the third trimester. The last three months are particularly tiring so you probably won't feel up to doing much anyway. You'll also get bigger sooner than someone who is having a single baby, and your size may preclude you from doing certain activities.

If you do want to be active, go for a gentle walk or swim, or to a pregnancy yoga or Pilates class. If you want to do anything more vigorous than this in the third trimester, check with your caregiver first.

Your caregiver will be monitoring your babies' progress and she may advise you on your level of activity if there is any slowdown in the babies' growth and development.

Whatever activity you're doing, always follow the guidelines for safe exercising (see p.18).

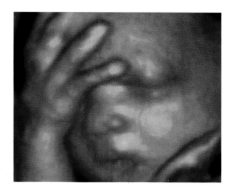

70 days to go...

YOUR BABY TODAY

Does your baby start to feel tired? Certainly on some scans it can look as if she is. In fact, your baby actually spends most of the time in a state of sleep rather than full wakefulness: it seems that during pregnancy your baby does need to spend most of the time asleep.

You probably won't want to stop working just yet, but you may need to make some adjustments if you're feeling very tired.

Later on in the third trimester you may begin to feel more tired than usual. The strain on your body may begin to show itself—you may find yourself uncomfortable and easily fatigued. Things that never bothered you previously, such as standing for long periods of time or walking a lot, may get increasingly difficult. For example, your trip to and from work may tire you much more than it did previously. If that is the case, find out whether you can alter your hours to avoid traveling at the busiest times of the day and, if you find yourself traveling during rush hours, don't be shy about asking someone to

give up their seat on the train for you. If there is a room in which you can rest at work, you may be able to take a short nap in the middle of the day or early afternoon, which might help to alleviate your fatigue a little.

You may want to discuss with your employer ways to make your job less physically demanding, or ask for help, for example if you need to carry heavy files or your job involves walking long distances. With a few adjustments you should be able to keep going until the start of your maternity leave, but above all, listen to your body: if you're tired, rest; if your feet and legs hurt, sit down.

FOCUS ON... TWINS

Cesarean birth

You're more likely to deliver twins by cesarean than a single baby (see pp.438–9). Many of these are elective: the decision is made in advance, and the mother doesn't go into labor. A cesarean is major surgery, but for the babies it's often the best way to arrive and a small price to pay for the mother.

Vaginal birth can be complicated for twins, especially the second twin who goes through two rounds of uterine contractions. It's considered high-risk if the babies are premature.

USING A BIRTHING POOL

Laboring and giving birth in water can not only relieve much of the pain, discomfort, and stress of childbirth, it can also induce relaxation and reduce blood pressure. Research shows that warm water on the lower back (the area of the spinal cord that receives the nerves from the lower abdominal region) can reduce labor pain, while the level of endorphins, or natural painkillers, rises in the same environment. Whether you choose a birthing pool or a warm bath, water is a great way to deal with contractions.

If you give birth in water, your baby's umbilical cord will continue to provide her with the oxygen she needs, but she will have to be brought to the surface quickly to encourage her to breathe on her own.

Water birth should be done with your caregiver's supervision, and some birthing centers and hospitals now offer the option (see p.343). Make sure you include these details on your birth plan (see p.303). Using a birthing pool will not be recommended if your birth is considered to be high risk.

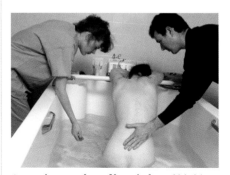

A growing number of hospitals and birthing centers offer birthing pools. If you'd like to have a water delivery, check the availability of a pool at your hospital when you tour the facility.

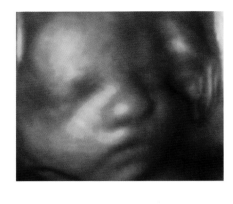

68 days to go...

YOUR BABY TODAY

You will be aware of times when your baby is especially active and times when he is more quiet. There is still a lot of space for your baby to move within the uterus but it is likely that there will be a favorite spot that receives more kicks than any other.

Your baby has now developed a clear rhythm of sleeping and waking that may mimic your own or be personal to him.

Exactly when and how your baby develops a cycle of sleeping and waking before birth remains a bit of a mystery. It's not known whether your own rhythms influence your baby's sleep–wake cycle or whether your baby develops his own internal clock. Indeed, such a clock might be triggered in response to the small amount of light that is able to penetrate through the uterus during the last few weeks of pregnancy. It's apparent from brain scans, however, that by this stage of pregnancy, your baby does have very separate periods of activity.

There is a clear cycle, alternating between periods of quiet rest, sleep with rapid eye movements (REM), wakefulness with activity but no eye movement, and wakefulness with lots of activity and eye movements. During this sleep–wake cycle, the baby's actions becomes more coordinated as periods of activity are linked to rhythmical breathing and increased heart rate, and eye movements.

By this stage of pregnancy, electrical activity in your baby's brain shows patterns reflecting periods of sleep or wakefulness. An EEG of your baby's brain would show that the quietest period, deep sleep, takes up almost half of the time. The next most common state is REM sleep (the sleep stage during which children and adults dream). This is a time of great electrical activity within your baby's brain. During REM sleep the baby may be quiet or making lots of movements, so it's not possible to tell whether your baby is truly awake at this time or if he's dreaming. Paradoxically, the least electrical activity happens when your baby is most awake—in fact less than 10 percent of your baby's time is spent truly awake at this stage.

STEM CELL COLLECTION

The blood in your baby's umbilical cord contains "cord blood," which is rich in stem cells. These cells are the building blocks of organ tissue, blood, and the immune system. Some parents save these cells and store them (in a private facility at a cost) in the event that their child or another family member needs their healing benefits (see p.302).

Studies have found that they are very effective in the treatment of more than 70 diseases including juvenile diabetes, cancers, heart disease, and brain injury.

Stem cells are widely used, but there is significant evidence to show that using cells from the cord blood of a sibling or other family member is more effective than using cells from an unrelated donor, or bone marrow from relatives.

Cord blood can be expensive to store. Some women choose to donate their blood to public cord blood banks. The donated blood is stored, and this is used to treat patients who need it most. Talk to your doctor if you'd like to do this.

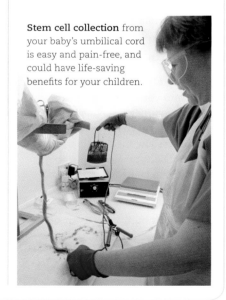

Stem cell collection from your baby's umbilical cord is easy and pain-free, and could have life-saving benefits for your children.

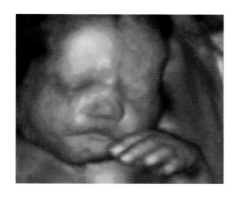

67 days to go...

YOUR BABY TODAY

It can come as quite a surprise to see that your baby will be increasingly making all sorts of expressions. Here the baby had his mouth turned down but the next minute will be yawning, grimacing, or peacefully sleeping.

Natural birth has many advocates, but the best birth is one that delivers your baby safely with minimum trauma for both of you.

Many women want a natural delivery, with no pain relief or other medical intervention. Giving birth naturally is for some reason perceived as the "best" way, and to do otherwise means that you somehow "failed" at childbirth. This pressure means that women can feel guilty or even depressed if they needed pain relief or a cesarean section, for example.

Bear in mind that some women have higher pain thresholds and can get through labor with simple breathing or relaxation techniques, while others need more help. Pain is subjective, no one else can feel your pain; if it is too much for you, then ask for help. Your options (see pp.402–7) will be explained to you by the doctor or midwife.

Childbirth is hard work, but the experience should not be so painful that it scars you. Being pain-free may mean that you have a more enjoyable, even empowering, labor experience. If you do decide you want pain relief, an epidural is the most common option—more than half of women having a baby in a hospital receive one.

Having a natural birth is high on the list of many women's priorities, but it's a good idea to prepare mentally for medical intervention, in case it becomes necessary.

ASK A PANEL ABOUT... NATURAL BIRTH

I want a natural birth but everyone says I'll change my mind once I'm in labor. Are they right?

Mom: Nothing can prepare you for the discomfort of labor, and I found my carefully laid plans were unrealistic and impractical when the pain kicked in. No matter how well prepared you are, you may change your mind during labor, and it's worth being prepared for that. I did feel a bit disappointed that I couldn't manage without pain relief. It helps if you focus on what's important—delivering a healthy baby. If you achieve this aim, you've succeeded, no matter

what happens along the way. I would say to stick it out for as long as you can, but you'll be doing yourself and your baby no favors if you both become exhausted and distressed.

Doctor: Many women are shocked by the intensity of the birth experience, and soon forget about their idealistic birth plan. It's better for all involved that you allow for contingency plans, and keep an open mind. Pain relief (see pp.396–407) and interventions

are designed to make the experience better for you and your baby, and will not be offered unless they're necessary, or you feel that you can't do without them. Some women get through labor naturally; others need some help. A lot of women do change their mind about "going natural," and there is nothing wrong with that. A mom who has her pain under control will find that the delivery is much quicker, and she'll have much more energy for her new arrival.

Twins

Just a few weeks to go. By now, you're probably quite large and, of course, excited at the imminent arrival of your twins, or more. However, you may also be concerned about how you will manage during and after the birth.

Getting ready for the birth

Although multiple pregnancies and births are more likely to have complications, they are now safer than ever as advances in prenatal and postpartum care have dramatically improved the outlook for premature babies—the main concern with multiples (see below).

You can prepare for the birth by getting plenty of rest. Putting your feet up, or even having a nap during the day, helps improve the blood flow to the placenta, which in turn helps your babies grow. Practicing Kegel exercises (see p.69) is important with a multiple pregnancy since your pelvic floor muscles are under additional strain.

(see p.69)

THIINKING AHEAD

Bonding with twins

Often, expectant moms of twins or more worry about how they will bond with more than one baby. It's true that bonding can be harder with twins, and even more so with higher multiples. After all, it's hard to fall in love with more than one person at a time, especially when you're exhausted caring for two babies or more. Being aware of this and arranging extra help for after the birth may ease your anxiety. Also, accept additional offers of help that allow you to rest or spend time with one twin. If someone offers to take the twins out, you might consider one twin going and the other spending time with you.

TWINS

How your babies lie in the uterus

In the final weeks, your babies will take up their positions for the birth. The most common position is with both babies lying vertically. With 75 percent of twins, the first is head down (cephalic); the second twin may be head down or breech, or one twin may lie across the uterus (transverse). You may suspect their position from the kicks, but only a scan confirms this.

A cesarean will be recommended if you have triplets or more, or your first twin is breech or transverse (25 percent of cases). A vaginal delivery is most likely if both twins are head down. If the first is head down and the second is transverse or breech, there are different opinions as to the best type of delivery, which you can discuss with your obstetrician.

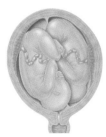 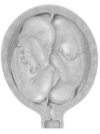 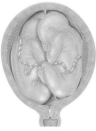 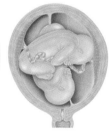

Both babies head down (cephalic) **One baby head down, and one breech** **Both babies in a breech position** **One baby head down and one transverse**

A shorter pregnancy Twins or more usually arrive earlier than singletons. Space in the uterus is one factor. In addition, with multiple pregnancies the placenta becomes less efficient toward the end of pregnancy. As a result, the average length of pregnancy is shorter: for twins 36 to 37 weeks is considered typical, for triplets the average pregnancy is 33 weeks, and for quadruplets pregnancy lasts about 30 weeks. The average birth weight for each twin is 5 lb 8 oz (2.5 kg) at full term.

You may deliver even earlier than this, since nearly 50 percent of twins are born prematurely. Nowadays expert care for premature babies means that about 75 percent of babies weighing 3 lb 5 oz (1.5 kg) at birth, and 57 percent of babies weighing 2 lb 3 oz (1 kg) at birth, survive.
.

Preparing for more than one

Even if your twins are identical they're individuals, and relating to them as separate people will help their development and your relationship with them. Even in pregnancy, some expectant moms notice how different their babies are from their different movement patterns in the uterus.

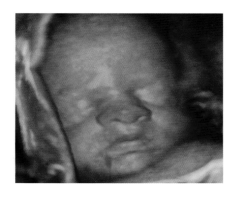

66 days to go...

YOUR BABY TODAY

In this 3D scan the baby's arm is held up next to the face. This type of scan shows external features but also looks inside the baby in 3D so you may see some parts of your baby "through" an arm or leg. Here, the baby's ear can be seen through the arm.

In the uterus and in the first months of his life, your baby relies on your immunity to various infections.

If your immune system thought your baby was foreign, it would mount an attack on him. You and your baby are designed so that this does not happen. Your baby does not have the ability to produce antibodies (which would attack you) in the uterus: he relies completely on you to protect him from infection, not only in the uterus but also after birth. Protection after birth is possible because antibodies from your immune system cross over the placenta into your baby's bloodstream, while you're pregnant. If you have immunity to a disease such as measles, mumps, polio, and many other severe infections, your baby will carry your antibodies to these conditions. This so-called passive immunity is lost with time and it is for this reason that, from two months onward, your baby will require a program of immunizations to protect against these and other illnesses.

FOCUS ON... YOUR BODY

There have been numerous studies over the past few years involving women exercising while they're pregnant. The bottom line is that exercise performed effectively and safely, at a moderate intensity and in healthy women, is beneficial.

In addition to being good for your health and making you feel more energized, exercising will get you into great shape for labor and childbirth, which is, in effect, a workout!

Here are the myths:

■ **Exercising will harm my baby if I move too much.** Your baby is protected by amniotic fluid and nourished by the placenta. By keeping within safe exercising guidelines (see p.18), and not doing any high-impact sports or activities where you are at risk of falling or injuries, you are not putting your baby at risk.

■ **Exercise will use up some of the nutrients my baby needs.** Your baby's growth will be monitored at doctor appointments, so you and your doctor will be able to tell whether your baby is growing at a usual rate or whether you should increase your calorie intake. If you're concerned, increase your calorie intake on the days that you exercise.

■ **Doing abdominal exercises will harm the baby.** You can do abdominal exercises but you should not do abdominal exercises lying on your back in the second and third trimesters. The risk of lying on your back is that the baby can press down on the vena cava (the large blood vessel that returns blood to your heart). This causes your blood pressure to fall and compromises the oxygen flow to the baby. The first sign of a problem will be feeling dizzy: if you roll on to your left side, any

symptoms should disappear. Don't hesitate to consult your doctor or midwife if you're concerned. The abdominal exercises shown on page 250 give you some great ways of doing safe abdominal exercises that do not put you or your baby at risk.

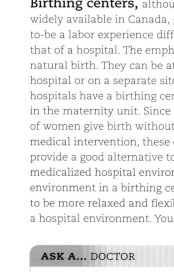

65 days to go...

YOUR BABY TODAY

Here the hands are holding the umbilical cord as it arises from what will become the belly button, or umbilicus. The umbilical coils and its covering of firm, clear jelly protect the cord from kinking and prying fingers.

If you want a home birth atmosphere with additional support, consider having your baby in a birthing center.

Birthing centers, although not widely available in Canada, give moms-to-be a labor experience different than that of a hospital. The emphasis is on a natural birth. They can be attached to a hospital or on a separate site. Some hospitals have a birthing center facility in the maternity unit. Since the majority of women give birth without needing medical intervention, these centers provide a good alternative to a more medicalized hospital environment. The environment in a birthing center tends to be more relaxed and flexible than a hospital environment. You'll have continuous support from a combination of labor nurses and midwives. Your doctor may also be affiliated with a birthing center. Furthermore, the medical team in these centers is very experienced at handling a birth without medical intervention. These factors increase your chances of a straightforward birth. To give birth in such a center, you need to have had an uncomplicated pregnancy and be unlikely to require specialized medical care or monitoring in labor and birth. If complications did occur, you would be transferred to the closest hospital, although this is rare.

HOME IS WHERE THE HEART IS

The prospect of sleeping in your own bed and being taken care of by people who love you are reason enough to opt for a home birth. It's natural to feel less inhibited at home, and you may be more inclined to move around more and for longer, be as vocal as you like, use gravity, and try different birthing positions, all of which can make labor and delivery shorter and easier. Your midwife will explain what's involved, so seek her advice. On the big day be flexible: you may want to head for the hospital.

ASK A... DOCTOR

I'm having a home birth. Can my older children, four and six, be present at the birth? There is nothing more wonderful or miraculous than the birth of a baby, and it's natural to want your older children to be present and witness it for themselves. However, do consider this carefully before you give them the go-ahead. For one thing, even the easiest of labors are painful, and young children will be distressed to see mom in pain. What's more, they may be slightly daunted to see their new sibling emerging from your body, probably covered with various substances. Having said that, many kids handle the experience well if they know what to expect, so outline everything, and explain that any cries, shrieks, or swearing on your behalf are necessary to help get the baby out. You could also mention that you may cry or even vomit, just so they are prepared. Let them know to expect some blood, and that baby will be attached to a (rather gruesome!) cord. If they're squeamish, get them to position themselves by your head, or bring them in immediately after.

Sit down with your partner and discuss what you both would like to happen during the whole labor and birth experience. Then start putting your hopes, thoughts, and feelings into a birth plan that you can discuss and expand on with your caregiver.

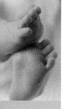

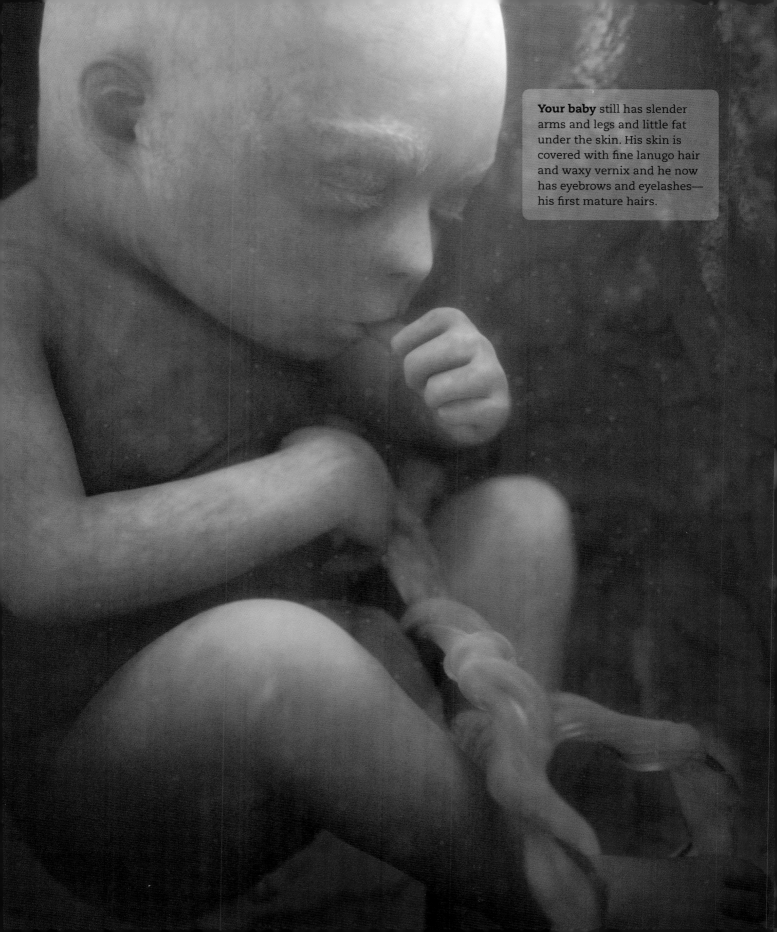

Your baby still has slender arms and legs and little fat under the skin. His skin is covered with fine lanugo hair and waxy vernix and he now has eyebrows and eyelashes—his first mature hairs.

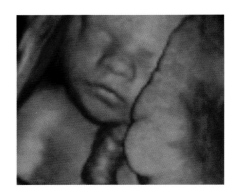

64 days to go...

YOUR BABY TODAY

Here the baby is resting on the placenta, seen at the right-hand side of the image, with the umbilical cord just below the baby's chin. The eyes are closed and this image was taken at a time when the baby was at his quietest, during deep sleep.

Once your baby's production of red blood cells is in full swing, in theory your immune system could begin to harm your baby.

At 30 weeks your baby's red blood cell production switches from the liver to the bone marrow. These red blood cells are unlikely to be of the same blood group as your own. Small numbers of these red blood cells often leak across the placenta; your body recognizes them as foreign and attacks them.

Your blood group is not important because, although antibodies to blood groups A, B, AB, or O attack your baby's cells in your circulation, they are too large to cross the placenta and attack your baby. Therefore differences in ABO blood groups do not matter. However, everyone is also Rhesus positive (85 percent) or negative (15 percent). If you are Rhesus negative (see p.123) and your partner is Rhesus positive, your baby may also be Rhesus positive.

Rhesus negative women produce antibodies to rhesus positive blood cells; these are smaller than ABO antibodies and can cross the placenta. Once they do, large numbers of antibodies can attack your baby's blood cells, leading to anemia. First pregnancies are rarely affected. In pregnancy you are given an injection of the rhesus antibody "Rh immunoglobulin (RhIg)" around now—with another after the birth. The Rh immunoglobulin (RhIg) is in a form that it is too large to cross the placenta. This mops up any of your baby's blood cells in your circulation, preventing your immune system from attacking your baby.

AMNIOTIC FLUID

Your baby excretes and reabsorbs about 16 fl oz (0.5 liter) of urine daily, and the amniotic fluid reaches a peak volume of 1.75 pints (1 liter) at 35 weeks. After this time the volume starts to decline and can be as little as 3.5–7 fl oz (100–200 ml) in an overdue pregnancy (see p.393).

Low levels of amniotic fluid, known as oligohydramnios (see p.473), can be a sign of a growth-restricted baby or a baby with kidney problems.

Excessive amniotic fluid, known as polyhydramnios (see p.473), may be seen in twin or triplet pregnancies, and is also associated with physical abnormalities in the baby or diabetes in the mother.

After 40 weeks, the fluid level needs to be checked regularly to ensure that there is not too steep a decline in fluid levels. If the overdue baby is thought to be at risk, an induction (see p.432) will be recommended.

FOCUS ON... YOUR HEALTH

A good night's sleep

Insomnia is a common problem during pregnancy and can lead to fatigue, feelings of stress and anxiety, and irritability. Whether it's brought on by your increased size, back pain, heartburn, getting up to empty your bladder, or something else, insomnia is not fun. Taking a warm bath or having a small snack before bed may help, as can relaxation techniques, such as deep breathing. A calming scent in a potpourri or fragrance on your pillow may aid relaxation. Make sure to exercise during the day. If you still can't sleep, get up and do something relaxing: read a book, watch TV, or listen to calming music until you feel sleepy. And try to make up for lost sleep with daytime naps.

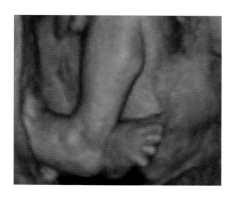

63 days to go...

YOUR BABY TODAY

One leg is shown here crossed over the other. Your baby can still stretch the legs out fully and even curl up in such a way that the feet can rest on top of the head: just because you're kicked on one side doesn't mean that the head will be on the other.

Epidural is a common form of pain-relief during labor and may be an option for you if you have a low pain threshold.

Many women have decided that they want a pain-free delivery with an epidural (see pp.404–5) even before they go into labor. It's good to know, however, that labor has to be well established before you can have an epidural, so you'll still experience some painful contractions. Epidurals generally work well, but sometimes the block isn't complete or is more effective on one side than the other. Some women decide to have an epidural because they know they're unlikely to cope well with labor pain. Many women start off saying that they don't want an epidural and change their minds halfway through—if it's your first pregnancy, you can't possibly know how you'll feel.

An elective cesarean (see pp.438–9) is one that is planned and generally performed for medical reasons—for example, because of a low-lying placenta (see p.212)—and not simply because a woman wants to have one. Having a cesarean is major abdominal surgery and in most circumstances it is safer to have a vaginal delivery. Recovery after a cesarean usually takes longer than after a vaginal birth, so one is only performed if necessary.

THE LOWDOWN

Tocophobia

This condition is an intense fear or dread of childbirth. There are two types: primary tocophobia predates pregnancy and can start as early as adolescence; secondary tocophobia is associated with an earlier traumatic experience in childbirth. This fear can manifest itself as nightmares, intense anxiety, or panic attacks.

If you have tocophobia, your doctor will refer you to a consultant obstetrician who deals in mental health issues, or you may be referred directly to a psychologist to discuss your fears. Some experts believe that hypnotherapy can help to tackle any subconscious fears of childbirth. An elective cesarean (see pp.438–9) may be recommended if your fear of having a vaginal birth cannot be overcome.

FOCUS ON... RELATIONSHIPS

Comfortable lovemaking

You may need to experiment to find lovemaking positions that are comfortable. Most women find that the missionary position becomes increasingly uncomfortable as your partner presses on your belly. You may find being on top is enjoyable and does not put pressure on your belly. Lying in the spoons position, with your partner behind you, can also be pleasurable. Other positions that don't restrict your pleasure and are comfortable include sitting together, kneeling while your partner enters from behind, and lying side by side with your legs entwined.

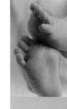

Your 32nd week

YOUR MIDWIFE WILL BE MONITORING YOUR BABY'S POSITION IN THE UTERUS

The baby has not settled into her final birth position just yet, but an assessment of how she's lying will be made at every routine checkup. There's still room in the uterus for your baby to exercise her limbs and she's getting much stronger and more active. You'll know all about it! As your belly gets bigger, it may become more difficult to be very active and to get comfortable when you're sitting or lying down.

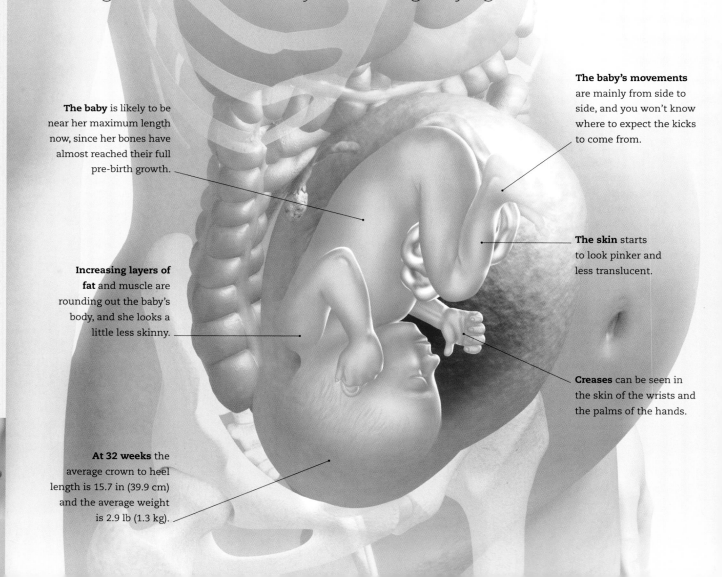

The baby's movements are mainly from side to side, and you won't know where to expect the kicks to come from.

The baby is likely to be near her maximum length now, since her bones have almost reached their full pre-birth growth.

The skin starts to look pinker and less translucent.

Increasing layers of fat and muscle are rounding out the baby's body, and she looks a little less skinny.

Creases can be seen in the skin of the wrists and the palms of the hands.

At 32 weeks the average crown to heel length is 15.7 in (39.9 cm) and the average weight is 2.9 lb (1.3 kg).

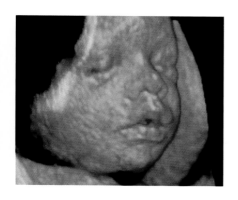

62 days to go...

YOUR BABY TODAY

The amount of amniotic fluid within the uterus is at its maximum over the next two weeks but will subsequently start to reduce gradually. Measurements of the four deepest pockets of amniotic fluid can add up to 6–8 in, allowing space for your baby to move.

If you listen to music while you're pregnant, your baby will be tuning in, too—and it might just benefit her.

You might have noticed that your baby becomes more active when you're listening to music. It's been noted that unborn babies move and even breathe in time to music, and there have been claims that by exposing your baby to certain types of music, you can enhance her brain development.

One study, relating to a "Baby Mozart" brain-enhancing product, claimed that the structure of, say, a particular Mozart arrangement, stimulated brain development to a greater extent than other genres, and even other classical composers. This theory has, however,

been debunked. Some research found that college-aged students who listened to classical music showed a brief and temporary improvement in spatial intelligence. However, the same research was not tested in children or babies. The research has not been repeated and the results are open to several different interpretations.

Whether or not it enhances your baby's intelligence, listening to classical music can relax you, which is always a good thing during pregnancy. And if you gently sway to the music, your baby may enjoy being "rocked" to sleep.

FOCUS ON... YOUR BODY

Protruding navel

You may be surprised to find that by now your perfectly formed navel is protruding. This protrusion is caused by the pressure of your rapidly expanding uterus, which presses against your abdomen and literally pops your belly button out.

Some women find their protruding navel unsightly, and choose to wear skirts or pants with a high waistband to cover it; you can also cover your protruding belly button with a Band-Aid.

A protruding navel is a normal consequence of pregnancy and it will return to normal a few months after the delivery. Although you may find that, like other parts of your body, your navel sags a little more than it used to.

ASK A... DOCTOR

What exactly is an "active birth"? Having an "active birth"—staying mobile during the first stage of labor and remaining upright, squatting, kneeling, or on all-fours during the second stage—can make labor and delivery easier and less painful. Working with gravity helps your pelvis to open and encourages the baby's head to press on your cervix, helping it to dilate. To get active:

■ **Practice squatting (see p.424):** it takes time to learn to do it, but it's an effective way to speed labor up. When squatting, make sure you have

sufficient support—from your partner, for example.

■ **Relax by kneeling** with a birth ball or beanbag.

■ **Use a birthing pool** if you want to relax in water for a while.

■ **If you need an IV,** because you've been induced (see p.432), ask for one with a long tube that will leave you free to move around a little.

■ **Choose a walking epidural,** which should enable you to stay active.

■ **If lying down** makes your contractions stop, get up and start moving again.

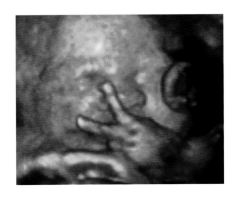

61 days to go...

YOUR BABY TODAY

Your baby's hand coordination continues to improve as her brain is better able to make sense of the feedback it receives. The eyes will often open but only for short periods at a time, reducing the chance of a stray finger coming too close.

By this stage, your baby is the length she'll be at birth, but she's still very thin and needs to gain fat and muscle.

At this stage of pregnancy, your baby's muscle mass and fat are continuing to increase. Her skin is now thicker and less translucent, and begins to look pink rather than red as the underlying blood vessels are overlaid with more flesh. Growth hormone is being produced by your baby's pituitary gland but before she's actually born this does not influence her growth. Instead insulin and insulin-like growth factors are key. As your baby's skeleton is now close to its final size, her overall length is established. Your baby is still, however, very skinny.

A sonographer can make a good estimate of your baby's weight from an ultrasound scan but her final birthweight will very much depend on when she is born. She'll continue to grow throughout the pregnancy, although in the last few weeks growth is mainly due to fat deposits rather than to muscle mass.

If you're trying to guess how heavy your baby will be at birth, the latest research indicates that the size of your baby has a lot to do with "imprinted" genes. These are genes that are marked as having come from the father, which promote the baby's growth, or the mother, which are growth limiting and attempt to preserve her resources.

FOCUS ON... TWINS

Dressing your babies

Twins look adorable when they're dressed alike, so you may be buying—and certainly will be given—lots of sets of matching clothing. But it's much easier to tell identical twins apart when they're dressed differently. It also helps everyone relate to them as individuals, which is good for their development.

Also keep practicalities in mind: every time one of your twins gets dirty, are you going to change them both? You may find it pays to be flexible: if there are only two clean onesies, then that is what they'll have to wear, regardless of style or color match.

Newborns don't care what they wear, but if you get in the habit of dressing them the same, they may become conscious of it in the toddler years and get distressed if they're wearing something different.

How you dress your babies is your decision, but you could:

■ **Dress your babies in matching outfits but different colors,** or the same colors but different styles.

■ **Only dress them identically on certain occasions,** for instance for a family photograph or special occasion.

■ **Give any identical outfits you receive to one twin.** The next batch of identical outfits goes to the other twin.

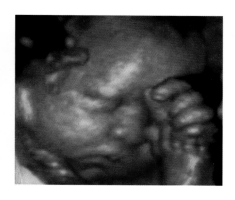

60 days to go...

YOUR BABY TODAY

Here the umbilical cord is seen lying over the baby's shoulder and next to the wrist. This is very common, in fact at some time every baby will have the umbilical cord lying close, especially during these next few weeks while the baby frequently changes position.

Jolts and jostles are all part of being pregnant—and your baby probably won't even notice them.

I'm finding it increasingly hard to focus at work. How can I best get through the next few weeks?

As your baby—and you—get bigger, you may find that you have less energy and your concentration span decreases accordingly. This is normal, but it can pose problems if you have a job to do! First of all, take regular breaks, putting your feet up or closing your eyes for a few minutes to rest. Make sure you drink enough, since dehydration can affect your performance. Similarly, eating healthy snacks, little and often, can keep you from flagging. Iron-rich foods, such as dried fruit, are particularly important: low iron levels can make you tire easily.

Carry a small notebook with you, and jot down anything that you need to remember, no matter how trivial. This can help overcome lapses of memory, and keep you focused on what needs to be done. It may also help to start your day with a "to-do" list, and check your way down it in order of priority. Finally, try to get enough sleep, which will give you at least half a chance of feeling refreshed the next morning.

Your belly is getting larger and larger. As you walk you may notice that your belly also appears to move, swaying from side to side with each step. It can be difficult to remember that you're so much bigger than you used to be. You may find yourself trying to squeeze through tight spaces, or between tables and chairs in a restaurant that previously you would have fit through and now find yourself

Keep a notebook to hand to jot down everything from what to do today, what to say when you make a call, and what you need to cover in a letter or e-mail.

a bit stuck! Even if you find that your belly is getting bumped around occasionally this really is nothing at all to worry about: your baby is safe, protected by the pool of amniotic fluid that acts as a cushion against the occasional jolt. Soon enough, though, you will be back to your normal shape, or nearly your normal shape, and it can be odd to think back to having to compensate for a belly.

Heart palpitations

Having a run of fast heartbeats, or missing a beat occasionally—or simply being acutely aware of your heartbeat—is defined as heart palpitations (see p.469). It's common to have these in late pregnancy. They are usually nothing to worry about and are simply the result of changes to your blood circulation, coupled with a large abdominal bulge, although unnecessary stresses and anxieties can play a part as well.

If, however, palpitations are accompanied by chest pain or breathlessness, or if you think they are occurring more frequently, mention this to your doctor.

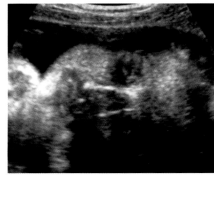

59 days to go...

YOUR BABY TODAY

Measurements around the head, abdomen, and thigh bones are used from the ultrasound image to estimate the weight of your baby. Interestingly, on average, boys are now starting to be slightly heavier than girls.

As your baby puts on muscle and its tone improves, she begins to be capable of more complex and stronger movements.

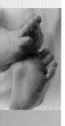

Your third trimester

Your baby's muscle tone takes some time to develop fully.

By this week of your pregnancy, head control is improving and in the legs muscle tone now allows for smoother and more complex movements. For once, the arms and hands lag behind the legs and feet in development, taking another three weeks to achieve the same level of tone and movement.

In the last few weeks the familiar "fetal position" is increasingly seen on scans: this is not only due to lack of space, but also because your baby's flexor muscles (those that bend the elbows, hips, and knees) have a better tone than her extensor muscles (the muscles that extend the arms and legs) in each limb.

You will also be aware that your baby is moving more now than at any other time. You only feel the movements that hit the lining of your uterus, but there will be many more small movements of which you are completely unaware. Movements inside the uterus are important: they help your baby's coordination, strengthen her bones, and increase muscle mass. The number of muscle cells increases up until 38 weeks. From this point on, individual muscle cells lengthen and expand in response to exercise, further increasing muscle mass and strength.

There is no need to feel left out when all around you are partying: enjoy fresh fruit juices over ice, topped with soda, tonic water, or ginger ale to add a little fizz.

NON-ALCOHOLIC DRINKS

Here are some ideas for delicious non-alcoholic drinks:
- Cranberry juice/orange juice/lemon juice/ginger ale
- Grapefruit juice/cranberry juice/soda or tonic water
- Sparkling apple juice/lime juice/sugar to taste
- Orange juice/bitter lemon
- Lemon juice/pineapple juice/orange juice/grenadine/soda
- Diced lemon/diced lime/diced orange/ginger ale/sugar to taste
- Apple juice/pear juice/ginger ale.

ASK A... DOCTOR

Will having an orgasm cause me to go into labor? In a pregnancy without problems, an orgasm will not cause premature labor (see p.431), and at full term orgasm will only cause the onset of labor if it's going to happen anyway. If you have had any signs of premature labor, or your water has broken (see p.411), you'll be advised to avoid sexual intercourse. This is because the hormone oxytocin increases during sexual arousal and oxytocin causes the muscles of the uterus to contact. Orgasm may increase practice, or Braxton Hicks', contractions (see p.410).

If you've gone past your due date and are at a point when your body is ready to go into labor, then sexual intercourse may help things to start for two reasons: the prostaglandins in semen will help the cervix to soften at this stage of pregnancy, and the contractions stimulated by orgasm have more chance of developing into early labor contractions.

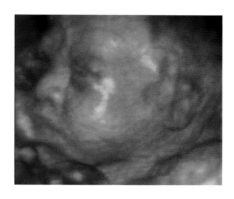

58 days to go...

YOUR BABY TODAY

This image shows a furrowed brow and an open-eyed expression. Just as the muscle tone in the limbs is strengthening, so the muscles of the face are being used and tested. This can produce some unusual expressions that do not necessarily reflect your baby's emotions.

How your baby is positioned can affect your delivery, but there is plenty of time at this stage for things to change.

Each time you are examined your doctor will assess your baby's lie and presentation (see p.336). Many babies are in the breech position earlier in the pregnancy, but most turn into the head down position by the end of the pregnancy. Still, breech births occur in about one in 25 full-term births. Between 32 and 37 weeks is the best time for your doctor to try to turn a breech baby. This is because there is plenty of room for the baby to turn around. After the 35th or 36th week, the baby is unlikely to change position since there is less room for large maneuvers. If your baby is breech, your doctor may try to turn the baby, a process called version and she may recommend an extra ultrasound scan at 37–38 weeks of pregnancy to check the baby's position. It may be difficult to be completely sure, on examination alone, whether the doctor is feeling the baby's bottom or head. If your baby is breech, your doctor may suggest a cesarean delivery.

FOCUS ON... DADS

Getting the balance right

Much of later pregnancy involves your partner doing less than normal. This may range from doing less exercise to not doing household chores. It may be challenging for your partner to realize that she's not able to do things as easily as before and, to a certain extent, is less independent.

You can be a great help to her in the final weeks of pregnancy, but be aware that there's a fine line between being supportive and being overly protective. Deep down you may want to turn into "superman" and do everything, but it might frustrate your partner if you become overly protective. Try to take the lead from her and give her help as and when she needs it, as well as space to do her own thing.

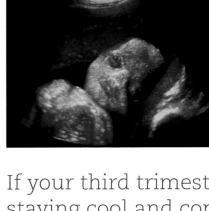

57 days to go...

YOUR BABY TODAY

You can see from this image just how much amniotic fluid is around your baby at this time. Ultrasound displays the fluid as black on the screen. Sometimes there will be speckles within the fluid: these represent skin and hair cells that are shed as your baby grows.

If your third trimester coincides with the summer months, staying cool and comfortable can be a real challenge.

When the weather is hot, your baby makes it sweltering! Keep yourself hydrated by drinking lots of cool water. Consider carrying a spray bottle of water (keep it in the fridge overnight so that it's nice and cold next day) to spritz you when you're too hot.

Opt for sleeveless clothing that is made of natural fabrics, such as linen and cotton, which will help keep the air circulating. If you want to keep some or all of your arms covered, wear short-sleeved jackets or cotton cardigans. Wear a sun hat and sunglasses, especially if you're in direct sunlight for any length of time.

Opt for flip-flops or low-heeled sandals to let your feet breathe—these can also be a good option if your feet are swollen (see pp.466–7).

FOCUS ON... YOUR BABY

Listening to your baby's heartbeat

From the very earliest stages of pregnancy, your baby's heart will be beating, and there can be nothing more uplifting and reassuring than hearing this for yourself. Your doctor can use a variety of instruments to hear your baby's heartbeat, including a stethoscope and a Doppler monitor (which uses ultrasound technology). A baby's heart beats between 120 and 160 times per minute (with slight variations)—quite a few more than your own heartbeat, which is normally under 100. The sole purpose of listening to the heartbeat is to ensure that it falls within a normal range, and to reassure moms-to-be that all is well. If there's an unusual rhythm or the heartbeat speeds or slows unexpectedly, your doctor can arrange for tests to confirm that all is well. Some women feel that hearing their baby's heartbeat helps the bonding process in advance of the birth.

THE LOWDOWN

First hours and days

To help you prepare for what will follow the birth of your baby, here's a few interesting facts you might like to know:

■ **You may shake all over** just after giving birth and don't be concerned if you vomit, this is quite normal and nothing to worry about.

■ **Newborn babies don't always master breast-feeding** (see pp.448–9) immediately. Just like you, they need to practice.

■ **After pains** (the clamping sensation in your uterus when your baby nurses) can hurt almost as much as contractions.

■ **The first time you urinate** and defecate after giving birth can be uncomfortable.

■ **You may feel very vulnerable,** and in need of your own mom, in the first few days of parenthood.

■ **Lochia** (after-birth bleeding) can be a challenge at first, even if you're using larger-sized sanitary pads.

■ **Bonding with a newborn doesn't always happen** immediately for all mothers, but it's worth the wait.

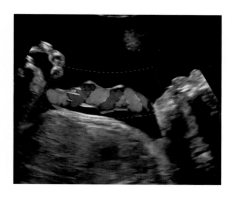

56 days to go...

YOUR BABY TODAY

The blood flow in the umbilical cord is highlighted in this image. The colors show the direction of flow. The smaller umbilical arteries that carry blood toward the placenta are seen in blue as they wrap around the more central umbilical vein (in red).

The best way to make sure you get enough sleep is to find ways to slow down mentally and relax.

You may find that you're having difficulty sleeping, partly because your belly makes it uncomfortable to lie down in certain positions, but also because you have lots to think about at the moment. Try to take some time out with your partner each evening relaxing and bonding together with your belly. Even spending 10 minutes doing nothing except focusing on yourself, your body, your partner, and your baby can be invigorating and rejuvenating.

Get yourself in a comfortable position, and try to focus inward on your body, turning your mind away from all your external worries. First focus on slowing down your breathing. Then turn your thoughts to a place and a time when you felt relaxed and happy—for example, when you were on vacation, walking on the beach. Next focus on clenching and then relaxing each set of muscles in turn, or imagine a ball of heat passing slowly through your limbs and body making them feel warm, heavy, and relaxed.

You might want to involve your partner, perhaps he could sit with you with his hands or head on your belly and try to adjust his breathing so it's in sync with yours. Just lying next to your partner, even without talking, can relax you and bring you close together.

DRESSING FOR EXERCISE

In this last trimester, dressing appropriately for exercise can make all the difference to your activities and the way that you feel.

During pregnancy it is possible to look good in your workout clothes, while still supporting your belly and your breasts. Ensure you wear the correct size clothes—trying to squeeze into a size you outgrew three months ago will be uncomfortable and restricting.

There are some great pregnancy exercise clothes on the market, which are cut well and have ample room for your belly. If, however, you'd rather

cover up while you're exercising, just wear a large T-shirt and baggy athletic pants or loose-fitting shorts. Wear whatever makes you feel confident and comfortable.

There are some good support belts available, which may make your cardiovascular exercise that much more comfortable. If you're carrying twins or more this will be even more of a welcome addition to your workout wardrobe. Most of the support belts are made from elasticized fabric with Velcro fastenings that can be adjusted to suit your belly size. These belts, available at many maternity stores, are inexpensive and can help ease back pain, too.

Your breasts will need additional support by this stage of pregnancy, but especially when you're exercising. A well-fitting sports bra is vital for any activity as the delicate breast tissue can weaken due to the increased pressure of your larger and heavier breasts. If your breasts are very large, and you feel they're unsupported by just wearing a sports bra, try wearing it on top of your usual bra.

Your 33rd week

IT'S HARD TO IMAGINE HOW LIFE WILL BE WITH A NEW BABY

All prospective moms, and not just first-timers, find it difficult to envisage the future after the arrival of the baby. The imaginings, dreams, and hopes of the last few months are about to become realities—which may be very different from what you expect. You may find that it helps to concentrate on practical matters, such as the birth celebrations and future child care. You could make plans for recovering your pre-pregnancy figure. The belly won't be with you forever, even if it feels like it!

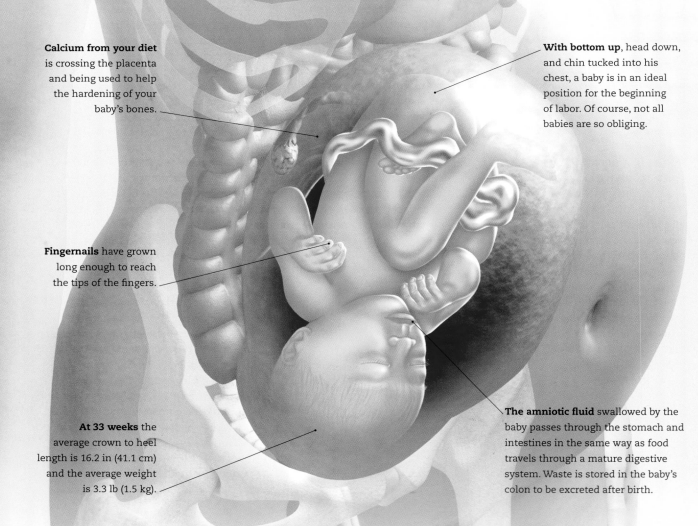

Calcium from your diet is crossing the placenta and being used to help the hardening of your baby's bones.

With bottom up, head down, and chin tucked into his chest, a baby is in an ideal position for the beginning of labor. Of course, not all babies are so obliging.

Fingernails have grown long enough to reach the tips of the fingers.

At 33 weeks the average crown to heel length is 16.2 in (41.1 cm) and the average weight is 3.3 lb (1.5 kg).

The amniotic fluid swallowed by the baby passes through the stomach and intestines in the same way as food travels through a mature digestive system. Waste is stored in the baby's colon to be excreted after birth.

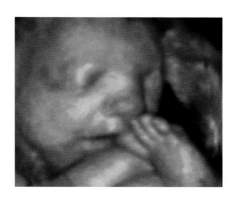

55 days to go...

YOUR BABY TODAY

In this image the hands are folded over beneath the chin and there's a foot up by the mouth and nose. It can look as if your baby is quite a contortionist but because he is still quite skinny, the joints allow for a great deal of flexibility.

If you feel you have little control over your own body, it's natural to think your figure will never be normal again—but it will!

At this stage of the third trimester, you'll still be gaining 1–2 lb (0.5–1 kg) per week but weight gain tends to slow down in the last few weeks of pregnancy. By now, your belly will have stretched and your belly button may have popped out—this can be quite protruding and may be seen through your clothes (see p.319). You may have developed a linea nigra in your second trimester, a dark line of pigmentation down the center of your abdomen (see p.170).

Like most women you are probably happy and excited about having a baby but a little concerned about getting your figure back after the birth. Some women get quite upset at the thought that their abdomens may not return to their previous shape, and this is completely normal. Rest assured that with a bit of hard work and exercise and the continuation of your healthy pregnancy diet after the birth, your figure can return to its pre-pregnancy state and your belly button should pop back to its normal shape of its own accord. The key is to remember it will take a bit of time: it did, after all, take nine months to gain the weight.

ASK A... DOCTOR

I want to work right up to the birth—is that allowed? Yes. Many women do, so they don't waste any maternity leave before baby. Check with your doctor to make sure it's okay for you. Think carefully before making this decision. Late pregnancy can be extremely tiring and, if your job is mentally and/or physically taxing, it may be better to begin your leave before your due date. You will also need time to prepare for the arrival of your baby.

A diet rich in foods containing fiber is good for health at any time of life but especially during these three months to relieve common symptoms such as constipation. Snack on whole-grain breads and cereals.

FOCUS ON... NUTRITION

Fabulous fiber

Fiber is very important in the third trimester, since it will help your digestive system work more efficiently. Dietary fiber—the indigestible part of plant foods—is the best natural way to keep the bowels regular. Most pregnant women who eat a diet based upon whole grains, fruits, and vegetables, are likely to be getting enough fiber.

Pregnant women should aim for 1 oz (25 g) of fiber daily. To give a sense of what it takes to achieve this, there are around 3 g in a medium avocado or banana, or a serving of broccoli, blueberries, brown rice, or beans. Eating three or four servings of fruit a day, vegetables with your meals, and eating whole-grain breads and brown rice will provide plenty.

Fiber makes you feel fuller sooner and longer, and can help to prevent overeating and excess weight gain. It also contributes to the management of diabetes, lowers cholesterol, and decreases the risk of heart disease.

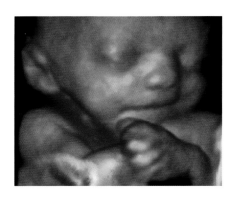

54 days to go...

YOUR BABY TODAY

During this week your baby's fingernails have become fully developed and now approach the tips of the fingers. Bathed in amniotic fluid, the nails are kept very soft: it's only after birth that your baby might tend to scratch and need to wear mittens.

Every 40 minutes, your baby swallows enough amniotic fluid to fill his stomach, before emptying it back into the amniotic sac.

Your baby is swallowing and recycling almost half a liter of amniotic fluid each day. In addition to providing him with nutrients, especially proteins, this fluid is important for the healthy development of the gut. Your baby's sense of taste is thought to have developed to such an extent now that if you have eaten spiced food he can distinguish this in the fluid he drinks.

Amniotic fluid does not enter the lungs but travels down the esophagus into the stomach where it is stored for a short time. At this stage, the stomach fills every 40 minutes, but, from 35 weeks, as the stomach enlarges, this rate slows down to every 80 minutes. Muscle contractions move the fluid in waves into the small and then large bowel. As it travels along the bowel, water is reabsorbed so that only waste material or "meconium," enters the colon, the final section of the large bowel. This meconium accumulates in the large bowel, which is completely full by the time your baby is born. Babies don't usually pass meconium before the birth but do so soon after. Meconium consists mainly of skin cells, lanugo hairs, and vernix. It has a greenish color due to the presence of bilirubin, a breakdown product from red blood cells.

FOCUS ON... THE BIRTH

False alarms

In the next few weeks, as you and your partner await your baby's arrival, you may experience one or two false alarms, especially if it's your first baby. A false alarm can come at any time of the day or night and it won't respect important meetings or deadlines.

It can help if you—as well as your partner—familiarize yourself with all the signs that indicate labor may be starting (see pp. 409–11). If, however, you're ever in doubt, do contact your doctor to ascertain that labor has not started, rather than assuming that this is the case. She will be very experienced in dealing with false alarms and won't mind you contacting her.

ITCHY SKIN

Having itchy skin on your belly is common: as the skin there stretches and thins, it can become dry. You could try using a moisturizing lotion to soothe this.

If, however, you have severe itching on your abdomen, or on the palms of your hands or soles of your feet, see your doctor. This itching can be a sign of obstetric cholestasis (see p.473), a rare pregnancy condition involving the liver, which causes bile salts to enter the bloodstream, making the skin (especially on the hands and feet) itchy, although there is no rash. The condition may also cause a vitamin K deficiency. Vitamin K helps the blood to clot, so a deficiency increases the risk of bleeding for both mother and baby. Medication to bind the bile salts and vitamin K supplements are effective treatments. Some studies suggest early induction of labor (at around 37 weeks) helps avoid complications. The condition resolves after delivery, usually without any long-term liver damage.

Your third trimester

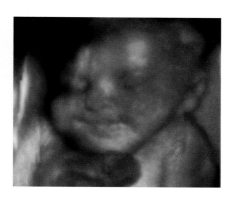

53 days to go...

YOUR BABY TODAY

Your baby's position in the uterus is influenced by your own posture. Gravity has some effect on your baby, so whether you are standing or sitting, and which side you lie down on affects the way your baby's back is turned and which side he rolls onto.

As your belly grows, it's normal to feel you want to support it when you're walking around.

You've probably had to change the way that you exercise by now due to your growing abdomen. You may well have had to replace jogging on the treadmill, for example, with going for long, brisk (or not so brisk!) walks. If you find that even walking makes your belly and pelvis sore or uncomfortable, you may find you naturally hold up your belly with your hands to try to give it some extra support and to give your pelvis and back a break. Some women say it feels as if the baby "might fall out."

You might want to invest in a pregnancy support band; made of stretchy fabric, this useful item supports the belly and can help prevent lower back pain.

Walking at a comfortable pace when you are heavily pregnant will cause your belly to shift around and your instinct may be to support your baby with your hands.

BUYING A BABY MONITOR

There are hundreds of monitors on the market, so choosing one can be daunting. Although monitors vary, they have the same basic components—a minimum of two units: one to transmit your baby's sounds, and one that stays with you so that you can hear if your baby is crying or fussing.

Additional features include: video screens, a moving lights-sound display, low power and out-of-range warnings, the option to use electricity or batteries, a talk-back function, and a temperature sensor. Some have a night-light function. With all these features available, your choice largely depends on your personal preferences and your budget. If your house is small, you don't necessarily need one.

FOCUS ON... YOUR BABY

Repositioning your baby

Your movements during late pregnancy can affect the position of your baby. Ideally, he'll lie head down, facing your back, with his chin tucked into his chest. You can encourage this optimum fetal position by:
- **Spending time on all fours,** wiggling your hips from side to side; or arch your back, then drop your spine down.
- **Sitting with your knees lower than your pelvis,** and your body tilted slightly forward.
- **Kneeling on the floor,** leaning over a beanbag, cushions, or birth ball.
- **Sitting on a birth ball,** with your legs positioned slightly apart and knees lower than your hips, then rocking your pelvis.
- **Assuming the tailor pose:** sit on the floor with your back straight and the soles of your feet together. Let your knees fall to the side and rest your elbows on your inner thighs.
- **Swimming:** breaststroke helps to open the pelvis.

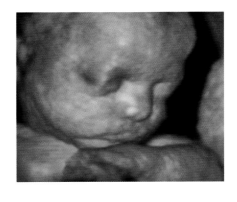

52 days to go...

YOUR BABY TODAY

This image shows that the bridge of your baby's nose is now more fully formed. The face is taking on a more rounded shape and some babies may look quite chubby from now on. Shadows around the top and sides of the head will increasingly give the illusion of hair.

By this stage of pregnancy, your baby's fingernails have grown and reach the tips of his fingers.

By now, your baby's fingernails have reached the tips of the fingers. The fingernails first appeared at 12 weeks, and since the development of the arms is consistently ahead of the legs, the toenails started to develop four weeks later. The future nail begins at the tip of each finger or toe, where a nail fold is formed. At the base of this nail fold, the cells start to harden into nail,

in a process known as keratinization. The nails grow from new cells formed in the soft nail bed. It takes nine weeks for the nails to reach the fingertips and it will be another four weeks before the toenails reach the tips of the toes.

The nail is actually all the same color, but the white part of the nail appears white because it does not have the nail bed, with its rich blood supply, beneath

it to give the illusion of color. Since the nails already reach the fingertips, it probably won't be long after the birth before your baby's nails need trimming—they are very fine and soft and you may find it easier to trim them by nibbling them away rather than trying to cut them. Or cut them with baby nail scissors while your baby is asleep and not wiggling around.

FOCUS ON... YOUR BODY

Yoga is excellent exercise for the mind and body while you're pregnant, and may be a cornerstone of your birth preparations if you choose to take active birth classes (see p.333). An instructor will tailor a routine for your body and the stage of your pregnancy. The individual stretches shown

below are ideal for opening up the pelvis and strengthening the legs. By practicing them while you're pregnant, you'll be able to use them more effectively and confidently during labor. When you're practicing squatting, it may help if your partner supports you from behind.

Get into a squatting position. Squat only if you find it easy to hold this position with your heels on the floor and your back straight.

Sit with your left leg stretched out in front of you and right leg bent. Gently twist your body, placing your hands on the floor for additional support.

Sit with one leg stretched out behind you, and the other tucked beneath your belly. Stretch upward, breathing deeply throughout.

Your third trimester

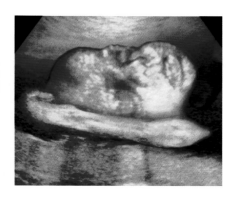

51 days to go...

YOUR BABY TODAY

In this image of the baby lying on his side, the arm is positioned beneath the head and is partly outside of the 3D view. This allows the ultrasound scan to look within the arm. Part of the bones in the elbow and forearm are seen here as bright reflections.

To get used to the fact that your newborn will arrive very soon, start focusing on life after the birth.

Friends and family might now begin talking about what will happen after the birth and what it will be like for you to have a baby.

If this is your first baby, you probably can't really envisage what it will be like to be a mom, and even if you have had a baby before you've never had a second or third and so don't know what it will be like to have another one. Of course you know that life will continue, but it can be difficult to see past the labor to the realities of life with a newborn. As ever, keep talking to those close to you about how you feel, be it excited or scared and unprepared (usually all three in rapid succession). Talk about what you think or hope it will be like after the baby is born, for example when are grandparents and other key people going to visit, and whether you would like a christening or naming party—or perhaps neither of these. This may help you get used to the idea that not only are you pregnant but there is a baby coming.

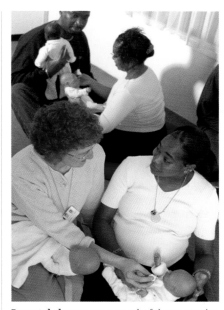

Prenatal classes are a wonderful opportunity to swap ideas and information with a group of people in the same position as you. Long-term friendships can be made here.

ASK A... DOCTOR

How will I benefit from going to prenatal classes? You'll get the opportunity to share information, ideas, fears, and concerns about childbirth in a comfortable environment, and to discuss and decide upon issues that will affect the way you choose to give birth. You'll also meet other parents-to-be. Often friendships formed at classes continue after the birth as you support each other in your new parenting role. In most classes, you'll be given advice about:

- **Tried-and-tested labor techniques,** such as breathing through the pain, massage, suitable sustenance, and some positive visualization exercises
- **Pain-relief options** and a range of natural alternatives (see pp.396–407)
- **How to present** (and preserve) your birth plan (see p.303)
- **The practical and emotional support** a birth partner can offer
- **The items required** for a hospital or home birth (see pp. 341 and 358).

You'll be advised on how to prepare yourself for the birth, what to expect in the first few days, and how to encourage healing afterward, as well as being given tips on caring for a newborn, including diaper changing, bathing, and establishing breast-feeding.

AS A MATTER OF FACT

In a first birth, the cervix dilates by about 1 cm every hour in active labor, compared to 1.5 cm an hour for subsequent babies.

First-time moms push for up to 2 hours, compared with about half an hour for a second baby.

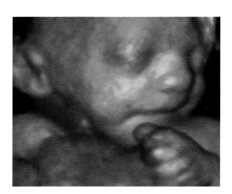

50 days to go...

YOUR BABY TODAY

This image may show the start of a smile. Your baby will often be smiling inside, sticking his tongue out, and making all sorts of faces. He may also still be experiencing hiccups that may be something that you are now becoming aware of.

The days and nights fly by with a newborn, so it's a good idea to start thinking about child care well before you need it.

It may seem impossible to believe that you should be considering child care before your baby is even born, but it can be useful to think through the options while you have the time. There are two main types of child care: in and out of your home. In the first case, you can have a live-in or live-out nanny or mother's help, an au pair (which may be acceptable if you work from home, for example, and can supervise), or perhaps a family member or friend who is prepared to come to your house to take care of your baby. If you choose outside child care, there are a number of options including day-care centers, relatives or babysitters in their homes, or on-the-job day care. Before you set your heart on one particular type of care, it's a good idea to investigate the costs and the availability in your area. You may want to pay a visit to some of the nurseries or other facilities close to you, just to get a feel for what's available, and establish now what you do and don't want. Secondly, remember that good-quality child-care facilities and babysitters are usually in demand, and, even if you aren't entirely sure when you will be going back to work, it's probably a good idea to put your baby's name (or last name, at least!) down for a few, to give you options when the time comes.

CALCIUM INTAKE

Your baby's skeleton began forming at the end of the first trimester, but the majority of your calcium is transferred to the baby from your body in the third trimester. This happens regardless of your calcium intake. If a mother-to-be's diet is low in calcium, it will be taken from the reservoir in her bones, which can affect her bone density.

The recommended amount of calcium in pregnancy is 1000 mg daily. Calcium needs to be accompanied by vitamin D in order to be absorbed by the body.

Dairy products are a rich source of calcium, and some, such as margarine and low-fat spreads, are often fortified with vitamin D. Vegetarian sources of calcium include tofu, leafy green vegetables, dried fruit, seeds, and nuts.

FOCUS ON... DADS

Being at the birth

Many dads-to-be are anxious about being with their partners during labor and birth. This is often because they will be witnessing their partner experience one of the most intense things a woman can ever do and they may be unsure of how to help.

There are plenty of ways in which you can support your partner during labor: being aware of her wishes, speaking for her if she is unable to, and repeating what doctors have said if she didn't hear clearly; passing her a drink; rubbing her back; holding a warm cloth to her face; switching music on or off; being encouraging and reassuring her.

Going to prenatal classes can be useful (see p.331). You will learn more about labor and birth, and how to support your partner physically and emotionally.

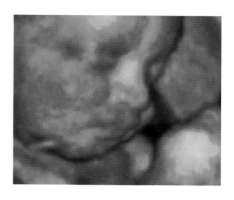

49 days to go...

YOUR BABY TODAY

Soon your baby will be approaching a time when the lungs can fully support him after birth. At 33 weeks though, most babies would still need some help with breathing if born this early. Your baby will be regularly practicing these breathing movements inside.

Choosing who will be present at the birth with you is a big decision, so start thinking about it in good time.

You can choose whoever you like to be your birth partner, though the doctors and nurses might object if you have a team of people! If you do want more than one partner, get approval ahead of the birth and put this in your birth plan (see pp.181 and 303). You may want to ask your mom, sister, or close friend in addition to your partner. You might also find that your partner is unable to be there, for example if he is unavoidably going to be out of the country. If you're comfortable with it and feel that you will benefit from someone else being there, then ask away. You can put who you want to be

your birth partner or partners on your birth plan. Of course, if you're going to ask someone else other than, or in addition to, your partner to be present, discuss it with him first. He might not be so thrilled at the idea of your mom being present, but explain why you would like her there. Remember that this is a special occasion for him as well and he may have his own preferences for who is or is not present at the birth.

Now might also be a good time to discuss things like whether you want a video made of the birth, but you may prefer that your partner supports you, rather than handling the camera!

Active birth classes teach you how to work with your body to deliver your baby more quickly and easily.

Active birth classes

The goal of active birth classes is to make women feel good about their bodies and give them the confidence that they have the mental and physical reserves to have a successful birth experience. Classes are generally appropriate regardless of fitness level, flexibility, and your stage of pregnancy.

■ **Active birth classes** promote the benefits of yoga and exercise as both physical and mental preparation for childbirth.
■ **Yoga strengthens the body,** improves posture and circulation, and teaches how to use relaxation and breathing techniques to relieve stress.
■ **Like prenatal classes,** active birth classes allow you to meet other parents-to-be and share their pregnancy experiences.
■ **The downside** is that these classes aren't widely available, so they get booked quickly and can be expensive. Ask your doctor about local classes. If you can't find a class in your area, read an active birth book or consider taking a prenatal yoga class.

Your 34th week

YOUR BABY IS ALMOST FULLY EQUIPPED FOR THE OUTSIDE WORLD

If your baby was born this week, she'd still need some help with breathing and feeding. But it's reassuring to know that basically she's in pretty good shape for survival. However, you are unlikely to go into labor this early. Now is your chance to start practicing the relaxation and pain-relieving exercises that you've been learning at your prenatal classes. The more familiar you are with the techniques, the more they will help you during labor.

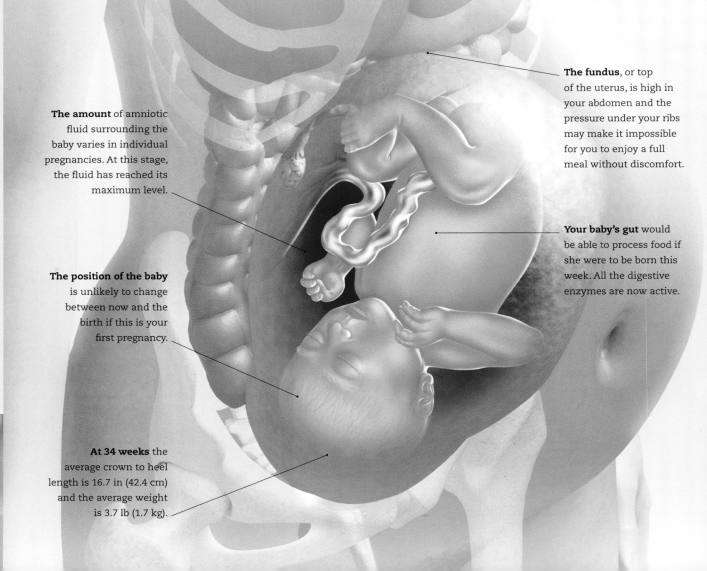

The fundus, or top of the uterus, is high in your abdomen and the pressure under your ribs may make it impossible for you to enjoy a full meal without discomfort.

The amount of amniotic fluid surrounding the baby varies in individual pregnancies. At this stage, the fluid has reached its maximum level.

Your baby's gut would be able to process food if she were to be born this week. All the digestive enzymes are now active.

The position of the baby is unlikely to change between now and the birth if this is your first pregnancy.

At 34 weeks the average crown to heel length is 16.7 in (42.4 cm) and the average weight is 3.7 lb (1.7 kg).

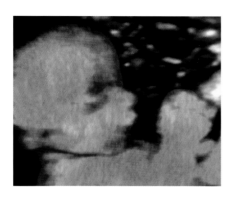

48 days to go...

YOUR BABY TODAY

Your baby may well be head down by this stage. The head is the heaviest part and gravity plus the shape of your uterus favors a head-down position. Ask your doctor at the next visit if she can determine the position for you.

Premature labor is highly likely in a twin pregnancy, so your doctor will be on alert and monitoring you closely.

There's still six weeks to go until the due date for a single pregnancy, but if you're expecting twins they may arrive any time from now. Most singleton pregnancies are 38 to 42 weeks, but if you're carrying twins, 37 to 39 weeks is optimal. But more than half of twins are born before 37 weeks. Women expecting twins are at higher risk of high blood pressure, preeclampsia, placental insufficiency, gestational diabetes, and premature labor. That said, many women do go on to deliver twins naturally and many doctors will allow you to continue to 40 weeks, after which time an induction or cesarean might be suggested.

If the babies are in any position other than "head down," or the placenta is in an awkward position, such as near the neck of the uterus, a cesarean may be recommended. Some doctors prefer to deliver twins by cesarean because the second twin may run into difficulties during the delivery, particularly if she is not head down. Premature babies are more at risk of complications than those who go to full-term. A cesarean delivery ensures the babies are delivered quickly without having to go through hours of potentially stressful labor.

Sometimes, one twin is born vaginally and the other by cesarean. This often happens if the lower twin is in the "head down" position and the higher twin isn't.

If you know your twin pregnancy is going to be induced or you've arranged a cesarean delivery, you have the advantage of being able to fully prepare for your babies' arrival.

AS A MATTER OF FACT

The average birth weight of twins is 5 lb 5 oz (2.6 kg).

This is compared to 7 lb 8 oz (3.5 kg) for singleton babies. It's not unusual for there to be a difference in birth weight between the babies. In fact, one twin may weight 2 to 3 lb (1 to 1.4 kg) more than the other.

ASK A... DOCTOR

I'm having my twins in a couple of weeks. Can they sleep in the same crib? Having shared the same tight space in the uterus for many months, it seems natural to allow twin newborns to sleep together and, in fact, research indicates that it may have some benefits. Not only has it been found to be safe for twins of roughly the same size to sleep together until three months of age, but one study found that putting newborn twins in the same crib helped regulate their body temperature and their sleep cycles.

They can be placed side by side, or head to head. To be safe, don't overdress them or use blankets, bumpers, or pillows. Make sure the mattress is firm with a fitted sheet over it. Like singletons, twins should be put to sleep in the safe sleeping position, on their backs (see p.444).

A double crib will last until your twins are old enough to move to a bed, but many experts believe twins should be given their own sleeping space from three months, so they can be given individual attention and the opportunity to develop their own sleep patterns.

Your 34th week

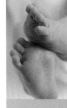

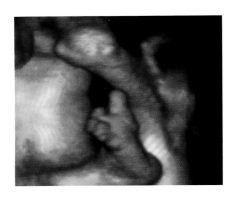

45 days to go...

YOUR BABY TODAY

A foot is shown here with the toes spread out. Not all of the movements that you feel will be due to kicks, some movements will be shrugs or punches and some from the bottom or head as it touches the sides of the uterus.

The size of your belly will increasingly be due to the baby alone as the amniotic fluid now reduces slightly each week.

The amount of amniotic fluid

that surrounds and protects your baby is now at its maximum and the placenta has almost completed its growth.

Amniotic fluid is essential for your baby's lung development, gut maturation, protein requirements, and temperature control. Adequate fluid also allows your baby to move easily since she is in an almost weightless state. There is about 800 ml of amniotic fluid around your baby. The range, however, is quite wide and "normal" can be anywhere between 300 ml and 2 liters. Sometimes there is too little, a condition known as oligohydramnios (see p.473), or too much fluid, a condition known as polyhydramnios (see p.473), surrounding the baby. In this situation you would be closely monitored and premature delivery may be necessary.

It's not surprising that the size of your uterus may not reflect the size of your baby since there can be so much variation in the quantity of fluid.

As the amount of amniotic fluid reduces in late pregnancy, your baby is not as well cushioned and her movements may become more obvious, although you should bear in mind that increasingly, as she grows, she has less space in which to move around.

AS A MATTER OF FACT

One of the most common concerns for women in late pregnancy is that their water will break in public.

The reality is that the amniotic fluid is unlikely to gush out. It is much more likely to trickle out because in a head-down position, the baby will press down on the cervix and prevent the liquid from escaping. If it does happen in public, don't worry—you won't be short of people offering help.

FOCUS ON... DADS

What's in your hospital bag?

Once your partner's labor begins, your attention will need to be focused on helping her both practically and emotionally. So in addition to helping your partner prepare her maternity bag (see p.358) in advance, it's a good idea to prepare a bag of your own.

Understandably, dads are not always well supported in delivery units, and certainly don't get fed. You'll also find that you're at the hospital for several hours.

Consider packing the following:

- Snacks
- Drinks
- A pillow
- Something to read or play
- A reasonable amount of change to pay for parking and to buy snacks, juice, and soft drinks if they're in vending machines
- A list of phone numbers, or enter them into your cell phone now
- A camera.

Text messaging is an effective way to inform some family and friends about the birth. Make sure you've entered all the numbers into your phone before the big day.

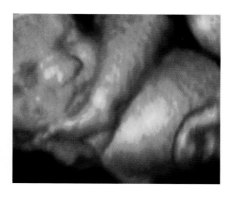

44 days to go...

YOUR BABY TODAY

At this stage your baby may lie transversely (see p.336) across your uterus as here, but such a position becomes increasingly less likely as the pregnancy advances. The more babies you have had the more likely it is that the shape of your uterus allows this lie.

You may be learning breathing and relaxation techniques at prenatal classes, but practice them at home, too.

When you are tense and frightened, pain can feel much worse, so teaching yourself to relax and stay calm can help. With around six weeks to go, you still have plenty of time to try out some of the breathing and relaxation techniques that will help you during labor. It's true that practice makes perfect and it can take some time to train your mind to relax at will, especially if you are in pain.

Spend a short period of time as often as you can, every day if possible, practicing your breathing—close your eyes and slow your breathing down, breathing in through your nose and out through your mouth. As you breathe in, imagine your breath entering your body and relaxing you and as you exhale you breathe out any pain or tension. You might want to involve your partner by asking him to breathe with you or count your breathing, a slow count to three or five for every inhale and exhale.

Some women like to practice using the techniques while pinching their arm temporarily to simulate a contraction—although of course it won't mimic the pain exactly! Practicing these techniques in a calm, relaxed manner in late pregnancy will help you to use them effectively on the big day.

A banana is a fabulous fruit to eat before exercising because it gives you a slow and steady release of energy.

AS A MATTER OF FACT

You're more likely to get a seat on public transportation in Japan due to the "manners squad"!

If you find that no one gives up their seat for you on public transportation, you're not alone. In Japan, however, the "manners squad" mission is to patrol trains and make sure that any seats are vacated by the young and offered to those who need them.

FOCUS ON... NUTRITION

Fuel for fitness

Demand for nutrients is higher when you're exercising and even higher when you're pregnant. This is not the time to reach for low-nutrient, high-calorie snacks; ensure you make careful choices when it comes to the nutrients you put into your body.

You should be eating a snack before you exercise, consisting of a complex carbohydrate and a protein. You should also eat frequent small meals and snacks if you are feeling hungry. It's fine to snack throughout the day.

Some healthy snack ideas are as follows:
- Half a bagel spread with two teaspoons of peanut butter
- An apple or banana and a handful of raw almonds
- A pear with two slices of Cheddar cheese
- Carrot, celery, and cucumber sticks and/or breadsticks dipped into two tablespoons of humus
- Cottage cheese or cream cheese spread on two large crackers or whole-wheat toast.

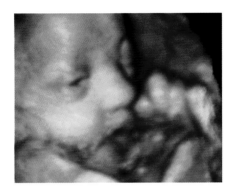

43 days to go...

YOUR BABY TODAY

Your baby is now capable of producing all of the enzymes that will process food within the digestive tract. If born early, your baby could now feed normally although some will still require help since they need to fine tune the coordination of their suckling reflexes.

Your baby is naturally nourished inside the uterus and her own digestive tract is now functioning well.

Eighty percent of your baby's energy needs are met by carbohydrates, mainly in the form of glucose, and almost 20 percent from protein. Fat is not used as an energy source but it is used for growth. All mineral, vitamin, and calcium needs are met from your own reserves and your diet. Two possible exceptions are iron and folate, a water-soluble vitamin that occurs naturally in foods; folic acid is the synthetic version. Folate does not easily cross the placenta to reach and nourish your baby. Your own iron reserves may already be low if you eat little or no red meat or if this pregnancy has followed on quickly from your last one. Your baby needs iron (and folate) to make red blood cells and because only a small percentage of iron in your diet is absorbed, iron supplementation is often recommended at this stage.

While all of your baby's gut structures were present by 20 weeks, it is not until this stage that all the enzymes needed for digestion are activated and the absorptive surface of the gut is established to a degree that would enable your baby to feed if she were born now.

GETTING UP FROM LYING DOWN

After you've exercised on the floor, or have been resting in bed, you may find it a struggle to get up from lying down. This simple maneuver can put a strain on your abdominal muscles, which are stretched, and it isn't helped by your altered center of gravity. The technique shown below was originally devised by yoga teachers to help you get up safely from a lying down position.

As with any strenuous maneuvers at this stage of pregnancy, always take your time and remember to breathe slowly and deeply throughout.

Step one: With your knees bent, roll on to your right side bringing the knee beneath you up to waist level. Keep your right hand aligned with your bent knee.

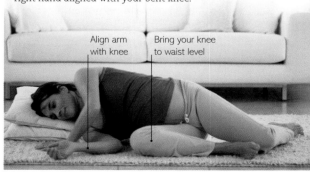

Align arm with knee

Bring your knee to waist level

Step two: Shift your weight onto your left hand and knee. Position your right knee under your right hip and your right hand under your shoulder and come up slowly on all fours.

Raise your head slowly as you get up

Place the weight on your left-hand side

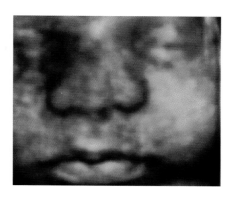

42 days to go...

YOUR BABY TODAY

A close-up of the baby's face clearly showing the lip shape and slightly separated eyelids. The slight shadowing seen to the left of the image is from the wall of the uterus, which at this stage of the pregnancy will always be very close to your baby.

If you've made the decision to have a home birth, you'll need to ensure you're fully prepared in good time.

ASK A... DOCTOR

What additional things do I need to think about if I'm having a home birth? Have all the items you need for labor and birth gathered in the place you intend to deliver, and organize your items separately from the baby's items.

As well as practical items, such as clothing, toiletries, and sanitary pads, you may also want to have on hand music, phone numbers, and a camera. It's a good idea to have a well-stocked fridge so make a list of nutritious foods to stock up on before your due date. This will help you during labor and in the first week of parenthood. Your baby will need diapers, cotton cloths, onesies, clothing, sheets, and blankets.

If you have other children, you may need to make arrangements for them to be taken care of.

Even though you're planning to have your baby at home, there are circumstances in which you may need to be transferred to a hospital. This can happen before, during, or after labor and so, even though you may not want to contemplate this outcome, have an emergency bag packed (see p.358) just in case.

Women had their babies at home for generations; it was only in the 20th century that women began to have hospital births. If you're considering a home birth, remember that the majority of pregnancies and deliveries are normal and do not need any medical intervention.

Be reassured that if you have decided to have a home birth and then change your mind, for example if you decide you want an epidural, or your midwife advises you that the baby needs help, you will be transferred to a hospital.

Your relationship with your midwife is even more important if you're giving birth at home as she will be your sole medical support.

Group B strep test

At least 30 percent of pregnant women carry the strep B bacteria in the vagina or rectal area. Known as GBS (group B streptococcus), it is not an STD and is usually harmless in adults, but can cause a rare and serious infection in newborn babies if untreated.

■ **Many women are now routinely screened for GBS,** at 35–37 weeks of pregnancy. If the result is positive, antibiotic treatment can be given during labor that will reduce the risk of the baby becoming infected. Some hospitals don't screen but if the bacteria is detected in a urine test or a swab is taken for another reason and is positive, antibiotic treatment may given in labor.

■ **The test is very straightforward** and involves taking a swab of the area around your vagina and rectum with results usually within 24–48 hours.

■ **If GBS is detected,** and treatment given as soon as labor starts, there is little risk to the baby.

■ **It is possible to be infected with GBS** in a second pregnancy, even if you didn't have it first time around.

Your 35th week

TRY TO STAY ACTIVE, EVEN THOUGH YOU MAY BE WADDLING BY NOW

Getting exercise is probably the last thing you want to do, but it's worth the effort. The more you move, the more energy you will gain. Gentle exercise will also help relieve some of the aches and twinges of late pregnancy. The baby's movements may change as he has less room to move around. Instead of kicks, he may be shuffling around. He's busy, though, practicing for the outside world, teaching himself to suckle and focus his vision.

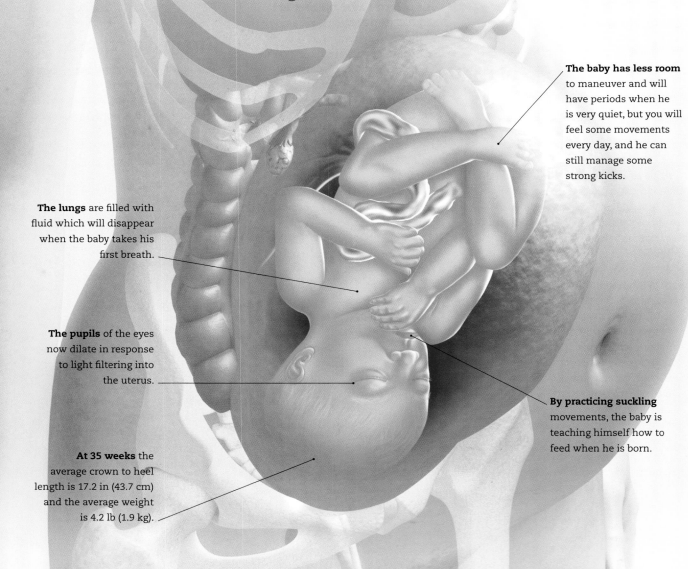

The baby has less room to maneuver and will have periods when he is very quiet, but you will feel some movements every day, and he can still manage some strong kicks.

The lungs are filled with fluid which will disappear when the baby takes his first breath.

The pupils of the eyes now dilate in response to light filtering into the uterus.

By practicing suckling movements, the baby is teaching himself how to feed when he is born.

At 35 weeks the average crown to heel length is 17.2 in (43.7 cm) and the average weight is 4.2 lb (1.9 kg).

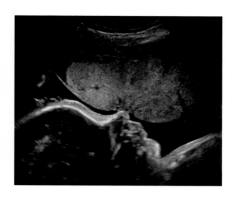

41 days to go...

YOUR BABY TODAY

This profile of the baby shows the tip of the nose touching the placenta. Your placenta will not be growing any more and now thins slightly. Within, the placenta continues to mature and it remains a highly efficient means of supplying your baby's energy needs.

As your size begins to have an impact on your daily activities, you'll find that a few practical adjustments are necessary.

Your posture will change as your belly continues to grow. To compensate for the heavy weight you're carrying, you might find that you lean back slightly, especially when you're walking downhill. You might also waddle when you walk as you shift your weight from side to side. In a few weeks' time, when the baby begins to engage into the pelvis (see p.361), you may find that you waddle even more.

It's normal at this late stage of pregnancy to move more slowly than normal. You may find yourself struggling to get out of bed or out of a chair, and picking something up off the floor can be more difficult than usual. Tasks such as tying your shoelaces or painting your toenails can seem impossible. You can overcome tasks such as these; for example by putting your feet on a stool to tie your shoelaces so you don't have to bend down so far. If you need help, there's no shame in asking. It can be difficult to be reliant on others but remember it's only temporary.

ASK A... DOCTOR

Can I have a water birth in the hospital? This depends on the maternity unit: some have birthing pools; others have facilities for you to rent a pool. More hospitals and birthing centers are offering this birthing option, so ask about renting a pool and bringing it in, but realize that just might not be an option. Some hospitals only allow you to labor in a pool, but not to deliver.

If your maternity unit does have a birthing pool, bear in mind that it may already be in use when you go into labor.

FOCUS ON... YOUR HEALTH

A diabetic pregnancy

Whether you develop diabetes in pregnancy (known as gestational diabetes—see p.473), or have preexisting diabetes, you'll require special care from your doctor. She will work out a plan for you, since diabetes poses risk in pregnancy.

If you have preexisting diabetes, your risks include high blood pressure, blood clots, preeclampsia (see p.474), diabetic kidney disease, and diabetic retinopathy, a condition that affects the retina in the eye. For the baby, there is an increased risk of congenital abnormalities and growth may be too fast or too slow.

The key to a healthy pregnancy and baby when you have diabetes is good blood-sugar control since your insulin requirements will change throughout pregnancy. Controlling blood-sugar levels reduces the risk of birth defects and stillbirth, or of you having a larger than expected baby, which can lead to problems during the birth.

If you have gestational diabetes, you will need to adapt your diet to include carbohydrates and fiber and reduce your intake of fats and sugar. You may also need insulin injections (see below) to help control your blood-sugar levels.

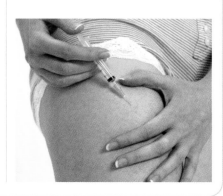

40 days to go...

YOUR BABY TODAY

At the back of your baby's eye, nerve cells that identify either black and white or color are maturing. The cells that respond to color signals are the last to develop but will eventually process more than half of the information that the eyes receive.

Your baby is blinking and learning to focus, and his pupils will dilate in response to light filtering through the uterus.

Your baby's eyes first began to develop two weeks after conception and then all of the major eye structures are formed over the following four weeks. The eye, however, keeps growing during the pregnancy and the optic nerve continues to develop after birth.

The eyes have been opening since 26 weeks of pregnancy but, until now, eye movements have been poorly coordinated. Eye movements are first seen at 18 weeks but they are random and infrequent. Movements become more frequent from 26 weeks and now, in the final few weeks, movements settle into a cycle of rest alternating with rapid eye movements (REM).

Some light does get through into the uterus and your baby is now much more responsive to strong lights.

Driving is still an option in late pregnancy, but you may find it uncomfortable to be in the car for long periods.

I'm concerned my maternity leave substitute will do a better job than me. Are these fears normal? Yes, completely normal. I remember being worried that the man filling in for me would outshine me. The amazing thing was that once my baby was born, anything work related was eclipsed by my new role. Far from losing skills, I think I became an efficient multitasker and when I returned to work, found the job easier than taking care of a baby.

Try not to worry. Not only do you have legal rights regarding the safety of your job (see pp.348–9), but you will have your chance to shine once again when your baby has settled into child care. In the meantime, enjoy your leave. It goes quickly, but also presents you with an opportunity to hone some important life skills.

GETTING OUT AND ABOUT

In most cases, it's perfectly safe to drive in the months leading up to the end of your pregnancy. However, if you feel that you're not able to concentrate at the wheel, or driving makes you uncomfortable, then give it a pass. When driving, it's very important that you position your lap belt directly under your belly (see p.253), to ensure that there is no danger to your baby if you are involved in an accident.

Traveling by public transportation is fine, too, but make sure you take full advantage of your condition to pointedly request a seat. Being jolted around on a train or bus is not ideal—not because it will damage your baby, but because your center of gravity has changed and you are more likely to fall or experience embarrassment and discomfort. Long periods of standing can also cause your ankles and feet to swell.

If you're feeling uncomfortable or dizzy, get off the train or bus and sit down in a cooler environment, preferably with your feet up, for about 20 minutes. Always carry water with you when you're out.

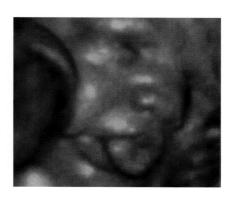

39 days to go...

YOUR BABY TODAY

Your baby will often stick his tongue out, as part of the development of the reflexes needed to feed. The rooting reflex enables your baby to find the nipple, then the strong suckling reflexes take over to coordinate breathing, feeding, and swallowing.

As maternity leave approaches, you might be looking for ways to save money, so here are ways to find baby clothes on a budget.

Dressing your newborn baby doesn't have to be expensive. Don't be shy about asking friends and family members for hand-me-downs. Those who aren't planning any more children will probably be glad to get rid of them. Get together with your women in your prenatal class, and arrange a swap session—many moms may have older children of a different sex than the new baby, and have no need for pink T-shirts, or polo shirts! While the idea of your baby wearing "used" clothing may take some getting used to, rest assured that most babywear is hardly worn.

Look on the internet for end-of-season sales, and even on some of the auction sites, where you can often pick up designer goodies for a fraction of the original price. Visit your yard sales or garage sales. Shop around; you don't have to pay a lot for items such as sleep sacks and will find inexpensive prices in the supermarket. Make a purchase with your weekly grocery shopping and you won't notice the cost as much.

Remember, too, that you will probably receive numerous gifts of clothing when your baby is born. If you know exactly what you'd like, you may like to create a gift registry from a favorite store or ask people for gift certificates for that store. When looking for more expensive

Knitting your own baby clothes is a great way to save money, and it can be rewarding to see your newborn in your own creations.

items of clothing, head for the three- to six-month-old rack, so that your baby will get plenty of use out of them. It can be disappointing if your newborn only gets a couple of weeks' wear out of an outfit you like.

A little squeamish?

It's quite normal to feel concerned about getting through labor on the day, and focusing on your partner and attending to her needs may help keep you distracted and reduce your anxiety. If possible, try to develop a good relationship in the coming weeks with your partner's caregivers. This way you'll feel more able to express any worries you're having, and hopefully get the reassurance and information you need.

If you find yourself feeling woozy on the day, try to leave the room since the nurses and doctor will be focused on caring for your partner. If you don't have time to leave the room to seek help when you feel faint, sit down immediately, with your head lower than your hips, or lie down with your feet raised. Try to stop yourself from panicking by taking slow, deep breaths. You'll find that the feeling passes quickly.

A good tip is to ensure that you are not too hot and to eat and drink regularly to prevent your feeling faint due to low blood sugar.

38 days to go...

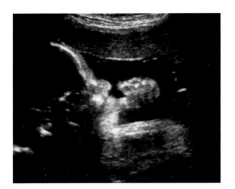

YOUR BABY TODAY

This 2D ultrasound has captured the moment that the baby is sucking his thumb. Your baby is gradually learning to coordinate this complex activity with breathing movements even though surrounded not by air but by the amniotic fluid.

Inside the uterus your baby is already practicing the suckling reflex, which will enable him to feed when he's born.

ASK A... DOCTOR

My mom has offered to stay with us after the birth. Is this a good idea? Some couples prefer to get to know their baby on their own, taking the first few days to settle in and get used to the idea of being new parents. It's also good to try to do things your own way when it comes to caring for your newborn. Having said that, you'll find an extra pair of hands invaluable.

It really depends on your relationship with your mom: if it's good and you feel she'll be supportive, then it's more likely to help than hinder. However, gently establish some guidelines—namely that while you welcome her help, you'd like to do things your way and have space to bond with your baby. Encourage your mom toward helping around the house, rather than just with the baby, not least so that your partner doesn't feel excluded at this important time.

By this stage of pregnancy you may not feel up to spending hours shopping for equipment and clothes for the baby. You can save a lot of time by getting catalogues from the major stores and making some preliminary decisions from the comfort of your armchair.

The suckling reflex is present earlier in pregnancy but it is known from assessing premature babies that it's usually not until around this time that the baby is strong and coordinated enough to suckle with ease. Your baby regularly practices suckling and this, in combination with the rooting reflex, will enable your baby to feed.

After birth you will see the rooting reflex as your baby turns toward anything that strokes his cheek. The head will turn, and your baby will move his mouth in a series of gradually diminishing circles until the object is found. Once feeding is well established,

at about four months, the rooting reflex disappears. From this point on, your baby has much more control over the process, able to turn and directly latch on (see pp.448–9) to the nipple.

While in the uterus, there is no chance of your baby accidentally swallowing amniotic fluid into the lungs. The lungs are already filled with fluid and the high pressure of this, together with your baby's larynx, keeps out amniotic fluid. After birth, babies have a series of reflexes designed to keep breathing and drinking separate. To help with feeding, babies always breathe through their nose.

ARE YOU READY FOR THE BABY?

You may find that you soon become too tired to shop. Try to buy items gradually, but there are certain things that it's worthwhile purchasing by around 37 weeks, just in case you go into labor. First, buy those small baby-care items you'll need right after the birth (see p.269) plus a car seat and a Moses basket or crib. You won't need a carriage immediately after the birth.

If going out shopping becomes difficult in late pregnancy, consider buying some items online.

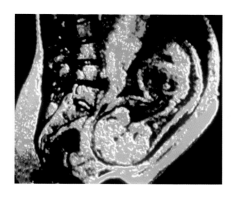

37 days to go...

YOUR BABY TODAY

This is an MRI image showing a cross section of the entire pregnancy. The mother's spine is on the left of the image, and the baby is lying head down within the pelvis. An MRI is rarely needed during pregnancy, but if recommended, it is entirely safe.

You'll probably find yourself analyzing every ache and pain in these final weeks of your pregnancy.

By this stage of pregnancy every time you get a twinge you may worry that it's the onset of labor. This is a normal concern, but try to remember that, even though you're heavily pregnant, most aches and pains are still likely to be due to constipation, or stretching ligaments, rather than labor.

You may begin to have Braxton Hicks' contractions; these practice contractions occur as the uterus tightens as a warm up for labor. They also help direct more blood to the placenta in the final weeks of pregnancy. Some women are unaware of them, while for others they can be quite uncomfortable. Relaxing the uterine muscles by changing your position, walking around, or taking a warm bath can help.

If you're unsure whether the pains you're having are Braxton Hicks', always consult your doctor or midwife.

ASK A... MOM

What will I need if I'm planning to breast-feed? I found all the following items really useful when I was breast-feeding my baby:
■ **Nursing bras** that can be unclipped at the front (see right) or have zip-open cups. Get properly fitted (bearing in mind that your breasts will be bigger once your milk comes in). You'll need at least two nursing bras and, thankfully, it's possible to get some attractive styles.
■ **Nipple cream**: this is soothing if you have cracked nipples.
■ **Breast pads** (disposable or washable). Slip them inside your bra to absorb any leaks between feedings. Alternatively, breast shells slot inside your bra to catch any excess milk.

■ **Breast-feeding pillow:** a V-shaped pillow isn't essential, but it will help you and your baby to get comfortable.
■ **Burp cloths** to catch dribbles.
■ **Breast pump** and bottles or bags for storing expressed milk.

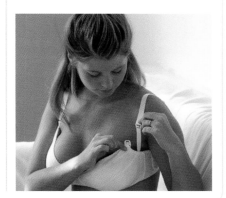

TIME TO THINK ABOUT

Breast-feeding

If you've decided to breast-feed, it's the best choice for you and your baby (see pp.448–9). However, it doesn't always come naturally so make it easier by being prepared:

■ **Read all about it.** If you're expecting some of the discomforts, they won't come as such a shock and you may be able to take measures to prevent them. It can help, for example, to know how to latch on your baby correctly (see p.448).
■ **Address any concerns** before your baby is born: ask your caregiver, or friends who've breast-fed.
■ **See how it's done** by visiting a breast-feeding group (ask your doctor to recommend one). You may have been concerned about breast-feeding in public, so it can help to see how discreetly it can be done. You could also ask a friend to let you watch her position and breast-feed her baby.
■ **Look for a lactation consultant**— available from your caregiver, or maybe a friend can recommend one, or contact the La Leche League (see p.480) for a list of counselors.

Your rights and benefits

Having a baby is a huge life change and many new parents find time and money are in short supply. Maternity and parental leave and benefits can help ease the transition, so it's worth finding out what you're entitled to.

Finding out about your maternity benefits can give you peace of mind that you will have some security during your maternity leave.

MATERNITY LEAVE EXTRAS

Leave vs. benefits

Trying to sort out what you are entitled to as a working mom-to-be can be confusing. In general, you may be eligible for provincially-legislated maternity and/or parental **leave**, which is unpaid, job-protected time off work. Your employer is not required to pay you during this time, although some of them do. You may also be entitled to maternity and/or parental **benefits**, in which the federal government pays a portion of your salary through the Employment Insurance Act (EI) during your time off work. Your employer may "top up" this amount.

Your rights

When you have a baby, you are entitled to take a certain amount of time off work to recover from the birth and to care for your newborn, and you retain your right to return to the same, or an equivalent position. Each province and territory has its own legislation regarding job protection during pregnancy, as well as maternity and parental leave, so you should check with your local government and your company's human resources department for the specifics of your situation.

Maternity leave (sometimes called pregnancy leave) is available for birth mothers, and ranges from 15–18 weeks. Parental leave can be taken by either parent, and ranges from 35–52 weeks. In some provinces, parental leave can be shared between the parents—however, a mother who chooses to take both maternity and a portion of the parental leave may not be allowed to exceed a certain maximum number of weeks. In most provinces and territories, you must have completed a specific period of continuous employment with a company to qualify for leave. Your employer is not required to pay you during your leave, although some of them do. You must give your employer written notice of at least 4–6 weeks before beginning your leave.

Some provinces require your employer to keep paying its share of contributions to your health or other benefit plans during your leave; otherwise, you may be required to pay the entire cost of the premiums if you wish your coverage to continue during your leave. You are protected from being

PAID LEAVE: THE FACTS

Dads at home

Dads are entitled to any part of the 35-week parental benefits offered by Employment Insurance, provided they have worked a minimum of 600 hours of insured work in the last 52 weeks. The proportion of fathers claiming this benefit has gone up significantly from 3 percent in 2000 to 20 percent in 2006, according to Statistics Canada. This is probably due in part to the EI parental benefits increasing from 10 to 35 weeks in 2001.

dismissed, laid off, or disciplined because you are taking maternity or parental leave; however, you may be dismissed for reasons unrelated to the leave (general downsizing, for example).

EI benefits

During your leave, you may be entitled to receive maternity and/or parental benefits through the federal Employment Insurance Act (EI), provided you have worked a minimum of 600 hours in the last 52 weeks and have been contributing to the EI program. The basic benefit is 55 percent of your average insured earnings, up to a certain maximum. There is a two-week waiting period before benefits are paid—the same as a deductible for any kind of insurance.

Eligible birth mothers are entitled to a maximum of 15 weeks of paid maternity benefits. If you choose to stop working

If I have to take a pregnancy-related absence, will my employer hold my job for me or will I be left without my job when I'm ready to return to work?

According to human rights laws in Canada, employers must hold open a job for a pregnancy-related absence for the same length of time that jobs are held open for employees on sick leave or on disability leave.

What happens to my eligibility for a bonus if I go on maternity or parental leave?

Whether or nor you'll receive a full bonus while on your leave will depend on your employer and your contract. But be aware that if you receive a bonus while on EI benefits, it may count as income and require a temporary adjustment of the amount that you receive from EI. Contact a Service Canada Center for more information.

I've just been offered my dream job, but I'm eight weeks' pregnant. Should I keep mum or should I say something to my new employer?

Human rights laws in Canada state that employers cannot refuse to hire a woman because of her pregnancy or because of a pregnancy-related condition.

---

before your due date, either for personal or medical reasons, you can start receiving your maternity benefits up to 8 weeks before your due date. Parental benefits of up to 35 weeks are available to either eligible parent, and can be shared between them. If the birth mother decides to take both the maternity and complete parental benefits, she could receive a total of 50 weeks' benefits. Parental benefits can be claimed starting from your baby's date of birth, and must be completed within a year of this date. EI benefits are considered taxable income, which means that both federal and provincial taxes will be deducted from your payment. You will need to apply for EI benefits as soon as you stop working, either in person at a Service Canada Center or online at www.servicecanada.gc.ca.

Your employer may also top up the amount that you receive from EI, and allow you to add on accumulated vacation or sick days to your leave. Speak to your human resources department about your specific circumstances.

Residents of Quebec are covered by the Quebec Parental Insurance Plan. Go to www.rqap.gouv.qc.ca for more details.

Going back to work

Before returning to work, consider the following:

■ Will life as a working mom be easier if you switch to a flexible working arrangement, such as a job share or part-time work? Give your employer ample time to consider any request.
■ If you're breast-feeding, will your employer provide a private, clean, and safe room for you to express milk? If not, would it be possible for you to pump inside a bathroom stall?
■ You're entitled to time off (which may be unpaid) for family emergencies.
■ You may be eligible for the Canada Child Tax Benefit, which can help with child-care costs.
■ You will need to give your employer at least 4 weeks notice before the date you intend to return to work.

Breast-feeding

Human rights laws protect a mother's basic right to breast-feed her child. But women may still experience negative reactions when they nurse in public. Your employer is responsible for accommodating your needs related to breastfeeding, within reason. Being able to pump at work prolongs the amount of time that you can breast-feed your baby, so these protections are important to breast-feeding moms. During an 8-hour workday, many moms find time to pump three times a day: during morning, lunch, and afternoon breaks. Since time is a premium at work, many moms get by by double-pumping with electric pumps, which should supply enough milk for the following day. La Leche League recommends that working moms should breast-feed their babies when they are at home mornings, evenings, and weekends.

Child care

If you will be returning to work, you will likely need child care for your baby. It is wise to look into your child care options while you are still pregnant, because it may take time to make a decision and some programs may have long waiting lists. Contact a local child-care resource and referral center for recommendations.

Health insurance for your baby

After the birth of your baby, you should apply for her provincial or territorial health insurance plan. Your doctor or midwife may provide you with a health plan application form, which will give you a copy of the number that will eventually be allocated to your baby. Otherwise, contact the government of your province or territory who will be able to advise you on where to get an application—many provincial or territorial government websites have applications that you can print out. In some jurisdictions, you can use your health card if you need to for your baby's first visit to the doctor.

Your rights and benefits

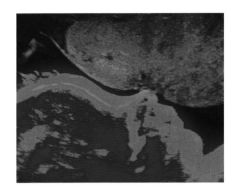

36 days to go...

YOUR BABY TODAY

The placenta, shown in red above the baby's green profile, is now receiving half a liter of blood each minute from your circulation. In order to accommodate this increase your blood volume expanded dramatically in the first few months of the pregnancy.

It's never too late to improve your fitness and whatever you do now will stand you in good stead for labor.

ASK A... DOCTOR

Why are some babies born prematurely? There are certain factors that may increase a woman's likelihood of having a premature baby. These include a previous obstetric history of prematurity of either themselves or a mother or sister; illness during pregnancy; the state of a woman's health prior to pregnancy; having a multiple pregnancy; fetal problems, such as reduced growth, which may be due to lifestyle factors such as smoking, and other fetal disorders.

You might be in the final few weeks but you still need to stay active. Exercising regularly and consistently will enable you to reap the rewards of your efforts: increased fitness, higher self esteem, and much more energy.

Find activities that you enjoy: swimming and walking are often favored by pregnant women in this late stage. As well as helping improve fitness, both of these activities will help you relax and unwind.

It is difficult to put an exact figure on how long you should be exercising for, but bear in mind that this will be determined by how hard you exercise—the two are linked. Consider the difference between a sprint and a marathon—each will have their own energy needs, one is short and has a very intense need for energy, while the other needs slow and sustained energy.

Always listen to your body and stop if you're in danger of overexerting yourself. It's important to eat plenty if you're exercising: choose snacks that will fuel your body (see p.339), especially given that the third trimester is the most demanding in terms of your baby's nutritional needs.

KANGAROO CARE

If your premature baby goes into a Neonatal Intensive Care Unit (NICU) (see pp.452–3) you may be able to take care of him using a method called kangaroo care. You will be asked to hold your baby on your chest between your breasts with his head turned so that his ear is next to your heart.

Developed in Bogota, Columbia, in response to a lack of incubators, kangaroo care is shown to have many benefits for NICU babies—mainly that their heart and breathing rates regularize quite quickly, allowing them to sleep for much longer periods. The baby's temperature is regulated by the temperature fluctuations in your breasts, meaning he doesn't have to expend energy keeping himself warm.

This, in addition to the extra sleep, preserves his energy for other vital functions, such as brain development and weight gain. Breast-feeding is also more sucessful and some kangarooed babies lose none of their birth weight.

If you go for a daily walk you will feel energized and it will be good preparation for all those strolls you'll be doing with your baby.

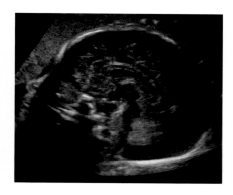

35 days to go...

YOUR BABY TODAY

Your baby's brain continues to mature. This ultrasound image shows that the folding pattern overlying the cerebral hemispheres has now developed giving rise to the familiar folds and grooves on the brain's surface. The bright reflections are from the bony skull.

The reality of being a mother will begin to hit you in these final weeks, and you have everything to look forward to.

Before the birth, it can be difficult to imagine having a relationship with your baby, even though you may feel a close bond during pregnancy.

Fortunately, bonding is a chemical process in your brain when you give birth. Other people's babies may leave you feeling cold, but it's highly likely that your own baby will spark all kinds of feelings that you never even knew you could experience. It's normal to worry about being a mother—coping

with the responsibility, taking care of a helpless baby, being "good enough," and making lifestyle changes. However, when your baby is born, your priorities will become abundantly clear, as will your affections—although bonding may not always be instant.

In some cases, postpartum depression (see p.475), or even the short-term baby blues (see p.450), can interrupt the natural progression of feelings a mother has for her newborn baby.

ASK A... DOCTOR

Will I be able to breast-feed my twins? Yes, but if possible, arrange for a lactation consultant with experience in feeding twins to be available after birth. If you get the positions correct and know how to latch on your babies (see p.448) at the outset, you'll feel much more confident continuing on your own.

Many moms of twins find that feeding them simultaneously, using a specially designed breast-feeding pillow, is the easiest way to manage. This is something you may want to buy now. There is a variety of effective breast-feeding positions for twins that the consultant or a midwife can show you.

FOCUS ON... YOUR BODY

Pamper yourself

You may not feel particularly lovely, but that's all the more reason to pamper yourself. There's unlikely to be time for beauty rituals once the baby is born.

- **Treat yourself to a manicure,** but don't have nail extensions for when your baby is born—sharp implements and babies don't mix.
- **Indulge in a facial:** it will make you feel good and help you relax.
- **Have your hair cut** since it may be some time before you get to the hairdresser again. It's a good idea to opt for a style that will be easy to manage once your baby arrives.
- **If you have aches and pains,** book a massage with someone who specializes in pregnancy.
- **Have a pedicure** a week or two before the birth. You'll be thrilled once your belly has gone and you're able to see your feet again.

If you're keeping a photographic record of your belly, you'll want it to look as good as possible. Gently exfoliating and moisturizing will ensure the skin is as smooth as possible. It won't, unfortunately, prevent stretch marks but it will improve the appearance of the skin.

Your 36th week

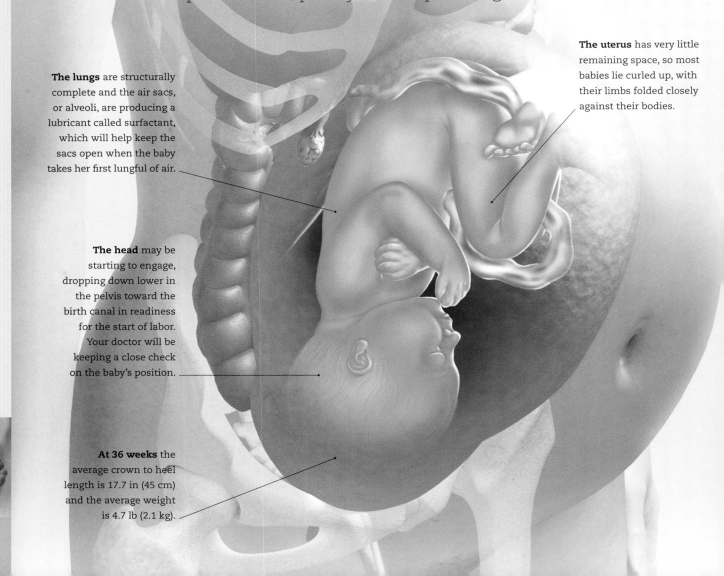

GET TOGETHER WITH YOUR PARTNER AND TALK THROUGH YOUR BIRTH PLANS

Don't leave crucial arrangements until the last minute. Have an action plan ready for when you go into labor—it might be sooner than you think. Babies can arrive ahead of schedule, so make sure you and your partner feel confident about managing. Figure out practicalities, such as arranging care for other children, or even the cat. Rope in your parents or friends to help if need be, pack your hospital bag, and relax.

The uterus has very little remaining space, so most babies lie curled up, with their limbs folded closely against their bodies.

The lungs are structurally complete and the air sacs, or alveoli, are producing a lubricant called surfactant, which will help keep the sacs open when the baby takes her first lungful of air.

The head may be starting to engage, dropping down lower in the pelvis toward the birth canal in readiness for the start of labor. Your doctor will be keeping a close check on the baby's position.

At 36 weeks the average crown to heel length is 17.7 in (45 cm) and the average weight is 4.7 lb (2.1 kg).

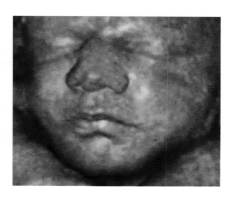

34 days to go...

YOUR BABY TODAY

Your baby's hair and eye color are all determined genetically and set before birth. Unfortunately, however detailed an ultrasound image is, it can only show the shape of structures and will never be able to show true color information.

You may be surprised to find that your social life is already changing, and the baby hasn't even arrived yet!

If you've become a homebody recently, be reassured it's quite normal. Wanting to stay at home is common in the final stages of pregnancy. You may be reluctant to plan social engagements for the next few weeks, just in case. For example, you don't want to spend money on a theater ticket that might not get used. Do, however, pencil in dates with friends because they will understand if you cancel last minute. You'll also find that once you're on leave, you're glad to get out of the house in the evenings.

Take the opportunity to go out with your partner in these last few weeks since dinner dates may not be on the agenda once the baby arrives.

ASK A... DOCTOR

My feet are swollen and tight; can I do anything about it? Swollen feet and ankles, known as edema, is due to excessive fluid seeping into the tissues because of the increased volume of blood (see pp.466–7). By late pregnancy, as blood volume continues to rise, this is a common problem. The swelling is usually worse later in the day and when the weather is warmer.

There are steps you can to take to help reduce the swelling, such as elevating your legs when sitting, rotating your feet, and lying on the floor with your feet up the wall. Wearing support hose (see p.225) also improves circulation. Make sure you drink plenty, particularly water, since this improves the kidney function and reduces water retention. Don't take diuretics—studies have found that these can adversely affect an unborn baby.

FOCUS ON... YOUR BODY

A soothing swim

Although you may feel too big to be exercising, swimming is a great activity for late pregnancy. The water supports the weight of your belly, so you may feel much lighter than you do normally. Try to do some gentle swimming as well as just relaxing in the water. Also consider going to prenatal water aerobics classes, which have exercises tailored for pregnant women.

When the weather is hot, relaxing in a swimming pool can be the best place to be. Use a float to support yourself and enjoy the wonderful feeling of weightlessness.

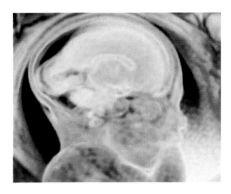

33 days to go...

YOUR BABY TODAY

This MRI scan shows detail of the baby's brain. MRI is particularly good at showing structures within the central nervous system. Taking and interpreting these images remains difficult and time consuming, however, so they are not part of routine testing.

Although the color is developing in your baby's eyes, the final color will not be known for some time.

What color will your baby's eyes be? The iris controls the amount of light that enters the eye and gives the eyes their color. Eye color is determined by the amount of melanin within the iris; this is the substance in the skin that gives different skin tones.

It certainly doesn't follow that your baby will have an identical eye color to that of you or your partner. Most fair-skinned babies will be born with only a small amount of melanin in the eye and the iris will appear gray or blue. If dark-skinned then there is a great deal of melanin and the color is usually dark gray or brown. The color continues to change after birth as melanin is produced in response to light. Your baby will be a year old before the final color of her eyes is fully developed.

You may have started to wonder whether your baby will have the same eye color as you or your partner. Her eye color may resemble either of yours, or it may be different than both of you.

PRACTICING VISUALIZATION

Visualization is an effective and positive way to help prepare for labor. Try practicing it in these final weeks, beginning with a basic relaxation exercise. So start at the top of your head and gently flex and relax every muscle down to your toes, concentrating on each muscle, and your breathing, as you do so. Now imagine the birth, with every step given a positive connotation. For example, your baby is floating in water, and is gently rocked as the contractions begin; the tightening you feel is the strong walls of your uterus, guiding your baby into the world; the contractions are waves on which you and your baby are riding, as your baby is washed out—you are both swimming together with the tide.

Cesarean birth

If you know you're going to have your baby by cesarean, it's good to being aware of what to expect following the birth. Although you should remain mobile after cesarean surgery, it's also important to get plenty of rest. Keep in mind that a cesarean section is major surgery so you will need to avoid lifting and carrying heavy loads for the first few weeks. Since this may be difficult if you have other small children or you are at home alone, you should try to recruit as much help as possible after the surgery. You should avoid doing any shopping since this usually involves carrying heavy bags. Order online if you can.

The advice is not to drive for six weeks. If you feel up to it before this time, check with your doctor that it is okay and make sure you're comfortable wearing a seatbelt and doing maneuvers, including emergency stops.

It is generally thought to take up to six weeks to fully recover from a cesarean delivery.

Your third trimester

354

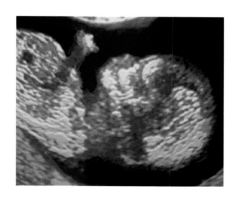

32 days to go...

YOUR BABY TODAY

In this week, the lungs become almost fully functional and able to support the baby if delivered early. This baby at this time is still considered preterm and it is not until 37 weeks that the baby's maturity is such that full term is reached.

Don't forget this is a life-changing time for your partner, too, so find positive ways to involve him in the time preceding the birth.

There is, understandably, a lot of focus on women in the lead-up to childbirth, but it's important not to neglect the dads-to-be. Your partner may be getting anxious about the birth itself, fearing that he might not manage well with being in the delivery room or just concerned about how it will affect him to see you in pain. Some men feel guilty that they cannot take their share of the pain and help more during labor.

Aside from thinking about the birth, your partner may be anxious about the fact he'll be responsible for a newborn baby in just a few weeks!

Talk to your partner if he appears anxious and involve him as much as possible—from helping you cope with pregnancy discomforts to preparing for the birth. If you've written a birth plan (see pp.181 and 303), go back over it now and discuss what might happen and how your partner could help on the day.

You could practice positions and breathing techniques for labor so that he feels more confident about helping you manage. If possible, he could go to your final prenatal appointments with you, where he can discuss any concerns he has with the doctor.

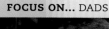
FOCUS ON... DADS

Getting ready

Have you done all your dad-to-be jobs? These include:

■ **Buy a car seat** and make sure you know how to install it safely in the car. You can't leave the hospital with your newborn without one.

■ **Assemble the crib** if you're going to use one in the early weeks.

■ **Ensure there is storage space** for the baby's clothes, bedding, diapers, and other bits and pieces.

ASK A... DOCTOR

I'm having my twins next week, but will I be able to love them both equally? Although this can be a concern, it is more likely to be the case that rather than favor one child over the other, a parent gives more love and attention to the baby who needs it most at that time.

It is also possible that the strain of having two babies in the house may increase the likelihood of delayed bonding, although this can also happen if the birth has been traumatic; if the mother or indeed the father is exhausted; or if one baby

has taken time to establish feeding, or is more fractious than the other. This does not mean that bonding will not take place over time.

In every family, there are bound to be ebbs and flows of love between parents and children. When a parent has two children born at different times, that parent may love one child differently than the other, but this does not mean that the love a parent has for one child is to the detriment of the other. If once your babies are born you still have concerns, speak to your doctor.

355

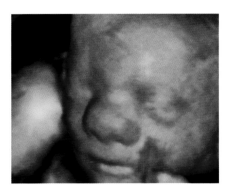

31 days to go...

YOUR BABY TODAY

Your baby's heart will beat quite fast, at between 110 and 160 beats every minute. Even after birth, your baby's heart will continue to beat at this speed. It will be several years before the heart rate is 70 or so beats per minute, the same as an adult.

The lungs don't become fully functional until these final weeks, but important development is taking place now.

If you imagine the lung as a tree, then the windpipe or "trachea" is the trunk of the tree. This then forms several branches or "bronchi," which divide several times, like twigs, to then produce the most delicate structures: the alveoli or leaves of the tree. It is within the alveoli that gas exchange will take place.

The alveoli began to develop at 24 weeks but they continue to increase in number throughout the pregnancy. The alveoli contain surfactant-producing cells to keep them open and these now become fully functional.

PRESCRIBED BEDREST

Toward the end of pregnancy, there are some circumstances when you may need to be admitted into the hospital for bedrest.
- **If you have contractions,** but your water hasn't broken.
- **If you develop preeclampsia** (see p.474). Measures will be taken to reduce your blood pressure.
- **If you have placental abruption,** where the placenta separates from the uterus (see p.473).

You may be closely monitored in hospital toward the end of your pregnancy if there is any concern about your health or that of your baby. A fetal monitoring machine will be used to check your baby's heartbeat.

FOCUS ON... YOUR BODY

Getting strong

Maintaining muscular strength, stretching, and doing gentle exercise right up until you give birth will help your posture—minimizing backaches, reducing stress on your skeleton, and making you feel more energized and relaxed.

As long as you feel good and adhere to the guidelines set out on page 18, you can continue with your activities.

Most importantly, at this time you should use common sense and listen to your body. If you're in pain, feel fatigued, or have dizzy spells, see your doctor immediately and stop exercising. You'll be feeling tired carrying around all that extra weight so adjust your activities accordingly. This could mean that you lower the intensity of your exercise and exercise for a shorter time, but if you feel good don't stop exercising entirely.

Look at the routines on pages 90 and 250, but don't do any exercises at this stage that require you to lie on your back.

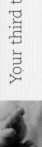

Your third trimester

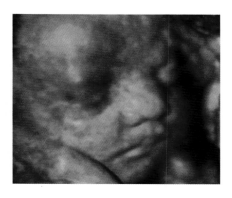

30 days to go...

YOUR BABY TODAY

Many babies will still have a good volume of amniotic fluid around them, but shadows from the placenta or side of the uterus, coupled with the curled up fetal position, will make imaging the baby harder and harder.

It's a good idea to make practical arrangements now for what might happen if you go into labor.

With only around four weeks to go, now is the time to make sure you have all your partner's contact details and know exactly how to get hold of him in case you go into labor when he's at work. He might want to be extra careful to ensure he has his cell phone switched on and at hand in these final few weeks, and that he's not traveling too far away.

If you have other children or other dependants (pets, for example, a dog) then you should arrange what will happen to them when you go into the hospital. You may want to explain to any older children what is going to happen so that they are prepared for when they go to stay with Grandma, or whoever will be taking care of them.

If you're having a cesarean, you might also want your older children taken care of once you're home from hospital.

Reassure your children that you will be coming back and that you're not sick, but that you have to go to the hospital when the baby comes. Depending on the age of your children, you could go with them to buy a present for the baby or you could give them a special job such as opening all the new gifts. Presents from the newborn to her elder siblings is also a good gesture.

In the lead-up to the birth, ensure your toddler spends time with any family members who will be taking care of him while you're in the hospital. This will help him manage without you without getting upset.

AS A MATTER OF FACT

In one study of women who anticipated that they would not need pain relief, 52 percent actually used it.

According to recent research from NICE (National Institute for Clinical Excellence), women underestimate how much giving birth will hurt, and don't find out enough about the pain-relief options available (see pp.402–7).

ASK A... DOCTOR

My baby was premature and is in the neonatal intensive care unit. I'm trying to express milk—am I helping? Yes, very much so. Breast milk helps ensure that the mother's natural immunity is passed on to her baby via her milk. Since premature babies are more prone to infection, expressing your breast milk is a great way to help your baby while she is in the NICU. Breast milk is much easier for a baby to digest: this is important for premature babies since their digestive tract may be less developed than a full-term baby's.

This is also a great way for you to bond and develop a relationship with your baby. It's likely to be a time of considerable stress for you and you may feel helpless, so knowing that you're doing such a great thing to help your baby will help enormously.

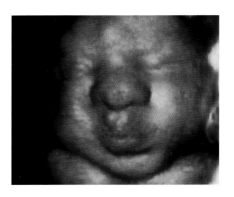

29 days to go...

YOUR BABY TODAY

Most babies will now be positioned longitudinally (lying straight up and down, with their head well in the pelvis). Even now, when space is limited in these final weeks, there is still time for the position to change to head down if your baby is bottom first (breech).

Complex developments are taking place in your baby's lungs that will enable her to breathe unaided once she is born.

The blood flow to your baby's lungs mirrors the development of the airways. Blood leaves the right side of the heart through a one-way valve into the main pulmonary vein. This then divides to give a pulmonary branch to each lung, and also a duct that allows blood to bypass the lungs and travel to the body directly. This will close soon after birth as the lungs expand and their resistance to blood flow falls.

Because your baby doesn't use his lungs for gas exchange in the uterus, the blood supply to them is quite small—only 10 percent of the post-birth supply. At this stage of pregnancy, the lungs' blood supply has completed its development, branching into finer and finer vessels as they come to lie closer to the alveoli.

When your baby is born, her chest is compressed in the birth canal and this helps to push the fluid out of the lungs in preparation for that incredible first breath. If your baby is born by cesarean, she will need first to bring the fluid up by herself. This is not a problem but for this reason the first breaths of a baby born by cesarean can be full of mucus.

Start figuring out now what you'll take to the hospital, since you won't want to be gathering items together once you're in labor.

ITEMS FOR YOUR HOSPITAL BAG

Make sure you have all the items you need for your hospital bag. Remember to include items for yourself as well as the baby and, if you know you're having a cesarean, pack enough items for a few days.

For yourself:
- Pajamas
- Underwear
- Nursing bras
- Slippers
- Dressing gown
- Hairbrush
- Toothbrush
- Toiletries

- Maternity sanitary pads
- Breast pads and nipple cream
- Comfortable loungewear in case you stay in and want to get dressed.

For your baby:
- Undershirts
- Footed onesies
- blanket
- Diapers
- Diaper bags
- Cotton pads
- Diaper cream, such as Desitin
- Baby wipes if you intend to use them
- Hat and cardigan for going home—you can also use the cardigan if your baby

needs layers to keep warm while she's in the hospital.

Other useful items:
- Camera—still camera and/or video camera
- Music for the delivery room
- Books and magazines
- Massage oil
- TENS machine (see p.399)
- Washcloths.

Your partner should also get a bag ready for himself (see p.338) and ensure the car seat is installed. Pack snacks and drinks closer to the time, but think about what you might need.

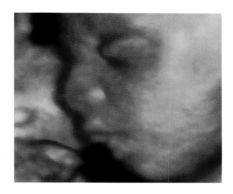

28 days to go...

YOUR BABY TODAY

You may notice a change in the character of your baby's movements, reflecting the reduced amount of amniotic fluid and, consequently, space to move around in. Each movement is more likely to be felt, however, as he touches the side of your uterus.

All pregnant women need support in the final weeks, but if you're single this can be even more important.

THE LOWDOWN

Baby showers

Throwing a baby shower to celebrate the imminent arrival is a great opportunity to get together with the girls. Arrange it yourself, or ask your best friend to do the honors. Note to best friend: surprise parties are great, but consider whether the mom-to-be will want to be the center of attention.

Think about:
- **A pampering theme:** the guests could give each other manicures and pedicures, or you could even hire a beautician for the afternoon.
- **Chipping in together to buy the mom-to-be something useful,** such as a car seat, or indulgent, such as a relaxing day out at a spa.
- **Games you could play,** such as inviting guests to guess the baby's sex, weight, and date she'll be born.
- **Refreshments:** Champagne, non-alcoholic drinks, nibbles, and a "birth" day cake.

At your baby shower you'll probably receive lots of gifts. It's common for there to be presents for both mom and the newborn.

Whether you're single by choice, or have unexpectedly found yourself in this position, you may be experiencing mixed feelings about the weeks to come. There is no doubt that going solo involves extra responsibilities and worries, but with a little help from your close friends and family, you can make these final few weeks of your pregnancy positive.

If you're concerned about going into labor alone, line up a close friend or family member who is on call at all times. He or she might want to get permission from their place of work to take leave to be with you should you go into labor. Keep yourself busy before your baby arrives, planning plenty of activities during your maternity leave.

Don't be afraid to ask people for help with shopping for last-minute baby buys or getting your home ready for your new arrival. Most people will be delighted with the honor of being asked to keep you company, and helping you get things ready.

Most importantly, take care of yourself: get organized by preparing meals you can freeze so you have plenty of healthy food in store for the weeks after the birth.

Your 37th week

YOUR BELLY MAY LOOK AS THOUGH IT'S STARTED TO SLIDE DOWNHILL

You're now about as big as you're going to get. Soon—maybe this week—the baby will drop down lower into your pelvis, ready for birth. Your belly may shift downward, too, giving you a different shape. This doesn't necessarily mean that labor is imminent, so don't worry about the baby "falling out." You're likely to still have some time to enjoy maternity leave and get organized.

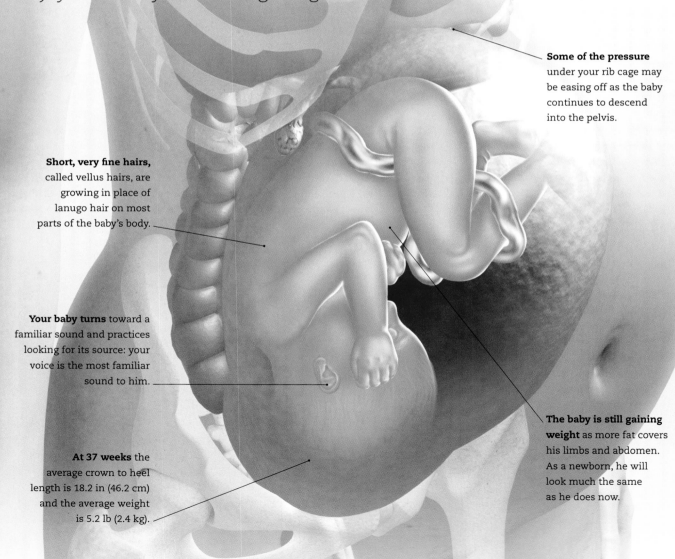

Some of the pressure under your rib cage may be easing off as the baby continues to descend into the pelvis.

Short, very fine hairs, called vellus hairs, are growing in place of lanugo hair on most parts of the baby's body.

Your baby turns toward a familiar sound and practices looking for its source: your voice is the most familiar sound to him.

The baby is still gaining weight as more fat covers his limbs and abdomen. As a newborn, he will look much the same as he does now.

At 37 weeks the average crown to heel length is 18.2 in (46.2 cm) and the average weight is 5.2 lb (2.4 kg).

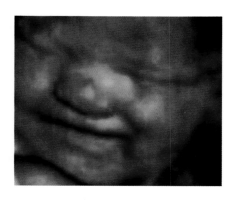

YOU ARE 36 WEEKS AND 1 DAY

27 days to go...

YOUR BABY TODAY

When scanned, this baby was lying with his back to his mother's. This "back to back" position is common at this stage but becomes less so as the pregnancy continues. Your doctor will be able to feel for the position of your baby's back from this point on.

You're in the home stretch now, and may start maternity leave soon. This can be a relief, but also a time of mixed emotions.

Going on maternity leave is a significant pregnancy milestone. As you leave your working role, the reality of beginning your role as a mother may hit you—but you hopefully have a few more weeks to get used to the idea!

It can be a welcome respite to take it easy and not have to rush around in the mornings, and you'll feel less tired by not having to travel to work. Although you need to take it easy, it's a good idea to plan some outings, since not having a routine can take some getting used to.

Although it's good to stay in touch with colleagues, try not to fall into the trap of logging on to work emails or staying up-to-date with what's happening at work. You might be worrying about losing some of your identity while you're on maternity leave; this is a common feeling but you'll find that before you know it your leave is over and you're settled back into work again.

Try to enjoy this lead-up to the birth and make the most of the time (see p.366) to get organized and prepare for your new arrival.

(see p.366)

ASK A... DOCTOR

Will I feel different when my baby drops? You will feel lighter, in that your breathing will be easier, with more room for your lungs to expand. Your abdomen may seem smaller, with your belly shifting down and forward, as your baby's head enters the birth canal. With pressure on your bladder, you may need to urinate more. You may also experience some pelvic pain.

WHEN YOUR BABY DROPS

Engagement is when your baby's head starts to move down into the pelvic brim in preparation for birth, and this can occur any time in these final few weeks of pregnancy, until the start of your labor. In the last weeks of pregnancy, your doctor will check to see if the head has started to engage, or drop, sometimes called "lightening."

Your doctor will do an examination to check to see where the baby's head is. This is called the station, and it's measured from -5 (the baby's head is floating above the pelvis) to +5, the head is at the opening of the vagina. This last stage is called crowning.

When your baby drops, you may find it easier to breathe, since your lungs will have more room to expand, or the need to urinate more because of more pressure on your bladder.

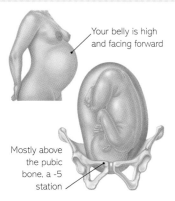

Your belly is high and facing forward

Mostly above the pubic bone, a -5 station

Not engaged: The baby's head has started to move into the pelvis, but more than three- or four-fifths can be felt above the pubic bone.

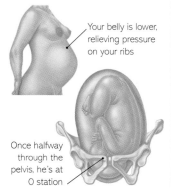

Your belly is lower, relieving pressure on your ribs

Once halfway through the pelvis, he's at 0 station

Engaged: The baby has dropped into the pelvis in preparation for birth. This causes your belly to change position and shape.

26 days to go...

YOUR BABY TODAY

Although almost invisible in the image, a very thin layer of vernix covers your baby. At first this helped to reduce the amount of water leaving your baby's skin, but now it helps to prevent direct contact with the skin and amniotic fluid.

Have you started nesting? The need to provide a safe, comfortable space for your new baby is a primitive desire.

THE LOWDOWN

Plaster casts!

Preserve your belly for posterity by making a plaster belly cast. You can either buy a kit or (far cheaper) purchase the plaster separately; it's all available online.

You will need:
- Plaster of Paris bandages, cut into several strips
- Large tub of petroleum jelly
- Bucket of warm water
- An assistant or two (not essential, but can be useful for speeding up the process and bringing refreshments).

Here's how to do it:
1. Strip down except for some old underwear (the smaller, the better)
2. Apply petroleum jelly liberally to your belly and breasts
3. Assume a comfortable pose
4. One by one, dip the plaster of Paris strips into the water, then apply, overlapping the layers until you have a thick coating
5. Sit and wait for it to dry—it's a good excuse to take a rest
6. Slip it off, when it's rock hard and paint it if you'd like.

The nesting instinct usually begins in the final weeks of pregnancy, accompanied by a surge of energy and an uncontrollable urge to get your home in ship shape.

Give in to your inner domestic goddess: cook, clean, organize, and de-clutter, but take it easy. If you spend hours on your hands and knees scrubbing, you may find yourself in labor sooner than you'd expected.

Some men develop a nesting instinct, but unfortunately this tends to be associated with cars and garden sheds. If this happens to your partner, at least you can look forward to a sparkling-clean car, spruced-up patio, and manicured lawn.

Nesting not happening for you? Pay the professionals to do a spring cleaning. Or forget it: your baby won't care whether the cupboards are clean.

Every nook and cranny of your home will get your attention once the cleaning bug hits you!

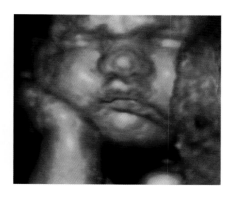

25 days to go...

YOUR BABY TODAY

A short portion of the umbilical cord is lying close to the mouth, which makes this baby appear to have a rather grumpy looking expression. The placenta is seen to the right of the image partially obscuring the view of the face.

You'll find that your beautiful belly is intruding on your life more and more, affecting your movements and eating patterns.

You might be getting a little frustrated by your size around now, which can make everyday activities more difficult. Simple maneuvers, such as fitting through doors or getting off the sofa, can be more difficult and you may find that everything takes a bit longer to achieve. All you can do is be patient and focus on getting through the next few weeks. You'll soon have your body back to normal.

During pregnancy, it's common to eat more often than previously but to eat less at each meal. This is because your uterus has grown so much that all your other organs have moved around and are squashed into much less space. Your stomach simply has less room in it to fit the food so you can't eat as much before feeling full. When your stomach empties you may find yourself hungry again. It's fine to snack, but make sure you're reaching for healthy foods and not the cookie jar!

Getting comfortable behind the steering wheel will become increasingly challenging in the late stages of pregnancy. Keep trips as short as possible or take regular breaks if you need to travel for any length of time. Always wear your seat belt (see p.252).

(see p.252)

THE LOWDOWN

VBAC

Doctors used to think that if you had one baby by cesarean, all future babies must also be born that way. This is not automatically the case; in fact, at least 50–60 percent of women who attempt a VBAC, or vaginal birth after cesarean, are successful. Your doctor or midwife will advise you if there are any reasons why you shouldn't attempt a VBAC, which may include being pregnant with multiples, abnormal presentation (including breech), placenta previa, or having had a classical (vertical) incision for your previous cesarean.

FOCUS ON... YOUR BABY

Working out with Mom

Your baby will usually move several times in the 20 to 30 minutes after you exercise. By keeping the intensity of your exercise at a moderate level you will not compromise the oxygen supply to your baby. When you exercise too hard and for too long, you may compromise this exchange and the result is the baby's movements will fall below their usual levels.

If you're concerned and unsure, keep a log of how much your baby is moving and compare this to the activity levels after exercise. If the level falls below what you consider to be "normal," speak to your caregiver.

24 days to go...

YOUR BABY TODAY

Your baby is now more suitably equipped for the time after the birth: his ears are fully formed on the outside and inside and he is used to hearing the sound of your blood circulating and your heart beating, and he recognizes your voice.

Your baby is losing the downy hair that he's had for several weeks, but if he's born now there may still be some visible.

Lanugo is extremely fine hair that covers your baby's body and, unlike adult hairs on the body, it is not associated with sweat glands. Lanugo hairs begin to be shed now since they are lost into the amniotic fluid in the last few weeks before birth. Your baby then swallows these lanugo hairs in the amniotic fluid but this is not a cause for concern: these hairs provide your baby with an important source of protein, essential to his development. It's been estimated that two-thirds of the protein in the fluid is swallowed and absorbed by the baby's gut each day, providing 15 percent of his protein needs.

The fine lanugo hairs are gradually replaced by vellus hairs, which are short, soft, nonpigmented hairs (often seen more on women and children). Terminal hair is the thicker, coarser, and longer hair that first grows on your baby's eyebrows, then his eyelashes, then his scalp. In adults, facial hair (beards), armpit, and pubic hair, is terminal hair.

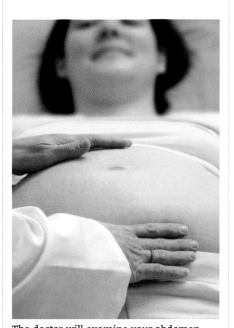

The doctor will examine your abdomen in late pregnancy to check the position of the baby. If the baby is breech, an ECV (see right) may be recommended to turn him into a head-down position. If he doesn't turn, a cesarean delivery may be necessary.

FOCUS ON... YOUR BODY

Desperate for a toilet

In the third trimester you'll be frequenting the bathroom regularly, as you did in the first trimester. At this stage it's due to the increasingly heavy baby pushing down on your bladder from above. If you find that it hurts when you expel urine, you may have a urinary infection and should contact your caregiver for a test.

ASK A... DOCTOR

I've heard about doctors "turning" breech babies. How does this work? Some obstetricians or midwives may try to turn a baby in late pregnancy using external cephalic version (ECV), which has a success rate of around 65 percent. The obstetrician tries gently to guide the baby into a head-down position by pressing his hands on the mother's abdomen, using an ultrasound as a guide. You may be given medication to relax the uterine muscles. You will be scanned first and if the baby is in an awkward position the procedure may not continue. If your baby is large this can affect the procedure, as can the amount of amniotic fluid: a low amount of fluid offers less protection to the baby.

If you're Rh negative, you may get an injection of Rh immunoglobulin (RhIg) after the version because of the small risk of a bleed around the placenta. An ECV is not recommended if you have a multiple pregnancy, have had bleeding, your placenta is low-lying (see p.212), your membranes have ruptured, or there is a known problem with the baby.

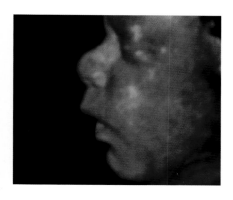

23 days to go...

YOUR BABY TODAY

3D views at this stage of the pregnancy will be extremely clear. Every part of the face is fully developed and your baby will be very expressive. Your baby is only a few days away now from being full term.

Don't be concerned about embarrassing yourself in labor—your caregivers will have seen it all before.

Many women worry about losing control during labor—for example that they will urinate or defecate when they are pushing. You might well pass a bit of stool when you're pushing but you probably won't notice; your doctor will put on a pair of gloves and use gauze to remove it.

The reality is that when you're in the throes of labor, you really won't care—you'll just want that baby out!

Keep an open mind about pain relief since you won't know how you'll handle the pain or what your pain threshold is until you're actually in labor.

ASK A... PANEL

What if I can't deal with the pain of labor?

Doctor: If you're concerned, take time to investigate the pain-relief options in advance of labor, so that you're aware of what's available, even if you don't plan to use it.

There's no shame in deviating from what you requested in your birth plan; the ultimate goal is to deliver a healthy baby, and to keep your energy levels and your spirits high. It's also important to ask for pain relief as soon as you feel that things are getting away from you.

Mom: When I was in labor, the pain literally took my breath away, and I really did feel that I would be unable to continue. Changing position, walking around, and using a birthing ball proved to be a good distraction, even if they passed the time rather than provided relief, and I chanted to myself, over and over, "You can do it!"

I dimly remembered that when the pain is at its worst you've hit "transition," which signals the beginning of the delivery itself, and it did help to know I was near the end, even if it did seem a long time in

coming. Focus on how much you want your baby in your arms, and view every contraction as one step closer to that moment.

Midwife: Moms who are prepared for the pain seem to find that it isn't as bad as they thought it might be, and are able to cope using breathing exercises and massage. The best advice is to know your limits. If you find the pain unbearable, then ask for some pain relief. Ask your caregiver what pain options are available to take the edge off of the discomfort, and make the process more bearable.

No woman can anticipate how her labor and delivery will proceed, and sometimes babies make things difficult by presenting themselves in awkward positions, or simply enjoying life inside a little too much to arrive promptly. Take things one step at a time, and when you know you've had enough, conserve your energy by getting the help you need. Any woman who delivers a healthy baby has had a successful delivery, and that's what's most important.

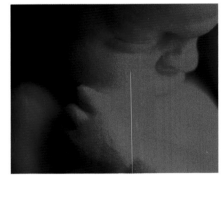

22 days to go...

YOUR BABY TODAY

Your baby will be able to recall and recognize the frequency and pattern of the most familiar sounds he hears within the uterus—your voice. Also, you might have noticed that loud noises may startle your baby during these final weeks.

If you're lacking in energy, try carb loading. This is also an effective measure in the days leading up to labor.

The idea behind carb loading comes from endurance athletes, who get 70 percent of their calorie intake from carbohydrates for three days prior to a big event. This enhances muscle uptake of fuel so that muscles are fully loaded with glycogen, the form in which carbs are stored in the body. If you're feeling tired, and especially prior to being active, ensure you take on plenty of carbohydrates.

In the days before your due date, base meals on carbohydrates, so that this food group provides up to 70 percent of your total calories. Include cereal or bread for breakfast, sandwiches for lunch, and include pasta, rice, or potatoes at dinner.

A baked potato is a great mini-meal, providing you with carbohydrates. Try different carbohydrate foods in the lead-up to labor to see which you like best.

MAKING THE MOST OF MATERNITY LEAVE

Maternity leave offers a great opportunity to prepare yourself for the birth of your baby.

■ **Take time to rest.** While it may seem like the optimum time to rush through a long "to-do" list, it's important to conserve your energy for the birth, and the weeks afterward.

■ **Prepare your hospital bag** (see p.358), or anything you may need for a home birth (see p.341).

■ **Make a list** of everyone you'd like contacted after the birth.

■ **Put together some natural remedies** to help you through labor and its aftermath. Lavender oil can be sniffed during labor to relax and calm. You may need ice packs if you end up having an episiotomy (placing ice pads or chilled witch hazel pads on the area may soothe your pain). Ask your doctor about safe pain medications for after delivery, or, if you want to avoid medications, ask him or her for drug-free suggestions.

■ **Prepare a few freezer meals.** There can be nothing better than having an already prepared, healthy meal on hand that can be taken right from the freezer when your arms are full with your new baby, and you lack the time and energy to get dinner on the table.

■ **Sort your baby's new clothes** into sizes, so you don't find yourself searching through piles to find something that fits.

■ **Get ahead** by preparing your birth announcements—address and stamp envelopes, or design something that can be sent via email, so that you only need to slot in your new baby's photo and details at the last moment.

■ **Get a manicure, pedicure, or massage.** Not only will time be tight after your baby arrives, but money may be, too! Take the opportunity to lift your spirits and feel your best.

■ **Produce something creative—** paint your baby's nursery, cross-stitch a little pillow or picture, make a crib bumper, start a scrapbook, or simply write a letter to your baby to put in a keepsake box. These personal touches are satisfying, and will be treasured for years to come.

■ **Catch up with friends and family for lunch.** It may be some time before you feel like going out again once you're getting used to being a parent and enjoying your new baby in the comfort of your home.

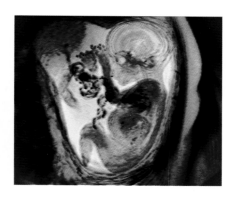

21 days to go...

YOUR BABY TODAY

This baby is lying in the breech position, with the umbilical cord seen as is travels toward the placenta in the top left-hand side of the image. Approximately 3 in every 100 babies will be in a breech position after 37 weeks.

Your baby is now able to hear many sounds that will all be familiar to him once he's born.

In this late stage of pregnancy, sounds penetrate the uterus easily and there is no doubt that the baby can hear and respond to these before birth. Your baby will startle at loud sounds but now also turn toward familiar sounds, and practice looking for the source of the sound. Your baby is not only recognizing a wider range of sound frequencies, but also discriminating between different sounds as well as learning and remembering familiar sounds, such as your voice and that of your partner.

Your baby breathes more quickly when he's concentrating on sounds and his heart rate increases. Although the baby can hear at birth, the ear drum continues to thin out, at the same time becoming more mobile and responsive to sounds. Your voice will be the most familiar sound to your baby at birth.

What if I can't breast-feed? It's normal to have doubts but be reassured that most women have enough milk, and with some help with positioning the baby can breast-feed without any problems. By this stage, you may even be leaking colostrum (see p.295).

Try to keep an open mind and remember that the breast milk does not come in straight after the birth (see p.448). Even if you have problems, try to persevere and don't feel pressured to give up just because it's convenient for the hospital staff or your partner, or because a friend or family member tells you it's not necessary.

Even if you don't end up breast-feeding, you can still get close to your baby by bottle-feeding.

It won't be long until you meet your baby. Meanwhile, talk to him. He'll recognize your voice—and your partner's—once he's born.

The final weeks

You aren't alone if you're a dad-to-be who's feeling a bit bewildered and shell-shocked by the imminent arrival of your baby. To begin with, you can expect a lot of changes at home. Once your partner starts maternity leave, she may start a whirlwind of activity in preparation for the new arrival, and will need your help to get everything ready.

While supporting your partner both practically and emotionally will be important in the coming weeks, take care of yourself, too. Take every opportunity to get some rest. Even if you've agreed that your partner will do the majority of the nighttime baby care, your sleep will still be disrupted in the weeks after the birth. Catch up with friends now, but not to the point where you tire yourself out, and keep up your exercise routine, if you have one.

It's normal to feel anxious about what's ahead—both being a birth partner and a dad—but be reassured that somehow everything will fall into place. Focus on the thought of holding your newborn baby.

Your 38th week

EVEN IF YOU HAVE ENJOYED YOUR PREGNANCY, YOU MAY BE LONGING FOR IT TO BE OVER

The baby is nearly ready, you are more than ready, so when is the birth going to happen? Probably not yet—especially if this is your first pregnancy. For another week or so, the uterus is still the best place for your baby while the finishing touches to her development take place. If you have other children, you can tell them that their new brother or sister won't keep everyone waiting much longer.

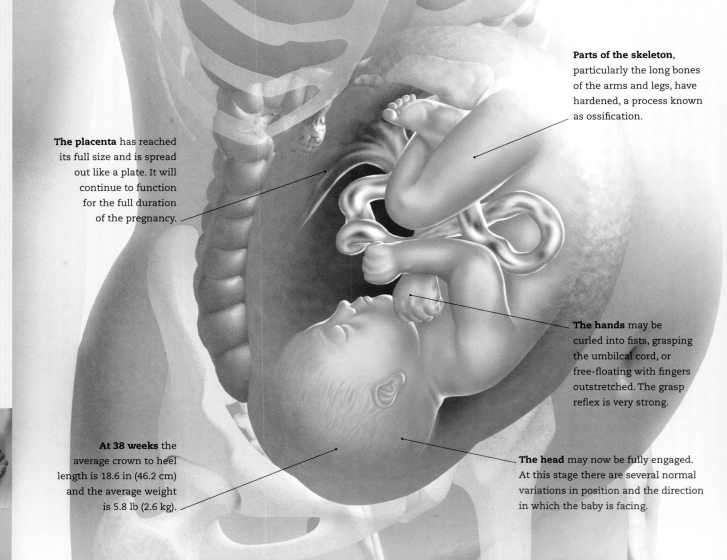

Parts of the skeleton, particularly the long bones of the arms and legs, have hardened, a process known as ossification.

The placenta has reached its full size and is spread out like a plate. It will continue to function for the full duration of the pregnancy.

The hands may be curled into fists, grasping the umbilcal cord, or free-floating with fingers outstretched. The grasp reflex is very strong.

At 38 weeks the average crown to heel length is 18.6 in (46.2 cm) and the average weight is 5.8 lb (2.6 kg).

The head may now be fully engaged. At this stage there are several normal variations in position and the direction in which the baby is facing.

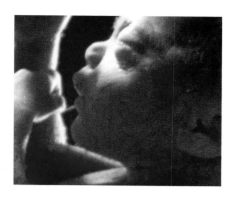

20 days to go...

YOUR BABY TODAY

Full term has been reached and your baby's features are now very clearly formed. To a certain extent from now on your baby is simply growing and putting on weight—factors necessary to provide energy after birth and help with temperature control.

Start preparing for the birth now: by being practical and positive, you can make it memorable for all the right reasons.

AS A MATTER OF FACT

Being hypnotized during pregnancy can make you more confident in the lead-in to labor.

A study found that first-time pregnant women also experienced a shorter labor. The average amount of time they pushed in the second stage was one hour, compared with the usual two hours for a first baby.

Probably the most effective way to remember as much as you can about your labor and the birth of your baby is to try to remain as healthy and rested as possible prior to the start of your labor; this will give you the best chance of staying strong and clear-headed throughout.

Feeling strong and having plenty of energy may also help you remain upright and active during the course of your labor, reducing the need for pain relief such as Demerol (see p.403), which can sometimes cause memory loss that makes it more difficult to remember the finer details of the birth. It's also helpful to have your birth partner with you throughout your labor so that he or she can help to fill in any blanks later. Photographs and videos are also good prompts.

After the birth, if you find that there are parts you can't remember, you can ask your doctor to let you see your birth notes. You might want to write up your experience in a journal.

FOCUS ON... DADS

Health professionals and you

When you get closer to the birth, and especially during labor, you will find that there is inevitably more contact with health professionals. These individuals are a source of reassurance and a font of knowledge, but as a male you may sometimes feel that you're being sidelined or that your opinion doesn't count. This can be very frustrating if you want to be highly involved in the pregnancy and birth.

Bear in mind that the health professionals are trying to provide care for the person who needs it the most—namely your partner. If you want to be heard, it's a good idea to write down any questions that you may have before you meet with health professionals. Labor nurses will make every effort to help you to feel involved, and support you in supporting your partner.

Try to keep in mind that the most important relationship your partner has is with you, and that a positive attitude on your part can make a substantial difference to your partner's pregnancy and birth. So be patient and persistent but not pushy.

Ensure you get plenty of rest in the next few weeks to get you in the best frame of mind for labor and birth.

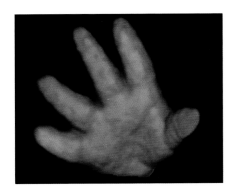

19 days to go...

YOUR BABY TODAY

A 3D close-up of the hand shows the skin folds. Just as fingerprints are unique, so are the deeper skin folds seen on the hands and feet. The grasp reflex is strong and your baby will start to grasp anything that touches the palm of her hand.

Your baby will benefit from extra time in the uterus, but her development is almost complete and she's now "full term."

THE LOWDOWN

Hair down there

One dilemma that's rarely discussed—but much pondered— among moms-to-be is whether they should shave or trim their pubic hair before giving birth.

It's really a personal choice and depends how much it bothers you: just because your best friend had her pubic hair waxed, you shouldn't feel pressure to do the same—aside from anything else, itchy regrowth will not be welcome in the days following the birth of your baby.

Before a cesarean, the top inch (at least) of your pubic hair may be trimmed in hospital— it generally isn't shaved as this could increase the risk of infection. If you know in advance that you are having a cesarean, you can trim yourself at home beforehand, or ask your partner to help you if you find it hard to see what you are doing!

Your baby will be very cramped in the uterus. It won't be long, however, until she's positioned head down and begins to engage in the pelvis as she prepares to make her entry into the world.

There is now less space for your baby to move and she will soon, if she hasn't already, settle down into a comfortable head-down position. The shape of the uterus encourages this head-down position and, once in it, turning would be a major effort for your baby. Plenty of amniotic fluid remains to cushion and protect your baby, who will still be attempting to be very active in this more confined space.

Your baby's behavior is now exactly the same as a newborn: she'll turn toward light and yawn just as much as a newborn, and she'll continue to practice breathing the amniotic fluid in and out with regular rhythmical movements.

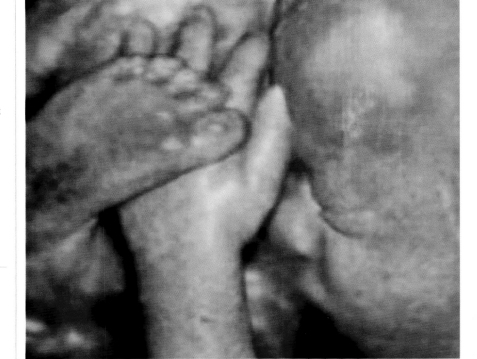

18 days to go...

YOUR BABY TODAY

With each day that goes by delivery is becoming ever more likely. You may experience Braxton-Hicks' contractions, which help to soften the cervix and prepare for labor. The amniotic fluid that surrounds your baby ensures she'll hardly notice these mild tightenings.

It's a good idea to give some thought to life after the birth, and ensure you have adequate help and support lined up.

Even at this late stage of pregnancy, it may still be hard to imagine your baby being born and living in your home. You and your partner may settle into life with your newborn with ease, and manage without any help, but it's still a good idea to have backup support just in case.

What you may not be prepared for is the fact that you're likely to be exhausted after weeks of poor sleep during pregnancy, and the rigors of labor itself. Add to this interrupted nights' sleep and the whole adjustment to being a new parent, and you may well find you'll need to call on people to help practically and emotionally.

It can help enormously to have a good support network set up in advance. Ideally, this will be close family and friends who you know you can rely on to drop in to help, but who will also know when you need to be left alone. Even an hour's help to prepare you a nutritious meal, or hold your baby while you get a much-needed rest or a shower, can give you some welcome respite.

Have the number on hand for your lactation consultant, so that you can ask for advice. Also get on the phone to moms-to-be whom you've met at prenatal classes; they more than anyone will be able to relate to how you're feeling.

Don't be too proud to accept help with housework and shopping. Knowing these tasks are taken care of will help you relax and focus on your baby.

Try to limit the number of guests you have in the early days, and make sure that they are warned that visits will be short. Although you will be desperate to show off your new baby, visits can be draining so it's better to wait until some routines are more established.

FOCUS ON... NUTRITION

Healthy snacking

Large meals are likely to leave you feeling uncomfortably full, especially late in the third trimester. If you go long periods of time between meals, you may become light-headed and feel weak from hypoglycemia—low blood sugar. This is because the baby is constantly drawing glucose from your bloodstream.

Healthy snacking is the key to eating well and comfortably:

■ **Keep lots of fresh fruit** on display in a bowl so you'll remember to eat it.
■ **Stock your cupboards** with a variety of dried fruits and nuts.
■ **Hard boil eggs** and keep them in the fridge. Try eating them with a sprinkle of salt to quell that salt craving.
■ **Buy or make some frozen juice pops** and keep them in the freezer. Some women also find it refreshing to suck on these during labor.

Yogurt is a nutritious and healthy snack for any time of day. For variety and additional nutrients, sprinkle granola or dried fruit on top.

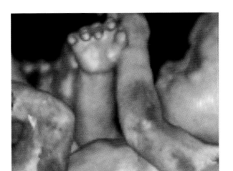

17 days to go...

YOUR BABY TODAY

What exactly triggers the start of labor is still a mystery. Does the signal come from your own body or does the baby play a part in the decision? Every labor is different, and the timing of your first labor can be quite different from your second.

Gradually, each of your baby's bones is becoming strengthened thanks to adequate amounts of calcium.

Your baby's bones are strengthened by the process of ossification in which hard bone is formed from calcium. To meet this increase in demand, you absorb calcium much more readily from your diet.

By this stage of pregnancy, the baby's humerus in the upper arm, femur in the upper leg, and tibia in the lower leg have undergone this process. As ossification occurs at specific weeks in your pregnancy, ultrasound can use these as markers to estimate the date of the pregnancy, if necessary.

The time at which this ossification occurs may be seen a few days earlier in girls than boys and, interestingly, the patella (knee bone), does not ossify until after birth.

ASK A... DOCTOR

I've had a small amount of bleeding. Should I be concerned? Bleeding in late pregnancy may be serious since it can be due to the placenta partially, or totally, detaching from the wall of the uterus, known as placental abruption (see p.473), or to a low-lying placenta, known as placenta previa (see p.212). If you have a mucus discharge tinged with blood in late pregnancy, this may be a "bloody show" (see pp.391 and 411).

Always seek medical advice for bleeding at any stage of pregnancy to rule out any problems.

One way to take Bach Flower Remedies (see below) is to put four drops into a glass of water and sip it at intervals. Alternatively, you can put the drops directly on to your tongue using the pipette. Always talk to your doctor before using any remedy.

AS A MATTER OF FACT

Just because your partner weighed above average at birth, it doesn't mean your baby will too.

The birth weight depends on the mix of genes your baby inherits. So, if your partner is tall and big boned and you're petite and were a tiny baby, keep your fingers crossed that you have the more dominant genes!

BACH FLOWER REMEDIES

Flower essence blends are designed to calm and center your energy, which some think can help you relax and encourage you to focus. Rescue Remedy and Emergency Essence, types of Bach Flower Remedy, are thought by some to be effective when used in labor, and in the weeks prior to and after the birth. The remedies are taken for a variety of symptoms including anxiety, shock, worry, stress, or simply for a boost during a long or painful labor.

A few drops may be taken on your tongue as required or mixed in water, as shown above. Both of these blends also come in cream form, to apply topically, or as a spray, to spritz yourself, and your environment.

Ask your doctor before you try these or other natural remedies, since they haven't been thoroughly studied.

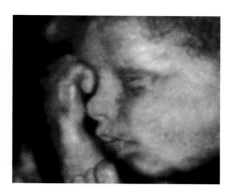

16 days to go...

YOUR BABY TODAY

The size of your uterus may have reduced slightly as your baby's head becomes more deeply engaged within your pelvis, allowing her body to move down. This can take some of the pressure away from your ribs, which is a welcome relief at this stage.

When there's going to be a new arrival on the scene, it's important to prepare the little members of your household.

How you handle introducing the new baby to your children will depend on their age. A toddler might be totally indifferent and unfazed, being more interested in your new baby's toys than the fact that she has a new brother or sister. An older child might be shocked and jealous by the arrival of a new baby, who appears to steal her limelight, and usurp his mommy and daddy's attention.

It's a good idea to prepare your little one several weeks in advance, explaining that the new baby will need a lot of time and attention, will need to be fed and changed regularly, and probably not be much fun for a few months. Focus on how your child can be a great helper, and show her what the new baby will need when she is born. Take some books out of the library that explain how families change when a new baby is born, and ask your child to talk about how she's feeling, and how she thinks things will be different when the baby arrives.

Encourage your child to choose a gift to give to the baby, and find something your child really wants as a gift from her new sibling. Ask grandparents or close friends to arrange a few treats or outings for your child both now and after the birth, so that she's occupied, and getting extra attention.

ASK A... DOCTOR

My mom had a difficult delivery with me. Am I likely to have the same experience as her? Like many women, you're obviously aware of the details of your own birth.

Some say you'll have the same sort of delivery your mom had with you—for example, your baby will be early or late or you'll have a very quick labor or a slow, assisted one. This isn't necessarily true.

Remember, depending on how old your mom is, there have probably been significant developments in obstetrics since your mom's days and, even if you face the same hurdles during your labor, they might be managed differently.

Also, you might be healthier and stronger than your mom was, so don't assume you're in for a difficult labor just because she had one.

Try to encourage a bond between your older child and your baby. Ask your child to imagine what the baby might be getting up to inside Mommy. Encourage her to suggest names, although don't promise to use them!

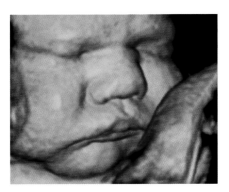

15 days to go...

YOUR BABY TODAY

Estimating your baby's size by measuring from the top of the uterus to the front of your pelvic bone can give you an idea of size, but this is less accurate now. Your baby may not yet have moved down into the pelvis and the amount of fluid around your baby is variable.

Newborn babies can tightly hold someone's finger because of the grasp reflex, and this is already functioning in the uterus.

Inside the uterus your baby has developed a strong grasp reflex. The grip is so strong after birth that it could support your baby's weight. This grasp reflex persists until your baby is about six months old; she will then have more choice over whether to grasp an object or not.

Interestingly, your baby also has a similar reflex in the foot. This is the "plantar reflex" and it causes the toes to attempt to curl around your finger if the sole of the foot is stroked. The plantar reflex takes slightly longer to disappear after birth, typically persisting until 12 months of age. Another reflex action causes the toes to spread out if the side of the foot is stroked. These reflexes and others seem to be quite primitive in nature and although they are thought to protect the baby, the precise function of each reflex is not fully understood.

In addition to being an effective way to relax, using a birthing pool can speed up labor. It is thought that water sets off a surge of the hormone oxytocin, which triggers contractions.

AS A MATTER OF FACT

Second labors are usually shorter in duration than first labors.

This usually means an easier labor, but a second baby could be bigger than a first, or positioned differently. There are many factors to consider.

THE LOWDOWN

Owls!

Could owls give us an insight into pregnancy and birth? It's doubtful, but these myths are entertaining!

■ **If a pregnant woman** hears the shriek of an owl, her child will definitely be a girl.

■ **An owl living in the attic** of a house will cause a problem with the baby.

■ **When the time comes to give birth** there should be no owls in the delivery room—if they hoot at the moment of birth the child will have a miserable life.

ASK A... DOCTOR

Is it true that natural or water births are best for the baby? Most childbirth experts would agree that a straightforward vaginal birth is the safest form of birth for both mother and baby. It is also generally considered safe to use water as a method of relieving the pain in uncomplicated labors.

However, it is sometimes not possible to achieve a straightforward vaginal delivery due to certain situations that can arise during labor and birth. If a problem with either the mother or baby occurs, the medical team will advise you on the safest way of delivering the baby.

It's important to think about the type of birth you would prefer and are comfortable with, but be prepared to be flexible and to see how labor unfolds. Speak to your doctor to find out if there's a birthing pool you can use at your hospital.

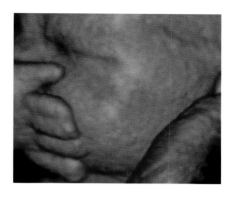

14 days to go...

YOUR BABY TODAY

The back of the hand is held up against the mouth in this image. Your baby will be practicing suckling at every opportunity, but this will be with parts of the hands, thumbs or fingers, since it's no longer easy to reach the toes.

If you haven't found out the sex of your baby, the excitement will be building; if you have, you can get very organized!

Knowing the sex of your baby enables you to decide on the name, buy specific outfits, and even decorate the nursery, if you have one, in a certain way. Remember, however, there's a chance that the scan (see pp.214–15) gave you misleading information. The only way to be absolutely certain of the baby's gender is if you found out following a diagnostic test, such as amniocentesis or chorionic villus sampling (see pp.152–3).

(see pp.214–15)

(see pp.152–3)

THE LOWDOWN

Boys and girls

Still wondering what you're having? Well, to help you guess, you might want to bear in mind a few more old wives' tales...

- If you have soft hands you're having a girl, rough hands you're having a boy.
- If the father-to-be is nervous, it's a girl, if he's relaxed it's a boy.
- If the mother picks up her coffee cup with two hands it's a girl, if she picks it up by the handle it's a boy.
- If you have a sensitive belly button it's a girl, if you have cold feet it's almost certainly a boy!

If you know the sex, you won't have the same incentive of a surprise at the end of your labor, but you may feel you can bond more closely with your baby during pregnancy and picture what he or she will be like as a newborn.

If you don't know the sex yet, then you will have a well-earned surprise after your hard work in labor. Some women who don't know the sex of their babies say that they have a strong instinct that the baby is a particular sex, but may be quite surprised when they have a baby of the opposite sex.

Try to keep an open mind and not raise your hopes about having a baby of a certain gender—the odds are slightly in favor of you having a boy.

While knowing the sex of your baby helps you make decisions, such as should you buy pink or blue, not knowing gives you a greater sense of anticipation.

ASK A... DOCTOR

My baby is in a posterior position. How will this affect my labor? In the posterior position the baby faces your belly instead of your spine (see p.336). This position may prolong your labor, which can be tiring, and cause more of a backache. If this is the case, you can try the same methods as for turning a breech baby (see p.329) to encourage your baby to move into an anterior position.

Sometimes the baby turns with the help of contractions when you are in fully established labor. If she doesn't turn, intervention such as the use of forceps or vacuum (see pp.436–7) may be needed.

(see p.336)
(see p.329)
(see pp.436–7)

AS A MATTER OF FACT

Your body is designed to handle the pain of labor!

Nobody likes pain, but your body's endorphin levels will increase during labor to help you cope with it. So it's reassuring to know that as the intensity of the contractions build, so does your ability to handle them.

Your 39th week

TIME MAY FEEL AS THOUGH IT'S STANDING STILL AND EVERY SMALL TWINGE HAS YOU ON THE ALERT

Know the signs that mean labor is really about to start. You may have some false alarms, so don't hesitate to call your doctor for advice and reassurance. Excitement will be competing with nerves—and that goes for your partner as well. No one can predict how labor is going to turn out, but before the big day it's helpful to agree on what your partner's role should ideally be.

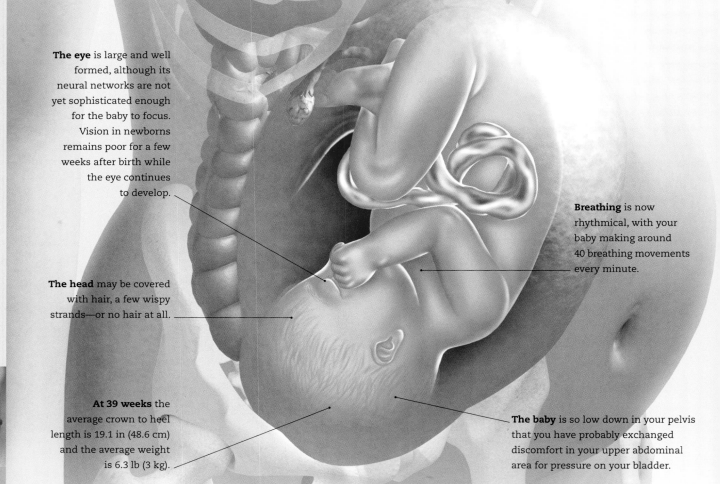

The eye is large and well formed, although its neural networks are not yet sophisticated enough for the baby to focus. Vision in newborns remains poor for a few weeks after birth while the eye continues to develop.

The head may be covered with hair, a few wispy strands—or no hair at all.

At 39 weeks the average crown to heel length is 19.1 in (48.6 cm) and the average weight is 6.3 lb (3 kg).

Breathing is now rhythmical, with your baby making around 40 breathing movements every minute.

The baby is so low down in your pelvis that you have probably exchanged discomfort in your upper abdominal area for pressure on your bladder.

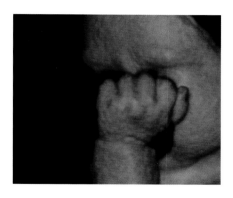

13 days to go...

YOUR BABY TODAY

This baby's hand is in the same position as in the image opposite, with the fist held tightly in front of the face. All of your baby's movements help build muscle strength and aid coordination, whether it's a kick or simply curling and uncurling the fingers.

With labor imminent, you'll be playing the waiting game. Staying active will help the time pass much more quickly.

You'll be resting a lot in the next two weeks. As your figure expands and you become more tired, it's natural to want to sit out the remainder of your pregnancy at home with your feet up, and put the answering machine on to field all the "Has it arrived?" inquiries!

It's fine to do this but it's good to remember that the very best way to stimulate labor is to keep active. What's more, the hormones produced by even gentle walking will lift your mood and help you feel more positive when your labor begins.

Try giving yourself one or two small tasks each day—perhaps meeting a friend for lunch, going for a very gentle swim, or purchasing some last-minute items for baby—being careful to stop and put your feet up when you feel tired. Be sensible about the type of activities you undertake, and avoid anything that could be exhausting or potentially dangerous; for example, bear in mind that your center of gravity is way off balance at the moment, and that wallpapering the nursery or carrying heavy groceries should definitely not be on your to-do list.

It may feel as though your life is on hold at the moment so that's why it's good to fill your time as best you can. Don't forget, however, that in just a couple of weeks you'll have your newborn occupying all your time.

THE LOWDOWN

The power of music

Research has shown that women who listen to music during labor tend to feel less stressed and are less likely to need pain relief. There's also some evidence to suggest that babies born to the accompaniment of music are calmer.

One study compared different beats and found that classical, instrumental sounds were the most relaxing. Familiar tunes and rhythms could distract you from the pain and—if you choose the right track— help you focus on your breathing. Line up a selection of tunes on your iPod well in advance of labor.

Try out a selection of music to discover what you find most soothing, or invigorating. Labor is a bit like a mini-marathon and listening to the right tunes might just help you get to the finish line.

Your 40th week

ALL THE MILESTONES ARE SAFELY PASSED AND YOU WILL MEET YOUR BABY ANY DAY NOW

Like many moms-to-be, you may have to linger in suspense beyond the "last" day of pregnancy. Without a doubt, the big event is about to happen very soon and it will be worth the waiting, wondering, and worrying. Once you see and hold your baby, you won't spend much time looking back over the past 40 weeks, but you'll certainly marvel at the miracle of it all.

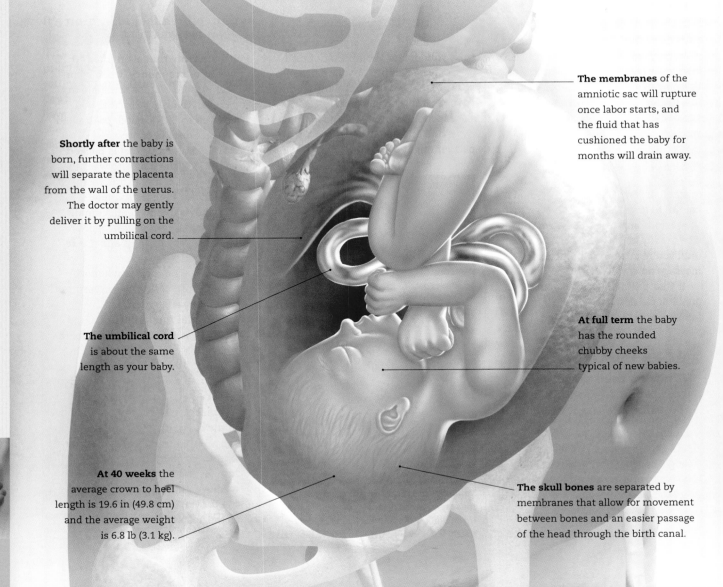

The membranes of the amniotic sac will rupture once labor starts, and the fluid that has cushioned the baby for months will drain away.

Shortly after the baby is born, further contractions will separate the placenta from the wall of the uterus. The doctor may gently deliver it by pulling on the umbilical cord.

The umbilical cord is about the same length as your baby.

At full term the baby has the rounded chubby cheeks typical of new babies.

At 40 weeks the average crown to heel length is 19.6 in (49.8 cm) and the average weight is 6.8 lb (3.1 kg).

The skull bones are separated by membranes that allow for movement between bones and an easier passage of the head through the birth canal.

Your third trimester

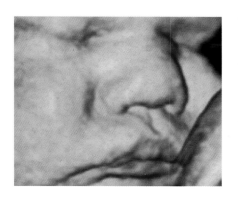

6 days to go...

YOUR BABY TODAY

If you are having a planned cesarean delivery, this is usually offered now—in order to balance the chance of labor starting unexpectedly with that of delivering your baby too soon. It is best for babies to be delivered as close to the due date as possible.

It's good to revisit your birth plan at this late stage since you may feel differently now about some of the requests you made.

A birth plan is usually filled in earlier in pregnancy, and you may not have given it much more thought since (see pp.181 and 303). Now that the birth is imminent, look over it with your partner to figure out whether you've changed your mind about anything. For example, you may be veering toward a more natural birth or, conversely, you may now be certain you want an epidural. Adapt it as you wish and discuss it with your caregiver, if necessary.

Since your partner will be your advocate in labor, putting your requests forward to your labor nurses and other caregivers if you're unable to express them, it's important that he understands your wishes and that they're fresh in his mind.

Remember, though, that you won't really know how you'll feel or what you want until you're in labor, so keep an open mind and be prepared to adapt your plans on the day if it's in the best interests of your baby's well-being.

Get your partner's view. Remember that this is a big event for him, too: the moment when he'll meet his baby for the first time. He may have anxieties and concerns and want reassurance about what his role will be on the day: tell him how you think he can best help you, whether it be a massage or just holding your hand throughout. Discuss how you both are feeling in the preparation for the birth—your concerns, hopes, and expectations.

ASK A... MOM

How many visitors can come see the new baby in the hospital?
Check the hospital's policy, but this is generally up to you. If you want your friends and family to come, by all means you can invite them—just be sure to check the visiting hours. Right now, you might think you want a roomful of visitors, but you may change your mind after you've been through labor and delivery, so wait to make your decision. You might just want to sleep or spend time alone with your partner and the baby. Remember, too, that young children (other than immediate family) may not be allowed to visit.

STAYING CLOSE

It can be difficult to think of anything but the birth and meeting your baby when you are this close to the end of pregnancy. Try to focus on other things, too:

■ **Spend time with your partner:** Enjoy quality time together while it is still just the two of you, before the baby makes demands on your time, and exhaustion sets in. Share your hopes and fears about how your lives are going to change.

■ **Make love:** you might feel you are too big, or too tired, but it is good to remind yourselves of your sexual relationship. And, you never know, making love could just get your labor started (see p.393).

5 days to go...

YOUR BABY TODAY

This close-up 3D ultrasound view shows that this baby's earlobe is particularly prominent. The dark flecks around the ear look like hair, but are in fact shadows (although many babies have hair at this stage).

Your baby's bones have hardened to a certain degree, but this process will continue right up to the teenage years!

Your baby's skeleton has gradually transformed, from soft cartilage to bone, a process called ossification (see p.372). This process starts in the center of each bone spreading outward. By the end of pregnancy, ossification is complete along the length of each bone but the ends of the long bones and the tips of the bones in the finger and toes remain as cartilage. This is necessary to allow later bone growth as the child develops.

The bones in the upper part of the skull are slightly different, developing from membranous structures rather than cartilage. These do not fully fuse until several years after birth and remain separated from each other by connective tissue. This connective tissue forms areas called sutures and where more than two bones meet, wider spaces called fontanelles. Their function is to allow space for movement or "molding" between the skull bones making it easier for the head to descend into the pelvis during labor. It is also these suture lines and fontanelles that help your doctor determine the position of the baby's head during labor.

After delivery you will notice that your baby's head shape is often elongated, but this soon changes as the bones realign back into their usual positions.

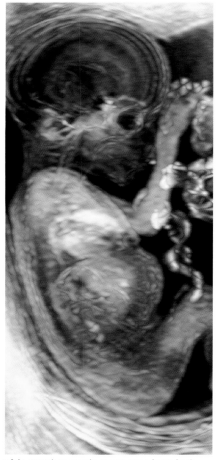

This MRI (magnetic resonance imaging) scan shows a fetus approaching full-term. The baby's brain, spinal column, heart, liver, and lungs are visible, and the umbilical cord can be seen to the right of the image.

THE LOWDOWN

Placenta on toast?

The thought of eating the placenta may turn your stomach, but some women choose to do exactly that. The organ is revered for its spiritual properties, and devotees of placentophagia believe the nutrients it contains, including vitamin B6, will help prevent them from developing postpartum depression. However, the evidence in favor of the health benefits of consuming a placenta is purely anecdotal.

An alternative and less controversial custom involves dressing the placenta with herbs, then burying it at a party to celebrate the baby's birth: this is thought to be an important bonding ritual for the extended family.

Art is another option: press the placenta against a piece of paper and you'll get a tree-shaped print.

Some cultures use the dried organ to make medicinal herbs.

Not sure how to cook placenta? Well just look online and you'll find plenty of placenta recipes, from pâté to lasagne, but, understandably, these might not be to everyone's taste.

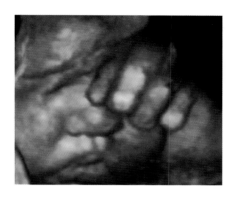

4 days to go...

YOUR BABY TODAY

Once labor starts your baby will no longer have room to place her hands on top of her head or by her face although, interestingly, she is still moving around—you probably won't notice these movements since you will have other things on your mind.

The inquiries may begin flooding in this week and it will feel as though the whole world is awaiting news of your baby's arrival.

In this final week of your pregnancy, the weight of expectation can be immense. It can feel as though everyone is waiting for you to pop, especially if it's your first baby.

You'll no doubt cope with it this week—and you may even enjoy getting all the attention—but if you happen to go overdue you might get frustrated by the constant calls and by having to repeat yourself. Try to be patient and remember people are simply excited for you and are just as frustrated with waiting as you are.

Matters aren't helped by the due date. Everyone will have this estimated date in mind, but unfortunately not many babies stick to a schedule and they enter the world exactly when they are ready (see p.378). Up to 42 weeks isn't really considered that late in medical circles. If it all becomes too much, rely on others close to you to field all the calls and make it clear that you promise to be in touch with an announcement just as soon as there is any news.

Text messaging can be a useful way of staying in touch with people in the final days. Sending out a circular "baby hasn't arrived yet" message is a good idea.

ASK A... DOCTOR

Is it worth paying extra for a private room when I'm in the hospital?
This is entirely up to you. It is expensive; it can cost a few hundred dollars a night, but some women find it money well spent. In addition to giving you more privacy and private time to bond with your new baby and your partner, a private room will be quieter, and you won't have as many interruptions, since you won't have medical staff coming in to treat a roommate. A private room can also make a difference in getting good rest at night, especially if you are a light sleeper.

FOCUS ON... YOUR BODY

False labor

You may experience deep and painful twinges, and practice contractions, known as Braxton-Hicks', particularly toward the end of pregnancy. It's easy to mistake these for the real thing, and you may find yourself rushing to the hospital when your body is really still practicing. You may also experience regular contractions for a period, which then stop. All of this is normal.

One sure sign that labor is imminent is that you lose your mucus plug (see p.411), another is your water breaking. In some cases, however, neither of these events takes place until labor is established, so don't panic if they don't happen to you.

You'll definitely know you're in labor when your contractions are occurring regularly, approximately every 15 minutes—time the gap between them. True contractions will get longer, stronger, and closer together as time goes on, and won't go away when you walk around or change position.

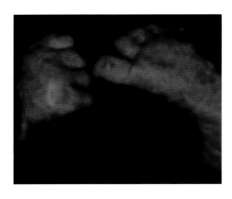

3 days to go...

YOUR BABY TODAY

This image shows that even at this time your baby will be able to reach down and touch her toes (see the foot on the right and the hand on the left). Because there is less space your baby will no longer be able to place her feet on top of her head.

Don't be too concerned if your baby hasn't engaged yet since this won't have any bearing on the final delivery date.

There are many reasons why your baby may not have engaged yet: the shape of your pelvis may mean that you need the pressure of the contractions to get the baby's head to engage. Very athletic women tend to have babies who engage late because their taut muscles hold the baby in a different position. Second and subsequent babies tend to engage later because the abdominal muscles are very loose, so the baby may move freely without feeling any need to get her head down. A big baby may not descend into the pelvis until the contractions start.

HOW YOUR BABY IS POSITIONED

Once the baby is head down and moves into the pelvis there are several positions she may adopt: six of the most common are shown below. The position is determined by where her back and occiput (the back of her head) are lying. The most usual position is LOT. If the baby is breech (see p.433), the position is determined by how the bottom is lying.

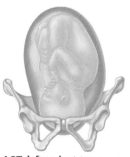

LOT: left occiput-transverse

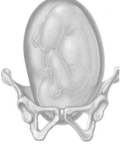

LOA: left occiput-anterior

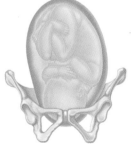

LOP: left occiput-posterior

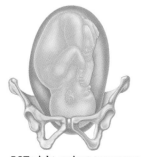

ROT: right occiput-transverse

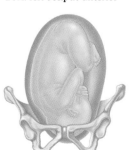

ROA: right occiput-anterior

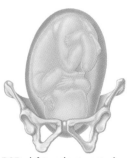

ROP: right occiput-posterior

LOT (left occiput-transverse): the back and occiput are positioned on the left-hand side of the uterus at right angles to the spine.

LOA (left occiput-anterior): the back and occiput are positioned closer to the front of the uterus on the left-hand side.

LOP (left occiput-posterior): the back and occiput are toward the spine on the left-hand side of the uterus.

ROT (right occiput-transverse): the back and occiput are at right angles to the spine on the right-hand side of the uterus.

ROA (right occiput-anterior): the back and occiput are toward the front of the uterus on the right-hand side.

ROP (right occiput-posterior): the back and occiput are toward the spine on the right-hand side of the uterus.

Your third trimester

388

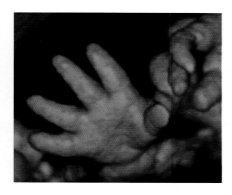

2 days to go...

YOUR BABY TODAY

This great image of the hands even shows the fine folds that have formed in the palms. Every baby has a unique pattern of folds on the palms and on the soles of the feet that you'll see when your baby finally arrives.

You'll be in labor very soon and it's normal to be anxious about what you need to go through to meet your baby.

You're bound to have mixed emotions about going into labor. While you'll want your baby to be born, you may be apprehensive about going through childbirth. Most women are understandably concerned about the pain, and may worry about their health and that of the baby. Remember that the majority of deliveries are normal and without complications and the majority of babies are fit and healthy.

Even though you've spent the past nine months preparing for the birth, you may still feel that you're not ready for the baby and that you won't be able to manage. Some of this will be the fear of the unknown—you have not yet met your baby and it's impossible to predict what the labor—and the weeks that follow it—will be like.

Although you may not feel fully prepared, be confident that you'll know how to take care of your newborn. In fact, you'll have probably already started the process of becoming a mother, wanting to nurture and protect your baby even before she's born, and this natural instinct will continue.

ASK A... DOCTOR

What's the difference between an emergency and elective cesarean?
An elective cesarean is when a planned decision is made during pregnancy to deliver the baby by cesarean section before the onset of labor. This is usually decided upon for medical reasons, although some women may decide to have an elective cesarean for practical reasons or to avoid having to go through labor.

An emergency cesarean is when a situation arises, usually in labor, that means the safest route for delivery is by cesarean section.

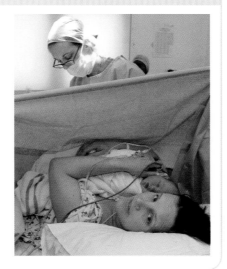

MRSA: IS IT A RISK?

There's a great deal of media coverage of "superbugs," such as MRSA. This is a bacterium that can live harmlessly on the skin of healthy people, but can lead to infection in vulnerable individuals. Good hygiene, particularly in the form of precautions such as hand-washing, is an effective method in the prevention of MRSA and your chances of acquiring the infection in hospital are low.

If cutlery and plates are washed using detergent and hot water this removes MRSA, and the risk of acquiring MRSA through contact with curtains, sheets, and pillows is very low. Health-care workers use antiseptic solutions, such as alcohol hand rubs, and more recently many hospitals are taking steps to prevent transmission of MRSA.

In addition to general hygiene measures, hospitals prevent the spread of MRSA by treating those infected with antibiotics, and by detecting cases early so that they can isolate affected patients. Infected patients are moved to a private room or to a room with others who have MRSA.

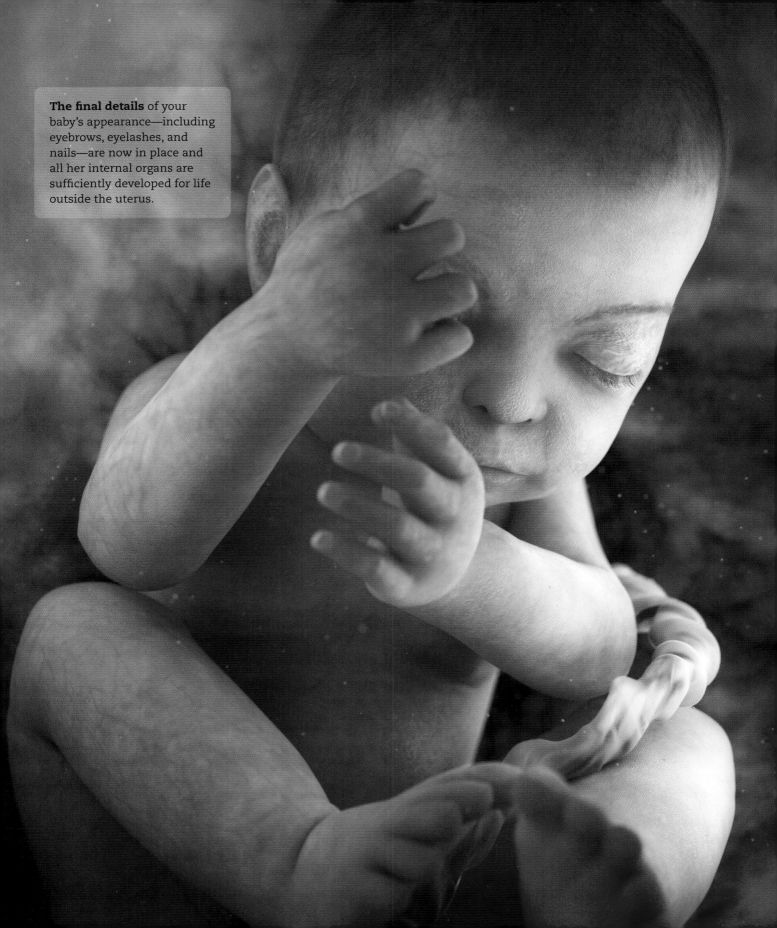

The final details of your baby's appearance—including eyebrows, eyelashes, and nails—are now in place and all her internal organs are sufficiently developed for life outside the uterus.

1 day to go...

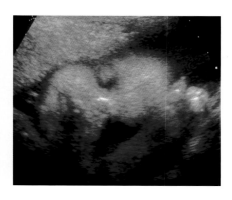

YOUR BABY TODAY

It's been wonderful to see your baby's progress and facial features as each day of the pregnancy has passed by. 2D and 3D ultrasound images, as well as MRI, have all played a part in giving us a glimpse into the fascinating and complex world of life before birth.

Your newborn's stomach will be fully developed, but low acid levels mean she can only be fed milk for the first few months.

RASPBERRY LEAF TEA

Raspberry leaf tea is a traditional remedy in Europe. European studies have found that drinking this tea in the months prior to delivery (not before week 30) helps shorten the second stage of labor by helping the uterine muscles to contract more efficiently, so that contractions are more effective.

The tea is also said to reduce the risk of having an assisted delivery, such as emergency cesarean or vacuum (see p.437).

In addition to this, raspberry leaf tea is believed to help the uterus to contract back to its normal size after the birth, and encourage the flow of breast milk.

As always you should talk to your doctor or midwife, before drinking any herbal teas or or taking any kind of herbal remedies.

Unlike an adult, your baby produces little gastric acid and keeps amniotic fluid in the stomach longer; it is this fluid that helps keep the acid content of her stomach low. While your baby is in the uterus hiccupping, turning upside down, and trying to coordinate breathing with swallowing, not having much hydrochloric acid in the stomach is a good idea.

After birth the acid content of your baby's stomach will increase quickly in the first 24 hours but not reach adult levels until three months. This is why solids aren't introduced until a baby is at least four months old, although six months is the current advice on when to start weaning. Babies have a reflex to spit out solid food if it's introduced too early and will only be able to take about 20–25 ml of food before the stomach is full. So it's easy to see how the stomach can quickly be overloaded, resulting in spitting up, which is when the baby brings the food and some milk back up.

ASK A... DOCTOR

What exactly is a "bloody show"? During pregnancy, a plug of jellylike mucus seals the lower end of your cervix and this prevents infection from getting into your uterus (see p.411). This "plug" comes away toward the end of pregnancy—known as a "bloody show"—and although this can mean that labor is going to start soon, it can also dislodge up to six weeks before your labor actually starts.

THE LOWDOWN

Take a break

Getting to know your newborn can be difficult if there's a constant stream of visitors bearing gifts and good wishes. Why not shut out the world and spend a few days home alone? Your newborn baby will sleep a lot, so take the opportunity to do the same. There will be plenty of time for people to meet the new member of your family.

Your hormones will be all over the place, so expect to experience lows as well as highs, especially when your milk comes in (see pp.448–9).

Your partner also needs time to bond with his baby, nurture you both, and come to grips with diaper changing.

So stick a message on the front door, switch on the answering machine, and snuggle up with your new family.

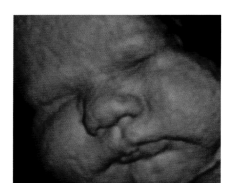

0 days to go...

YOUR BABY TODAY

Your baby is now ready for the outside world. Sudden changes will take place with that first breath after delivery, as she immediately adapts from her time within the fluid-filled environment of the uterus to life in the air outside.

You've reached 40 weeks exactly! It may have seemed like a long wait, but it will be worth it once you're holding your baby.

Congratulations! If you don't yet have your newborn baby in your arms, you soon will, and your life will be changed forever. Even the longest pregnancy seems unaccountably short when your labor begins, and the reality begins to hit that you'll soon be holding your newborn.

You'll get through the labor; and you'll forget about the discomfort after a few good sessions detailing it to family and close friends. In fact, everything that precedes that moment when you hold your newborn baby for the first time becomes inconsequential when you realize that you have created the most wondrous thing of all: a new life. So good luck and well done! This is only just the beginning of the most amazing years of your life.

Your pregnancy is coming to an end so rather than nurturing your belly, you'll soon be nurturing your amazing newborn baby.

AS A MATTER OF FACT

58 percent of parents questioned in a recent survey believed that the name they gave their baby would contribute to his or her success in life.

More found it easier to name a boy than a girl, and just 3 percent said they would change the name they'd given their baby if they could.

Overdue baby

Your baby is described as being overdue if you have not gone into labor by the time you are 40 weeks' pregnant. This is not unusual since most women do not go into labor at exactly 40 weeks, and anything between 37 and 42 weeks is considered to be normal.

Why labor is late As the exact trigger that sets off labor is unknown, it's not clear why some women are overdue. You are more likely to be overdue if this is your first baby, if you've had an overdue baby before, or if the condition runs in your family. Some think it's more common in well nourished women, and there is even evidence that pregnancies are longer in the summer than in the winter. If your due date was figured out from an early ultrasound, this gives a more accurate dating of pregnancy than the date of your last menstrual period, and you'll be less likely to be classified as overdue.

What will be done
After 41 weeks, there is a slightly increased risk to your baby's health that may be due to the reduced efficiency of the placenta. After 42 weeks the risk increases, but is still small. Depending on hospital policy, you will be offered an induction around 41 weeks (see p.432). The following may also be done.

Stripping the membranes After 40 weeks, your doctor may do an internal examination to "strip the membranes." She'll insert a gloved finger into the cervix and pull the membranes in a circular pattern. This can soften the cervix and increase the chance of you going into labor by 30 percent in the next 48 hours. It's safe for you and your baby, but can cause cramps and slight bleeding.

Assessments after 42 weeks Many doctors induce labor by 41 or 42 weeks. If your pregnancy goes beyond 42 weeks and you don't want to be induced, your

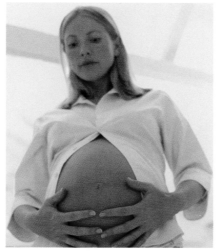

Going over your due date can be stressful, but it may help to remind yourself that it's also extremely common and quite normal.

doctor may offer monitoring with scans to measure the baby's pulse and volume of fluid around the baby; or you may have a NST (see p.418) once or twice a week until labor to pick up any signs that the placenta is failing. If a problem is found, you'll be advised to have a cesarean or an induction of labor.

How you're feeling
You might find the physical and mental stress of being pregnant beyond your due date considerable but it can help to know that unless you have a medical condition, being overdue does not significantly increase your health risks. You may worry that your baby will grow too large, causing difficulty in labor, but your baby isn't likely to put on enough weight in the last week or so to make a big difference and most overdue babies have a normal birthweight.

AT-HOME STRATEGIES

Bringing on labor

Although no "home" or alternative remedy has been proven to bring on labor, there are several harmless techniques that are thought to assist the body's natural processes.

■ **Probably the most enjoyable way to try to bring on labor is to make love** with your partner. Sperm contains prostaglandins that may act as a natural uterine stimulant, although the evidence that this works is inconclusive. Making love is not dangerous to your baby, unless your doctor has specifically told you to refrain from intercourse for a medical reason, such as fetal growth restriction or placental bleeding.

■ **Nipple stimulation during sex** or by itself can cause the release of oxytocin from your pituitary gland, which is linked to contractions and cervical ripening.

■ **Walking and exercise** may cause a mild increase in uterine contractions by helping the baby move down the pelvis, putting pressure on the cervix.

■ **Raspberry leaf** has been associated with increased uterine activity. Very little research has been done studying the use of raspberry leaf in pregnant women, so it's best to avoid this herbal remedy unless your doctor gives you the go-ahead and your pregnancy is already full-term.

 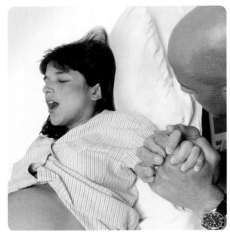 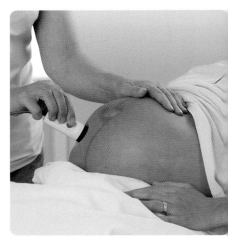

As the moment you've so eagerly anticipated approaches, you may have increasing concerns about what lies in store for you during the labor and delivery, and doubts as to whether you'll be able to cope with the physical and mental demands during this crucial time. Being as informed as possible about the progress of labor and your options for pain relief are both important first steps in enabling you to face labor and birth with a positive mindset.

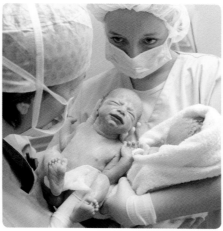

Labor
and birth

Pain relief options

A PRIOR KNOWLEDGE OF PAIN RELIEF WILL HELP YOU MAKE INFORMED CHOICES IN LABOR

Once in labor, in addition to needing emotional and physical support, which your doctor, nurse, or midwife and birth partner will provide, you may also need some form of pain relief to help you cope. They will help you work with your labor pain by employing natural methods such as breathing techniques. If you need stronger pain relief, they'll advise you on medical methods, such as analgesics or an epidural (see pp.402–407).

Coping with pain

To help you cope with labor and birth, it's important to have an understanding of the progress of pain during labor.

Labor pain is unique and quite different from everyday chronic and acute pain. Generally, pain is a warning sign that something is wrong, but labor pain acts as an "alert" that the birth process is underway and that you need a safe environment in which to give birth. Some women prefer a homelike environment, which has been shown to have many benefits, including reducing the need for medical forms of pain relief. For this reason, many labor rooms in maternity units and especially birth centers have homey decoration and furnishings to make them feel less medicalized. Other women need the reassurance provided by hospitals that stronger forms of pain relief and medical backup are available.

Being informed about the pain of labor can reduce your anxiety and help you manage.

How women react to pain

No one really knows what starts labor and every woman's labor is unique. Likewise, the pain associated with labor can vary enormously between women. Some women have relatively painless labors, while some describe the pain as moderate, and others experience severe pain. One thing that does seem clear is that anxiety and fear increase the levels of adrenaline, which in turn can increase the intensity of the pain experienced. The strength of labor pain can also be affected by factors such as your emotional state and anticipation of labor; your previous experiences, if any; cultural beliefs; and, in particular for first-time mothers, the fear of the unknown. Thorough preparation prior to labor and sensitive and caring support throughout labor and birth can help reduce anxiety and fear considerably.

Thinking ahead

The sensation of pain is different during the different stages of labor, and as labor progresses the intensity and duration of the pain increases. The most effective methods of dealing with pain will also change as your labor progresses (see box, left).

The more familiar you are with the methods of dealing with pain and with the several natural and drug-induced methods of pain relief available (see following pages), the easier it will be for you to manage during labor and birth. To make decisions about pain relief, you will also need to understand the changes that take place in your body during the three different stages of labor (see pp.408–29).

PAIN RELIEF THROUGHOUT LABOR

Your pain-relief requirements may change during labor, so it helps to be aware of different types of pain relief.

Early first stage In this phase, the cervix begins to dilate. Contractions are mild, and you may find that natural methods, such as massage and breathing, are helpful. If you need stronger pain relief, you may be given analgesics, which dull pain but allow you to remain active since you won't lose all feeling or muscle movement.

Active first stage The cervix now starts to dilate more quickly and contractions are stronger and closer together. Some women are happy to continue with natural or analgesic pain relief; others may need stronger relief and an epidural may be given at this point (see pp.404–5).

Transition Contractions are intense and frequent as the cervix dilates fully. Systemic (intravenous or intramuscular) analgesics aren't usually given this close to the birth since they could affect the baby. If you have an epidural already in place, this can be topped off.

Second and third stages Second stage lasts from full dilation of the cervix until birth; contractions are strong and longer lasting, but easier to manage since you start pushing. Analgesics may be used. In the 3rd stage, delivery of the placenta, contractions are mild and you shouldn't need pain relief.

Natural pain relief

Many women opt for natural pain relief in labor, or choose to complement medical pain relief with natural methods.

During your labor, encephalins and endorphins (feel-good hormones) are released to provide you with some naturally induced pain relief. Many women now are also more aware of natural techniques, such as staying active, and of the availability of complementary therapies that they can use in addition to, or instead of, medical pain relief during pregnancy, childbirth, and following the birth. Some of these therapies are self administered and some are practitioner administered. A knowledge of the benefits of different therapies and how to use them is important if you are considering using them to deal with pain in labor.

Staying active

Being active in labor has been shown to help women to deal with pain and reduce the length of labor. Historically, women have been active in labor for centuries, but a medicalization of childbirth in the West led to an acceptance that women lie in bed, and a common image of a laboring woman is one lying in bed. Although during labor you may want to rest on a bed between contractions, many women find that when they feel supported, they will instinctively move around and do not cope well lying down, which can increase pain and hamper the progress of labor as your baby pushes against gravity. You may find it helpful to take a walk, roll on a birthing ball, rock in a rocking chair or change positions when you get too uncomfortable. There are certain interventions, such as the use of electronic fetal monitoring (see p.418), IVs, and some types of analgesia, that will limit your mobility.

RELAXATION TECHNIQUES

There are various techniques you can use to help you relax during labor; if you're relaxed, it will be easier to stay calm and in tune with your body. These techniques include focusing on your breathing (see below); listening to music (perhaps humming to the beat of a favorite tune during a contraction); and listening to a meditation CD.

Learning how to breathe slowly and steadily in labor helps you focus and stay calm. Usually, your breathing responds to how you're feeling and may increase slightly during a contraction, or you may hold your breath, which can make you feel light-headed. If this happens, you need to focus and steady your breathing. Your nurse will remind you to breathe slowly and steadily. Breathing in for five and out for seven slows your breathing down, helps you relax, and stops you from panicking.

Concentrating on your breathing in labor is calming and helps you focus (top). **Leaning forward while breathing** steadily can be comforting during contractions (bottom).

Listening to some of your favorite music in the first stage of labor is a great way to relax between contractions, enabling you to let go and reserve energy for later in labor.

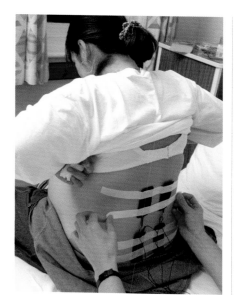

Once the electrodes for TENS are positioned on your back, you will be free to move around and find comfortable positions.

TENS

TENS stands for Transcutaneous Electrical Nerve Stimulation, and is a small electrical device that reduces pain signals sent to the brain. In addition to being used in labor, the device can also be used at the end of pregnancy (after 36 weeks) if you have a backache or uncomfortable Braxton Hicks' contractions (see p.410).

The battery-operated TENS machine has thin wires that are connected to four electrodes, or sticky pads, which are taped to the lower back. The machine is thought to work by sending electrical impulses from the machine along nerve roots to the pain pathways in the brain, thereby blocking pain impulses. It's also thought to stimulate the brain to produce "feel good" encephalins and endorphins, which can modulate the pain.

TENS is most effective in early labor, particularly for lower back pain, and it is therefore important to have the device available at the beginning of labor. It's therefore worth finding out if your hospital has TENS machines or whether you need to rent one in advance. You can hold the device or have it near you in labor and can increase the strength of the electrical impulse with a button as your contractions get stronger.

There are several advantages to TENS. It has few side effects; it allows you to remain active; and it can be used in combination with other types of pain relief. The disadvantages are that there hasn't been much research done about its safety for the baby, so a theoretical risk exists, and it is generally effective with just mild to moderate pain; the sticky pads mean that a back massage is not possible; and it isn't possible to labor in water or have an epidural inserted while using the device.

Water

Many women find being in warm water during labor very soothing and an excellent way to cope with labor pain.

The warmth of the water soothes muscles, promoting relaxation, and being in water aids buoyancy, which can help relieve the pressure on your pelvis. Over the last decade or so, this natural method has become more available for women and some hospitals and birth centers provide bathtubs. Whether or not you can actually deliver your baby in the water will depend on the hospital's policy and whether there are any doctors or midwives trained in water births (see p.427). You can also purchase or rent a birthing pool.

Hypnosis

Self-hypnosis, using visualization and breathing techniques to induce a state of deep relaxation and banish fear, is an increasingly popular means of dealing with labor, and is referred to as "HypnoBirthing." This is based on the "fear-tension-pain" syndrome of

Laboring in warm water can be deeply soothing. In addition to helping take the pressure off your pelvis, water also relaxes muscles, in turn easing tension and stress.

QUESTIONS AND ANSWERS

Will I be able to stay active in labor?
Yes, most women are able to remain active through labor and are encouraged to do so, perhaps using props such as a chair, beanbag, or birthing ball. Staying active can help since this can speed up labor, and changing your position can help you deal with labor pain. When you arrive at the hospital or birth center, discuss your birth plan with the doctor and inform her that you want to be as active as possible.

Will I lose control if I use hypnosis during my labor? No, you will simply feel deeply relaxed, but will still be in control and know what you are doing. Don't worry—self-hypnosis will help you be less anxious and frightened during your labor, which will help you to deal with labor pain. With preparation, your partner can help you stay focused and use some hypnotic techniques too.

I've had a previous cesarean. Does this mean that I won't be able to labor in water this time? It depends on the procedures that your health-care provider follows for women who have already had a cesarean. After a cesarean, the doctors will want to monitor you and the baby either continuously or frequently during labor, because there is a very small chance that your uterus may rupture, which is often only detected through a change in the baby's heartbeat. But waterproof monitoring systems are widely available and some practices may perform WBAC—water birth after cesarean.

At what point can I get into the birthing pool? This is up to you. Relaxing in warm water is often suggested in the early stages of labor, as long as your contractions are progressing. You can sit in the warm water for 1½ to 2 hours for pain management, but then get out. Changing your environment helps keep your labor active.

childbirth first described by the English obstetrician Grantly Dick-Read (see p.303), who believed that fear prevents the release of the "feel good hormones," endorphins and encephalins. He maintained that when fear is eliminated, most women can give birth naturally. With HypnoBirthing, you are fully aware of what is happening around you, but may feel as though you're daydreaming or drifting off to sleep. You and your birth partner can attend HypnoBirthing classes anytime during pregnancy to learn the techniques before labor. To find a class in your area, visit hypnobirthing.com/findapract.htm.

Acupuncture
This uses fine needles placed at specific points on the body to reduce pain by stimulating the production of endorphins. Acupuncture is a traditional form of Chinese medicine that believes there are channels within the body through which energy, or "chi" runs. Blockages can occur in these channels, and so by inserting needles at certain points, energy is unblocked, relieving pain and restoring balance to the body. Many women find acupuncture helpful to treat mild pregnancy symptoms, and some women use this therapy during labor. Acupuncture has no harmful side effects for the mother or baby and in labor, needles will usually be inserted in points that do not restrict your movement, for example in the ear. If you want to have acupuncture during labor, you will need to look for an acupuncturist who specializes in this area and arrange to have him or her with you during labor.

MASSAGE AND TOUCH

Many women find massage helpful in labor to induce relaxation, bring about a sense of well-being, and alleviate pain. Your birth partner may find it relaxing and therapeutic too. Ideally, he or she will have had a chance to see massage techniques demonstrated in prenatal classes and to practice before labor. Massaging the lower back helps relieve pain in this area; head, neck, and shoulder massage is beneficial for relieving tension and fatigue.

The touch therapies shiatsu and acupressure can also help relieve pain and tension. They involve application of pressure to specific points to increase endorphin levels. You or your partner will need to learn the techniques from a trained practitioner. Ask your doctor if she can put you in touch with a practitioner.

Your partner can use the heel of his hand to apply firm pressure to your sacrum. The hands can be alternated to stroke around the lower back.

Using the thumbs to massage the lower back in a circular motion, working from the base of the spine down to the buttocks, can release tense muscles.

Applying deep pressure to the buttocks and lower back with the thumbs can help you focus and release held-in tension during contractions.

Homeopathy

This is based on the principle of treating like with like. Talk to your doctor before using any homeopathic products during pregnancy or labor, since homeopathy is an area of complementary and alternative medicine that's associated with much debate and scientific controversy. If your doctor or midwife gives you the okay, a certified homeopath can prescribe remedies based on your individual needs. There is a lack of scientific evidence on the effectiveness of homeopathy, although many women find the remedies helpful.

Aromatherapy

Aromatherapy (essential) oils are derived from plants and used for their therapeutic properties. The use of these oils in childbirth can stimulate, refresh, and soothe you and to some extent your partner. There is some evidence that oils, such as lavender, reduce anxiety in labor, which in turn helps you cope with pain. Hot and cold compresses with essential oils added to the water used to wet the cloth can be soothing and massaging diluted essential oils (in a carrier oil) into the skin is therapeutic. Many experts recommend against aromatherapy during pregnancy and labor because some scents may be hazardous to pregnant women. The effects of most plant oils on pregnant women is unknown.

Reflexology

Reflexology involves massaging reflex zones on your feet that correspond with different parts of your body to improve your blood circulation and relax any tension you may be feeling. Reflexology is gaining some popularity as a coping technique in the early stages of labor. However, because many women naturally want to be active and move around during their labor, this may be more helpful in between early contractions.

BIRTH STORY: A NATURAL HOME BIRTH

Jenna is a 31-year-old mom and this is her second labor. She had a straightforward birth with her daughter, now three. This pregnancy was uneventful, so she decided to have a home birth this time.

Jenna's story: When I was eight days overdue, my midwife did a "stretch and strip" (see p.393) of my cervix to encourage labor. I then had a couple of bloody shows (see p.411) and irregular contractions. In the night I woke with contractions 20 minutes apart. I couldn't get back to sleep, so I had a warm bath, took a couple of acetaminophens, and went back to bed. My daughter woke at 6:45 am and we had breakfast. My contractions were every 10 minutes and getting stronger, so my husband stayed home.

By 8:00 am, my contractions were every 5 minutes, stronger, and lasting 50–60 seconds. My husband called the midwife. She said she was on her way and advised me to stay active. I started to use the TENS machine (see p.399) on a low setting, which helped me focus. I found standing and rocking my pelvis back and forth and from side to side helpful and I used a birthing ball. My husband was supportive, massaging my shoulders and under my abdomen where it hurt most; I found the heat from his hands soothing. My daughter held my hand.

At 8:40 am, the midwife arrived. She checked my blood pressure, pulse, and temperature, felt my belly, listened to the baby's heart, and took a urine sample, which relieved some pressure in my pubic area. She confirmed that I was in established labor since my cervix was 5 cm dilated. My cervix was thinning, the head was pressing down, and my membranes were intact. I remained active, using TENS, and leaning forward. My husband put on a relaxing CD.

At 9:50 am my contractions were every two minutes, very strong, and lasting 60 seconds. I tried walking and marching on the spot. My mom arrived and took my daughter to the park. I felt hot and so I had a cool drink and my midwife dabbed my face with a cool, wet cloth. I found kneeling on all fours, rocking and arching my back, helpful.

By 10:30 am my contractions were very painful. My midwife listened to the heartbeat intermittently.

By 11:00 am I felt an urge to push. My water broke and my contractions were very strong and each minute. I felt panicky, but my midwife encouraged me, saying she thought the baby would be born soon; my husband helped me focus by breathing slowly. My midwife confirmed that I was fully dilated and ready to push. I somehow found the energy to bear down and felt the head emerge. I took a breath, concentrated, and pushed my baby out. My baby boy was born at 11:14 am, 8 lb 2 oz, and my husband cut the cord once it had stopped pulsating. I delivered my placenta without drugs (see p.429). My midwife advised me to put my baby to my breast to stimulate the hormone oxytocin, which causes contractions and helps the placenta to come away. My placenta was delivered at 11:40 am.

The midwife's comments: Jenna and her husband prepared well and worked as a team. Jenna was active for most of labor, and stayed focused. Her feelings of panic in the transition period were normal, but her husband and I gave her extra support. By working with her instincts she found inner strength and had a normal birth. Her labor was nine hours, about average for a second-time mom.

Drugs for pain relief

Various types of medication are available for pain relief during labor; many can be used alongside natural forms of pain relief.

Discussing different pain relief options with your doctor prior to labor can help you assess the merits of each type and to think about what type of pain relief you would prefer.

For some, natural pain relief may not be sufficient to enable them to deal with the increasing intensity of contractions, and they may choose to use medication in combination with natural techniques. In some situations, for example if labor is induced (see p.432) or augmented (see p.415), contractions may start strongly rather than build up gradually and a stronger type of pain relief may be needed.

There are several types of medical pain relief available, which fall into two groups. Analgesic drugs dull the perception of pain, while anesthesia, which may be regional or general, numbs pain totally. In regional anesthesia, also known as a nerve block, local anesthetic drugs are injected around nerves that supply a particular area. There are several types of regional nerve block: epidurals and spinal blocks numb sensation in the abdomen and are used to reduce the pain of contractions; a pudendal block numbs sensation in the vagina and perineum and may be used in a forceps delivery. Occasionally, a general anesthetic is given during a cesarean.

Since all labors are different, it's not possible to have a "one size fits all" approach to pain relief. Being flexible and informed will help you feel in control. Read any literature from your doctor, go to prenatal classes, and ask questions. Try to eliminate any worries by increasing your knowledge, for example by asking if it's possible to attend a childbirth education class at the hospital that discusses the pros and cons of each type of pain relief. Keep in mind that some childbirth classes, like Lamaze and the Bradley method, can teach you breathing and relaxation techniques that may help reduce your need for pain medication during labor.

THINK ABOUT

Natural pain relief

Whether you're still at home and it's too early in labor to get pain medication, or you're trying to wait it out at the hospital to see if you really need drugs, you can try any or all of the following techniques that may help to relieve pain without medication:

- Taking a warm bath or shower
- Changing your position
- Meditation
- Hypnosis
- Getting a back massage from your partner
- Walking around
- Meditation

Pain relief plan

Having a birth plan ahead of time that outlines the circumstances during which you would resort to using medication for pain relief may be helpful for some women. For example, you may want to try to remain medication-free unless the pain is so intense, it interferes with your ability to hold a normal conversation, or it doubles you over in pain. Perhaps you'll seek relief if your labor drags on hours longer than you expected and you need some respite to sleep for a while to regain your strength for the upcoming pushing that you'll be doing. Whatever the case, you may feel more in control if you know ahead of time what your limits are and when you want to say yes to pain medication, rather than being overwhelmed by the situation, if you don't give it much thought beforehand.

Opioids

These belong to a group of drugs called narcotics (which literally means sleep-inducing), which includes morphine.

They attach themselves to receptors in the brain or nerves and block the transmission of pain.

Tranquilizers These drugs don't relieve pain, but they can help to relieve anxiety and help a women relax for several hours during early labor. Some women who are very anxious about the impending pain or of labor and childbirth may seek this sort of medication. Tranquilizers may be given orally, intravenously, or injected into a large muscle. Oral dosage takes the longest to take effect. Some women dislike what tranquilizers do to them, since they may feel drowsy and out of control. If the dose is very high, women may nod off between contractions. It may be hard for a woman to fully remember her labor experience if she's taken tranquilizers. The drugs also effect the baby, decreasing his activity and muscle tone during and after birth. For these reasons, tranquilizers are not for everyone and are rarely used, but in certain circumstances, they can help a woman feel less anxious about labor.

Considering an epidural

Pros

■ An epidural provides absolute pain relief in 90 percent of cases; 10 percent of women have some degree of residual pain, but still have a marked improvement in their overall discomfort.
■ Epidurals do not pose any risk to your baby.
■ The presence of an effective epidural means that if intervention is needed at any time, the epidural can be topped off with anesthetic for either an assisted delivery with forceps or vacuum, or a cesarean delivery. This also reduces the likelihood that a general anesthetic will be needed.

Cons

■ Around 1 in 10 women do not experience absolute pain relief with an epidural.
■ Some women develop a headache that persists after an epidural (see p.406).
■ A rare complication is patches of heaviness in the legs or feet.

There are a few very rare risks with an epidural

■ In common with all invasive procedures, inserting an epidural can result in infection. Meningitis occurs in around 1 in 100,000 women and an epidural abscess occurs in about 1 in 50,000 women.
■ There is a 1 in 170,000 risk of developing a blood clot in the epidural space (epidural hematoma).
■ There is a 1 in 100,000 risk of the epidural tube moving into the fluid around the spine and resulting in unconsciousness, and there is a 1 in 250,000 chance of the epidural causing some form of paralysis.

Epidurals

An epidural is a regional anesthetic that can be given at any stage of labor to numb the abdomen and therefore block the pain of contractions, but it's typically given when the woman is at least 4 cm dilated. In some cases, if a woman's labor progresses very quickly and she doesn't request one right away, she may not be able to get one before delivery. Epidurals are the most popular form of pain relief during labor in Canada, with more than half of pregnant women delivering in hospitals choosing this treatment.

How epidurals work A hollow needle is inserted between two vertebrae in the lower back. A tiny plastic tube is then passed through the needle and into the epidural space surrounding the spinal cord. A local anesthetic is injected into the needle and flows through the tube into the epidural space so that the nerve roots carrying the pain stimulus to the brain are coated with anesthetic and pain is reduced or completely blocked. This will affect sensation in your legs so that you need to remain in bed and your baby will be closely monitored. A stronger epidural also affects sensation in your bladder, so you will need to have a catheter. Used late in labor, a stonger epidural may mean that you need help to push the baby out, since the pelvic floor muscles will be heavy and ineffective. In this case, your nurse or midwife will put a hand on your abdomen to feel when a contraction starts and will tell you when to push. In some cases, an assisted delivery (see pp.436–7) becomes necessary.

When are epidurals used? Epidurals can be used throughout labor, but they're typically given during active labor when a woman is 4–5 cm dilated. Since everyone has varying pain thresholds, the time when one is requested varies. There are factors to bear in mind should you opt for an epidural late in labor. To minimize the risks, you must remain completely still during the placement of the epidural tube. If your labor has progressed too far to enable you to do this, the anesthesiologist may refuse to proceed with an epidural for your own interest. Also, if you choose to have an epidural late in labor, it may be necessary to give a high dose so that it takes effect in time, which has disadvantages (see left).

If you're considering using an epidural, inform your doctor early in labor so that she can consult the anesthesiologist. The anesthesiologist may then discuss this with you and take a brief medical history to ensure that it's safe for you to have an epidural. She will discuss any risks, and answer any questions that you or your partner has, all of which can save time later on if you decide to go ahead.

There are occasions when an epidural is not advised. These include cases where a woman has had spinal surgery or is taking blood-thinning medication. Rarely, a woman may have an infection that could be exacerbated by an epidural.

Side effects There are a number of minor side effects. The medication can cause blood pressure to fall, so this will be monitored (see p.405). If it does fall, you'll be given fluids and medication, and subsequent doses may be reduced.

It's common to expericene itching with epidurals, caused by the release of histamine from the opioid component of a mobile epidural. Histamine is a substance released by the body during an allergic reaction that can cause itching. The itch can be treated, but in most cases it gets better on its own. If you develop an itch, a greater concentration of local anesthetic alone will be used.

It's not unusual to shiver with an epidural, although this is a more common side effect if a concentrated local anesthetic is used, as is the case for a cesarean delivery.

Epidural pain relief can cause a rise in temperature. If this occurs, you'll have a

If you opt for an epidural, the doctor should explain the procedure to you, and you should have the opportunity to ask the anesthesiologist any questions.

Getting ready for an epidural Before starting the epidural, a plastic tube will be placed in a vein in the back of your hand or in your arm, to which an IV containing fluid will be connected. You are given fluids during an epidural to stop your blood pressure from dropping. The doctor will then help you into the correct position to receive the epidural, which will either be sitting up with your legs over the side of the bed leaning forward, or curled up on your side on the edge of the bed. The position may depend on the preference of the anesthesiologist.

Your lower back will be cleaned with antiseptic and a drape placed over the rest of your back to reduce the risk of infection. Before the epidural needle is inserted, a local anesthetic will be given into the skin and surrounding tissues. This creates a numb patch to ensure that the insertion of the large epidural needle is not painful. When the local anesthetic is injected, you may feel a scratching sensation and experience a very short-lived sting in the area between the vertebrae bones

The procedure Since it's important for you to remain still during the procedure, the anesthesiologist will insert the epidural between your contractions. If this is difficult, you should try to concentrate on your breathing and remain as still as possible until the procedure is completed. You will feel a pushing sensation in your back while the anesthesiologist is trying to find the very small epidural space with the hollow needle. When the space is located, a tiny plastic tube will be fed into it through the needle. The epidural needle is then removed and the tube, which is secured onto your back with sticky tape, remains in the epidural space. The tube remains in place until your baby is delivered and, because it is very thin, soft, and pliable, it is perfectly safe to lie on the tube and to move around.

Managing the epidural Once the epidural tube is successfully in place, the anesthesiologist will give the first dose of medication through it by means of a syringe. Once she is satisfied that the epidural is in the correct position and is working effectively, all subsequent doses, or "top ups," can be given without another injection. Your blood pressure will be taken once the epidural is in place and will be monitored for the next half an hour or so, and then regularly thereafter, including after each top up. Each dose of medication takes around 10–20 minutes to take its full effect and can last between one and two hours. The epidural will be topped up as required, usually around every three to four hours, to keep you comfortable throughout your labor. An anesthesiologist should be available 24 hours a day to manage any concerns or problems that may arise with the epidural.

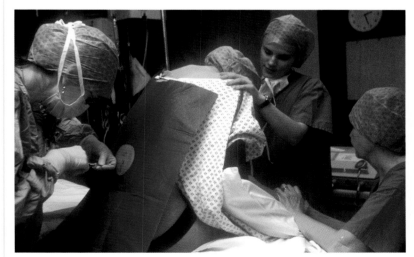

Before the epidural is given, your back will be covered with a sterile sheet and then a local anesthetic will be given to numb the area so that you don't experience pain when the larger epidural needle is inserted.

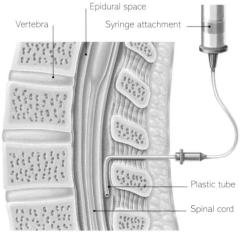

Epidural space

Syringe attachment

Vertebra

Plastic tube

Spinal cord

The anesthetic is given through a tube that is inserted into the epidural space, avoiding the spinal cord and its covering.

Drugs for pain relief

blood test to eliminate an infection since this can also cause your temperature to rise. You will be given preventative antibiotics while waiting for the blood test results, and acetaminophen to bring your temperature back to normal.

Problems with epidurals In addition to side effects, there can occasionally be problems with the effectiveness of an epidural. The anesthetic may not spread evenly in the epidural space, which may be caused by the epidural tube sitting on one side of the epidural space. This can mean that pain relief only occurs on one side of the body. If this occurs, the anesthesiologist will try to reposition the tube and give another dose of anesthetic. If this doesn't work, the only other solution is to redo the entire epidural.

Sometimes, one spot can remain painful, usually in the groin area or low down in the front of the abdomen, which is referred to as a "missed segment." This results from a single nerve root not being coated with the local anesthetic. Again, the anesthesiologist may reposition the tube. Sometimes, a stronger local anesthetic or an opioid is used to numb the area. If a persistent missed segment is too uncomfortable, the anesthesiologist may do a combined spinal epidural block, known as a CSE (see opposite).

It's thought that epidural pain relief may prolong the second stage of labor. It also increases your chances of having an assisted delivery, especially if a high dose of anesthetic is given toward the end of labor, which affects your ability to push. However, an epidural doesn't increase the chance of a cesarean and doesn't, despite common misconceptions, cause long-term backache after the birth.

Spinal block

This is similar to an epidural in that a needle is put in your back and pain relief is achieved by blocking nerve fibers that supply the pelvic organs. However, in a spinal block, the needle is passed through the epidural space to pierce the membrane covering the spinal cord (the dura) so that anesthetic can be injected into the fluid around the spinal cord; no tubes are left in place. The needle used for a spinal block is smaller than that used for an epidural, which means it's less painful to insert. There is still a risk of a headache as with an epidural (see left) and the side effects should be treated the same way.

A smaller dose of anesthetic is needed and it works very quickly: pain relief is almost immediate, whereas an epidural takes 10–20 minutes. However, the use of a spinal block is limited because only a single dose of medication can be administered. As a result, spinal blocks are usually reserved for use during a cesarean, or for an assisted delivery when an epidural isn't in place.

Combined spinal epidural (CSE) or "walking epidural"

This involves both a spinal injection and putting an epidural in place. It's sometimes done when problems are encountered with an epidural (see left) and is also used for a cesarean. A CSE gives pain relief throughout labor. However, it's a specialized technique and isn't offered in all units.

Pudendal blocks

This type of regional anesthesia involves injecting a local anesthetic into the vagina where the pudendal nerves are located to reduce pain in the vagina and perineum. The pudendal needle is quite long and thick, so before the injection is given, a cold anesthetic spray is applied to the area. The anesthetic has no effect on the baby and can be used with other medications. It takes effect very quickly and is sometimes used just before birth to aid an assisted forceps delivery.

General anesthesia

Most cesareans are conducted using regional anesthesia. However, in some cases general anesthesia, where the mother is put to sleep, is necessary. This may be because of a failure of regional anesthesia, blood-clotting problems in the mother, an infection in the mother's bloodstream, or persistent fetal distress.

AN EPIDURAL "HEADACHE"

Some women report a headache after an epidural, which can develop more than 24 hours after the delivery and tends to be at the front of the head. It is made worse by sitting up and moving around and is much improved by lying down. This occurs in around 1 in 100 women and is caused by the epidural needle moving too far forward and cutting the dura sheath, the membrane maintaining the fluid around the spinal cord and brain. This small hole results in a loss of fluid from the sheath, which causes a headache. The risk is hugely reduced by remaining still during the placement of the epidural. In around 70 percent of women, the hole heals on its own.

You will be advised to drink plenty of fluids and to take simple painkillers, such as acetaminophen and ibuprofen and you will be reviewed at regular intervals by an anesthesiologist.

If the headache persists, a procedure called a "blood patch" will be done. This is done in the sterile environment of an operating room by an anesthesiologist, who will place an epidural needle in your back and take around 20 ml of blood from a vein in your arm. The blood is then passed down the needle into the epidural space. This forms a clot that seals the hole and prevents further leakage of fluid from around your spine, therefore relieving the headache.

Alice was having her first baby. Her pregnancy had been uncomplicated and she had written a birth plan with her husband outlining her desire for a natural childbirth by keeping active and using TENS and then warm water to deal with contractions. Alice also stated that she wanted to avoid an epidural if possible.

Alice's birth story: My husband and I arrived at the delivery suite in early labor. I started to use a TENS machine for pain relief. However, as my labor progressed, I became very distressed since I hadn't anticipated that the contractions would be so painful. When I was around 3 cm dilated, I decided to remove the TENS machine and get into the bath. My husband gave me a back massage and provided emotional support. However, I think he struggled to understand my discomfort and he needed support from the nurse. After 15 minutes, I decided to get out of the bath since it was providing little pain relief. I used a birth ball to stay active and my husband gave me more massage and acupressure. I coped well for the next hour, but then became increasingly exhausted and upset. When I was

examined, I was only 5 cm dilated. We both felt despondent because we had hoped I was further along.

My nurse then suggested that I talked to the anesthesiologist about my options for further pain relief, and as a result of my conversation with the anesthesiologist, I decided to have an epidural. I told the anesthesiologist that I'd had an epidural a few years ago for knee surgery and how it had provided excellent pain relief, but that I had itched for hours afterward. The anesthesiologist surmised that the itch was caused by one of the painkilling medications (fentanyl) in the epidural top up and agreed that this medicine wouldn't be used.

The anesthesiologist agreed to do a low dose combined spinal epidural that gave absolute pain relief within five minutes. My legs were a little heavy at first, but they felt fine within an hour. I felt that we were both able to take time out after the epidural and that I was able to refocus on my labor. I felt pleased that I'd managed a large part of my labor without pain relief, and was happy with the decision to have an epidural when I did. I had an unassisted delivery later that evening and gave birth to a beautiful baby girl.

The anesthesiologist comments: Alice kept an open mind regarding pain relief and understood that different methods of pain relief could be used at different times during labor. After the epidural, she no longer felt that her labor was an endurance test and was able to focus again on her labor and on delivering a healthy baby.

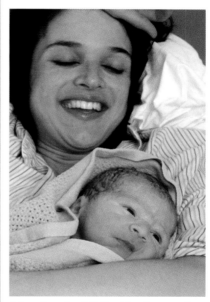

A low dose "mobile" epidural means that you maintain some feeling in your legs and can remain active during labor.

The procedure Precautions are taken to minimize the risks to you and your baby. You'll be given an antacid to reduce stomach acid. Often a catheter is inserted into the bladder and antiseptic is applied to the abdomen before you're put to sleep to minimize the baby's exposure to the anesthetic.

As the mother is put to sleep, a face mask is held tightly over her nose and mouth. Because a major risk during general anesthesia is undigested food or liquids in the stomach re-entering the mouth and going into the lungs (which can cause damage) you'll likely

be told not to eat or drink anything once labor begins (because labor usually slows digestion), in case you need general anesthesia. You may be able to have ice chips, though. Once asleep, an anesthesiologist inserts a tube through your mouth and down your throat so that oxygen can easily reach your lungs. You may therefore have a sore throat when you wake up.

During the surgery the anesthesiologist cares for the mother, giving painkillers and anti-nausea medicine when needed. The baby is cared for by the doctor.

After the surgery The procedure takes about an hour. The mother is woken 5–10 minutes after the surgery. The baby is kept with the mother at all times unless he needs extra care.

Since general anesthesia doesn't give localized pain relief, it's normal to need pain relief afterward. Oral medicine will be given regularly and morphine-based medication may be given for a day or two. Your anesthesiologist may set up a patient-controlled analgesia, or a PCA, via an intravenous route, which will deliver a prescribed amount of painkiller on demand.

Drugs for pain relief

1st stage of labor

WAITING FOR YOUR LABOR TO START CAN BE BOTH FRUSTRATING AND TERRIBLY EXCITING.

You may be anxious to get your delivery over with, or feel that you aren't ready for labor. This can be an emotional time, so try to stay calm. This section helps you identify the symptoms and signs of labor and takes you through the changes that occur as your body gets ready to give birth.

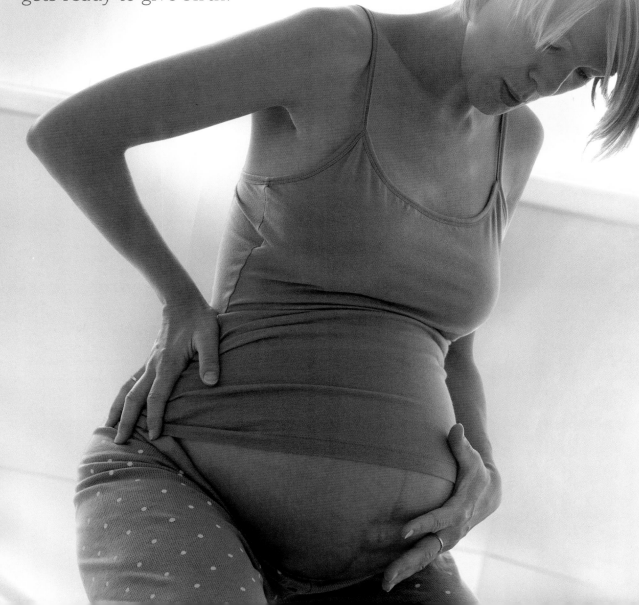

Approaching labor

As your pregnancy comes to an end, your cervix starts to soften as your body prepares for the forthcoming labor and birth.

As labor approaches, your body starts to prepare itself for the task ahead and you may notice various physical symptoms and signs that labor is about to start. Not every woman experiences labor in the same way, and certain signs can occur either before labor starts or during labor.

Common physical symptoms

Toward the end of your pregnancy, you may experience a sensation of building pressure or cramping in your pelvic or rectal area. This pelvic cramping can feel very similar to monthly menstrual cramps. A dull pain in your lower back that comes and goes is common too. You may also notice an increase in heartburn (acid reflux) and gassiness. Unless you have a high-risk pregnancy, there is no need to go to the hospital or call your doctor if you experience any of these symptoms in the later stages of your pregnancy.

Your emotional state

This is a time of waiting and many women busy themselves with household tasks. These bursts of activity are often thought to be instinctual, as the mother prepares the home for the new arrival, referred to as "nesting." The anticipation of what will happen during labor can give rise to a mixture of emotions, from fear and anxiety to excitement and impatience. Women may feel fearful about how much pain they will feel or how uncomfortable they will be with bodily functions. Nothing can prepare you fully for how you will feel in labor, but the more you understand about pain relief options (see pp.397–401) beforehand, the more confident you will feel about your ability to manage. It's also thought that by being informed and prepared, you are likely to reduce your anxiety during labor, which in itself can enable you cope better with the pain of contractions.

(see pp.397–401)

CHECKLIST

Preparing for labor

The period before labor starts can last for hours or even days, particularly with a first labor. So that you can manage when you go into labor, you need to take care of yourself during this pre-labor stage.

■ **Stay well rested** so that you aren't completely exhausted when you go into labor.

■ **If you're having trouble resting,** possibly because of anxiety or discomfort, try practicing relaxation techniques, such as breathing or visualization techniques, whereby you focus on a tranquil setting to induce a state of calm.

■ **Continue eating to keep your energy levels up** and provide fuel for the days ahead. You may not feel like eating a large meal; instead eat little and often. Opt for wholesome snacks such as dried fruit, nuts, or a whole-wheat sandwich, and drink lots of fluids.

■ **If you're suffering with back pain, try showering in warm water or taking a warm bath.** However, be careful when showering, since pregnancy increases your chances of feeling dizzy, and avoid a prolonged bath in very hot water since this may not be good for your baby.

■ **A lower back massage is comforting** and a good way to relax and ease discomfort—ask your partner to give you a soothing massage.

To prepare your body for the task ahead, ensure that you get plenty of rest and relaxation. In addition to getting a good night's sleep, take a light nap during the day if you feel fatigued.

No one is sure exactly what triggers labor, but it seems the process varies with each species.

In sheep, a drop in progesterone signals the start of labor. In mice, babies release proteins to signal their maturity, which in turn triggers labor. In humans, little is known about the signals that start labor although there are many theories. Studies suggest that the production of hormones such as corticotrophin-releasing hormone (CRH) by the uterus and placenta may play a role. It's also thought that an increase in pro-inflammatory substances known as cytokines may be involved. Whatever the trigger, it's likely that the onset of labor involves a biological communication between your baby and your body to indicate that your baby is ready to be born.

Braxton Hicks' contractions

One of the most common symptoms of approaching labor is an increase in the strength and frequency of Braxton Hicks', or practice, contractions (see p.387), which may be occurring up to four times an hour. The purpose of these practice contractions is to prepare your uterus to deal with real labor contractions so that labor progresses smoothly. Some women find Braxton Hicks' relatively painless, while others find these practice contractions fairly uncomfortable, especially if the baby is quite low and contractions cause increased pelvic pressure.

Apart from the level of pain, one of the main ways to distinguish Braxton Hicks' from real contractions is that Bracton Hicks' are irregular and they fade away, whereas labor pains occur at regular intervals and gradually become stronger, more intense, and closer together. The other main difference between Braxton Hicks' contractions and real ones is that, unlike Braxton Hicks', real contractions cause your cervix to dilate, which indicates that labor is beginning.

Engagement of the head

With a first baby, dropping down of the baby's head into your pelvis, known as engagement, usually means that labor is likely to start soon. In second and subsequent pregnancies, engagement may not occur until the start of labor.

You can usually tell that your baby's position has changed in two ways. First, you may notice that you have less discomfort in your upper abdomen or around your ribs because the downward movement releases some pressure. Second, you may notice increased pressure or pain in your pelvic or vaginal area as the baby's head moves into position. Your walking may become more of a waddle and you may have to use the bathroom more frequently than before. In some cases, your baby's head may pinch some of the nerves that run through your pelvis and you may

SIGNS OF APPROACHING LABOR

Although each woman's experience of labor differs and there are no hard and fast rules as to what will happen when, there are signs that indicate that labor is likely to start either imminently or within a matter of days. One of the classic signs that labor isn't far away is a "bloody show" (see opposite), when you lose the plug of mucus that has protected your baby during pregnancy. The other indisputable sign that labor will be shortly underway is that your cervix begins to dilate, although of course this will only be visible during an internal examination.

One other sign that labor may be about to start is if your water breaks (see opposite). However, for the majority of women this happens later on during established labor.

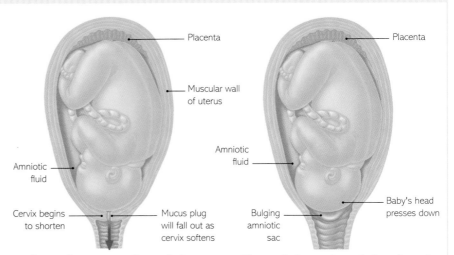

As the cervix starts to soften and shorten, the thick plug of mucus that protected your baby from infection during pregnancy comes away and falls out of the vagina, an event referred to as a "bloody show." When this happens, you may notice a yellowish discharge.

The amniotic membrane bulges through the cervix as the baby's head presses down. When the membranes break (water breaking), labor is imminent, or may have already started. The amniotic fluid may pass out as a gush of fluid or a trickle.

When to seek help

Make your way to the hospital or seek advice if any of the following occur:

■ **You have vaginal bleeding** that is like a period or heavier.

■ **You're leaking amniotic fluid** or leaking greenish fluid that could indicate the baby is distressed.

■ **The baby isn't moving as expected** (ask your doctor for advice).

experience sciatica, a sharp electric pain that runs down the outside of your leg to your outside toes (see p.470).

The "bloody show"

In pregnancy, a plug of mucus forms at the end of the cervix to prevent infection from entering the uterus. At the end of pregnancy, as the cervix softens and widens, this plug is dislodged and comes out through the vagina. When this occurs, you may see a discharge known as the "bloody show"; although some women don't notice anything. The discharge may appear as a thick, clear or yellow clump that looks like mucus from your nose. It's common for small amounts of blood to be present due to small tears in the cervix as the plug comes away.

Losing the plug of mucus usually means that labor will begin soon and you should make plans to leave for the hospital in the near future (within 12 hours). However, if loss of the plug is accompanied by other symptoms, such as painful, frequent contractions, heavy bleeding or leaking fluid (indicating your water has broken), you should call your doctor or hospital immediately.

Water breaking

Rupture of the amniotic membranes, called the water breaking, usually occurs once labor has started, but it can happen earlier. If this happens, it often means that labor is imminent. For some, a big gush of fluid is a clear sign that their water has broken, while for others there may be a trickle and it can be hard to determine if the amniotic fluid is leaking. Also, since many women have trouble controlling their bladder in pregnancy, telling the difference between urine and amniotic fluid can be hard. One way to tell is to wear a sanitary pad. If the pad quickly becomes soaked, your water has probably broken. Amniotic fluid also has an odor that is different than urine, even to nonprofessional noses.

Monitoring after the water breaks

If you think your water has broken but contractions haven't started, contact your doctor or the hospital for advice. If you're due, there are no complications, and your baby's head is engaged, you may be advised either to stay at home for a while to see if labor starts, or will be asked to be seen at the hospital. This is because, once your water has broken, your baby has lost the protective membrane surrounding him or her, which means there is an increased risk of an infection reaching your baby. The doctor should check your file to see if you're Group B Strep (GBS)-positive, and if you are, you'll be admitted and started on IV antibiotics. She may also monitor your baby's heartbeat (see p.418) to check that your baby isn't distressed. If you're GBS-negative and all is well, you may be able to return home, or stay at home, for a set amount of time and an appointment will be made to see how you're progressing. If labor doesn't start within 24 hours (the timeframe may be shorter in some hospitals), the hospital may suggest an induction (see p.432).

Early contractions

As your body prepares to go into labor, you will start to experience mild and irregular contractions. These differ from Braxton Hicks' since they build gradually and will soften and dilate the cervix.

As you approach labor, you will experience irregular contractions; these will increase in strength and regularity as labor progresses.

When am I in labor?

A common concern of many women is how they will know when they are in labor. The following are indications that labor is truly underway.

■ **You are having contractions that are becoming stronger** and more intense, lasting longer, and the interval between the contractions is getting shorter.

■ **Changing your position or** walking around doesn't ease the intensity of the contraction.

■ **The contractions start high in your abdomen and** move down through the uterus and lower back, rather than occurring only in the lower abdomen.

■ **Your water breaks** (see left) while you're having contractions.

How labor progresses

Stronger and more regular contractions continue to stretch your cervix until, at around 10 cm, it is fully dilated.

SUDDEN BIRTH

Although uncommon, labor and birth can occur unexpectedly fast, resulting in an unplanned home birth or a birth on the way to the hospital. Sudden birth is more likely to happen in second and subsequent labors or if you've had a previous sudden birth.

If you're alone at home. Try to stay calm and phone the emergency services for an ambulance. Also ask them to contact your doctor, whose number should be in your address book. Try to contact a friend, relative, or a neighbor who can help. If someone is with you, ask him or her to contact the ambulance and doctor.

Wash your hands and gather newspapers, clean towels, or clean clothing, or if you have an assistant ask him or her to prepare in this way. If there is time, the floor or bed should be covered with a plastic sheet, open trash bags, or newspapers and have a plastic bowl for the amniotic fluid and blood.

If you have an urge to push, breathe slowly; panting and blowing can help. Sit or kneel on the floor or your bed on top of a clean towel so that your baby doesn't fall onto a hard surface. Your water may break and an assistant can watch for a sudden bulging of the perineum and for your baby's head to appear, at which point you can push.

Once the head is delivered, you will feel another contraction and can push the body out. You may be able do this alone, or an assistant can put his or her hands either side of the head and apply gentle pressure. If your baby is born in the amniotic bag, this can be punctured with fingers; the baby's face will need wiping so that the airway is clear. Try to record the time of birth. Give your baby immediate skin-to-skin contact to keep him warm; then dry him and wrap him in a towel or blanket. Putting him to your breast stimulates contractions to deliver the placenta. An assistant can watch for a gush of blood or lengthening of the cord, a sign that the placenta has come away. Put the placenta in a towel in a bowl to be checked. Clamp the cord with string or a shoe lace; the doctor or paramedic will cut it when he or she arrives.

If you're in a car. If you feel an urge to push, your partner should pull over and put the hazard lights on. If your baby is born in the car, your partner can put him on your belly for warmth. If you have towels, dry your baby, wrap him in a clean towel, and call an ambulance.

If you have an uncontrollable urge to push on your way to the hospital, you may need to pull over and call emergency services.

Since every woman's experience of labor is different, it's hard to say exactly what your experience will be like. However, the stages of labor are common for all women. The first stage, when labor becomes established, starts when contractions start to open, or dilate, the cervix (see box, p.415). For some women, especially those who don't want strong pain relief, this is the hardest part of labor. Waiting for the cervix to dilate can be a long process with your first baby, and there isn't much you can do to hurry the process. The first stage of labor can be broken down into different phases, referred to as the early, or latent, phase, and the active phase (see below). After these phases comes transition, when your cervix becomes fully dilated and before you start to push your baby out (see p.416).

The early (latent) phase During the early phase, which can last for over a day or so in a first labor, your contractions gradually become more uncomfortable, but still relatively mild, and occur more frequently, although they may be irregular. During this phase, your cervix gradually shortens, a process known as effacement (see box, p.414) and begins to dilate. When the cervix is approximately 3–4 cm dilated and you're having regular, strong contractions, the active phase has begun (see below). The changes to your cervix during the early phase can be slow or fast and are hard to predict.

The active phase The active phase of the first stage is the individual point for each woman where cervical change happens more quickly and predictably.

Many couples feel unsure about when to go to the hospital. If your pregnancy is low risk, you will almost certainly be more comfortable at home at the start of labor and should wait until you're in active labor, when your contractions are regular, occurring every 5–10 minutes, and painful, before going to the hospital. At this stage, the hospital will want to assess how your baby is responding to strong contractions, and you may want some medication for pain. This needs to be administered in a setting where you can be monitored and, in the case of an epidural (see p.404), can only be given in the hospital.

If your pregnancy is high risk, you have had a prior cesarean, have a breech baby, or carry the streptococcus B bacterium, call the maternity ward to discuss when to go to the hospital.

Once you're in active labor, a final reason to go to the hospital is to make sure your baby is born there. An unplanned home (or car) birth is not best for you or your baby. This is unusual in a first pregnancy, but with subsequent births women are more likely to arrive at the hospital quite dilated or to have an unintended home birth.

Getting to the hospital Arrange for someone to drive you to the hospital, either your partner, or a friend or relative; don't consider driving yourself. Map the route ahead of time, consider a dry run before the big day, and have a bag packed with everything you will need for you and your baby (see p.358).

Admission procedure When you get to the hospital, you'll be checked in and will be put into a labor room if you look like you're in active labor, or into an assessment bed if this isn't clear. Usually you will be asked for a urine specimen, and a nurse will check your temperature, pulse, and blood pressure, check your cervix, and review your pregnancy history. If you're in early labor, you may be sent home. This doesn't mean you were unwise to come in; it's good to ensure all is well.

Once you've been admitted, you and your baby will be assessed by a doctor or nurse. Sometimes an intravenous (IV) line will be placed and blood tests may be done. You can make your room comfortable with items from home.

On your arrival at the hospital you will be assessed to see if you are in established labor and should remain at the hospital.

However, exactly when you enter active labor can be hard to establish, even for a doctor. For most women, active labor occurs at around 4 cm dilation. Your contractions are regular and may be every 5 minutes or so and getting closer together until they're 2 to 4 minutes apart and lasting from 45 seconds to one minute or more. From the start of active labor to the birth can last for around 10 to 12 hours, although this may be considerably shorter in a second labor.

In active labor, the nature of your contractions change, with pain becoming less concentrated in the lower abdomen, instead starting higher in the abdomen and moving down toward the pelvis and lower back as your baby is pushed down. Contractions are caused by a painful tightening of the muscles that may start off feeling like a severe period pain and

As labor begins

If you're having a home birth, your midwife will have talked to you in advance about how to contact her once you're in labor. Since she will be traveling to you, bear in mind local traffic conditions. If the streets might be busy, it's worth phoning her in early labor. She may ask you to phone again when your contractions are closer together.

While waiting for the midwife, you may want to move around, or relax in a warm bath. If you've purchased or rented a birthing pool, ensure that this is ready to use. Ask your partner to lay down old sheets or plastic sheeting over the floor. Eating small, nourishing snacks and drinking water will provide energy for the hours ahead.

Home births are not for everyone. They're only an option for you if you're having a healthy, low-risk pregnancy. Remember that not all attempts at home birth are successful, and you may need to be transferred to a hospital before delivery if complications arise. Your midwife will have lots of experience in these situations and will advise you based on what's best for you and your baby.

How labor progresses

413

The cervix is comprised of firm muscle that forms a strong base at the bottom of the uterus. For your baby to be born, the cervix needs to stretch and soften so that it can open, or dilate, and your baby can pass out of the uterus and into the vagina.

Toward the end of pregnancy, substances in your blood called prostaglandins start to soften the cervix so that it becomes more malleable. While you are pregnant, your cervix is usually around 2 to 3 cm long. In late pregnancy or early labor, Braxton Hicks' practice contractions start to shorten the cervix, a process known as effacement. Most women have a cervix that has shortened to 1 cm during the very early stages of labor. This is also referred to as 50 percent effaced. As the cervix continues to shorten, the cervix is gradually drawn up by the uterus, and by the time it is 100 percent effaced, the cervix will have started to open. Eventually the cervix becomes fully dilated (see box, opposite), and the baby can be pushed out.

As labor approaches, the cervix starts to lose its firmness and starts to soften in response to the presence of prostaglandins in the blood.

Lower segment of uterus

Cervix

Once the cervix has softened, it starts to shorten. This process is referred to as effacement and needs to occur before the cervix can begin to dilate.

Cervix drawn up by uterus

Cervix shortened

The "station" refers to the position of your baby's head in relation to your pelvis. This is recorded as a number between -5 and +5. Zero station means the head is "engaged" and has entered the vaginal canal within the pelvic bones. A negative number (-5 to 0) means that the head isn't engaged in the pelvis. A positive number (0 to +4) means that your baby's head is moving down the pelvis and +5 means your baby is crowning (being born). Ideally, you should not push until the head is engaged in the pelvis, even if you're fully dilated.

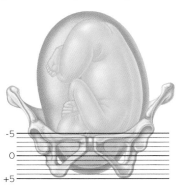

-5

0

+5

The position of the head in relation to the pelvis is marked on a scale of -5 to +5.

---

increase in intensity as they reach their peak. Your doctor will assess if you're in active labor by observing your pain levels, the frequency and strength of contractions, and by using a tool called a labor curve, which plots cervical change and the position of your baby's head in relation to your pelvis over time (see partograms, p.419).

It's important for your doctor to determine when you enter active labor so she can assess how labor is progressing. For first labors, 90 percent of women have a cervical dilation of about 1 cm per hour, whereas labor moves faster in subsequent births. Once it's established that you're in active labor, the doctor can predict when you may deliver. However, since women vary widely in how long it takes them to have a baby, bear in mind that this is only an estimate.

During active labor, you may want to have medical pain relief if you haven't so far, such as analgesics or an epidural (see pp.402–6).

Abdominal and vaginal examinations

You will have several internal vaginal examinations and your abdomen will be palpated to assess the baby's position. If your doctor is assessing if amniotic fluid is leaking, a speculum examination may be done, but in most cases this isn't necessary. Usually, the doctor uses her fingers to assess the baby and the progress of labor. She will try to check you often enough to make sure that your labor is progressing, but not so often that it causes you extra discomfort or increases your risk of infection. The following are assessed during a vaginal examination.

The station The doctor will check how far the head has descended into the pelvis (see box, above).

Cervical effacement The doctor will assess how your cervix is shortening,

known as effacement (see box, top left). Once the cervix is sufficiently shortened, it begins to dilate, or open.

Cervical dilation The doctor assesses how dilated, or open, your cervix is (see box, below). Active labor is established at 3 to 4 cm dilation and full dilation occurs at around 10 cm. You can't push your baby out until you're fully dilated.

Fetal position Fetal presentation refers to the part of your baby that is coming out first. Babies can be born head first or bottom first (breech) (see p.433). Your doctor will also assess which way your baby is facing in the birth canal. The easiest way for a baby to be born is head down with the back of the baby's head (occiput) and spine toward the front (anterior) of your uterus, known as an occiput anterior position. Your baby can also be born vaginally from an occiput posterior position (back of baby's head and spine toward the back of your uterus), but

this can take longer and be more painful. Vaginal tears are more common when babies are born in the occiput posterior position. A final position is when your baby faces your side, known as occiput transverse. Full-term babies can't be born in the transverse position since the head is too big to fit this way. However it's not uncommon for babies to rotate around during labor, although this would need to happen before you start to push. If this doesn't happen, labor may need to be assisted with forceps or a vacuum and suction cup (see pp.436–7).

Descent with contractions Although most of the time your doctor will try to examine you inbetween contractions, sometimes it helps to see how much the baby's head comes down in the pelvis during a contraction, referred to as the descent. If there is a good descent during contractions this means that the baby is fitting well into your pelvis and that your contractions are efficient.

DILATION

Once your cervix is stretched and softened (see box, opposite), it begins to open, or dilate, so that your baby can pass through into the vagina to be born. Regular contractions cause the cervix to dilate, and in first labors the cervix dilates at an average of 1 cm per hour; this rate is often faster for subsequent labors. You cannot push your baby out until you are fully dilated, which occurs at 10 cm.

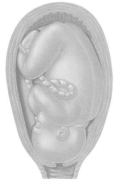 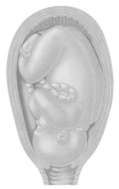 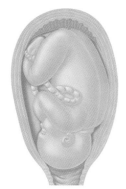

At 2 cm dilation, the cervix has shortened and is beginning to open. Contractions may still be irregular.

At 6 cm dilation, you are in active labor. Your contractions will be more frequent, regular, and stronger.

At 10 cm dilation, you are fully dilated. Contractions may be almost continuous and you are nearly ready to start pushing your baby out.

QUESTIONS AND ANSWERS

Am I likely to have medical interventions in labor in the hospital?
The reality of a hospital birth is that medical interventions may be suggested, some of which may be more helpful than others. Procedures that can be done include artificially breaking the water; inserting a catheter or an IV line; and speeding up labor with drugs.

Is artificial rupture of the membranes routine in the hospital?
Artificially breaking the bag of water, known as amniotomy or ARM (see p.432) is offered routinely in some hospitals in labor. This is a painless, low-risk procedure that is thought to shorten the time of labor by one to two hours, reduce the chance of a low early APGAR score in your baby (see p.428), and significantly decrease the chance that you'll need drugs to speed up labor (see below). ARM is usually optional. The one time it is necessary is if a fetal scalp electrode needs to be put on the baby's head (see p.419) since this cannot be done without breaking the water. It may also be done as part of the induction process (see p.432).

How is labor speeded up with medication?
A slow labor may be speeded up with the medication oxytocin, a procedure known as augmentation. Oxytocin is naturally released from your pituitary gland in labor. Synthetic oxytocin can be given via an intravenous (IV) line to strengthen contractions. When this is done, it's usual to have continuous fetal monitoring (see p.418) since, if the contractions become too strong, your baby may show signs of distress. Since oxytocin is quickly cleared from your system once the IV is turned off, contractions that are too strong can be weakened quickly. Oxytocin is also given during an induction of labor (see p.432).

Transition

Transition is the end of active labor as your cervix becomes fully dilated and you ready yourself to begin pushing. This is one of the shortest stages of labor, lasting from 15 minutes to two hours, although on average it's about 30 minutes. This can be one of the most challenging parts of labor because your contractions intensify and can begin to feel continuous since they now occur every 30–90 seconds. If you haven't had an epidural, transition can be especially difficult since you may feel a lot of pressure on your lower back and rectum and have an overwhelming desire to push, but will be unable to push until your cervix is fully dilated. Even if you've had an epidural, you may notice increasing pelvic pressure. If you do push before your cervix is ready, you may tear your cervix or cause your cervix to swell and thicken, which will prolong the process of labor.

It's not uncommon to vomit now, a side effect of the stretching of your cervix and the pelvic pressure. You may also tremble or shake and have hot flashes.

How you can cope You may feel very uncomfortable during this period as your contractions become stronger and you try to hold back from pushing. Significant pelvic pressure during the transition phase can make it difficult to relax between contractions, and you will therefore need plenty of support from your birth partner and nurse at this time, since you may be feeling exhausted, out of control, possibly frightened, and may even think that you can't continue.

Work with your nurse to find the best position for you. This is the one stage of labor where it can be helpful not to adopt an upright position, since you can take some of the pressure off the pelvis. Sitting or being on all fours with your bottom raised may help. Keep breathing during your contractions; your nurse may show you how to pant and breathe shallowly to help resist the urge to push. If possible, moving around during contractions can sometimes help since you will focus on doing something else until you can actively push. You could try rocking on a birthing ball or in a rocking chair. If there is time between your contractions, ask your partner to massage your lower back if this helps relieve pressure.

It can be easy to lose sight of the purpose of labor at this point, so try to focus on the fact that your baby will soon be born.

Pain relief Your doctor may not give you intravenous pain relief now, since these can cause your baby to be too sleepy if they are given close to the birth. Depending on hospital procedure, you may or may not be able to have an epidural now (see p.404).

Support in the first stage

During the first stage, your partner has a varied and important role. In adddition to helping you feel comfortable and assisting you with positions, your partner can also support you mentally. This is especially important at the end of the first stage, when you reach transition (see above), a point when women often feel panicky and out of control. Your partner can offer reassurance that you're doing well and that the delivery of your baby is not far off. He can also improve your comfort, for example by applying a damp, cool washcloth to your face and neck, and he can help you focus on your breathing, reminding you to pant or blow to help you resist the urge to push before the cervix is fully dilated.

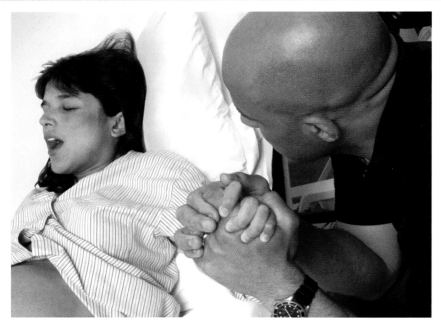

During transition, you may be overwhelemed by the strength and frequency of your contractions. Your partner's support is crucial during this stage and his encouragement can help keep you focused on your labor.

If your cervix is not dilating, or your baby is not descending, as quickly as expected during the first stage, your doctor will try to assess why this is and if something can be done. Usually, your doctor will assess the three P's: the passenger (the size of the baby and his position in the uterus); the powers (the efficiency of your contractions); and the passage (the size and shape of your pelvis). These three elements work together and each one is important for your labor to progress smoothly.

There are several reasons why a labor may not progress. These include if the baby's head is too large for the mother's pelvis, known as cephalopelvic disproportion (CPD); if contractions are inefficient; and if the baby is in a posterior position with his back facing the mother's back.

Cephalopelvic disproportion

Sometimes CPD may be suspected before labor, in late pregnancy. This may be the case if the doctor thinks that you have a narrow pelvis or a prominent sacral bone, both of which may make birth slower or more difficult. However, an assessment of the pelvis alone is not an accurate way to predict if you'll be able to have a successful vaginal birth and, even if the pelvis is not an optimal shape, the doctor may be happy for you to continue trying for a vaginal birth. This is because it's not the shape of your pelvis alone that is important, but the interaction between your baby (the passenger) and your pelvis.

If CPD is suspected, but the baby's head has engaged, a vaginal birth can still be attempted. The labor will be monitored with a labor graph (see p.419) and if there are signs that the baby is in distress, an emergency cesarean may be performed. If the head hasn't engaged toward the end of labor, a planned cesarean may be offered.

If your doctor suspects CPD in labor, she will reassess the baby's size to check if she originally underestimated his or her weight. Even though the combination of a large estimated weight and a slow labor can suggest that there may be delivery problems, often labor proceeds normally.

Inefficient contractions If your labor isn't progressing because your cervix is dilating slowly or has stopped dilating, your doctor will assess the frequency of your contractions, which should be every 2 to 3 minutes. She'll also assess how strong the contractions are by palpating your abdomen: the firmer it feels during contractions, the more likely they are to be effective. If contractions are more widely spaced than they should be and their strength indicates they're unlikely to be effective, she may use one or two techniques to speed up labor, known as augmenting labor. First, she may artificially rupture the membranes if they haven't already ruptured, a process known as ARM (see p.432). This can shorten the duration of labor by around one to two hours.

If ARM has no effect, you may be given the drug oxytocin to increase the strength and frequency of contractions (see p.432). Initially, a small dose is given and then increased over time until you're having three or four moderately strong contractions every 10 minutes. If this is done, you'll have continuous electronic fetal monitoring (see p.418) to check that the baby is not distressed by the sudden onset of stronger contractions.

If your labor is still not progessing several hours after the drugs have been started, then a cesarean may be recommended.

Posterior presentation The best position for your baby in labor is an occipito-anterior position with the back of the head (occiput) facing your front. If the back of the head faces your back (occipito-posterior) this can make it hard for the baby to turn and move down the birth canal and can prolong labor. The doctor may suggest that you change positions to encourage the baby to turn. If the baby fails to rotate, forceps or vacuum may be needed to aid the delivery (see pp.436–7).

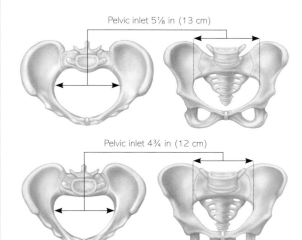

Pelvic inlet 5⅛ in (13 cm)

Pelvic inlet 4¾ in (12 cm)

A gynecoid pelvis is the name given to a pelvis that has a circular shape. The generous proportions of this more typical "female-shaped" pelvis provides room for the head to pass through during the birth.

An android pelvis is the term used to describe a pelvis that has a more triangular shape. This reduces the room available for the baby's head to pass through and is more likely to cause problems during a vaginal delivery.

Monitoring during labor

Throughout labor, your baby's heartbeat and your contractions will be monitored to make sure that your labor is progressing as it should be and that the well-being of you and your baby is not threatened.

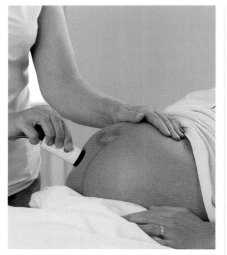

A handheld device can monitor your baby's heartbeat at intervals, leaving you free to move around during labor.

Your baby's heart rate is an indication of how well your baby is dealing with labor and it is monitored at regular intervals, called intermittent monitoring. If a problem is found or you have a high-risk pregnancy, then you may be advised to have fetal electronic monitoring, in which your baby's heart rate and your contractions are monitored continuously by a electronic fetal heart monitor (see box, below). All the information about your labor is recorded on a chart, called a labor graph (see opposite).

Intermittent monitoring

This is done using a handheld battery-operated device known as a Doppler sonicaid, which is held against your abdomen to listen to your baby's heartbeat. When you are pushing in the second stage of labor, the fetal heart needs to be monitored more frequently.

Electronic fetal monitoring

In this type of fetal monitoring, two devices monitor your baby's heart rate and the strength and frequency of your contractions. Your baby's heart rate is monitored with a circular ultrasound-like device. If you want, you can hear the heartbeat, or ask that the volume be turned down if this is distracting. Your contractions are monitored with a small plastic circular device. One or two elastic belts are placed around your abdomen to secure the monitors. You should be able to stand, sit, or squat with the monitors in place, and some hospitals

---

HOW MONITORING IS DONE

External fetal monitoring

The baby's heartbeat and the strength and frequency of your contractions are measured by devices strapped to your abdomen with wires that connect to a machine that produces a printout of the readings and an ongoing digital log on the computer.

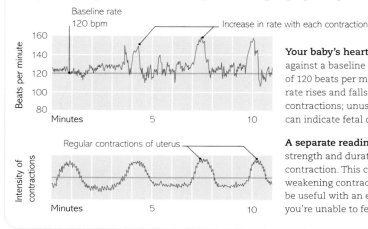

Baseline rate 120 bpm — Increase in rate with each contraction

Beats per minute: 160, 140, 120, 100, 80

Minutes 5 10

Your baby's heartbeat is recorded against a baseline measurement of 120 beats per minute. The heart rate rises and falls naturally with contractions; unusual variations can indicate fetal distress.

Regular contractions of uterus

Intensity of contractions

Minutes 5 10

A separate reading records the strength and duration of each contraction. This can detect weakening contractions and can be useful with an epidural when you're unable to feel contractions.

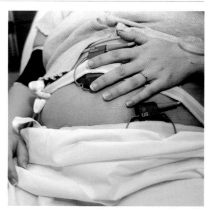

Continuous monitoring of your baby's heart rate and your contractions is done by means of monitors strapped to your abdomen.

Scalp electrode

If there are concerns about the baby's heartbeat, a small electrode attached to the scalp can give a more precise reading than external electronic fetal monitoring. The electrode is passed through the cervix and attached to the head.

Electrode is attached to baby's head

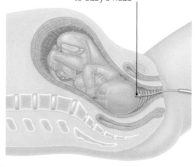

have monitors that allow you to walk around and be monitored by radio signal.

Internal monitoring If your baby's heart-rate reading indicates the baby is distressed or the signal from an electronic monitor is poor, the doctor may suggest internal fetal monitoring. In this technique, a small electrode is attached to the baby's scalp and detects the electrical impulses of his heart. A wire from the electrode comes out via the cervix and attaches to the EFM machine (see box, above). You still wear a strap around your abdomen, which holds the device for detecting the rate and strength of your contractions.

The electrode is placed during a vaginal examination and is no more uncomfortable than this. Placing a scalp electrode may be mildly uncomfortable for your baby and there is a small risk that your baby could get a scalp infection, which can be treated with antibiotics. Even though these risks are small, a

scalp electrode is not placed routinely. Your doctor will discuss how it works before it is placed, and you should understand why it's being done. Electrodes should also be avoided if you have a viral disease that can be transmitted to your baby during labor, such as hepatitis B or C, or HIV. Once a scalp electrode has been placed, you can't move far from the monitor, although you may be able to change position.

If a EFM reading from the scalp electrode indicates that your baby is distressed, a blood sample may be taken from the scalp to check acidity levels. If these are high, a cesarean or assisted delivery may be suggested.

Labor graphs

A labor graph is a large chart that contains several graphs which provide information on your labor, allowing the doctor to monitor the progress of your labor. One of the most useful tools in this chart is a graph showing your labor curve. This plots cervical change and the position of your baby's head in relation to your pelvis over time. The graph enables the doctor to establish when your labor became active. Also recorded with your baby's heart-rate monitoring are your blood pressure, pulse, temperature, and the rate of your contractions, as well as your pain levels.

Should you have electronic fetal monitoring?

Although monitoring during labor is an important part of the care of you and your baby, there is some debate as to the benefits of continuous monitoring and some believe there may be associated maternal risks. As a result, most hospitals suggest intermittent fetal monitoring. Although you can refuse monitoring entirely, the staff may be unhappy about this and ask you to sign a form or statement releasing them from liability if anything goes wrong during the labor and birth.

Risks Studies suggest that women who are monitored continuously are more likely to have a cesarean section or an assisted delivery with forceps or vacuum (see pp.436–7). This is because your doctor may see changes in the fetal heart rate that concern her. Some changes, such as a faster heart rate (more than 160 beats a minute), known as tachycardia, or decreases in the heart rate that occur after your contractions, can be caused by decreased oxygen to your baby. If

your doctor sees these changes, she may be unable to determine if they were caused by low oxygen or if your baby is actually fine.

If it's thought that your baby may be at risk, an emergency cesarean section may be recommended. If there are fetal heart rate changes while you are pushing, a forceps or vacuum delivery may be offered.

Benefits The benefits of continuous electronic fetal monitoring are not entirely clear. You are able to hear your baby's heartbeat and some women may find this comforting. Also, experts agree that continuous monitoring reduces the chance that your baby will have a seizure after the birth, a symptom of brain injury from low oxygen. Seizures are rare, occurring in around 2.5 per 1000 births with monitoring and 5 per 1000 births without monitoring. It is harder to prove that electronic fetal monitoring can prevent rarer complications such as cerebral palsy or fetal death.

Positions for first stage of labor

Being active during the first stage of labor is thought to help labor progress. If you're well prepared and practice different postures and positions for labor during pregnancy, you will instinctively be able to use these during childbirth.

Leaning forward onto a pile of cushions with your knees apart is a soothing and relaxing position, and can also encourage your cervix to dilate.

Many different postures and positions can help you in the first stage, and there is evidence that changing your position in this stage increases the effectiveness of your contractions and reduces the pain. Assuming upright positions in particular uses gravity to assist the descent of the baby.

Active positions

Positions that allow you to remain active are thought to help labor progress. Some women find rocking the pelvis backward and forward, and then rotating the pelvis in a clockwise and then counterclockwise direction while standing or sitting on a birthing ball, helps ease the pain. Adopting an all-fours position on your hands and knees can help you stay focused and also allows you to rotate your pelvis. Moving backward and forward in a rocking chair can also be comforting. Many women find walking in place and walking around helpful.

Supported positions

Supported positions can be especially helpful if your baby is in an occiput-posterior position (baby's back to your back). Leaning forward with your hands on a table or chair during a contraction and breathing slowly and steadily helps you focus. If you find it comforting, your partner can massage your shoulders and back at the same time. A lot of women find either sitting astride on a chair facing the back of the chair or sitting on a toilet and facing the tank with a pillow for their head and arms, a comfortable position. This also allows you to "catnap" between contractions.

Using a birthing ball during labor enables you to adopt upright positions while feeling supported. While sitting on a birthing ball, or adopting a supported kneeling position with one, you will be able to rotate your hips to encourage the progress of labor.

Kneeling in an all-fours position helps take the weight off your back. This position also allows you to move your hips back and forth or rotate them, which can be comforting during early contractions.

Kneeling and leaning forward onto cushions with your bottom raised also helps ease a backache and can be a helpful position to adopt during transition (see p.416) when you may need to resist the urge to bear down.

Sitting astride a chair can be a relaxing position because this enables you to lean forward with your legs astride while remaining supported.

Lying on your side with your knee bent and supported with pillows can be a relaxing postion between contractions, enabling you to rest and re-energize. You may also want to adopt a supported lying position during some contractions.

2nd and 3rd stages

THE MOMENT OF DELIVERY IS WITHIN SIGHT AND YOU WILL SOON MEET YOUR LONG-AWAITED BABY

The second stage begins when your cervix is fully dilated and your baby has moved deep into the pelvis. These signs may be accompanied by an overwhelming urge to bear down and, once your doctor is satisfied that you are ready to do it, you will be able to push your baby out. The third stage, the delivery of the placenta, marks the end of labor.

Delivering your baby

In the second stage, your labor starts to accelerate as you actively push your baby out into the world.

As you enter the second stage of labor, you will probably experience an overwhelming desire to bear down. Once your doctor has established that you are fully dilated and are ready to start pushing, you may start to feel more in control of your labor since your pushing helps move your baby farther down into the pelvis.

The second stage

The second stage of labor starts when your cervix is completely open, at about 10 cm, and ends with the birth of your baby. This stage usually lasts for around 45 minutes to two hours during a first labor and from 15 to 45 minutes in subsequent deliveries. The second stage is intense and during this time your contractions will become stronger, but may occur less frequently, occurring around every two to five minutes. At this point you may feel a sensation of fullness in your vagina or bowel and have a strong urge to push. Many women find labor pains more bearable

THE MECHANISMS OF LABOR

The birth passage, far from being straight, involves a series of rotational maneuvers known as the "mechanisms of labor."

This curve, known as the "curve of Carus," is thought to result from the evolution of humans from being on all fours to being upright. This caused the spine to curve, the pelvis to tilt, and gave a curve to the birth canal. Your pelvic floor muscles help the head rotate through the birth canal.

FOCUS ON...YOUR BIRTH PARTNER

Support in the second stage

In the second stage, your partner's support is invaluable. His or her role is to make you feel supported and safe and to offer lots of encouragement.

Your birth partner can provide verbal support to help you deal with the strenuous task of pushing your baby out with each contraction. There may be times when you're not lucid and your partner will need to speak for you and liaise with medical staff.

In addition to emotional support, your birth partner can act as your physical support in whatever position you adopt in the second stage, whether this is a squatting position or another position that you find comfortable. Your partner will be able to massage your back if this is helpful, and can hold you and comfort you and help you focus on your breathing during and between each contraction.

Your partner can also watch as your baby's head crowns and describe what he or she can see, or hold a mirror for you to see the baby's head, which can be deeply reassuring as you realize that the end is in sight.

The emotional and physical support provided by your birth partner can be crucial during the second stage of labor, the time when you are having to exert yourself physically to push your baby down in your pelvis and out through the birth canal.

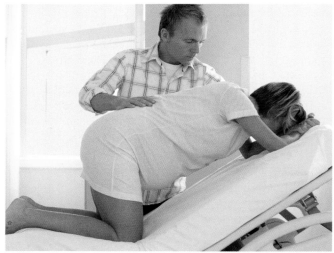

In a kneeling position, both your partner and the nurse can support you as you bear down (top left). Being on all fours with the hospital bed for support can be a comfortable position (bottom left).

An upright squatting position is good for pushing and can be adopted if you have firm support from your partner. He can support you under the arms while you put your hands around the back of his neck.

in the second stage since they can now actively work with the contractions and push their baby out. Other women find this a particularly hard part of labor because they start to feel exhausted from the effort of prolonged pushing.

Second stage positions

Although you may be tired and want to lie down, it's recommended that you resist this urge in the second stage. Your partner and nurse can give you plenty of support to help you adopt the most comfortable position.

Staying upright Adopting an upright position during the second stage of labor has several advantages. The main one is that you are using gravity to assist your baby's descent, which will also help you bear down and push. Being upright can also improve the alignment of your baby in the birth canal; can increase the efficiency of your contractions; and widens the passageway through the pelvis.

There is also evidence that adopting upright positions in the second stage of labor can reduce the length of time you

take to bear down and give birth, and make it less likely that you will have an instrument delivery or episiotomy (see pp.436–7 and p.427).

Which positions to adopt Upright positions during the second stage of labor include upright sitting and squatting positions.

If you prefer a sitting position, try to sit in an upright or semi-recumbent position. If you adopt a sitting position on a bed, sitting at a 45-degree angle can help your breathing and reduce the risk of a condition known as aortocaval compression, which can affect how well your blood is circulated around your body and to your baby. This is caused by the weight of your uterus and the baby pressing on major blood vessels (the aorta and vena cava), reducing the amount of oxygen that circulates around your body, which makes you feel light headed and dizzy. If this happens, you will be advised to lie on your left side to relieve pressure and increase the amount of oxygen circulating.

Because kneeling or squatting increases the pelvic outlet, many women will naturally adopt a squatting or all-fours position to give birth since they find that this is the most comfortable and easy position in which to deliver their baby. Upright squatting and kneeling positions help increase your pelvic outlet by around 28 percent compared to when you're in a lying-down position. This means that there is more room for your baby to descend through your pelvis and into the birth canal. Some women find it hard to squat down comfortably because they are not used to being in this position and tire easily. If this is the case, ask your partner to support you as you squat.

Alternatively, you may find that lying on your side is your preferred position; your partner can help you by supporting one of your legs to keep your pelvis as open as possible. There is also some evidence that lying on your side can protect your perineum from tearing.

Using props Some women find using props such as a beanbag, birthing ball, pillows, or a large cushion while kneeling and leaning forward helpful.

When to push

Your baby will start to rotate his or her head and shoulders to enable these to descend through your pelvis to be born, and you will feel the urge to bear down and push as this is happening. Your doctor will help you focus and

encourage you to push when you feel the urge, which will come naturally with a contraction. With each contraction, you will need to concentrate on pushing down deep into the pelvic area and bottom. It can help to put your chin on your chest and to bear down for as long as possible during a contraction, during which time you may need to take several steady breaths. You may feel like grunting and making noises when bearing down, or you may prefer to breathe deeply and quietly; you should do whatever you find helpful and works best. You will need to work with your body's instincts and adopt the position you find most comfortable and easy to give birth in (see above). Pushing your baby out into the world takes a huge amount of effort and energy, but you have the ability and are very capable of doing this.

Your doctor and birth partner will encourage and support you throughout this stage and help you to believe in your ability to give birth.

Your baby's descent

The time it takes to push your baby out once he or she is deep within the pelvis can take around 30 minutes to one hour for a first labor, although this time may be considerably reduced in subsequent labors, sometimes taking just a few minutes. The combined force of the contractions (which are now around every two to five minutes) and your pushing moves your baby farther down into the pelvic outlet. As this occurs, the pressure on your back and rectum will intensify and you may experience a stinging sensation as your vagina becomes fully stretched. Your doctor may tell you to stop pushing at this point so that your perineum can thin further and so that the baby's head isn't delivered too suddenly, which could

PUSHING WITH AN EPIDURAL

If you have had an epidural, this can affect your awareness of when to bear down and push. If this is the case, your doctor will first check that your baby isn't showing signs of distress, and may then decide to wait a while for the epidural effect to wear off slightly so you can feel when to bear down and push. Alternatively, the doctor will feel the top of your uterus so that she is aware of when a contraction is starting and will then guide you to bear down and push.

After your baby is born

Shortly after your baby's birth, the cord will be cut and your uterus will start to contract again to deliver the placenta.

The third stage
This is from the birth of your baby until the delivery of the membranes (the amniotic bag that surrounded your baby) and placenta. The placenta can be actively managed with the help of drugs or delivered without drugs, known as passive management or a physiological third stage. Your doctor will discuss these options with you before labor.

Cutting the cord
Once your baby has been delivered, it may be left for two minutes before it is cut. Some believe that allowing the cord to pulsate for a few minutes means your baby receives more blood from the placenta, which may boost his or her blood volume. The cord will be clamped in two places, about 1 cm and 4 cm from the baby's belly, and is cut with scissors between the clamps.

Delivery of the placenta
How your placenta is delivered depends on your doctor. Many wait for it to happen naturally, but others offer an intramuscular (IM) injection of an oxytoxic drug in your thigh to make the uterus contract so that you can deliver the placenta and membranes quickly. Helping the uterus contract in this way reduces the risk of heavy bleeding occurring during the third stage, known as a postpartum hemorrhage (see box, right) and speeds up the delivery of the placenta, which can happen within 5 to 15 minutes after the birth of the baby. The risk of a postpartum hemorrhage occurring is the reason many units advise an active delivery. If you have a fibroid, active delivery will be advised because there is a heavy risk of bleeding.

Your doctor will place one of her hands just above your pubic bone to prevent the uterus from being pulled

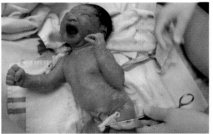

The umbilical cord will be clamped and cut, a few minutes after the birth, severing the link between your baby and the placenta.

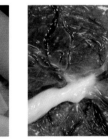

The disc-shaped placenta, weighing around 1 lb 2 oz (500 g), has a network of blood vessels surrounding the umbilical cord in its center.

FIRST CHECKUPS

Apgar score

At 1, 5, and 10 minutes, your baby's breathing, pulse, movements, skin color, and responses are assessed. In South Asian and black babies, the color of the mouth, palms of the hands, and soles of the feet are checked. Each is given a score between 0 and 2, called the Apgar score. A total of 7 or more at 1 minute is normal; under 7 means help is needed.

Apgar score	2	1	0
Skin color	Pink all over	Body pink; extremities blue	Pale/blue all over
Breathing	Regular strong cry	Irregular, weak cry	Absent
Pulse/heart rate	Greater than 100 bpm	Less than 100 bpm	Absent
Movements/muscle tone	Active	Moderate activity	Limp
Reflexes after given certain stimuli	Crying or grimacing strongly	Moderate reaction or grimace	No response

downward when she pulls on the cord. With her other hand, she will then apply gentle traction to the cord to help deliver the membranes and placenta. This is known as "controlled cord traction" (CCT).

Delivering the placenta naturally

If you decide to deliver the placenta without drugs, known as a physiological third stage, this can take up to an hour. Your doctor will encourage you to bear down and you may find squatting helps. The doctor will check the placenta to ensure it's complete and that none of it remains in the uterus, which can cause a postpartum hemorrhage (see box, below).

How you feel after the birth

After the huge effort of giving birth, it's common to have a physical reaction. Many women experience uncontrollable shaking or shivering, and some feel nauseous and may even vomit. In addition to your physical reaction, you are also likely to be feeling overwhelmed and emotional. Once you and your baby have been given the all clear, you should be given some quiet time alone to get to know each other.

YOUR BABY'S APPEARANCE

Newborn babies are usually surprisingly unattractive. Fortunately, as parents, we usually think they are beautiful. Newborns are covered in a waxy substance called vernix, together with amniotic fluid and blood from the birth canal. Babies who have passed meconium before the delivery may also have brown stained skin and nails.

In addition, newborn babies often have a molded, elongated head, with a swollen area on top known as a "caput," which is due to the pressure on the baby's head as it passes through the birth canal. Also, the nose may be squished to one side and the eyes may be swollen. Sometimes the genitals are swollen too. Rest assured that all of these features are temporary and within 24 hours or so the molding will work itself out and your baby will

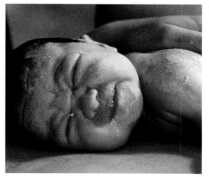

Your newborn baby may have a squashed appearance, but this will smooth out within a day or two.

begin to look more like the baby you were expecting to meet.

Many babies are born with birthmarks that are referred to as "stork marks." These are red birthmarks on the eyelids and at the nape of the neck, which fade in time.

Skin-to-skin contact with your newborn baby will help keep her warm—newborns don't have very good temperature control—and will also help the two of you start bonding.

Special cases

EACH LABOR IS DIFFERENT AND THERE ARE TIMES WHEN SOME TYPE OF INTERVENTION IS NEEDED

You may know in advance that a condition or factor in your pregnancy means that intervention, such as an induction or a cesarean section, will be needed. At other times, events can occur in labor that mean assistance is needed, or a premature labor can mean that your baby needs special care. In all cases, rest assured that procedures are in place to ensure your own and your baby's safety.

Premature birth

The term "premature" describes both the time of birth, before 37 weeks, and how well prepared your baby is for life outside of the uterus. Premature births account for about 16 percent of Canadian births.

Your baby may be born prematurely either because an early delivery is advised on medical grounds (see below), or you go into spontaneous preterm labor. The earlier the birth, the higher the chance of complications in the baby, such as breathing problems or infections. Nowadays, however, huge advances in the care of premature babies means that babies born as early as 23 or 24 weeks may survive. If your baby is premature, he may need to spend time in a neonatal intensive care unit (NICU, see p.452).

Advising an early delivery

A decision may be made to deliver a baby early if the mother's or baby's health is in danger. For example, an early delivery may be recommended if the mother has a medical problem, such as a heart condition that could increase her physical stress, or preeclampsia (see p.474), which could endanger her own and her baby's health. An early delivery may also be advised if a scan shows that the placenta is not functioning well and the baby is not receiving enough oxygen. Almost 39 percent of babies in Canada delivered before 37 weeks are born by cesarean section.

Spontaneous preterm labor

The cause of spontaneous labor before 37 weeks is often unknown. However, it is more likely if a woman has a major abnormality of the uterine wall, such as large fibroids (see p.218), a weakness in the cervix, which may have been present from birth, or has occurred after surgery to the cervix or is pregnant with more than one baby.

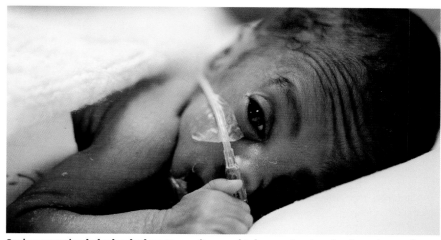

Seeing your tiny baby hooked up to monitors and tubes can be alarming, but take comfort from the fact that these are helping your baby to breathe and feed and in turn to develop.

Infections like bacterial vaginosis can also set off contractions at an early stage.

What might be done? Preterm labor can't be stopped, but medication can slow the process and reduce some risks.

Steroids can promote the production of a natural chemical in the baby's lungs that reduces the effort of breathing. They must be given 24 to 48 hours before the birth to have maximum benefit.

You may also be given oral medicine or an injection to reduce the frequency of contractions. This can prolong pregnancy for a few days, during which time the steroids can take effect. Also, if necessary, you can be transferred to a hospital with NICU facilities.

Finally, you may be advised to have injected antibiotics since preterm babies are susceptible to bacterial infections caught via the cervix during birth.

PREDICTING PREMATURE LABOR

It's hard to predict who will go into labor prematurely. However, if you've had a previous preterm birth, tests may be done to find out if it is likely in your current pregnancy. A cervical scan may be done around 23 weeks since a shorter cervix increases the risk of early labor. Pelvic swabs detect bacteria that are linked to preterm labor, and "fetal Fibronectin" test between 24 and 34 weeks shows whether a protein is present that, during the second half of pregnancy, generally can't be detected until 1–3 weeks before labor and delivery. Sometimes, a short cervix is strengthened with a stitch. Antibiotics can be given if abnormal bacteria are found.

Induction of labor

For about 19.7 percent of women in Canada, labor is started by artificial means, or induced, to reduce the risks to mother and baby.

An induction may be offered if it's felt that continuing the pregnancy poses a risk to your health or to the health of your baby. The most common reason for an induction is the continuation of a pregnancy beyond 41 or 42 weeks, in which case the placenta may begin to fail. Induction may be offered earlier if you have twins, or a medical condition such as diabetes. Before setting a date for induction, your doctor may offer to strip your membranes (see p.393) to help you go into spontaneous labor.

Induction is not the same as an augmentation of labor, which is when drugs are used to increase the efficiency of your contractions when you've already gone into labor spontaneously (see p.415).

Assessing the cervix

Before an induction, you'll have an internal examination to assess the cervix. Induction is easier if your cervix is short and soft, described as "favorable" or "ripe," rather than long and firm. The findings may be logged in a table called the Bishop's Score, which also assesses how far the cervix is dilated (see p.415), the position of the cervix, and the station of the fetal head in the pelvis (see p.414). A total score over six indicates good conditions for an induction of labor.

Softening the cervix

If your cervix isn't ripe, it can be softened with prostaglandins. These are naturally occurring chemicals that help stimulate contractions. Artificial prostaglandins can be given in the form of a gel or "string" of a drug called Cervidil, which is placed at the top of the vagina near the cervix, or a vaginal suppository or an oral pill. This is usually effective, but sometimes prostaglandins fail to soften the cervix and may be tried again after a few days. On the other hand, some women experience dramatic effects after a small dose.

Breaking the water

Amniotomy, or artificial rupture of the membranes (ARM), is one of the most important steps in the induction process, often referred to as "breaking the water" and it's done once the cervix is soft and slightly dilated, and the head has started to enter the pelvis. A thin plastic probe is passed through your cervix and used to make a small hole in the amniotic membranes, which allows some of the fluid around your baby to leak out. This softens the cervix even more and can provoke contractions in the muscular wall of the uterus. If contractions don't become established after ARM, then you'll require treatment with Syntocinon or Pitocin (see below).

Oxytocin, Syntocinon, Pitocin

Oxytocin is a natural hormone that stimulates the uterus, increasing the frequency and strength of contractions. A synthetic form, Syntocinon or Pitocin, is used with the same effect. It's diluted in fluid then dripped into a vein in your arm or injected into a large muscle. This is safe and effective when used correctly; however, it must be used with care since excessive contractions can reduce your baby's oxygen supply in labor. Your contractions and your baby's heartbeat will be continuously monitored (see p.418).

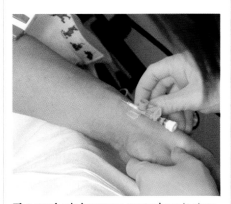

The synthetic hormone syntocinon is given via an intravenous line to stimulate the strength and frequency of your contractions.

Breech baby

At 32 weeks, 15 percent of babies are breech (bottom first). With time, most turn, with just 3 percent remaining breech at term.

Breech labors and births are usually more difficult, so if your baby is still in a breech position in late pregnancy, you may be offered a procedure to turn your baby (see below).

Turning your baby

The procedure to turn your baby, external cephalic version (ECV), is usually offered at around 37 weeks if a baby is still in a breech position. The doctor presses on the lower part of your belly to elevate your baby's bottom out of the pelvis. Pressure is used to rotate your baby until he is head down. The procedure may feel uncomfortable, and you may be given medication to relax the uterus. A scan is often done before and after the procedure.

The success rate for ECVs is often over 50 percent. Complications, such as bleeding behind the placenta and premature rupture of the membranes, are rare. If an ECV is unsuccessful and you want to try for a vaginal birth, you will be advised to deliver in a hospital so help can be provided quickly if needed. In most cases, a cesarean will be advised as the position of a breech baby is likely to make vaginal delivery difficult.

Breech diagnosed in labor

Occasionally it isn't discovered that your baby is in breech until you're in labor. This happens because it can be hard to distinguish between a baby's head and bottom by feeling your belly alone.

If a breech is diagnosed in labor, you may be able to have an ECV but at this stage it has a lower success rate. An ECV may not be possible in labor if the water has broken, if you're in advanced labor, or if there's no one to do the procedure.

Delivery of your baby

If you try for a vaginal birth, you should be in a hospital with an ob/gyn present, since you may need an assisted delivery or an emergency cesarean. Fetal monitoring should be done throughout labor, since babies in distress will need to be delivered by cesarean. Sometimes a breech baby has problems getting oxygen and blood through the umbilical cord, if it's squeezed into the wrong position.

You'll be advised to have your baby's heartbeat monitored throughout labor, and you may have an IV in case you need a cesarean. You may be asked to lie on your back with your feet in stirrups so that the doctor can access the baby. An alternative position is to stand or be on all fours. Your bladder may be emptied with a catheter and an episiotomy cut may be done to prevent a more serious tear (see p.427). The doctor may apply gentle pressure to the baby's arms or legs during birth, but you're unlikely to notice this. Except for these differences, the birth is likely to feel the same as the birth of a head-first baby. During the birth, the head will be eased out of the birth canal either by hand or with forceps. to control the speed of the birth, which should be neither too fast nor too slow.

A cesarean is likely if complications arise, for example the baby shows signs of distress; the cord slips below the baby's bottom; the cervix dilates too slowly; or the baby isn't descending.

POSITIONS OF A BREECH BABY

A breech baby can lie in one of three positions, known as extended (frank); flexed (complete); or footling. With an extended breech, the hips are flexed, knees extended, and the feet are by the head. A vaginal delivery is most likely with this type of breech. With a flexed breech, the hips and knees are flexed, with the feet above the buttocks, and a vaginal birth may be possible. In a footling breech, the hips are extended with the feet below the buttocks, so a vaginal delivery is unlikely.

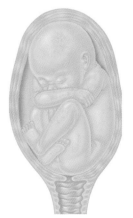

| Extended (frank) breech | Flexed (complete) breech | Footling breech |

Multiple births

Carrying twins or more increases the risk of complications during birth and you and your babies will be closely monitored.

Twin pregnancies occur naturally in around 1 in 53 women, but some factors increase the chance of you conceiving twins or more, including the use of some fertility treatments, becoming pregnant when you're older, already having children, and having a family history of twins.

Monitoring during pregnancy

Because multiple pregnancies are high risk, you'll receive extra monitoring; the type of delivery depends on the position of your twins and other complications. A concern is whether twins will be born prematurely with a small birth weight, which can mean spending time in a neonatal intensive care unit (see p.452).

Toward the end of pregnancy, you may have extra scans to monitor the babies' growth, since the ability of the placenta to provide oxygen can be reduced in a twin pregnancy. The volume of the fluid around each baby and their heart rates may be measured to check their well-being.

Possible complications

Certain complications with the babies or the mother can influence the delivery and mean that a cesarean is planned.

Fetal complications Twin-to-twin transfusion syndrome (TTTS) is a condition unique to identical twins who

share a placenta (see p.51). It occurs if there is a direct link in the blood supply between the babies and can put the lives of both at risk. Babies with TTTS need specialized treatment that may involve reducing the fluid around one baby or using a laser to separate the circulations.

Rarely, twins can develop in the same sac, known as monoamniotic twins. The main risk of this condition is that the cords become tangled, affecting the oxygen supply. The twins may have heart traces at the end of pregnancy and are delivered early by cesarean.

Maternal complications When you're carrying twins, you're at a higher risk of

With a twin delivery a larger medical team will be on hand to deal with any complications and to take care of both babies at birth.

QUESTIONS AND ANSWERS

Will I have a say in how I deliver my twins?

If you are having twins, you will get the chance to discuss your plans for giving birth with your obstetrician during the pregnancy. Your decision to have a vaginal birth or a cesarean section will probably be based upon several factors, such as the position of the babies, with the safety of you and your babies as the most important factor. Currently, an international twin birth study is underway to determine the best way for twins to be delivered.

Can I have a home birth with twins?

The Society of Obstetricians and Gynecologists of Canada and many midwives recommend against the home birth of twins because of the potential for complications. For the safety of your babies, a hospital birth is recommended.

Gillian found out she was having twins at an early scan. At first she was worried that the pregnancy and birth would be hard, but her confidence grew as she saw her babies growing well. She went into labor at 35 weeks.

Gillian's story: I was shocked when they told me I was carrying twins, since none of my family has had twins. The pregnancy was tough because I was so tired and I had such a big belly. I enjoyed the scans though because they were really reassuring.

I went into labor at just over 35 weeks. After initial contractions, my water broke at 2 am. My husband got me to the hospital in 15 minutes; I think he was in a bit of a panic. Jonathan, our first twin, was born just after 4 pm, so the first part of my labor was quite long. I managed without much pain relief medication. Celia came 20 minutes later. They broke my second bag of water since her heartbeat was low, but she was fine at birth. I remember the birthing room being crowded, and even though people introduced themselves to me, I couldn't have told you who they were. However, they all disappeared soon after the birth and left us to spend some time alone with our babies. That was the best time. All the worries disappeared and we could just get on with being a mom and a dad.

The doctor's comments: Like many women with a twin pregnancy, Gillian was worried about what might happen to her and her babies during labor. She had talked at length to me and the doctor during her pregnancy, but still felt anxious. When she arrived on the labor ward however, she could see that the people caring for her were highly professional and experienced. This gave her the confidence to deal with events as they unfolded. Both babies were doing very well when they left the hospital and Gillian was making an excellent recovery too.

Despite being higher risk, a twin birth is most likely to result in the safe delivery of both babies.

complications, such as preeclampsia (see p.474), possibly because of the additional strain on the kidneys; the liver condition cholestasis (see p.473), for reasons that are unclear; and thrombosis, because there is an additional strain on your circulation. These conditions may also mean that an early cesarean is recommended.

Going into labor
You're more likely to go into labor early and your babies may be lighter than average. With twins, you're likely to go into labor around 37 weeks; with triplets around 33 weeks; and with quadruplets around 30 weeks. The average birthweight for twins is 5.5 lb (2.5 kg); triplets and quadruplets are almost always low-birthweight.

Labor and birth with twins
Current recommendations are that an obstetrician should attend a twin birth.

If you're planning to have a vaginal birth, the labor should be almost as quick as it is with one baby.

Continuous monitoring of both heartbeats is recommended during a multiple labor. This is usually done by putting one strap around your belly for each baby, but sometimes the second baby is monitored in this way and the first baby may have a scalp electrode put on his head (see p.419), which gives a clearer picture of the first baby's heartbeat if it has been difficult to find.

Delivering the first twin For your first baby, the chance of using forceps or vacuum is the same as for a singleton birth, although the birth of the first twin may need to be assisted so that the doctor can gain quick access to the second twin. After the first twin's delivery, his cord is clamped and cut, but the placenta usually remains in the uterus until the second baby has been born.

Delivering the second twin The medical team will confirm whether your second baby is head- or bottom-first, either by feeling your abdomen, doing an internal examination, or by scanning you. As the second baby's head or bottom enters the pelvis, the second bag of water may be broken to encourage strong contractions. A normal birth should follow in about 30 minutes, and forceps or vacuum are only used if problems arise. If the second twin is bottom-first, a doctor should be on hand to help. It's unusual for the first twin to be born vaginally and the second to be born by a cesarean, but this may happen if the second baby needs an urgent delivery and a vaginal birth seems unsafe.

Delivering the placenta There is a greater risk of postpartum hemorrhage with twins, which means that an active management of the third stage may be advised (see p.428).

Multiple births

435

Assisted birth

In Canada, at least 2.5 percent of babies has an assisted birth. These are considered safe and can prevent further complications.

UNDERSTANDING WHY

Reasons for an assisted birth

There are several factors that can make an assisted birth more likely.

■ **Your baby has an abnormal heart rate,** which suggests that he might be in distress.

■ **You have been pushing a long time,** but your labor is progressing slowly.

■ **You're exhausted** and can't manage any more pushing.

■ **You have a medical condition** and have been told not to push for long.

An assisted birth is a birth in which either forceps or a vacuum suction cup (also called a vacuum or ventouse extractor) are used to aid a vaginal delivery. There may be some mild side effects such as bruising after an assisted birth, but major complications are rare.

As with all medical interventions, the use of forceps or a vacuum extractor will only be offered when it is thought to be necessary for the health of the baby and/or mother.

The procedure

First, your doctor will discuss with you the need for the procedure and may also explain to you the potential complications. You may be asked to sign a consent form, although not all hospitals insist on this. Before the birth takes place, you will probably be given an episiotomy and local anesthetics or epidural anesthesia. Fresh covers may be placed over your legs and abdomen and a catheter will be inserted to empty your bladder. The doctor will then place the forceps around the baby's head or attach the vacuum cup and will encourage you to start pushing again when you have a contraction. Your baby should be born within another 20 minutes from this time, give or take. There is less of a risk for a vaginal injury with a vacuum extraction than there is with forceps.

Forceps

Modern surgical forceps were invented by the British doctor Chamberlen in the seventeenth century and so have been in use for hundreds of years, although they have been modified over time. Forceps are an effective and reliable way to assist a delivery, but they have to be used with care by a properly trained doctor.

The forceps are placed so that they hold the sides of the baby's head near the ears and cheeks. The operator of the forceps then gently pulls the baby's head downward while you push during a contraction, and then will guide the baby out of the birth canal.

Forceps can also be used to adjust the the baby's head before the birth if the baby is lying in an occiput posterior position, which is with his back facing the mother's back (see p.417), toward the end of labor. After turning the baby's head and body, delivery is then completed as in the same way as described above.

METHODS OF ASSISTING BIRTH

Assisting your baby's birth with vacuum or forceps is a safe, well practiced procedure, which can prevent the need for an emergency cesarean. Whether you have forceps or vacuum may depend on the particular expertise and experience of the doctor doing the procedure.

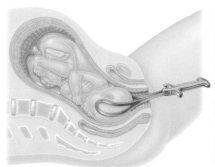

With forceps, your baby's head is cradled on either side with metal tongs that guide him down in time with your contractions.

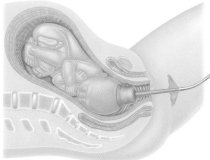

With vacuum, a soft suction cup is attached to your baby's head and then your baby is gently guided out.

Pros and cons of forceps There are several advantages of forceps over vacuum. First, they do not rely on any kind of machinery that could cause a problem during the birth. They also work well even if your contractions are weak or if you are finding it hard to push due to exhaustion. Lastly, forceps have a low failure rate: if the doctor can get the forceps around your baby's head easily, he will usually be able to complete the vaginal birth of your baby without having to resort to a cesarean. The disadvantage of forceps is that you may be more likely to have vaginal or perineal damage than with vacuum.

Vacuum extractor

The vacuum, or vacuum extractor, was invented in the 1950s. It consists of a cup attached to a tube that connects to a suction pump. The cup, which can be hard or soft plastic or metal, is placed on top of the baby's head and held in place while the suction creates a vacuum that makes the cup adhere to the baby's scalp. The doctor pulls downward while you push during a contraction.

Vacuum births are known to be very safe as long as you are at least 34 weeks pregnant. Before this time your baby's head may be too fragile to deal with the suction and few doctors use a vacuum before 32 weeks.

Pros and cons of vacuum The vacuum has some advantages over forceps; it is often a little easier to apply and may be less uncomfortable for you. It is also less likely to cause vaginal and perineal damage and you will be less likely to need an episiotomy. However, vacuum fails in up to 20 percent of cases, and it is especially likely to fail if your baby is not in the ideal position for the birth. Some doctors think it is also more likely to fail if your contractions are weak, if there is already a lot of natural swelling on your baby's head, or if you are too tired to push. If a vacuum does come off during the

birth, it can be reapplied, or the doctor can reach for a pair of forceps instead. Sometimes, however, a cesarean section has to be performed if the vacuum fails.

Pain relief

It can be painful having an assisted vaginal birth, so it is important that you have sufficient pain relief to help you cope with the delivery. In some situations, an injection of a local anesthetic in and around the vagina is sufficient to help you deal with the pain, particularly if the doctor is anticipating the birth to be fairly quick, and if your baby has already traveled most of the way through your pelvis. For more difficult assisted births, for example where the baby is not in an occiput anterior position (see p.417), an epidural may be given (see p.404). This is especially useful if you're going to give birth in the operating room instead of the delivery room because forceps or vacuum have a high chance of failing, leading to the need for a cesarean. Finally, if you already have an epidural in place, this can be topped up with additional medication if necessary.

Cesarean section

A cesarean delivery may be suggested if there is a potential benefit to your own or your baby's health, or sometimes both.

A cesarean section is the delivery of your baby by means of a cut in the abdomen. A cesarean rate of around 10–15 percent is thought to be reasonable, although in most Western countries the rate has risen beyond 20 percent and around 30 percent of all babies in Canada are now delivered by cesarean, an all-time high.

The increase is due to a higher incidence of cesareans in first-time mothers and a lower incidence of vaginal birth after cesarean (VBAC) in subsequent pregnancies. Some women may think that cesareans are safer for the baby than a vaginal birth. In fact, if you've had an uncomplicated pregnancy, a cesarean is hard to justify on medical grounds.

Types of cesarean

Cesareans are either emergency or elective (planned) procedures. The need for a cesarean may be apparent well before labor begins, so you, your partner, and your obstetrician will have time to talk through the procedure and what will happen—this is an elective cesarean. For an emergency cesarean, the need only becomes apparent once labor is underway and a risk develops for either the baby or the mother.

Emergency cesareans An emergency cesarean is most commonly carried out when the baby is thought to be at risk, for example if the baby's oxygen supply has been reduced and there are signs of fetal distress. In this case, the staff will try to do the cesarean rapidly—within 30 minutes when possible, although it's important that shortcuts aren't taken that could put your own health at unnecessary risk.

Urgent cesareans take place when there's no immediate threat to life, and these are more common than emergency cesareans. An urgent cesarean may be done if your baby's heart rate is causing concern very early in labor and the prospect of a vaginal delivery taking place within a reasonably short time is low. Another reason for an urgent cesarean is if you are not progressing in your labor.

Elective cesareans Around one-third of cesareans are elective, or planned, procedures, and the number of these has increased greatly in recent years. Reasons for an elective cesarean include a breech baby; a tear involving the back passage, (or another traumatic event during a previous vaginal delivery); a previous cesarean; a larger

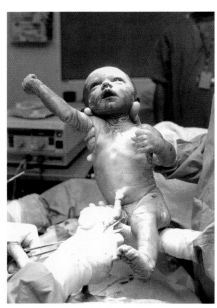

Your baby is gently lifted out of the uterus and the cord is clamped and cut.

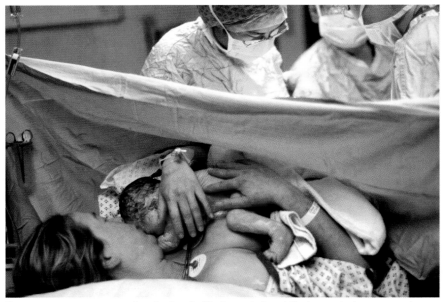

You or your partner can enjoy the first hold of your baby while the surgical team completes the operation by delivering the placenta and stitching the incision.

than average baby, and maternal choice. In these situations, although a cesarean is reasonable, an attempt at a vaginal birth is also reasonable with the right precautions. It's uncommon for maternal choice to be the sole reason for a cesarean, and there's likely to be another factor, such as one of those cited above.

In some situations, it would be hazardous for either you or your baby if you were to try for a vaginal birth; for example you've had multiple previous cesareans or other major surgery to the uterus; the baby can't be moved from lying horizontally; the placenta is lying very low (see p.212); or there are severe pelvic abnormalities in the birth canal. Some maternal medical conditions also mean that vaginal birth is not advisable.

Giving your consent

The doctor will need your consent prior to doing a cesarean. He should tell you why the procedure is being proposed, and what its benefits and risks are. Ideally, you should have plenty of time to decide whether you want the surgery or not, although with an emergency cesarean, the time to think things over may be limited. Even so, you are always within your rights to say no to a cesarean, even if this means that your life or that of your baby is at risk.

Your anesthesia

Before the surgery, you will meet an anesthesiologist, who will make sure that you have no pain during your surgery and will help you with pain control afterward. Most women are awake during a cesarean. An injection of medication into the spinal fluid in your back, called a spinal block, numbs any sensation of pain (see p.406). Or, if you've been using an epidural for pain relief in labor (see p.404), this can be used for the surgery. After your anesthetic has been given, the anesthesiologist will check that it is working properly.

Being awake usually means that your birthing partner can stay with you and it's also a little safer for you and for your baby than a general anesthetic. Very occasionally a general anesthetic is needed (see pp.406–7).

The surgery

Before the surgery, an IV line will be put in your hand or your arm so that fluids or medications can be given intravenously if necessary. Also, the pubic hair on your belly may be clipped downward by about 1 in (3 cm) to clear the way for the cut. Both of these may be done before you go to the operation room or after you arrive there.

Once the anesthesiologist is assured you're pain free, a catheter will be inserted into your bladder and will stay in until the next day while your sensation recovers. Your abdomen will be cleaned with an antiseptic solution and sterile drapes will be placed over you, which prevent you and your partner from seeing the surgery.

During the surgery, a 4 in (10 cm) long cut will be made, usually horizontally, on the abdomen wall, across the bikini line, although occasionally an up-and-down cut below the belly button is done. Your bladder will be pushed down and the front of the uterus opened so that the doctor can access the baby. If your water hasn't already broken, this will be done now before the baby and placenta are delivered. The surgeon will release the baby's head from the pelvic brim and lift the baby out. Sometimes, another member of the team needs to put pressure on the uterus to assist this.

You'll be able to see your baby when the cord has been cut, and once initial checkups have been done on your baby, either you or your partner should be able to hold him while the surgery is completed. After the umbilical cord is cut, your doctor will remove the placenta.

To finish the cesarean, the uterus will be closed up with one or two layers of

POSSIBLE COMPLICATIONS

There are several common, but minor, problems associated with cesareans. These include bleeding during the surgery, or a day or so later; the need for a blood transfusion; or getting a minor infection in the bladder or in the abdominal incision.

You will most likely be given antibiotics before the surgery, so getting a major infection is far less common. Consequently, having to have a major second surgery because of a life-threatening incision infection is extremely rare. The chance of a blood clot forming in the pelvic veins is also very small.

Other rare complications: Since sharp implements are used during the surgery, there is a small risk that your bladder, or even your baby, could be cut during the surgery. Your bowels are less likely to be damaged and your other internal organs are highly unlikely to be injured.

stitches, then the abdomen wall will be stitched in separate layers. This takes about half an hour, although it can take longer, especially if you've had previous surgeries. You may have dissolvable stitches, or stitches that have to be taken out after four or five days; less commonly, small staples may be used. The choice is usually made by the doctor, but if you have a preference, make this known to the team caring for you before the surgery starts.

Your recovery

Your nurses will encourage you to get out of bed the following day, and by the day after this you may be well enough to do most things for yourself, with help. Women usually go home on the fourth day after the cesarean.

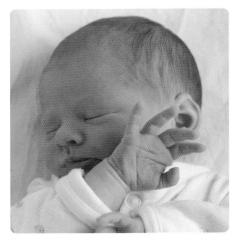

You've spent the last nine months anticipating this moment, but nothing can quite prepare you both for how you'll feel when you meet your baby. In the coming weeks, you'll recover from the birth, but your world will change dramatically as you grapple with your baby's everyday care. You may feel an array of emotions, from pure joy to frustration at your level of exhaustion. Most importantly, you'll be getting to know your tiny baby and marveling at this new addition to your family.

Life with your new baby

The first 12 hours

A few minutes ago you were a couple—and now you are parents! The moment you have been dreaming of for nine months has finally arrived... so what happens next?

Of course your experiences will depend on your labor and birth and local procedures, but here is what usually occurs in your first 12 hours after birth.

🕐 **1–2 hours** As long as he is well, your baby can be placed in your arms, and you can cuddle him and make the most of these first magical moments. The doctor or your partner will cut the umbilical cord after a few minutes, or once it stops pulsating. You may feel elated, relieved, or just exhausted. Don't be alarmed if you start to vomit, shake vigorously, or feel too exhausted to even hold your baby at first. These are all very normal post-birth sensations.

If your baby is fine and you want to breast-feed, put him to the breast, but he may just nuzzle at first. Snuggle him close, skin to skin: the warmth of your body is all he needs right now.

At 1, 5, and 10 minutes, your baby will be observed and given an Apgar score (see p.428). He will be wiped with a soft towel and his fingers and toes checked. He will then be weighed and his head circumference measured. He will also have a hearing test in the first hours.

But you also have work to do. As soon as your baby is born, you have to push once more to expel the placenta. You'll have milder contractions that detach the placenta from your uterus. After about 10 or 20 minutes (sometimes longer), you'll be done (see p.428).

If your perineum tore, or you had an episiotomy (a cut to ease your baby out), you may need stitches. You'll be given a local anesthetic, unless you already have an epidural, so you don't feel a thing. Your partner can hold your baby and sit close by while you are stitched.

🕐 **2–3 hours** Time to refuel: many women say their first drink of water and snack after giving birth are the best they've ever tasted... enjoy.

If you're feeling fine and there are no concerns about your condition, you'll likely be moved to the room on the maternity ward where you'll spend the remainder of your time in the hospital. You'll be taken there in a wheelchair with your baby in your arms. (In some hospitals, you'll never leave the room where you deliver; some labor and delivery rooms are designated as postpartum rooms, as well.)

🕐 **3–4 hours** After the exertion of giving birth, you'll be sweaty, sticky, and in need of a shower, which you can

Nothing compares with the moment when you meet your baby face to face.

Life with your new baby

have now if you didn't have an epidural. Ask a nurse or your partner to walk with you if you're wobbly. Afterward you'll feel like a new woman and can put on a breast-feeding bra for comfort.

5–6 hours Off to the bathroom? The first time you urinate it can sting, especially if you had stitches, so pour a cup of warm water over your perineum as you urinate. The hospital needs to know everything is in good working order before you leave its care. You'll need to use sanitary pads to soak up the vaginal blood loss (lochia).

7 hours This might be the first chance you've had to look at your baby's tiny toes, scrunched-up legs, or fine head of hair. There may be traces of greasy vernix on his skin. Perhaps he has long, flaky fingernails that need trimming or a downy fuzz of hair called lanugo on his back. He's unique and gorgeous.

8 hours If your baby is awake, he may be hungry. At this stage, you're producing nutrient-rich colostrum, a fluid containing antibodies. Position him at the breast: he should open his mouth wide and take the entire areola, known as "latching on." Breast-feeding stimulates the release of the hormone oxytocin, which contracts the uterus. This can cause afterpains, more noticeable in second and subsequent births, which can feel like contractions. The only consolation is that with each contraction, your uterus—and hence your abdomen—shrinks back down.

9 hours If you're up to it, you might be ready for visitors, either at home or on the unit, to admire your baby. Don't let them tire you out, though.

10 hours Your baby's newborn checkups will take place when he is between 4 and 48 hours old. A staff pediatrician at the hospital will examine him from top to toe; listen to his heart,

THE FIRST MEDICAL CHECKUP

In the first 12 hours a pediatrician will give your baby a checkup. In addition to a head-to-toe examination, there will be checks made on skin color, temperature, and muscle tone, and on reflexes, such as sucking and grasping.

Heart and lungs are checked to ensure they sound normal.

Head shape and fontanelles (soft areas between the skull bones) are examined.

Hands and feet are checked for reflexes, and fingers and toes are counted.

Mouth and palate—the separate sections should have fused together.

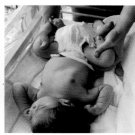

Hips are rotated and the legs are bent upward to check for signs of dislocation.

Spine is checked to ensure it is straight and free from abnormalities.

check his hips (and testes in a boy); and ask about the contents of his diapers.

11 hours In many hospitals, you can spend your first night as a new family together, since rooming-in with the baby is a common practice and new dads often sleep over. This lets the nurses see how mother and baby interact. If you need to get a few hours of uninterrupted sleep after a long or difficult labor, a nurse can collect the baby from you.

12 hours After a whirlwind of agony, ecstasy, and sheer hard labor, you need to rest when you can. If your baby is sleeping, fend off visitors, draw the curtains around your bed, or take the phone off the hook, and sleep.

Your recovery

Although you've had major surgery, you'll be encouraged to get up to get your circulation going. After an epidural, this will be as soon as you've regained the feeling in your legs. After a general anesthetic, you'll be encouraged to get up when you no longer feel sleepy, usually within an hour. You won't be able to shower yet, but your nurse or midwife can give you a bed bath to help you freshen up.

You'll probably feel very tired and sore, so ask for help with positioning your baby at the breast, and take pain medication when you need it.

Getting acquainted

YOUR BABY TODAY

In the first 24 hours, your baby should pass urine and meconium, the first black, sticky feces, that are made up of waste products and bile. You'll be changing plenty of diapers, and in no time, you'll be a diapering pro.

Finally, your baby is in your arms! As you recuperate in the hospital, you'll get to know the baby you've waited to meet.

CHECKLIST

Safe sleeping

Crib death is a concern for all new parents. Follow the guidelines from the Canadian Pediatric Society's "Safe Sleep for Babies" to minimize the risks.

■ **Put your baby on his back** to sleep.

■ **Don't let your baby get too hot.** He really doesn't need a blanket. If it's chilly, add layers and make sure his feet are covered, but don't go overboard. In the summer, he may be most comfortable sleeping in just a onesie—but make sure the fan or air conditioning vent isn't directly overhead.

■ **Don't let anyone smoke** around your baby.

■ **Never sleep with** your baby on a sofa or armchair.

■ **The safest place for your baby to sleep is in a crib or co-sleeper** near where you sleep. If you bring the baby into your bed to breast-feed, put him back in his crib or co-sleeper when done.

■ **Keep all soft objects,** like pillows, toys, and loose bedding out of the baby's crib. A firm mattress covered by a fitted sheet is best.

At last, you're a mom! You may feel love at first sight, when you first hold your baby after the birth, but for many women bonding takes place over the next few days or weeks. For both parents, skin-to-skin contact with your baby helps the bonding process and is particularly beneficial for premature babies (see p.452). Try not to be anxious when you pick up your baby. In the first few weeks, your baby has little head control, so support him with a hand under his head and shoulders, or both hands under his arms and with your fingers supporting his head.

The nurses in the maternity ward are there for help and support. You'll be asked if you've urinated and will be given help with breast-feeding if needed. A lactation consultant will likely also be on hand to guide you through the initial difficulties you may encounter when nursing is unfamiliar. If your hospital offers "rooming in," you'll get to spend most of the day with your baby present, except when he is taken by the nurses for routine testing or examinations by the staff pediatricians. You'll also be visited by your doctor every day that you're in the hospital so he or she can check on your progress.

YOUR BABY'S REFLEXES

Newborn babies have reflexes that form part of their survival skills. In addition to the rooting and grasping reflexes shown here, babies also have a startle reflex, whereby they will fling out their arms if unsupported, and a stepping reflex, which means they will step their feet up and down if held upright on a surface.

Rooting reflex: If you touch or stroke your baby's cheek, he will turn toward that side with his mouth open in search for food.

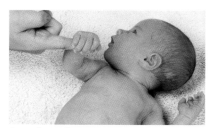

Grasping reflex: If you place your finger in the palm of your baby's hand, he will instinctively tightly grip your finger.

1st **WEEK:** DAY 2

Settling in

YOUR BABY TODAY

Newborn babies sleep around 16 hours a day, although some sleep for most of the first few days while others seem awake and fretful. If your baby is very sleepy, you may need to wake her for feedings, which should be at least every four hours.

You may be feeling anxious about your new responsibilities, but be reassured by the support network around you.

Your ob/gyn will visit in the hospital today. She will ask how you are managing and check that you have emergency contact numbers. You may be asked to watch short films or read brochures about the risks of Shaken Baby Syndrome and/or Sudden Infant Death Syndrome. A pediatrician will also examine your baby in the hospital today.

It's important that you eat a healthy diet and rest during the day whenever possible. Kegel exercises (see p.69) are vital to strengthen your muscles. If you were given painkillers or anti-inflammatory medicine, take these as necessary. If you get visitors, make sure they wash their hands before touching the baby.

Do I need to clean the cord stump before it drops off?

Your baby's cord stump, which is the end of the umbilical cord, will shrivel up and fall off naturally around 7–10 days after the birth. Many parents feel uneasy about touching the stump and are unsure whether or not to clean it. Some pediatricians recommend swabbing it regularly with rubbing alcohol but others say to leave it alone. However, if it does become dirty, clean with soap and water and dry well. If the cord stump or the surrounding

area are sticky, inflamed, or smelly, contact your doctor for advice. It's important to keep the cord stump dry. Exposing it to air at times helps avoid the risk of infection.

While you're in the hospital, you may get lots of visitors. And while it's fun to show off your beautiful baby to friends and family, make sure that you take time to sleep, because once you bring your baby home, you won't have much opportunity to sleep. In most hospitals, your baby will stay in your room and sleep in a crib beside your bed, so you or your partner will be able to tend to her in the night.

BURPING YOUR BABY

Burping simply means helping your baby burp after a feeding. After a feeding, air bubbles in your baby's stomach need to rise to the top and you can help this happen by sitting her on your lap or holding her upright against your shoulder. You don't need to rub or pat her, but this often feels right and babies seem to like it! It's a good idea to burp half way through a feeding and again at the end, especially for bottle-fed babies, since air fills up the stomach, slows down the feeding, and makes a baby more likely to vomit.

Holding your baby upight over your shoulder after a feeding can help your baby burp and therefore ease discomfort.

EASING DISCOMFORT

Stitches and hemorrhoids

The following can increase comfort.

■ When you urinate, pour warm water over the area to ease stinging.

■ Sit on an inflatable ring.

■ Apply a cooling gel or ice pack.

■ Take a warm bath or spray water on your stitches in the shower.

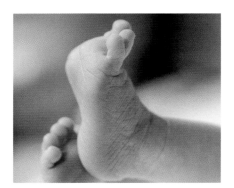

Going home

YOUR BABY TODAY

A new baby's skin is often quite dry in the first few weeks. This is normal and the skin will eventually correct itself. Although you don't need to put moisturizer on a baby's skin, if you want you could gently massage in some baby or olive oil.

Once your breast milk arrives, your baby may start to appear more relaxed and contented and go longer between feedings.

Your first day at home with your tiny new baby can be daunting. You are also probably feeling tired after feeding and changing your baby at night.

Keeping your baby's crib close to your bed can make life easier at night when you feed or change her. A crib with sides that can be lowered put next to your bed lets you feed her and place her back in her crib without actually getting out of bed. Try to deal with night wakings with a minimum of fuss. Keep lights low and don't talk much or stimulate your baby. Only change your baby's diaper if it is really necessary and, once the feeding is done, put her right back down in her crib.

You'll discover that babies don't like being dressed—especially having clothes pulled over their head. Keep life simple by buying machine-washable, front-fastening onesies and only change outfits if a diaper leaks. In the first weeks, there is no need to change her into a daytime outfit. If she is cold, simply add layers.

Today, you may notice that swelling in your hands and feet subsides as you pass more urine. However, you still need to drink plenty of fluids—two to three quarts a day—to prevent bladder infections, avoid constipation, and help breast milk production. Today or tomorrow may be the first time you move your bowels since giving birth. Eat lots of fruit and vegetables and adequate amounts of fiber to help bowel movements return to normal.

Until now, your breasts have produced colostrum, the watery premilk rich in nutrients and antibodies. By the end of the third day your milk will come in and your baby will start to feel more satisfied. Once your milk is in, your breasts will likely feel engorged and uncomfortable. As feeding establishes over the next few days this discomfort should start to recede.

Fathers will be proud to have the new baby at home. Apart from breast-feeding, dads can be involved in all aspects of care, including calming the baby, changing diapers, bathing, and dressing.

The doctor will do a checkup before you go home to make sure the uterus has contracted; your blood loss (lochia) to ensure it isn't too heavy; and any stitches.

SPONGE BATHS

Babies don't need frequent baths. Two or three times a week is enough, or their skin can dry out. For the first week or two, before the umbilical cord stump falls off, give sponge baths. Wrap your baby in a towel and lie her on a flat surface. Get ready a baby washcloth, a bowl of warm water, and mild baby soap. Uncover only the body parts you're actively washing, then rewrap them in the towel. Start with the face, with water only, then use soap on the body and end with the diaper area.

Using a damp washcloth, gently clean your baby's face, using water only.

To clean her hands, wipe the backs and palms and between the fingers.

Wash the diaper area last, making sure to clean between the creases in the skin.

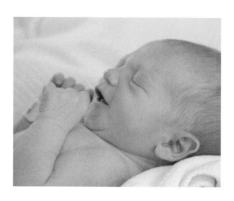

First outing

YOUR BABY TODAY

The pediatrician will examine your baby today. She will ask if he is alert and check for any signs of jaundice (see p.477). She will also weigh him and will ask how he is getting along with feeding and whether there are any problems.

Your body is gradually recovering from the birth, and you may be starting to feel like facing the world once again.

Your breasts should be feeling a bit more comfortable by now as feeding becomes established, and your uterus will be steadily reducing in size, but can still be felt by pressing on your abdomen.

Your blood loss will have started to ease off by now, although you may find that it's heavier first thing in the morning and also while you're breast-feeding.

You'll visit the pediatrician today for the baby's first in-office checkup. She will look for any signs of dehydration, such as your baby not having plenty of wet diapers and any feeding problems. She'll also measure your baby's weight, length, and head circumference. The measurements will be plotted on a graph to track your baby's own growth curves at all of his subsequent appointments. The doctor willl also examine the soft spots (fontanelles) on your baby's head; look into his ears, eyes, and mouth; listen to his heart and lungs; and examine his abdomen, hips, legs, and genitals.

You'll likely head home from the hospital today. If you had stitches or staples these will likely be removed today before you're discharged, although many obstetricians now use subcuticular stitches (just under the skin layer) that do not need to be removed since they gradually absorb over a few weeks.

A properly installed baby car seat is a legal requirement when traveling with your baby in a car.

AS A MATTER OF FACT

By day four about a third of all babies are visibly jaundiced.

Jaundice in newborn babies is usually harmless and is due to an elevated level of the waste product bilirubin in the blood, caused by the baby's immature liver. Very high levels of bilirubin can cause problems and are treated with light therapy (see p.477).

CHECKLIST

Taking your baby out

If you haven't been out yet, cabin fever may be setting in. Make sure you have everything you may need before venturing out on a trip.

■ **Pack a diaper bag with** two diapers, wipes or cotton pads, a spare onesie, a cloth, and a bottle of formula if you're bottle-feeding.

■ **Take layers of clothing** on outings, including an undershirt, onesie, and cardigan. In winter, add an all-in-one babysuit and a blanket in a carriage.

■ **A third of a baby's heat is lost through his head,** so on cool days, add a hat or hooded top. Socks and booties are easy to lose, so footed onesies are more practical; mittens are only needed in cold weather.

■ **In hot weather, make sure your baby is covered** and protected from direct sunlight at all times.

■ **Figure out how to use a baby sling.** If traveling by car or public transportation, learn how to fold and unfold a stroller.

■ **Do not carry your baby far in a car seat** because it's bad for your back.

Feeding your baby

Breast-feeding provides your baby with the best nutritional start in life and has a range of other benefits, outlined here. If you decide to bottle-feed, you can also be confident that your baby will thrive. The key to both methods is preparation.

QUESTIONS AND ANSWERS

How often should I feed my baby?

If you have a healthy, full-term baby, you should feed her on demand, which means feeding her when she cries and seems hungry. This can mean that sometimes she'll be fed every couple of hours and sometimes she'll go for four to six hours without a feeding. Although you may not feel as if you're producing much milk initially, your baby only needs small quantities of colostrum, the first watery milk. Her demands will grow after the first few days, which will coincide with your milk coming in (see right).

Will I be able to breast-feed my twins?

Milk is produced on a supply and demand basis, so it's perfectly possible to breast-feed twins and more. If your babies are born early, breast milk is beneficial since it protects against infections, which premature babies are more susceptible to, so it's worth breast-feeding, even for a few weeks, but you'll need rest and ample nutrition. Start by feeding your twins separately. If you then want to feed them together, take time to position them well. An under-arm hold works well (see p.449) and cushions and a willing helper are useful. Expressing (see p.449) means the babies can be fed together, alternating on the breast. If you think that they aren't getting enough milk, consult your doctor. A lactation consultant, La Leche League, or the local chapter of Multiple Births Canada can offer support too.

The benefits of breast-feeding

Breast-feeding is the perfect first food for your baby; it contains all the nutrients your baby needs and works on a supply and demand basis, so that as your baby feeds, your body responds by producing more milk. Breast milk is thought to reduce a baby's risk of developing an allergic condition, such as asthma and eczema, to make childhood obesity and diabetes less likely, and it may reduce the long-term risk of heart disease.

Breast-feeding also provides benefits for you. It helps your uterus contract to its pre-pregnancy shape more quickly. It helps you get back into shape quicker since your body uses additional energy to produce breast milk, and it reduces your risk of getting breast and ovarian cancer.

Lastly, and importantly, breast-feeding helps you and your baby to be close both physically and emotionally.

When your milk comes in

In the first few days your breasts produce colostrum, a watery substance that contains essential nutrients and antibodies that help your baby to fight off infections such as those of the ear, chest, and gastrointestinal tract.

At around day three, or sometimes a bit later, you will start to produce milk, which contains all the nutrients your baby needs. Your breasts may feel uncomfortably full

THE RIGHT TECHNIQUE

Latching on

Taking the time to ensure that your baby is latched on properly before a feeding is important because you could otherwise develop sore nipples. A baby that is properly latched on has her mouth wide open, with the whole areola (the area surrounding the nipple) in her mouth; her bottom lip will be curled back and she will be noticeably sucking. You'll feel a sucking effect over the entire area.

Once you've positioned your baby so that she is level with your breast, hold her with her nose and mouth facing your nipple.

When your baby opens her mouth wide, bring her to the breast, ensuring that she takes all of the nipple and the areola into her mouth.

To remove your baby from the breast insert your finger into the corner of her mouth to break the seal so that she doesn't pull the nipple.

Holding your baby tummy-to-tummy is a comfortable position for you both, enabling your baby to latch on well (top, left). **An under-arm "football" hold** can help keep a restless baby still (bottom, left). **Lying side by side** is often recommended after a cesarean (right).

and tender at this time, and you'll need to make sure they're properly emptied at each feeding to prevent them from becoming engorged (see p.456).

Successful breast-feeding

Despite the fact that breast-feeding is a natural process, it can sometimes prove difficult. Getting comfortable before a feeding, positioning your baby well, and ensuring that she latches on properly (see box, left), are all prerequisites for successful feeding.

For your baby to latch on properly, it's important that you're both positioned well. Ensure that you're comfortable and that your back is well supported; using cushions for support may be helpful. You may find sitting and cradling your baby at chest level is comfortable with her tummy facing your tummy. Or you could try a football hold with your baby under your arm. Some women find it helpful to lie on their side to latch their baby on. You'll soon discover which positions suit you best and will gradually gain confidence in your ability to feed.

Once your baby is latched on, the "letdown" reflex is triggered. You will feel a tingling sensation as milk is released, which in turn stimulates the production of more milk. Your baby will pause during

feedings and stop when she is full. It's advisable to always have water or juice during or just after a feeding to replace the fluids lost from breast milk.

Bottle-feeding

This involves more preparation, but your partner can help and become involved with feeding. You'll need in advance 4–6 bottles: larger 8 fl oz (250 ml) bottles, and smaller 4 fl oz (125 ml) ones; newborn bottle nipples; a bottle brush; and infant formula. If you have chlorinated tap

Bottle-feeding helps dads strengthen the bond with their baby and allows you to have some welcome time off from feeding.

EXPRESSING MILK

An extra supply

Expressing your milk boosts your milk production and enables you to go out or have an unbroken night's sleep while your partner feeds the baby. You can express milk as soon as you like after the birth, although often women wait until feeding is established, at about four weeks. Your fresh milk can be stored in a milk-storage bag or bottle for 3–8 days in the fridge or frozen for 3–6 months and defrosted in the fridge or a bowl of warm water, never the microwave.

Many women use a breast pump, either electric or manual, to express milk. You can also express manually.

water, it's okay to put bottles in the dishwasher or wash by hand. Otherwise, clean all of the parts, then boil in water for 5–10 minutes. Put filtered or cooled boiled water in the bottle, then add the formula according to the manufacturer's instructions. Test the temperature of the milk by squeezing a drop on your inner wrist: it should feel warm, but not hot. Cool the milk if necessary by placing the bottle in a pitcher of cold water, or running it under cold water while shaking the bottle all the time. When ready, hold your baby half sitting with her head in the crook of your elbow and her back along your forearm. Gently put the nipple into her mouth and tip the bottle so the milk covers the nipple to stop her from swallowing any air. Discard any formula leftover in the bottle.

Feeding your baby

449

Baby blues

YOUR BABY TODAY

If you had a cesarean and your baby is healthy, he'll likely come home from the hospital with you today, after passing his final in-hospital pediatric exam. Make sure you have the correct car seat for him, and pack a blanket or two to keep him warm.

Try to spend some time focusing on the needs of older children too and helping them to adapt to the new arrival.

Today, you might feel emotional and weepy, known as the "baby blues." This is caused by hormonal changes and exacerbated by fatigue and a feeling of anti-climax after the build up to the birth. The baby blues last a day or so and with rest and emotional support you will start to feel better. If the feelings fail to subside after a few days, talk to your doctor since you may be suffering from postpartum depression (see p.475).

Your breasts will still feel tender and full today. Feeding your baby on demand (see p.448) will help relieve this. Feeling tired interferes with the "letdown" reflex (see p.449), so it's vital to rest or sleep in the day to make up for broken nights. It's important to continue breast-feeding at night to prevent milk stagnation, which leads to problems such as abscesses and mastitis (breast inflammation) (see p.475).

Your baby's arrival is a major adjustment for an older child, but there are ways to help him welcome the baby. Give your older child a gift from the baby and encourage him to help with the baby's care as is appropriate for his age. A two-year old may want to touch the baby, hold his hand, and bring diapers and other things that are needed, while a five-year old can hold the baby with support and sing to him.

Giving older siblings attention and time avoids them feeling left out and helps them to accept the new arrival.

TIPS FOR COPING

Coping strategies

Setting yourself some guidelines can help you cope with the added demands of twins or more.

- Make time to be with your babies.

- Prioritize activities ruthlessly, enlist practical help, and shop online.

- Don't bathe your babies daily unless you and they enjoy it.

- Let visitors make their own coffee.

- Consider using pacifiers if your twins cry a lot. This helps you attend to the twin most in need.

- Make time for yourself every day.

Finding your way

YOUR BABY TODAY

It's likely that both you and your baby are becoming more confident with feeding. It's common for new babies to bring up some milk after each feeding, known as spitting up, and this is unlikely to cause any harm. Talk to the doctor if you're at all concerned.

By now, you and your partner will be starting to feel more confident about holding, handling, and feeding your baby.

Many parents feel uneasy about giving their baby a bath since they worry about dropping a slippery baby. Many also find that their baby objects strongly to being undressed and immersed in water. Bathing should be fun, so if your baby hates baths at first, sponge bathe him most of the time (see p.446). Make bathtime as stress-free as possible by gathering everything you need before you start and make sure

the room you undress your baby in is warm and draft-free. After the bath, dry and dress your baby immediately.

Diapers will be a part of your life for the next couple of years. There is no need to routinely change a diaper before or after feedings—just when there is a stool or it is heavy with urine. After opening a diaper, wipe away all visible feces with the diaper. Clean your baby's bottom thoroughly with wet cotton

pads, wiping from front to back to avoid spreading germs. If using a cloth diaper, use a cream to avoid diaper rash. If your baby wears disposable diapers you may not need a diaper cream, but if he starts to get a diaper rash, you may find that diaper cream will clear it up.

BATHING YOUR BABY

Before you bath your baby, have a towel ready to dry him and a clean diaper and change of clothes at hand so that he doesn't get cold after the bath. Half fill a baby bath with water that feels lukewarm to your elbow. After bathing, dry him quickly. Don't use talcum powder, which he could inhale.

Wrap your baby in a towel, and support his head and shoulders while you wet his head with the other hand.

While supporting his head and shoulders and under his bottom, lower him carefully into the water.

Still supporting his head, wash him with a washcloth or sponge; start with the face and end with the bottom.

CHECKLIST

Exercise basics

You will be encouraged to do some gentle exercise as soon as you feel able, although it's best to wait until the six-week checkup (see pp.462–3) before starting a strenuous program.

■ Try to maintain good posture since this will help relieve backaches.
■ Continue Kegel exercises (see p.69) after giving birth.
■ If you had a cesarean, wait until at least six weeks before starting an exercise program.
■ Start with low-impact exercises, such as walking and Pilates. Gradually increase the duration and intensity. You can also begin to strengthen your abdominal muscles (see p.456).
■ If you have any bleeding or feel faint, stop and consult your doctor.
■ Set realistic goals.

451

Neonatal intensive care babies

Around 14 to 15 percent of all babies born in Canada need to spend time in a neonatal intensive care unit (NICU). Babies most often need extra care to assist them with breathing until their lungs have matured.

There are many reasons why your baby may need special care, the most common one being prematurity (being born before 37 weeks). Babies may need to spend days, weeks, or sometimes months in a NICU until they are big enough and well enough to go home.

Neonatal intensive care unit

If your baby is in a NICU, this is a particularly stressful time. It helps to understand a bit about who will be caring for your baby, what they will be doing, and how to make sure you're fully informed at all times.

In Canada most hospitals have a unit to provide special nursing and medical care for babies; these are divided into three levels depending on the degree of care offered. Level one is the most basic level. These units don't provide long-term ventilatory support, but they are expert at caring for babies who are slightly premature, need frequent nursing, or have previously been ventilated and are ready to be transferred to less intensive care. Level two units ventilate and give intensive care to babies from 32 weeks' gestation. Level three units offer intensive care for babies born as early as 23 weeks, and can often do neonatal surgery.

All these units are staffed by special nurses and doctors who will be happy to show you around before the baby is born if there is time.

Ward rounds Most units have rounds each morning, and the more intensive units will have another round later in the day. Some allow parents to be present and to ask questions during rounds, while others prefer parents to wait outside and then make time to talk to them afterward.

Communication and visiting You may be able to spend some time with your baby before he is sent to a NICU. However, if your baby needs to be on a ventilator, or has another serious problem, he will be sent immediately to neonatal intensive care, and you may not have any time together after the birth. You'll be encouraged to see your baby as soon as he has been transferred, and if you're unable to go immediately, you may be given a photo of your baby.

You should be able to see your baby any time of the day or night and the nurses will be happy to update you regularly. The doctors will also give you an update on an ad hoc basis or arrange to meet you for a more formal chat. Other family members may be able to visit the unit with your permission.

THE ROLE OF PARENTS

How you can help your baby

For most, the experience of having their baby in a NICU is extremely stressful. Parents may feel that they have no role in the care of their baby; however, this is not the case. The most important thing you can do for your baby is to start expressing breast milk. Breast milk will nearly always be the best milk for a premature baby and can be stored in a freezer until needed.

You may be able to touch and stroke your baby and can be helped to cuddle him while he is on a ventilator. Babies thrive on skin-to-skin contact, called kangaroo care. You'll be encouraged to tuck your baby on your chest inside your shirt so that he can enjoy a close bond. Talking, reading, and singing to your baby helps him become familiar with you. You may be able to change his diaper and help with feedings, even if these are through a nasogastric tube.

Spend plenty of time with your baby, especially when breast-feeding since this may help the letdown reflex (see p.449), but save some time for yourself too so that you conserve energy for when you return home with your baby.

Carrying your baby close to your body and enjoying skin-to-skin contact together will help your tiny baby thrive.

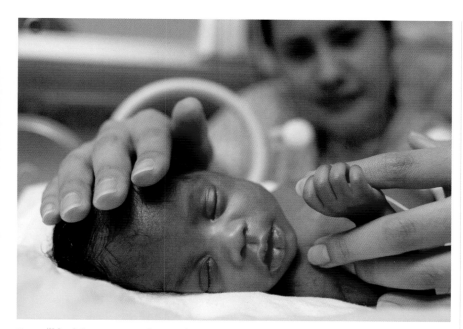

You will both be encouraged to touch, stroke, and caress your small baby, and to spend as much time as possible talking and singing to him.

Your baby's care

While your baby is in the NICU, he may be treated with medication and have various tests and checkups. In some cases, he will need to be on a ventilator.

Tests and X-rays Your baby may have blood tests to check for infection and anemia, to check kidney function, oxygen, and carbon dioxide levels, sugar levels, and to identify his blood group. The frequency of these depends on how ill or premature your baby is. In neonatal intensive care, babies need blood tests periodically. Some babies need an X-ray while they're there, and very premature babies often need many chest X-rays and sometimes abdominal ones.

Assisting your baby Some babies need a little extra oxygen, while others need constant oxygen through a nasal tube. For very premature babies, a tube may be placed into the trachea (windpipe) and connected to a ventilator that blows oxygen into the lungs. Babies are monitored to see when they can be weaned off the ventilator.

Most babies in intensive care need one or more IVs to give fluids, blood, and antibiotics. Very small babies may be fed through a long, fine feeding tube running through the mouth or nose to the stomach. They may also need at least one blood transfusion, for some cases of conditions like anemia and jaundice.

Antibiotics are often given to prevent infection. Some babies need medicine to keep their blood pressure up, and many who are ventilated need medicine to sedate them and to prevent or treat pain.

YOUR BABY'S CAREGIVERS

Who's who on the neonatal unit

Neonatal nurses

Most of the care in a neonatal intensive care unit is carried out by highly trained nurses. These include registered nurses and neonatal clinical nurse specialists who have advanced training. Some intensive care units also have neonatal nurse practitioners, who have advanced education and training and can perform many procedures.

Doctors

Neonatologists are the doctors who run the neonatal intensive care units. These are the doctors who will coordinate your baby's daily care plan. They are pediatricians who have received advanced training to care for sick and premature newborns. The neonatologist in charge of the department is known as the attending doctor. In addition to neonatologists, there are often neonatology fellows and pediatric residents, as well. Neonatology fellows are pediatricians who are getting advanced training to care for sick newborns. Pediatric residents are doctors who are being trained in the specialty area of pediatrics.

Other members of staff

A neonatal intensive care unit depends on a number of other staff members. These include a registered dietitian, physical and occupational therapists, technicians (who can draw blood or take X-rays), pharmacists, and, in some neonatal intensive care units, a psychotherapist to offer much needed emotional support to parents.

Tuning in

YOUR BABY TODAY

Some "tummy time" is good for infants as long as they are awake and being observed. But don't lie your baby down on her stomach for bed—it's dangerous and can lead to Sudden Infant Death Syndrome (SIDS).

As the bond between you and your baby continues to grow, you will start to feel more intuitive about his needs.

CHECKLIST

Your baby's cries

Follow the checklist below to help you identify the cause of your baby's cries. If your baby cries for three hours or more a day, consult your doctor.

■ **Hunger is the main reason** for crying; he will stop once he is offered the breast, a bottle, a finger, or a pacifier.

■ **A cry of pain** is easy to interpret since your baby may be inconsolable, draw up his legs in pain, or arch his back. If you're unsure how to remedy the pain, consult your doctor.

■ **A wet or dirty diaper** can be uncomfortable and cause crying.

■ **Your baby may want to be held** if you can see no other reason for his crying. Babies can't be spoiled by too much cuddling. Carrying him in a sling while you do chores may comfort him.

■ **Your baby may be overstimulated.** If nothing else works, put him down in a quiet room; in our anxiety as new parents, it can be easy to forget that babies need quiet time.

You will soon start to recognize your baby's cries and will feel increasingly confident about how to tend to his needs.

Crying is the only way your baby can get your attention. Parents-to-be often worry about how they'll know what their baby wants. Although his cries may seem indistinguishable at first, you'll soon start to interpret them (see box, left).

Ideally, you'll have continued Kegel exercises (see p.69) in this first week. It's important to continue doing these since they strengthen the muscles that support your bladder, helping to prevent stress incontinence (see p.475). They also help promote healing and ease discomfort if you've had stitches since they increase the blood flow to your perineum.

SWADDLING

Swaddling: If your newborn cries a lot, is fussy, or has trouble sleeping, try swaddling her. Being wrapped tightly in blankets, with the arms bound, makes babies feel the way they did in when they were in the uterus, and it calms them. In fact, some babies sleep an extra hour or two when swaddled and may even need to be unswaddled to wake up for their feedings. Be sure that any blankets you use for swaddling are tightly wrapped around the baby, because loose blankets can cover a baby's face and so become a factor for Sudden Infant Death Syndrome (SIDS). You may have learned how to swaddle your baby in the hospital. If not, your pediatrician should know how to do it. There are also simple swaddling products on the market that use Velcro tabs for a snug fit, thus eliminating the need to learn how to properly swaddle. These products can be found online or in stores.

Healthy living

YOUR BABY TODAY

Whether you're breast-feeding or bottle-feeding can have an effect on your baby's stools. The stools of breast-fed babies tend to be slightly runnier and can have a fairly sweet aroma, while bottle-fed babies may have firmer, stronger smelling stools.

A healthy lifestyle benefits your physical and mental well-being and helps you deal with the demands of parenthood.

It's important to eat a well-balanced diet (see pp.14–17) to help you deal with the demands of motherhood. If you're breast-feeding, you'll need an extra 500 calories a day. Drink plenty of clear fluids, being careful to limit your caffeine intake. If you were anemic during pregnancy, or had a heavy blood loss after the birth, eat lots of iron-rich foods, such as broccoli or spinach. Foods and drinks rich in vitamin C will help you absorb iron.

If you smoke and didn't manage to stop during pregnancy, this is an ideal time to try to stop. Ask your doctor to refer you to a local smoking cessation group. Limiting your alcohol intake is also wise, and drinking while breast-feeding isn't recommended.

It can be easy to take over your baby's care, but it's important that your partner is involved too and doesn't feel left out. Your partner is adjusting to fatherhood and may have his own anxieties and concerns. Sharing the practical care will help him forge his own bond with the baby. As his confidence grows, you'll be able to take some time out while he cares for the baby. Keeping the lines of communication open is vital since this is a time of huge change for you both. It takes time to adjust to being a family, but if you work together you'll manage the transition more smoothly.

Eating a variety of fresh produce will ensure a good intake of vitamins and minerals.

AS A MATTER OF FACT

You'll need to register your baby's birth with your provincial or territorial government

Once this is done, you can apply for a birth certificate and your baby's Social Insurance Number (SIN). Usually this paperwork is given to you by the hospital staff or your midwife.

YOUR BABY'S DIAPER: WHAT'S NORMAL AND WHEN TO WORRY

The color and consistency of a baby's stools are highly variable, but most are normal and not a cause for concern. However, some types of stool can indicate a problem and it's important that you know what to look for. A change in the color of urine or the presence of blood might also alert you to a problem.

What's normal

■ Once your baby has passed the first dark meconium (see p.444), stools may become dark green, green-yellow, bright yellow, orange, or brown; all are normal and may vary in the same day.
■ If your baby is breast-fed, stools may be loose and seedy.
■ If your baby is bottle-fed, stools tend to be smooth and firmer.

■ Frequency of stools varies from after every feeding to every 2–3 days.
■ Urine may be yellow or clear.
■ A pink or red-orange stain on the diaper due to urate crystals (which form from concentrated urine); these are common in the first few weeks, especially in breast-fed babies and are nothing to worry about.

What's not normal

■ White or putty-colored, which could indicate a liver problem.
■ Blood mixed in the stools, which could suggest a milk allergy.
■ Dark urine could be a sign of dehydration or jaundice.
If you notice any of these signs, ask your doctor for advice.

The 2nd week

455

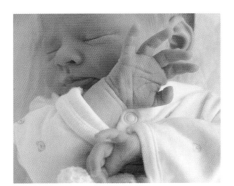

Focus on you

YOUR BABY TODAY

If your baby vomits large amounts and isn't thriving, this may suggest a problem such as gastroesophageal reflux (see p.477). This is caused by the immaturity of the stomach muscles and does resolve over time and with treatment.

Now that you've begun to adapt to the topsy-turvy world of motherhood, try to carve out some time for yourself each day.

To help you deal with broken nights and constant demands, you need to develop coping skills, such as taking an afternoon nap. You may also be dealing with feelings of isolation and may even find it hard to keep track of what day it is as days and nights merge into one. To revive your spirits, arrange for a friend or relative to take care of your baby while you have a break. You and your partner also need to make more of an effort to make time for each other.

TIPS FOR MOM

Tummy-flattening

Strengthening your abdomen enables your body to work more efficiently during any activity and helps you regain your pre-pregnancy tone.

■ Sit up straight; pull in your tummy for 60 seconds at least once each hour.

■ Stand tall and straight to keep you abdominal muscles firm.

■ Massage your abdomen with oil or body lotion in circular movements.

■ When you feel able, you can start doing gentle sit-ups to strengthen your abdomen, but wait for at least six weeks after a cesarean.

BREAST-FEEDING PROBLEMS

For some women, breast-feeding is a straightforward process that both mother and baby take to without a hiccup. However, for many women breast-feeding can be surprisingly hard and extra support is needed to overcome problems. Engorged (swollen) breasts and sore nipples are a common complaint; knowing how to avoid or treat these problems can be the difference between continuing with breast-feeding or giving up.

The secret to avoiding sore nipples is to make sure that your baby latches on to your breast properly (see p.448).

Engorged breasts can make it hard for your baby to latch on, so try expressing a little milk before a feeding to relieve some pressure. Whenever possible, let the air get to your nipples, and use breast pads at other times to keep the nipples dry.

You can relieve engorged breasts by continuing with breast-feeding and expressing milk frequently inbetween feedings to relieve the pressure. Placing a warm, clean washcloth on your breast or putting a chilled cabbage leaf inside your bra can also be soothing.

Positioning your baby well at the breast and ensuring that he latches on properly will help to avoid sore, painful nipples.

Putting a chilled cabbage leaf inside your bra can be surprisingly soothing, especially if your breasts are feeling inflamed.

Getting checked

YOUR BABY TODAY

Sometimes babies develop skin rashes or irritations and sore bottoms around this time and, if this is the case, you can call your pediatrician for advice on how to relieve these minor problems, which may require a prescription.

If you find that you need some additional help with the baby, there are several options to consider.

Adjusting to life with a newborn is difficult for some mothers, especially those recovering from cesareans. Sleep deprivation may make it hard to handle all of the new responsibilities. If your husband took time off during the first week, you may want another pair of hands to take his place. If you're able to hire a babysitter or visiting nurse for a few hours a day, you'll get some relief. If not, consider asking a good friend or relative for assistance. But before calling in any favors, make sure that the person

you ask will actually provide the type of help you need. Do you want someone to care for the baby so you can nap, make dinner, or run errands? Do you want someone to cook or clean while you tend to the baby? Do you need someone to get groceries and pick up your preschooler? Be clear about your needs so your helper isn't upset that she won't get to hold the baby the whole time she's helping.

Your baby loves to be stimulated. He can focus about a foot away and will

watch a simple object such as a mobile. Babies soon recognize familiar faces and he will love to watch you talk. Being part of your daily life provides plenty of stimulation. Tell him what you are doing and your plans for the day, read him stories, and listen to music together. When he is awake, give him time on his tummy to develop strength in the arms and prevent a "flat" head, a common problem in babies who spend a lot of time on their back. Always supervise your baby while he is on his tummy.

SLEEPING BABES

Newborn babies have a least two naps each day and many simply rotate sleeping and eating throughout the day. In the early days, you'll find that there is little routine to your baby's sleep pattern since he can't go for a long period without being fed.

You will probably find that your baby isn't fusssy about where he naps and that this can be wherever it's convenient for you, whether this is in the car, the stroller, or baby sling. If you're at home, you may prefer to put your baby somewhere quiet for a nap, such as in his crib, or you might want to keep him close by in a playpen or on a towel on the floor, if this is safe.

Many babies find being carried close in a baby sling deeply comforting and may sleep happily while being transported.

TIPS FOR BABY CARE

Nails and scratching

Babies' nails grow quickly and are also very tricky to cut! However, to stop your baby from scratching her face, you'll need to keep them trimmed. Be careful not to rip the edge of the nails since this can cause infection.

■ You can buy special baby scissors, although these may not cut the nails short enough to prevent scratching.

■ Using a soft emery keeps them short.

■ You may want to put mittens on your baby until she is past the scratching stage.

Taking stock

YOUR BABY TODAY

Many babies have spots known as milia, or "milk spots." These tiny whitish yellow spots appear on the face in the first two days and disappear by four weeks. Occasionally babies have spots resulting from the mother's hormones that take longer to disappear.

Part of becoming a parent is learning to trust your own instincts, even if this sometimes means ignoring the advice of others.

There are many approaches to baby care, and once you have a baby you may find that everyone has a tip to offer. Although many of these suggestions are helpful, the advice can become a bit overwhelming and is often conflicting. One area where there is a great deal of advice is breast-feeding (see p.448). If you are struggling with breast-feeding and wondering why it all seems so much harder than it looks, you may find that advice from professionals, friends, family, and books is increasingly unhelpful. It can help to take a step back, decide which of your friends or relatives has a similar approach to yours in other areas of life and pay most heed to their advice. Above all, have confidence in your own ability and trust your instincts, reminding yourself that there are many right ways to do things.

CHECKLIST

Your first trip to the supermarket

Some advance planning and management can help to take the stress out of a supermarket shop.

■ **Giving your baby a good feeding before setting out** may mean that he sleeps peacefully at the supermarket.

■ **Supermarkets can be very cold,** so dress your baby appropriately.

■ **Check to see if your car seat clips onto a cart** since this can make life easier. Otherwise, use the supermarket's own cart with a baby seat or put your baby into a sling while you walk around the supermarket.

■ **Make a shopping list before you go** so that you don't forget essentials if you're distracted by your baby crying.

BABY MASSAGE

Babies love to be touched and massaging your baby can be a great way to bond with your baby. All you need is some olive oil (avoid nut or aromatherapy oils) and a towel on the floor or bed. Ensure the room is warm and that your baby isn't hungry or too full. Undress your baby, rub some oil into your palms, and gently rub his tummy, limbs, fingers, and toes, watching his face to check that he is enjoying the massage. A baby massage class is a good way to make friends with other moms in your area.

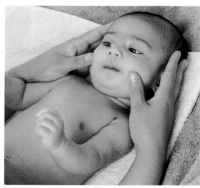

Lay your baby on a soft towel and then use the tips of your fingers to gently stroke your baby's head, avoiding the soft area, or fontanelles, at the top of the head.

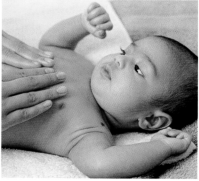

With gentle downward strokes massage your baby's chest and then use your fingertips to rub his tummy with outward circular strokes.

Looking back

YOUR BABY TODAY

By now, you may feel that your baby is begining to interact a bit more as you notice that he loves to gaze at faces and enjoys watching you talk and smile. However, he won't be able to smile back for a few weeks yet.

For some, reliving a traumatic birth is painful and you and your partner may need support to work through difficult memories.

ASK A ... DOCTOR

My baby's eye is constantly sticky. What can I do about this? Many newborn babies wake up with sticky eyes. This is due to a temporary blockage of the tear ducts, which are tiny in newborn babies. Clear his eye by wiping it with a cotton pad soaked in cooled, boiled water, using a fresh piece for each wipe. The problem usually resolves with time, but if the secretions become yellow and look infected, tell your doctor because your baby may need antibiotic eye drops.

FOCUS ON... YOUR BABY'S SENSES

Your baby's world

Your baby will focus on your face when being fed. He has been able to hear since he was in the uterus, and loves the sound of voices and music. He is startled by sudden noises, but can't locate them yet. He can taste; he loves the sweetness of breast milk and can tell if you've eaten something different! He can recognize your smell, and loves being cuddled, stroked, and carried close to you in a sling.

Your baby is fascinated by your face and loves making eye contact with you.

Once the acceptance and realization that you have had a baby sinks in and you are beginning to adapt to your new role as a mother, you may start to reflect on your birth experience and may want to share this with your relatives and friends. You will remember your birth story for the rest of your life and later share it with your baby.

Sometimes the labor and birth may not have gone as you wanted or anticipated. For example, you may have gone over your due date and had to be induced, and this may have led to interventions and possibly an instrumental delivery or an emergency cesarean section. You may feel some

disappointment and be unsure about why certain things happened and whether you could have been able to do anything to prevent them from happening.

Occasionally some women, and their partners, who had a particularly difficult birth experience can suffer from post-birth trauma. If the birth was traumatic and you feel upset and unsettled, make an appointment with your doctor to discuss your birth experience. She will be able to explain events that you are unsure about and, if necessary, may be able to arrange for you to see the obstetrician who cared for you during labor, although this isn't

standard, or recommend a mental health professional for you to speak with. If your partner feels traumatized by your birth experience and felt helpless during the process, he can also talk to the doctor, or if he prefers, to a mental health professional.

Talking to your partner about the labor and birth can help you relive good memories and to come to terms with the more unsettling ones. Your partner is one of the best placed people to reassure you about how you managed during labor, and talking together can help you open up and express your feelings about the birth.

459

Feeling close

YOUR BABY TODAY

It's inevitable that your baby will be exposed to viruses and some believe this reduces the risk of allergies later on. However, small babies can be quite sick with a cold so try to avoid people with colds at first. Breast-feeding provides protection against viruses.

Now that you and your partner are adapting to your new roles, you can start to think about how to make time for each other.

Finding time alone together can be hard and resuming your love life can take time. Some women resume their love life without any problems, but for many it takes a little longer, especially if they had stitches and are sore. Also, a difficult birth can affect you emotionally, as can fatigue from lack of sleep. It's recommended that you wait two to three weeks after giving birth before sexual intercourse to let your uterus reduce in size and for the bleeding to stop. Many women prefer to wait until after their six-week checkup (see pp.462–3). Initially, cuddling and nonpenetrative sex can help you and your partner experience closeness. When you both feel right you can resume sex, but the first time needs to be gentle and you may need a lubricant since your hormones can cause vaginal dryness, especially when breast-feeding. If intercourse is painful, talk to your doctor who can make sure you're healing.

You will need to consider contraception now. If you're undecided as to what to use and want to resume intercourse, it's a good idea to use condoms until your six week checkup when you can discuss the issue further.

Adapting to family life can mean learning to juggle your time to meet each other's needs.

GETTING YOUR FIGURE BACK

Most women lose around 10–15 lb (4–7 kg) in the first two weeks after the birth since, in addition to the loss of the weight of the baby, placenta, and amniotic fluid, you will lose the water that you retained in pregnancy. This water will be mobilized from your tissues and reabsorbed back into your bloodstream, and you'll eliminate it through your urine. Often women can feel more swollen after the delivery than they were before, but this extra fluid will be eliminated naturally in the next two weeks since you will probably pass large amounts of urine.

After two weeks, your weight loss will slow down. It's important to not try to lose weight too quickly after the birth, especially if you're breast-feeding, when you need around 500 extra calories each day. If you don't meet these extra nutritional needs, you will probably find that your energy will be low from a lack of calories. Eat a balanced diet that consists of whole grains, fruits, vegetables, and protein and drink plenty of fluids to avoid constipation.

New beginnings

YOUR BABY TODAY

Now that you are getting the hang of being a new mom, seek out other new parents for some exercise or socializing. There should be many options available to you in your local area.

Life will never be the same again and by now you will understand the unconditional love of a parent for their child.

Babies like to suck, even when they're not hungry anymore. Some suck their fingers or thumbs, but others do nicely with pacifiers. Some parents have strong feelings about whether or not to give a baby a pacifier, but they won't hurt your baby at all and have been linked to a reduction in Sudden Infant Death Syndrome (SIDS) when used during sleep. If you decide to use pacifiers, look for models with soft nipples and a one-piece design that are dishwasher-safe. Have several on hand, since pacifiers tend to fall on the floor. Keep in mind that if a baby depends on a pacifier to sleep, he may wake up and cry if it falls out of his mouth. If you are breast-feeding, many experts recommend waiting one month before introducing a pacifier, to avoid nipple confusion.

You may now be getting out more by yourself since your partner may be back at work. Ask your pediatrician about times and venues for support groups in your local area and any carriage-walking groups or baby massage classes since these are excellent ways to meet other moms.

At two weeks, you'll be getting the hang of being parents. Life will never be the same again, and although this means that you will always have to put your baby first and will not have as much time for yourself, in return you have the most beautiful, fascinating child with her own personality whom you will always love unconditionally. There is nothing that compares with the love of parent and child, and by now, you will understand exactly what that means.

ASK A... DOCTOR

Should I try to get my baby into a routine? In the first few weeks, it's too early to establish routines. To establish breast-feeding, newborn babies need to be fed on demand and most, in time, will figure out their own routine. If you want to try to establish set feeding times, you will have to consider how you will cope with a screaming baby. However, it's worth starting a nighttime routine early on. Bathing your baby, singing to him, feeding him, and putting him down in his crib to sleep will help him develop good sleep patterns later on.

RECORDING YOUR BABY

It's tempting to take photos and videos almost constantly when your first baby is born. Subsequent children often remark on how relatively few photos there are of them! Digital photography means that you can email family and friends immediately with new baby photos, however, try not to go overboard since, although you will never tire of looking at your own baby, other people's baby photos are of more limited interest.

The first pictures together provide precious memories.

You'll be fascinated by your new baby's every moment.

Don't forget to include pictures of the proud dad.

Your six-week checkup

At about four to eight weeks following the birth, you will have a postpartum checkup with a doctor at your ob/gyn's practice. This checkup is to see if you are physically and emotionally well. Your baby will also have a physical and developmental checkup around this time.

Your six-week postpartum checkup is the ideal time to talk to your doctor about any problems or concerns you have, and to receive reassurance that you have recovered well after the birth.

Your assessment

In the first couple of months following the birth of their baby, the majority of women don't experience any major health concerns and will revert back to their prepregnant health status. However, it's good practice to have a general assessment to reassure you that you are well and coping with the early transition to motherhood.

Your postpartum checkup is an ideal opportunity for you to consult your doctor about any concerns you have following the birth of your baby. Any worries about yourself can be discussed at this appointment, from your mood to any apprehensions about having sex again. Your doctor will offer you advice and possibly treatment, and will also be able to refer you to a specialist for further treatment if necessary.

Your physical checkup

Your doctor will do routine checkups, such as taking your blood pressure. He or she will also ask if you have any concerns, how you're feeding your baby, and, if you are breast-feeding, whether you've had any problems with your breasts and lactation.

Your uterus will have returned to nearly its prepregnancy size (about the size of the palm of your hand) and will not be able to be felt. However, your doctor may check your abdomen to see if the muscles are returning to normal since occasionally the abdominal muscles separate after birth, known as "diastasi recti." If the muscles are more than four fingers apart, you may be referred to a physical therapist. Pilates and core conditioning exercises (see p.250) can help and your doctor may talk to you about these exercises.

Backaches can be a problem after the birth, exacerbated by the pregnancy hormone relaxin (see p.197), which softens muscles and ligaments and remains in the body for a few months after pregnancy. If you're suffering from backaches, your doctor may talk to you about your posture, particularly when you're carrying or feeding your baby, and about the benefits of exercise.

If you had a cesarean, the incision will be looked at to check that it has healed well. You may still feel numbness around the site of the incision, but sensation should gradually return as the nerve endings renew themselves.

If you haven't had a Pap smear in the last three years, you will likely be given one on the spot, unless you're bleeding heavily.

Checking your bladder You will be asked if you have problems urinating, and may be asked for a urine sample if you have symptoms such as frequent urination or stinging when passing urine. Stress incontinence, or leaking urine (see p.475), is common after childbirth, so don't feel embarrassed to mention this to your doctor. He or she may encourage you to do Kegel exercises (see p.69), and if the problem persists you may be referred to a physical therapist for bladder-training exercises.

Your stitches If you're still sore from stitches, your doctor will check that these are healing properly. Although most stitches are absorbable, they can take up to three months to completely absorb. Bathing can sometimes help the stitches absorb, but if you continue to have problems your doctor may recommend Sitz baths two or three times a day or a topical anesthetic cream (see also Perineal problems, p.475).

Your emotional well-being

In addition to checking you physically, the doctor will also assess your emotional and mental health. Many women feel extremely tired in these early weeks, as night feedings and constant demands begin to take their toll. However, if you are feeling low, overly tired, or depressed a lot of the time, you may be suffering from postpartum depression (see p.475), so it's important not to ignore these symptoms. Talk to your doctor about how you are feeling; he will be able to offer support and refer you to experts in treating depression.

Looking at your lifestyle

Your doctor will advise you on healthy eating and lifestyle measures. If you smoke, you'll be given information about support groups in your local area to help you stop smoking.

QUESTIONS AND ANSWERS

Is it true that I don't need to worry about getting pregnant again while I'm breast-feeding?
If you are breast-feeding, you may not have a period for a while after giving birth. Although this means you are less likely to conceive, you can still ovulate, so you shouldn't assume that you don't need to use contraception. The doctor or nurse will discuss contraception and sexual health with you and may recommend the progesterone-only pill, which can be prescribed from 21 days if you're breast-feeding.

I'm bottle-feeding my baby and am worried about getting pregnant again. How soon could this happen?
If you decided to bottle-feed, you will probably have had your first period prior to this checkup and so certainly could become pregnant again. Although your doctor will have already discussed contraception with you, this will be addressed again at your six-week checkup. The doctor or nurse will want to check that you have contraceptive measures in place; if not, he or she will offer you guidance and advice.

I had stitches and have felt too anxious to have sex since the birth. Is this normal?
Yes, plenty of women feel this way and many wait to resume sex until after their postpartum checkup. During this checkup, the doctor or nurse will be able to confirm that your incision has healed, and offer reassurance about resuming sex. On the other hand, there is nothing wrong with having sex before this checkup as long as you have stopped bleeding. When you do have sex, you may need to use a lubricant (KY jelly), particularly if you're breast-feeding since your hormones can cause some vaginal dryness.

ASSESSING YOUR BABY

Your baby's checkup

A pediatrician will want to see your baby at around 4 days, 1 month, and 2 months to do a physical checkup and look at how your baby is growing and developing.

The doctor will perform a similar examination to the newborn checkup (see p.443). He or she will examine your baby's hips, spine, eyes, heart, and the pulses at the top of the legs. In boys, it's important to check that the testes are located in the scrotum. This is also a chance to look for subtle problems such as a heart murmur, which can develop after birth. Your baby will be weighed and his head circumference measured. The doctor will ask how your baby is feeding and check for signs of jaundice. Your baby's development will be checked too: whether he has head control, is starting to smile, and can focus on an object or face a foot away, and follow a moving object. Your baby should receive some immunizations during these early visits. All of these findings will be recorded in a record of your baby's growth and development.

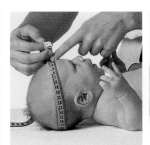

The head circumference is taken and the fontanelles, the soft areas on your baby's head, are checked.

Your baby's heart rate will be listened to and the doctor will monitor and check his breathing.

To check head control, your doctor will gently lift your baby up by his arms to see how he holds his head.

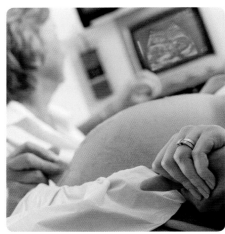

Rarely does pregnancy pass without some complaint. The majority of problems are minor and due to normal pregnancy changes. Some, however, are more serious and require medical attention. Today, high-quality prenatal care means that potentially serious conditions are usually successfully managed, both during pregnancy and in labor. Problems after the birth, either in the baby or the mother, may need medical attention with careful follow-up and sometimes referral to a specialist.

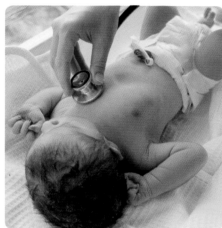

Concerns and complications

Common concerns in pregnancy

Pregnancy hormones affect every system in your body. In this section, you will find a list of common concerns with an explanation of the adaptation process that may cause these symptoms, information on whether medical help is likely to be required, and advice on measures you can take yourself to alleviate symptoms.

General symptoms

Fatigue

An overwhelming feeling of fatigue is often one of the earliest signs of pregnancy. Such feelings usually subside during the second trimester, but are likely to return in the third trimester.

CAUSES The main causes of extreme fatigue in early pregnancy are massive hormonal changes and the extra demands on the body made by an increase in blood volume of up to 50 percent. It's this increase in blood volume that helps the lining of the uterus to thicken and the placenta to develop. In the second trimester, energy levels usually return to normal as hormone changes settle down. Late in pregnancy, fatigue may recur because your extra size and weight and the demands of the growing baby means that your body systems need to work harder. In both early and late pregnancy, difficulty sleeping (see p.95) can contribute to feelings of fatigue. Fatigue in pregnancy can also be caused by anemia (see p.472).

WHAT TO DO If you are working, take regular breaks and get some fresh air at least once a day. Ensure that your fluid intake is adequate; caffeine is not helpful because it dehydrates your body and will leave you feeling worse. Take more time for sleep if you need to; housework can wait and you may need to cut back on social commitments.

Difficulty sleeping

It's very common to have sleeping difficulty in pregnancy, especially in the first and third trimesters.

CAUSES A common cause of disturbed sleep is the need to urinate frequently. Early in pregnancy, this is due to the amount of blood in your body, leading to the kidneys filtering out more fluid, which ends up in your bladder. As pregnancy progresses, another factor is expansion of the uterus within the pelvic cavity, so that it competes for space with the bladder. This leads the bladder to require more frequent emptying, which will interrupt your sleep. Many women also feel hungry during the night and need to snack, while others find that nausea and vomiting interrupt their night or lead to early waking. From about 20 weeks of pregnancy, the uterus moves up out of the pelvis, taking pressure off the bladder, and nausea often subsides, which means that sleep improves. Toward the end of pregnancy, sleep patterns can once again be disturbed. Unborn babies are often active just when you want to rest; your body is bulky and finding comfortable sleeping positions becomes difficult; and as the baby becomes bigger and heavier pressure on the bladder may return.

WHAT TO DO If frequent urination is keeping you awake, don't drink large quantities of fluid close to bedtime, and to avoid waking up hungry include foods high in unrefined carbohydrates, such as whole-wheat bread, in your evening meal. If you do wake up, don't lie there for long periods, since this is frustrating and may lead to habitual sleeplessness. Get out of bed and engage in a simple activity that won't overstimulate your brain, have a warm, caffeine-free drink, and return to bed when you're sleepy. Later in pregnancy when you find it difficult to get comfortable, experiment with different sleeping positions: use plenty of pillows, under your head and belly and between your knees. A rest during the day is essential during late pregnancy, but limit this to a 20-minute power nap or an hour reading or watching television with your feet up. If you sleep for long periods during the day, you will further lessen your ability to sleep at night.

Headaches

Headaches are common in pregnancy, especially in the first trimester.

CAUSES Most headaches are unlikely to be a cause for concern and are probably due to hormonal changes and the need for additional fluids. Headaches occurring in the third trimester that are accompanied by other symptoms, such as abdominal pain or nausea, may be a sign of preeclampsia and should be assessed by a doctor (see p.474).

WHAT TO DO Making sure you drink enough clear fluids (around five cups a day) and avoiding caffeine should help reduce the number and severity of headaches. If you're working or concentrating on a task, have a break every two to three hours, and get some gentle exercise in fresh air. For a sinus headache, apply a warm compress to the front and sides of your face. For tension headaches, place a cool compress on the back of your neck. If you suspect your headache is due to lack of sleep, get more sleep. And make sure you're eating enough, since hunger and low blood sugar can cause headaches. Relieve stress—another headache trigger—with deep breathing, meditation, yoga, or massage. Always discuss your symptoms with your doctor before taking medication.

If you have a headache in late pregnancy that is accompanied by swelling of the legs and ankles, generalized body swelling, abdominal pain, or nausea and vomiting, contact your doctor immediately.

Swollen feet and ankles

Some women experience a small amount of swelling in their feet, ankles, hands, and wrists, which can be particularly pronounced in hot weather.

CAUSES Swelling is the result of fluid retention, which in turn results from the extra blood produced during pregnancy to provide for the growing baby.

WHAT TO DO This is best managed by alternating light activity with periods of rest during which your feet are elevated. However, staying in bed or sitting in a chair for very long periods may increase the risk of deep vein thrombosis (DVT) (see p.186). DVT is a potentially serious condition in which a blood clot forms in a vein; if the clot breaks off, it may travel to the lungs and block a major blood vessel. Swollen feet and ankles can also be a sign of other problems such as preeclampsia (see p.474), so should always be reported to your doctor who can check for other symptoms.

Skin changes

Itching and dry skin
Many pregnant women suffer from itchy, dry patches of skin that worsen in late pregnancy. Such skin irritation is a reaction to hormonal changes and can be eased by a perfume-free moisturiser. Rarely, itching in late pregnancy may be due to a serious condition called obstetric cholestasis (see p.473). Itching caused by this condition is much more severe, usually constant, and often concentrated on the hands and feet.

Spider veins
Clusters of broken capillaries (tiny red blood vessels) called spider veins may appear during pregnancy, mainly on the cheeks. These occur as a result of increased blood circulation and the softening effect of pregnancy hormones on blood vessels. Spider veins are painless, but if you are worried about their appearance you can cover them with makeup. They usually disappear soon after the birth.

Increased pigmentation
An increase in skin pigmentation is common in pregnancy, probably due to the increased production of hormones. Most women notice a darkening of the area around the nipple (the areola), and a dark line, called the linea nigra, forming vertically through the middle of the belly from the umbilicus to the pelvis. Also common are dark patches on the cheeks, nose, and chin, known as melasma (also known as chloasma, or the "mask of pregnancy.") On women with dark skin, the patches may apppear lighter than surrounding skin. Exposure to sunlight can make the patches more obvious, so use a high-protection sunscreen on your face.

Stretch marks
Rapid stretching of the skin during pregnancy often leads to the development of pink or purple lines, known as stretch marks. These marks, which can look quite alarming, with a scarlike appearance, usually appear in late pregnancy, commonly on the abdomen, hips, thighs, and upper breast. There is no clear evidence that any cream will prevent or remove stretch marks, although a light unscented moisturizer can help keep the skin supple, as will staying well hydrated and avoiding excessive weight gain. As time passes after the birth, stretch marks become silvery and almost invisible.

Breast problems

Breast tenderness
For many women, breast tenderness and an increase in the size of their breasts are the first signs of pregnancy. Sometimes breasts are so painful that you can't bear them to be touched, and they may also throb and feel hot. Breast tenderness usually subsides by the end of the first trimester.

CAUSES Tenderness is a sign that the breasts are preparing for their role of feeding your baby after the birth: the milk ducts are starting to enlarge and blood flow increases.

WHAT TO DO Wearing a properly fitting bra will help support your breasts and reduce discomfort. An ill-fitting or tight bra will be uncomfortable and may put pressure on the milk ducts. You may also find it helpful to wear a soft sleep bra at night. If your breasts feel hot, applying a cool washcloth to them may bring relief.

If you have a painful or red patch on a breast, you should report this to your doctor because it could be a sign of mastitis (see p.475).

Nipple problems
Each woman has breasts and nipples individual to her. Women who have flat nipples that do not protrude or whose nipples are inverted (concave) may worry that they may not be able to breast-feed. However, all healthy women can breast-feed because babies feed by taking in a mouthful of breast, not just the nipple.

CAUSES Inverted or flat nipples are thought to be due to shorter ligaments in the underlying breast tissue that pull the nipples inward.

WHAT TO DO If you have any concerns about the suitability of your nipples for breast-feeding, talk to your doctor who can refer you to a lactation consultant. There are also products available that will draw out nipples in preparation for breast-feeding. However, these are by no means essential because when babies latch on to the breast they are able to draw out even a flat or inverted nipple (although you may eventually need help by a lactation consultant to show you the best way to help your baby do this).

Digestive problems

Nausea and vomiting
Approximately 80 percent of women are troubled by the unpleasant symptoms of nausea and vomiting in early pregnancy. During this period it can be difficult to eat large meals, and strong smells and tastes can become unbearable. Many women also find some vegetable and acidic foods more difficult to digest and worry that their usually healthy eating pattern has deteriorated. Early pregnancy nausea and vomiting usually subside between 12 and 20 weeks; however it's not uncommon to experience some return of these problems late in the pregnancy.

CAUSES Early in pregnancy, the pregnancy hormones interact with hormones that control other body systems, particularly those involved with blood sugar regulation, and this results in feelings of nausea and vomiting. Late in pregnancy, problems with digestion may occur because the uterus takes up most of the space in your abdomen, displacing your intestines and stomach and leaving little room for the digestion of large amounts of food.

WHAT TO DO The best way to manage the nausea and vomiting of pregnancy is to drink plenty of water throughout the day

and also eat small amounts of food on a regular basis, which will help to avoid long gaps between meals, and snacking on complex carbohydrates such as whole-wheat and whole-grain products, whole-grain cereals, and brown rice dishes. Avoid snacks with a high sugar content because, although these will give you a quick boost, they will soon leave you feeling worse than before because your blood sugar plummets. Reducing your overall intake of the refined sugar found in candy, cake, cookies, and sugary drinks will help reduce the symptoms of nausea and vomiting and will also lessen your risk of developing gestational diabetes.

The "little and often" principle, coupled with healthy snacks is equally good advice for the late phase of pregnancy.

Gastroenteritis

This is inflammation of the lining of the stomach and intestines, most commonly due to infection. It causes vomiting and diarrhea that usually come on suddenly. In most cases, the condition clears up on its own and is not a cause for concern. However, if it's severe, you could become dehydrated, and this can affect blood flow to your baby through the placenta. Infection with listeria bacteria can, rarely, cause late miscarriage.

CAUSES Gastroenteritis is caused by infection contracted either through contact with an infected person, or by consuming contaminated food or drink (food poisoning). Food poisoning is often the result of poor food hygiene.

WHAT TO DO Drink plenty of water, and try to avoid cross infection with other members of the household (see below). If you're unable to retain even small sips of water, or your vomiting and diarrhea have lasted for 24 hours, you should seek medical advice from your doctor. If you can't reach your doctor, go the nearest hospital emergency room for treatment. If you have a preexisting medical condition such as diabetes, you should seek help immediately. You may be treated with intravenous fluids if you are dehydrated, and fetal monitoring may be done to check the health of your baby. Infection with listeria is treated with antibiotics.

AVOIDING GASTROENTERITIS It is important that you try to avoid gastroenteritis by practicing good food hygiene (see p.17).

If someone else in your household has gastroenteritis, avoid infection by using separate soap, towels, cutlery, and dishes. If you have more than one toilet, get the infected person to use one separate from the rest of the household. Wipe toilets, sinks, and faucets with a mild bleach solution after each use. Infected individuals should also avoid preparing food for others.

Indigestion and heartburn

Many women start to experience episodes of indigestion and heartburn during the second trimester.

CAUSES Indigestion results from slower movements of the digestive tract under the influence of pregnancy hormones combined with reduced space in the stomach from the growing baby. The muscular valve at the top of the stomach is also softened by hormones and this can allow stomach acid to flow up into the espohagus, causing heartburn.

WHAT TO DO Avoiding large meals, especially late at night, helps prevent indigestion and heartburn. If you suffer from heartburn at night, try sleeping in a propped up position with your head higher than your feet. For relief from heartburn, a liquid antacid preparation can be helpful; ask your doctor for advice on which medications are safe. Some women find that slowly drinking a glass of milk eases the discomfort.

Constipation

During the second trimester, constipation often becomes a problem.

CAUSES Under the influence of the softening effect of pregnancy hormones, the digestive tract becomes less active. As a result, fecal matter spends more time in the large intestine, allowing reabsorption of fluids and leaving solids hard and difficult to pass. Not drinking enough fluids increases the likelihood of constipation.

WHAT TO DO Dietary fiber in the form of vegetables and whole foods, with an increase in fluid intake usually corrects the problem. Laxatives are not recommended during pregnancy. They can stimulate contractions and lead to dehydration. Talk to your doctor if these steps don't resolve your constipation.

Hemorrhoids

Hemorrhoids are dilated blood vessels around the inside of, or protruding from, the anus. Their constriction by the anal muscles and sensitivity to the acidic environment leads to a feeling of discomfort in mild episodes and pain in more severe cases. They are more likely to occur during the third trimester.

CAUSES The hormonal softening of the tissues around the anus increases the risk of developing hemorrhoids. Pressure of the baby's head on the blood vessels is also a factor, as is constipation.

WHAT TO DO Treatment of constipation and avoiding pushing or straining to pass a stool are important in the prevention of hemorrhoids. Ask your doctor which over-the-counter creams for relieving discomfort are safe. If hemorrhoids are protruding and causing great discomfort, it's often possible for a health professional to "reduce" them by pushing them gently back into place.

Heart & circulation problems

Dizziness and faintness

Throughout pregnancy, occasional dizziness or feelings of faintness can be a problem.

CAUSES In early pregnancy, feeling faint may occur even when you are sitting down and is likely to be due to low blood sugar. This can happen as a result of not eating enough, a common problem at this stage of pregnancy when many women suffer from morning sickness. In the second trimester, dizziness or faintness that comes on when getting up from a sitting position or as a result of standing for long periods is likely to be caused by low blood pressure. Blood pressure is lowered in pregnancy because the pregnancy hormone progesterone softens blood vessels to enable blood to flow more freely to your baby. When you stand, the low blood pressure may mean that not enough blood reaches your brain, leading to dizziness and faintness.

As pregnancy advances, you may find that you feel dizzy lying on your back. This happens because in this position the heavy uterus puts pressure on the main blood

vessels running through the trunk and reduces the blood flow to the brain.

WHAT TO DO To help prevent low blood sugar, have small snacks of foods high in complex carbohydrates (see p.92). Staying well hydrated, taking regular breaks from work, not standing in one position for too long, and getting fresh air are also helpful in preventing faintness. If you start to feel dizzy, sit down and put your head between your legs, which will relieve the unpleasant feeling. Stay seated until you feel completely recovered and then get up slowly. Any time you feel dizzy or faint, call your doctor immediately, especially if you also have stomach pain, vaginal bleeding, blurry vision, headaches, or heart palpitations, or the dizziness is persistent. If you have fainted and bumped your head or injured any part of your body then you should go to the hospital for a checkup.

If you experience dizziness when lying on your back, turning onto your side will quickly help you feel better. Lying on your left side is preferable because this helps to pump blood around the body.

Palpitations

A feeling that your heart is racing, or beating irregularly is common in pregnancy, particularly between 28 and 32 weeks, but can occur at any time.

CAUSES The reasons for palpitations remain unclear and hypotheses range from the effect that progesterone has on the heart muscle, to the heart coping with the extra blood flow needed to maintain both mother and fetus.

WHAT TO DO Palpitations are usually fleeting and nothing to worry about. However, if you have frequent palpitations or they are accompanied by chest pain, dizziness, or breathlessness, you should consult your doctor. If you have a history of heart disease or a heart abnormality, seek advice immediately.

Nosebleeds

Nosebleeds occur frequently in pregnancy, and although they are a nuisance they are rarely a serious problem.

CAUSES As with all other blood vessels in the body, those in the nose are softened and expanded during pregnancy. In addition,

your body has an increased blood volume in pregnancy, which puts pressure on these delicate structures. You are more likely to have a nosebleed if you have a cold or sinus infection or if your nasal membrane is dry, which can happen in cold weather or air conditioned rooms.

WHAT TO DO To manage a nosebleed, sit down, keep your head in a normal position, and apply pressure to the bottom of the nose with your thumb and forefinger. You will need to maintain this pressure constantly for about 10 minutes before checking to see if the bleeding has stopped. Do not be tempted to tip your head back or lie down, since this will cause you to swallow the blood, leading to nausea and possible vomiting. Ice or a cold compress applied to the nose and facial area in conjunction with the nasal pressure can help constrict the blood flow and halt the bleeding. Seek medical advice if the nosebleed results from a head injury or if heavy bleeding continues for more than 20 minutes. Mention frequent small nosebleeds at your prenatal appointment to enable the elimination of more serious conditions.

Bleeding, tender gums

Bleeding from the gums and gum tenderness are both common complaints during pregnancy.

CAUSES These problems occur as a result of increased blood volume coupled with the softening effect of pregnancy hormones on blood vessels. Allowing plaque to accumulate may exacerbate these symptoms and also makes the start of gum disease more likely.

WHAT TO DO Good dental hygiene is vital; don't be tempted to avoid brushing your teeth if they feel tender, but switch to a softer brush. Brushing your teeth and gums and flossing regularly are particularly important during pregnancy. Also, visit your dentist regularly during pregnancy and the postpartum period.

Varicose veins and vulval varicosities

Varicose veins are enlarged, distorted veins that may develop in the legs or around the vulval area. Varicose veins in or around the anus are known as hemorrhoids (see p.468). Varicose veins may become troublesome

during the later stages of pregnancy, causing discomfort and sometimes itching; they may also be unsightly. Varicosities in the vagina or vulva areas do not inhibit a normal birth and are not at risk of rupture during the birth.

CAUSES The increased blood flow and softened vessels mean that many women experience varicose veins and vulva varicosities during pregnancy. The growing uterus puts pressure on veins in the pelvis which, in turn, leads to increased pressure in the legs and vulva area.

WHAT TO DO Support hose designed for pregnancy can be helpful, Avoid tight clothes that constrict the waist, groin, or legs As with all conditions, varicose veins should be reported to your doctor for assessment and advice. Varicose veins usually improve within three months after the birth of the baby.

Aches and pains

Backaches

Lower generalized backaches are extremely common during pregnancy, particularly in the third trimester; around two thirds of all pregnant women suffer from backaches.

CAUSES As pregnancy progresses, the increased weight of your abdomen tends to pull on the lower spine so that it curves inward and your center of gravity shifts forward. As you try to correct this, you may strain the the lower back muscles. In addition, pregnancy hormones soften your ligaments, causing them to stretch and provide less support for your back.

WHAT TO DO Maintaining good posture and avoiding tilting your pelvis forward helps relieve pressure on your back and helps both prevent and alleviate backaches. Regular, moderate exercise to keep your muscles toned and supple is also beneficial. See pages 90 and 250 for suggested exercise routines. Yoga, pilates, and water aerobics are also recommended.

Try to avoid standing in one position for too long and vary your daily tasks, if possible breaking them down into shorter stints. If your work involves standing or sitting for long periods, take regular short breaks, and while sitting, make sure your lower back is supported. Avoid lifting heavy objects.

Massage and warm water can help relieve backaches. If back pain is particularly troublesome, talk to your doctor about wearing a supportive maternity belt.

Pelvic girdle pain (PGP)

Also known as symphysis pubis dysfunction, pelvic girdle pain (PGP) refers to discomfort and pain felt in the pelvic area and groin. The pain may be concentrated in the buttocks or travel down one leg, and for this reason is sometimes mistaken for sciatica (see below). PGP is often worse when doing activities such as walking or going up stairs; it may also be troublesome at night, but this is usually related to activities done during the day. PGP is most common toward the end of pregnancy and may range in severity from mild to serious enough to need a walking aid.

CAUSES Various factors may contribute to PGP. The pelvis is made up of three bones: the sacrum and the two iliac (hip) bones. The bones are connected at the front by the symphysis pubis joint, and at the back by the sacroiliac joints. The joints are stabilized by ligaments and usually move very little. During pregnancy, however, ligaments soften and stretch more easily so that there is more movement at these joints. This results in instability of the pelvis. In addition, postural changes due to the enlarging abdomen may mean that one joint is more mobile than the other, putting extra strain on the joints. The result is inflammation of the joints and discomfort or pain.

WHAT TO DO If there is increased movement in one side of your pelvis, a pelvic support belt may be recommended, which often gives instant relief. You may be referred to a physical therapist who will show you how to modify everyday activities, such as walking and getting up, in order to avoid pain, and may also recommend abdominal and Kegel exercises (see p.69). Acupuncture can help relieve pain, and prenatal water aerobic classes are helpful. Preventative measures include avoiding activities that cause pain, and avoiding heavy lifting, lying on your back, and sustained periods of activity. It's also important to get plenty of rest.

Round ligament pain

The two round ligaments run from the top of the uterus on either side and attach to the side walls of the abdomen. As the uterus enlarges, the round ligaments gradually become stretched, which can cause an ache or brief, sharp pain on one or both sides of the lower abdomen or in the groin. Round ligament pain usually starts during the second trimester.

WHAT TO DO See your doctor, who will rule out other causes for the abdominal pain. Once you have been reassured, you should find it easier to deal with the pain. When you have an episode, try to rest and relax. Lying on your side and bringing your knees up toward your chest may be helpful, as can taking a warm bath.

Sciatica

This is pain in one or both buttocks that may radiate down one leg. There may also be tingling or numbness in the legs, although this occurs only in a small percentage of women. Sciatica is most likely to occur after the second trimester.

CAUSES Sciatica is caused by trapping or compression of the sciatic nerve as it runs through the spinal column. The pain is termed referred pain, that is, pain felt in an area away from the problem site. Sciatica is not caused by compression of the nerve by the fetus's head. The causes of sciatica in pregnancy are the same as in women who are not pregnant and include poor posture, wear and tear on vertebral joints, and poor lifting techniques.

WHAT TO DO Specific exercises can help to stretch muscles gently and release pressure on the sciatic nerve. Your doctor may be able to advise you on exercises or may refer you to a physical therapist for help.

Coccygeal pain

The coccyx, or tailbone, is the small bone found at the base of the spine. This bone is usually fairly immobile; however in pregnancy it becomes more mobile, which facilitates the passage of the baby through the birth canal during labor. Pain in this area can make sitting for long periods extremely uncomfortable, particularly at work or during travel. Coccygeal pain can occur throughout pregnancy.

CAUSES Coccygeal pain may predate pregnancy due to a previous injury to the area; the discomfort may then be exacerbated by the hormonal and mechanical changes of pregnancy. Alternatively, coccygeal pain may arise in pregnancy, since increased movement in the coccyx during this time makes injury more likely. Sometimes the coccyx is injured during labor by the baby's head, and coccygeal pain therefore develops after the birth.

WHAT TO DO Moving around frequently and gently massaging the area can help relieve discomfort. Ask your doctor which analgesics are safe for you to take. The condition usually gets better within 6 weeks of delivery.

Leg cramps

Cramps in the legs, particularly in the calf muscles, are a common problem during pregnancy. These occur most commonly at night, but may sometimes come on when walking, and their frequency can increase as your pregnancy advances.

CAUSES There is debate as to the cause of leg cramps in pregnancy. They are likely to be caused by a combination of factors including maternal posture, increasing body weight, restriction in the blood flow to the legs, and the pressure of the uterus on the pelvic nerves. Some suggest that leg cramps in pregnancy may be due to a lack of salt in the diet. However, research demonstrates that low levels of salt are healthy in pregnancy, and that it is very unlikely that anyone who is eating a balanced diet will suffer from salt depletion.

WHAT TO DO Leg cramps may be relieved by changing position, flexing the toes of the affected leg upward, and massaging the cramped muscle. To avoid leg cramps, massage your legs before bed and avoid sitting or standing in one position for long periods. A warm bath before bed may also help. Stay well hydrated and alternate regular periods of moderate exercise with periods of rest.

If you have persistent pain, redness, or swelling in your calf, this may be a sign of deep vein thrombosis (DVT) (see p.186), which requires prompt medical attention.

Restless leg syndrome

Restless leg syndrome is an uncomfortable feeling or unpleasant tingling that creates an overwhelming desire to move your legs, or causes legs to jerk uncontrollably,

especially during sleep. Sufferers describe the sensation as being like an electric current passing through the legs or like having itchy bones. During pregnancy, the problem is most likely to occur during the third trimester.

CAUSES Restless legs syndrome is frequently triggered or aggravated by pregnancy. The cause is unknown, but some studies indicate that it might be related to low iron levels. Many sufferers have a family history of the condition.

WHAT TO DO If you're suffering from restless leg syndrome, talk to your doctor about having a blood test to check your iron levels. If levels are low, a simple iron supplement may be prescribed. Some women find it helpful to exercise or stretch their legs, to use hot or cold compresses, or to have a leg massage. If the condition occurs for the first time in pregnancy, there is a very good chance that it will disappear after the baby is born.

Carpal tunnel syndrome

The carpal tunnel is a small tunnel in the wrist through which nerves run from your forearm into your hands and fingers. Carpal tunnel sydrome occurs when the nerves are compressed, resulting in tingling and pain in the fingers, which is often worse at night. In severe cases, there may be considerable discomfort and a reduced grip. In pregnancy, this is most likely to occur in the second and third trimesters.

CAUSES Carpal tunnel syndrome is caused by pressure on nerves running through the tunnel due to swelling of surrounding tissues. During pregnancy, swelling in the hands and feet is common as a result of the extra fluid and blood volume.

WHAT TO DO If you think you may have carpal tunnel syndrome, talk to your doctor. You may be referred to a physical therapist for treatment, who will recommend specific exercises to help relieve the discomfort. You may also be advised to wear a lightweight splint to support your wrists, which can be especially beneficial if the pain is disturbing your sleep. Carpal tunnel syndrome usually disappears after the birth. However, if it persists, a simple surgery can be performed to relieve the pressure on the nerves.

Urinary and vaginal problems

Yeast infections (candidiasis)

During pregnancy, an increased vaginal discharge is normal. However, if the discharge is creamy and thick, and you have some soreness and itching in your vaginal area, you may have yeast, a fungal infection. If you have a vaginal discharge with an odor, you could have trichomoniasis or bacterial vaginosis, which are sexually transmitted infections that can lead to premature delivery if not treated with antibiotics. You are more prone to yeast during pregnancy, particularly during the third trimester.

CAUSES A yeast infection is caused by a fungus called *Candida albicans*. The organism exists normally in small numbers in the intestines and vagina, and doesn't cause problems. However, during pregnancy, the environment in the vagina changes, causing overgrowth of the fungus. If you are under stress, feeling generally unwell, taking antibiotics, or have diabetes, you may be more likely to develop a yeast infection.

WHAT TO DO If you think you have a yeast infection, contact doctor, who can take a vaginal swab to confirm the diagnosis. He or she may recommend an over-the-counter vaginal cream. Yeast infections can be harder to control during pregnancy, and may take up to two weeks to go away. To prevent additional infections, wear cotton underwear and always wipe from front to back after a bowel movement.

Stress incontinence

If you have stress incontinence, you pass small amounts of urine unintentionally, particularly when coughing, sneezing, or laughing, and when exercising or lifting heavy objects. Stress incontinence can happen at any time during pregnancy, but is most common in the last trimester.

CAUSES The pelvic floor muscles are under additional strain during pregnancy and are also affected by hormonal changes. Therefore any increase in abdominal pressure caused by coughing, sneezing, laughing, or other activities that puts these muscles under pressure may result in leakage of a small amount of urine.

WHAT TO DO Stress incontinence can be embarrassing and distressing; however, you should mention the problem to your doctor who will be able to advise you on Kegel exercises (see p.69), which should help reduce the problem if you practice them regularly. It's important too to empty your bladder whenever you need to. You may want to wear a sanitary pad for additional reassurance.

Urinary tract infections

During pregnancy, you're more susceptible to urinary tract infections. Most commonly, such infections are confined to the badder, when they are known as cystitis. Symptoms of cystitis include a frequent, urgent need to urinate and a painful burning sensation when passing urine; there may be some blood in your urine. Occasionally, an infection can travel up from the bladder to the kidneys. In this case you may also have pain in your lower back on one side (over the kidney area), have a high temperature, and may feel nauseous or vomit. Sometimes a urinary tract infection is present but causes no symptoms. Prompt treatment of urinary tract infections is especially important in pregnancy because if an infection reaches the kidneys, it can trigger early labor.

CAUSES Urinary tract infections are caused by bacteria entering the body through the urethra (the outlet from the bladder) and multiplying. Such infections are probably more common during pregnancy because the effect of hormones on the urinary tract slows the passage of urine.

WHAT TO DO If you have any symptoms of a urinary tract infection, see your doctor right away. The doctor will take a mid-stream urine sample and the sample will be sent to a laboratory to identify the type of bacteria that is causing the infection. Your doctor may prescribe a seven to ten day course of antibiotics that are safe for both you and your baby. Symptoms usually improve in a few days after the start of treatment. Because some urinary tract infections are asymptomatic, all pregnant women have urine tests at prenatal doctor's visits, and if bacteria are found, appropriate antibiotics are prescribed.

Resources

Fertility

www.ahrc-pac.gc.ca
(866) 467-1853
Assisted Human Reproduction Canada

www.cfsh.ca
(613) 241-4474
Canadian Federation for Sexual Health

www.iaac.ca
(800) 263-2929
Infertility Awareness Association
of Canada

www.myfertility.ca
Information on fertility and fertility
clinics

Pregnancy, Labor, and Birth

www.babycenter.ca
Information on pregnancy and
childbirth

www.babyzone.com

www.canadianmidwives.org
(514) 807-3668
Canadian Association of Midwives

www.cappacanada.ca
(866) 236-2478
Childbirth and Postpartum Professional
Association

www.dona.org
(888) 788-3662
Doulas of North America

www.fitpregnancy.com

**www.healthycanadians.ca/hp-gs/
index_e.html**
Guide to a healthy pregnancy

www.hypnobirthing.com

www.ican-online.org
International Cesarean Awareness
Network

www.icea.org
(919) 863-9487
International Childbirth Education
Association

www.lamaze.org
(800) 368-4404
Lamaze International

www.motherisk.org
(416) 813-6780
Information on the safety of
medications, infections, chemicals,
personal products and everyday
exposures during pregnancy and
breastfeeding

Breast-feeding

www.breastfeedingcanada.ca
(416) 465-8265
Breastfeeding Committee for Canada

www.lllc.ca
(613) 774-4900
La Leche League Canada

Support Groups

www.asthma.ca
(866) 787-4050
Asthma Society of Canada

www.autismsocietycanada.ca
(613) 789-8943
Autism Society Canada

www.bereavedparentsofcanada.ca
Bereaved Parents of Canada

www.cdss.ca
(800) 883-5608
Canadian Down Syndrome Society

www.cmha.ca
(613) 745-7750
Canadian Mental Health Association—
Helping with depression and
postpartum psychosis

www.cysticfibrosis.ca
(800) 378-2233
Canadian Cystic Fibrosis Foundation

www.diabetes.ca
(800) 226-8464
Canadian Diabetes Association

www.marchofdimes.ca
Working against the threats of birth
defects, premature birth, and infant
mortality

www.meningitis.ca
(800) 643-1303
Meningitis Research Foundation
of Canada

www.multiplebirthscanada.org
(705) 429-0901 / (866) 228-8824
Multiple Births Canada

www.preeclampsia.org
Preeclampsia Foundation

www.preemie-l.org
Parents of Premature Babies Inc.

www.sbhac.ca
(204) 925-3650 / (800) 565-9488
Spina Bifida and Hydrocephalus
Association of Canada

www.sidscanada.org
(905) 688-8884
Canadian Foundation for the Study of
Sudden Infant Death

www.smiletrain.org
(800) 932-9541
International charity for children born
with cleft palate

Parents

www.canadianequalparentinggroups.ca
Directory of groups to support children's
relationships with both parents after
divorce or separation

www.canadianparents.com

www.childwellbeing.org
Center for Child Well-Being

www.parentscanada.com

www.safekid.org
(888) 499-4444
Children's Safety Association of Canada

www.todaysparent.com

Rights and Benefits

www.rqap.gouv.qc.ca/index_en.asp
Quebec Parental Insurance Plan

www.servicecanada.gc.ca/eng/sc/ei/
benefits/maternityparental.shtml
Information on EI maternity and
parental benefits

General

www.aboutkidshealth.ca
Trusted answers from The Hospital for
Sick Children

www.caringforkids.cps.ca
(613) 526-9397
Children's health information

www.cfpc.ca
(905) 629-0900 / (800) 387-6197
College of Family Physicians of Canada

www.cps.ca
Canadian Pediatric Society

www.hc-sc.gc.ca/fn-an/food-guide-
aliment/index-eng.php
Canada's Food Guide – Health Canada

www.healthycanadians.ca/smoke-
fumee_e.html
Healthy Canadians—Go Smoke-Free

www.noharm.org
Health Care Without Harm—
Environmentally responsible health care

www.sexualityandu.ca
Resources for sexual well-being

www.sogc.org
(613) 730-4192 / (800) 561-2416
Society of Obstetricians and
Gynaecologists of Canada

www.tc.gc.ca/RoadSafety/SafeDrivers/
childsafety/car/cartime/stage1.htm
Transport Canada—infant car seat
safety

www.womenshealthmatters.ca
Women's Health Matters

Index

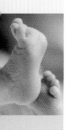

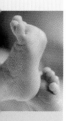

491

Acknowledgments

Maggie Blott's acknowledgments

I would like to thank the Pregnancy and Childcare team at Dorling Kindersley for their help, guidance, and expert knowledge. In particular I would like to thank Andrea Bagg for her patience and support. I would also like to thank my children Polly, Jess, and Eddie for their love and for putting up with me and my preoccupation during this project.

Publisher's acknowledgments

Indexer Hilary Bird
Proofreader Angela Baynham
Additional Editorial Assistance Suhel Ahmed, Ann Baggaley, Terry Moore, Helen Murray, Diana Vowles
Additional Design Assistance Isabel de Cordova, Charlotte Seymour
Illustration Assistance Amanda Williams
Additional illustrations Philip Wilson
Picture Librarian Romaine Werblow
Additional Picture Research Jenny Baskaya
Hair & Makeup Stylist for Photography Alli Williams
Photographer's Assistants Sarah Bailey and Carly Churchill
Assistant to Art Director for Photography Susie Sanford
Location Agency www.1st-Option.com

Dorling Kindersley would like to thank all the authors and illustrators for their expertise and dedication. We are grateful to the following individuals and organizations for their help:
Dr. Mary Steen RGN, RM, BHSc PGCRM, PGDipHE, MCGI, PhD for consultancy work and editorial assistance.
Catharine Parker-Littler SRN, RSCN, SCM, DPSM (Advanced midwifery), BscMid (Hons) for permission to reuse text from *Ask a Midwife*.
Dr. Paul Moran MD, MRCOG for consultation and expert advice on all embryonic and fetal images. His invaluable contribution provided not only the fetal text and all fetal captions, but he also sourced, scanned, and supplied images when all other image sources had been exhausted. Paul would like to thank the women who helped him to provide the images for this book and Maggie Blott for the opportunity to work on such a fascinating title.
Dr. Pranav Pandya BSc, MRCOG, MD for advice on embryonic and fetal images.
The women at the Royal Victoria Infirmary who gave permission for their scans to be used in this book.
Nicola, Joe and Leo Hayward, and **Reuben Marcus** for allowing us to use photographs of themselves.

A special thank you to:
University College Hospital London for permission to photograph in the new Elizabeth Garrett Anderson (EGA) Wing. Many thanks also to the midwives, who helped and advised during photography and who also in some cases modeled for us.

The new University College Hospital Elizabeth Garrett Anderson (EGA) Wing opened its doors to women and their babies in the first week of November 2008. The £70 million wing includes three floors dedicated to the care of mothers and babies and has been specially designed to ensure all women have ready access to the integrated care they and their babies may require. Maternity care is provided by midwifery, obstetric, neonatal, and anesthetic consultants with their teams and core midwifery staff working together to deliver up to 6,000 babies a year.

Mothers will receive care from the same team of midwives throughout their pregnancy. All women who are anticipated to have low risk pregnancies and deliveries will be offered the facilities of the Bloomsbury Birthing Centre—providing a home-from-home philosophy.

The Elizabeth Garrett Anderson (EGA) Wing houses prenatal and postpartum beds, high-dependency maternity unit beds, birthing rooms, birthing pools, special care cribs, and neonatal intensive care cribs. In addition to providing care for women with normal pregnancies, the staff also cares for women with very complicated, high risk pregnancies and treats some of the sickest and most vulnerable babies in the UK with the most modern equipment and up-to-date and highly trained medical, midwifery, and nursing teams.

Picture credits

Most of the scans and photographs of the developing baby in this book are of the embryo and fetus live in utero, pictured using endoscopic and ultrasound technology. When this has not been possible, images have been taken by reputable medical professionals as part of research or to promote educational awareness.

Dorling Kindersley would like to thank the following for their kind permission to reproduce their photographs:
(Key: a-above; b-below/bottom; c-center; f-far; l-left; r-right; t-top)

Alamy Images: 322tl; Angela Hampton Picture Library 266bc; Avatra Images 33cra, 84br; Marie-Louise Avery 135cl; Peter Banos 58cr; Bubbles Photolibrary 10tr, 20br, 148br, 185cr, 233bc, 242br, 317br, 328br; Adam Burton 125br; Camera Press Ltd 255bc, 268bc; Form Advertising 338br; David J. Green 76bc; Jennie Hart 47bl; Juergen Hasenkopf 95br; Janine Wiedel Photolibrary 405bl, 438br; Martin Hughes-Jones 154cr; Medical-on-Line 381cl; Picture Partners 235c, 369br, 380c; Pregnancy Maternity And Motherhood/Mark Sykes 365bl; Profimedia International s.r.o. 3fcla; Chris Rout 119bc, 148bc, 193c, 232cr; **babyarchive.com:** MJ Kim 42cl; **Babybond® www.babybond.com:** 2clb, 146tl, 149bc, 149bl, 149fbl, 173tl, 183tl, 199tl, 206bc, 206bl, 206br, 218tl, 256bc, 257tl, 258tl, 262fcl, 262ftl, 262tl, 263bc, 281tl, 282tl, 283tl, 286tl, 287tl, 288tl, 289tl, 292tl, 294tl, 306tl, 310tl, 311tl, 320tl, 323br, 327tl, 328tl, 329tl, 330tl, 332tl, 333tl, 336tl, 337tl, 338tl, 339tl, 340tl, 353tl; **BSIP:** 166tl, 235tl, 253tl; Ramare 174tl, 240bc, 343tl, 350tl, 351tl; SGO 131tl, 270tl, 271tl, 296tl; **Bubbles:** Moose Azim 333bl; **Corbis:** Heide Benser / zefa 180br; Brooke Fasani 341bc, 382bl; Rolf Bruderer 198c; Cameron 426c; Kevin Dodge 77bl; Annie Engel / zefa 200bl, 335bc, 375bc; Wolfgang Flamisch / zefa 387c; Owen Franken (sidebar); Rick Gomez 3fcrb, 10tc, 32cra, 158bc, 177c; Ole Graf/zefa 32bc; Rune Hellestad 389bc, 438bl; A. Inden / zefa 171cl; JLP/Sylvia Torres 2fcla; Michael A. Keller 60cr, 64bc; Jutta Klee

140c; Mika / zefa 80bl, 101bc; Markus Moellenberg/zefa 2crb, 31tc; Moodboard 273cl; Kevin R Morris 314br; Peter Pfander / zefa 351bc; Shift Foto / zefa 261bc; Ariel Skelley 6fbl, 464cl; Tom Stewart 245cr; Larry Williams 6fcr, 205br, 289br, 297cr, 395cr; **Custom Medical Stock Photo:** 127tl; **Dreamstime.com:** Monkey Business Images 37br, 57bc, 65cr, 292bc; Pliene 159tl; Shahar 204br; Shipov 180tl; Starush 256bl; Studio1one 162tl; **fotolia:** Liv friis-larsen 134cl; Nyul 75cr; **Getty Images:** 83bc, 311cr, 374c; Altrendo 412bc; Altrendo Images 356bl; B2M Productions 54l; Blend Images 73cr; Blend Images/Jose Luis Pelaez Inc 6cra, 30tr; Blend Images/PBNJ Productions 33bl; Leland Bobbe 313cr; Daniel Bosler 287br; Noah Clayton 164bc; Taxi / Colorstock 157br; Donna Day 270bc; DK Stock 63br; DK Stock / Michael Rowe 172br; Dorling Kindersley / Sian Irvine 173br; Gazimal 117bl; George Doyle 339bc; Vladimir Godnik 309bc; Sammy Hart 354c; Frank Herholdt 263br; Dorling Kindersley / Ian Hooton 209br; Ian Hooton 295br; Iconica 45c; Iconica / Andersen Ross 241br; Image Bank/Tracy Frankel 263bl; Image Source 149cra; Blend Images / Jose Luis Pelaez Inc 251br; Ruth Jenkinson 306cr; Christina Kennedy 223br; Jutta Klee 169cr; The Image Bank / Bernhard Lang 115cr; Lecorre Productions 145cr; StockFood Creative / Louise Lister 114br; LWA 462c; LWA/The Image Bank 367c; Laurence Monneret 385br; Nacivet 371br, 373br; Peter Nicholson 131br; Sarma Ozols 357cr; Barbara Peacock 262bc; Iconica / Jose Luis Pelaez 110c; Photonica 97bc; Louie Psihoyos 453tl; Riser 44cr, 116bc; Riser/ Frank Herholdt 3crb; Riser/Laurence Monneret 263cr; Stockbyte 86c, 263ftl, 327bc; Stockbyte/George Doyle 2cla; StockFood Creative 33ca; Stone 39c, 105br; Stone / James Baigrie 207br; Stone/Jerome Tisne 148; Jonathan Storey 246bc; Studio MPM 283c; Taxi 66br; Taxi / Bernd Opitz 252tl; Taxi / DreamPictures 106br; Jerome Tisne 151br; Titus 275bc; Tobias Titz 127cl; Paul Venning 379cr; Simon Wilkinson 139br; ZenShui / Laurence Mouton 316cr; **iStockphoto.com:** Alex Bramwell 104br; Dirk Richter 259c; **Prof. J.E. Jirasek MD, DSc.:** 3cra, 11tl, 32br, 33tc, 33tl, 68tl, 69tl, 71tl, 72tl, 73tl, 75tl, 76bl, 83tl, 87tl, 96cr, 96tl, 101tl, 104tl, 107tl, 110tl, 114tl, 115tl, 149tl, 149tr, 232tl, 242tl, 249tl; **jupiterimages:** Pixland 91c; **Lennart Nilsson Image Bank:** 33ftl, 65tl, 87cr, 91tl, 93cr, 93tl, 99tl, 100tl, 107cr, 126cr, 156cr, 219tl, 231c; **Life Issues Institute:** 125tl, 181tl, 200tr, 260tl; **LOGIQlibrary:** 113br, 138c; **Masterfile:** 191cl, 237bc; Jerzyworks 224c, 304cr; Michael A. Keller 180bc; **Mediscan:** 120tl, 211tl, 237tl; **Mother & Baby Picture Library:** 262br, 282bc, 426cl, 435cr; Dave J. Anthony 238bc; Moose Azim 307br, 427bc, 427br; Ian Hooton 6bl, 6cla, 6fcl, 6tr, 12tr, 26br, 28br, 30tc, 33br, 103bc, 122bc, 122cb, 138b, 142l, 146cl, 199c, 229bc, 230c, 243cr, 262tr, 263tl, 267cr, 278br, 279br, 286bc, 299c, 300br, 302br, 321bc, 348, 383bc, 393c, 394cl, 397c, 402cr, 411tr, 465cl; Ruth Jenkinson 3fcra, 6cl, 6crb, 11tc, 13tr, 239cr, 288br, 319cr, 331cr, 394c, 399tl, 407cr, 409bl, 416br, 432bc, 441tc; Eddie Lawrence 6cr, 395cl, 399b; Paul Mitchell 8-9, 31tl, 149cl, 203cr, 320br; James Thomson 13tc, 19; **Dept of Fetal Medicine, Royal Victoria Infirmary, Newcastle upon Tyne:** 97tl, 111, 140tl, 161tl, 165tl, 167tl, 170tl, 187tl, 188tl, 274tl, 275tl, 276tl, 277tl, 278tl, 279tl, 297tl, 299tl, 300tl, 304tl, 305tl, 314tl, 316tl, 317tl, 325tl, 370tl, 374tl, 375tl, 377tl, 378tl, 379tl, 380tl, 381tl, 382tl, 383tl, 385tl, 386tl, 388tl, 389tl, 392tl; **Dr. Pranav P Pandya:** 143c, 143cr, 285c, 285cr; **Photolibrary:** Banana Stock 2fclb, 103cl, 429b, 464c; Pierre Bourrier 133cr; Brand X Pictures 167bc; Neil Bromhall 226bl; OSF / Derek Bromhall 190tl; OSF / Neil Bromhall 221tl, 223tl, 229tl, 233tl, 255tl; OSF / Densey Clyne 193tl, 194br, 194tl, 203tl; Fresh Food Images/Robert Lawson 32tl; Henry Horenstein 366tl; Robert Lawson 322c; Graham Monro 430; Andersen Ross 323bc; Joy Skipper 332c; **Phototake:** Dr Benoit/Mona Lisa 365tl; Sovereign 355tl; **PunchStock:** 442; **Reflexstock:** Agencja Free / Rafal Strzechowski 221br; **Rex Features:** 309tl; Prof Stuart Campbell 105tl, 106tl, 151tl, 154tl, 172tl, 189tl, 198tl, 209tl, 216tl, 217tl, 225tl, 226tl, 245tl, 252, 261tl, 269tl, 293tl, 295tl, 307tl, 321tl, 345tl, 361tl, 363tl, 387tl; **Science Photo Library:** 21tl, 77tl, 120bc, 169tl, 207tl, 240tl, 262c, 284tl; AJ Photo 335tl; Anatomical Travelogue 49tl, 63tl, 64tl, 67cl, 79tl, 81tl, 84tl, 86tl, 89tl, 92tl, 117tl, 129tl, 133tl, 145tl, 158tl, 174c, 197tl, 291tl, 344tl, 362tl, 364tl, 371tl; Samuel Ashfield 343br, 364c; Bernard Benoit / Kretz Technik 341tl; Thierry Berrod, Mona Lisa Production 354tl; Biophoto Associates 36tl; Neil Borden 215tc, 215tl; Neil Bromhall 230tl, 241tl, 243tl; Neil Bromhall / Genesis Films 227tl; BSIP Estiot 57tl; BSIP VEM 40tl; BSIP, ASTIER 395c, 434bl; BSIP, ATL 324tl; BSIP, Cavallini James 124bl; BSIP, Laurent 418br; John Burbridge 47tl; CIMN, ISM 266tl, 273cr; Clouds Hill Imaging Ltd 10tl; Clouds Hill Imaging Ltd. 53cr; CNRI 428c; Kevin Curtis 378bl; Dopamine 135tl, 163tl, 175tl, 178tl, 179tl; Dr Keith Wheeler 43tl; Du Cane Medical Imaging Ltd 367tl, 386c; Edelmann 41c, 72cr, 100c, 109tl, 119tl, 124tl, 132tl, 134tl, 144tl, 148ftr, 148tr, 155tl, 157tl, 166bl, 171tl, 182br, 185tl, 213tl, 222tl, 234tl, 238tl, 239tl, 256tl, 347tl, 369tl; Simon Fraser 141tl, 370br; GE Medical Systems 372tl, 373tl; Steve Gschmeissner 37tl, 41tl, 46tl, 48tl; Ian Hooton 1c, 2cra, 2fcrb, 3cla, 4-5c, 6fbr, 14, 24bc, 46br, 103bl, 129c, 149cb, 149ftl, 188cl, 214bc, 263c, 398br, 455c, 464cr, 465cr; Dr Isabelle Cartier, ISM 45tl; Jean-Claude Revy-A. Goujeon, ISM 66tl; K.H. Kjeldsen 60tl; Mehau Kulyk 186tl, 246tl, 251tl; Dr Najeeb Layyous 95tl, 116tl, 121tl, 126tl, 130tl, 137tl, 156tl, 182tl, 186bc, 204tl, 208tl, 212tl, 222bl, 231tl, 267bc, 268tl, 274br, 313tl, 357tl, 358tl, 359tl; Living Art Enterprises, Llc 215c, 215cl; Cecilia Magill 6fcra, 31tr; Manfred Kage 39tl; Matt Meadows 346tl, 391tl; Hank Morgan 206tl; Dr Yorgos Nikas 50bl, 50br, 50fbr; Dr Yorgos Nikos 59bc, 59tl; Susumu Nishinaga 44tl; Lea Paterson 20bc; D. Phillips 50fbl, 53tl; Photo Researchers, Inc / Nestle / Petit Format 205tl; Alain Pol, ISM 248tl; Prof. P. Motta / Dept. of Anatomy / University 56tl; Prof. P. Motta / Dept. of Anatomy / University "LA SAPIENZA", Rome 49bc; Professors P.m. Motta & J. Van Blerkom 32tr; Professors P.M. Motta & S. Makabe 35tr; R. Bick, B. Poindexter, UT Medical School 67tl; P. Saada / Eurelios 138tc; Sovereign, ISM 139tl, 177tl, 178cr; James Stevenson 259tl; BSIP, Kretz Technik 319tl; Tek Image 310br; Alexander Tsiaras 132cr, 162cr; Zephyr 38tl, 331tl; **University College London Hospitals:** 271cr; **Wellcome Library, London:** 80tl, 164tl, 190br, 191tl, 195tl, 224tl, 265tl; Yorgos Nikas 61tl; Anthea Sieveking 429tr; **Wikipedia, The Free Encyclopedia:** Acaparadora 43bl

All other images © Dorling Kindersley
For further information see: www.dkimages.com